Contents

D0784675

Published by the National Gardens Scheme, Hatchlands Park, East Clandon,
Guildford, Surrey GU4 7RT

Editor: The Director, National Gardens Scheme

Cover illustration of Flintham Hall, Nottinghamshire, by Val Biro

A catalogue record for this book is available from the British Library.

Typeset in Linotron Bell Centennial by Land & Unwin (Data Sciences) Limited, Bugbrooke.

Text printed and bound by Wm Clowes Ltd, Beccles.
Cover printed by George Over Limited, Rugby.
Colour illustrations printed by MN Productions, Northampton

Trade Distributor: Seymour, Windsor House, 1270 London Road, Norbury, London, SW16 4DH.

ISBN 0-900558-28-8   ISSN 0141-2361

Why Carr Sheppards are supporting the National Gardens Scheme

It may seem strange for a private client stockbroker to be involved with gardens, but the reason is very simple. We believe that those of you whose gardens appear in this book, and those who buy it, are the backbone of England and Wales.

In this way, you are very similar to our private clients, and the nature of the service we strive to give them resembles the care and long term commitment that show their results in these gardens.

The National Gardens Scheme does wonderful work for charity, and we cannot think of a more revered and worthwhile organisation with whom to be associated.

We are very happy to continue our support.

Fred Carr

Fred Carr, Chief Executive

CARR SHEPPARDS
Banque Indosuez Group

122 Leadenhall Street, London EC3V 4SS. Tel: 0171-303 1234. Fax: 0171-303 1212.
Carr Sheppards is a member of the London Stock Exchange and regulated by the Securities and Futures Authority.

The National Gardens Scheme

- *What is the National Gardens Scheme?*

  A charity founded in 1927 which raises money by opening gardens to the public.

- *How is the money raised?*

  Owners generously open their gardens to the public on specific days and money is raised from entry fees plus the sales of teas and plants.

- *How many gardens are there and where are they?*

  3,500 spread throughout England and Wales.

- *Who are the main beneficiaries?*

  The Scheme provides long-term financial assistance to the charities listed on page 9.

- *How much money is donated to the charities supported?*

  In 1995 over £1.3 million.

- *How can I help?*

  The more gardens you visit the more the National Gardens Scheme will raise for charity.

Start your gardening week every Wednesday

Garden News is first with the latest gardening news, views and advice and it's available every Wednesday. Written by gardeners for gardeners it ensures you get the most from your gardening week. So don't miss out! Order your copy from your newsagent today!

The essential monthly guide

....to plants, planting and garden design

Every month Practical Gardening brings you inspired design ideas and the very best of practical gardening advice . Pick up a copy this month and we'll show you how to create and get the most from your beautiful garden. **Practical GARDENING**

Patron, President and Council of The National Gardens Scheme Charitable Trust

The Secret Garden (and other gems) revealed.

Country Houses Association has nine beautiful houses in the south of England, each with extensive gardens and grounds. Five of them are open under the National Gardens Scheme.

You'll find a warm welcome at: **Aynhoe Park**, Aynho, near Banbury; **Flete**, near Plymouth; **Greathed Manor**, at Lingfield, Surrey; **Swallowfield Park**, close to Reading. And at **Great Maytham Hall** (pictured), near Cranbrook in Kent, you'll discover *The Secret Garden* of Francis Hodgson Burnett's children's classic.

Do come and visit. You might even decide to become a member of the Association - a recognised charity, committed to preserving these treasures of our heritage. And, if you really can't bring yourself to leave, we'll be delighted to explain how you could become a resident, because each of these houses is home to active retired people who enjoy a carefree retirement.

THERE ARE COUNTRY HOUSES ASSOCIATION PROPERTIES IN BERKSHIRE, DEVON, KENT, OXFORDSHIRE, SURREY, SUSSEX, WILTSHIRE

To find out more, contact Country Houses Association, Room L35, FREEPOST, London WC2B 6BR. Telephone: 0171- 836 1624 (weekdays) or 0171-240 1676 (weekends).

COUNTRY HOUSES
ASSOCIATION

Beneficiaries

The National Gardens Scheme provides long-term
financial support to the following:

- **The Queen's Nursing Institute** – for the
welfare of elderly and needy district nurses

- **Cancer Relief Macmillan Fund** – for the
provision and training of Macmillan cancer
nurses

- **The Nurses Welfare Service** – for assistance
to nurses in personal difficulty

- **The Gardeners' Royal Benevolent Society**
– for assistance to retired gardeners

- **The Royal Gardeners' Orphan Fund** – for
assistance to the orphans of gardeners

- **The Gardens Fund of the National Trust** –
for the restoration of historic gardens

- **Additional Charities Nominated by Owners
(ACNO)** – Over 600 charities chosen by
Garden Owners

THE ROYAL
HORTICULTURAL
SOCIETY

Join the Royal Horticultural Society today and save £5

As a special introductory offer for readers of *Gardens of England and Wales*, we are offering a saving of £5 on your first year subscription.

For just £26, you will receive the very best advice and inspiration available to gardeners (normal price £31 – £24 plus £7 enrolment fee). Membership of the RHS is just like having a panel of experts on hand whenever you need them.

Free gardening magazine subscription

You can look forward to a monthly copy of **the** gardening magazine. *The Garden* is an entertaining combination of news, horticultural problem pages, in-depth articles about garden design and interesting plants and a range of exclusive offers for members.

Free visits

You can also start planning days out at 17 of Britain's most beautiful gardens including the RHS Gardens at Wisley in Surrey, Rosemoor in Devon and Hyde Hall in Essex. Your membership entitles you to unlimited free visits to the gardens, and you can even bring a guest in free to the RHS Gardens. You can book privileged tickets – both special prices and members-only days – to the world's top flower shows, including Chelsea and Hampton Court Palace Flower Show. You also get free entrance to the monthly Westminster Flower Shows: an ideal opportunity to buy the very best plants from Britain's top nurseries.

Free advice

Other highlights include free advice from RHS experts and free seeds from Wisley, and you'll find that *The Garden* features regular new benefits such as gardens to visit or special RHS plant offers.

Your membership is vital to Britain's gardening heritage

The Royal Horticultural Society has been promoting horticultural excellence throughout the world since 1804. Today, gardening is Britain's most popular hobby and our extensive programme of education. conservation and scientific work ensures that future generations will continue to enjoy our gardening heritage too.

As a registered charity, we are dependent on money that we raise ourselves – and your support is a vital contribution.

We are pleased to offer readers of *Gardens of England and Wales* a £5 saving when you join the RHS – or perhaps enrol a friend – today.

Please make your cheque payable to The Royal Horticultural Society and send it to the **Membership Department, The Royal Horticultural Society, PO Box 313, London SW1P 2PE**. If you are enrolling a friend, please enclose their name and address on a separate sheet; we will send the new members' pack to you to pass on. If you would prefer not to cut this coupon, please write to us with all the details required – including code 722. This offer expires 31 October 1996.

For further information please call the RHS Membership Department on 0171-821 3000.

Royal Gardens

SANDRINGHAM HOUSE AND GROUNDS Norfolk
By gracious permission of Her Majesty The Queen, the House and grounds at Sandringham will be open on the following days: from 4 April to 6 October inclusive daily. Please note that the **house only** will be **closed** to the public from 23 July to 6 August inclusive and that the house and grounds will be closed from 27 July to 6 August inclusive. Coach drivers and visitors are advised to confirm these closing and opening dates nearer the time. Picnicking and dogs are not permitted inside the grounds.

Hours
Sandringham House: 11 to 4.45; museum: 11 to 5 and grounds: 10.30 to 5.

Admission Charges
House, grounds and museum: adults £4.00, OAPs £3.00, children £2.00. Grounds and museum only: adults £3.00, OAPs £2.50; children £1.50. Advance party bookings will be accepted. There are reductions in admission fees for pre-paid parties. Free car and coach parking.

Sandringham Church
Subject to weddings, funerals and special services, when the grounds are open as stated above, opening times will be 11-5 April to October. At other times of the year the church is open by appointment only.

Sandringham Flower Show
Wednesday 31st July 1996.

Enquiries
The Public Access Manager, Estate Office, Sandringham or by telephone 9-1, 2-4.30 Monday to Friday inclusive on King's Lynn 772675.

FROGMORE GARDENS Berkshire
By gracious permission of Her Majesty The Queen, Frogmore Gardens, Windsor Castle, will be open from 10.30-7 (last admission 6.00 pm) on the following days: **Wednesday May 1 and Thursday May 2**. Entrance to gardens and mausoleum through Long Walk gate. Coaches by appointment only: apply to the National Gardens Scheme, Hatchlands Park, East Clandon, Guildford, Surrey, GU4 7RT (Telephone 01483 211535) stating whether May 1 or 2, and whether morning or afternoon. Admission £2, accompanied children free. Dogs not allowed.
Visitors are requested kindly to refrain from entering the grounds of the Home Park. Light refreshments will be available at the free car park (near the outer gate to the gardens). Also open:

Royal Mausoleum
Open, free of charge, both days.

Frogmore House
Open in aid of the Royal Collection Trust. Entrance only from Frogmore Gardens. Admission Adults £3, over 60's £2, under 17 £1, children under the age of 8 not admitted.

National Trust Gardens

Certain gardens opened by The National Trust are opened in aid of the The National Gardens Scheme on the dates shown in this book. National Trust Members are requested to note that where a National Trust property has allocated an opening day to the National Gardens Scheme which is one of its normal opening days, members can still gain entry on production of their National Trust membership card (although donations to the Scheme will be welcome). However, where the day allocated is one on which the property would not normally be open, then the payment of the National Gardens Scheme admission fee will be required.

Famous for fine Jewellery
and an incomparable service

Richard Ogden

International Jeweller

General Information and Symbols

‡   Following a garden name in the Dates of Opening list indicates that those gardens sharing the symbol are near each other and open on the same day.

‡‡   Indicates a second series of gardens near each other and open on the same day.

¶   Opening for the first time.

❀   Plants/produce for sale if available.

♿   Gardens with at least the main features accessible by wheelchair.

✗   No dogs except guide dogs but otherwise dogs are usually admitted, provided they are kept on a lead.

●   Gardens marked thus do not necessarily give all their takings to the National Gardens Scheme. Instead they give a guaranteed contribution.

▲   Where this sign appears alongside dates in the descriptive entry for a garden it denotes that this garden is also open regularly to the public on days other than those for the NGS.

Additional Charities Nominated by Owner (ACNO) Where the owners of private gardens (not normally open to the public) have nominated some other cause to receive an agreed share from the admission money, the name of the other cause is included in the descriptive entry as (Share to ....) with an ® or © to indicate whether it is a Registered Charity or a Charitable Cause.

Tea When this is available at a garden the information is given in capitals, e.g. TEAS (usually with home-made cakes) or TEA (usually with biscuits). There is, of course, an extra charge for any refreshments available at a garden. TEAS in aid of ... is used where part or all the proceeds go to another organisation.

Open by appointment Please do not be put off by this notation. The owner may consider his garden too small to accommodate the numbers associated with a normal opening or, more often, there may be a lack of car parking. The minimum size of party is either stated in the garden description or can be found out when making the appointment. If the garden has normal open days, the entrance fee is as stated in the garden description.

Coach parties Please, by appointment only unless stated otherwise.

Photographs Photographs taken in a garden may not be used for sale or reproduction without the prior permission of the garden owner.

Lavatories Private gardens do not normally have outside lavatories. Regretably, for security reasons, owners have been advised not to admit visitors into their houses to use inside toilets.

Children All children must be accompanied by an adult.

Distances and sizes In all cases these are approximate.

FIRST AID FOR FLOPPY FLOWERS

◀ BEFORE

AFTER ▶

The **Easy, Unobtrusive** plant support made of strong brown pointed aluminium tube, with a pliable green plastic coated wire fork at the top.

BEND THE FORKS TO SUIT YOUR PLANTS

Upright for lilies, gladioli, etc

Wide for Bushy plants

Horizontal to train climbers

Two or more joined with ties through the "eyes". Two will encircle about six feet!

Y-Stakes are so easy to use at any time, you do not need to put them in before a plant has fully grown. They are much tidier than netting and less obtrusive than rings. They avoid the unnatural bunched up look which can happen with other forms of staking.

Y-Stakes can be used as a simple prop in exactly the same way as a forked stick, but you can bend the arms to suit your plant, or with a quick twist, join them together with flexible wire ties (through their eyes) at any distance apart.

Y-Stakes are suitable for a very wide range of plants, throughout the gardening season, from geraniums to hollyhocks. They are so easy to move, when your early plants such as peonies are over they can quickly be transferred to later plants e.g. delphiniums, dahlias or chrysanthemums.

Y-Stakes are available in five sizes from 1ft plus 9" arms to 5ft plus 16" arms. A **Trial Set** of 3x1ft, 3x2ft, and 3x3ft (9 stakes in total) is a good way to test the lengths needed for your various plants. You will find that you have uses for all of the sizes as the season progresses.

The **Trial set** is available at the **special offer** price of £17.90 including postage, (please mention the "Yellow Book" when ordering). Telephone, fax, or write your order with cheque or credit card number to Davies Systems, Brandsby Lodge, Brandsby, York. YO6 4SJ. **Tel. 01347 888 224.** Fax 01347 888 337. Orders are sent by return, or ask for free leaflet and complete price list.

GARDENS
ILLUSTRATED
Photographic Competition

THE NATIONAL GARDENS SCHEME CHARITABLE TRUST AND GARDENS
ILLUSTRATED ANNOUNCE AN EXCITING COMPETITION FOR 1996 OPEN TO
ANYONE WITH A CAMERA

LOAD YOUR CAMERAS

To mark the 70th anniversary of The
National Gardens Scheme Charitable Trust
in 1997, we are running a major
photographic competition in conjunction
with Gardens Illustrated this
spring and summer.

THE CRITERIA

The judges will be looking for a set
of eight to ten colour transparencies
(slides) which capture the spirit of one
of the participating NGS gardens. The
pictures should document the layout of
the garden and show the excellence of
the planting, originality of the design
features and include portraits of
the owner or gardeners, if
appropriate.

THE PRIZE

The winner will receive the brand
new **Pentax MZ-5**, the world's smallest
SLR camera, worth £700. Plus their
photographs will illustrate a major feature
in GARDENS ILLUSTRATED. The winner
and runners-up will also have their work
published in the special anniversary
edition of *Gardens of England and Wales*
in 1997.

THE JUDGES

The judging panel will include: Claudia
Zeff, Art Director of GARDENS
ILLUSTRATED; Andrew Lawson, the
internationally acclaimed photographer;
Daphne Foulsham, Chairman of The
National Gardens Scheme Charitable
Trust; and John Dickins, Pentax Product
Manager, Photographic Division.

TO ENTER

Each entrant must apply in writing,
including a large SAE, to: The National
Gardens Scheme, Hatchlands Park, East
Clandon, Guildford, Surrey GU4 7RT. In
return you will receive an accreditation
pass with a personal identification code
number, the rules of the competition and
detailed instructions. The panel will be
judging blind, so we request that entrants
do not put their name on their slide
mounts but use their code number
instead. All work submitted will become
the property of the NGS. No other
correspondence will be entered into and
the judges' decision is final.

**The closing date for submissions to
the photographic competition is
October 1 1996. We will announce the
winners in the February/March 1997
issue of Gardens Illustrated and the
1997 anniversary edition of Gardens
of England and Wales.**

SPECIAL EVENTS DIARY

The National Gardens Scheme has arranged a number of special events during 1996 which we hope you will support and enjoy. Details are below. Directions and further information about the gardens can be found in the relevant county section of this book.

Evening Garden Openings
This is an opportunity to visit an NGS garden and enjoy refreshments with friends in the scent and beauty of the early evening. Admission and refreshments £2.50.

County/Garden	Date	Time
Essex		
Park Farm	16, 17 June	7.00-9.00 pm
Kent		
Cares Cross (£3)	17 July	5.00-8.00 pm
London		
103 Thurleigh Road	19 June	6.30-9.00 pm
Little Lodge	19 June	6.30-9.00 pm
Southwood Lodge	20 June	6.30-8.30 pm
Surrey		
Moleshill House	3 July	6.30-9.00 pm
Chilworth Manor (£2)	10 July	6.00-8.00 pm
Sussex		
Gaywood Farm	12 June	5.00-7.30 pm
Frith Hill	15, 27 June	5.00-8.00 pm
Frith Lodge	15 June	5.00-8.00 pm
The White House	25 June	5.30-7.30 pm
Hurst Mill	28 June	5.00-7.30 pm
Casters Brook	28 June, 1 July	5.00-7.30 pm
Neptune House	3 August	5.30-7.30 pm
Great Allfields	Throughout June	By appointment; ring 01403-820226
64 Old Shoreham Rd	Throughout the Season	By appointment; ring 01273-889247

Royal Horticultural Society Gardeners Question Time

This presents an opportunity to visit an NGS garden and have your gardening questions answered by an expert from the RHS free of charge.

County Garden	Date	Time
Devon		
Bickham House	19 May	2.00-5.00 pm
Dorset		
Steeple Manor	30 June	1.30-6.00 pm
Shropshire		
Gate Cottage	16 June	1.00-5.00 pm

Royal Horticultural Society Gardeners Question Time *continued*

Somerset
Coombe House | 4 August | 2.00-6.00 pm

Warwickshire
8 Vicarage Road | 30 June | 2.00-6.00 pm

Worcestershire
The Manor House | 5 June | 11.00-5.30 pm

Meet the NGS Gardener

This presents an opportunity to visit an NGS garden and receive a conducted tour from the Garden Owner. The tours normally last about 30 minutes and several will take place within the opening times shown. There will be a small extra charge; details available on arrival. National Trust members will be charged for events at National Trust properties.

County/Garden	Date	Time
Cheshire		
The Mount	14 July	2.00-5.30 pm
Dunham Massey (NT)	18 August	11.00-5.00 pm
Lyme Park (NT)	12 May, 1 Sept	11.00-5.00 pm
Derbyshire		
Field House Farm	22 May, 19 June, 17 July	2.00-6.00 pm
Essex		
Glen Chantry	30 June, 15 Sept	2.00-5.00 pm
Warwick House	9 June	2.00-6.00 pm
Hampshire		
Little Court	13 May, 22 July, 19 Aug	11.00-7.00 pm
Kent		
Pevington Farm	19 May, 16 June	11.00-5.00 pm
Lancashire		
Old Barn Cottage	26 May	12.00-5.00 pm
The Ridges	6 May	11.00-5.00 pm
Norfolk		
Lexham Hall	26 May, 23 June	2.00-6.00 pm
Shropshire		
Wollerton Old Hall	14 June	12.00-5.00 pm
Worcestershire		
Yew Tree House	7 July	2.00-6.00 pm

ENGLAND

Avon

Hon County Organiser:	Mrs Mary Bailey, Quakers, Lower Hazel, Rudgeway, Bristol BS12 2QP Tel 01454 413205
Assistant Hon County Organisers:	Dr Margaret Lush, Hazel Cottage, Lower Hazel, Rudgeway, Bristol BS12 2QP Tel 01454 412112
	Mrs Amanda Osmond, Church Farm House, Hawkesbury, nr Badminton, Avon GL9 1BN Tel 01454 238533
	Mrs Ann Pockney, Chester House, Blackmoor, Lower Langford, Bristol BS18 7HJ Tel 01934 863190
Avon Leaflet:	Mrs Jean Damey, 2 Hawburn Close, Bristol BS4 2PB Tel 0117 9775587
Hon County Treasurer:	J K Dutson Esq., The Firs, Rockhampton, Nr Berkeley, Glos GL13 9DY Tel 01454 413210

DATES OF OPENING

February 26 Monday
The Urn Cottage, Charfield
March 10 Sunday
Algars Manor & Algars Mill, Iron Acton
March 17 Sunday
Jasmine Cottage, Clevedon
March 25 Monday
The Urn Cottage, Charfield
March 30 Saturday
The Brake, Tockington‡
Old Down House, Tockington‡
March 31 Sunday
The Brake, Tockington‡
Brook Cottage, Upper Langford
Old Down House, Tockington‡
Sherborne Garden, Litton
April 7 Sunday
Algars Manor & Algars Mill, Iron Acton
Coombe Dingle Gardens, Bristol
Failand Court, Lower Failand
The Urn Cottage, Charfield
April 8 Monday
Algars Manor & Algars Mill, Iron Acton
Coombe Dingle Gardens, Bristol
April 14 Sunday
Coley Court & The Little Manor, Farrington Gurney
The Manor House, Walton-in-Gordano
April 15 Monday
Stockwood Gardens, Stockwood
April 16 Tuesday
The Manor House, Walton-in-Gordano
Stockwood Gardens, Stockwood

April 18 Thursday
Jasmine Cottage, Clevedon
April 20 Saturday
Brackenwood Garden Centre, Portishead
April 21 Sunday
Brackenwood Garden Centre, Portishead
Crowe Hall, Widcombe
April 23 Tuesday
The Manor House, Walton-in-Gordano
April 25 Thursday
Jasmine Cottage, Clevedon
April 28 Sunday
Jasmine Cottage, Clevedon
April 29 Monday
The Urn Cottage, Charfield
April 30 Tuesday
The Manor House, Walton-in-Gordano
May 2 Thursday
Jasmine Cottage, Clevedon
May 4 Saturday
Frenchay Gardens, Bristol
May 5 Sunday
Frenchay Gardens, Bristol
May 7 Tuesday
The Manor House, Walton-in-Gordano
May 8 Wednesday
Highview, Portishead
May 9 Thursday
Jasmine Cottage, Clevedon
May 12 Sunday
Dyrham Park, Chippenham
The Manor House, Walton-in-Gordano
Petty France Hotel, Badminton

May 14 Tuesday
The Manor House, Walton-in-Gordano
May 15 Wednesday
Gardener's Cottage, Upton Cheyney
Windmill Cottage, Backwell
May 16 Thursday
Jasmine Cottage, Clevedon
May 18 Saturday
Highview, Portishead
Parsonage Farm, Publow
May 19 Sunday
Algars Manor & Algars Mill, Iron Acton
Church Farm, Lower Failand
Hill House, Wickwar
Parsonage Farm, Publow
May 21 Tuesday
The Manor House, Walton-in-Gordano
May 23 Thursday
Jasmine Cottage, Clevedon
May 26 Sunday
Jasmine Cottage, Clevedon
Pearl's Garden, Coalpit Heath
Stanton Prior Gardens, nr Bath
May 27 Monday
Pearl's Garden, Coalpit Heath
The Urn Cottage, Charfield
May 28 Tuesday
The Manor House, Walton-in-Gordano
May 29 Wednesday
Highview, Portishead
May 30 Thursday
Jasmine Cottage, Clevedon
June 2 Sunday
Barrow Court, Barrow Gurney
Rock House, Elberton

June 4 Tuesday
The Manor House,
Walton-in-Gordano
June 5 Wednesday
Highview, Portishead
June 6 Thursday
Jasmine Cottage, Clevedon
June 9 Sunday
Clifton Gardens, Bristol
The Manor House,
Walton-in-Gordano
Tranby House, Whitchurch, Bristol
June 11 Tuesday
The Manor House,
Walton-in-Gordano
June 13 Thursday
Jasmine Cottage, Clevedon
June 15 Saturday
Goblin Combe, Cleeve
June 16 Sunday
Crowe Hall, Widcombe
Goblin Combe, Cleeve
Sherborne Garden, Litton
The Urn Cottage, Charfield
June 18 Tuesday
The Manor House,
Walton-in-Gordano
June 19 Wednesday
Gardener's Cottage, Upton
Cheyney
Highview, Portishead
Windmill Cottage, Backwell
June 20 Thursday
Jasmine Cottage, Clevedon
June 23 Sunday
Badminton House, Badminton
Canok Garth, Clevedon ‡
Doynton House, Doynton ‡‡
Jasmine Cottage, Clevedon ‡
Old Rectory, Doynton ‡‡
June 25 Tuesday
The Manor House,
Walton-in-Gordano
June 26 Wednesday
Brooklands, Burnett ‡
2 Old Tarnwell, Upper Stanton
Drew
Stanton Prior Gardens, nr Bath ‡
June 27 Thursday
Jasmine Cottage, Clevedon
June 30 Sunday
Bourne House, Burrington
Brooklands, Burnett
Church Farm, Lower
Failand
Highview, Portishead
Stanton Drew Gardens
July 2 Tuesday
The Manor House,
Walton-in-Gordano
July 4 Thursday
Jasmine Cottage, Clevedon
2 Old Tarnwell, Upper Stanton
Drew

July 7 Sunday
Failand Court, Lower Failand
University of Bristol Botanic
Garden
July 9 Tuesday
The Manor House,
Walton-in-Gordano
July 10 Wednesday
Highview, Portishead
July 11 Thursday
Jasmine Cottage, Clevedon
2 Old Tarnwell, Upper Stanton
Drew
July 14 Sunday
Brewery House, Southstoke
The Manor House,
Walton-in-Gordano
Sherborne Garden, Litton
July 16 Tuesday
The Manor House,
Walton-in-Gordano
2 Old Tarnwell, Upper Stanton
Drew
July 17 Wednesday
Highview, Portishead
Windmill Cottage, Backwell
July 18 Thursday
Jasmine Cottage, Clevedon
Stockwood Gardens, Stockwood
July 19 Friday
Stockwood Gardens, Stockwood
July 20 Saturday
Tranby House, Whitchurch, Bristol
July 21 Sunday
Jasmine Cottage, Clevedon
Lady Farm, Chelwood
Tranby House, Whitchurch,
Bristol
July 23 Tuesday
The Manor House,
Walton-in-Gordano
July 24 Wednesday
Gardener's Cottage, Upton
Cheyney
July 25 Thursday
Jasmine Cottage, Clevedon
July 27 Saturday
Highview, Portishead
July 28 Sunday
Highview, Portishead
July 30 Tuesday
The Manor House,
Walton-in-Gordano
August 1 Thursday
Jasmine Cottage, Clevedon
August 3 Saturday
Bryncrug, Mangotsfield
August 4 Sunday
Bryncrug, Mangotsfield
August 6 Tuesday
The Manor House,
Walton-in-Gordano
August 7 Wednesday
Highview, Portishead

August 8 Thursday
Jasmine Cottage, Clevedon
August 11 Sunday
The Manor House,
Walton-in-Gordano
Quakers, Lower Hazel
August 13 Tuesday
The Manor House,
Walton-in-Gordano
August 15 Thursday
Jasmine Cottage, Clevedon
August 17 Saturday
Highview, Portishead
August 18 Sunday
Highview, Portishead
Tranby House, Whitchurch, Bristol
August 20 Tuesday
The Manor House,
Walton-in-Gordano
August 21 Wednesday
Highview, Portishead
Windmill Cottage, Backwell
August 22 Thursday
Jasmine Cottage, Clevedon
August 25 Sunday
Jasmine Cottage, Clevedon
August 27 Tuesday
The Manor House,
Walton-in-Gordano
August 29 Thursday
Stockwood Gardens,
Stockwood
August 30 Friday
Stockwood Gardens,
Stockwood
August 31 Saturday
Highview, Portishead
West Tyning, Beach
September 1 Sunday
University of Bristol Botanic
Garden
West Tyning, Beach
September 3 Tuesday
The Manor House,
Walton-in-Gordano
September 10 Tuesday
The Manor House,
Walton-in-Gordano
September 11 Wednesday
Highview, Portishead
September 14 Saturday
Highview, Portishead
Old Down House, Tockington
September 15 Sunday
Old Down House, Tockington
Sherborne Garden, Litton
September 17 Tuesday
The Manor House,
Walton-in-Gordano
September 18 Wednesday
Gardener's Cottage, Upton
Cheyney
Highview, Portishead
Windmill Cottage, Backwell

September 30 Monday
The Urn Cottage, Charfield
October 12 Saturday
Brackenwood Garden Centre,
Portishead
October 13 Sunday
Brackenwood Garden Centre,
Portishead
October 14 Monday
The Urn Cottage, Charfield
October 16 Wednesday
Gardener's Cottage, Upton
Cheyney

Regular openings
For details see garden description

Crowe Hall, Widcombe
Pearls Garden, Coalpit Heath
Sherborne Garden, Litton
Stanton Prior Gardens, nr Bath
University of Bristol Botanic Garden

By appointment only
*For telephone numbers and other
details see garden descriptions.
Private visits welcomed*

10 Linden Road, Clevedon
Madron, Bathford
Old Tarnwell, Upper Stanton Drew
Vine House, Henbury

DESCRIPTIONS OF GARDENS

Algars Manor & Algars Mill ❀ Iron Acton 9m N of
Bristol. 3m W of Yate/Chipping Sodbury. Turn S off Iron
Acton bypass B4059, past village green, 200yds, then
over level Xing (Station Rd). TEAS **Algars Manor**. *Combined adm £1.50 Chd 20p. Sun March 10 (No Teas or
Plants) Easter Sun, Mon April 7, 8, Sun May 19 (2-6)*
    Algars Manor ❀ (Dr & Mrs J M Naish) 3-acre wood-
land garden beside R Frome; mill-stream; native plants
mixed with azaleas, rhododendrons, camellias, magnolias, eucalyptus. Picnic areas. Early Jacobean house
(not open) and old barn. Featured in NGS video 3. *Private visits also welcome* **Tel 01454 228372**
    Algars Mill (Mr & Mrs J Wright) entrance via Algars
Manor. 2-acre woodland garden beside R Frome;
spring bulbs, shrubs; early spring feature of wild Newent daffodils. 300-400 yr old mill house (not open)
through which mill-race still runs *(Share to Histio-
cytosis Research Trust®)*

Badminton ⌖❀ (The Duke of Beaufort) 5m E of Chipping Sodbury. Large garden designed 11 years ago. Still
in the process of being created. Mixed and herbaceous
borders; many old-fashioned and climbing roses; conservatories and orangery; walled kitchen garden recreated in
Victorian style ¼m from house with a new glasshouse.
TEAS. *Adm £1.50 OAPs/Chd £1 under 10 free. Sun June
23 (2-6)*

Barrow Court ❀ Barrow Gurney 5m SW Bristol. From
Bristol take A370 and turn E onto B3130 towards Barrow
Gurney; immediate right, Barrow Court Lane, then ½m,
turn R through Lodge archway. 2 acres of formal gardens,
designed by Inigo Thomas in 1890. Architectural garden,
with sculpture and pavilions; arboretum; on going reno-
vations to stonework; replanted yew hedging and parterres. C17 E-shaped house (not open). Parking limited.
TEAS. *Adm £1 Chd 50p. Sun June 2 (2-6)*

Bourne House ⌖❀ (Mr & Mrs Christopher Thomas)
Burrington nr Bristol BS18 7AF 12m S Bristol. N of Burrington. Turning off A38 signposted Blagdon-Burrington;
2nd turning L. 4 acres, and 2 paddocks. Stream with
waterfalls & lily pond; new pergola; mature trees, and
shrubs. New mixed borders; roses; bulbs. TEAS. *Adm
£1.50 Chd free. Sun June 30 (2-6). Private visits welcome
following written application*

Brackenwood Garden Centre Woodland Garden ⌖❀
(Mr & Mrs John Maycock) 131 Nore Rd, Portishead. From
Bristol A369 (10m). M5 Junc 19. 1m from Portishead on
coast rd to Clevedon. 8-acre woodland garden. Rhododendrons, camellias, Japanese maples and pieris; secluded woodland pools with waterfowl; many rare trees
and shrubs. Magnificent coastal views. Japanese maples
in full colour in the Autumn. Restaurant and Tea Room
open every day. *Adm £1.50 OAPs £1.25 Chd 60p.* ▲ *Sat,
Sun, April 20, 21 (9-5) Sat, Sun Oct 12, 13 (10-4),* **Tel
01275 843484**

The Brake ⌖ (Mr & Mrs D C J Skinner) Vicarage Lane,
Tockington. 10m N of Bristol. From A38 turn L signposted
Tockington/Olveston after bridging M4. R at Triangle in
Tockington and L 50yds on - Old Down Hill. L at top of
hill then immediate R. Alternatively follow brown signs to
Oldown. Fine views of Severn Estuary and both bridges.
Long mixed borders with emphasis on plants and shrubs
that thrive on dry, exposed hillside; woodland walk with
interesting ground cover, bulbs, cyclamen. *Adm £1 Chd
free. Sat, Sun March 30, 31 (2-6)*

Brewery House ❀ (John and Ursula Brooke) 2½m S of
Bath off A367, L onto B3110, take 2nd R to Southstoke or
bus to Cross Keys. House is ¼m down Southstoke Lane.
Please park where signed and walk down. ⅔-acre garden
on 2 levels. Fine views; top garden walled. Many unusual
plants. Water garden. All organic. Partly suitable for
wheelchairs. Plants for sale. Cream TEAS in aid of Village
Hall. *Adm £1.20 Chd free. Sun July 14 (2-6). Private or
group visits welcome, May-Sept by appt, please* **Tel
01225 833153**

Brook Cottage ⌖❀ (Mr & Mrs J S Ledbury) Upper
Langford. 13m S Bristol on A368 NW of Burrington
Combe, adjacent to the Blagdon Water Garden Centre.
Mature garden of 2½ acres with stream. Interesting col-
lection of trees, shrubs and spring bulbs. Walled garden
with good selection of fruit trees. TEAS in aid of St John's
Church. *Adm £1.50 Chd free. Sun March 31 (2-5.30)*

Brooklands ⌖❀ (Mr & Mrs Patrick Stevens) Burnett.
2m S Keynsham on B3116. Turn R into Burnett Village.
1½-acre garden; mature trees and variety of ornamental
shrubs; rose garden; herbaceous border; extensive planting of shrub roses and clematis; fine views of distant
Mendip Hills. Ploughman lunches and TEAS (on Sun in
aid of St Michael's Church, Burnett). *Adm £1.50 Chd free.
Wed June 26 (11-5), Sun June 30 (11-6)*

Bryncrug ✿❀ (Mrs Margaret Jones) 23 Charnhill Ridge Mangotsfield. ½m from Staplehill on the Mangotsfield Rd B4465 and at the bottom of the hill turn R into Charnhill Drive and in 30yds turn L to Charnhill Ridge. Small town garden, densely planted with interesting trees and shrubs, many in dry shade; pond; conservatory and unusual front garden. Featured in Nov 93 Practical Gardening. Welsh TEAS in aid R.S.P.C.A. *Adm £1 Chd 20p. Sat, Sun Aug 3, 4 (11-5)*

¶**Canok Garth** ⅊ (Mr & Mrs Peter Curtis) 9 Channel Rd Clevedon. 12m W of Bristol (Junction 20 off M5). Follow signs to seafront and pier, continue N on B3124 past Walton Park Hotel, turn R at St Mary's Church. ½-acre garden with a little of everything. Herbaceous border, interesting shrubs and trees, annuals, lawns, fruit and vegetables. Fairly intensively cultivated, but with ample room for grandchildren. *Adm £1 Chd free. Sun June 23 (2-6)*

Church Farm ⅊❀ (Mr & Mrs N Slade) Lower Failand. 5m SW Bristol. Take B3128 Bristol to Clevedon, turn R at Xrds opp Failand Stores, Beggar Bush Lane and L at T junction; or M5 junction 19 towards Bristol but turn R in 50yds to Portbury. On leaving village turn L Failand Lane, turn L at T junction. Organic garden. Many clematis. Interesting trees and plants. Cream TEAS Sun May 19 only. *Adm £1.50 Chd 20p (Share to Friends of Bristol Eye Hospital®). Suns May 19, June 30 (2-5). Private visits welcome (min 6 people) by appt, please Tel 01275 373033*

Clifton Gardens ✿ Bristol. Close to Clifton Suspension Bridge. *Combined adm £1.50 Chd 25p. Sun June 9 (2-5.30)*
   9 Sion Hill ❀ (Mr & Mrs R C Begg) Entrance from Sion Lane. Small walled town garden, densely planted; climbing & herbaceous plants; herb garden; old roses
   16 Sion Hill ⅊ (Drs Cameron and Ros Kennedy) Entrance via green door in Sion Lane, at side of No 16. Small pretty town garden with pond, several interesting shrubs and trees
   17 Sion Hill ⅊ (Mr & Mrs Philip Gray) Entrance from Sion Lane. Town garden with trees and shrubs. TEAS

Coley Court & The Little Manor ✿❀ Teas at **Manor Farm**. *Combined adm £1.50 Chd free. Sun April 14 (2-6)*
   Coley Court (Mrs M J Hill) East Harptree, 8m N of Wells. Take B3114 through East Harptree turn L signed Coley and Hinton Blewitt. From A39 at Chewton Mendip take B3114 2m, sign on R, Coley, Hinton Blewitt, follow lane 400yds to white house on L before bridge. 1-acre garden, open lawn, stone walls, spring bulbs; 1-acre old Somerset orchard. Early Jacobean house (not open)
   The Little Manor (Mrs K P P Goldschmidt) Farrington Gurney on A39. Turn E in village on to A362 towards Radstock-600yds turn L. ¾-acre spring garden; many varieties of bulbs, flowering trees, many rare shrubs; rose garden. Early C17 house with attractive courtyard

Coombe Dingle Gardens ⅊❀ 4m NW of Bristol centre. From Portway down Sylvan Way, turn left into the Dingle and Grove Rd. From Westbury-on-Trym, Canford Lane sharp right at beginning of Westbury Lane. From Bristol over Downs, Parrys Lane, Coombe Lane; turn left and sharp right into the Dingle and Grove Rd. TEAS Hillside.

Combined adm £1.50 Chd free. Easter Sun, Mon April 7, 8 (2-6)
   Hillside (Mrs C M Luke) 42 Grove Rd. 2 acres late Georgian lay-out. Victorian rose garden; fine trees, shrubs. Walled kitchen garden
   Pennywell (Mr & Mrs D H Baker) Grove Rd. 2 acres; varied collection trees and shrubs, fritillaries, spring bulbs and flowers naturalised in grass, organic kitchen garden. Views over adjoining Blaise Castle Estate, Kingsweston Down and the Trym Valley. Exhibition of sculpture by Mary Donington. Plant stall in aid of Friends of Blaise

Crowe Hall ❀ (John Barratt Esq) Widcombe. 1m SE of Bath. L up Widcombe Hill, off A36, leaving White Hart on R. Large varied garden; fine trees, lawns, spring bulbs, series of enclosed gardens cascading down steep hillside. Italianate terracing and Gothick Victorian grotto contrast with park-like upper garden. Dramatic setting, with spectacular views of Bath. New trellis and water garden created in 1995. Featured in NGS gardens video 2. Dogs welcome. TEAS. *Adm £1.50 Chd 50p. Suns March 24; May 12, 26; July 14. For NGS Suns April 21, June 16 (2-6). Also private visits welcome, please Tel 01225 310322*

Doynton House ⅊❀ (Mrs C E Pitman) Doynton. 8m E of Bristol 7m N of Bath. ¾m NE of A420 at E end of Wick. Mature, old fashioned 2-acre garden with herbaceous borders, shrubs and lawns. TEAS. *Adm £1 Chd 50p (Share to Doynton Parish Church®). Sun June 23 (2-6)*

Dyrham Park ✿❀ (The National Trust) 8m N of Bath. 12m E of Bristol. Approached from Bath-Stroud Road (A46), 2m S of Tormarton interchange with M4, exit 18. Situated on W side of late C17 house. Herbaceous borders, yews clipped as buttresses, ponds and cascade, parish church set on terrace. Niches and carved urns. Long lawn to old west entrance. Deer Park. TEAS in aid of NT. *Adm incl Deer Park £2.60 Chd £1.30. Sun May 12 (11-5.30)*

Failand Court ⅊❀ (Mr & Mrs B Nathan) Lower Failand. 6m SW of Bristol. Take B3128 from Bristol towards Clevedon. Past Long Ashton Golf Club, over traffic lights in Failand. Second turning R to Lower Failand. Or M5 junction 19 towards Bristol. 1st R through Portbury, turn L into Failand Lane. 1m to top of hill. Turn L past church first R. Park in Oxhouse Lane. 1¼-acre mature garden originally landscaped by Sir Edward Fry. Further developed by Miss Agnes Fry. Interesting trees, shrubs and vegetable garden. TEAS. *Adm £1.50 Chd free. Suns April 7, July 7 (2-5)*

¶**Frenchay Gardens** ✿ 5m N of Bristol. From M32 take Exit 1 towards Downend. Follow signs towards Frenchay Hospital. At t-lights turn R, take 4th turn L at mini roundabout for parking at Church and Frenchay Common. Limited parking in Malmains Drive. TEAS in aid of Frenchay Church. *Combined adm £2.50 Chd 25p. Sat, Sun May 4, 5 (2-6)*
   ¶**Lluestowen** ⅊ (Mrs B Wiltshire) Bristol Rd. 1-acre old established spacious garden with a specimen Tulip Tree and other unusual trees. Many flowering cherries and pine trees. Paved courtyard with moongate entrance. Large area of strawberry beds

¶**20 Malmains Drive** (Mr & Mrs P G Mayall) Approx ⅕-acre divided into 3 areas with mixed borders of shrubs and herbaceous plants. Part woodland

¶**29 Malmains Drive** ♿ (Mr & Mrs G E Bayley) Approx ⅓-acre. Long narrow garden with established trees creating areas for shade loving plants leading to an open area with summerhouse. Access to neighbour's garden with fish and water features

¶**33 Malmains Drive** ♿❀ (Mr & Mrs Eric White) ⅓-acre plantsman's garden designed by owners since 1983 for low maintenance with unusual trees and shrubs. A yr-round garden split up into different planting areas - mixed shrub and perennial borders, heather bed with grasses, wild area, rock garden plus container planting

Gardener's Cottage ✂❀ (Mr & Mrs M J Chillcott) Wick Lane, Upton Cheyney. 6m NW of Bath; 8m SE of Bristol off A431, turn L near Bitton signposted Upton Cheyney; ¾m up Brewery Hill, 1st turning L after Upton Inn, parking at Upton Inn. 1-acre part walled garden, formerly kitchen garden of early C18 Manor House. Picturesque setting overlooking the Mendips. Garden created by present owners with the introduction of a large variety of trees/shrubs, mixed/herbaceous borders, several pergolas, rock gardens/conifer beds and a fine selection of ornamental grasses. Also a formal and large informal Koi pond and bog garden with streams, bridges and other interesting water features. TEAS. *Adm £1 Chd free. Weds May 15, June 19, July 24 (3-8); Weds Sept 18, Oct 16 (2-6). Also by appt for groups of 10 or more, please* **Tel 01272 9326767**

Goblin Combe ✂❀ (Mrs H R Burn) Cleeve. 10m S of Bristol on A370, turn L onto Cleeve Hill Rd just before Lord Nelson Inn. After 300 yds turn L onto Plunder St, first drive on R. Car parking near the bottom of the drive just beyond the Plunder St turning. 2 acre terraced garden with interesting collection of trees, shrubs and borders, surrounded by orchards, fields and woodlands. Magnificent views. TEAS. *Adm £1.50 Chd free (Share to The Music Space Trust®). Sat, Sun June 15, 16 (2-5.30)*

Highview ✂ (Mike & Mary Clavey) Portishead. From Bristol take the A369 (10m) M5 Junction 19, 1½m from Portishead on Coast Rd to Clevedon, take L turn into Hillcrest Rd. Property found at end of a private drive bottom of steep hill. Please park in Hillcrest Rd. 1-acre garden made from scratch by owners since 1987. Large collection of heathers, variety of plants in mixed borders. Herbaceous and rockery plants, miniature rose bed, water features. Alpine bed. Lovely channel views. Garden slightly on slope. TEAS. *Adm £1 Chd free. Weds May 8, 29; June 5, 19; July 10, 17; Aug 7, 21; Sept 11, 18; Sats May 18; July 27; Aug 17, 31; Sept 14; Suns June 30, July 28, Aug 18 (2-5.30). Also private visits welcome, please* **Tel 01275 849873**

Hill House ♿✂❀ (Dr & Mrs Richard Adlam) 4m N of Chipping Sodbury on B4060. Through Wickwar, L by wall signed to M5; then 200yds on L. 7 acres of land, of which 4 acres of gardens originally designed and planted by Sally, Duchess of Westminster. Gold/silver plantings in gravel; pleached lime walk; wild flowers and bulbs; owls and pheasant aviaries, peacocks, flock of Southdown sheep. TEAS. *Adm £2 Chd £1. Sun May 19 (2-6)*

Jasmine Cottage ✂❀ (Mr & Mrs Michael Redgrave) 26 Channel Rd, Clevedon. 12m W of Bristol (junction 20 off M5). Follow signs to seafront and pier, continue N on B3124, past Walton Park Hotel, turn R at St Mary's Church. Medium-sized garden created by owners from a wooded shelter belt for interest in all seasons. Old--fashioned roses; clematis, pergola; mixed shrub borders; island beds; gravel beds, pond and potager. Many unusual herbaceous, tender perennials and climbers. Plants propagated from the garden available in small nursery area. Toilet facilities. Pre-booked Teas only on Thurs in April and May. TEAS Thurs in June to Aug and all Suns. Groups to pre-book. *Adm £1 Chd free. Suns March 17, April 28, May 26, June 23, July 21, Aug 25 (2-6). Every Thurs April 18 to Aug 22 (2.30-5.30). Private visits welcome April to Sept, please* **Tel 01275 871850**

Lady Farm ♿✂❀ (Mr & Mrs M Pearce) Chelwood. On the A368 ½m E of Chelwood Bridge Xrds (A37 & A368) 9m S of Bristol and 9m W of Bath. The existing garden, started 10 yrs ago, covers an area of 1 acre, but a further 6 acres are currently being developed. Surrounding the farmhouse and courtyard are shrub and herbaceous borders, climbers, roses and a terrace overlooking a recently created, spring fed watercourse which flows into a lake in the valley with adjacent rock features. Extensive shelter belts have, and are, being planted, and woodland and lakeside walks are in the early stages of development. This garden is NOT recommended for children under 14. Ample parking. TEAS in aid of Chelwood Church. *Adm £1.50 Chd 50p. Sun July 21 (2-6). Private parties welcome, please* **Tel 01761 490770**

10 Linden Road ❀ (Ruth & William Salisbury) Clevedon. Coming from the seafront, head up Alexandra Rd opp the pier, cross the roundabout. Linden Rd is between the Midland and Barclays Banks. No 10 is 150yds on the R. A very small but richly planted seaside town garden. Over 400 different species of trees, shrubs and plants grow in 3 areas, the largest being 35′ × 40′. A garden developed with children in mind and having shape, form and colour throughout the year. TEAS. *Adm £1 Chd free. Open by appt only Suns March to Oct, please* **Tel 01275 874694**

Madron ✂❀ (Mr & Mrs Martin Carr) Ostlings Lane, Bathford. Approx 3½m E of Bath close to A4. At Batheaston roundabout take A363 Bradford-upon-Avon Rd; then 1st turning L, Ostlings Lane is immediately on R alongside Crown Inn. At top of short rise 100yds, stone pillars on L are entrance to Madron - 2nd house on L along drive. 1½ acres overlooking Avon valley. Conifers, trees, hardy and tender perennials, water garden and fine lawns. Designed with an artist's eye for plant and colour associations. Featured in RHS book 'Planting your Garden'. TEAS. *Adm £1.50 Chd free. June 10 to July 26 by prior appt only. Parties and painters welcome, please* **Tel 01225 859792**

By Appointment Gardens. These owners do not have a fixed opening day usually because they do not like crowds or have insufficient parking space. Owner will often give guided tour

The Manor House &*❀* (Mr & Mrs Simon Wills) Walton-in-Gordano, 2m NE of Clevedon. Entrance on N side of B3124, Clevedon to Portishead Rd, just by houses on roadside nearest Clevedon. Clevedon-Portishead buses stop in Village. 4-acres; trees, shrubs, herbaceous and bulbs mostly labelled. Coaches by appt only. TEAS (Suns only) in aid of St Peter's Hospice Bristol. *Adm £1.50, Acc chd under 14 free (Share to St Peter's Hospice, Bristol®). Tues April 16 to Sept 17 (10-4); Suns April 14, May 12, June 9, July 14, Aug 11 (2-6). Private visits welcome all year, please* Tel 01275 872067

Old Down House &*❀* (Mr & Mrs Robert Bernays) Tockington, 10m N of Bristol. Follow brown Tourist Board signs to Oldown from A38 at Alveston. 5 acres divided into small formal and informal gardens by hedges and walls; topiary, shrubs; extensive lawns; rock garden; fine trees (weeping beeches, etc). Herbaceous borders, semi-wild areas with spring and autumn cyclamen; fine views to Severn and Welsh hills. TEAS. *Adm £1 Chd free (Share to Bristol Age Care®). Sat, Sun March 30, 31; Sept 14, 15 (2-6). Private parties welcome, please* Tel 01454 413605

¶**Old Rectory** &*❀* (Sheila & Robert Sawyer) Doynton. 2-acre garden surrounding Rectory with mature woodland and walled garden. Old-fashioned roses, shrubs and herbaceous plantings in mixed borders. Some new planting over past 2 yrs. Homemade ice cream and lemonade. *Adm £1 Chd 50p (Share to Doynton Parish Church®). Sun June 23 (2-6)*

2 Old Tarnwell *❀*❀ (Ken & Mary Payne) Upper Stanton Drew. Lies 6m S of Bristol between the B3130 and A368 just W of Pensford. Detailed directions given when appt. is made. A quart of good plants poured into a quarter pint sized plot featuring various colour themed borders, ornamental grasses, ferns, clematis and a well stocked "puddle"! Possibly the smallest, most intensively planted garden in the Yellow Book (total 0.02 acres). Plenty of ideas for small gardeners! Regret not suitable for children. Gold Award Garden (Garden News). TEAS and plants at nearby nursery. *Adm £1.25. Only by appt. Wed June 26, Thurs July 4, 11, Tues July 16 (10-9), please* Tel 01275 333146

Parsonage Farm *❀*❀ (Mr & Mrs Andrew Reid) Publow. 9m S of Bristol. A37 Bristol-Wells; at top of Pensford Hill, almost opp B3130 to Chew Magna, take lane which runs down side of row of houses; 250yds on R. 3½-acre woodland garden with large collection of trees and shrubs incl rhododendrons, azaleas and conifers; tuffa-stone rockery and heather garden. Partly suitable for wheelchairs. TEAS in aid of All Saints, Publow. *Adm £1.50 Chd free. Sat, Sun May 18, 19 (2-5)*

Pearl's Garden &*❀* (Mr & Mrs D Watts) Coalpit Heath. NE Bristol. Take Downend (Westerleigh Rd) to Tomarton Rd past Folly Public House over motorway and garden is 500yds on L. From junction 18 on M4, turn N on the A46 and almost immed L signposted Pucklechurch. After 5½m the garden is on R shortly before bridge over motorway. 2 acres developed since 1966; mixed trees, flowering shrubs with 100 varieties of hollies; herb and water gardens; peafowl. Good views over Bristol from outside stairs. TEAS. *Adm £1.50 Chd free.*

Each Sun in May and June. For NGS Sun, Mon May 26, 27 (11-5). Ploughman's Lunch available. Also private visits welcome May and June, please Tel 01179 562953

Petty France Hotel &❀ (W J Fraser Esq) Badminton. On A46 5m N exit 18 M4. Edge of Badminton Estate. Chipping Sodbury 5m. 2 acres of mature shrubs and trees incl specimen cedar, 200-yr-old yew hedge, medlar and tulip tree. Vegetable garden and herbs. Many spring flowers and shrubs. TEAS. *Adm £1 Chd free. Sun May 12 (2-6) Private parties also welcome please* Tel 01454 238361

¶**Quakers** &*❀* (Mrs Mary Bailey) Lower Hazel. 10m N of Bristol. Turn off A38 in Rudgeway, signposted to Lower Hazel and Old Down. ¼m at bottom of hill. Mature ¾-acre garden set against a backdrop of natural woodland. A large herbaceous and other colour themed mixed borders planted for seasonal interest. Surrounding the main lawn which is dominated by a large magnolia are mature shrubs. A ¼-acre 'paddock' with large pond; marginal planting, trees and ornamental shrubs. A vegetable plot screened by roses and clematis, shade plantings and extensive climbers on the house. Ploughman's lunch and TEAS. *Adm £1.50 Chd free. Sun Aug 11 (11-5)*

Rock House *❀*❀ (Mr & Mrs John Gunnery) Elberton. B4461 Severn Bridge to Alveston. From bridge, in Elberton, take 1st turning L to Littleton-on-Severn and turn immed R. 1-acre walled garden undergoing improvement. Pond and old yew tree. Mixed borders. Cottage garden plants. *Adm £1 Chd free (Share to St John's Church, Elberton®). Sun June 2 (2-6)*

Sherborne Garden &❀ (Mr & Mrs John Southwell) Litton. 15m S of Bristol, 7m N of Wells. On B3114 Litton to Harptree, ½m past Ye Olde Kings Arms. 4 acre landscaped garden developed from fields since 1964 offering wide variety of shrubs, trees and herbaceous plants, incl. many unusual items. Collections of hollies, ferns, hostas, species roses, grasses, daylilies; ponds, pinetum. Picnic area. Featured on 'Gardeners World' and 'Garden Club'. Home-made TEAS June 16. At other times tea and biscuits. *Adm £1.50 Chd free. Suns, Mons June through Sept. For NGS Suns March 31, June 16, July 14, Sept 15 (11-6). Private visits and parties welcome throughout year, please* Tel 01761 241220

Stanton Drew Gardens &*❀*❀ 7m S Bristol A37 Bristol-Wells; at top of Pensford Hill take B3130 to Chew Magna. After 1m turn towards Stanton Drew at thatched round house. Cautiously negotiate humpbacked bridge and the gardens are just after the bridge. Parking is supervised. Refreshments in aid of Village Funds. *Combined adm £2 Chd free. Sun June 30 (12-6)*

> **Hall Cottage** (Ivor & Kate Watkins) This small garden is typically cottage, with a strong emphasis on vegetables neatly set in plots surrounded by grass paths, with colour from herbaceous and bedding borders, pond and fruit areas. 2 greenhouses provide the facilities for raising all the stock and many more interesting plants are available for sale
>
> **Rectory Farm House** (Dr & Mrs J P Telling) ½-acre garden surrounding C15 Church House later used as a farmhouse. Garden completely redesigned and replanted over the past 2yrs. Trees, shrubs, mixed borders, pond and new rock garden

Stanton Court (Dr R J Price & Partners) A new garden established from 1986 to complement the recreational needs of a Nursing Home. Ideal for disabled visitors. Access for elderly persons a priority. Our aim is minimal maintenance with maximum variety. The wide range of plants have been largely donated by the locality. Pond; terrace garden; patio; large sweeping borders; cut flower beds and fruits in season. Mature copper beech and cedars

Stanton Prior Gardens &❀ 6m from Bath on A39 Wells Rd; at Marksbury turn L to Stanton Prior; gardens either side of Church set in beautiful countryside in unspoilt village. Ploughman's lunch & cream TEAS. *Combined adm £2 Chd free. Every Wed May 1 to Aug 28 (11-5). For NGS Sun May 26, Wed June 26 (11-5). Parties by appt all year, please* Tel 01761 471942
   Church Farm (Mr & Mrs Lesley Hardwick) Herbaceous borders, rock garden, scree garden; shrub roses, many unusual plants, wild area with ¼-acre pond; ducks and geese
   The Old Rectory (Lt Col & Mrs Patrick Mesquita) 1-acre garden incl medieval pond. Landscaped and replanted since 1983, with unusual shrubs and plants, apple and pear arches and pergola with white roses and clematis; a newly-created knot garden
   ¶**The Gables** (Mr & Mrs Alistair Hardwick) Newly created cottage garden open for NGS days

¶**Stockwood Gardens** ❀❀ nr Bristol. A37 Wells Rd. At Whitchurch t-lights (Black Lion) turn into Staunton Lane. Two gardens within 1m of each other. *Adm £1 each garden (not suitable for children). Mon, Tues April 15, 16 Thurs, Fris July 18, 19; Aug 29, 30 (2-dusk) Private visits welcome*
   ¶**19 Derricke Rd** (M Tucker) 6th L turn on Staunton Lane then 1st R. This garden demonstrates what can be done with a corner plot on a housing estate in 3 yrs. Densely and colourfully planted with all yr-round interest incl spring and summer bulbs, climbers, herbaceous perennials, conifers, ferns, grasses, trees, shrubs, tubs, hanging baskets, statues & small pond. Tel 01275 542727
   ¶**74 Cowling Drive** (B Brooks) Turn L at 1st roundabout on Staunton Lane then 1st L (Craydon Rd). Take 5th L (Cowling Rd) and at T-junction L into cul-de-sac. Peaceful mature garden (not large) planted for yr-round interest with trees, shrubs, conifers, herbacious plants, bulbs, tubs and hanging baskets. TEAS in aid of NSCA. Tel 01275 831898

Tranby House ❀❀ (Paul & Jan Barkworth) Norton Lane, Whitchurch. ½m S of Whitchurch Village. Leave Bristol on A37 Wells Rd, through Whitchurch Village 1st turning on R, signposted Norton Malreward. 1¼-acre informal garden, designed and planted to encourage wildlife. Wide variety of trees, shrubs, and flowers; ponds and new wild flower meadow. Plants and pressed flower pictures for sale in aid of The Wildlife Trust. Partly suitable for wheelchairs. TEA. *Adm £1.50 Chd free. Sun June 9; Sat July 20, Suns July 21, Aug 18 (2-5.30)*

University of Bristol Botanic Garden &❀❀ Bracken Hill, North Rd, Leigh Woods, 1m W of Bristol via Clifton. Cross suspension bridge, North Rd is 1st R. As featured on Gardeners World 1993, 1994 and 1995, Superintendent Nicholas Wray, (presenter). 5-acre garden supporting approx 4,500 species; special collections incl cistus, hebe, ferns, salvia and sempervivum, plus many native plants. Range of glasshouses and large Pulhams rock garden. TEAS. *Adm £1 Chd 50p (Share to Friends of Bristol University Botanic Garden®). Private visits welcome all year, please* Tel 01179 733682. *For NGS Suns July 7, Sept 1 (11-5)*

The Urn Cottage &❀❀ (Mr A C & Dr L A Rosser) 19 Station Road, Charfield, Wotton-under-Edge, Glos GL12 8SY. 3m W of Wotton-under-Edge and 3m E of M5 exit 14. In Charfield turn off main road at The Railway Tavern, then 400 yds on L: short walk from parking. ¾-acre cottage garden made from scratch by owners since 1982 surrounding stone built cottage in country setting. Wide variety and profusion of plants in mixed borders of differing character, incl small streamside gardens. TEAS in aid of CLIC and Bournstream. *Adm £1.50 Chd 30p. Suns April 7 (2-5), June 16, Mons Feb 26, March 25, April 29, May 27, Sept 30, Oct 14 (2-4) Sun June 16 (2-6). Disabled please contact us before visiting. Parties by appt all year*

Vine House & (Mrs T F Hewer) Henbury Rd, Henbury. 4m N of Bristol. Bus stop: Salutation, Henbury, 50yds. 2-acres; trees, shrubs, water garden, bulbs, naturalised garden landscaped and planted by present owner since 1946. TEAS. *Adm £1 OAPs/Chd 50p (Share to Friends of Blaise®). Private visits welcome all year, please* Tel 01179 503573

West Tyning &❀❀ (Mr & Mrs G S Alexander) Beach. From Bath (6m) or Bristol (7m) on A431. From Bitton village turn N up Golden Valley Lane, signposted Beach. Continue up lane for 2m to Wick–Upton Cheyney Xrds, turn R towards Upton Cheyney for 200yds. Parking in nearby field. 1¼-acre garden; roses and clematis over a series of pergolas which separate and join different areas; lawns with curved mixed borders in both sun and shade; woodland with ferns, hellebores and other shade plants; rough grass with fruit and shrubs; rock garden and vegetable garden. TEAS with home-made cakes by Bitton WI. *Adm £1.50 Chd free. Sat, Sun Aug 31, Sept 1 (2-6)*

Windmill Cottage ❀❀ (Alan & Pam Harwood) Hillside Rd, Backwell. 8m SW of Bristol. Take A370 out of Bristol to Backwell, ½m past Xrds/traffic lights, turn L into Hillside Rd. Parking available in Backwell and New Inn (10 min walk). Hillside Rd is single track lane with no parking (unless for special reasons). Into a 2-acre plot put a plentiful variety of plants, add to this a pinch of knowledge and a sprinkling of wildflowers, together with a reasonable amount of ground cover; blend in some colour and a generous dash of fragrance. Bind the whole thing together with a large collection of clematis, balanced with a proportion of vegetables. A good supply of enthusiasm to be added at regular intervals. TEAS. *Adm £1.50 Chd 50p. Weds May 15, (2-5.30) June 19, July 17; Aug 21 (2-7.30) Sept 18 (2-5.30). Groups welcome by appt, please* Tel 01275 463492

Bedfordshire

Hon County Organiser: Mr & Mrs C Izzard, Broadfields, Keysoe Row East, Bedford MK44 2JD

DATES OF OPENING

March 16 Saturday
Swiss Garden, nr Biggleswade
March 31 Sunday
Broadfields, Keysoe Row East
April 7 Sunday
King's Arms Path Garden,
Ampthill
April 14 Sunday
Broadfields, Keysoe Row East
April 21 Sunday
Woburn Abbey, Woburn
April 28 Sunday
Howard's House, Cardington
May 7 Tuesday
Seal Point, Luton
May 12 Sunday
Luton Hoo Gardens, Luton
Odell Castle, nr Bedford
The Old Stables, Hockliffe
May 19 Sunday
Aspley Guise Gardens,
Buckinghamshire
May 26 Sunday
88 Castlehill Rd, Middle End,
Totternhoe

Milton House, nr Bedford
June 2 Sunday
Southill Park, nr Biggleswade
June 4 Tuesday
Seal Point, Luton
June 9 Sunday
The Old Stables, Hockliffe
Woburn Abbey, Woburn
Yelden Gardens
June 16 Sunday
Dean and Shelton Gardens,
Huntingdon
June 23 Sunday
The Old Rectory, Pertenhall
Odell Castle, nr Bedford
Toddington Manor, Toddington
June 30 Sunday
88 Castlehill Rd, Middle End,
Totternhoe
Grove Lodge, 6 Deepdale, Potton
Howard's House, Cardington
Woodleys Farm House,
Melchbourne
July 2 Tuesday
Seal Point, Luton
July 14 Sunday
Barton-Le-Clay Gardens

6 High Street, Clophill
The Old Stables, Hockliffe
July 20 Saturday
Broadfields, Keysoe Row East
July 21 Sunday
Broadfields, Keysoe Row East
July 28 Sunday
Crosshall Manor, nr St Neots
August 6 Tuesday
Seal Point, Luton
August 18 Sunday
The Old Stables, Hockliffe
September 3 Tuesday
Seal Point, Luton
September 21 Saturday
Swiss Garden, nr Biggleswade

Regular openings
For details see garden description

Luton Hoo Gardens, Luton
Toddington Manor, Toddington

DESCRIPTIONS OF GARDENS

Aspley Guise Gardens 2m SW of M1 (Exit 13) towards Woburn Sands. Entrance from Church Rd. *Combined adm £2 Chd £1. Sun May 19 (2-6)*
   Aspley House ⚹ (Mr & Mrs C I Skipper) House on E side of village. 5 acres; shrubs and lawns. William and Mary house (not open). Woburn Sands Band and local childrens orchestra in attendance and other special activities. TEAS
   The Rookery ⚹ (C R Randall Esq) 5 acres; rhododendrons and woodland

Barton-Le-Clay Gardens & 6m N of Luton on the B655 Barton-le-Clay to Hitchin rd. Hitchin 5m. TEAS at The Rectory. *Combined adm £2.50 Chd £1. Sun July 14 (2-6)*
   47 Hexton Road ✿ (Mrs S H Horsler) ¼-acre cottage garden with mixed borders
   The Rectory (Canon Peter Whittaker) 2 acres with background of Chilterns; moat, herbaceous border, mature trees, lawns; overlooked by C12 church

Broadfields &✿ (Mr & Mrs Chris Izzard) Keysoe Row East. Leave Bedford on Kimbolton Rd B660 approx 8½m. Turn R at Keysoe Xrds by White Horse public house ½m on R. 3 acres; herbaceous borders; spring bulbs, summer bedding, fuchsias; mature trees; shrubs; vegetable and fruit gardens. TEAS. *Adm £1.50 Chd 50p. Suns March 31, April 14 (2-6) Sat July 20 (2-6) Sun July 21 (10-2). Private visits welcome, please* **Tel 01234 376326**

88 Castlehill Road ⚹✿ (Chris & Carole Jell) Middle End, Totternhoe. 2m W of Dunstable, R turn off B489 Aston-Clinton Rd. Fronting main rd approx ½m through village. Elevated position with fine views across Aylesbury Vale and Chilterns. Adjoining Totternhoe Knolls Nature Reserve. ½-acre, S sloping on limestone and clay, entirely created by owners. Plantsman garden for all seasons; designed as small gardens within a garden since 1986; shrubs; climbers and herbaceous. TEAS. *Adm £1.50 Chd free. Suns May 26, June 30 (2-6). Also private visits welcome, please* **Tel 01525 220780**

¶**Crosshall Manor** & (Mr V Constantine) Crosshall, Eaton Ford. Just off A1 on the B1048 NW of St Neots. C18 manor house situated in 1½ acres of formal lawned gardens with mature trees, mixed borders, shrubs, currently being developed to include terrace, pools with fall fountains; formal rose gardens, pergolas, pots, trough plantings and other features. TEAS. *Adm £1.50 Chd 50p. Sun July 28 (2-6)*

¶**Dean & Shelton Gardens** N of Bedford on Northants/Cambs border, 4m W of Kimbolton. Home-made TEAS. Tickets and maps in each village. Please use free car parks. No coaches. *Combined adm £3 OAP £2 Chd £1 (Share to All Hallows Church, Dean; St Mary's Church, Shelton®). Sun June 16 (2-6)*

Lower Dean

¶**Inglenook House** & (Mr & Mrs Bill Ashby) ¾-acre garden, shrubs, trees, herbaceous, pond and water garden

¶**The Old Butcher's Shop** &❀ (Mr & Mrs P Draper) ⅓-acre artist's garden with emphasis on form, texture and colour. Studio also open

Upper Dean

¶**Dean House Farm** & (Mr & Mrs Paul Cook) C16 farmhouse with ½-acre garden being gradually rescued by owners. Pond with geese and ducks

¶**Francis House** ❀ (Mr & Mrs David Butter) Traditional garden begun in 1991 around restored C16 farmhouse. Many choice and unusual plants. Monksilver plant stall

¶**Highbank House** & (Mr & Mrs D J Gray) 1-acre garden, interesting trees, shrubs, herbaceous borders. Pond and knot garden

Shelton

¶**Squirrel Cottage** & (Mr & Mrs D A Saunders) ¾-acre garden with deep herbaceous borders, specimen shrubs and trees

¶**The Little House** & (Mr & Mrs I W Burns) Cottage garden, herbaceous and shrub borders, vegetable garden

¶**The Old Rectory** &❀ (Mr & Mrs J H Wells) Approx 6-acres, sweeping lawns, herbaceous border, roses, orchard

Grove Lodge ❀❀ (Peter Wareing & Jean Venning) 6 Deepdale, Potton. 2m E of Sandy on 1042 towards Potton, past RSPB Reserve, downhill to Xrds. L at 'Locomotive' - lane to TV mast; first house on R. 1½-acre sandy hillside garden; conifers; heathers, shrubs, incl rhododendrons, climbing roses, herbaceous border, orchard with wild flowers, rockery banks with pond. TEAS and plant sale in aid of R.A.T.S. *Adm £1.50 OAP £1 Chd 50p. Sun June 30 (2-6). Private visits welcome for parties of 12 and over, please* Tel 01767 261298

¶**6 High Street** &❀ (Mrs Janice Rogers) Clophill. Midway between Bedford and Luton. Turn R just N of the A6, A507 roundabout. Limited parking on the village green, if full use the Flying Horse and Green Man car parks. ½-acre informal gardens bordering the R Flit. Beds densely planted with shrubs and herbaceous perennials, many unusual with thought given to the plant and colour combinations. Climbing roses, mature trees and bog garden containing interesting moisture loving plants. *Adm £1.50 Chd 50p. Sun July 14 (2-6). Private visits welcome, please* Tel 01525 860 853

Howard's House & (Humphrey Whitbread Esq) Cardington. 2m SE of Bedford. Large walled flower and vegetable gardens; flowering cherries and clematis, mature trees. *Adm £1.50 Chd 50p. Suns April 28, June 30 (2-6)*

Kings Arms Path Garden &❀❀ Ampthill Town Council (Mrs N W Hudson) Ampthill. Free parking in town centre. Entrance opp. old Market Place, Ampthill, down Kings Arms Yard. Small woodland garden of about 1½ acres created by plantsman the late William Nourish. Trees, shrubs, bulbs and many interesting collections. Maintained since 1987 by 'The Friends of the Garden.' Tea at adjacent Bowling Club or nearby tea shops. *Adm 50p Chd 25p. Suns Feb 11, (2-4). May 26, June 23, Aug 25 (2.30-5). For NGS Sun April 7 (2.30-5). Private group visits welcome, please* Tel 01525 402030

Luton Hoo Gardens ❀❀ Luton; junction 10 M1. Entrance at Park St gates. The mansion house where you can view the Wernher Collection is set in a Capability Brown landscape with formal gardens and a secluded rock garden. TEAS. *Adm gardens only £2.50 OAPs £2.25 Chd £1. Easter to Oct 13, Fris, Sats, Suns (12-5). For NGS Sun May 12 (12-5)*

Milton House &❀ (Mr & Mrs Clifton Ibbett) nr Bedford. N of Bedford on the A6. The drive to the house is on the R, S of the village of Milton Ernest. Formal, terrace and sunken gardens set in large grounds with lakes and waterfall. TEAS in aid of All Saints Parish Church, Milton Ernest. *Adm £2 Chd 50p. Sun May 26 (2-6)*

Odell Castle (The Rt Hon Lord Luke) Odell. NW of Bedford. From A6 turn W through Sharnbrook; from A428, N through Lavendon and Harrold. Station: Bedford 10m. Terrace and lower garden down to R. Ouse. House built 1962 on old site, using original stone. TEA. *Adm £1 Chd free. Suns May 12, June 23 (2-6)*

¶**The Old Rectory** &❀ (Mr & Mrs F R Finiston) Pertenhall. Situated on B660 approx 10m from Bedford 1½m from Kimbolton. 4 acres of mature gardens approached through lime avenue. Walled garden with special features, ancient (perhaps the largest) mulberry and rare medlar. Shrubberies and herbaceous borders; scented and kitchen gardens, views over large pond and paddocks. Many interesting and developing features. *Adm £2 Chd free. Sun June 23 (2-6)*

The Old Stables ❀❀ (Mr & Mrs D X Victor) 3m N of Dunstable. From A5 in Hockliffe, W on A4012. Turn R after ¼m (signposted Church End), then L at Church. Follow lane for ½m and take field track on R. 2 acres incl walled garden. Alpines, mixed herbaceous and shrub borders. Wide range of plants incl hardy geraniums, erodiums, dianthus, saxifrages, euphorbias, deutzias and clematis. National collections of alpine dianthus and erodium. *Adm £1.50 Chd 50p (Share to Milton Keynes City Orchestra®). Suns May 12, June 9, July 14, Aug 18 (2-6)*

Seal Point ❀❀ (Mrs Danae Johnston) 7 Wendover Way. In NE Luton, turning N off Stockingstone Rd into Felstead Way. A small sloping most exciting town garden with many unusual herbaceous plants, climbers and trees; water features, topiary cats and bonsai; beds with oriental flavour representing yin and yang; original ornaments, grasses, ferns, architectural plants and much more. TEA by arrangement. *Adm £2 Chd under 14 free. Tues May 7, June 4, July 2, Aug 6, Sept 3 (2-6). Private visits welcome, also small groups, please* Tel 01582 611567

Southill Park &❀ (Mr & Mrs S C Whitbread) 5m SW of Biggleswade. Large garden, rhododendrons, renovated conservatory. *Adm £2 Chd £1 (Share to The Tradescant Trust®). Sun June 2 (2-5.30)*

Swiss Garden ᴅ✦ (Bedfordshire County Council) Old Warden, Biggleswade. Signposted from A1 and A600. 2m W Biggleswade, next door to the Shuttleworth Collection. 9 acres of landscaped gardens set out in 1830s alongside a further 10 acres native woodland with lakeside picnic area. Garden includes many tiny buildings, footbridges, ironwork features and intertwining ponds. Romantic landscape design highlighted by daffodils, rhododendrons and old rambling roses in season. *Adm £2.50 Concessions and Chd £1.25 (Share to Friends of the Swiss Garden©). Sats March 16, Sept 21 (1-5)*

Toddington Manor ᴅ✦ (Sir Neville & Lady Bowman-Shaw) Exit 12 M1. Signs in village. House and gardens restored by present owners. Walled garden with greenhouses and herb garden; beautiful roses and shrubs; lakeside walks in the woods. Rare Breeds Centre and Vintage Tractor collection. Cricket on pitch in front of house at weekends. Best months June and July. Gift Shop, home made TEAS. *Adm £3.50 OAP's £2.50 Chd £1.50. Special rates for parties. Open April 10 to Sept 29 daily (11-6). (Closed Mon & Tues incl Bank Hols). For NGS Sun June 23 (11-6)*

Woburn Abbey ✦ (The Marquess of Tavistock) Woburn. Woburn Abbey is situated 1½m from Woburn Village, which is on the A4012 almost midway from junctions 12 and 13 of the M1 motorway. 22 acres of private garden originally designed by Wyattville, with recent restoration of the The Duchess' rose garden. Unique hornbeam maze with C18 temple by Chambers. TEAS. *Adm £1 Chd free. Suns April 21 (gardens), Sun June 9 (gardens & maze) (11-5)*

Woodleys Farm House ᴅ✦✿ (Hon Mrs Hugh Lawson Johnston) Melchbourne. Leave A6 10m N of Bedford, or 4m S of Rushden. House reached by lime avenue before reaching village of Melchbourne. Small garden 1½ acres, with roses, lawns, shrubs and herbaceous plants. TEAS in aid of Melchbourne Church. *Adm £1 Chd free. Sun June 30 (3-6)*

Yelden Gardens ✦✿ Beds, Northants border 14m N of Bedford, 4m S of Rushden. Adjacent to A6 and A45. TEAS at The Manor. *Combined adm £2.50 Chd free. Sun June 9 (2-6)*
> **The Manor** (Mr & Mrs E Woolf) 2.5 acres. Formal rose garden surrounding fish pond. Shrubberies leading to tennis court. Herbaceous borders, ornamental garden, greenhouses. Dried flowers for sale and TEAS
> **The Old Rectory** (Mr & Mrs P Rushton) 2.5 acres of established gardens. Many fine trees, ornamental pond, herb garden, shrubberies

Berkshire

Hon County Organiser: Bob Avery Esq, 'Jingles', Derek Rd., Maidenhead, SL6 8NT Tel 01628 27580

Asst Hon County Organisers: The Hon Mrs J A Willoughby, Buckhold Farm, Pangbourne Tel 01734 744468
(NW) Mrs C M J Povey, Bussock Mayne, Snelsmore Common, Newbury Tel 01635 248347
(SW) Mrs P P A Meigh, Fishponds, West Woodhay, Nr Newbury Tel 01488 668269
(Central) Mrs M A Henderson, 'Ridings', Kentons Lane, Wargrave, RG10 8PB Tel 01734 402523
(Publicity & Brochures) Mrs J Bewsher, Arcturus, Church Road, Bray, Berks SL6 1UR Tel 01628 22824

Hon County Treasurer: Bob Avery Esq

DATES OF OPENING

March 17 Sunday
Foxgrove, Enborne, nr Newbury
March 31 Sunday
Welford Park, nr Newbury
April 8 Monday
Swallowfield Prk, nr Reading
April 14 Sunday
Blencathra, Finchampstead
Folly Farm, nr Reading
Kirby House, Inkpen ‡
Odney Club, Cookham
Scotlands, Cockpole Green, nr Wargrave

West Woodhay House, Inkpen ‡
April 21 Sunday
Foxgrove, Enborne, nr Newbury
The Harris Garden, Whiteknights, Reading
The Old Rectory, Farnborough, Wantage
April 24 Wednesday
The Old Rectory, Burghfield, nr Reading
May 1 Wednesday
Frogmore Gardens, Windsor
May 2 Thursday
Frogmore Gardens, Windsor

May 5 Sunday
Blencathra, Finchampstead
Bussock Wood, Snelsmore Common, nr Newbury
Simms Farm House, Mortimer, nr Reading
May 6 Monday
Simms Farm House, Mortimer, nr Reading
May 12 Sunday
Beenham House, Beenham ‡
Englefield House, Theale ‡
Hurst Gardens, nr Reading
The Old Rectory, Farnborough, Wantage

Padworth Common Gardens
Silwood Park, Ascot

May 19 Sunday
Old Rectory Cottage,
nr Pangbourne
Priory House, Sunningdale
Silwood Park, Ascot ‡
Sunningdale Park ‡

May 23 Thursday
Meadow House, nr Newbury

May 26 Sunday
Alderwood House, Greenham
Common
Bowdown House, Newbury
Englemere, nr Ascot
Little Bowden, Pangbourne
Waltham Place, White Waltham

May 27 Monday
Folly Farm, nr Reading

June 2 Sunday
Aldermaston Park, Aldermaston
Trunkwell Park, Beech Hill

June 6 Thursday
Meadow House, nr Newbury

June 9 Sunday
Bear Ash, Hare Hatch
Foxgrove, Enborne, nr Newbury
Meadow House, nr Newbury
Padworth Common Gardens

June 15 Saturday
Eton College, Windsor

June 16 Sunday
Fox Hill, Inkpen

June 23 Sunday
Alderwood House, Greenham
Common
Basildon Park, Lower Basildon
Folly Farm, nr Reading
Kirby House, Inkpen ‡
Peasmore Gardens
West Woodhay House,
Inkpen ‡

June 26 Wednesday
Rooksnest, Lambourn

June 30 Sunday
Combe Manor, Hungerford ‡
Donnington Grove Country Club,
Donnington, nr Newbury
The Old Rectory, Farnborough,
Wantage
Ockwells Manor, Maidenhead
Old Rectory Cottage,
nr Pangbourne
Withers Farmhouse, Inkpen ‡
Woolley Park, nr Wantage

July 7 Sunday
Little Bowden, Pangbourne
Stanford Dingley Village
Gardens

July 11 Thursday
Meadow House, nr Newbury

July 14 Sunday
Englefield House, Theale
Inkpen House, Inkpen

July 21 Sunday
The Old Mill, Aldermaston

Scotlands, Cockpole Green, nr
Wargrave
Waltham Place, White Waltham

July 25 Thursday
Meadow House, nr Newbury

July 31 Wednesday
The Old Rectory, Burghfield, nr
Reading

August 4 Sunday
Padworth Common Gardens

August 11 Sunday
Whiteknights, The Ridges,
Finchamstead

August 18 Sunday
Hurst Gardens, nr Reading
Meadow House, nr Newbury

September 1 Sunday
Trunkwell Park, Beech Hill

October 6 Sunday
Silwood Park, Ascot

Regular openings
For details see garden description

Englefield House, Theale
The Old Rectory, Burghfield, nr
Reading
Swallowfield Park, nr Reading
Waltham Place, White Waltham

DESCRIPTIONS OF GARDENS

Aldermaston Park ఉ֍ (Blue Circle Industries plc) Newbury 10m W; Reading 10m E; Basingstoke 8m off A340 S. 137-acres, surrounding Victorian Mansion (1849) with modern offices making interesting contrast of architecture. Fine trees; specimen rhododendrons and shrubs; large lawns; 11-acre lake with lakeside walk. TEA. *Adm £2 Chd free. Sun June 2 (1-4.30)*

Alderwood House ֍֍ (Mr & Mrs P B Trier) Greenham Common. S of Newbury take A 339 towards Basingstoke for approx 3m. Turn L towards New Greenham Park. Turn R immediately before gate along track to house. Interesting 2½-acre garden started in 1904. On many levels with a number of rare trees and shrubs. Old roses, herbaceous border, conservatory and fine vegetable garden. TEAS. *Adm £1 Chd 50p. Suns May 26, June 23 (2-6)*

Basildon Park ఉ֍֍ (Lord & Lady Iliffe; The National Trust) Lower Basildon, Reading. Between Pangbourne and Streatley, 7m NW of Reading on W of A329. Private garden designed and planted by Lady Iliffe with help of Lanning Roper. Open once a year for this occasion. Mainly old roses but other interesting plants constantly being added by owner. TEAS in NT house. *Adm £1 Chd free.* ▲*For NGS Sun June 23 (2-6)*

Bear Ash ֍֍ (Lord & Lady Remnant) Hare Hatch. 2m E of Wargrave. ½m N of A4 at Hare Hatch, between Read-

ing and Maidenhead. 2 acres charming garden overlooking lake in parkland; silver and gold planting; shrub and specie roses. TEAS. *Adm £2 Chd free (Share to NSPCC Berkshire Appeal®). Sun June 9 (2-6)*

Beenham House ఉ֍ (Prof & Mrs Gerald Benney) Beenham. ½-way between Reading and Newbury, 1m N of A4; entrance off Webbs Lane. 21 acres of grounds and garden; old Lebanon cedars, oaks, hornbeams; recent plantings. Good views of park and Kennett Valley. Regency house (not open). Coach parties by appt. TEAS. *Adm £1.50 Chd free (Share to St Mary's Church, Beenham®). Sun May 12 (2-6)*

Blencathra ఉ֍֍ (Dr & Mrs F W Gifford) Finchampstead. Entrance at the NW end of Finchampstead Ridges on B3348. Disabled passengers may alight near the house. 11-acre garden which present owners started in 1964, laid out and maintained with minimum of help. In 'Good Gardens Guide' since 1993. Many varied mature trees; lawns; heathers; rhododendrons; azaleas; wide range of conifers; three small lakes and stream; bog areas and spring bulbs. Interesting throughout year. TEAS. *Adm £2 Chd free. Suns April 14, May 5 (2-6); also private visits welcome individuals or parties, please* **Tel 01734 734563**

By Appointment Gardens. See head of county section

Bowdown House ૬ (Mr & Mrs M Dormer) Newbury. 3m Newbury, Greenham Common N. On Bury's Bank Rd 2m past Greenham Golf Club. Lutyen's parterre gardens in style of Gertrude Jekyll; fine trees and rare shrubs. 50 acres of ancient woodland, now a nature reserve in care of BBONT. House by Sir Oswald Partridge Miln. TEA. *Adm £1.50 Chd free (Share to BBONT®). Sun May 26 (2-5.30)*

Bussock Wood ❀ (Mr & Mrs W A Palmer) Snelsmore Common. 3m N of Newbury. On B4494 Newbury-Wantage Rd. Bluebells, fine trees and views; sunken garden with lily pond. Early Briton Camp. TEAS in aid of Winterbourne Parish Church. Plants for sale. *Adm £1 Chd 10p. Sun May 5 (2-5.30)*

Combe Manor ✿❀ (Lady Mary Russell) Combe. Approx 10m from Newbury or from Andover. From M4 in Hungerford, turn L after passing under railway bridge; over cattle grid onto Hungerford Common; turn R 400yds later and follow signs to Inkpen; pass The Swan on L, bear R at junction and then almost immediately L to Combe Gibbet and Combe. The Manor stands ½m from the village beside the church. 2 acres of lawns, borders, roses, shrubs and fruit trees. Walled garden with C17 gazebo, C11 church adjoining will be open. TEAS. *Combined adm with* **Withers Farm** *£2 Chd under 12 free. Sun June 30 (2-6)*

¶Donnington Grove Country Club ❀ (Shi-Tennosi Int Ltd) Donnington. Leave M4 at Junction 13; take A34 to Newbury. Leave A34 at 1st junction, turn R then L towards Donnington Castle for 2m. Cross 1st mini roundabout. At 2nd, turn R into Grove Rd. From Hungerford take the A4 Bath Rd, turn L at Oxford Rd B4494 and L into Grove Rd. Country Club 200yds on R. Buddist Temple and water garden set within 25-acre walled English garden, being centrepiece of approx 80 acres of C18 country parkland. Lake, river and woodland walks. The temple garden contains fish ponds and wide selection of rhododendrons and azaleas. The remaining garden is laid out to herbaceous borders, shrubs and lawns with small mature yew maze. TEA. *Adm £2 Chd free (Share to Riding for the Disabled®). Sun June 30 (11-5)*

Englefield House ૬✿❀ (Sir William and Lady Benyon) nr Theale. Entrance on A340. 7 acres of woodland garden with interesting variety of trees; shrubs; stream and water garden; formal terrace with fountain and borders. Commercial garden centre in village. Deer park. Part of garden suitable for wheelchairs. Home made TEAS Long Gallery NGS days only. *Open every Mon all yr and Mons, Tues, Weds, Thurs from April 1 to June 30 incl (10-dusk). Adm £2 Chd free (Share to St Mark's Church®). For NGS Suns May 12, July 14 (2-6). Private parties for House and Garden welcome, please* **Tel 01734 302221**

Englemere ❀ (The Chartered Institute of Building) From M3 leave at junction 3 follow the A332 signposted Ascot. Englemere is located on the R. From M4 leave at junction 6 signposted Windsor travel on A355 then A332 through Windsor Great Park signposted Ascot. At the Racecourse roundabout continue on A335 signposted Bagshot. Englemere is a few 100yds from the roundabout on the L. 14-acre garden featuring pleasant lawns surrounded by mature trees providing walks in shady undergrowth. The garden is particularly noted for its variety of azaleas and rhododendrons. The grounds surround the historical mansion which is a former home of Field Marshall Lord Roberts of Kandahar and the estate was declared a royal residence by King George VI. Part ground floor open. Englemere is the HQ of The Chartered Institute of Building who have cared for the ground since 1972. TEAS. *Adm £1.50 Chd free (Share to CIOB Benevolent Fund®). Sun May 26 (2-6). Parties welcome, please* **Tel 01344 23355**

Eton College Gardens ૬✿❀ (Provost & Fellows) Stations: Windsor ¾m Eton ½m. Bus: Green Line 704 & 705 London-Windsor 1m. Luxmoore's Garden is an island garden created by a housemaster about 1880; reached by beautiful new bridge; views of college and river. Provost's and Fellows' Gardens adjoin the ancient buildings on N and E sides. Parking off B3022 Slough to Eton rd, signposted. TEAS in aid of Datchet PCC. *Combined adm £1 Chd 20p. Sat June 15 (2-6)*

Folly Farm ૬✿ (The Hon Hugh & Mrs Astor) Sulhamstead, 7m SW of Reading. A4 between Reading/Newbury (2m W of M4 exit 12); take rd marked Sulhamstead at Mulligans Restaurant 1m after Theale roundabout; entrance 1m on right, through BROWN gate marked 'Folly Farm Gardens'. One of the few remaining gardens where the Lutyens architecture remains intact. Garden, laid out by Gertrude Jekyll, has been planted to owners' taste, bearing in mind Jekyll and Lutyens original design. Raised white garden, sunken rose garden; spring bulbs; herbaceous borders; ilex walk; avenues of limes, yew hedges, formal pools. House (not open). TEAS. *Adm £1.50 Chd free (Share to West Berkshire Marriage Guidance Trust®). Sun April 14, Mon May 27, Sun June 23 (2-6)*

Foxgrove ૬✿❀ (Miss Audrey Vockins) Enborne, 2½m SW of Newbury. From A343 turn R at 'The Gun' 2m from town centre. Bus: AV 126, 127, 128; alight Villiers Way PO 1m. Small family garden with adjoing nursery (Foxgrove Plants); interesting foliage plants, troughs, raised beds, spring bulbs, naturalised in orchard; double primroses, snowdrop species and varieties; peat bed. TEAS. *Adm £1 Chd free. Suns March 17 (2-5.30), April 21, June 9 (2-6)*

Fox Hill ૬❀ (Mrs Martin McLaren) Inkpen. Between Hungerford and Newbury, turn off A4 at sign saying Kintbury and Inkpen. Drive into Kintbury. Turn L by shop onto Inkpen Rd. After approx 1m, turn R at Xrds. After passing village signpost saying Inkpen, turn 1st L down bridleroad. Garden 2nd on L. Car park in field. 3-acre garden, blossom, bulbs, many interesting shrubs. New rose garden. Small formal garden and duck pond. TEAS. *Adm £1 Chd free. Sun June 16 (2-6)*

Scotland's Gardens Scheme. The National Gardens Scheme has a similar but quite separate counterpart in Scotland. Called Scotland's Gardens Scheme, it raises money for the Queen's Nursing Institute (Scotland), the Gardens Fund of the National Trust for Scotland and over 160 registered charities nominated by garden owners. The Handbook is available (£3.25 incl p&p) from Scotland's Gardens Scheme, 31 Castle Terrace, Edinburgh EH1 2EL.
Telephone 0131-229-1870, Fax 0131-229-0443

Frogmore Gardens &✿ (by gracious permission of Her Majesty The Queen) Windsor Castle; entrance via Park St gate into Long Walk (follow AA signs). Visitors are requested kindly to keep on the route to the garden and not stray into the Home Park. Station and bus stop; Windsor (20 mins walk from gardens); Green Line bus no 701, from London. Limited parking for cars only (free). 30 acres of landscaped gardens rich in history and beauty. Large lake, fine trees, lawns, flowers and flowering shrubs. The Royal Mausoleum, within the grounds, will also be open free of charge. Refreshment tent in car park on Long Walk (from where there is a 5 min walk to the gardens). **Coaches by appointment only** (apply to NGS, Hatchlands Park, East Clandon, Guildford, Surrey GU4 7RT enc. s.a.e. or **Tel 01483 211535** stating whether May 1 or 2; am or pm). *Adm £2 Chd free. Wed May 1, Thurs May 2 (10.30-6.30; last adm 6)*

The Harris Garden & Experimental Grounds &✿✿ (University of Reading, School of Plant Sciences) Whiteknights, Reading RG6 6AS. Turn R just inside Pepper Lane entrance to University campus. 12-acre research and teaching garden extensively redeveloped since 1989. Rose gardens; herbaceous borders, winter garden, herb garden etc. Flowering cherry circle, new in 1995. Extensive glasshouses. Many plants labelled. TEAS in aid of Friends of The Harris Garden. *Adm £1 Chd free. Sun April 21 (2-6)*

Hurst Gardens & On the A321 between Twyford and Wokingham. Both gardens are in the village of Hurst but quite a distance apart. They offer an interesting contrast in age, size and approach. TEAS at Hurst Lodge only. *Combined adm £2 Chd free (Share to Helen House Childrens Hospice®). Suns May 12, Aug 18 (2-5.30)*
    Hurst Lodge ✿ (Mr & Mrs Alan Peck) Large 5 acre old garden which has been cared for by members of the same family for over 75 yrs. It features lawns and mature trees, a recently created rockery, pond and bog garden, a formal parterre, a walled garden with herbaceous borders, a large kitchen garden as well as camellias, azaleas, rhododendrons, magnolias, flowering cherries, a variety of Japanese maples and bulbs
    Reynolds Farm (Mr & Mrs Christopher Wells) The owners freely admit to a lack of classical design, but like Topsy the garden just grew. Having been drowned in the winter of 94/95 and baked in the summer of 95 it is amazing there is anything to look at. However because of a considerable planting programme there are no gaps and owing to continuous buying of irresistable plants and propagating many others, there will be a greater collection on view than before

Inkpen House ✿ (Mr & Mrs David Male) Inkpen. Between Hungerford and Newbury; turn off A4 at sign marked Kintbury and Inkpen. Drive into Kintbury. Turn L by shop onto Inkpen Rd. After approx 1m turn R at Xrds. After passing sign marked Inkpen take R fork signposted Lower Inkpen. After red telephone kiosk on R take 2nd turn on L marked C13 Ch. Car park in field on L. 4-acre garden laid out at beginning of C18 in the Versailles style with formal planting of avenues and bosquets. Pleached lime walk and walled kitchen garden. TEAS. *Adm £1.50 Chd free. Sun July 14 (2-6)*

Kirby House ✿✿ (Richard Astor Esq) Turn S off A4 to Kintbury; L at Xrds in Kintbury towards Combe. 2m out of Kintbury. Turn L immediately beyond Crown & Garter. House and garden at bottom of hill. 6 acres in beautiful setting. Formal rose borders, replanted herbaceous border in kitchen garden, newly planted colour theme border between yew buttress hedges. C18 Queen Anne house (not open). TEAS at West Woodhay House. *Combined adm with* **West Woodhay House** *£2 Chd 25p (Share to St Swithins Church®). Suns April 14, June 23 (2-6)*

Little Bowden &✿ (Geoffrey Verey Esq) 1½m W of Pangbourne on Pangbourne-Yattendon Rd. Large garden with fine views; woodland walk, azaleas, rhododendrons, bluebells. Heated swimming pool 50p extra. TEAS. *Adm £2 Chd free. Suns May 26, July 7 (2.30-6). Parties welcome, please* **Tel 01734 843441**

Meadow House &✿✿ (Mr & Mrs G A Jones) Ashford Hill is on the B3051 8m SE of Newbury. Take turning at SW end of village signposted Wolverton Common. Meadow House on R approx 300yds along lane. Approx 1¾-acre plantsman's garden. Pond with waterside planting; mixed shrub and herbaceous borders. Many unusual plants. *Adm £2 Chd free.* ▲*Open for NGS Sun June 9, Aug 18 (2-6). TEAS in aid of Church. Thurs May 23, June 6, July 11, 25 (10-5). Private visits welcome by appt, please* **Tel 01734 816005**

North Ecchinswell Farm, nr Newbury see Hampshire

Ockwells Manor &✿✿ (Mr & Mrs B P Stein) Maidenhead. Exit 8/9 off M4. A404M towards Henley. 1st slip rd to L to Cox Green and White Waltham. R at 1st roundabout. L at 2nd roundabout. Follow rd to end and turn R. 3½ acres of formal garden around mediaeval Manor House. Listed grade 1 (not open); walled garden; new herb garden, rose garden, over 100 pots; clipped yews; small maze; lime avenue; swimming pool; peacocks, ornamental ducks and geese; farm animals; woodland walk. TEAS. *Adm £1.50 Chd free. Sun June 30 (2-6)*

Odney Club &✿ (John Lewis Partnership) Cookham. Car park in grounds. 120 acres; lawns, garden and meadows on R Thames; specimen trees. Cream TEAS River Room. *Adm £1.50 Chd free (Share to Sue Ryder Foundation®). Sun April 14 (2-6)*

The Old House, Silchester see Hampshire

The Old Mill & (Mrs E M Arlott) Aldermaston. On A4 between Reading and Newbury, take A340 then follow signs. 7 acres; lawns; walks; flower beds; shrubs; R Kennet flows through with sluices and hatches. Fine Old Mill House (not open). TEAS. *Adm £1 Chd free. Sun July 21 (2-6)*

Old Rectory Cottage ✿ (Mr & Mrs A W A Baker) Tidmarsh, ½m S of Pangbourne, midway between Pangbourne and Tidmarsh turn E down narrow lane; L at T-junction. 2-acre cottage garden and wild garden with small lake bordered by R Pang. Unusual plants, spring bulbs, roses climbing into old apple trees, ferns, hellebores and lilies. White doves and golden pheasants. Featured on TV and in many gardening books. *Adm £1 Chd free (Share to BBONT®). Suns May 19, June 30 (2-6)*

The Old Rectory, Burghfield &#&✿ (Mr R R Merton) 5m SW of Reading. Turn S off A4 to Burghfield village; R after Hatch Gate Inn; entrance on R. Medium-sized garden; herbaceous and shrub borders; roses, hellebores, lilies, many rare and unusual plants collected by owners from Japan and China; old-fashioned cottage plants; autumn colour. Georgian house (not open). TEAS in aid of NSPCC. *Adm £2 Chd free. Open 2nd and last Wed of month Feb to Oct incl (11-4). For NGS Wed April 24, July 31 (11-4)*

The Old Rectory, Farnborough ✿✿ (Mrs Michael Todhunter) 4m SE of Wantage. From B4494 Wantage-Newbury Rd, 4m from Wantage turn E at sign for Farnborough. Outstanding garden with unusual plants; fine view; old-fashioned roses; collection of small flowered clematis; herbaceous borders. Beautiful house (not open) built c.1749. Near church with John Piper window in memory of John Betjeman who lived at The Old Rectory. Teas in village. *Adm £1.50 Chd free (Share to Farnborough PCC®). Suns April 21, May 12, June 30 (2-6). Private visits by written appt*

Padworth Common Gardens ✿✿ Rectory Rd, Padworth Common. ½-way between Reading and Newbury. 1½m S of A4 take Padworth Lane at Padworth Court Hotel. TEAS. *Combined adm £1.50 Chd free. Suns May 12, June 9, Aug 4 (2-6)*

   Bloomsbury (Mr & Mrs M J Oakley) 20-acre farm now grazing and gardens with plant nursery. Obsessive plant collector owners versus free-draining gravel hilltop. Sissinghurst-planned White Garden. Woodland plantings round orchard trees, shady gravel yard by barn, pool with paved surround and pots of Agapanthus, etc. 'Ligularia' bog garden. ShCh Red Setters and Grand Bleus de Gascogne. Field walk to C11 Church
   Honeyhanger & (Mrs Jenny Martin) Rectory Rd. 2-acres of traditional and woodland gardens containing many special and unusual trees, shrubs and perennials, acquired by obsessive plant collector. Courtyard with pots incl world-wide half hardies: collection of bonsai in Oriental-style garden. Tropical house, orchid house, aviary, ornamental fountain pond, waterfall; woodland ponds

Peasemore Gardens 7m N of Newbury on A34 to M4 junction 13. N towards Oxford then immed L signed Chievely. Through Chievely and onto Peasemore approx 3½m or B4494 from Newbury 6m R signposted Peasemore. TEAS at The Old Rectory. *Combined adm £1.50 Chd free (Share to Invalids at Home®). Sun June 23 (2-6)*

   Hill Green House &✿ (Sir Brian McGrath) Pretty house (not open). Approx 2 acres; shrubs, roses, lily pond etc. Extensive lawns and fine views
   The Old Rectory, Peasemore &✿ (Mr & Mrs I D Cameron) Georgian house with fine trees in lovely setting. Shrub roses, peonies, large rose border and herbaceous border
   Paxmere House &✿ (The Marchioness of Lansdowne) Opp The Old Rectory. 4-acre cottage garden. Roses, shrubs, etc

¶**Priory House** ✿✿ (Mr & Mrs J Leigh) Priory Rd, Sunningdale. Take turning opp Waitrose, Ridge Mount Rd, Priory Rd 1st L. 2¼-acre garden designed in 1930's by Percy Cane (copies of original planting plans on view) planted for yr-round interest and colour. Garden created by previous owners over 60 yrs. Original York stone paths and ornamental pond restored by present owners. Large lawn with shrub borders, yew hedges and rare trees; rock garden, heathers and large vegetable garden; rhododendrons and azaleas planted with impressive hostas by stream. Mature camellias, fine shrubs and conifers. NO PARKING, please at Priory House or in Priory Rd. Free parking at Sunningdale BR station; courtesy bus to garden at regular intervals. TEAS. *Adm £2 Chd free (Share to Make-a-Wish Foundation®). Sun May 19 (2-6)*

Rooksnest ✿✿ (Dr & Mrs M D Sackler) Earls Court Farm, Lambourn Woodlands. Situated approx 3m from the A338 (Wantage) Rd along the B4000. Nearest village, Lambourn. Rooksnest signposted on the B400 in both directions, ie whether approaching from Lambourn or from the A338. Approx 10-acre exceptionally fine traditional English garden. Recently restored with help from Arabella Lennox-Boyd. Includes terraces; rose garden; lilies; herbaceous borders; herb garden; many specimen trees and fine shrubs. TEA. *Adm £1.50 Chd 50p. Wed June 26 (2-5)*

Scotlands &✿ (Mr Michael & The Hon Mrs Payne) In centre of triangle formed by A4130 (was A423) E of Henley-on-Thames, the A321 to Wargrave and the A4 at Knowl Hill - midway between Warren Row Village and Cockpole Green. 4 acres; clipped yews; shrub borders; grass paths through trees to woodland and pond-gardens with Repton design rustic summer house. Rocks with waterfall and new gazebo. Featured in Good Gardens Guide. TEAS. *Adm £2 Chd free. Suns April 14, July 21 (2-6). Private parties welcome, please* Tel 01628 822648

Silwood Park (Imperial College) Ascot. 1½m E of Ascot in the junction of A329 and the B383. Access from the B383 200 metres N of the Cannon Inn. 240 acres of parklands and natural habitats, surrounding fine C19 house by Waterhouse, architect of the Natural History Museum. Japanese garden under restoration; pinetum, young arboretum specialising in oaks and birches. Two nature walks (1m & 2m) through oak and beech woodland to lake. TEAS. *Adm £1.50 Chd free. Suns May 12, 19; Oct 6 (2-6). Parties by appt, please* Tel 01344 23911

Simms Farm House &✿✿ (The Rev His Hon. Christopher & Mrs Lea) Mortimer, 6m SW of Reading. At T-junction on edge of village, from Grazeley, turn R uphill; L by church into West End Rd; at next Xrd L down Drury Lane; R at T-junction. 1-acre garden with mixed shrub borders, small rockery; bog garden; formal pond; unusual plants. Lovely view. TEA. *Adm £1 Chd 50p. Sun, Mon May 5, 6 (2-6); Private visits welcome, please* Tel 01734 332360

Sonning Village Gardens ✿ 4m E of Reading in Sonning Lane off the A4 (9m W of Maidenhead off the A4) 400 metres heading N along Sonning Lane. School found on L. TEAS. *Combined adm £2 Chd free. Sun June 9 (2-5)*

   Reading Blue Coat School (Headmaster) The school is in 45 acres of fields and woods with paths running down to the R Thames and Sonning Lock. The garden consists mainly of annual bedding, roses and shrubs mixed with trees eg magnolias in Magnolia Walk

South Hill (Mr & Mrs Tomlinson) Entrance opp Reading Blue Coat School. 5 acres of lawns; specimen trees beautifully planted with shrubs; walled garden

Thatched Cottage も (Dr & Mrs Grenfell Bailey) 3 acres well laid out; lawns, specimen trees, herbaceous border

Stanford Dingley Village Gardens ❀❀ Between Reading and Newbury. 5m from junction 12, M4; turning by Queen's Head to South End and Bradfield. Pretty village with ancient Church and bridge over R Pang. Parking in field. TEAS. *Combined adm £2 Chd free. Sun July 7 (Share to Abbeyfield Reading Soc®) (2-6) including:*

Bradfield Farm も (Mr & Mrs Newton) ½-acre. Wide variety of plants. Further 5-acres mixed broadleaf planting in 1990. *Private visits by appt* Tel 01734 **744113**

Bridge Cottage も (Mr & Mrs M Ranwell) Pretty ½-acre cottage garden. Deep mixed borders. Interesting terrace and tub planting

Mill Cottage (Mr A Roberts) Pretty small cottage gardens to both front and rear, bordering R Pang to rear

The Mill (Mrs P Stinton) Interesting and unusual wild garden with bog area, adjoining village green. Recently restored to former glory

Sunningdale Park ❀ (Civil Service College) Ascot. 1½m E of Ascot off A329 at Cannon Inn or take Broomhall Lane off A30 at Sunningdale. Over 20 acres of beautifully landscaped gardens designed by Capability Brown. Terrace garden and victorian rockery designed by Pulham incl cave and water features. Lake area with paved walks; extensive lawns with specimen trees and flower beds; impressive massed rhododendrons. Beautiful 1m woodland walk. Limited access for wheelchairs. Cream TEAS. *Adm £2 Chd free. Sun May 19 (2-5)*

Swallowfield Park も❀ (Country Houses Association) 5m S of Reading off B3349, entrance nr village hall. Level grounds of 25 acres which incl a large walled garden and herbaceous borders, rose beds, vegetable gardens, massed rhododendrons and many specimen trees. There are wide lawns and gravel paths, with a small lake and a wooded walk to the R Loddon. Visit dogs' graves. The distinguished house (open) was built in 1689 for Lord Clarendon. Home-made TEAS. *Adm £2.50 Chd free. (Share to Country Houses Association®). Weds, Thurs May 1 to Sept 30. Parties welcome, please* Tel 01734 **883815.** *For NGS Easter Mon April 8 (2-5)*

Trunkwell Park も❀ (Trunkwell Project) Beech Hill. From Reading: M4 junction 11 follow Basingstoke sign approx. ¼m at roundabout turn L and follow Three Mile Cross-Spencers Wood. Centre of Spencers Wood look for Beech Hill Rd on R and follow into Beech Hill Village (centre) and follow signs. From Basingstoke follow A33 to Wellington roundabout turn L following Beech Hill signs. At village turn R. Located in grounds of Trunkwell House Hotel. Parking and toilets. Conducted tours. This 3-acre site with large Victorian walled garden is run by the Charity Horticultural Therapy as a teaching and therapeutic centre where people with special needs are encouraged to participate in a wide range of horticultural activities designed to improve skills and to gain confidence. Located on Berkshire/Hants border in very attractive surroundings, Trunkwell caters to an increasing

number of clients daily, so why not come and witness that disability is no handicap to rewarding and successful gardening. Part of garden dedicated to Wildlife Conservation. Plants for sale, bedding in June. TEAS. *Adm £1 Chd free (Share to Horticultural Therapy®). Suns June 2, Sept 1 (2-6)*

Waltham Place も❀ White Waltham. 3½m S of Maidenhead. Exit 8/9 on M4, then A423(M) or M40 exit 4 then A404 to A4 Maidenhead exit and follow signs to White Waltham. 40 acres of organic gardens with woodland and lake. Specimen trees incl splendid weeping beech, herbaceous borders, japanese, herb, butterfly, kitchen, iris and wonderful walled garden. Many interesting and unusual plants. Small organic farm with tamworth and berkshire pigs, bagot goats, castlemilk moorit and jacob sheep, jersey cattle. Home-made cream TEAS, plants and dried flowers (May 26 & July 21 only). *Adm £2 Chd 50p (Share to Thames Valley Adventure Playground®). Suns May 26, July 21 (2-7), Wednesdays during April to September (2-5)*

Welford Park も❀ (Mrs J L Puxley) 6m NW of Newbury on Lambourn Valley Rd. Entrance on Newbury/Lambourn Rd (fine gates with boot on top). Spacious grounds; spring flowers; walk by R. Lambourn. Queen Anne house (not open). TEAS. *Adm £2 Chd free (Share to Welford Church®). Sun March 31 (2-4.30)*

West Silchester Hall, nr Reading see Hampshire

West Woodhay House も (H Henderson Esq) 6m SW of Newbury. From Newbury take A343. At foot of hill turn R for East Woodhay and Ball Hill. 3½m turn L for West Woodhay. Go over Xrds in village, next fork R past Church. Gate on L. Parkland; large garden with bulbs, roses, shrubs, lake, woodland garden. Large walled kitchen garden, greenhouses. TEAS. *Combined adm £2 Chd 25p (Share to West Woodhay Church®) with* **Kirby House.** *Suns April 14, June 23 (2-6)*

Whiteknights も❀ (Mr & Mrs P Bradly) Finchampstead. Midway along Finchampstead Ridges on B3348 between Finchampstead War Memorial and Crowthorne Station. 2½ acres, lawns, Japanese water garden, dwarf conifers, interesting plantings, fruit and vegetable garden. New Mediterranean garden. Tudor Life in Miniature Exhibition. Cream TEAS in aid of Guide Dogs for the Blind. *Adm £1.50 Chd 50p. Sun Aug 11 (2-5.30). Private visits and parties welcome, please* Tel 01734 733274

¶**Withers Farmhouse** も (Mrs A L Hoare) Inkpen. Approx 3m from Hungerford. From M4 in Hungerford turn L after passing under railway bridge; over cattle grid onto Common turn R 400yds later and follow signs to Inkpen; pass Swan on L; turn R at junction by telephone kiosk and bear R, signed Ham and Shalbourne - ¼m house on L of turning L up hill to church. Car park in field. Cottage garden of 1 acre, borders, roses, shrubs. *Combined adm with* **Combe Manor** *£2 Chd free. Sun June 30 (2-6)*

Woolley Park も❀ (Mr & Mrs Philip Wroughton) 5m S of Wantage on A338 turn L at sign to Woolley. Large park, fine trees and views. Two linked walled gardens beautifully planted. Teas close to Old Rectory, Farnborough. *Adm £1. Sun June 30 (2-6)*

Buckinghamshire

Hon County Organiser: Mrs Sue Wright, Brudenell House, Quainton, Aylesbury, Bucks HP22 4AW
Tel 01296 655250
Assistant Hon County Organisers: Mrs Angela Sanderson, Wellfield House, Cuddington, Aylesbury HP18 OBB
(supplies) Tel 01844 291626
Mrs Joy Try, Favershams Meadow, Mumfords Lane, Gerrards Cross, SL9 8TQ
Tel 01753 882733
Hon County Treasurer: Dr H Beric Wright

DATES OF OPENING

February 18 Sunday
Great Barfield, High Wycombe
March 3 Sunday
Campden Cottage, Chesham Bois
Waddesdon Manor, nr Aylesbury
March 10 Sunday
Springlea, Seymour, Marlow
March 31 Sunday
Walmerdene, Buckingham
April 7 Sunday
Overstroud Cottage, Great
Missenden
Springlea, Seymour, Marlow
Turn End, Haddenham
April 8 Monday
Great Barfield, High Wycombe
April 14 Sunday
Campden Cottage, Chesham Bois ‡
The Old Vicarage, Padbury
6 Oldfield Close, Little Chalfont ‡
Quoitings, Marlow
April 21 Sunday
Long Crendon Gardens, nr Thame
6 Oldfield Close, Little Chalfont
April 28 Sunday
Nether Winchendon House,
nr Aylesbury
The White House, Denham Village
Whitewalls, Marlow
May 5 Sunday
The Manor House, Bledlow,
nr Princes Risborough
Overstroud Cottage, Great
Missenden
Springlea, Seymour, Marlow
May 6 Monday
Gracefield, Lacey Green
Turn End, Haddenham
Winslow Hall, nr Buckingham
May 12 Sunday
Ascott, nr Leighton Buzzard
Campden Cottage, Chesham Bois
Cliveden, Taplow
Oaklands, Main Street, Weston
Turville
Peppers, Great Missenden
Quainton Gardens, nr Aylesbury
May 14 Tuesday
Stowe Landscape Gardens,
Buckingham

May 19 Sunday
Chalfont St Giles Gardens ‡
Favershams Meadow, Gerrards
Cross ‡
May 26 Sunday
Brill Gardens, nr Thame
The Edge, Chalfont St Giles
Sheredon, Longwick
May 27 Monday
Brill Gardens, nr Thame
May 29 Wednesday
Spindrift, Jordans,
Beaconsfield
June 2 Sunday
Springlea, Seymour, Marlow
June 8 Saturday
The Manor House, Princes
Risborough
June 9 Sunday
Chilton Gardens, nr Thame
Cublington Gardens, Leighton
Buzzard
Overstroud Cottage, Great
Missenden
Pasture Farm, Longwick,
nr Princes Risborough
Weir Lodge, Chesham
Whitchurch Gardens
June 11 Tuesday
Pasture Farm, Longwick,
nr Princes Risborough
June 16 Sunday
Campden Cottage, Chesham Bois
Gipsy House, Great Missenden
Hillesden House, nr Buckingham ‡
Tythrop Park, Kingsey, nr Thame
Walmerdene, Buckingham ‡
June 19 Wednesday
Walmerdene, Buckingham
June 23 Sunday
Askett Gardens, Princes
Risborough
Dinton Gardens, nr Aylesbury ‡
Favershams Meadow, Gerrards
Cross
59 The Gables, Haddenham ‡
The Manor House, Bledlow,
nr Princes Risborough
The Manor House, Hambleden,
nr Henley-on-Thames
Old Vicarage, Padbury

June 26 Wednesday
Cublington Gardens, Leighton
Buzzard
59 The Gables, Haddenham
June 30 Sunday
Cheddington Gardens,
nr Leighton Buzzard
The Edge, Chalfont St Giles
Flint House, Penn Street Village,
nr Amersham ‡
Great Barfield, High Wycombe
Long Crendon Gardens, nr Thame
The Manor Farm, Little Horwood,
nr Winslow
Quainton Gardens, nr Aylesbury
Watercroft, Penn ‡
July 7 Sunday
Campden Cottage, Chesham
Bois
Overstroud Cottage, Great
Missenden
Springlea, Seymour, Marlow
July 10 Wednesday
Dorneywood Garden, Burnham
by written appointment only
July 14 Sunday
Nether Winchendon House,
nr Aylesbury
Sheredon, Longwick
The White House, Denham
Village
July 17 Wednesday
Dorneywood Garden, Burnham
by written appointment only
July 21 Sunday
Hughenden Manor, High
Wycombe
Whitewalls, Marlow
July 28 Sunday
14 Well Street, Buckingham
August 4 Sunday
Campden Cottage, Chesham Bois
Springlea, Seymour, Marlow
August 10 Saturday
Dorneywood Garden, Burnham
by written appointment only
August 17 Saturday
Dorneywood Garden, Burnham
by written appointment only
August 18 Sunday
Ascott, nr Leighton Buzzard

August 25 Sunday
Peppers, Great Missenden

September 1 Sunday
Campden Cottage, Chesham Bois

September 8 Sunday
Cliveden, Taplow
Overstroud Cottage, Great Missenden
Quoitings, Marlow ‡
Springlea, Seymour, Marlow ‡
West Wycombe Park, West Wycombe

September 15 Sunday
Great Barfield, High Wycombe

September 22 Sunday
Turn End, Haddenham

September 25 Wednesday
59 The Gables, Haddenham

September 29 Sunday
59 The Gables, Haddenham

October 6 Sunday
Campden Cottage, Chesham Bois

1997
February 16
Great Barfield, High Wycombe

By appointment only
For telephone numbers and other details see garden descriptions. Private visits welcomed

Blossoms, nr Great Missenden
Hall Barn, Beaconsfield
Harewood, Chalfont St Giles
Tramway Farm, Brill, nr Thame

The Wheatsheaf Inn, Weedon
Wichert, Ford, nr Aylesbury

By appointment – Parties only

Campden Cottage, Chesham Bois
Gracefield, Lacey Green, Princes Risborough
Great Barfield, High Wycombe
Ketchmere Close, Long Crendon Gardens
Overstroud Cottage, Great Missenden
Springlea, Seymour Plain, Marlow
Turn End, Haddenham
Walmerdene, Buckingham
Whitewalls, Marlow

DESCRIPTIONS OF GARDENS

Ascott ⚧✿ (Sir Evelyn and Lady de Rothschild; The National Trust) Wing, 2m SW of Leighton Buzzard, 8m NE of Aylesbury via A418. Bus: 141 Aylesbury-Leighton Buzzard. Beautiful surroundings and layout. Garden part formal, part natural; many specimen trees, shrubs, naturalised bulbs, spring and summer bedding, fountains; lily pond. *Adm (incl NT members) £3 Chd £1.50 Under 5 free. ▲For NGS Suns May 12, Aug 18 (2-6). Last adm 5pm*

Askett Gardens ✿ 1m from Princes Risborough on A4010 to Aylesbury. At Black Horse roundabout, turn into Askett village. Parking off Letter Box Lane 1st turning L. TEAS. Plant stall in car park. *Combined adm £2 Chd free (Share to Iain Rennie Hospice®). Sun June 23 (2-6)*

  The Bell House ✿ (Mr & Mrs J R Hughes) Approx ⅓ acre. Charming old-fashioned country cottage garden with stream and herbaceous border, informally planted

  The Bell House Barn ⚧ (Mrs Christine Ramsay) Approx ⅔-acre. Large romantic cottage garden with hardy perennials, shrubs and roses, (formerly part of Bell House garden). Backcloth of mature trees in parkland setting

  Mulberry House ⚧✿ (Mr & Mrs M D Ashby) 1-acre garden with large variety of shrubs, herbaceous borders, rockery and pond. Several specimen trees incl mulberry

  Old Rose Cottage ⚧✿ (Mr & Mrs G A Davies) 1-acre garden with long N facing walled border mainly herbaceous and shrubs, specimen trees of whitebeam, spruce, beech and maple. Collection of hardy geraniums, old roses and holly. Herb garden, island heather and conifer bed. TEAS

  The Old Wick ⚧✿ (Mr & Mrs P Dewe) A larger village garden planted for all-yr interest with fine spruce and conifer trees, small stream and pond

  Three Ways Cottage ⚧✿ (Dr & Mrs P N J Appleton) 1-acre garden in what had been the orchard behind 3 cottages. Informal garden with mixed beds of herbaceous plants and shrubs, some self seeded annual poppies. Small kitchen garden of fruit trees, herbs and vegetables. TEAS

Blossoms ⚧✿ (Dr & Mrs Frank Hytten) Cobblers Hill, 2½m NW of Great Missenden by Rignall Road (signed to Butlers Cross) to King's Lane (1½m) then to top of Cobblers Hill, R at yellow stone marker and in 50yds R at stone marked Blossoms. [Map ref SP874034]. 4-acre garden begun as hill-top fields in 1925, plus 1-acre beechwood. Lawns, trees, old apple orchard, small lake, water gardens, woodland, troughs, scree garden and several patios. Large areas of bluebells, wild daffodils, fritillaria and other spring bulbs. Flowering cherries and many interesting trees incl small collections of acer, eucalyptus and salix; foliage effects throughout the year. TEAS. *Adm £1.50. Private visits only, please* **Tel 01494 863140**

Bovingdon Gardens see Herts

Brill Gardens 7m N of Thame. Turn off B4011, (Thame to Bicester), or turn off the A41 at Kingswood, both signed to Brill. C17 windmill open Suns 2.30-5.30. Teas available at The Pheasant, The Red Lion and The Sun. *Combined adm £2 Chd free. Sun, Mon May 26, 27 (2-6)*

  Commoners ⚧✿ (Mr & Mrs R Wickenden) Tram Hill. Cottage garden, under ¼ acre. Much from seed and cuttings. Lovely views over low walls in all directions. *Private visits welcome, please* **Tel 01844 237418**

  Old Farm ✿ (Dr & Mrs Raymond Brown) South Hills, off Windmill St. ½-acre established garden around 3 terraces of old shrub roses; secluded position with high open views over Otmoor; kitchen garden, soft fruit, many self-sown perennials, S African annuals and plants in pots. Garden featured in 'Homes & Gardens' Aug 94. *Private visits welcome, please* **Tel 01844 238232**

  The Old Vicarage ⚧✿ (Mr & Mrs P Toynbee) The Square. ¾-acre, partly-walled garden with areas of interest in sun and shade. Arches and ornamental features. Small formal herb and vegetable garden. Ideas to interest children, as seen on 'Gardeners World'

  14 The Square ✿ (Mrs Audrey Dyer) Secret paved garden behind small terraced cottage. Handbuilt pots packed with plants for yr-round interest. *Private visits welcome, please* **Tel 01844 237148**

Campden Cottage ✿❀ (Mrs P Liechti) 51 Clifton Rd, Chesham Bois, N of Amersham. From Amersham-on-the-Hill take A416; after 1m turn R (E) at Catholic Church. From Chesham take A416; and first turning L after beech woods. ½-acre derelict garden restored by owner since 1971; plantsman's garden of yr-round interest; fine collection of unusual and rare plants. Hellebores in March. Featured on 'Gardeners' World' and in the 'Good Gardens Guide 1996'. Please use car park signed on main rd. Teas Old Amersham. No push chairs. *Adm £1.50 Chd free. Suns March 3, April 14, May 12, June 16, July 7, Aug 4, Sept 1, Oct 6 (2-6). Also by appt for parties with TEAS. No coaches. Please* **Tel 01494 726818**

Chalfont St Giles Gardens Off A413. TEAS in aid of Iain Rennie Hospice. *Combined adm £3 for 3 gardens or £1.50 per garden Chd free. Suns May 19 (2-6)*

  Concordia ✗ (Mr & Mrs D E Cobb) 76 Deanway. Parking in Deanway. A small challenging garden on a difficult sloping site. Herbaceous and shrub borders; rock garden; fruit trees; collection of epiphytic orchids. *Private visits also welcome, please* **Tel 01494 873671**
  Halfpenny Furze ✗✿❀ (Mr & Mrs R Sadler) Mill Lane. From London take A413 signed Amersham. Mill Lane is ¼m past mini roundabouts at Chalfont St Giles. Limited parking in Mill Lane, 1-acre plantsman's garden on clay: part woodland (rhododendrons, azaleas, acers, magnolias, cercis, cercidiphyllum) part formal (catalpa, cornus, clerodendrum, unusual shrubs, roses and mixed borders). TEAS. *Private visits also welcome, please* **Tel 01494 872509**
  North Down ✗✿❀ (Mr & Mrs J Saunders) From Halfpenny Furze, short uphill walk L into Dodds Lane. Garden is 250yds on R. Limited parking in Dodds Lane. Approx ¾-acre garden with interest throughout yr, some unusual plants, vistas. Mixed beds, shrubs, with rhododendrons, azaleas, acers; spring bulbs. Small bog garden; climbers; sempervivums; patio with water feature. *Private visits also welcome, please* **Tel 01494 872928**

Cheddington Gardens 11m E of Aylesbury; turn off B489 at Pitstone. 7m S of Leighton Buzzard; turn off B488 at Cheddington Station. Gardening books stall. TEAS on the green. *Combined adm £2 Chd free (Share to Methodist Chapel and St Giles Church, Cheddington®). Sun June 30 (2-6)*

  Chasea (Mr & Mrs A G Seabrook) Medium-sized garden on clay; assorted tubs and baskets; 2 half-round pools backing onto rockeries; conifers; perennials and bedding. *Private visits welcome, July only, please* **Tel 01296 668923**
  Cheddington Manor ✗ (Mr & Mrs H Hart) 3½-acres; small lake and moat in informal setting, roses, herbaceous border, and interesting mature trees
  34 Gooseacre (Mrs Barbara Smith) A well-designed partly paved small garden with magnificent views over the Chilterns. Delightful water feature, patio, mixed shrubs and climbers for all yr interest

---

Regular Openers. Too many days to include in diary. Usually there is a wide range of plants giving year-round interest. See end of county section for the name and garden description for times etc.

The Old Reading Room ✗❀ (Mr & Mrs W P Connolley) ⅓-acre cottage garden; small fern collection; trees incl ginkgo biloba
Rose Cottage ❀ (Mr & Mrs D G Jones) ¼-acre cottage garden planted for all yr interest with accent on colour; old roses; small scree area with unusual plants and conservatory. Partly suitable for wheelchairs. *Private visits welcome, please* **Tel 01296 668693**
21 Station Road ✗ (Mr & Mrs P Jay) ½-acre informal garden with wildflower conservation area; herbaceous and shrub borders; herbs and kitchen garden
Woodstock Cottage ✗ (Mr & Mrs D Bradford) 42 High Street. Delightful cottage garden with rear courtyard and patio

Chilton Gardens ✗ 3m N of Thame. In Long Crendon turn off B4011 follow signs to Chilton; village has C18 mansion house C12-C16 church, parking available. TEAS in aid of church. *Combined adm £2 Chd free. Sun June 9 (2-6)*

  The Old School House ✗ (Mr & Mrs John Rolfe) Working cottage garden; extended pond; extensive views; fruit garden
  ¶**The Old Thatch** ❀ (Mr & Mrs N Lucas) SW facing, sloping terrain of ⅓ acre. Good variety of shrubs, perennials and annuals
  The Old Vicarage ❀ (Mr & Mrs G Rosenthal) Approx ½-acre walled garden; mature trees, mixed borders, vegetables and plants for shady areas
  Signpost Cottage ✗ (Mr & Mrs G Baker) Approx ⅔-acre colourful village garden behind C17 thatched cottage. Bright containers on terrace

Cliveden ✗✗ (The National Trust) 2m N of Taplow. A number of separate gardens within extensive grounds, first laid out in the C18 incl water garden, rose garden; herbaceous borders; woodland walks and views of the Thames. Suitable for wheelchairs only in part. TEAS. *Adm grounds only £4. Parties £3.50 Chd £2.* ▲*For NGS Suns May 12, Sept 8 (11-6)*

Cublington Gardens ✗✗❀ From Aylesbury take Buckingham Rd (A413). At Whitchurch (4m) turn R to Cublington. TEAS. *Combined adm £2.50 Chd free. Sun June 9, Wed June 26 (2-5)*

  Old Manor Farm (Mr & Mrs N R Wilson) Reads Lane. Large garden in process of being redesigned; rose and 'yellow' gardens, herbaceous borders; swimming pool with collection of planted tubs; ha ha and walled vegetable garden. **Private visits by written appt**
  The Old Rectory (Mr & Mrs J Naylor) 2-acre country garden with herbaceous border, rosebeds, shrubs and mature trees; vegetables; ponds, climbing plants

Dinton Gardens 4m SW Aylesbury or 4m NE Thame. Gardens signed in village. TEAS in Village Hall in aid of Dinton Church Bell Restoration Fund. Parking at Perryfield. *Combined adm £2 Acc chd free. Sun June 23 (2-6)*

  Appletree Cottage ✗ (Mr & Mrs J K Mitchell) High St. A village centre garden begun from scratch in 1985. A blend of trees, shrubs, conifers and flowers on several levels designed to give privacy on an exposed site and good foliage colour whilst complementing neighbouring gardens

Honeysuckle Cottage & (Shaun Lee) ½-acre garden developed from meadow in last 4yrs. Designed, planted and maintained by young man with special needs. Mixed borders planted mainly with perennials for colour all summer. Vegetable garden, fruit trees and soft fruit

Orchard Cottage ❀ (Mr & Mrs H C Bingham) High St. ⅓-acre designed for minimum maintenance and all yr colour, variety and interest; sculpted lawns, hidden vistas, pergola and patios; shrubberies, ornamental and fruit trees, roses, mixed borders, plants for perfume and to attract butterflies

Perryfield &❀ (Mr & Mrs J Gray) New Rd. ⅓-acre with mature trees and planted for colour contrast; small water garden; island beds, mainly herbaceous and shrubs; some bedding

Westlington House &❀ (Mr & Mrs J Archer) Large manor house garden approx 3 acres incorporating walled gardens, orchard, vegetable gardens, greenhouses. Many specimen trees set in 20 acres of parkland

Dorneywood Garden &❀❀ (The National Trust) Dorneywood Rd, Burnham. From Burnham village take Dropmore Rd, and at end of 30mph limit take R fork into Dorneywood Rd. Dorneywood is 1m on R. From M40 junction 2, take A355 to Slough then 1st R to Burnham, 2m then 2nd L after Jolly Woodman signed Dorneywood Rd. Dorneywood is about 1m on L. 6-acre country garden with shrubs, rose garden, mixed borders and dell. TEAS. *Adm £2.50 Chd under 15 free. Garden open* **by written appt only** *on Weds July 10, 17, Sats Aug 10, 17 (2-5.30). Apply to the Secretary, Dorneywood Trust, Dorneywood, Burnham, Bucks SL1 8PY*

The Edge ❀❀ (Mr & Mrs D Glen) London Rd, Chalfont St Giles. Garden is ¼m towards Chalfont St Peter from The Pheasant Xrds on A413 nr Kings Rd. Georgian cottage with landscaped garden of ¾ acre, created by owners. Partially enclosed with walls and yew hedges, interesting shrubs incl magnolias, wisterias, climbing and shrub roses. Small exhibition by Misbourne Art Society. TEAS. *Adm £1 Chd free. Suns May 26, June 30 (2-6)*

Favershams Meadow &❀❀ (Mr & Mrs H W Try) 1½m W of Gerrards Cross on A40. Turn N into Mumfords Lane opp lay-by with BT box. Garden ¼m on R. 1½-acre garden. Mixed herbaceous, knot, parterre and separate blue and white garden. Beautiful roses on house and in David Austin rose garden. Attractive brick paved vegetable garden. Garden maintained to a very high standard, always being improved. TEAS in aid of the Red Cross and The Wexham Gastrointestinal Trust. *Adm £1.50 Chd free. Suns May 19, June 23 (2-6)*

Flint House &❀❀ (Mr & Mrs David White) Penn Street Village, 2m SW of Amersham. Turn S off A 404 into village. Opp church (open). Parking in church car park. 1½-acre garden surrounding C19 flint vicarage; herbaceous borders, shrub and climbing roses, raised alpine bed, herb garden; rose 'hoops' beside tennis court. Geraniums in garden room. TEA in aid of the Church. *Adm £1.50 Chd 20p. Sun June 30 (2-6)*

59 The Gables &❀ (Mrs A M Johnstone) Haddenham. Off A418 6m W of Aylesbury, 3m E of Thame. Travelling S along Churchway, The Gables is 2nd turning L after

Miles' Garage. This small garden (60' × 35') has recently undergone some changes; herbaceous border widened; new mini pond. Planted for all season interest. Bonsai, ferns, ivies. *Adm £1 Chd under 10 free. Suns June 23, Sept 29 (2-6); Weds June 26, Sept 25 (2-5)*

Gipsy House &❀❀ (Mrs F Dahl) Gt Missenden. A413 to Gt Missenden. From High St turn into Whitefield Lane, continue under railway bridge. Large Georgian house on R with family additions. York stone terrace, pleached lime walk to writing hut; shrubs, roses, herbs, small walled vegetable garden, orchard, gipsy caravan and maze for children. Limited access for wheelchairs. Teas locally. *Adm £1.20 Chd 30p (Share to Roald Dahl Foundation®). Sun June 16 (2-5)*

Gracefield &❀ (Mr & Mrs B Wicks) Lacey Green. Take A4010 High Wycombe to Aylesbury Rd. Turn R by Red Lion at Bradenham, up hill to Walters Ash; L at T-junction for Lacey Green. Brick and flint house on main rd beyond church facing Kiln Lane. 1½-acre mature garden; many unusual plants, trees, mostly labelled; orchard, soft fruit, shrub borders, rockery; plants for shade, sink gardens. Two ponds. Ploughman's lunches, TEAS and plants in aid of local Macmillan Nurses Group. *Adm £1.50 Chd free. Bank Hol Mon May 6 (11.30-5). Parties welcome by* **written appt** *May to Sept*

Great Barfield &❀❀ (Richard Nutt Esq) Bradenham, A4010 4m NW of High Wycombe 4m S of Princes Risborough. At Red Lion turn into village and turn R. Park on green. Walk down No Through Road. 1½-acre garden, designed for views, lay out, contrast and colour, as background for unusual plants. Michael Gibson in 'The Rose Gardens of England' says that it is a plantsman's garden in the best possible sense of the term and not to be missed to see how all plants should be grown to the best advantage. Feb now not only famous for snowdrops and hellebores but willows and a variety of bulbs; drifts of crocus; April unique collections of Pulmonarias and Bergenias; also red Trilliums now naturalised. June old-fashioned and climbing roses, Lilies including naturalised L. martagon. Sept considerable collection of colchicum, autumn colour and Sorbus berries. NCCPG national collection of leucojum (spring & April); celandine (April); iris unguicularis (Feb). Sales of unusual plants. TEAS. *Adm £1 Chd under 16 free (Share to Berks, Bucks and Oxon Group of NCCPG®). Sun Feb 18 (2-5), Mon April 8 (2-5.30), Suns June 30 (2-6), Sept 15 (2-5). Private visits and parties welcome, please* **Tel 01494 563741**. *First opening in 1997 Sun Feb 16 (2-5), subject to unforeseen events*

Hall Barn (The Dowager Lady Burnham) Lodge gate 300yds S of Beaconsfield Church in town centre. One of the original gardens opening in 1927 under the National Gardens Scheme, still owned by the Burnham family. A unique landscaped garden of great historical interest, laid out in the 1680's. Vast 300-yr-old curving yew hedge. Extensive replanting in progress after severe gale damage. Formal lake. Long avenues through the Grove, each terminating in a temple, classical ornament or statue. Obelisk with fine carvings in memory of Edmund Waller's grandson who completed the garden about 1730. *Garden open* **by written appointment only**. *Applications to The Dowager Lady Burnham, Hall Barn, Beaconsfield, Buckinghamshire HP9 2SG*

Harewood ✿✗ (Mr & Mrs John Heywood) Harewood Rd, Chalfont St Giles. Chalfont and Latimer Met Line tube station ¾m. From A404 Amersham-Rickmansworth Rd, at mini roundabout in Little Chalfont Village turn S down Cokes Lane. Harewood Rd is 200yds on L. 1 acre; fine yew and box hedges; established conifers; wide variety unusual shrubs and hardy plants; many climbers incl roses, clematis, wisterias; pool, sink gardens; planted for yr-round interest. Emphasis on foliage and colour contrast. Cream TEAS. *Adm £1.50 Chd free (Share to Arthritis & Rheumatism Council®). Private visits welcome, please* **Tel 01494 763553**

Hillesden House ✿✗✿ (Mr & Mrs R M Faccenda) Hillesden, 3m S of Buckingham via Gawcott. Follow Hillesden signs after Gawcott on Calvert Rd. 6 acres developed since 1978 from virgin land on site of C16 Manor House by superb Perpendicular Church 'Cathedral in the Fields'; large lawns, shrubberies; rose, alpine and foliage gardens; interesting clipped hedges; conservatory; large lakes and deer park; commanding views over countryside. TEAS in aid of Hillesden Church. *Adm £1.50 Chd under 12 free. Sun June 16 (2-6)*

Hughenden Manor ✿✗✿ (The National Trust) 1½m N of High Wycombe on W side of Great Missenden Rd A4128; [Grid ref: SU866955 on OS sheet 165]. 5 acres with lawns, terraced garden, herbaceous border, formal annual bedding, orchard and woodland walks. The Trust has undertaken restoration work in accordance with photographs taken at the time of Disraeli's death. Teas available. *Adm House & Garden £3.70 Chd £1.85 Family £9. Adm garden only £1 Chd 50p.* ▲*For NGS Sun July 21 (1-5). Last adm 4.30*

Long Crendon Gardens 2m N of Thame B4011 to Bicester. TEAS. *Combined adm £2 Chd free (Share to Church House Roof Fund©)* **Sun April 21 (2-6)**
  Manor House ✿✿ (Sir William & Lady Shelton) turn R by church; house through wrought iron gates. 6 acres; lawns sweep down to 2 ornamental lakes, each with small island; walk along lower lake with over 20 varieties of willow; fine views towards Chilterns. House (not open) 1675. TEAS
  The Old Crown ✿ (Mr & Mrs R H Bradbury) 100yds past Chandos Inn. 1 acre on steep SW slope. Old-fashioned and other roses and climbers. Flowering shrubs, herbaceous plants. Spring bulbs, assorted colourful containers in summer; 2 vegetable patches
  Old Post House ✿✿ (Mr & Mrs Nigel Viney) In the picturesque High St. Attractive cottage garden. Interesting spring & summer shrubs, and planting. Small produce stall
  Springfield Cottage ✿✿ (Mrs Elizabeth Dorling) 6 Burts Lane. ¼-acre very secluded, mature garden. Foliage predominating all yr with primroses, bluebells, herbaceous borders, flowering shrubs and many clematis
  Windacre ✿✿ (Mr & Mrs K Urch) 62 Chilton Rd, next to Primary School. 1-acre; roses, interesting shrubs, herbaceous plants, lenten roses, main features sunken lawns, conifers and trees. Cream TEAS

Sun June 30 (2-6)
  Croft House ✿ (Cdr & Mrs Peter Everett) Thame Rd. In square, white wrought iron railings. ½-acre walled garden; plants and shrubs of botanical interest especially to flower arrangers. TEAS
  8 Ketchmere Close ✿✿ (Mr & Mrs A Heley) 1991, 1992 & 1993 award winner incl Booker Garden Centre Competition for the best kept garden under 100ft in Buckinghamshire. Colourful split level garden with extensive views. Wide range of shrubs, conifers, rockery and water feature. *Parties welcome in June and July, please* **Tel 01844 201422,** *evenings*
  Manor House ✿✿ (Sir William & Lady Shelton) Description with April opening
  The Old Crown ✿ (Mr & Mrs R H Bradbury) Description with April opening
  Springfield Cottage Description with April opening
  Windacre Description with April opening. Cream TEAS

The Manor Farm ✿✗✿ (Mr & Mrs Peter Thorogood) Little Horwood 2m NE Winslow signposted off A413. 5m E Buckingham and 5m W Bletchley S off A421. Hilltop farmhouse garden on acid clay, laid out and replanted 1986. Wide range of alpines and plantsman's plants for yr-round interest in colour, form and foliage; good roses, pergola, 100' hosta border, herbaceous, wild flower meadow, damp garden, lovely views. Cream TEAS in aid of Gt. Horwood W.I. *Adm £2 Chd free (Share to REACT®). Sun June 30 (2-6). Private visits welcome April to Sept, please* **Tel 01296 714758**

The Manor House, Bledlow ✗✿ (The Lord & Lady Carrington) ½m off B4009 in middle of Bledlow village. Station: Princes Risborough, 2½m. Paved garden, parterres, shrub borders, old roses and walled kitchen garden. House (not open) C17 & C18. Water and species garden with paths, bridges and walkways, fed by 14 chalk springs. Also a new 2-acre garden with sculptures and landscaped planting. Partly suitable wheelchairs. TEA May, TEAS June. *Adm £3 Chd free (Share to Garden History Society® June only). Suns May 5, June 23 (2-6); also private visits welcome May to Sept by written application (2-4.30)*

The Manor House, Hambleden ✗ (Maria Carmela, Viscountess Hambleden) Hambleden. NE of Henley-on-Thames, 1m N of A4155. Conservatory; shrubs and old-fashioned rose garden. TEA at Hambleden Church. *Adm £1.50 Chd 20p. Sun June 23 (2-6)*

The Manor House, Princes Risborough ✗✿ (Mr & Mrs J Vellacott) From High Wycombe take A4010 to Princes Risborough. Turn L down High St. L at Market Square and bear R. The house is R of church, public car park beyond. From Aylesbury-Thame follow signs to town centre and turn R at Market Square. 2 acres surrounding C17 house (not open), large walled garden designed by NT in 1972 with pond, box balls and mixed borders, orchard with blue and white borders leading to gazebo. Informal rose garden bordered by nut walk and woodland. TEAS in aid of St Marys Church. *Adm £2 Chd under 15 free. Sat June 8 (2-5)*

Nether Winchendon House ♿✿❀ (Mr & Mrs R Spencer Bernard) Nether Winchendon, 5m SW of Aylesbury; 7m from Thame. Picturesque village, beautiful church. 5 acres; fine trees, variety of hedges; naturalised spring bulbs; shrubs; herbaceous borders. Tudor manor house (not open) home of Sir Francis Bernard, last British Governor of Massachusetts. TEA weather permitting. *Adm £1.50 Chd under 15 free.* ▲For NGS Suns April 28, July 14 (2-5.30). *Private visits welcome by written application*

¶**Oaklands** ♿✿❀ (Mr & Mrs Roy Brunswick) 35 Main St, Weston Turville. 2m SE of Aylesbury. Turn off A413 or A41 onto B4544. Garden is opp Five Bells inn (car park). Secluded mature ½-acre garden offering something for everyone. A loft of tumbler pigeons overlooks the pond, which is a haven for visiting birds and animals. Flower borders, incl some of the 100 varieties of clematis in the garden, surround the bog garden and duck jacuzzi. The magic grotto and fairy paths are a delight to children and lead to the apiary where bee demonstrations can be seen, weather permitting. TEAS in aid of 14th Vale of Aylesbury Venture Sea Scouts. *Adm £1.20 Chd free. Sun May 12 (2-6)*

The Old Vicarage, Padbury ♿✿❀ (Mr & Mrs H Morley-Fletcher) Padbury 2m S of Buckingham on A413 follow signs in village. 2½ acres on 3 levels; flowering shrubs and trees. Display collection of hebes, geometric vegetable garden; pond and sunken garden; parterre; work in progress. TEAS in aid of League of Friends of Buckingham Hospital. *Adm £1.50 Chd free. Suns April 14 (2-5), June 23 (2-6)*

6 Oldfield Close ✿❀ (Mr & Mrs Jolyon Lea) Little Chalfont. 3m E of Amersham. Take A404 E through Little Chalfont, turn 1st R after railway bridge, then R again into Oakington Ave. From M25 junction 18 take A404 to Amersham. In 2m turn L at Xrds (Lodge Lane & Church Grove) then bear R into Oakington Ave. Plantsman's ⅛-acre garden of borders, peat beds, rock plants, troughs and small alpine house. Over 2,000 species and varieties of rare and unusual plants. Plant stall in aid of Bethany Village Leprosy Society, in India. Cream teas at bakery in village. *Adm £1 Chd free. Suns April 14, 21 (2-5). Private visits welcome all yr, please Tel 01494 762384*

Overstroud Cottage ✿❀ (Mr & Mrs J Brooke) The Dell, Frith Hill. Amersham 6m Aylesbury 10m. Turn E off A413 at Gt Missenden onto B485 Frith Hill to Chesham. White Gothic cottage set back in layby 100yds up hill on L. Parking on R at Parish Church. Cottage originally C16 hospital for Missenden Abbey. Garden of yr-round interest; on 2 levels carved from chalk quarry. Artistic planting schemes; ornamental potager/herb garden; lily pond; sink gardens; collection of hellebores; bulbs; primulas, pulmonarias, hardy geraniums, species roses, clematis and traditional cottage plants. Not suitable for children or push chairs. TEAS at Parish Church. *Adm £1 Chd 50p (Share to The Ralph Sutcliffe Fund for Meningitis Research®). Suns April 7, May 5, June 9, July 7, Sept 8 (2-6). Parties welcome by appt, please Tel 01494 862701*

Pasture Farm ♿✿❀ (Mr & Mrs R Belgrove) Thame Rd. Longwick, nr Princes Risborough. 1m W of Longwick on A4129. 4m E of Thame. Farm entrance 50yds from layby. Garden at top of farm track. ½-acre plantswoman's garden. Herbaceous border, rockery and white garden. Integral nursery with perennials incl unusual white varieties. TEAS. *Adm £1 Chd free (Share to Aston Sandford Church Appeal®). Sun June 9, Tues June 11 (2-6). Also private visits welcome, please Tel 01844 343651*

Peppers ♿✿❀ (Mr & Mrs J Ledger) 4 Sylvia Close, Gt Missenden. A413 Amersham to Aylesbury Rd. At Great Missenden by-pass turn at sign. Great & Little Kingshill (Chiltern Hospital). After 400yds turn L, Nags Head Lane. After 300yds turn R under railway bridge. Sylvia Close 50yds on R. Approx 1 acre. Wide variety of plants, shrubs, trees, incl uncommon conifers, collection of acers, unusual containers, all year colour. TEAS. Donation from plant sale and teas to Workaid. *Adm £1 Chd free. Suns May 12, Aug 25 (10-5). Private visits welcome, please Tel 01494 864419*

Quainton Gardens 7m NW of Aylesbury. Nr Waddesdon turn N off A41
Sun May 12 *(2-6)* Combined *adm £1.50 Chd free*
    Brudenell House ♿✿ (Dr & Mrs H Beric Wright) Opp Church. 2-acre garden with specimen trees planted about 1830. Blossom, bulbs and primroses. Double herbaceous borders backed by rose hedges. TEAS
    Capricorner ♿ (Mr & Mrs A Davis) Small garden created in former stable yard, planted for yr-round interest with many scented plants; semi-wild area with trees
    Hatherways ❀ (Mr & Mrs D Moreton) A cottage garden which has gradually emerged from near wilderness. Bog garden, interesting shrubs, herbaceous plants and bulbs. Plant stall in aid of NSPCC
    Thorngumbald ♿ (Mr & Mrs J Lydall) Cottage garden heavily planted with wide selection of old-fashioned plants, organically grown; small pond, conservatory; attempts to encourage wild life
Sun June 30 *(2-6)* Combined *adm £2 Chd free*
    Brudenell House (description with May opening). TEAS in aid of Quainton Sports Club
    Capricorner (description with May opening)
    Cross Farmhouse (Mr & Mrs E Viney) 1-acre garden flanking hill with old farm pond. Mixed shrub and herbaceous planting emphasising shape, texture and colour of foliage. Fine view
    35 Lower Street ♿ (Mr D Burn) Small, S-facing rear garden with mixture of curved herbaceous and shrub borders. Raised vegetable and flower beds
    Thorngumbald (description with May opening)

Quoitings ♿ (Kenneth Balfour Esq) Oxford Rd, Marlow, 7m E of Henley, 3m S of High Wycombe; at Quoiting Sq, in Marlow turn N out of West St (A4155); garden 350yds up Oxford Rd on L. 2½-acres secluded garden with wide range of conifers and magnificent trees incl tulip, lime and pomegranate. Grand display of self propagated tulips followed by colourful mixed flower and dahlia beds; lawns; ha-ha; vistas. C17/18 house (not open) formerly home of Historiographer Royal to William IV and Queen Victoria. Marlow Town Band. TEAS. *Adm £2 Chd free. Suns April 14 (1-5), Sept 8 (1-6)*

Sheredon ظ۞ (Mr & Mrs G Legg) Thame Rd, Longwick. Between Princes Risborough and Thame on A4129 next to Longwick PO. Winner of several garden awards. ⅓-acre colourful garden. Large pond with bog plants, large selection of roses and unusual plants. Arches leading to smaller gardens. Organic vegetable garden. Orchard with various berries and grapes. Chickens and aviary. Many garden and water plants for sale. Cream TEAS July only. *Adm £1 Chd 25p. Suns May 26, July 14 (11-5)*

Spindrift ۞ (Norma Desmond) Jordans, nr Beaconsfield. On L of school, park in playground. Garden for all seasons on different levels full of surprises. Herbaceous border, variety of unusual hardy plants, fine hedges and specimen trees; hosta and hardy geranium collection; dell with pond; acid-loving shrubs. Model terraced vegetable and fruit garden with greenhouses and vines. Inspired by Monet, nasturtium arches surrounded by iris, poppies and peonies. Partly suitable for wheelchairs. Member of Horticultural Research Assoc. TEAS. *Adm £2 Chd under 12 20p. Wed May 29 (2-5). Private visits welcome, please Tel 01494 873172*

Springlea ظ۞۞ (Mr & Mrs M Dean) Seymour Plain. 1m from Marlow, 2½m from Lane End off B482. From Lane End pass Booker airfield on L then in 1m pass Seymour Court, L at pillar-box on grass triangle. ⅓-acre secluded garden backed by beechwoods. Flower arrangers' garden for colour, foliage and all yr interest. Spring bulbs, azaleas, rhododendrons, unusual trees, shrubs. Rockery, pond, waterfall, bog garden, hostas. Arched walkway with labelled clematis collection. 60' herbaceous border against high brick wall with many climbers, racing pigeon loft. Award winner of large garden 1991 and 1992 in Buckinghamshire. Great selection of unusual plants. TEAS by WI (not March or April). *Adm £1.50 Chd free. Suns March 10 (1-5), April 7, May 5, June 2, July 7, Aug 4, Sept 8 (2-6). Private visits and groups welcome March to October, please Tel 01628 473366*

Stowe Landscape Gardens ۞ (The National Trust) 3m NW of Buckingham via Stowe Ave. Follow brown NT signs. One of the supreme creations of the Georgian era; the first, formal layout was adorned with many buildings by Vanbrugh, Kent and Gibbs; in the 1730s Kent designed the Elysian Fields in a more naturalistic style, one of the earliest examples of the reaction against formality leading to the evolution of the landscape garden; miraculously, this beautiful garden survives; its sheer scale must make it Britain's largest work of art. TEAS. *Adm £4 Chd £2. ▲For NGS Tues May 14 (10-5). Last adm 4pm*

Tramway Farm ۞ (Mr & Mrs K Richardson) Ludgershall Rd, Brill. 7m N of Thame, turn off B 4011, Thame-Bicester or turn off A41 at Kingswood; both signed. 1-acre clay garden in hidden valley along the banks of a stream with wildlife pond; herbaceous borders with long season of interest, vegetable plot and mature spinney with spring bulbs. *Adm £1. Private visits welcome April-Sept, please Tel 01844 238249*

Turn End ۞ (Mr & Mrs Peter Aldington) Townside, Haddenham. From A418 turn to Haddenham between Thame (3m) and Aylesbury (6m). Turn at Rising Sun into Townside. BR Hadd and Thame Parkway. This acre seems

much more. Through archways and round corners are several secret gardens. A sweeping lawn bounded by herbaceous beds and a wooded glade with snowdrops, narcissi and bluebells. Old roses, iris and climbers abound. A sunny gravel garden has raised beds, alpine troughs and sempervivum pans. The house designed and built by the owners encloses a courtyard and fish pool. Featured in 'Country Life', 'The Garden', 'Practical Gardening'. TEAS by Stoke Mandeville Ambulance Station. *Adm £1.50 Chd 50p. ▲For NGS Suns April 7, Sept 22, Bank Hol Mon May 6 (2-6). Groups by appt at other times, please Tel 01844 291383/291817*

Tythrop Park ظ۞ (Mr & Mrs Jonathan Marks) Kingsey. 2m E of Thame, via A4129; lodge gates just before Kingsey. 4 acres. Replanting of wilderness. Walled kitchen garden, fully productive. Muscat and black (Muscat) d'Hamburg vine propagated from vine at Hampton Court 150 yrs ago in vine house. Courtyard now planted as grey garden. Parterre to S of Carolean house (not open). TEAS. *Adm £1.50 Chd free. Sun June 16 (2-6)*

¶**Waddesdon Manor** ظ۞۞ (The National Trust) On A41 between Aylesbury and Bicester. Follow signs to The Manor. The gardens were laid out between 1874 and 1898 under the direction of Baron Ferdinand de Rothschild. Innovative use of trees and shrubs coupled with the flamboyant displays of high Victorian bedding gives Waddesdon its own special identity. The restored Water Garden is open for the first time with one of the finest displays of Pulham rockscape where naturalistic outcrops of rock, cascading water, still ponds and intricate planting provide overwhelming drama. Water Garden conducted visits booked on a timed ticketing basis from the Manor gardens. Refreshments available all day in the restaurant. *Adm Manor Gardens £3 Chd (under 12) £1.50; Adm (incl NT members) Water & Rock Garden £1 Chd 50p (unsuitable for wheelchairs). ▲For NGS Sun March 3 (11-5)*

Walmerdene ظ۞۞ (Mr & Mrs M T Hall) 20 London Rd Buckingham. From Town Centre take A413 (London Rd). At top of hill turn R. Park in Brookfield Lane. Cream House on corner. Small town garden, unusual plants mostly labelled; species and hybrid hellebores; bulbs; herbaceous; euphorbias; climbing, shrub and species roses; geraniums; clematis. Sink garden, rill garden, 2 ponds, white and yellow border; 2 greenhouses. TEA in March, TEAS in June. *Adm £1 Chd free. Sun March 31 (2-5, hot soup if cold & wet), Sun, Wed, June 16, 19 (2-6). Private visits and parties welcome, May, June, July, also evening group visits, please Tel 01280 817466*

Watercroft ۞ (Mr & Mrs P Hunnings) Penn 3m N of Beaconsfield on B474, 600yds past Penn Church. Medium-sized garden on clay; white flowers, culinary herb garden planted 1993, rose walk, weeping ash; kitchen garden; pond, wild flower meadow. Plants and honey for sale. C18 house, C19 brewhouse (not open). Cream TEAS in aid of Holy Trinity Church, Penn. *Adm £1.50 Chd 30p. Sun June 30 (2-6)*

By Appointment Gardens. See end of county section

Weir Lodge &♨♿ (Mr & Mrs Mungo Aldridge) Latimer Rd Chesham. 1m SE of Chesham. Turn L from A416 along Waterside at junction of Red Lion St and Amersham Rd. From A404 Rickmansworth-Amersham Rd turn R at signpost for Chenies and go for 4m. Parking at Weir House Mill (McMinns). ¾-acre garden on bank of R. Chess. Recovered from dereliction in 1983 by owners. Stream and ponds with planted banks. Gravelled terrace with sun loving plants. Assorted containers; mixed beds. Mature trees, incl fine beeches in adjoining paddock. TEAS in aid of Chesham Society. *Adm £1 Chd free. Sun June 9 (2-6)*

14 Well Street &♨♿ (Mr & Mrs P Bradley) Buckingham. Well St is off Town centre (S side). 14 is opp The Woolpack inn. Small enclosed and private town garden; paved and walled with raised beds, troughs, pots and colourful annuals. Smaller secondary garden of shrubs and trees accessible through covered passageway; hanging baskets to front. TEAS. *Adm £1 Chd free (Share to Motorneurone Disease Society®). Sun July 28 (2-5)*

West Wycombe Park & (Sir Francis Dashwood; The National Trust). West Wycombe. 3m W of High Wycombe on A40. Bus: from High Wycombe and Victoria. Landscape garden; numerous C18 temples and follies incl Temple of the Winds, Temple of Venus, Temple of Music. Swan-shaped lake with flint bridges and cascade. *Adm (grounds only) £2.50 Chd £1.25 (incl NT members).* ▲*For NGS Sun Sept 8 (2-5)*

The Wheatsheaf Inn &♨♿ (Mrs W Witzmann) Weedon. 2m N of Aylesbury off A413 Buckingham-Aylesbury rd. Black and White thatched Tudor Inn opp 15' brick wall of 'Lilies'. Parking in courtyard and village. Since 1985 3 acres of field turned into a formal, flower and wild garden; with pond, roses, shrubs, perennials, spring bulbs, heather, conifers. Badminton and croquet lawn. Yr-round interest and fine views. Front has a preservation 400-yr-old walnut probably planted when the Old Wheatsheaf Coaching Inn was built. Many other old trees incl hazel grove for thatching. New paved area developed for shade-loving plants. Recommended by Gardening 'Which' magazine. *Adm £1 Chd free. Private visits welcome by appt only, please* **Tel 01296 641581**

Whitchurch Gardens 4m N of Aylesbury on A413. TEAS. *Combined adm £2 Chd free. Sun June 9 (2-6)*
  Kempsons Farm & (Mr G Band & Miss S Wells) Church Headland Lane. Converted barn set in 1-acre garden established in 1993. Set high on outskirts of the village behind the church, surrounded by paddocks and far-reaching views towards Cresslow Manor, the garden features a large natural looking pond stocked with assorted fish incl Koi carp, cascading waterfall and Japanese bridge; young shrubs and continuing planting, with patio and stable courtyard
  Mullions (Dr & Mrs L I Holmes-Smith) ⅓-acre picturesque cottage garden behind C17 cottage. 2 ponds and garden on 3 terraces
  The Old Cottage &♿ (Mr Roger Gwynne-Jones) ¾-acre cottage garden with herbaceous border, herb garden and wild area. Sloping lawn with views over Vale of Aylesbury. Partly suitable for wheelchairs

The Old Granary ♿ (Mr & Mrs P V Betts) Formerly part of a farmyard, now entering its 4th season, the garden is being developed as mixed borders, retaining walls of local stone. Gravel paths lead past the old farm granary to a paddock with views of open countryside
Quenington House &♨ (Mr & Mrs D F Ryder Richardson) 7 High Street. A family garden with croquet lawn bordered by roses and shrubs with far-reaching views to Waddesdon Manor. A secret garden lies in the most westerly corner
Yew Tree Cottage &♿ (Mr & Mrs B S Foulger) 3 tier garden with fish pond, patios and small wooded area, the whole offering sanctuary for wildlife. Panoramic views over the Vale of Aylesbury

The White House & (Mr & Mrs P G Courtenay-Luck) Denham Village. Approx 3m NW of Uxbridge, off A40 between Uxbridge and Gerrards Cross. Denham Village is signposted from A40 or A412; nearest main line station Denham Green. Underground Uxbridge. Parking in village rd. The White House is opp the Norman church in centre of village. 17 acres comprising 6 acres formal garden and an 11-acre paddock. Old flagstone terrace surrounds 2 sides of C18/19 house, leading to new yorkstone terrace; garden being restored to former glory; rejuvenation of old yew hedges, reclamation of lawns and shrubberies. R Misbourne meanders through lawns containing shrubberies, flower beds, orchard and developing rose garden. Large walled vegetable garden and restored Victorian greenhouses. Cream TEAS. *Adm £2 Acc chd free (Share to St Mary's Church, Denham Village®). Suns April 28, July 14 (2-5)*

Whitewalls &♿ (Mr W H Williams) Quarry Wood Rd, Marlow. From Marlow town centre cross over bridge. 1st L white garden wall, 3rd house on L. Thames-side garden approx ½-acre with spectacular view of weir. Large lily pond, interesting planting of trees, shrubs and herbaceous perennials. Many colourful containers. Sight of large conservatory with exotic plants. Teas available in Marlow. *Adm £1.50 Chd free. Suns April 28, July 21 (2-6). Private visits and parties welcome, please* **Tel 01628 482573**

Wichert &♿ (Mr & Mrs C Siggers) Ford. 5m SW of Aylesbury, 5m ENE of Thame. From Aylesbury A418 towards Thame. L at Bugle Horn into Portway. After 3m L into Ford. Approx 100yds beyond Xrds L into drive immed after Old Bakehouse. Approx 1½ acres developed into separate gardens since 1990. Silver and Pearl, shade, fern, kitchen and pavement gardens; maze, pond and wild garden with indigenous British trees. *Adm £1 Chd free. Private visits welcome, please* **Tel 01296 748431**

Winslow Hall & (Sir Edward & Lady Tomkins) Winslow. On A413 10m N of Aylesbury, 6m S of Buckingham. Free public car park. Winslow Hall (also open), built in 1700, designed by Christopher Wren, stands in a beautiful garden with distant perspectives, planted with many interesting trees and shrubs. In spring, blossom, daffodils and the contrasting foliage of trees combine to make the garden particularly attractive. TEAS. *Adm house & garden £3 garden only £1.50 Chd free. Bank Hol Mon May 6 (2-6)*

Cambridgeshire

Hon County Organisers:

South: Lady Nourse, Dullingham House, Dullingham, Newmarket, Suffolk CB8 9UP Tel 01638 508186

North: Mrs M Thompson, Stibbington House, Wansford, Peterborough PE8 6JS Tel 01780 782043

Assistant Hon County Organisers:

South: John Drake Esq., Hardwicke House, High Ditch Road, Fen Ditton, Cambridge CB5 8TF Tel 01223 292246

Timothy Clark Esq, Netherhall Manor, Soham, Ely CB7 5AB Tel 01353 720269

North: Mrs M Holmes, Manor House, Alwalton, Peterborough PE7 3UU Tel 01733 233435

Hon County Treasurers
(South Cambridgeshire): John Drake Esq.
(North Cambridgeshire): Michael Thompson Esq.

DATES OF OPENING

March 24 Sunday
Barton Gardens, Cambridge
March 31 Sunday
Trinity College, Fellows' Garden, Cambridge
April 5 Friday
Stibbington House, Wansford
April 7 Sunday
Netherhall Manor, Soham, Ely
April 8 Monday
Hyset, Horseheath ‡
Padlock Croft, West Wratting ‡
Scarlett's Farm, West Wratting ‡
Stibbington House, Wansford
Weaver's Cottage, West Wickham ‡
April 14 Sunday
Chippenham Park, nr Newmarket
King's College Fellows' Garden, Cambridge
April 19 Friday
Wimpole Hall, Royston
May 5 Sunday
Downing College, Cambridge
Netherhall Manor, Soham, Ely
Wytchwood, Great Stukeley
May 6 Monday
Ely Gardens
May 12 Sunday
Docwra's Manor, Shepreth
May 19 Sunday
Tetworth Hall, nr Sandy
May 25 Saturday
Hyset, Horseheath ‡
Padlock Croft, West Wratting ‡
Scarlett's Farm, West Wratting ‡
Weaver's Cottage, West Wickham ‡
May 26 Sunday
Fen Ditton Gardens, Fen Ditton
Godmanchester Gardens
Ramsey Gardens

Tetworth Hall, nr Sandy
May 27 Monday
Hyset, Horseheath ‡
Padlock Croft, West Wratting ‡
Scarlett's Farm, West Wratting ‡
Weaver's Cottage, West Wickham ‡
June 2 Sunday
Leckhampton, Cambridge
Thorpe Hall (Sue Ryder Foundation), Peterborough
Willingham Gardens
June 9 Sunday
Ely Gardens
83 High Street, Harlton
Madingley Hall, Cambridge
Orton Longueville Gardens, Peterborough
June 16 Sunday
Alwalton Gardens
Duxford Gardens, Cambridge ‡
Inglethorpe Manor, nr Wisbech
Melbourn Bury, Royston ‡
Melbourn Lodge, Royston ‡
The Old Post Office, Brington
31 Smith Street, Elsworth
Whittlesford Gardens ‡
June 19 Wednesday
Alwalton Gardens
June 22 Saturday
The Manor, Hemingford Grey
Padlock Croft, West Wratting ‡
Scarlett's Farm, West Wratting ‡
Weaver's Cottage, West Wickham ‡
June 23 Sunday
Chippenham Park, nr Newmarket ‡
Fordham Abbey, Fordham ‡
Hemingford Abbots Gardens
Horningsea & Waterbeach Gardens
Milton, Peterborough
Swaffham Bulbeck Gardens ‡

June 30 Sunday
Barton Gardens, Cambridge ‡
Clare College, Fellows' Garden, Cambridge ‡
Grantchester Gardens, Grantchester ‡
Sutton Gardens, nr Ely
West Wratting Park, West Wratting
July 6 Saturday
Emmanuel College Garden & Fellows' Garden
July 7 Sunday
Greystones, Swaynes Lane, Comberton
Mill House, North End, Bassingbourn
Nuns Manor, Frog End, Shepreth
Ramsey Gardens
July 12 Friday
Wimpole Hall, Royston
July 14 Sunday
Anglesey Abbey, Cambridge
Whittlesford Gardens
Willingham Gardens
July 21 Sunday
King's College Fellows' Garden, Cambridge
Pampisford Gardens, nr Cambridge
July 27 Saturday
Hyset, Horseheath ‡
Padlock Croft, West Wratting ‡
Scarlett's Farm, West Wratting ‡
Weaver's Cottage, West Wickham ‡
August 4 Sunday
Netherhall Manor, Soham, Ely
August 11 Sunday
Anglesey Abbey, Cambridge
Netherhall Manor, Soham, Ely

August 17 Saturday
Unwins Seeds Trial Gardens, Histon, Cambridge
September 1 Sunday
Docwra's Manor, Shepreth
October 13 Sunday
Chippenham Park, nr Newmarket

Regular openings
For details see garden description

The Crossing House, Shepreth
Docwra's Manor, Shepreth

By appointment only
For telephone numbers and other details see garden descriptions. Private visits welcomed

92 Bannold Road, Waterbeach
Elm House, Elm, Wisbech

DESCRIPTIONS OF GARDENS

Alwalton Gardens ⚘ Alwalton. 4m W of Peterborough, next to E of England showground. Parking at Village Hall. TEAS. *Combined adm £2 Chd free. Sun, Wed June 16, 19 (12-5)*

The Forge & (Mr & Mrs M Watson) Large cottage garden. Deep bed vegetables
Manor House ❀ (Mr & Mrs M Holmes) Walled garden divided into garden 'rooms' by yew and beech hedges. Borders and topiary surrounding C17 farmhouse (not open). Developing woodland walk with views over Nene valley
Oak Cottage & (Mr & Mrs J Wilson) Small enclosed garden with roses and lilies
9 Oundle Road & (Mr & Mrs C Leary) Medium-sized garden, mixed borders, pond, shrubs, rose arbour

Anglesey Abbey &⚘❀ (The National Trust) 6m NE of Cambridge. From A14 turn N on to B1102 through Stow-cum-Quy. 100 acres surrounding an Elizabethan manor created from the remains of an abbey founded in reign of Henry I. Garden created during last 60 years; avenues of beautiful trees; groups of statuary; hedges enclosing small intimate gardens; daffodils and 4,400 white and blue hyacinths (April); magnificent herbaceous borders (June). Lunches & TEAS. *Adm house and garden £6.50; garden only £3.20 Chd £1.60.* ▲*For NGS Suns July 14, Aug 11 (11-5.30)*

92 Bannold Road ⚘ (Mr & Mrs R L Guy) Waterbeach. 7m N of Cambridge on E of A10. Plantsman's tiny garden with over 300 plants in 150 varieties. Teas provided for garden clubs by arrangement. *Collection box. Private visits welcome June, July, please Tel 01223 863661*

Barton Gardens 3½m SW of Cambridge. Take A603, in village turn R for Comberton Rd. Teas in village hall. *Combined adm £1.25 Chd 25p (Share to GRBS®). Suns March 24, June 30 (2-5)*

¶**13 Allens Close** (Mrs R Wright) Small patio walled garden
Farm Cottage &⚘ (Dr R M Belbin) 18 High St. Cottage garden with water feature. Courtyard garden
The Gables & (P L Harris Esq) 11 Comberton Rd. 2-acre old garden, mature trees, ha-ha, spring flowers. *March 24 only*
14 Haslingfield Road & (J M Nairn Esq) Orchard, lawns, mixed domestic. *March 24 only*
Kings Tythe & (Maj C H Thorne) Comberton Road. Small domestic garden; good through way to larger gardens of **Town's End** and **The Gables**. *March 24 only*
31 New Road & (Dr D Macdonald) Cottage garden
Orchard Cottage, 22 Haslingfield Road &

(Mr J Blackhurst) Interesting mixed domestic. ½-acre garden with raised vegetable beds. *March 24 only*
The Seven Houses &⚘❀ (GRBS) Small bungalow estate on L of Comberton Rd. 1½-acre spring garden; bulbs naturalised in orchard. Colourful summer borders. Gift stall
Town's End &⚘ (B R Overton Esq) 15a Comberton Rd. 1-acre; lawns, trees, pond; extensive views. Raised vegetable beds. *March 24 only*

Chippenham Park &❀ (Mr & Mrs Eustace Crawley) Chippenham 5m NE of Newmarket, 1m off A11. 3½m of walled park landscaped by Mr Eames and Mr Lapidge to incl "a beautiful sheet of water ¾m long, small stretches of canal existing from the old formal garden, 2 lines of lime trees on each side of the park said to represent the Anglo-Dutch and French fleets at the Battle of La Hogue in May 1692". Restored C18 dovecote. 7-acre garden with borders of unusual and rare shrubs, trees and perennials. Daffodils by the lake in spring, summer borders and dramatic autumn colour. Many specialist Plant Stalls. Refreshments. *Adm £1.50 Chd free (Share to St Margaret's Church, Chippenham®). Suns April 14, June 23, Oct 13 (11-5)*

Clare College, Fellows' Garden ⚘ (Master & Fellows) Cambridge. The Master and Fellows are owners of the Fellows' Garden which is open; the Master's garden (nearby) is not open to the public. Approach from Queen's Rd or from city centre via Senate House Passage, Old Court and Clare Bridge. 2 acres; one of the most famous gardens on the Cambridge Backs. TEAS. *Adm £1.50 Chd under 13 free. Sun June 30 (2-6). Private visits welcome, please Tel 01223 333 222*

The Crossing House & (Mr & Mrs Douglas Fuller and Mr John Marlar) Meldreth Rd, Shepreth, 8m SW of Cambridge. ½m W of A10. King's Cross-Cambridge railway runs alongside garden. Small cottage garden with many old-fashioned plants grown in mixed beds in company with modern varieties; shrubs, bulbs, etc, many alpines in rock beds and alpine house. *Collecting box. Open daily, any reasonable time. Parties by appt, please Tel 01763 261071*

Docwra's Manor &⚘❀ (Mrs John Raven) Shepreth, 8m SW of Cambridge. ½m W of A10. Cambridge-Royston bus stops at gate opposite the War Memorial in Shepreth. 2½-acres of choice plants in series of enclosed gardens. Small nursery. TEA May 12, Sept 1 only, in aid of Shepreth Church Funds. *Adm £2 Chd free. All year Mon, Wed, Fri (10-4), Suns April 7, May 5, June 2, July 7, Aug 4, Oct 6 (2-5), also Bank Hol Mons (10-4). Proceeds for garden upkeep. Also private visits welcome, please Tel 01763 261557. For NGS Suns May 12, Sept 1 (2-6)*

Downing College ᕼᕼ (The Master & Fellows of Downing College) Regent Street. Centre of Cambridge opp the University Arms Hotel to the S of Parkers's Piece. Approach from Regent St only. Fine example of 16-acre garden in a classical setting. Wilkins' Greek revival buildings frame wide lawns and paddock. Mature and newly planted rare trees. Unusual view of the Roman Catholic Church. Master's garden. Fellows' garden and walled rose garden with period roses. TEA. *Adm £1.50 Chd 50p (Share to Friends of Arthur Rank House®). Sun May 5 (2-6)*

¶**Duxford Gardens** ᕼᕼ 9m S of Cambridge, junction 10 off M11, follow signs for Duxford Village. Teas at St Peters Church in aid of Restoration Appeal. *Combined adm £2. Sun June 16 (2-6)*

¶**Kings Head House** (Mr & Mrs P Milton) 1-acre walled garden, herbaceous borders, shrubs, old roses. Courtyard area with conservatory

¶**8 Moorfield Road** ❀ (Maggi Stewart) Started 5yrs ago from scratch by Maggi Stewart. Full of ideas for planting using unusual plants with emphasis on the use of water, ponds, fountains, fish and wildlife. All can be found in this secret garden

¶**Robynet House** (Gordon Lister) 1-acre of old roses, box hedging, herbaceous borders and formal garden with fountain and urns

¶**Elm House** ᕼᕼ (Mrs D Bullard) Wisbech. On B1101 approx 2m from Wisbech. Free parking. Walled garden approx 1½ acres with young arboretum, shrubs, perennials and annuals. (House not open). *Adm £1.50 Chd free. Private visits welcome by appt June 17 to July 19, please* **Tel 01945 583021**

Ely Gardens ᕼᕼ❀ 16m N of Cambridge on A10. (*Share to Old Palace Sue Ryder Home®)*
Mon May 6 (2-5) *Combined adm £1 Chd 50p*

Old Bishops Palace 1½ acres with small lake, iris walk and herbaceous border wonderfully restored by two expert voluneers to its original C17. Famous for its plane tree - oldest and largest in country

The Old Fire Engine House Restaurant and Gallery (Mr & Mrs R Jarman) Delightful walled country garden with mixed herbaceous borders and wild flowers. Situated just W of the Cathedral. TEAS
Sun June 9 (2.30-5.30) *Combined adm £3 Chd 50p single garden £1*

Belmont House, 43 Prickwillow Rd (Mr & Mrs P J Stanning) Designed ½-acre garden with interesting and unusual plants

¶**Queen's Hall** (Mr & Mrs R H Youdale) In Cathedral Close. Recently re-created in theme of "medieaval garden" using as much as possible plants available pre 1600

Rosewell House 60 Prickwillow Road. (Mr & Mrs A Bullivant) Well stocked garden with emphasis on perennial planting and splendid view of cathedral and surrounding fenland

The Bishops House To R of main Cathedral entrance. Walled garden, former cloisters of monastery. Mixed herbaceous, box hedge, rose and kitchen garden

31 Egremont St (Mr & Mrs J N Friend-Smith) A10 Lynn Rd out of Ely. 2nd L. Approx 1 acre. Lovely views of cathedral, mixed borders, cottage garden. Ginkgo tree, tulip tree and many other fine trees

Old Bishops Palace Description with May opening. TEAS

48 St Mary's Street (Mr J Hardiment) Formal walled garden with a wide variety of beautiful and unusual plants

Emmanuel College Garden & Fellows' Garden ᕼᕼ in centre of Cambridge. Car parks at Parker's Piece and Lion Yard, within 5 mins walk. One of the most beautiful gardens in Cambridge; buildings of C17 to C20 surrounding 3 large gardens with pools; also herb garden; herbaceous borders, fine trees inc Metasequoia glyptostroboides. On this date access allowed to Fellows' Garden with magnificent Oriental plane and more herbaceous borders. Teashops in Cambridge. *Adm £1 Chd free. Sat July 6 (2.30-5.30). Private visits welcome, please* **Tel 01223 334241**

Fen Ditton Gardens ᕼ❀ 3½m NE of Cambridge. From A14 Cambridge-Newmarket rd turn N by Borough Cemetery into Ditton Lane; or follow Airport sign from bypass. Flower Festival in Parish Church. Teas in church hall. *Combined adm £2 Chd 50p (Share to Parish Church ®). Sun May 26 (2-5.30)*

Hardwicke House ᕼ❀ (Mr J Drake) 2 acres designed to provide shelter for plants on exposed site; divided by variety of hedges; species roses; rare herbaceous plants; home of national collection of aquilegias, collection of plants grown in this country prior to 1650. Please park in road opposite. Large sale of plants in aid of NGS; rare aquilegias from National Collection; foliage plants and rare herbaceous plants. **Exceptional rare plant sale for NGS**. *Private visits welcome by appt, please* **Tel 01223 292246**

The Old Stables (Mr & Mrs Zavros) Large informal garden; old trees, shrubs and roses; many interesting plants, herbs and shrubs have been introduced. House (not open) converted by owners in 1973 from C17 stables. *Private visits welcome by appt, please* **Tel 01223 292507**

The Rectory (Revd & Mrs L Marsh) Small rectory garden. Largely mediterranean flowers, extensive range of climbers, Tromp l'oeil. Intensive organic vegetable garden which supplies household throughout the year, incl 34' long decorative arch support for beans, sugar peas, spaghetti marrows, cucumbers and tomatoes

¶**Fordham Abbey** ᕼᕼ❀ (Mr & Mrs John Lewin Smith) Fordham. On A142 at edge of village towards Newmarket. 4-acre garden surrounding Georgian house (not open), lawns, mature trees, pond, orchard with wild flowers, shrubs roses and mixed borders, redwood avenue. TEAS. *Adm £1.50 Chd 50p. Sun June 23 (2-6)*

LARGE PLANT STALL

HARDWICKE HOUSE

Sun May 26 (2-5.30)
A unique and exciting opportunity to purchase rare plants, Turkish and pre 1660 plants, aquilegia, rare native plants.

PROCEEDS IN AID OF THE NATIONAL GARDENS SCHEME

¶Godmanchester Gardens ✲ TEAS in aid of Godmanchester Church Fund. *Combined adm £3 Chd free £2 per garden. Sun May 26 (2-5)*

Farm Hall ❀ (Prof & Mrs Marcial Echenique) Godmanchester. Fronting West St (Offord/St Neots rd B1043) 2m S of Huntingdon, 15m NW of Cambridge (A14). Early C18 country house (not open) on edge of Godmanchester. Set in 24 acres of parkland with mature trees. Formal layout on its main axis: in front a rectangular pond or canal flanked by an avenue of poplars ending at the R Ouse; behind a long avenue of limes more than 200yrs old. Charming walled garden with formal box hedges, herbaceous borders and fruit trees. Rose garden with lily pond surrounded by yew hedge; statuary; wooded walk with wild flowers

Island Hall ❀ (Mr Christopher & The Hon Mrs Vane Percy) Godmanchester. In centre of Godmanchester next to car park, 1m S of Huntingdon (A1) 15m NW of Cambridge (A604). Station: Huntingdon (1m). 3-acre grounds, of important mid C18 mansion. Tranquil riverside setting with replica of original Chinese bridge over millstream to island. The garden has been restored during last 10 yrs. New shrubberies have been planted, vistas created. There are new formal borders and blue and white borders. Wild flowers have been encouraged on the island

Grantchester Gardens ❀ 2m SW of Cambridge. AI0 from S, L at Trumpington (Junction 11, M11). M11 from N, L at Junction 12. Palestrina Singers will be performing at the Old Vicarage. Craft Fair at Manor Farm, quality handmade goods; wooden toys; pottery, stained glass; glass blowing demonstration; honey and demonstrations of beekeeping. TEAS. *(Share to Grantchester Church®). Sun June 30 (2-6)*

Home Grove ♿ (Dr & Mrs C B Goodhart) 1-acre mature, orchard-type garden with shrub roses. Specimen trees and lawns and carefully planned kitchen garden

North End House (Mr & Mrs A Frost) 1 acre, shrub and herbaceous borders; old-fashioned roses; water garden and rockery. Small conservatory

The Old Vicarage ♿✲❀ (Lord & Dr Archer) 2½ acres; house dating from C17; informal garden laid out in mid C19 with C20 conservatory; lawn with fountain; ancient mulberry tree; many other interesting trees incl cut-leaf beech; beyond garden is wilderness leading to river bank bordered by large old chestnut trees immortalised by Rupert Brooke, who lodged in the house 1910–1912

Greystones, Swaynes Lane ♿✲❀ (Dr & Mrs Lyndon Davies) Comberton. 5m W of Cambridge. From M11 take exit 12 and turn away from Cambridge on A603. Take first R B1046 through Barton to Comberton; follow signs from Xrds. Plantswoman's garden of approx ½ acre attractively planted with wide range of flowering plants framed by foliage and shrubs. Gravel bed and troughs give contrast; vegetable garden. TEAS. *Adm £1.50 Chd 50p (Share to Herbal Research®). Sun July 7 (2-5.30). Private visits welcome, please* **Tel 01223 264159**

Hardwicke House See Fen Ditton Gardens

Hemingford Abbots Gardens 4m E of Huntingdon. Turn off A14 at Little Chef. In village turn R into Common Lane. Parking opp Meadow Lane. TEAS at 68 Common Lane. *Combined adm £2 Chd free (Share to Parkinsons Disease Society®). Sun June 23 (2-6)*

Heathermead ♿ (Mr & Mrs Nigel Everdell) 25 Common Lane. ⅓-acre, 250 rose bushes, variety of shrubs, pink and white border, pond with great crested newts, small bog garden, organic vegetable plot, specimen and fruit trees

¶Lane End Cottage (Mr & Mrs R W Horner) 65 Common Lane. Approx ¾-acre mature cottage garden. Collection of large specimen trees, herbaceous island beds, 2yr yet already mature 'olde worlde' paved pergola area with unusual climbing plants, shrubbery, rockeries and small woodland area. Pots, plants and interesting features

68 Common Lane ♿❀ (Mr & Mrs D W Flanagan) Informal garden of approx 1-acre. Very colourful herbaceous borders framed by mature pines and woodland, rose walk, vegetable garden and wild area

83 High Street, Harlton ♿✲❀ (Dr Ruth Chippindale) 7m SW of Cambridge. A603 (toward Sandy); after 6m turn L (S) for Harlton. ⅓-acre interesting design which includes many different features, colours and a wide diversity of plants. TEAS. *Adm £1 Chd free (Share to Harlton Church Restoration Fund®). Sun June 9 (2-6); also by appointment* **Tel 01223 262170**

Horningsea Gardens ✲ Waterbeach. TEAS. *Combined adm £2 Chd 50p (Share to Village Church® & Arthur Rank Hospice®). Sun June 23 (2-5.30)*

15 Abbots Way (Mr & Mrs D Edwards) Horningsea. 4m NE of Cambridge from A1307 Cambridge Newmarket Rd. Turn N at borough cemetery to Horningsea or take B1047 N from A14. 1-acre developing plantswoman's garden on old flood bank of R Cam; overlooking river and water meadows. Spring and natural pond. Clematis and solomon's seal amongst fine collection of rare and unusual plants, shrubs and trees. Entrance to car park and garden signposted nr village hall; no access to garden via Abbots Way

The Lodge ♿ (N M Buchdal) Clayhithe Road, Horningsea. 5m NE of Cambridge to Newmarket Rd. 1½m of A14 on Clayhithe Rd (B1047), ¾m out of Horningsea on L towards R Cam. 3 acres of well landscaped garden framed by mature willows and old native trees; many shrubs and old roses; large water garden and many wide herbaceous borders. Unusual plants for sale from specialist nursery on site. Car park

¶32 Station Road ♿❀ (Mr & Mrs Reeve) Waterbeach. Visitors please park at station or village green. Small S facing enclosed garden. Large variety of interesting plants, conservatory with selection of vines

¶Hyset (Mr & Mrs S Agnew) Cardinals Green. A604 between Linton and Haverhill. On opp side of bypass A604 to Horseheath Village. Take turning signed 'The Camps'. Hyset is 2nd on R. ⅓-acre garden being developed by professional plantsman/horticulturist who is very able to give advice. Interesting range of herbaceous, shrubs, climbers and alpines. Attractive water feature displaying host of plants and insect life. Poly tunnel growing range of salads. *Combined adm £2 Chd 50p with* **Padlock Croft, Scarletts Farm** *and* **Weavers Cottage.** *Mons, Sats April 8, May 25, 27, July 27 (2-6). Private visits welcome, please* **Tel 01223 892982**

Inglethorpe Manor ✿❀ (Mr & Mrs Roger Hartley) Emneth, near Wisbech. 2m S of Wisbech on A1101. 200yds on L beyond 40mph derestriction sign. Entrance opp Ken Rowe's Garage. Large garden with interesting mature trees, lawns, mixed and herbaceous borders, shrub roses, rose walk and water garden. Victorian house (not open). TEAS in aid of NSPCC. *Adm £1.50 Chd free. Sun June 16 (2-6)*

King's College Fellows' Garden ♿✿ Cambridge. Fine example of a Victorian garden with rare specimen trees. Colour booklet available £1.50, free leaflet describing numbered trees. TEAS. *Adm £1 Chd free. Suns April 14, July 21 (2-6)*

Leckhampton ♿✿ (Corpus Christi College) 37 Grange Rd, Cambridge. Grange Rd is on W side of Cambridge and runs N to S between Madingley Rd (A1303) and A603; drive entrance opp Selwyn College. 10 acres; originally laid out by William Robinson as garden of Leckhampton House (built 1880); George Thomson building added 1964 (Civic Trust Award); formal lawns, rose garden, small herbaceous beds; extensive wild garden with bulbs, cowslips, prunus and fine specimen trees. TEAS. *Adm £1.50 Chd free. Sun June 2 (2-6)*

Madingley Hall Cambridge ✿ (University of Cambridge) 4m W, 1m from M11 Exit 13. C16 Hall set in 7½ acres of attractive grounds. Features incl landscaped walled garden with hazel walk, borders in individual colours and rose pergola. Meadow, topiary and mature trees. TEAS. *Adm £1.50 Chd free (Share to Madingley Church Restoration Fund®). Sun June 9 (2.30-5.30)*

The Manor ❀ (Mr & Mrs P S Boston) Hemingford Grey. 4m E of Huntingdon off A14. Entrance to garden by small gate off river towpath. No parking at house except disabled by arrangement with owners. Car park sign posted. Garden designed and planted by the author Lucy Boston, surrounds the C12 manor house on which her Green Knowe Books were based. 4 acres divided into different areas with topiary; one of the best collections of old shrub roses in Cambridgeshire, and herbaceous borders with mainly scented plants. Enclosed by river, moat and wilderness. TEAS in aid of WI. *Adm £1.50 Chd 50p. Sat June 22 (2-5.30)*

Melbourn Bury ♿✿❀ (Mr & Mrs Anthony Hopkinson) 2¼m N of Royston; 8m S of Cambridge; off the A10 on edge of village, Royston side. 5 acres; small ornamental lake and river with wildfowl; large herbaceous border; fine mature trees with wide lawns and rose garden. TEAS. *Combined adm with Melbourn Lodge £2 Chd free. Sun June 16 (2-6). Private visits welcome for parties of 4 and over, please Tel 01763 261151*

Melbourn Lodge ♿✿❀ (J R M Keatley Esq) Melbourn 3m N of Royston, 8m S of Cambridge. House in middle of Melbourn village. 2-acre garden maintained on 9 hrs work per week in season. C19 grade II listed house (not open). TEAS at Melbourn Bury. *Combined adm with Melbourn Bury £2 Chd free. Sun June 16 (2-6)*

Mill House ♿✿❀ (Anthony & Valerie Jackson) Fen Road, North End. On the NW outskirts of Bassingbourn 1m from Church, on the rd to Shingay. Take North End at the war memorial in the centre of Bassingbourn which is just W of the A1198, 2m N of Royston (do not take Mill Lane). Garden created out of open countryside by garden designer owners. Clever use of walls, pergolas, water and varying land levels provide a backdrop for many very fascinating plants notably viticel la clematis, giving interest and colour throughout the year. Rare plants for sale. *Adm £1.50 Chd free. Sun July 7 (2-5.30). Private visits welcome in July, please Tel 01763 243491*

¶**Milton** ✿ (The Hon Lady Hastings) Peterborough. Turn N off A47 just W of Peterborough into Bretton Way. Turn 1st L into Milton Park (just before entrance to Fitzwilliam Hospital). 35 acres. Pleasure grounds by Repton. Orangery by John Carr of York. Walled herbaceous and shrub garden recently replanted. Newly planted knot garden. TEA. *Adm £2 Chd free. Sun June 23 (2-6) Private visits welcome following written application*

Netherhall Manor (Timothy Clark) Soham. Enter Soham from Newmarket, Tanners Lane is 1st R 80yds after Webbs Store. Enter Soham from Ely, Tanners Lane is 2nd L after War Memorial. 1-acre walled garden incl courtyard featured on Geoffrey Smiths 'World of Flowers' and 'Gardeners World'. April-Crown Imperials, Victorian hyacinths and old primroses. May-florists ranunculus (picotee and bizarre), and tulips (rose, bizarre, byblomen). Also during Aug formal beds of Victorian pelargoniums, calceolarias, lobelias and heliotropes an organic seasonal kitchen garden. Teas at Soham Windmill. *Adm £1 Chd 50p. Suns April 7, May 5, Aug 4, 11 (2-5). Private visits welcome, please Tel 01353 720269*

Nuns Manor ♿✿❀ (Mr & Mrs J R L Brashaw) Frog End Shepreth. 8m SW of Cambridge 200yds from A10 Melbourn-Shepreth Xrds. C16 farmhouse surrounded by 2-acre garden; interesting plants, large pond, woodland walk, kitchen garden. Mixed and herbaceous borders. **Unusual plants for sale for NGS**. TEA in aid of Shepreth Church. *Adm £1.50 Chd free. Sun July 7 (2-5.30); also group visits by appt April to July, please Tel 01763 260313*

¶**The Old Post Office** ❀ (The Hon Mrs Sue Roe) Brington, nr Huntingdon. Turn off A14 onto B660 northbound approx 7m W of junction with A1. Then follow signs to Brington. In Brington go towards Old Weston. Last house on L. A packed, newly planted cottage garden with plenty of unusual plants. Approx ¾-acre. The boundary between garden and countryside is deliberately left blurred to encourage wildlife. Pond, small wild flower meadow. TEA. *Adm £1. Sun June 16 (2-6). Private visits at weekends welcome April to Sept by appt, please Tel 01832 710223*

¶**Orton Longueville Gardens** ✿ Off 605 Oundle Rd, Peterborough, 2½m E of intersection with A1 after junction with Nene Parkway. Teas at 16 The Village. *Combined adm £1 Chd 50p. Sun June 9 (2-5)*

   ¶**The Old School** ❀ (Dr & Mrs Ross Gordon) The Village. A converted 1853 village school, playground, school master's house and garden. Formal layout with informal planting of ⅓-acre gardens in picturesque village lage

¶**Lane End** (Mr & Mrs R M Bulkeley) 9 St Botolph Lane. After junction with Nene Parkway, take 1st R into Royston Ave; park near junction with Sheringham Way take signed footway to St Botolph Lane. Please do not park in Lane. Designers secluded garden enclosed by tall hedges, contains a range of unusual small trees, shrubs and herbaceous plants. Emphasis on organic gardening and encouraging wildlife

Padlock Croft ಈ✿❀ (Mr & Mrs P E Lewis) West Wratting. From dual carriageway on A604 between Linton and Horseheath take turning N (Balsham W Wratting); Padlock Road is at entry to village. Plantsman's organic garden of ⅔-acre, home of the National Campanula Collection; mixed borders, troughs, alpine house etc incl rare plants; rock and scree gardens; potager with raised beds; bantams and ducks. *Combined adm £2 Chd 50p with* Hyset *(not June 22)*, Scarletts Farm *and* Weavers Cottage. *Sats, Mon April 8, May 25, 27; June 22, July 27 (2-6). Private visits also welcome, weekdays, please* Tel 01223 290383

Pampisford Gardens ಈ✿❀ 8m S of Cambridge on A505. TEAS at the Old Vicarage in aid of RDA. *Combined adm £2 Chd free. Sun July 21 (2-5.30)*
> **Beech Corner** (Dr & Mrs B E Bridgland) 22 Church Lane. Rear garden has been planned as a small paved courtyard leading round into mini woodland
> **The Dower House** (Dr & Mrs O M Edwards) 7 High Street. Medieval house surrounded by well designed and interesting garden
> **Glebe Crescent** A group of pensioners houses with very colourful small gardens
> **The Old Vicarage** (Mr & Mrs Nixon) Next to Church in village. 2½-acres; mature trees; shrub and herbaceous borders with good ground cover plants; small Victorian style conservatory planted with rare species

¶**Ramsey Gardens** nr Huntingdon
Sun May 26 (2-5) *Combined adm £1.50 Chd free*
> ¶**The Elms** (Mr & Mrs K C Shotbolt) From Ramsey travel through Ramsey Forty Foot, just before bridge over drain, turn R, 300yds on R. Large water garden beautifully landscaped with shrubs, water lilies, ferns and large tank koi carp. Mirror carp, golden orfe in lakes. 2-acres full of unusual plants; spring flowers
> ¶**77 Great Whyte** ✿ (Mr & Mrs H Holden) Cottage garden 55′ × 45′ well stocked with trees, shrubs and flowers, many interesting plants and features
> ¶**7 Hollow Lane** ಈ❀ (Mrs Yvonne Wright) Medium-sized garden with shrubs and perennials, ornamental and wild pond. Pergola, rockery, vegetable and fruit garden. Beautiful view of Ramsey abbey. TEAS in aid of MacMillan Hinchinbroke Cancer Care Appeal
Sun July 7 (2-6). Map and TEAS at **Yesteryear**. *Combined adm £2.50 Chd free*
> ¶**The Elms** (for description see above)
> ¶**Great Whyte** (for description see above)
> ¶**7 Hollow Lane** (for description see above)
> ¶**Glencairn** ಈ (Mrs Anne How) Large garden with shrubs, heathers, vegetables, container patio, extensive lawns, views over fields and golf course
> ¶**18 Little Whyte** (Mr & Mrs R Sisman) Small interesting garden with unusual plants, trees and shrubs, vegetable garden

¶**Yesteryear Guest House** ಈ❀ (Mr & Mrs W Staley Grace) Small town garden full of colour with rockeries and pond, greenhouses. Patios full of hanging baskets and containers. Pergola, gazebo

Scarlett's Farm ಈ✿❀ (Mr & Mrs M Hicks) Padlock Rd, West Wratting. From dual carriageway on A604 between Linton and Horseheath taking turning N (W Wratting 3½); Padlock Road is at entry to village. Scarlett's Farm at end of Padlock Road. ⅓-acre mixed country garden, planted for long season of interest; small nursery attached. TEAS. *Combined adm £2 Chd 50p with* Hyset *(not June 22)*, Padlock Croft *and* Weavers Cottage. *£1 garden on its own. Sats, Mon April 8, May 25, 27; June 22, July 27; (2-6). Private visits welcome, April to Oct incl please* Tel 01223 290812

31 Smith Street ಈ✿❀ (Drs J D & J M Twibell) Elsworth. Approx 9m from Cambridge, Huntingdon, St Ives and St Neots. From A428 (St Neots) enter village and turn L at T-junction at "Poacher" public house. 2nd house on L. 2nd house on R on entering village from Hilton end. ¾-acre cottage garden. Herbs, scented, insectivorous and other unusual plants. National collections of artemisia (featured Channel 4 Garden Club Sept 1992) and nerium oleander. TEA. *Adm £1 Chd 50p (Share to NCCPG®). Sun June 16 (2-5.30). Private visits welcome, please* Tel 01954 267414

Stibbington House (Mr & Mrs Michael Thompson) Wansford. 8m W of Peterborough W of A1 on B671 Elton Rd S of Wansford. Approx 3 acres of trees, shrubs, spring flowers and bulbs, lawns running down to mill stream (R Nene). Site of old paper mill. River walks. TEAS April 8 only. *Adm £1.50 Chd free. Fri, Mon April 5, 8 (12-5)*

Sutton Gardens ಈ✿❀ 6m W of Ely on A142, turn L at roundabout into village. Teas at 5 Church Lane in aid of Sutton WI. *Combined adm £2.50 Chd free. Sun June 30 (2-6)*
> **1 Church Lane** ಈ❀ (Miss B M & Miss B I Ambrose) Small garden near church, filled with an unusual range of trees, shrubs, climbers, alpines; and perennials incl penstemon border. Plants for shade, raised beds, troughs, greenhouse. Teas at 5 Church Lane in aid of Sutton WI
> **51 High Street** (Mr A Wilkinson) Medium-sized garden on sloping site, herbaceous borders, terrace, conservatory with vine. Tender perennials include salvias, daturas, gloriosa lilies and summer flowering bulbs
> **7 Lawn Lane** ಈ❀ (Mr & Mrs R Kybird) Small garden with many hanging baskets and containers; fuchsias, penstemons, hardy geraniums, roses, hostas, clematis and shrubs incl photinia
> **8 Lawn Lane** ❀ (Mr & Mrs H J Fortin) Small garden closely planted and colourful, with rockery, formal pool, terrace and curved lawns on 2 levels. Secluded vegetable corner. Meticulously cared for by plantaholic
> **91 The Row** ಈ❀ (Mr & Mrs M Cooper) Recently created organic garden bordering open fenland. Traditional English hedgerow and pond to encourage wildlife. (Great crested newts in pond). Collection of herbs; secluded scented garden. TEAS in aid of Sutton Scout Group

¶**Swaffham Bulbeck Gardens** 8m E of Cambridge off B1102 past Anglesey Abbey. TEAS in aid of St Mary's Church, Swaffham Bulbeck. *Combined adm £1.50 Chd free. Sun June 23 (2-6)*

¶**Martin House** (Prof & Mrs L Sealy) New garden with Chinese influence, designed and made by Mrs Sealy. Herb garden

¶**The Merchant's House** ⅄ (Mr & Mrs H L S Bevington) Commercial End. 1-acre walled gardens to C17 house originally used for canal-based merchanting business. Gardens still being restored; potager, orchard, old roses, mixed herbaceous borders

Tetworth Hall ❀ (Lady Crossman) 4m NE of Sandy; 6m SE of St Neots off Everton-Waresley Rd. Large woodland and bog garden; rhododendrons; azaleas, unusual shrubs and plants; fine trees. Queen Anne house (not open). TEA in aid of Waresley Church. *Adm £1.50 Chd free. Suns May 19, 26 (2-6). Private visits welcome April 15 to June 15, please* Tel 01767 650212

Thorpe Hall ⅄❀ (Sue Ryder Foundation) Thorpe Rd, Longthorpe, Peterborough. 1m W of Peterborough city centre. Thorpe Hall 1665 Grade I house in Grade II listed garden with original walls; gate piers; urns and niches. Historic planting restoration. Unique garden in course of replanting. Victorian stone parterre; iris collection; rose garden and 1650 herbaceous borders; ferncry. TEA. *Adm Garden only £1 Chd 50p (Share to Sue Ryder Foundation®). Sun June 2 (2-5.30)*

Trinity College, Fellows' Garden ⅄❀ Queen's Road, Cambridge. Garden of 8 acres, originally laid out in the 1870s by W B Thomas; lawns with mixed borders, shrubs, specimen trees. Drifts of spring bulbs. *Adm £1 Chd free. Sun March 31 (2-6)*

Unwins Seeds Ltd ❀ (Mr & Mrs David Unwin) Impington Lane, Histon. 3m N of Cambridge, 1m off A14 on B1049. Follow signs for Histon and Cotterham. At traffic lights nr Rose & Crown in centre of Histon, turn R into Impington Lane. Trial gardens of approx 6 acres where 4,500 varieties of annuals, biennials, perennials and vegetables from seed are assessed. Many new and experimental strains are on show. The company uses the gardens to determine the garden worth of new varieties and monitor the trueness to type of strains it already lists. TEA. *Adm £1.50 Chd under 14 free. Sat Aug 17 (12-5)*

Weaver's Cottage ⅄❀❀ (Miss Sylvia Norton) Streetly End, West Wickham. 1m N of A604 between Linton and Haverhill. ½-acre garden planted for fragrance with bulbs; shrubs; herbs; perennials; honeysuckle; old shrub and climbing roses. National Lathyrus Collection. TEA. *Combined adm £2 Chd 50p with* Hyset *(not June 22),* Padlock Croft *and* Scarletts Farm*. Sats, Mon April 8, May 25, 27; June 22, July 27 (2-6). Visitors welcome any time by appt* Tel 01223 892399

West Wratting Park ⅄❀❀ (Mr & Mrs Henry d'Abo) 8m S of Newmarket. From A11, between Worsted Lodge and Six Mile Bottom, turn E to Balsham; then N along B1052 to West Wratting; Park is at E end of village. Georgian house (orangery shown), beautifully situated in rolling country, with fine trees; rose and herbaceous gardens. TEA. *Adm £1 Chd free. Sun June 30 (2-7)*

Whittlesford Gardens ❀ 7m S of Cambridge. 1m NE of Junction 10 of the M11 and A505. TEAS. Flower festival in parish church. *Combined adm £2 Chd 50p (Share to Whittlesford Memorial Hall Fund®). Suns June 16, July 14 (2-6)*

The Guildhall ❀ (Dr P & Dr M Spufford) North Road. Small knot garden next to medieval half-timbered building (not open). *June 16 only*

Cherrytree Cottage ❀ (Mr & Mrs J Eastwood) Organic low maintenance garden, planted to encourage wildlife. Fishpond and small bog garden, lots of pretty places to sit and enjoy

58 Duxford Road ⅄ (Mr & Mrs J Bryant) Large garden with mature fruit trees, lawns, mixed borders, pond and summerhouse. *June 16 only*

¶**13 West End** ❀ (Mr & Mrs C Taylor) Interesting range of climbers, ground cover plants in small paved garden, pond. *June 16 only*

15 West End (Mr & Mrs A Watson) Small garden with ornamental pond and mixed borders

26 West End ❀ (Mrs & Mrs W Wight) 2 acres of casual wild garden consisting of paths, shrubs, trees and other items, populated with chickens, pheasants and assorted pigeons. *July 14 only*

¶**23 Newton Road** ⅄ (Mr & Mrs F Winter) Featured on C4's 'Garden Club'. Exceptionally large allotment 55 × 34m with fine range of vegetables, soft and stoned fruit, flowers for cutting. Compost making. Around the house a garden with shrubs, perennial plants, alpines and fish pond. *July 14 only*

5 Parsonage Court ⅄❀ (Mrs L Button) Medium-sized garden with wide range of trees, shrubs and annual plants, large pond and attractive terrace with pergola. Please park on main rd

Brook Cottage ❀ (R Marshall Esq & Ms J Lewis) Newton Road. Small untidy cottage garden with good variety of plants bordered by stream. Peaceful setting

11 Scotts Garden ❀ (Mr & Mrs M Walker) Shady walled garden, mixed herbaceous borders with many foliage plants. Small formal pond

12 Swallow Croft (Miss J Woodley) Small garden with shrubs, tubs and hanging baskets. *July 14 only*

Willingham Gardens ❀❀ 10m N of Cambridge on B1050 off new A14. TEAS in aid of WI. *Combined adm £1.50 Chd 50p. Sun June 2 (2-6)*

66 Balland Field (Mr & Mrs G Burton) Interesting garden with unusual containers holding annuals among shrubs and hardy plants; pond. Runner-up in BBC Look East Gorgeous Gardens Competition 1994

60a Church Street (Mrs Y Rutherford & Dr M Spratling) Small intimate garden with unexpected detail and numerous scented plants, Pergola, pools, parterre and conservatory; raised beds

15a High Street (Mr & Mrs A Robinson) Informal garden with herbaceous perennials, shrubs, unusual trees, fruit and vegetables

40 Over Road (Mrs M & Mr R F Burdett) Small cottage-style garden with herbaceous borders, alpine troughs, unusual plants and a small pond to encourage wildlife

4 Rampton End (Mr & Mrs R Curtis) A shrub and hardy plant collection laid out in a series of rooms, with holly 'carousel', mediterranean and vegetable garden. Greenhouses. Featured on C4's 'Gardening Club'

Sun July 14 (2-6). TEAS. *Combined adm £1 Chd 30p*

66 Balland Road (Mr & Mrs G Burton) Description above

43a Church Street (Mr & Mrs S Dyson)

45a Church Street (Mr & Mrs K Ellwood) These 2 long narrow gardens display immaculate large kitchen gardens and bright arrays of annuals and bedding plants, hanging baskets. In attention to detail the owners bring to each garden a quite distinct identity. 100yd long ⅓-acre garden with lawn, flower borders, mixed containers, large vegetable garden with greenhouse and fruit

Wimpole Hall ♿✿ (National Trust) Arrington. 5m N of Royston signed off A603 to Sandy 7m from Cambridge or off A1198. Part of 350-acre park. First sight of reinstatement of Victorian Parterres on N lawns. Rose garden and fine trees, marked walks in park. National Collection of Walnuts. Massed plantings of daffodil. Guided tours available 11.00, 15.00 hrs given by Head Gardener. Lunches & TEA. *Adm £1.50 Chd free (Guided Tours £2).* ▲*For NGS Fris April 19, July 12 (10.30-5)*

Wytchwood ✿❀ (Mr & Mrs David Cox) Gt Stukeley. 2m N of Huntingdon. Turn off B1043 into Owl End by Great Stukeley village hall. Parking at village hall and in Owl End. 1½ acre yr-round interest. Lawns, shrubs, perennial plants, trees, ponds, roses, area of wild plants and grasses. Vegetables and rare poultry. TEAS. *Adm £1.50 Chd 50p. Sun May 5 (2-5.30)*

Cheshire & Wirral

Hon County Organiser: Nicholas Payne Esq, The Mount, Whirley, Macclesfield, Cheshire SK11 9PB
Tel 01625 426730

Assistant Hon County Organisers: Mrs T R Hill, Salterswell House, Tarporley, Cheshire CW6 0ED
Tel 01829 732804
Mrs N Whitbread, Lower Huxley Hall, Hargrave, Chester CH3 7RJ
Tel 01829 781481

DATES OF OPENING

April 14 Sunday
Poulton Hall, Bebington
The Well House, Tilston

April 17 Wednesday
35 Heyes Lane, Timperley

April 21 Sunday
Penn, Alderley Edge
85 Warmingham Road, nr Crewe

April 24 Wednesday
2 Rose Cottage, Whitegate, Northwich

April 28 Sunday
The Old Hall, Willaston

May 5 Sunday
Penn, Alderley Edge
Tushingham Hall, Whitchurch
Willaston Grange, South Wirral

May 6 Monday
Orchard Villa, Alsager
Penn, Alderley Edge

May 12 Sunday
Haughton Hall, nr Bunbury
Lyme Park, Disley
Rode Hall, Scholar Green

May 14 Tuesday
Orchard Villa, Alsager

May 18 Saturday
Peover Hall, Knutsford

May 19 Sunday
Bolesworth Castle, Tattenhall
Dorfold Hall, Nantwich
Hare Hill Gardens, Over Alderley
Peover Hall, Knutsford
5 Pine Hey, Neston ‡
17 Poplar Grove, Sale
The Quinta, Swettenham
Rosewood, Puddington ‡

May 21 Tuesday
Orchard Villa, Alsager

May 22 Wednesday
Cholmondeley Castle Gardens, Malpas
35 Heyes Lane, Timperley
Reaseheath, nr Nantwich

May 26 Sunday
Manley Knoll, Manley
Penn, Alderley Edge

May 27 Monday
Ashton Hayes, Chester
Penn, Alderley Edge

May 28 Tuesday
Orchard Villa, Alsager

May 29 Wednesday
Reaseheath, nr Nantwich

June 1 Saturday
Arley Hall & Gardens, Northwich

June 2 Sunday
Henbury Hall, nr Macclesfield
Little Moreton Hall, Congleton

June 5 Wednesday
35 Heyes Lane, Timperley
The Quinta, Swettenham

June 8 Saturday
The Old Parsonage, Arley Green

June 9 Sunday
The Old Parsonage, Arley Green
The Stray, Neston

June 11 Tuesday
Orchard Villa, Alsager

June 12 Wednesday
Reaseheath, nr Nantwich

June 16 Sunday
Norton Priory, Runcorn
The Old Hough, Warmingham
The Well House, Tilston

June 18 Tuesday
Orchard Villa, Alsager

June 19 Wednesday
Reaseheath, nr Nantwich

June 23 Sunday
Cherry Hill, Malpas
The Mount, Higher Kinnerton, Chester
The Old Hall, Willaston ‡
Poulton Hall, Bebington ‡

June 24 Monday
The Mount, Higher Kinnerton, Chester

Tatton Park, Knutsford

June 25 Tuesday
Orchard Villa, Alsager

June 26 Wednesday
Reaseheath, nr Nantwich

June 29 Saturday
Old Fanshawe Vicarage,
Siddington

June 30 Sunday
Burton Village Gardens, Burton
73 Hill Top Avenue, Cheadle
Hulme
Old Fanshawe Vicarage,
Siddington
85 Warmingham Road, nr Crewe

July 3 Wednesday
Reaseheath, nr Nantwich

July 7 Sunday
17 Poplar Grove, Sale
Stonyford Cottage Nursery,
Northwich

July 10 Wednesday
Reaseheath, nr Nantwich

July 14 Sunday
The Mount, Whirley
Wood End Cottage, Whitegate

July 17 Wednesday
Reaseheath, nr Nantwich

July 24 Wednesday
Reaseheath, nr Nantwich

August 4 Sunday
Bluebell Cottage, Lodge Lane,
Dutton

August 7 Wednesday
Capesthorne, Macclesfield

August 18 Sunday
Dunham Massey, Altrincham

August 26 Monday
Thornton Manor, Wirral

September 1 Sunday
Lyme Park, Disley

Regular openings
For details see garden description

Cholmondeley Castle Gardens,
Malpas
Dunge Farm Gardens
Norton Priory, Runcorn
Peover Hall, Knutsford
The Quinta, Swettenham
Stonyford Cottage Nursery,
Northwich

_____

By appointment only
*For telephone numbers and other
details see garden descriptions.
Private visits welcomed*

37 Bakewell Road, Hazel Grove
2 Stanley Road, Heaton Moor
Willow Cottage, Prestbury

_____

DESCRIPTIONS OF GARDENS

Arley Hall & Gardens &.❀ (The Viscount Ashbrook) 6m W of Knutsford. 5m from M6 junctions 19 & 20 & M56 junctions 9 & 10. 12 acres; gardens have belonged to 1 family over 500 yrs; great variety of style and design; outstanding twin herbaceous borders (one of earliest in England); unusual avenue of clipped Ilex trees, walled gardens; yew hedges; shrub roses; azaleas, rhododendrons; herb garden; scented garden; woodland garden and walk. Arley Hall and Private Chapel also open. Lunches and light refreshments (in C16 converted barn adjacent to earlier 'Cruck' barn). Gift shop. Specialist plant nursery. *Adm Gardens & Grounds only £3.30, Chd under 16 £1.70. Hall £2.50 extra; Chd £1.25 under 5 free (Share to The Samaritans®). April to Sept (hall opening times vary during April & Sept) every Tues to Sun incl & Bank Hols (12-5) last adm to gardens 4.30. For NGS Sat June 1 (12-4.30).* **Tel 01565 777353**

Ashton Hayes (Michael Grime Esq) Chester. Midway between Tarvin and Kelsall on A54 Chester-Sandiway rd; take B5393 N to Ashton and Mouldsworth. Approach to Ashton Hayes can be seen halfway between Ashton and Mouldsworth. The ¾m drive is beside former lodge. About 12 acres, incl arboretum and ponds. Predominantly a valley garden of mature trees and flowering shrubs. Great variety of azaleas and rhododendrons; notable embothrium. TEAS. *Adm £1.50 OAPs £1 Chd 50p (Share to Church of St John the Evangelist, Ashton Hayes®). Mon May 27 (2-6). Private visits welcome, please* **Tel 01829 751209**

37 Bakewell Road ❀ (Mr & Mrs H Williams) Hazel Grove. From Manchester on A6 following signs to Buxton, bear R at Rising Sun Public House, Hazel Grove. Taking the Macclesfield Rd (A523) take 1st R (Haddon Rd) then 1st L into Bakewell Rd. Small suburban garden 17yds × 6½yds heavily planted with azaleas, rhododendrons (several rare and unusual varieties), hydrangeas; pool and waterfall. Excellent example of how much can be planted in a small area. *Adm £1.50 Chd free. May 1-July 1. Private visits welcome for parties of 6 and under, May & June, please contact Mrs Williams* **Tel 01625 260592**

Bluebell Cottage &.❀ (R L & D Casey) Lodge Lane, Dutton. From M56 (junction 10) take A49 Whitchurch Rd for 3m, turn R on A533 towards Runcorn at traffic lights. Lodge Lane is the 1st turning L approx 1.5m. 1½-acre garden with ave of young trees leading to canal. The cottage garden has been developed into a series of rooms. Large lawn areas with herbaceous borders filled with wide selection of plants. Additional beds with Mediterranean theme and ornamental grasses currently being added. Adjacent is a 3-acre wild flower meadow and nursery. TEAS in aid of Cheshire Wildlife Trust. *Adm £1.50 Chd 50p. Sun Aug 4 (1-5.30). Private visits welcome, please* **Tel 01928 713718**

Bolesworth Castle &.❀ (Mr & Mrs A G Barbour) Tattenhall. Enter by lodge on A41 8m S of Chester or 1m N of Broxton roundabout. Landscape with rhododendrons, shrubs and borders. Woodland walk replanted 1993/4. TEAS. *Adm £2 Chd free (Share to Harthill & Burwardsley Churches®). Sun May 19 (2-5.30)*

Bridgemere Garden World &.❀ On A51 7m S of Nantwich, 1m N of Woore. Follow brown tourist signs from Nantwich. The Garden Kingdom over 22 enjoyable and peaceful gardens showing many different styles of plant grouping. It includes the recreated Bridgemere Garden World prize winning exhibition gardens from Garden Festivals, Chelsea Flower Show Gold Medal gardens and the garden where the Gardeners' Diary television programme is filmed. *Adm £1.50 OAPs and Chd over 8yrs £1. Sat July 13 (10-5)*

Burton Village Gardens ✿✤ 9m NW of Chester. Turn off A540 at Willaston-Burton Xrds (traffic lights) and follow rd for 1m to Burton. Ample free parking. TEAS at Rake House. *Combined adm £2 Chd free (Share to St Johns Hospice and Clatterbridge Hospital, Bebington®). Sun June 30 (2-6)*

> **Bank Cottage** (Mr & Mrs J R Beecroft) Small, very colourful, mixed cottage garden with old roses backing on to village cricket ground
>
> **Rake House** (Mr & Mrs R I Cowan) Enclosed sandstone courtyard, relaid with original cobbles and York stone, with pond; old orchard and potagered vegetable garden. TEAS in aid of St John's Hospice
>
> **Briarfield** ✤ (Mr & Mrs P Carter) About an acre of rare trees and shrubs together with fruit and vegetable garden in woodland setting. Short woodland trail to and from **Lynwood**
>
> **Lynwood** ✤ (Mr & Mrs P M Wright) On the fringe of the village on the Neston Road. ⅓-acre garden with shrub borders; rockery, pond with waterfall, pergola, arbour with climbers, heathers and alpines

Capesthorne ⅊ (Mr & Mrs W A Bromley-Davenport) 5m W of Macclesfield. 7m S of Wilmslow on A34. Bus stop: Capesthorne (Congleton to Manchester route). Medium-sized garden; daffodil lawn; azaleas, rhododendrons; flowering shrubs; herbaceous border; lake, pool and arboretum. Georgian chapel built 1722 on view. Hall open from 1.30-3.30 (extra charge). Illustrated book on garden/woodland walks available at £1. Historic parks and gardens. TEAS and LUNCHES. Free car park. *Adm garden £2.25 OAPs £2 Chd £1; Hall extra £2.50 Chd £1. Combined tickets £4, £3.50, £1.50. March-Oct incl; Weds and Suns, also Good Fri & Bank hols. For NGS Wed Aug 7 (12-6).* Tel 01625 861221

Cherry Hill ⅊✤ (Mr & Mrs Miles Clarke) Malpas. 2m W of Malpas signed from B5069 to Chorlton. Massed bulbs in spring; walks through pine woods and rhododendrons to trout lake; walled garden, herbaceous borders, shrub roses. Ornamental vegetable garden. TEAS in attractive house overlooking Welsh mountains. Cricket ground. *Adm £2 Chd 50p. Sun June 23 (2-5.30)*

Cholmondeley Castle Gardens ⅊✤ (The Marchioness of Cholmondeley) Malpas. Situated off A41 Chester/Whitchurch rd and A49 Whitchurch/Tarporley rd. Romantically landscaped gardens full of variety. Azaleas, rhododendrons, flowering shrubs; rare trees; herbaceous borders and water garden. Lakeside picnic area; rare breeds of farm animals, incl llamas, gift shop. Ancient private Chapel in the park. Tearoom offering light lunches etc. TEAS. *Adm gardens only £2.60 OAPs £1.80 Chd 75p. April Suns & Bank Hol Mons (12-5.30); May to October, Weds, Thurs (12-5.30); Suns & Bank Hol Mons (12-5.30). Reduced rate for coach parties. For NGS Wed May 22 (12-5.30).* Tel 01829 720383 or 720203

Dorfold Hall ✿✤ (Mr & Mrs Richard Roundell) Nantwich. 1m W of Nantwich on A534 between Nantwich and Acton. 18-acre garden surrounding C17 house with formal approach; lawns and recently planted herbaceous borders; spectacular spring woodland garden with rhododendrons, azaleas, magnolias and bulbs. TEAS in aid of Acton Parish Church. *Adm £2 Chd 75p. Sun May 19 (2-5.30)*

● **Dunge Farm Gardens** ✿✤ (Mr & Mrs David Ketley) Kettleshulme. Take B5470 rd from Macclesfield. Kettleshulme is 8m from Macclesfield. Turn R in village signed Dunge Valley Gardens and Goyt Valley and in ½m at Xrds, turn R down lane to Dunge Farm. Surrounded by romantic hills and set in 5 acres, at 1000ft, this is the highest garden in Cheshire; mature trees, woodland, streams, bog gardens, herbaceous borders, species rhododendrons, magnolias, acers and meconopsis plus roses. Yr-round interest an oasis in the Pennine foothills. TEAS. *Adm £3. Sats, Suns, Bank Hols £2.50 Mons to Fri Chd free (Share to NGS®). Open daily April 1 to Aug 31 (10.30-6).* Tel 01663 733787

Dunham Massey ⅊✿✤ (The National Trust) Altrincham. 3m SW of Altrincham off A56. Well signed. Garden over 20 acres, on ancient site with moat lake, mount and orangery. Mature trees and fine lawns with extensive range of shrubs and herbaceous perennials suited to acid sand, many planted at waterside. Set in 350 acres of deer park. TEAS. *Adm £2.50 Chd £1 (car entry £2). ▲For NGS Sun Aug 18 (11-5)*

Hare Hill Gardens ⅊✤ (The National Trust) Over Alderley. Between Alderley Edge and Prestbury, turn off N at B5087 at Greyhound Rd [118:SJ85765]. Bus: Cheshire E17 Macclesfield–Wilmslow (passing BR Wilmslow and Prestbury) to within ¾m. Stations: Alderley Edge 2½m, Prestbury 2½m. Attractive spring garden featuring a fine display of rhododendrons and azaleas. A good collection of hollies and other specimen trees and shrubs. The 10-acre garden includes a walled garden which hosts many wall shrubs including clematis and vines. The borders are planted with agapanthus (African lily) and geraniums. Partially suitable for wheelchairs. *Adm £2.50 Chd £1.25. ▲For NGS Sun May 19 (10-5)*

Haughton Hall ✤ (Mr & Mrs R J Posnett) Tarporley. 5m NW of Nantwich off A534 Nantwich/Wrexham Rd, 6m SE of Tarporley via A49. Medium-sized garden; species of rhododendron, azaleas, shrubs, rock garden; lake with temple; waterfall. Collection of ornamental trees. Home-made TEAS. *Adm £2 Chd 50p. Sun May 12 (2-6)*

Henbury Hall ⅊✿✤ (Mr & Mrs Sebastian de Ferranti) nr Macclesfield. 2m W of Macclesfield on A537 rd. Turn down School Lane, Henbury at Blacksmiths Arms: East Lodge on R. Large garden with lake, beautifully landscaped and full of variety. Azaleas, rhododendrons, flowering shrubs, rare trees, herbaceous borders. TEAS in aid of East Cheshire Hospice. *Adm £2 Chd 50p. Sun June 2 (2-5)*

35 Heyes Lane ✿✤ (Mr & Mrs David Eastwood) Timperley. Heyes Lane is a turning off Park Rd (B5165) 1m from the junction with the A56 Altrincham-Manchester rd 1½m N of Altrincham. Or from A560 turn W in Timperley Village for ¼m. Newsagents shop on corner. A small suburban garden 30' × 90' on sandy soil maintained by a keen plantswoman member of the Organic Movement (HDRA). An all yr round garden; trees; small pond; greenhouses; fruit and vegetables with a good collection of interesting and unusual plants. TEA. *Adm £1.50 Chd free. Weds April 17, May 22, June 5 (2-5)*

73 Hill Top Avenue ✿ (Mr & Mrs Martin Land) Cheadle Hulme. Turn off A34 Wilmslow Rd at t-lights (Waggon & Horses) into Stanley Rd (B5094). After 1m turn L into Gill Bent Rd, signposted Cheadle Hulme Sports Centre. Go to end, small roundabout, turn R into Church Rd. 2nd rd on L is Hill Top Ave. No. 73 is 400yds on R. From Stockport or Bramhall turn R into Church Rd by The Church Inn. Hill Top Ave is last rd on R. ⅙-acre plantswoman's garden designed to disguise its long narrow shape. Established and new plantings of herbaceous, shrub and climbing roses, clematis, pond and damp area, shrubs and small trees. TEAS. *Adm £2 Chd free (Share to Arthritis & Rheumatism Council®). Sun June 30 (2-5)*

Little Moreton Hall &✿✿ (The National Trust) Congleton. On A34, 4m S of Congleton. 1½-acre garden surrounded by a moat and bordered by yew hedges, next to finest example of timber-framed architecture in England. Herb and historic vegetable garden, orchard and borders. Knot garden based on design in 'The English Gardener' published by Leonard Meager in 1670, though probably Elizabethan in origin. Adm includes entry to the Hall with optional free guided tours. Wheelchairs and electric mobility vehicle available. Disabled toilet. Picnic lawns. Shop and restaurant serving coffee, lunches and afternoon teas. TEAS. *Adm £3.60 Chd 1.80.* ▲*For NGS Sun June 2 (12-5.30 last admission 5)*

Lyme Park ✿ (The National Trust) Disley. 6m SE of Stockport just W of Disley on A6 rd. 17-acre garden retaining many original features from Tudor and Jacobean times; high Victorian style bedding; a Dutch garden; a Gertrude Jekyll style herbaceous border; an Edwardian rose garden, a Wyatt orangery and many other features. Also rare trees, a wild flower area and lake. TEAS. Donations to NGS. *Adm £3 per car to estate, £1.50 Chd 75p to gardens.* ▲*For NGS Suns May 12, Sept 1 (11-5)*

Manley Knoll & (Mrs D G Fildes) Manley, NE of Chester. Nr Mouldsworth. B5393. Quarry garden; azaleas and rhododendrons. TEAS. *Adm £1.50 Chd 25p. Sun May 26 (2-6). Private visits welcome for parties 20 to 30, please* Tel 01928 740226

The Mount, Higher Kinnerton &✿ (Mr & Mrs J Major). 6m W of Chester, L off A5104 just after it crosses A55. Approx 2½-acre garden with mature trees; shrubs and lawns; kitchen garden, variety of perennial plants some interesting and unusual. TEA and plant stall Sun only. *Adm £2 Chd free. Sun June 23 (Share to Help the Aged®) (2-6) Mon June 24 (Share to All Saints Kinnerton®) (5-8). Cheese and wine. Private parties welcome, please* Tel 01244 660275. *Best months June and July*

The Mount, Whirley &✿✿ (Mr & Mrs Nicholas Payne) The Mount is situated about 2m due W of Macclesfield along A537 rd. Opp Blacksmiths Arms at Henbury, go up Pepper St, turn L into Church Lane which becomes Andertons Lane in 100yds. The Mount is about 200yds up Andertons Lane on L. Adequate parking. The garden is approx 1½ acres and has interesting trees including eucryphia nymansensis, fern leaved beech and sciadopitys. The garden is very much compartmentalized with lawns; shrubberies; herbaceous border; swimming pool and short vista of Irish Yews. TEAS. *Adm £2 Chd 50p. Sun July 14 (2-5.30). Parties welcome, please* Tel 01625 426730

Norton Priory &✿ (Norton Priory Museum Trust Ltd) Tudor Road, Manor Park, Runcorn. Runcorn New Town 1m, Warrington 5m. From M56 Junction 11 turn for Warrington and follow signs. From Warrington take A56 for Runcorn and follow signs. 16 acres well established woodland gardens; Georgian summerhouses; rock garden and stream glade; 3-acre walled garden of similar date (1760s) recently restored. Georgian and modern garden designs; fruit training; rosewalk; colour borders; herb garden, cottage garden and exhibition. New projects underway: restoration of ancient pear orchard; cydonia (tree quince) collection. Plants for sale from the Walled Garden collection. Priory remains of museum also open. TEA. *Combined adm £2.60 Chd £1.40. Daily April to October (12-5) weekends and bank hols (12-6) Nov to March (12-4) (Walled garden closed Nov-Feb). For NGS Sun June 16 (12-6). Horticultural Show Sept 22.* Tel 01928 569895

Old Fanshawe Vicarage ✿✿ (Mr & Mrs William Wrather) Siddington. 4½m S of Alderley Edge, 4m W of Macclesfield. Use drive off A34, ¼m S of entrance to Capesthorne Hall and ¾m N of B5392. Ample parking. 5 acres, attractive setting next to Redesmere Lake. Interesting natural old garden with some formality, pond, stream, bog garden, woodland walk, herb and vegetable garden. TEAS. *Adm £2 Chd 50p (Share to RNIB®). Sat, Sun June 29, 30 (2-5)*

The Old Hall &✿✿ (Dr & Mrs M W W Wood) Hadlow Rd, Willaston S Wirral, 8m NW of Chester on village green. ¾-acre; mixed border; interesting plants; bulbs; winter flowering shrubs and colour. C17 house. TEAS June only. *Adm £1.50 Chd free (Share to Neuromuscular Centre®). Suns April 28 (2-5), June 23 (2-6); also private visits welcome, please* Tel 0151 327 4779

The Old Hough &✿✿ (Mr & Mrs D S Varey) Warmingham. 2m from Middlewich on A50 to Nantwich, turn L to Warmingham and L again at T; or L on A533 from Sandbach to Middlewich and R at T. 2½ acres owner-designed and maintained garden, enhancing period house and farm buildings. Architectural in character, with much use of reclaimed materials. Varied borders with some choice plants. Wildlife pond and interesting young trees protected by mature oak wood. Lily pond and rill amidst formal lawns and rose borders. Ample parking and WCs. TEAS in aid of Warmingham Church. *Adm £2 Chd 50p. Sun June 16 (2-6)*

The Old Parsonage &✿ (The Viscount & Viscountess Ashbrook) Arley Green; 5m NNE of Northwich and 3m Great Budworth; M6 junctions 19, 20 and M56 junction 10. Follow signposts to Arley Hall and Gardens and notices to Old Parsonage which lies across park at Arley Green. 2-acre garden yew hedges, herbaceous and mixed borders, shrub roses, climbers, woodland garden and pond, with unusual young trees and foliage shrubs. Waterplants, rhododendrons, azaleas, meconopsis. Plant stall. TEAS. *Adm £2 Chd under 16 £1 (Share to Save the Children®). Sat, Sun June 8, 9 (2-6)*

Orchard Villa &✿ (Mr & Mrs J Trinder) 72 Audley Rd, Alsager. At traffic lights in Alsager town centre turn S towards Audley, house is 300yds on R beyond level Xing. Long and narrow, this ⅓-acre has been designed to grow a wide range of herbaceous plants, iris and alpines ferns and grasses in scree, peat, raised, light and shade beds. TEAS. *Adm £1.50 Chd free. Bank Hol Mon May 6; TEA Tues May 14, 21, 28; June 11, 18, 25 (1.30-5.30); also private visits welcome for parties of 2 and over, please* **Tel 01270 874833**

Penn ✿✿ (R W Baldwin Esq) Macclesfield Rd, Alderley Edge. ¾m E of Alderley Edge village, on B5087, Alderley Edge-Macclesfield rd. Turn L into Woodbrook Rd for car parking. 2½ acres. This garden contains an exceptional collection of flowering shrubs and trees, on a hillside looking over the Cheshire plain. The many hundreds of rhododendron species and cultivars include some Himalayans (now small forest trees), yellow & blue species (wardii, augustinii etc.), masses of azaleas plus a wide range of camellias & magnolias including superb varieties from Cornwall, and many fairly rare trees including gingko, davidia (handerchief tree), golden elm, embothriums, plus for added interest 2 sequoia sempervirens (now 30ft high struck in 1965 from a block of wood bought in the Muir woods across the Golden Gate in San Francisco). TEA. *Adm £2 OAPs £1.50 Chd 50p. Suns April 21, May 5, 26, Mons May 6, 27 (2-5). Parties welcome by written appt*

Peover Hall ✿ (Randle Brooks Esq) Over Peover. 3m S of Knutsford on A50, Lodge gates off Blackden Lane. 15-acres. 5 walled gardens: lily pond, rose, herb, white and pink gardens; C18 landscaped park, moat, C19 dell, rhododendron walks, large walled kitchen garden, Church walk, purple border, blue and white border, pleached lime avenues, fine topiary work. Dogs in park only. TEAS. *Adm £1.50 Chd £1. Mons & Thurs (2-5) May to Oct. NOT Bank Hols. Other days by appt for parties. For NGS Sat, Sun May 18, 19 (2-6)*

5 Pine Hey &✿✿ (Mr & Mrs S J Clayton) Neston. A540 Chester to Hoylake Rd. Turn off at the Shrewsbury Arms (Roast Inn) traffic lights towards Neston. Turn R at T-junction drive through Neston past cross on the L, then fork L at traffic lights and continue along Leighton Rd, Pine Hey is on L. The garden covers approx ¾ acre and is laid out informally with different areas, including a copse, water garden, stream and lawns each with its own character. The main objective is to make it an all-yr garden. TEAS in aid of Wirral Methodist Housing Association. *Adm £1.50 Chd free (Share to Wirral Methodist Housing Association). Sun May 19 (2-5). Private parties welcome, please* **Tel 0151 3363006**

17 Poplar Grove ✿✿ (Gordon Cooke Esq) Sale. From the A6144 at Brooklands Station turn down Hope Rd. Poplar Grove 3rd on R. This recently englarged town garden has been created by the owner who is a potter and landscape designer. It has a special collection of unusual plants in an artistic setting with many interesting design features and details. TEA. *Adm £1 Chd 50p (Share to North Manchester General Hospital®). Suns May 19, July 7 (2-6)*

Poulton Hall ✿ (The Lancelyn Green Family) Poulton Lancelyn, 2m from Bebington. From M53, exit 4 towards Bebington; at traffic lights (½m) R along Poulton Rd; house 1m on R. 2½ acres; lawns, ha-ha, wild flower meadow, shrubbery, walled gardens with literary associations. Cream TEAS. *Adm £2 Chd 20p. Suns April 14, June 23 (2-6)*

The Quinta &✿ (Sir Bernard Lovell) Swettenham. Turn E off A535 at Twemlow (Yellow Broom Cafe) and follow signs to Swettenham. 15-acre collection of rare trees and shrubs leading to woodland walks overlooking the Dane Valley and to the thirty-nine step descent to Swettenham Brook. A site of special scientific (SSSI) and biological importance. TEA NGS days, & parties by arrangement. *Adm £2 Acc chd free (Share to St Peter's Church, Swettenham®). Open daily until sunset. For NGS Sun May 19, Wed June 5 (10-sunset). Parties welcome, please* **Tel 01477 571254**

Reaseheath &✿✿ (Reaseheath College) nr Nantwich. 1½m N of Nantwich on the A51. The Gardens, covering 12 acres, are based on a Victorian Garden surrounding Reaseheath Hall and contain many mature trees of horticultural interest. The gardens are used as a teaching resource. There are specialised features of particular interest including, glasshouses; model fruit garden; rose garden; woodland garden; lakeside bog garden and extensive shrub borders, lawns and sports facilities. TEA. *Adm £2. Weds May 22, 29, June 5, 12, 19, 26, July 3, 10, 17, 24 (2-4.30). Parties welcome, please* **Tel 01270 625131**

Rode Hall ✿ (Sir Richard & Lady Baker Wilbraham) Scholar Green [National Grid reference SJ8157] 5m SW of Congleton between A34 and A50. Nesfield's terrace and rose garden with view over Humphrey Repton's landscape is a feature of Rode gardens, as is the Victorian wild flower garden with a grotto and the walk to the lake past the old Stew pond. Other attractions include a restored ice house and working walled kitchen garden. TEAS. *Adm £2 Chd 50p (House extra £2) (Share to All Saints Odd Rode and St Mary's, Astbury Parish Churches®). Sun May 12 (2-5.30)*

2 Rose Cottage ✿ (Mr & Mrs Paul Field) Whitegate. Turn S off A556 (Northwich/Chester) at Sandiway t-lights, Dalefords Lane. Follow rd approx 2m, do not go into Whitegate village. Turn L into Beauty Bank by large thatched house; garden 80 yds on L. ½-acre plantsman's garden, plus further 2 acres being developed. National Collection of over 100 varieties of Daphnes. Unusual shrubs and trees incl snowdrop tree, lindera, maackia. Scree bed, troughs, pond, tree house. *Adm £1.50 Chd free (Share to NCCPG®). Wed April 24 (2-5)*

Rosewood ✿ (Mr & Mrs C E J Brabin) Puddington. 6m N of Chester turn L (W) off Chester to Hoylake A540 to Puddington. Bear L at village green and follow NGS signs. 1-acre garden incl small wood, pond well planted with bogside species, mixed herbaceous, shrub beds with new plantings of rhododendron, azalea species and hybrids; many unusual trees. Most of the new plantings are grown from seed by owner. TEAS. *Adm £2 Chd free (Share to St Winefride's Church, Neston®). Sun May 19 (2-6). Private visits by appt, please* **Tel 0151353 1193**

2 Stanley Road ✿❀ (Mr G Leatherbarrow) Heaton Moor. Approx 1½m N of Stockport. Follow Heaton Moor Rd off A6. Stanley Rd on L. 1st house on R. Tiny town garden with all year interest, packed with interesting plants, creating a secret cottage garden atmosphere. Old species and English roses, clematis, hardy geraniums, ivies, varied evergreens, daphnes, hellebores, delphiniums, mixed herbaceous; ponds. Max no. of visitors 2 — no room for more. Not suitable for less agile. TEA. *Adm £2 Chd 75p. Private visits welcome April to Sept, please* **Tel 0161 442 3828**

Stonyford Cottage Nursery & Garden ♿✿❀ (Mr & Mrs Anthony Overland) Cuddington. 6m W of Northwich. Turn R off A556 (Northwich to Chester). At Xrds ¾m past A49 junction (signpost Norley-Kingsley). Entrance in ½m on L. Set in a sheltered valley, the gardens feature a 'Monet' style pool with bridges to an island and woodland walk. The adjacent nursery has herbaceous perennials and less common plants for sale. TEAS in aid of special Olympics (Cheshire) (NGS day only). *Adm £1.50 Chd 50p. April to Oct Tues to Sun & Bank Hols (10-5.30). For NGS Sun July 7 (1.30-5.30)*

The Stray ♿✿❀ (Mr & Mrs Anthony Hannay) Neston. Approx 10m NW of Chester. ½m NW of Shrewsbury Arms (traffic lights). Turn off A540 into Upper Raby Rd. After ³⁄₁₀m turn R into unmade lane and The Stray is immediately on the L. 1½ acres of newly planted shrubs, herbaceous and mixed borders. Interesting colour schemes and unusual plants. Replanting commenced in 1991. A chance to see a new garden maturing. TEAS in aid of RNLI. *Adm £1.50 Chd 50p. Sun June 9 (2-6)*

Tatton Park ♿✿❀ (Cheshire County Council: The National Trust) Knutsford. Well sign-posted on M56 junction 7 and from M6 junction 19. 2½m N of Knutsford. Considered to be the very finest and most important of all gardens within The National Trust they rank among England's 'Top Ten'. Features include orangery by Wyatt, fernery by Paxton, Japanese, Italian and rose gardens. Greek monument and African hut. Hybrid azaleas and rhododendrons, swamp cypresses, tree ferns, tall redwoods, bamboos and pines. TEAS. *Adm £2.50 Group £2 Chd £1.70 Group £1.40.* ▲*For NGS Mon June 24 (10.30-5)*

Thornton Manor ❀ (The Viscount Leverhulme) Thornton Hough, Wirral. From Chester A540 to Fiveway Garage; turn R on to B5136 to Thornton Hough village. From Birkenhead B5151 then on to B5136. From M53, exit 4 to Heswall; turn L after 1m. Bus: Woodside-Parkgate; alight Thornton Hough village. Large garden of yr-round interest. TEAS. *Free car park. Adm £2 OAPs £1 Chd 50p. Bank Hol Mon Aug 26 (12-7)*

Tushingham Hall (Mr & Mrs P Moore Dutton) 3m N of Whitchurch. Signed off A41 Chester-Whitchurch Rd; Medium-sized garden in beautiful surroundings; bluebell wood alongside pool; ancient oak, girth 26ft. TEAS. *Adm £2 Chd 50p (Share to St Chad's Church, Tushingham®). Sun May 5 (2-5.30)*

85 Warmingham Road ✿❀ (Mr & Mrs A Mann) Approx 3m N of Crewe town centre on the road between Leighton Hospital and Warmingham Village. Close by White Lion Inn, Coppenhall. ⅓-acre plantsman's garden, with shrubs, perennial borders, raised beds, troughs, rock garden, peat garden, pond and greenhouse with cacti and succulents. Speciality alpines. TEAS. *Adm £2 Chd free. Suns April 21, June 30, (1-5). Private visits welcome March to Sept, please* **Tel 01270 582030**

The Well House ✿ (Mrs S H French-Greenslade) Tilston, nr Malpas 12m S of Chester on A41, 1st turn R after Broxton roundabout, L on Malpas Rd through Tilston. House and antique shop on L. Field parking signed. 1-acre cottage garden, bridge over natural stream, many bulbs, herbs and shrubs. TEAS. *Adm £2 Chd 25p (Share to Cystic Fibrosis Trust®). Suns April 14, June 16 (2-5.30). Private visits by appt March-July, please* **Tel 01829 250332**

Willaston Grange ♿ (Sir Derek and Lady Bibby) Willaston. A540 Chester to West Kirby until opposite the new Elf Garage. Proceed down B5151 Hadlow Rd, towards Willaston. Borders, rock garden, vegetable garden, orchard, about 3 acres. Special feature - woodland walk. TEAS. *Adm £1.50 OAPs £1 Chd free. Sun May 5 (2-6)*

Willow Cottage ✿ (Mrs Martin Tolson) Prestbury. Straight behind the Admiral Rodney Public House in Prestbury. An intensively planted small cottage garden of less than ⅒-acre. *Adm £2 Chd £1. Private visits (max of 10) welcome May to July (2.30-5), please* **Tel 01625 828697**

Wood End Cottage ✿❀ (Mr & Mrs M R Everett) Whitegate. Turn S off A556 (Northwich by-pass) to Whitegate village; opp. school follow Grange Lane for 300yds. ½-acre plantsman's garden sloping to a natural stream. Mature trees, many clematis, herbaceous, raised beds, shade and moisture loving plants. Large plant stall. TEAS. *Adm £1.50 Chd 50p (Share to David Lewis Centre for Epilepsy®). Sun July 14 (2-6) also by appt, please* **Tel 01606 888236**

Clwyd

See separate Welsh section beginning on page 310

Cornwall

Hon County Organiser:	G J Holborow Esq, Ladock House, Ladock, Truro, Cornwall TR2 4PL Tel 01726 882274
Assistant Hon County Organisers:	Mrs D Morison, Boskenna, St Martin, Manaccan, Helston TR12 6BS Tel 01326 231 210
	Mrs Richard Jerram, Trehane, Trevanson, Wadebridge PL27 7HP Tel 01208 812523
	Mrs Michael Latham, Trebartha Lodge, North Hill, Launceston PL15 7PD Tel 01566 82373
Leaflet/Yellow Books	Tony Shaw Esq, Rope House, Cliff Street, Mevagissey, nr St Austell, Cornwall PL26 6QL Tel 01726 842819
Publicity	Mrs Elizabeth Waldron-Yeo, Pembre, Trelill Bodmin, PL30 3HZ Tel 01208 850793
Hon County Treasurer:	Mrs Cynthia Bassett, 5 Athelstan Park, Bodmin, PL31 1DS Tel 01208 73247

DATES OF OPENING

March 14 Thursday
Catchfrench Manor, St Germans
March 16 Saturday
Trengwainton, Penzance
March 24 Sunday
Ince Castle Gardens, Saltash
March 30 Saturday
Catchfrench Manor, St Germans
April 7 Sunday
Tremeer, St Tudy
April 13 Saturday
Glendurgan, Mawnan Smith
April 14 Sunday
Penjerrick, Budock, nr Falmouth
Trelissick, Feock
April 20 Saturday
Catchfrench Manor, St Germans
April 21 Sunday
Penwarne, nr Falmouth
St Michael's Mount, Marazion
April 28 Sunday
Polgwynne, Feock
May 5 Sunday
Bodwannick, Nanstallon ‡
Estray Parc, Budock
Oak Lodge Woodland Garden,
    Nanstallon ‡
Pinetum, Harewood
Tregrehan, Par
May 8 Wednesday
Antony, Torpoint
May 12 Sunday
Boconnoc, nr Lostwithiel
Creed House, Creed
High Noon, Ladock ‡
Ladock House, Ladock ‡
Trenance, Launceston
May 17 Friday
Cotehele House, St Dominick,
    Saltash
May 19 Sunday
Carclew Gardens,
    Perran-ar-Worthal

Lanhydrock, Bodmin
Paradise Park, Hayle
Pinetum, Harewood
May 23 Thursday
Headland, Polruan
May 26 Sunday
Lamorran House, Upper Castle
    Road, St Mawes
Nansawsan House, Ladock
Peterdale, Millbrook
Pine Lodge Gardens, Cuddra, St
    Austell
May 29 Wednesday
Treloyhan Manor Hotel, St Ives
May 30 Thursday
Headland, Polruan
Treworder Mill, Truro
June 2 Sunday
Higher Truscott, St Stephens
June 6 Thursday
Treworder Mill, Truro
June 9 Sunday
Trevegean Manor Way, Heamoor
Zoar, Mylor
June 13 Thursday
Treworder Mill, Truro
June 16 Sunday
Bodwannick, Nanstallon ‡
Mary Newman's Cottage, Saltash
Newton House, Lanhydrock ‡
Oak Lodge Woodland Garden,
    Nanstallon ‡
Tregilliowe Farm, Ludgvan
June 20 Thursday
Treworder Mill, Truro
June 23 Sunday
Jimmers, St Neot ‡
Newton House, Lanhydrock
Northwood Farm, St Neot ‡
The Old Barn, St Neot ‡
Tremarkyn, Wenmouth Cross, St
    Neot ‡
Water Meadow, Luxulyan
June 27 Thursday
Treworder Mill, Truro

June 30 Sunday
Roseland House, Chacewater
Scawn Mill, nr Liskeard
July 7 Sunday
Long Cross Victorian Garden,
    Trelights
Treviades Gardens, Constantine
July 14 Sunday
The Hollies, Grampound, nr Truro
Roseland House, Chacewater
Tregilliowe Farm, Ludgvan
Trenance, Launceston
July 21 Sunday
Peterdale, Millbrook
July 28 Sunday
Trenarth, Constantine
August 4 Sunday
Pinetum, Harewood
August 21 Wednesday
Trerice, nr Newquay
September 29 Sunday
Trebartha, nr Launceston

Regular openings
For details see garden description

Carwinion, Mawnan Smith
Catchfrench Manor, St Germans
Heligan Gardens, Mevagissey
Ken Caro, Bicton, nr Liskeard
Lanterns, Restronguet, nr Mylor
Paradise Park, Hayle
Pencarrow, Bodmin
Peterdale, Millbrook
Prideaux Place, Padstowe
Roseland House, Chacewater
Trebah, Mawnan Smith
Tregrehan, Par
Trevarno Gardens, Sithney Helston
Trewithen, Probus, nr Truro
Woodland Garden, Garras, nr
    Helston

By appointment only
*For telephone numbers and other
details see garden descriptions.
Private visits welcomed*

Bosavern Mill, St Just, Penzance
Chyverton, Zelah
Furzeball, Lanteglos-by-Fowey

Scotland's Gardens Scheme. The National Gardens Scheme has a similar but quite separate counterpart in Scotland. Called Scotland's Gardens Scheme, it raises money for the Queen's Nursing Institute (Scotland), the Gardens Fund of the National Trust for Scotland and over 160 registered charities nominated by garden owners. The Handbook is available (£3.25 incl p&p) from Scotland's Gardens Scheme, 31 Castle Terrace, Edinburgh EH1 2EL. Telephone 0131-229-1870, Fax 0131-229-0443

DESCRIPTIONS OF GARDENS

Antony ✗ (National Trust: Trustees of the Carew Pole Trust) 5m W of Plymouth via Torpoint car ferry; 2m NW of Torpoint, N of A374; 16m SE of Liskeard; 15m E of Looe. In a Repton landscape with fine vistas to the R Lynher. Features a formal courtyard, terraces, ornamental Japanese pond and knot garden. **Antony Woodland Garden and Woods:** an established woodland garden and natural woods extending to 100 acres. TEAS. *Adm £1. Combined Gardens adm £2.50 Chd ½ price.* ▲*For NGS Wed May 8 (1.30-5.30)*

Boconnoc ᴅ✿ (Mr & Mrs J D G Fortescue) 2m S of A390. On main rd between middle Taphouse and Downend garage, follow signs. Privately owned gardens covering some 20 acres, surrounded by parkland and woods. Magnificent old trees, flowering shrubs and views. TEAS. *Adm £1.50 Chd free (Share to Boconnoc Church Window Fund®). Sun May 12 (2-6)*

¶Bodwannick ✗ (P M & W M Appleton) Nanstallon. 2½m W Bodmin. Turn at Bodmin Trailer Centre (A30) signposted Nanstallon, L at Xrds signposted Hoopers Bridge then sharp R. Approx 1-acre compact garden incl water garden, herbaceous, granite Cornish cross, roses, shade garden and shrubs. TEAS. *Combined adm with Oak Lodge £2 Chd free. Suns May 5, June 16 (2-6). Private visits welcome, please* **Tel 01208 831427**

¶Bosavern Mill ✗ (Mrs Jennifer Hilliard) St Just. From Penzance take A3701 bypass to St Just before reaching St Just turn L onto B3306 to Sennen and Airport. ¾m through Kelynack turn sharp R at brow of hill through farmyard, single tarmac lane, 1st house on R ½m, ltd parking. 1-acre garden started in 1989. Terraced with granite, incl rockery, 2 ponds and a stream. The garden was created from a near vertical N facing slope with a wide variety of ramblers, perennials and shrubs, a plantsman's garden. TEAS. *Adm £1.50 Chd free. (2-6) By appt, please* **Tel 01736 787659**

Carclew Gardens ✗ (Mrs Chope) Perran-ar-Worthal, nr Truro. From A39 turn E at Perran-ar-Worthal. Bus: alight Perran-ar-Worthal 1m. Large garden, rhododendron species; terraces; ornamental water. TEAS. *Adm £2 Chd 50p (Share to Barristers Benevolent Fund®). Sun May 19 (2-5.30)*

●Carwinion ✿ (Mr H A E Rogers) Mawnan Smith via Carwinion Rd. An unmanicured or permissive valley garden of some 10 acres with many camellias, rhododendrons and azaleas flowering in the spring. Apart from an abundance of wild flowers, grasses, ferns etc, the garden holds the premier collection of temperate bamboos in the UK. TEAS April to Oct (2-5.30). *Adm £2 Chd free. Open daily throughout the year (10-5.30). Private visits welcome, please* **Tel 01326 250258**

●Catchfrench Manor ᴅ✗✿ (Mr & Mrs J R Wilks) St Germans. To south of A38 5 miles E of Liskeard signposted Catchfrench. Under restoration: 25-acre historic Repton landscaped garden to 'Red Book' design; vined courtyard, Elizabethan and Quarry gardens. A fine spring garden with magnolia, rhododendrons, camellias and azaleas. TEAS. *Adm £2.50 Chd 5-14 £1. Mon to Sat March 1 to Nov 2. For NGS Thurs March 14, Sats March 30, April 20 (10.30-4.30)*

Chyverton (Mr N T Holman) Zelah, N of Truro. Entrance ¾m SW of Zelah on A30. Georgian landscaped garden with lake and bridge (1770); large shrub garden of great beauty; outstanding collection magnolias, acers, camellias, rhododendrons, primulas, rare and exotic trees and shrubs. Visitors personally conducted by owner. Featured in NGS video 3. *Adm £3.50 (parties over 20 persons by arrangement Adm £3) Chd under 16 free. Private visits welcome weekdays March to June by appt, please* **Tel 01872 540324**

Cotehele House ᴅ✗✿ (The National Trust) 2m E of St Dominick, 4m from Gunnislake (turn at St Ann's Chapel); 8m SW of Tavistock; 14m from Plymouth via Tamar Bridge. Terrace garden falling to sheltered valley with ponds, stream and unusual shrubs. Fine medieval house (one of the least altered in the country); armour, tapestries, furniture. Dogs in wood only and on lead. Lunches and TEAS. *Adm garden, grounds & mill £2.80 Chd half price. Fri May 17 (11-5.30)*

Creed House ᴅ✿ (Mr & Mrs W R Croggon) Creed. From the centre of Grampound on A390. Take rd signposted to Creed. After 1m turn L opp Creed Church and the garden is on L. Parking in lane. 5-acre landscaped Georgian Rectory garden. Tree collection; rhododendrons; sunken alpine and formal walled herbaceous gardens. Trickle stream to ponds and bog. Natural woodland walk. Restoration began 1974 – continues & incl recent planting. TEAS. *Adm £1.50 Chd free.* ▲*Sun May 12 (2-5.30).* **Tel 01872 530372**

Estray Parc ✗ (Mr & Mrs J M Williams) Penjerrick. Leave Penjerrick main entrance on R follow the rd towards Mawnan Smith until entrance to The Home Hotel on L. Directly opp turn R and follow the signs. In 1983 most of this 3-acre garden was a bramble thistle-infested field. A considerable variety of plants have been introduced and continuous grass cutting has produced passable sloping lawns interspersed by a large collection of trees and shrubs. *Adm £1.50 OAPs £1 Chd 50p (Share to Mermaid Appeal®). Sun May 5 (2-6)*

Furzeball ♿❀ (Phyllis & Eric Milner Kay) Pont. 1½m Fowey-Bodinnick Ferry. Follow unclassified rd Bodinnick-Polruan. After Whitecross, bottom of hill bear L into small lane. [Nat. Grid Ref: SX145527]. No access for coaches. 1-acre sheltered cottage garden. Outstanding views over countryside. Garden designed to exploit natural features: contrasting flower beds, rhododendrons and azaleas, springs, small water garden, gunnera, ferns etc. Lawns, fruit trees, vegetables, also wild flower sanctuary. All areas connected by footpath/steps made from local stone. Visitors conducted by owners. *Adm £2.50. Mid-May to mid-June, closed Mons. By appt only, please* **Tel 01726 870600** *pref after 6pm*

Glendurgan ✄❀ (The National Trust) Mawnan Smith, take rd to Helford Passage, 5m SW of Falmouth. Follow NT signposts. Walled garden, laurel maze, giants stride, valley with specimen trees, bluebells and primulas running down to Durgan fishing village on R Helford. Large car park. TEAS. *Adm £2.90 Chd half price. ▲For NGS Sat April 13 (11.30-5.30)*

Headland ✄ (Jean & John Hill) Battery Lane, Polruan. On E of Fowey estuary; leave car in public park; walk down St Saviour's Hill, turn L at Coast Guard office. 1¼-acre cliff garden with sea on 3 sides; mainly plants which withstand salty gales but incl sub-tropical. Spectacular views of Coast; cove for swimming. Cream TEAS. *Adm £1 Chd 50p. Open every Thurs June, July, Aug, Sept. For NGS Thurs May 23, 30 (2-7)*

●**Heligan Gardens** ♿❀ (Mr Tim Smit) Pentewan. From St Austell take B3273 signposted Mevagissey, follow signs. Heligan Gardens is the scene of the largest garden restoration project undertaken since the war. Of special interest in this romantic Victorian garden are; the fern ravine, 4 walled gardens with peach houses, vineries, melon grounds, a splendid collection of Bee boles, crystal grotto, Italian garden with a pool, an Elizabethan beacon 'Mount' and a large tropical Japanese valley garden. All are connected by an intricate web of over 2½m of ornamental footpaths, most unseen for more than half a century. TEAS and light refreshments. *Adm £2.90 OAPs £2.50 Chd £1.70. Open every day (10-4.30). Groups welcome,* **Tel 01726 844157**

High Noon ♿ (R E Sturdy) Ladock. 7m E of Truro on A39. 3½ acres ornamental trees, rhododendrons, camellias, and magnolias, 10yrs old; rose garden; daffodils; lawns; formal pool; S-facing slope with good views. *Combined adm with* **Ladock House** *£2 Chd free. Sun May 12 (2-5.30)*

Higher Truscott ♿✄❀ (Mr & Mrs J C Mann) St Stephens. 3m NW of Launceston between St Stephens and Egloskerry. Signposted. Yr-round elevated garden of 1 acre in a natural setting. Trees, shrubs, climbers, herbaceous plants and alpines (many unusual). Splendid views. Ornamental vegetable garden. TEAS. *Adm £1 Chd free. Sun June 2 (2-6)*

The Hollies ♿✄❀ (Mr J & Mrs N B Croggon) Grampound, nr Truro. In centre of village on Truro-St Austell rd. 2-acre garden of unusual design; unusual mixed planting of trees, shrubs and alpines. TEAS. *Adm £1 Chd free. Sun July 14 (2-5.30).* **Tel 01726 882474**

Ince Castle Gardens ♿❀ (Viscount & Patricia, Viscountess Boyd of Merton) 3m SW of Saltash. From A38 at Stoketon Cross take turn signed Trematon, then Elmgate. 5 acres with lawns and ornamental woods; shell house and dovecote. TEAS. *Adm £1.50 Chd free. Sun March 24 (2-5.30)*

Jimmers ❀ (Mr & Mrs P Kent) St Neot. On L up Bush Hill. ¾-acre garden laid out in rooms with surprises and changes in atmosphere; varied planting; interesting trees; shrubs incl small collection of hollies, perennials, pond, patio, lawns and views; pergola; tranquil setting. *Combined adm with* **The Old Barn, Northwood Farm** *and* **Tremarkyn** *£3 Chd free. Sun June 23 (11-5)*

●**Ken Caro** ✄❀ (Mr & Mrs K R Willcock) Bicton, Pensilva, 5m NE of Liskeard. From A390 to Callington turn off N at Butchers Arms, St Ive; take Pensilva Rd; at next Xrds take rd signed Bicton. 2 acres mostly planted in 1970, with a further 2-acre extension in 1993; well-designed and labelled plantsman's garden; rhododendrons, flowering shrubs, conifers and other trees; herbaceous. Panoramic views. Collection of aviary birds. Featured in NGS video 2. *Adm £2 Chd 50p. April 14 to June 30 every Sun, Mon, Tues, Wed; Tues & Weds only July & Aug (2-6).* **Tel 01579 362446**

Ladock House ♿ (Mr G J & Lady Mary Holborow) Ladock. 7m E of Truro on A39. Car park and entrance by church. Georgian old rectory with 4 acres of lawns, rhododendrons, camellias and azaleas with woodland garden. All planted during last 15yrs. TEAS in aid of Ladock Church. *Combined adm with* **High Noon** *£2 Chd free. Sun May 12 (2-5.30)*

Lamorran House ✄❀ (Mr & Mrs Dudley-Cooke) Upper Castle Rd, St Mawes. First turning R after garage; signposted to St Mawes Castle. House ½m on L. Parking in rd. 4-acre sub-tropical hillside garden with beautiful views to St Anthonys Head. Extensive water gardens in Mediterranean and Japanese settings. Large collection of rhododendrons, azaleas, palm trees, cycads, agaves and many S hemisphere plants and trees. TEA. *Adm £2 Chd free. Sun May 26 (10-5).* **Tel 01326 270800**

Lanhydrock ♿✄❀ (The National Trust) Bodmin, 2½m on B3268. Station: Bodmin Parkway 1¾m. Large-sized garden; formal garden laid out 1857; shrub garden with good specimens of rhododendrons and magnolias and fine views. Lunches and TEAS. Closed Mondays. *Adm garden only £3 Chd half price. ▲Sun May 19 (11-5.30; last adm to house 5)*

●**Lanterns** ❀ (Mrs I Chapman) Mylor. 1m NE of Mylor. From Mylor follow the Restronguet Passage/Pandora Inn rd signs, Lanterns is on the RH-side before reaching the waterfront. ½-acre mature garden in natural setting planted by owners. Wide variety of shrubs, bulbs, herbaceous perennials, climbers, conservatory/greenhouse plants. Interesting in any season; small streams and dry areas; waterside walks. Owner always pleased to advise on plants and planting. *Collecting box. Open every day throughout the year (11am-dusk)*

Regular Openers. See end of county section.

Long Cross Victorian Gardens &※ (Mr & Mrs Crawford) Trelights, St Endellion. 7m N of Wadebridge on B3314. Charm of this garden is mazelike effect due to protecting hedges against sea winds; views of countryside and sea scapes (Port Isaac and Port Quin Bays) Garden specially designed to cope with environment of Cornwall's N Coast. Cream TEAS, coffee, evening meal. *Adm £1.25 Chd 25p.* ▲*Sun July 7 (10.30-6.30). Private visits welcome for parties of 25 and over, please* **Tel 01208 880243**

Mary Newman's Cottage ※※ (Tamar Protection Society) Culver Rd, ¼m from Saltash town centre; park on waterfront. Cottage garden with herbaceous, annuals and herbs. Overlooks R Tamar and Bridges. Recently restored C15 cottage, former home of Sir Francis Drake's first wife. TEA. *Adm £1 Chd 50p (Share to Tamar Protection Society®).* ▲*Sun June 16 (2-4.30).* **Tel 01579 347993**

Nansawsan House ※※ (Mr & Mrs Michael Cole) Ladock. 7m E of Truro on A39. Parking at Falmouth Arms or Parish Hall. Car parks. 1½ acres, part of a once larger Victorian garden. Rhododendrons, camellias, shrubs, trees and borders. CREAM TEAS in aid of Ladock Church. *Adm £1.50 Chd free. Sun May 26 (2-5)*

Newton House &※ (Mrs Michael Trinick) Lanhydrock. 3½m SE of Bodmin on W bank of R. Fowey nr Respryn Bridge. Follow signs to Lanhydrock and Respryn. Surrounded by woods in the beautiful valley of the R. Fowey. 3 acres of old-fashioned walled garden, lawns, shrubs, herbaceous border and old shrub roses, fruit, vegetables and orchard. TEAS. *Adm £1.50 Chd free (Share to Lanhydrock Church®). Suns June 16, 23 (2-6)*

Northwood Farm ※ (Mr & Mrs P K Cooper) St Neot. Take rd out of village to Wenmouth Cross. L and first R. Follow very narrow rd and NGS posters to Farm on R. House & garden on site of a China Clay Dri used 150 yrs ago. House rebuilt from barn and garden from old sunken pits still being developed. Discovery of several natural springs led to creation of ponds now with collection of water birds. *Combined adm with* **The Old Barn, Tremarkyn** *and* **Jimmers** *£3 Chd free. Sun June 23 (11-5)*

Oak Lodge ※※ (Mr & Mrs Miller) Nanstallon, Nr Bodmin. From Bodmin, take A30 SW following signs for Redruth, for approx 2m. Turn R at top of hill and follow signs to Nanstallon. Proceed through village and take 2nd turning R on a L bend. Oak Lodge is approx 1.3m along this road on the R. Set at the edge of woodland, the 7-acre property is gradually being developed around the original trees into informal gardens, natural woodland walks carpeted with bluebells and other wild flowers in springtime, and an arboretum. TEAS in aid of The British Heart Foundation. ▲*For NGS Combined adm with* **Bodwannick Manor Farm** *£2 Chd free. Suns May 5, June 16 (2-6)*

The Old Barn &※ (Mrs H S Lloyd) St Neot nr Liskeard. Turn R by garage, down lane to Holy Well. Cross field. 1st on L. Park in field. Riverside garden, mature trees, shrubs; mixed perennials, roses, clematis, pelargoniums, lawns, pond with water lilies. TEAS. *Combined adm with* **Northwood Farm, Jimmers** *and* **Tremarkyn** *£3 Chd free. Sun June 23 (11-5)*

Paradise Park &※※ (Mr Michael Reynolds) Hayle. Follow the A30 to Hayle, go to St Ives/St Erth roundabout then follow official brown and white signs to Paradise Park. The 2-acre walled garden is part of the 14 acres opened in 1973 as 'The rare and endangered birds breeding centre'. Much effort has been expended to make the gardens a suitable setting for a bird breeding collection of international importance. The World Parrot Trust is based here. Walled garden with pergolas, trellis and gazebos; climbing roses, clematis, lilies and passiflora are featured. *Open throughout the yr from 10am to 5pm.* Cafe in Park. *Adm £4.95 Chd £2.95 (Share to World Parrot Trust®).* ▲*Sun May 19 (10-4)*

●**Pencarrow** &※ (Molesworth-St Aubyn Family) 4 miles N.W. Bodmin, signed off the A389. 50 acres of formal and woodland gardens laid out in the 1840's by Sir William Molesworth Bt. Marked walks past the Victorian Rockery, Italian and American Gardens, Lake and Ice House. Over 650 different varieties of rhododendrons, also an Internationally known specimen conifer collection. *House, Tearooms and Craft Centre open Sun to Thurs. Open daily Easter Sun to October 15. Adm garden only £1.50 Chd free. Gardens open daily (1.30-5)*

Penjerrick Garden ※ (Rachel Morin) Budock. 3m SW of Falmouth between Budock and Mawnan Smith. Entrance at junction of lanes opp. Penmorvah Manor Hotel. Parking on verge along drive. Room to park one coach at gate. 15-acre garden of historical and botanical interest. Home of Barclayi and Penjerrick rhododendron hybrids. The upper garden with lovely view to the sea, contains many rhododendrons, camellias, magnolias, azaleas, bamboos, tree ferns and magnificent trees. The lower luxuriant valley garden features ponds in a wild woodland setting. *Adm £1.50 Chd 50p (Share to Alzheimer's Disease Society®).* ▲*For NGS Sun April 14 (11.30-4.30). Guided tours* **Tel 01872 870105**

Penwarne (Dr & Mrs H Beister) 3¼m SW of Falmouth. 1½m N of Mawnan. Garden with many varieties of flowering shrubs, rhododendrons, magnolias, New Zealand shrubs, formal and informal garden; walled garden. Ornamental ducks. *Adm £1 Chd 50p. Sun April 21 (2-5)*

Peterdale ※ (Mrs Ann Mountfield) St John's Road, Millbrook. Take new rd to Southdown. 1st L at new roundabout, straight ahead up St Johns Rd. Peterdale last bungalow on L. Small garden started 1980 from field; designed and created by owner on different levels; interesting collection of shrubs, trees, herbaceous plants combined with many old roses, recent waterfall and pond area. Truly a plantsperson's garden. Won Best Family Garden in GB RHS Award 1995. TEA. *Adm £1.50 Chd free. Weds May and June. For NGS Suns May 26, July 21 (10.30-5.30).* **Tel 01752 823364**

By Appointment Gardens. These owners do not have a fixed opening day usually because they do not like crowds or have insufficient parking space. Owner will often give guided tour.

General Information. For general information on the use of this book see Page 15.

Pine Lodge Gardens &✿❀ (Mr & Mrs R H J Clemo) Cuddra. On A390 E of St Austell between Holmbush and Tregrehan. Follow signs. 30-acre estate comprises gardens within a garden. The wide range of some 5,500 plants all of which are labelled, have been thoughtfully laid out using original designs and colour combinations to provide maximum interest for the garden lover. In addition to rhododendrons, magnolias, camellias, herbaceous borders with many rare and tender plants, marsh gardens, tranquil fish ponds, lake within the park, pinetum. TEAS. *Adm £2 Chd free. Sun May 26 (1-5). Also open by appt* **Tel 01726 73500**

Pinetum &✿❀ (Mr & Mrs G R Craw) Harewood. 6m SW of Tavistock. From A390 Tavistock-Callington Rd proceed towards Calstock. After 1m follow sign to Harewood Parish Church. At church continue straight on. 3rd house on R. Walkways meander through 2-acre pinetum full of maturing, uncommon, specimen trees of botanical and ornamental intrigue interspersed with shrubs, plants and garden features for yr-round colour and interest. TEAS. *Adm £1.50 Chd free. Suns May 5, 19; Aug 4 (2-5.30)*

Polgwynne &✿❀ (Mrs P Davey) Feock. 5m S of Truro via A39 (Truro-Falmouth rd) and then B3289 to 1st Xrds: straight on ½m short of Feock village. 3½-acre garden and grounds. Fruit and vegetable garden, woodlands extending to shore of Carrick Roads; magnificent Ginkgo Biloba (female, 12′ girth) probably the largest female ginkgo in Britain; other beautiful trees; many rare and unusual shrubs. Lovely setting and view of Carrick Roads. TEAS. *Adm £2 Chd free. Sun April 28 (2-5.30).* **Tel 01872 862612**

●**Prideaux Place** & (Mr & Mrs Prideaux-Brune) Padstow. On the edge of Padstow follow brown signs for Prideaux Place, from ring rd (A389). Surrounding Elizabethan house the present main grounds were laid out in the early C18 by Edmund Prideaux. Ancient deer park with stunning views over Camel estuary; Victorian woodland walks currently under restoration. Newly restored sunken formal garden. A garden of vistas. Cream TEAS. *Adm £2 Chd £1. Easter Sunday to Oct 17 (1.30-5); Bank Hols (11-5)*

Roseland House ❀ (Charlie & Liz Pridham) Chacewater. 4m W of Truro, at Truro end of main st. Parking in village car park (100yds) or surrounding rds. 1-acre garden subdivided by walls and trellises hosting a wide range of climbers. Mixed borders of unusual plants, Victorian conservatory and greenhouse extend the gardening yr. TEAS. *Adm £1.50 Chd free. Tues May, June, July (1-6). Suns June 30, July 14 (2-5).* **Tel 01872 560451**

St Michael's Mount ✿❀ (The Rt Hon Lord St Levan; The National Trust) Marazion. ½m from shore at Marazion by Causeway; otherwise by ferry. Flowering shrubs; rock plants; castle walls; fine sea views. TEAS. *Adm Castle & gardens £3.70, Chd £1.85 (under 16).* ▲*For NGS Sun April 21 (10.30-4.45)*

Scawn Mill ✿❀ (Mrs A Ball & Dr Julian Ball) St Keyne. From the A38 at the E end of Dobwalls take the signpost to Duloe, Herodsfoot and Looe for 1½ m. Turn R at sign for Scawn and continue for 1m down to the river. Water lily lake lying beside the West Looe River terraced with

azaleas, black pines and Japanese Maples. Walks beside primulas, herbaceous border and Japanese garden. Public footpath following West Looe River through woodland to Herodsfoot. TEAS. *Adm £1.50 Chd free. Sun June 30 (2-5.30)*

●**Trebah** ❀ (Trebah Garden Trust) Mawnan Smith 4m from Falmouth. Follow tourism signs from Hillhead Roundabout on A39 approach to Falmouth. Excellent parking (free) and access for coaches. 25-acre S facing ravine garden, planted in 1850's. Extensive collection of rare and mature trees and shrubs incl glades of huge tree ferns over 100 years old and sub-tropical exotics. Hydrangea collection covers 2½ acres. Water garden with waterfalls and rock pool stocked with mature Koi Carp. A magical garden for plantsman, the artist and family. Play area and trails for children. Use of private beach. New Coffee Shop. *Adm £2.90 OAPs £2.50 Chd and disabled £1. Open every day throughout year (10.30-5 last admission).* **Tel 01326 250448**

Trebartha (The Latham Family) North Hill, SW of Launceston. Nr junction of B3254 & B3257. Wooded area with lake surrounded by walks of flowering shrubs; woodland trail through fine woods with cascades and waterfalls; American glade with fine trees. TEAS. *Adm £1.50 Chd 50p. Sun Sept 29 (2-5.30)*

Tregilliowe Farm &❀ (Mr & Mrs J Richards) Penzance-Hayle A30 Rd from Penzance turn R at Crowlas Xrds. After approx 1m turn sharp L on to St Erth Rd. 2nd farm lane on R. 2-acre garden still developing. Herbaceous beds with wide range of perennials and grasses. Raised Mediterranean bed. TEAS June in aid of Save The Children. July in aid of St Julias Hospice. *Adm £1.50 Chd free. Suns June 16, July 14 (2-6).* **Tel 01736 740654**

●**Tregrehan** &✿❀ (Mr T Hudson) Entrance on A390 opp Britannia Inn 1m W of St Blazey. Access for cars and coaches. Garden largely created since early C19. Woodland of 20 acres containing fine trees, award winning camellias raised by late owner and many interesting plants from warm temperate climes. Show greenhouses a feature containing softer species. TEA. *Adm £2.50 Chd free. Mid March to end June daily. Not open Easter Sunday. For NGS Sun May 5 (10.30-5)*

Trelissick &✿❀ (The National Trust; Mr & Mrs Spencer Copeland) Feock, 4m S of Truro, nr King Harry Ferry. On B3289. Planted with tender shrubs; magnolias, camellias and rhododendrons with many named species characteristic of Cornish gardens. Fine woodlands encircle the gardens through which a varied circular walk can be enjoyed. Superb view over Falmouth harbour. Georgian house (not open). TEAS. *Adm £3.80 Chd half price. Car park £1.* ▲*For NGS Sun April 14 (1-5.30)*

¶**Treloyhan Manor Hotel** &✿ (Mr T Rogers) St Ives. Situated on the A3074 as you drive down into St Ives on the RH-side. Approx 7 acres of gardens overlooking St Ives bay. A pleasant garden thoughtfully laid out incl many trees, shrubs and rare ferns. Suited to the mild winter climate. TEAS. *Adm £1.50 Chd free. Wed May 29 (2-5.30)*

¶**Tremarkyn** ✿✿ (Mr & Mrs J E Thomas) Wenmouth Cross, St Neot. Turn R off A38 (Liskeard and Bodmin) approx ¾m past Doublebois signposted St Neot and Carnglaze Caverns. In St Neot turn sharp R (signposted St Cleer) up steep hill; within ½m as soon as road levels out [201:194677]. ½-acre drive lined with trees and shrubs. Gardens around old granite buildings - still evolving. Bog garden, kitchen garden; unusual conifers. 2 acres of grassed areas with trees and shrubs. Coffee. *Combined adm with* **Jimmers, Northwood Farm** *and* **The Old Barn** *£3, Chd free. Sun June 23 (11-5)*

Tremeer Gardens St Tudy, 8m N of Bodmin; W of B3266, all rds signed. 7-acre garden famous for camellias and rhododendrons with water; many rare shrubs. *Adm £1 Chd 50p. Sun April 7 (2-5).* **Tel 01208 850313**

Trenance ✿✿ (Mr & Mrs J Dingle) Launceston. Follow signs for Leisure Centre along Dunheved Rd. At College end of rd take sharp L bend and immed after this take another L turning into Windmill Hill. Trenance is approx 200yds on L. A 1¾-acre garden for all seasons. A wide variety of trees and shrubs incl rhododendrons, camellias, azaleas, acers and magnolias; heathers and conifers, primulas, herbaceous borders, roses and clematis with several smaller gardens within the main garden. TEA. *Adm £1.50 Chd 50p. Suns May 12, July 14 (2-6)*

¶**Trenarth** ✿ (Mrs L M Nottingham) High Cross. Nearest main rds A39, A394 Truro, Falmouth, Helston. 1½m E of Constantine, 2m W of Mawnan Smith, 1½m S of Treverva. Nearest landmark High Cross Garage. From Treverva with garage on L take lane to L, then immed R down dead-end lane. Trenarth is ½m at end of lane. Diverse 2-acre gardens round old farmhouse. Courtyard, conservatory, C18 garden walls, yew hedging, herbaceous and rockery beds, shrub borders, ha-ha, orchard and woodland walk to Helford. Extensively replanted during past 2 yrs, with further wilderness areas awaiting reclamation. TEAS. *Adm £1.50 Chd free. Sun July 28 (2-5)*

Trengwainton ✿✿✿ (The National Trust) 2m N W of Penzance, ½ mile West of Heamoor on Penzance-Morvah rd (B3312), ½m off St Just rd (A3071) The garden of mainland Britain perhaps most favoured for the cultivation of exotic shrubs and trees. Plantsman's delight. TEAS. *Adm £2.90 Chd half price.* ▲*For NGS Sat March 16 (10.30-5.30)*

Trerice ✿✿✿ (The National Trust) Newlyn East 3m SE of Newquay. From Newquay via A392 and A3058; turn R at Kestle Mill (NT signposts). The summer-flowering garden is unusual in content and layout and there is an orchard planted with old varieties of fruit trees. A small museum traces the history of the lawn mower. Lunches & TEAS. *Adm house & garden £3.80 Chd half price.* ▲*For NGS Wed Aug 21 (11-5.30). Children's Garden Trail*

●**Trevarno Gardens** ✿ (Mr M Sagin & Mr N Helsby) Sithney Helston. Signed from Crowntown on the B3303, 3m NW of Helston. Set within beautiful and historic Trevarno Estate dating back to 1296, one of Cornwall's most romantic and secret woodland gardens covering 40 acres. Extensive collection of rare shrubs, specimen trees, walled gardens, mysterious rockeries, grotto, enchanting lake, cascade and fountains and abundant wildlife; now subject of major restoration and replanting programme. TEA. *Adm £2.50 Chd under 14 £1.25, under 5 free. Open daily (10-5) Jan 1 to Dec 24.* **Tel 01326 574274**

Trevegean ✿ (Mr & Mrs E C Cousins) 9 Manor Way. Take Penzance by-pass; take first L off roundabout towards Treneere and Heamoor. Sharp R turn for Manor way. ⅓-acre divided into series of enclosed areas; planting some formal, informal, topiary garden, shrubs and perennials; connected by brick and slab paths some edged with box. TEAS. *Adm £1 Chd free (Share to St Julias Hospice Hayle®). Sun June 9. Private visits welcome for parties of under 30 April 1 to end of July (2-5), please* **Tel 01736 67407**

Treviades Gardens ✿✿ Off the Falmouth to Constantine R at High Cross - 1m on the Falmouth side of Constantine and N of Port Navas. At High Cross, turn to Port Navas. The gardens are on the L going down the hill. Travelling from the Truro area follow the A39. Use the Penryn by-pass. At Hillhead Roundabout, follow the signs to Constantine. Cream TEAS. *Combined adm £2 Chd free (Share to Mermaid Appeal®). Sun July 7 (2-5.30)*

    Treviades Barton (Mr & Mrs M J Ford) Series of walled gardens, each one with own character (i.e. roses in one); vegetable garden and small arboretum

    Treviades Wollas (Mrs Watson) S facing medium-sized garden in two parts - leading down to small water garden fed by two springs

●**Trewithen** ✿✿ (Mr A M J Galsworthy) Truro. ½m E Probus. Entrance on A390 Truro-St Austell Rd. Signposted. Large car park. Internationally renowned garden of 30 acres laid out by Maj G Johnson between 1912 & 1960 with much of original seed and plant material collected by Ward and Forrest. Original C18 walled garden famed for towering magnolias and rhododendrons; wide range of own hybrids. Flatish ground amidst original woodland park. Featured in NGS video 2. TEAS. *Adm £2.80 Chd £1.50 Group £2.50. Mon to Sat March 1 to Sept 30, Suns April-May only (10-4.30). Special arrangements for coaches. Mrs Norman* **Tel 01726 882763**

Treworder Mill ✿✿ (Derek & Pearl Rutter) Kenwyn. 2½m W of Truro. A390 Truro to Redruth. Turn at Treliske Hospital roundabout. Pass Duchy Hospital. Turn L at T junction. Car parking at bottom of hill. R Kenwyn Valley Garden. 2¾ acres with streams and a wide range of moisture-loving plants including Candelabra primulas and hostas in a tranquil woodland setting. Interesting and well-planted natural pond area. *Adm £1.50 Chd free. Thurs May 30, June 6, 13, 20, 27 (10-12 noon and 2-5).* **Tel 01872 73314** *evenings*

Water Meadow ✿ (Philip & Rose Lamb) Luxulyan 5m NW of St Austell, 6m S of Bodmin. [Map ref SX 052582.] Park in village street between church and school. Turn by church, garden 200yds downhill on L. 1½-acre garden on sloping site with Grade II listed grotto. Large pond with waterside planting and bog garden with extensive primula, astilbe, gunnera, arum lilies etc. Gravel garden surrounded by shrub roses & herbaceous planting. Specimen trees and shrubs with recently established mixed borders. TEAS in aid of WI. *Adm £1.50 Chd free. Sun June 23 (2-5) also by appt please* **Tel 01726 851399**

●**Woodland Garden** ✸❀ (Mr & Mrs N Froggatt) Garras. On Helston-St Kererne Rd B3293, turn R ¼m past Garras at Woodland Garden sign. Entrance on R after ½m. Peaceful 2½-acre valley garden designed to encourage wildlife. 9 acres heather downland (Erica vagans, July/Aug). Spring succession of wild daffodils, primroses, bluebells, camellias, rhododendrons. Unusual plants set sympathetically among mature woodland. Yr-round foliage colour and form. Dogs allowed only on Downs. *Adm £1 Chd free. Sat April 13 to Sept 28 (2-5).* **Tel 01326 221295**

¶**Zoar** ✸❀ (Mrs Pixie Wells) Mylor. [O/S Map 204, ref: 807367.] From Truro take A39 to Falmouth for approx 7m. 2nd turning L after Norway Inn, follow signs to Restronguet and Mylor Bridge for 2¼m. At Xrds by large yellow house turn R, Zoar is 1st house on L. From Falmouth take A39 to Penryn. At Kessells Garage turn R, signed to Mylor. Drive through village, up Passage Hill, Zoar is last house on R. An unusual 1-acre garden mostly planted since 1986. Some mature shrubs and an interesting collection of dwarf conifers. Small pond and arboretum. Bounded on two sides by cornish hedges. *Adm £2 Chd free. Sun June 9 (2-5)*

Cumbria

(including 4 gardens open under Scotland's Gardens Scheme)

Hon County Organiser: (South)	Mrs R E Tongue, Paddock Barn, Winster, Windermere LA23 3NW
Assistant Hon County Organiser: (North)	Mrs E C Hicks, Scarthwaite, Grange-in-Borrowdale, Keswick CA12 5UQ
Hon County Treasurer:	Derek Farman Esq, Mill House, Winster, Windermere LA23 3NW

DATES OF OPENING

April 6 Saturday
Copt Howe, Chapel Stile, Ambleside
April 7 Sunday
Copt Howe, Chapel Stile, Ambleside
April 8 Monday
Copt Howe, Chapel Stile, Ambleside
April 13 Saturday
Copt Howe, Chapel Stile, Ambleside
April 14 Sunday
Copt Howe, Chapel Stile, Ambleside
April 20 Saturday
Copt Howe, Chapel Stile, Ambleside
April 21 Sunday
Copt Howe, Chapel Stile, Ambleside
Winderwath, nr Penrith
April 22 Monday
Levens Hall, Kendal
April 27 Saturday
Copt Howe, Chapel Stile, Ambleside
April 28 Sunday
Copt Howe, Chapel Stile, Ambleside ‡
Green Bank, Grasmere ‡
May 4 Saturday
Copt Howe, Chapel Stile, Ambleside

May 5 Sunday
Copt Howe, Chapel Stile, Ambleside
Dallam Tower, Milnthorpe
Rydal Mount, Eskdale Green, Gosforth
Stagshaw, Rothay Road, Ambleside
May 6 Monday
Copt Howe, Chapel Stile, Ambleside ‡
Green Bank, Grasmere ‡
May 8 Wednesday
Rydal Mount, Eskdale Green, Gosforth
May 11 Saturday
Acorn Bank, Temple Sowerby, nr Penrith
Copt Howe, Chapel Stile, Ambleside
May 12 Sunday
Browfoot, Skelwith Bridge, Ambleside ‡
Copt Howe, Chapel Stile, Ambleside ‡
Fell Yeat, Kirkby Lonsdale
Holme Crag, Witherslack
The Nook, Helton, nr Penrith
May 15 Wednesday
Fell Yeat, Kirkby Lonsdale
May 18 Saturday
Copt Howe, Chapel Stile, Ambleside ‡
St Annes, Great Langdale ‡

May 19 Sunday
Browfoot, Skelwith Bridge, Ambleside ‡
Copt Howe, Chapel Stile, Ambleside ‡
Halecat, Witherslack
Holehird, Windermere
Matson Ground, Windermere
St Annes, Great Langdale
May 25 Saturday
Copt Howe, Chapel Stile, Ambleside
Galesyke, Wasdale
May 26 Sunday
Browfoot, Skelwith Bridge, Ambleside ‡
Copt Howe, Chapel Stile, Ambleside ‡
Galesyke, Wasdale
Green Bank, Grasmere ‡
High Beckside Farm, Cartmel
May 27 Monday
Copt Howe, Chapel Stile, Ambleside
Palace How, Brackenthwaite, Loweswater
May 29 Wednesday
Windy Hall, Windermere
June 2 Sunday
Blakeholme Wray, Newby Bridge ‡
Dalswinton House, Auldgirth
Hazelmount, Thwaites, Millom
Hutton-in-the-Forest, Penrith
Lindeth Fell Country House, Bowness-on-Windermere ‡

Stagshaw, Rothay Road,
Ambleside
June 5 Wednesday
Brackenburn, Manesty, Keswick
June 6 Thursday
Lingholm, Portinscale
June 8 Saturday
Bush Green Cottage,
Broughton-in-Furness
June 9 Sunday
Bush Green Cottage,
Broughton-in-Furness
Craigieburn Garden, Moffat
Station House, Lamplugh,
nr Workington
June 12 Wednesday
Brockhole, Windermere
June 15 Saturday
Acorn Bank, Temple Sowerby,
nr Penrith
Bush Green Cottage,
Broughton-in-Furness
Rannerdale Cottage, Buttermere
June 16 Sunday
Bush Green Cottage,
Broughton-in-Furness
Fell Yeat, nr Kirkby Lonsdale
Holme Crag, Witherslack
Rannerdale Cottage,
Buttermere
June 19 Wednesday
Fell Yeat, nr Kirkby Lonsdale
June 22 Saturday
Sizergh Castle, nr Kendal
June 23 Sunday
Dallam Tower, Milnthorpe

Yews, Middle Entrance Drive,
Bowness-on-Windermere
June 30 Sunday
Askham Hall, Penrith ‡
The Mill House, Sebergham ‡
Whitbysteads, Askham ‡
Windy Hall, Windermere
July 7 Sunday
Nunwick Hall, Great Salkeld
July 10 Wednesday
Brockhole, Windermere
July 13 Saturday
Acorn Bank, Temple Sowerby,
nr Penrith
July 14 Sunday
Argrennan House, Castle Douglas
Halecat, Witherslack
High Cleabarrow, Windermere
Marton House, Long Marton,
nr Appleby
July 21 Sunday
Dallam Tower, Milnthorpe
38 English Street, Longtown
Hensol, Castle Douglas
Hutton-in-the-Forest, Penrith
August 8 Thursday
Lingholm, Portinscale
August 18 Sunday
Holehird, Windermere
Rydal Mount, Eskdale Green,
Gosforth
August 21 Wednesday
Rydal Mount, Eskdale Green,
Gosforth
September 1 Sunday
Craigieburn Garden, Moffat

September 8 Sunday
Matson Ground, Windermere
September 23 Monday
Levens Hall, Kendal

Regular openings
For details see garden description

Brockhole, Windermere
Higham Hall College, Cockermouth
Holker Hall & Gardens
Holehird, Windermere
Hutton-in-the-Forest, Penrith
Levens Hall, Kendal
Lingholm, Portinscale
Winderwath, nr Penrith

By appointment only
*For telephone numbers and other
details see garden descriptions.
Private visits welcomed*

Greencroft House, Great Strickland
Greystones, Embleton
High Rigg, Grange-in-Borrowdale
Langholme Mill, Woodgate, Lowick
Green
Scarthwaite, Grange-in-Borrowdale
Wood Hall, Cockermouth

DESCRIPTIONS OF GARDENS

Acorn Bank &⚙❀ (The National Trust) Temple Sowerby. 6m E of Penrith on A66; ½m N of Temple Sowerby. Bus: Penrith-Appleby or Carlisle-Darlington; alight Culgaith Rd end. Medium-sized walled garden; fine herb garden; orchard and mixed borders; wild garden with woodland/riverside walk. Dogs on leads only woodland walk. *Adm £1.70 Chd 80p. April 1 to Oct 31 daily (10-5).* ▲*For NGS Sats May 11, June 15, July 13 (10-5)*

Askham Hall ⚙❀ (The Earl & Countess of Lonsdale) 5m S of Penrith. Turn off A6 for Lowther and Askham. Askham Hall is a pele tower, incorporating C14, C16 and early C18 elements in courtyard plan. Formal outlines of garden with terraces of herbaceous borders and original topiary, probably from late C17. Shrub roses and recently created herb garden. Kitchen garden. TEAS. *Adm £1.50 Chd free (Share to Askham & Lowther Churches®). Sun June 30 (2-5.30)*

Blakeholme Wray ⚙ (Mr & Mrs W T Rooney) Newby Bridge. [Grid Ref GR 384 895] Blakeholme Wray is 2m N of Newby Bridge on A592. 4 acres garden, 22 acres woodland. An outstanding position with lawns sweeping down to the shore of Windermere. Informal planting is ongoing under present owners: massed rhododendrons and azaleas, damson orchard, wild orchids, bluebell car-

pets, ancient woodland walk, abundant wildlife. Partially suitable for wheelchairs. TEA. *Adm £1.50 Chd free. Sun June 2 (12-5)*

Brackenburn (Prof & Mrs D C Ellwood) Manesty. Take rd signed Portinscale and Grange off A66. Follow all signs for Grange. Garden is 1½ acres on the mountainside on RH-side of rd 3½m from A66. The Garden has wonderful views of Lake Derwent Water. There are several water features planted for damp acid conditions with many rhododendrons, azaleas, ferns and primulas. Brackenburn is the former home of author Sir Hugh Walpole. TEA. *Adm £1.50 Acc chd free (Share to Scottish terrier emergency care scheme®). Wed June 5 (2-5)*

Brockhole & (Lake District National Park) Windermere. 2m NW of Windermere on A591 between Windermere and Ambleside. 10 acres formal gardens, designed by Thomas Mawson. Acid soils and mild aspect, many unusual or slightly tender plants, shrub roses, herbaceous borders, scented garden. 20 acres informal grounds, wide variety of trees and shrubs. Picnic area, adventure playground, boat trips on Lake Windermere. Garden walks. Restaurant and tea rooms. *Adm free (Multi-tariff parking available, season ticket for car park. Adm charge on special event days (not NGS days)). Daily March 30 to Nov 3; for NGS Wed June 12, July 10 (10-5).* **Tel 015394 46601**

Browfoot ❀ (Mr Trevor Woodburn) Skelwith Bridge 2½m SW of Ambleside on A593. Turn down lane at Skelwith Bridge. Woodland garden developed by owner; rhododendrons; azaleas; species trees and natural rock garden. Approx 2 acres. TEAS provided by and in aid of the Community Centre, only on May 12. *Adm £1.30 Chd 40p. Suns May 12, 19, 26 (11-5)*

¶**Bush Green Cottage** ⬥❀❀ (Mr & Mrs James Haunch) Broughton-in-Furness. On A590 on edge of Broughton. 1½m from Foxfield on RH-side. Approx 1-acre cottage garden. Streams and pool. Originally Crossing Keepers Cottage on Furness Railway; large collection geraniums. Wide variety hardy plants; new areas under development. *Adm £1.50 Acc Chd under 12 free. Sats, Suns June 8, 9; 15, 16 (11-5)*

Copt Howe ❀ (Professor R N Haszeldine) Chapel Stile. Great Langdale ¼m W of Chapel Stile. 2-acre plantsman's garden, newly extended. Scenic views Langdale Pikes. Extensive collections of acers (especially Japanese), camellias, azaleas, rhododendrons, quercus, fagus, rare shrubs and trees, unusual perennials; herbaceous and bulbous species; alpines and trough gardens; rare dwarf and large conifers; Expedition plants from Far East. Featured by the media, gardening magazines. *Adm £2; OAP £1.50; Chd free. Sats, Suns April, May and Bank Holidays (12-5). Cream TEAS and plants May 5, 26 (10-5.30). Plants on many other days (Share to Langdales Society© May 5, Friends of the Lake District® other days). Private visits welcome April to end Sept, please* **Tel 015394 37685**

Dallam Tower ⬥ (Brigadier & Mrs C E Tryon-Wilson) Milnthorpe, 7m S of Kendal. 7m N of Carnforth, nr junction of A6 and B5282. Station: Arnside, 4m; Lancaster, 15m. Medium-sized garden; natural rock garden, waterfalls, rambler and polyanthus roses; wood walks, lawns, shrubs. *Adm £1 Chd free. Suns May 5, June 23, July 21 (2-5)*

38 English Street ❀❀ (Mr & Mrs C Thomson) Longtown, Carlisle. M6 junction 44, A7 for 6m into Longtown. 300yds on L next door to Annes Hairdressers. Entrance through open archway. Terraced house garden. Red sandstone and water features; containers and troughs, pergola and herbaceous. TEA. *Adm £1 Acc chd free (Share to Cat Protection League®). Sun July 21 (2-5). Private visits and parties welcome, please* **Tel 01228 791364**

Fell Yeat ⬥❀❀ (Mr & Mrs O S Benson) Casterton, nr Kirkby Lonsdale. Approx 1m E of Casterton Village on the rd to Bull Pot. Leave A65 at Devils Bridge, follow A683 for a mile, take the R fork to High Casterton at the golf course, straight across at two sets of Xrds, the house is immediately on the L about ¼m from no through rd sign. 1-acre informal country garden with mixed borders, herbaceous, old roses, small fernery, herb garden and small pond and is building up the National Collection of Ligularias. TEAS in aid of Holy Trinity Church, Casterton. *Adm £1.50 Chd 20p. Suns, Weds May 12, 15, June 16, 19 (1-5)*

Galesyke ⬥❀ (Christine & Mike McKinley) Wasdale. From the N enter Gosforth and follow signposts to Nether Wasdale. Pass through Nether Wasdale, following signs to the Lake and Wasdale Head. After approx ¾m, entrance on R. From the S head towards Santon Bridge turn off A595 at Holmrook or app from Eskdale. Turn R at Santon Bridge following signs to Wasdale Head. Approx 3m to entrance. Secluded landscaped riverside garden of approx 1½ acres containing a variety of mature trees and flowering shrubs. Riverside meadow and secluded woodland walks. TEAS. *Adm £1.50 Chd under 12 free. Sat, Sun May 25, 26 (11.30-5)* **Tel 019467 26267**

Green Bank ❀ (Mr & Mrs Reg Gifford) Grasmere. 4m from Ambleside off the A591 Keswick Rd. Turn R between Swan Hotel and its car park. 5-acre steep hillside garden with woodland walks and mountain stream under a 5yr renovation plan. Features a unique collection of rare trees, rhododendrons, camellias and azaleas brought to England by the late Michael Black from Bhutan, Chile, Nepal, etc. Great interest to plant enthusiasts. Teas in adjacent hotels or cafes in Grasmere. *Adm £2 Chd/OAPs £1. Suns April 28, May 2, Mon May 6 (10.30-5). Private visits welcome Mon to Fri, by appt April 1 to June 28, please* **Tel 015394 35496**

Greencroft House ⬥❀ ❀ (Mr & Mrs W Irving) Gt Strickland, 7m S of Penrith. Off A6 at Hackthorpe, signed to Gt Strickland ¾m. Approx 1-acre of a series of small gardens of different character: herbs; alpines; shrubs; water and herbaceous plants. *Adm £1.50. Private visits welcome June, July and August for parties of 6, please* **Tel 01931 712236**

Greystones ❀❀ (Mr & Mrs D Cook) Embleton. Just off A66, 4m E of Cockermouth, 2m W of Bassenthwaite Lake. Take turning marked 'Wythop Mill' with watermill sign. Lane 200yds on R. 1 acre of mostly new garden being developed on various levels around mature trees, with shrubs, herbaceous beds and borders, woodland garden, ponds, scree, spring bulbs. Organic fruit and vegetable beds. *Adm £1 Chd free. Private visits welcome, please* **Tel 017687 76375**

Halecat ⬥❀❀ (Mrs Michael Stanley) Witherslack, 10m SW of Kendal. From A590 turn into Witherslack following the Halecat brown signs. L in township at another brown sign and L again, signpost 'Cartmel Fell'; gates on L [map ref. 434834]. Medium-sized garden; mixed shrub and herbaceous borders, terrace, sunken garden; gazebo; daffodils and cherries in Spring, over 70 different varieties of hydrangea; beautiful view over Kent estuary to Arnside. Nursery garden attached. TEA. *Adm £1 Chd free. Suns May 19, July 14 (2-5). Also private parties welcome, please* **Tel 0144 852229**

Hazelmount ⬥❀❀ (Mrs J Barratt) Thwaites, Millom, 2m from Broughton-in-Furness off A595 up hill after crossing Duddon River Bridge. 5-acre woodland garden, small lake with stream; spring display of species rhododendrons, azaleas and flowering shrubs. Mature trees and exceptional views of Duddon Estuary and sea. Cream TEAS. *Adm £1.50 Chd free. Sun June 2 (2-5.30)*

By Appointment Gardens. See end of county section

High Beckside Farm ✿ (Mr & Mrs P J McCabe) Cartmel. 1¼m N of Cartmel. Take the Haverthwaite Rd, from the PO in the village. A newly created conservation area, a wild garden with ponds, waterfalls, waterfowl; flowering bushes and a number of rare trees. An arboretum in the very early stages of formation. 11 acres of wild flowers on a hillside with fine views. A small house garden. Approx ¼m from house to conservation area. Stout shoes. TEA. *Adm £1.25 Chd free. Sun May 26 (1-5). Private visits welcome, please* **Tel 015395 36528**

High Cleabarrow ♿✿❀ (Mr & Mrs R T Brown) 3m SE of Windermere off B5284 Crook to Kendal Rd (nr Windermere Golf Course). 2-acre newly designed and planted comprising formal rose garden, old-fashioned roses, new pond waterside planting, large collection of geraniums, hostas and hydrangeas. Unusual plants, woodland area. TEAS. *Adm £1.50 Chd free under 12. Sun July 14 (1.30-5.30)*

¶**High Rigg** (Miss B Newton) Grange-in-Borrowdale. From Keswick take B5289 to Grange; cross rd bridge, suitable for mini-buses. House ½m on L. ¾-acre fellside garden created over 30 yrs by Miss F M Birkett. Mixed shrub/herbaceous border, rock and bog gardens. Rhododendrons, azaleas and many other shrubs and trees. *Adm £1.50 Acc chd free. Private visits and parties welcome, please* **Tel 017687 77206**

Higham Hall College ♿ (Alasdair Galbraith) Bassenthwaite Lake. 7m N of Keswick 4m SE of Cockermouth. Take rd signed Castle Inn off A66 at N end of Bassenthwaite Lake. Higham Hall is signed after ½m. 4 acres of informal Victorian gardens incl pond, woodland walk, specimen trees, lawns, sunken rose garden. Rhododendrons. Parkland views towards Skiddaw. *£1 donation in Honesty Box. Open all year, every day (9-dusk).* **Tel 017687 76276**

Holehird (Lakeland Horticultural Society) ✿ Patterdale Road, Windermere. ½m N of Windermere town on A591. Turn R onto A592 to Patterdale. Garden signposted on R ¾m on A592. Car park along private drive. The garden of nearly 5 acres is set on a hillside with some of the best views in Lakeland, with a great diversity of plants that grow well in this area, incl alpine and heather beds and a collection of rhododendrons and azaleas. The walled garden is mostly herbaceous. National collections of astilbes, polystichum ferns and hydrangeas. Partially suitable wheelchairs. *Garden always open. Entrance by donation £1 Chd free. Warden available throughout summer (10-5). Coach parties by appointment, volunteer guides available* **Tel 015394 46008**. *For NGS Suns May 19, Aug 18 (10-5)*

●**Holker Hall & Gardens** ♿✿❀ (Lord & Lady Cavendish) Cark-in-Cartmel. 4m W of Grange-over-Sands. 12m W of M6 (junction 36). Formal and woodland gardens developed by the Cavendish family over two centuries. Exotic trees beside ancient oaks, sycamore and beech. Spring carpets of bulbs with rhododendrons, azaleas, magnolias. Summer: Rose and elliptical garden, extensive cascade, wild flower meadow, rare trees and shrubs, eucryphias. National Collection of Styracacrae, Lakeland Motor Museum, Adventure Playground, Deer Park, shop, cafeteria. Garden Festival May 31, June 1, 2. *Adm prices not available at time of going to press. Groups by arrangement, Garden tours. Open Sun to Fris April 2 to Oct 31 (10-6 last entry 4.30)*

¶**Holme Crag** ✿ (Mr Jack Watson) Witherslack, Grange-over-Sands. Off A590 Barrow Rd through Witherslack. Turn L Helecat. Turn L at next rd on junction. Just past telephone kiosk in Newton Rd signpost approx 1m. Partially suitable for wheelchairs. 4 acres designed to encourage wildlife. Award winning bird garden with large pond and rockeries; 22 different species nest. Scree beds. Azaleas, rhododendrons and mature shrubs and trees, spring garden, primulas - species bulbs. *Adm £1.50 Acc chd under 12 free. Suns May 12, June 16 (1.30-5)*

Hutton-in-the-Forest (Lord Inglewood) 5m NW of Penrith. 3m from exit 41 of M6. Magnificent grounds with C18 walled flower garden, terraces and lake. C19 Low garden, specimen trees and topiary; woodland walk and dovecote. Mediaeval House with C17, C18 and C19 additions. TEAS. *Adm £2 gardens, grounds, £3.50 house, gardens & grounds Chd free gardens, grounds £1.50 house & garden & grounds. Gardens and grounds open daily all year except Sats (11-5). House and tea room open (1-4) Easter Sun, Mon, Tues, Wed, Thurs, April 7, 8, 9, 10, 11; Thurs, Fris, Suns, Bank Hols and Aug Weds May 2 to Sept 28. For NGS Suns June 2, July 21 (11-5)*

¶**Langholme Mill** ✿ (Dr W E Gill) Woodgate, Lowick Green. On the A5092 Greenodd to Workington rd 3m from Greenodd on a short stretch of dual carriageway. Park in front of the house. Approx ¾-acre of woodland garden with a beck running the length of it. Dwarf rhododendrons smaller rhododendrons, yak species and hybrids Japanese azaleas and azaleas; acers, bamboos, hostas, astilbes and waterside plants. *Adm £1.50 Chd under 12 free. Private visits welcome please write or* **Tel 01229 885215** *after 1pm*

Levens Hall ♿✿❀ (C H Bagot Esq) 5m S of Kendal on Milnthorpe Rd (A6); Exit 36 from M6. 10 acres incl famous topiary garden and 1st ha-ha laid out by M Beaumont in 1694. Winner of the HHA/Christies Garden of the year award 1994. Magnificent beech circle; formal bedding; herbaceous borders. Elizabethan mansion, added to C13 pele tower, contains superb panelling, plasterwork and furniture. Steam collection. Only gardens suitable for wheelchairs. *Adm House & Garden £4.80 Chd £2.50. Garden only £3.50 Chd £1.80. Reduction for groups. April 1 to Sept 30. House and garden, gift shop, tearoom. children's play area, picnic area. Sun, house (11-4.30), Mon, Tues, Wed, Thurs, house (12-4.30) grounds (10-5), steam collection (2-5). Closed Fri & Sat. For NGS Mons April 22, Sept 23 (10-5)*

Lindeth Fell Country House Hotel ♿ (Air Commodore & Mrs P A Kennedy) 1m S of Bowness on A5074. 6-acres of lawns and landscaped grounds on the hills above Lake Windermere, probably designed by one of the Mawson school around 1907; majestic conifers and specimen trees best in spring and early summer with a colourful display of rhododendrons, azaleas and Japanese maples; grounds offer splendid views to Coniston mountains; rose garden and herbaceous border newly developed. Top terrace suitable for wheelchairs. TEAS in hotel £1. *Adm £1 Chd free. Sun June 2 (2-5). Also private parties welcome, please* **Tel 01539 443 286**

Lingholm &⚘❀ (The Viscount Rochdale) Keswick. On W shore of Derwentwater; Portinscale 1m; Keswick 3m. Turn off A66 at Portinscale; drive entrance 1m on left. Ferry: Keswick to Nicol End, 10 mins walk. Bus: Keswick to Portinscale, 1m. Formal and woodland gardens; garden walk 1m; rhododendrons, azaleas, herbaceous borders etc. Spring daffodils, autumn colours. Plant centre. Free car park. TEAS. *Adm £2.70 (incl leaflet) Chd free. April 1 to Oct 31 daily. For NGS Thurs June 6, Aug 8 (10-5)*

Marton House ⚘❀ (Mr & Mrs M S Hardy-Bishop) Long Marton, Turn off A66 2m W of Appleby signposted Long Marton. Follow rd through village under bridge. House/Car park on R. A 4½ acre walled garden nestling in the foothills of the Pennines. Magnificent Cedar of lebanon, herbaceous borders. Italian garden leading to small lake, ducks, woodland walk, views. Ongoing landscaping and refurbishment. Cream TEAS. *Adm £1.50 Chd 25p. Sun July 14 (1-5.30)*

Matson Ground &⚘❀ (Matson Ground Settlement) Windermere. From Kendal turn R off B5284 signposted Heathwaite, 100yds after Windermere Golf Club entrance. Lane joins another in ¼m. Continue straight on. Garden is on L after ¼m. From Bowness turn L onto B5284 from A5074. After ¾m turn L at Xrds follow sign to Heathwaite. Garden on L ¾m along lane. Watercourse flows through ornamental garden to large pond in the wild garden of meadow grassland, spring bulbs later wild flowers. Azaleas, rhododendrons, large mixed shrub/herbaceous borders, imaginative topiary work. Landscape designer John Brookes has made recent changes in the garden. A ½-acre walled kitchen garden being run on organic methods, greenhouses and dovecote. Adjacent to ornamental garden a 2-acre amenity woodland. TEAS. *Adm £1.50 Chd 50p. Suns May 19, Sept 8 (1-5)*

The Mill House ⚘❀ (Mr & Mrs R L Jefferson) Sebergham. Take junction 41 off M6 A5305 Penrith to Wigton Rd into Sebergham turning to L into an easily missed lane just before bridge over river Caldew. 200 yds up lane, after bungalow take L fork in drive. Ample parking. ½-acre garden set in secluded valley around the water mill; features millstream and pond, a large herbaceous border and a gravel garden; fruit and vegetable garden. TEAS in aid of Welton School Trust. *Adm £1.50 Chd free. Sun June 30 (1.30-4.30)*

The Nook &❀ (Mr & Mrs P Freedman) Helton. Penrith N 5m from B5320, take signs to Askham-Haweswater. Turn R into Helton. ½-acre terraced rock garden, beds and tubs, alpines, ornamental pool, goldfish, bog plants, fruit and herb garden; magnificent views over R Lowther and parkland. Homemade provisions and cakes for sale. TEAS. *Adm £1.50 Chd free. Sun May 12 (11-4)*

Nunwick Hall &⚘❀ (Mr & Mrs C M & Mr O H Thompson) On outskirts of Great Salkeld, 5½m NE of Penrith. Parkland and walks to R Eden. 7 acres of garden, with terrace, parterre, lawns with rose garden, borders and large Victorian rockery. The original walled garden has flowers, fruit, vegetables and an orchard. Picnics in park. TEAS. *Adm £2 OAP's £1.50 Chd under 12 free (Share to St Cuthbert's Church, Great Salkeld®). Sun July 7 (1.30-5)*

Palace How ⚘❀ (Mr & Mrs A & K Johnson) Brackenthwaite, Loweswater, 6m SE of Cockermouth on B5292 and B5289 or from Keswick 10m over Whinlatter Pass, through Lorton village, follow signs for Loweswater. Established damp garden set in lovely situation amongst mountains. Unusual trees and shrubs, especially rhododendrons and acers. Pond with bog plants; candelabra primulas; Himalayan poppies, roses and alpines. Cream teas at Loweswater Village Hall in aid of NSPCC. *Adm £1.50 Chd free. Sun May 27 (11-5). Private visits and parties welcome, please Tel 01900 85648*

Rannerdale Cottage ❀ (The McElney Family) Buttermere. 8m S of Cockermouth, 10m W of Keswick. ½-acre cottage garden with beck and woodland walk overlooking Crummock Water, splendid mountain views. Herbaceous, shrubs, roses, perennial geraniums, tree peonies, pond with fish. TEAS. *Adm £1.50 Chd free. Sat, Sun June 15, 16 (11-5)*

Rydal Mount ❀ (Don & Toni Richards) Eskdale Green, Holmrook, nr Gosforth. Turn off A595 where signed 6m to Eskdale Green. Turn sharp R opp Eskdale Stores. 2nd house on R. 1½-acre garden on natural rock facing SW. Heathers and tree heaths with shrubs and small trees favouring acid soil; eucalyptus and American blueberrys; water garden. Blueberry TEAS. *Adm £1 Chd free (Share to West Cumbria Hospice at Home®). Suns, Weds May 5, 8; Aug 18, 21 (2-5). Also private visits welcome, please Tel 019467 23267*

St Annes ❀ (Mr & Mrs R D Furness) Great Langdale. 5m from Ambleside on B5343. Follow signs for Langdale/Old Dungeon Ghyll. At Skelwith Bridge take R hand fork and at Elterwater take R hand. Through Chapel Stile, ¾m on L hand side travelling W. 3-acre partial woodland with established variety of conifers and trees, azaleas and rhododendrons. Natural rock faces with alpines, streams and rocky paths. Magnificent views Langdales. Partially suitable for wheelchairs. TEAS. *Adm £1.50 Chd free. Sat, Sun May 18, 19 (12-5). Open for groups by appt, please Tel 015394 37271*

Scarthwaite ⚘ (Mr & Mrs E C Hicks) Grange-in-Borrowdale. From Keswick take B5289 to Grange; cross on road bridge, suitable for mini buses, house ¼m on L. ¼m walk from far side of bridge for coach parties. Ferns, cottage garden plants and many others closely packed into ⅓ acre. *Adm £1.50 Acc chd free. Private visits and parties welcome, please Tel 01768 777 233*

Sizergh Castle &⚘❀ (The National Trust) nr Kendal. Close to and W of the main A6 trunk road, 3m S of Kendal. An approach road leaves A6 close to and S of A6/A591 interchange. ⅔-acre Limestone Rock Garden largest owned by the National Trust; large collection of Japanese maples, dwarf conifers, hardy ferns, primulas, gentians and many perennials and bulbs; water garden with bog and aquatic plants; on walls around main lawn are shrubs and climbers, many half-hardy; rose garden contains specimen roses along with shrubs, climbers, ground cover and lilies; wild flower banks, herbaceous border, crab apple orchard with spring bulbs and 'Dutch' garden. *Castle & gdn adm £3.30 Chd £1.70; Gdn adm £1.70 Chd 90p. ▲For NGS Sat June 22 (12.30-5.30)*

Stagshaw ⚘ (The National Trust) ½m S of Ambleside. Turn E off A 591, Ambleside to Windermere rd. Bus 555 Kendal-Keswick alight Waterhead. Woodland gdn incl fine collection of rhododendrons and azaleas. Ericaceous trees & shrubs incl magnolias, camellias, embothriums. Views over Windermere. *Adm £1.20 Chd 60p.* ▲*For NGS Suns May 5, June 2 (10-5.30)*

Station House ⌒⚘ (Mr & Mrs G H Simons) Wright Green. Lamplugh approx 6m from Workington, White-haven and Cockermouth signposted off A5086 Lilyhall-Workington from Cockermouth-Egremont Rd ½m under disused railway line from Workington-Whitehaven A595 at Leyland roundabout take rd signposted Branthwaite-Loweswater. 2-acre garden created over site of disused railway line and station. Features shrubs and trees; ve-getable and fruit garden. Morning coffee/TEAS. *Adm £1 Chd 50p. Sun June 9 (10.30-4.30)*

Whitbysteads ⚘ (The Hon Mrs Anthony Lowther) Ask-ham nr Penrith 8m from Penrith. Turn R at Eamont Bridge off the A6. Turn L at Y fork after Railway Bridge signed Askham. Through village, turn R at Queen's Head. 1-acre garden on several levels surrounding farmhouse on edge of fells, featuring wide variety shrub roses, un-usual herbaceous plants and geraniums. Pergola; foun-tain. Magnificent views over Eden Valley. TEAS. *Adm £1.50 Chd free (Share to St Michael & All Angels Church, Lowther®). Sun June 30 (2-5)*

¶**Winderwath** ⚘⚘ (Miss Jane Pollock) 5m E of Penrith N of A66. Mature garden laid out at turn of C19 with in-teresting trees and borders. Recently established rock garden with many specialist alpines. Surplus plants and secondhand garden tools for sale. TEA. *Adm £1.50 Acc chd free (Share to Cliburn Church®). March to Oct Mon-Fri (10-4) Suns May to Sept (2-6) For NGS April 21 (1-5)*

¶**Windy Hall** ⚘⚘ (Diane & David Kinsman) Crook Road, Windermere. 8m from Kendal on B5284 ½m after Win-dermere golf club on L up Linthwaite Country House Hotel driveway. From Bowness-on-Windermere take Ken-dal Rd A5074 and turn up B5284 driveway on R. Garden of 3-4 acres maintained by owners and developed from a wilderness over past 15 years. Woodland garden, herba-ceous and alpine gardens, water gardens and large kit-chen garden. Wide variety of plants, especially rhododendrons, camellias, magnolias, sorbus, hydrangeas and many climbers. Special collections of aconitum, arun-cus and filipendula. Waterfowl garden with many species of ducks and geese, stewartias and awesome gunneras. Rarebreed sheep. TEAS. *Adm £1.50 Chd 25p. Wed May 29, Sun June 30 (10-6) Private visits and parties by appt, please* Tel 015394 46238

Wood Hall ⚘⚘ (Mr & Mrs W Jackson) Cockermouth. Entrance to drive in large lay-by ¼m N (towards Carlisle) off the A595/A594 roundabout nr Cockermouth. A 5½-acre Thomas Mawson garden, with terraces, walls, small feature gardens, lawns, woods and paths. Venerable trees and newer planting. Alpines, shrubs and herbaceous plants. *Adm £1.50 and Acc chd free. Private visits and par-ties welcome, please* Tel 01900 823585

Yews ⚘⚘ (Sir Oliver & Lady Scott) Bowness-on-Winder-mere. Middle Entrance Drive, 50yds. Medium-sized for-mal Edwardian garden; fine trees, ha-ha, herbaceous borders. TEAS. *Adm £1.50 Chd free (Share to Marie Curie Cancer Care®). Sun June 23 (2-5.30)*

Gardens open under Scotland's Gardens Scheme

Argrennan House ⌒ (Robert Reddaway & Tulane Kidd) Castle Douglas 3½m, Kirkcudbright 3½m on A711. Geor-gian house (not open) set in beautiful parkland with spe-cimen trees. A large walled garden with traditional herbaceous borders, shrub borders and rose garden. Water garden with box parterres and 1840 rockery. Woodland walks. Water garden, ponds and bog gardens. TEAS served in old kitchen. *Adm £1.50 Chd 50p (Share to Crossroads Care Attendant Scheme, Stewartry branch®). Sun July 14 (2-5)*

Craigieburn Garden ⚘ (Janet Wheatcroft) Moffat. 2m E of Moffat on A708 Selkirk rd round bad bends on L, not R. Parking limited. A plantsman's garden specialising in plants of SE Asia. A spectacular gorge and sheltered woodland provide ideal conditions for the National Col-lection of Meconopsis. Also formal borders, roses, bog garden, peat beds and alpines. Specialist plant nursery. *Adm £1.50 Chd free (Share to Gurkha Welfare Trust®). Suns June 9, Sept 1 (12.30-8)*

Dalswinton House ⚘ (Sir David & Lady Landale) Auld-girth. Dumfries 7m. Dumfries/Auldgirth bus via Kirkton stops at lodge. Woodland and lochside walks. Cake and plant stall. Home baked TEAS. *Adm £1.50 (Share to Kirk-mahoe Parish Church®). Sun June 2 (2-5)*

Hensol ⌒⚘ (Lady Henderson) Castle Douglas. A762, 3m N of Laurieston. Cars free. An early C19 granite house designed by Lugar. Established garden surrounding house. Alpines, shrubs, water garden and new woodland garden. River walks. TEA in house. *Adm £1.50 Chd 50p (Share to RNLI®). Sun July 21 (2-5)*

Scotland's Gardens Scheme. The National Gardens Scheme has a similar but quite separate counterpart in Scotland. Called Scotland's Gardens Scheme, it raises money for the Queen's Nursing Institute (Scotland), the Gardens Fund of the National Trust for Scotland and over 160 registered charities nominated by garden owners. The Handbook is available (£3.25 incl p&p) from Scotland's Gardens Scheme, 31 Castle Terrace, Edinburgh EH1 2EL. Telephone 0131-229-1870 Fax 0131-229-0443

Derbyshire

Hon County Organiser:

Mr & Mrs R Brown, 210 Nottingham Rd, Woodlinkin, Langley Mill, Nottingham NG16 4HG Tel 01773 714903

Hon County Treasurer:

Mrs G Nutland, 4 Sadler Close, Adel, Leeds LS16 8NN

DATES OF OPENING

March 31 Sunday
Bluebell Arboretum, Smisby
Bowbridge House, Mackworth

April 3 Wednesday
Bluebell Arboretum, Smisby

April 14 Sunday
32 Heanor Road, Codnor
Meynell Langley, Kirk Langley ‡
Radburne Hall, nr Derby ‡
Shottle Hall Guest House, Belper

April 21 Sunday
Field House Farm, Rosliston,
nr Burton-on-Trent

April 24 Wednesday
Bluebell Arboretum, Smisby ‡
Field House Farm, Rosliston,
nr Burton-on-Trent ‡

April 28 Sunday
Bowbridge House, Mackworth
Fir Croft, Calver, nr Bakewell
The Riddings, Kirk Ireton

May 5 Sunday
Bluebell Arboretum, Smisby
Cherry Tree Cottage, Hilton

May 6 Monday
Cherry Tree Cottage, Hilton

May 11 Saturday
Broomfield College, Morley

May 12 Sunday
Broomfield College, Morley
Fir Croft, Calver, nr Bakewell
The Limes, Apperknowle

May 15 Wednesday
Bath House Farm, Ashover ‡
Oaks Lane Farm, Brockhurst ‡

May 19 Sunday
Dam Farm House, Yeldersley
Lane, Ednaston
Field House Farm, Rosliston,
nr Burton-on-Trent
The Limes, Apperknowle
Locko Park, Spondon
57 Portland Close, Mickleover

May 22 Wednesday
Field House Farm, Rosliston,
nr Burton-on-Trent

May 26 Sunday
Bowbridge House, Mackworth
Darley House, nr Matlock
Dove Cottage, Clifton, Ashbourne
The Limes, Apperknowle

June 2 Sunday
Dam Farm House, Yeldersley
Lane, Ednaston ‡

Fir Croft, Calver, nr Bakewell
Green Farm Cottage, Offcote,
nr Ashbourne
The Limes, Apperknowle
Thatched Farm, Radbourne ‡

June 6 Thursday
Kedleston Hall, Derby

June 9 Sunday
Bluebell Arboretum, Smisby
Cherry Tree Cottage, Hilton
Corner Cottage,
Osmaston-by-Ashbourne
Darley House, nr Matlock
Field Farm, Kirk Ireton

June 12 Wednesday
Bluebell Arboretum, Smisby

June 16 Sunday
Dam Farm House, Yeldersley
Lane, Ednaston
Field House Farm, Rosliston,
nr Burton-on-Trent
Fir Croft, Calver, nr Bakewell
32 Heanor Road, Codnor ‡
210 Nottingham Road,
Woodlinkin ‡
The Old Slaughterhouse, Shipley
Gate
57 Portland Close, Mickleover

June 19 Wednesday
Field House Farm, Rosliston,
nr Burton-on-Trent

June 23 Sunday
Birchwood Farm, Coxbench
Cashel, Kirk Ireton
Darley House, nr Matlock
Dove Cottage, Clifton, Ashbourne
42b Shop Lane, Nether Heage
Thatched Farm, Radbourne
White Gate, Arleston Meadows,
Derby

June 29 Saturday
Mount Cottage, Ticknall
Stainsborough Hall, Hopton,
nr Wirksworth

June 30 Sunday
Bowbridge House, Mackworth
Cherry Tree Cottage, Hilton
32 Heanor Road, Codnor
Mount Cottage, Ticknall
Oaks Lane Farm, Brockhurst
Tudor House Farm, Kirk Langley
White Gate, Arleston Meadows,
Derby

July 7 Sunday
Fanshawe Gate Hall, Holmesfield
32 Heanor Road, Codnor ‡

Lea Gardens, nr Matlock
The Limes, Apperknowle
159 Longfield Lane, Ilkeston
23 Mill Lane, Codnor ‡

July 10 Wednesday
Fanshawe Gate Hall, Holmesfield
Oaks Lane Farm, Brockhurst

July 13 Saturday
Fanshawe Gate Hall, Holmesfield

July 14 Sunday
Bath House Farm, Ashover
Bluebell Arboretum, Smisby ‡
Dam Farm House, Yeldersley
Lane, Ednaston
Darley House, nr Matlock
Dove Cottage, Clifton, Ashbourne
Field Farm, Kirk Ireton
Field House Farm, Rosliston,
nr Burton-on-Trent ‡
Hardwick Hall, Doe Lea
Lea Hurst, nr Matlock

July 17 Wednesday
Bluebell Arboretum, Smisby ‡
Field House Farm, Rosliston,
nr Burton-on-Trent ‡

July 20 Saturday
Tissington Hall, nr Ashbourne

July 21 Sunday
Corner Cottage,
Osmaston-by-Ashbourne ‡
Daisy Hill Cottage, Longford ‡
32 Heanor Road, Codnor
The Limes, Apperknowle
Shottle Hall Guest House,
Belper

July 24 Wednesday
Calke Abbey, Ticknall

July 28 Sunday
Dove Cottage, Clifton,
Ashbourne
The Limes, Apperknowle

August 4 Sunday
32 Heanor Road, Codnor ‡
23 Mill Lane, Codnor ‡

August 11 Sunday
Bluebell Arboretum, Smisby
Dam Farm House, Yeldersley
Lane, Ednaston

August 14 Wednesday
Bluebell Arboretum, Smisby

August 18 Sunday
Dove Cottage, Clifton, Ashbourne
White Gate, Arleston Meadows,
Derby

August 26 Monday
Tissington Hall, nr Ashbourne

September 11 Wednesday
Bluebell Arboretum, Smisby
September 14 Saturday
Broomfield College, Morley
September 15 Sunday
Broomfield College, Morley
September 29 Sunday
Bowbridge House, Mackworth
October 16 Wednesday
Bluebell Arboretum, Smisby

October 20 Sunday
Bluebell Arboretum, Smisby

Regular openings
For details see garden description

Lea Gardens
Renishaw Hall, nr Sheffield

By appointment only
For telephone numbers and other details see garden descriptions. Private visits welcomed

Birchfield, Ashford in the Water
Darley House, nr Matlock
Gamesley Fold, Glossop
Valezina Hillside, Heage

DESCRIPTION OF GARDEN

Bath House Farm &✿❀ (Mr & Mrs Hetherington) Ashover. 4½m N of Matlock on A632 Chesterfield Rd. Take 1st R after leaving village of Kelstedge and next R at T-junction. Overlooking Ashover and with extensive views this recently landscaped garden has a wide variety of heathers and mixed borders and a large water feature with waterfall, pond and stream surrounded by well chosen plants and rare shrubs and trees. Recently planted dell for spring flowers. TEA. *Adm £1.50 Chd free. Wed May 15 (1-4.30), Sun July 14 (11-4.30) Private visits May to Sept by appt, please* **Tel 01246 590562**

Birchfield &✿ (Brian Parker) Dukes Drive, Ashford in the Water. 2m NW of Bakewell on A6 to Buxton. Beautifully situated terraced garden of approx ¾ acre mostly constructed within last 9 yrs. Designed for all-yr-round colour, it contains a wide variety of shrubs and perennials, bulbs, roses, water and scree gardens. Areas of copse with wild flowers are being developed in adjacent field. TEA. *Adm £1 Chd free (Share to Bakewell and District Mobile Physiotherapy Assoc®). Private visits welcome April to Sept, please* **Tel 01629 813800**

¶**Birchwood Farm** ✿❀ (Stuart & Janet Crooks) Coxbench. 5m N Derby. From A38 take B6179 by Little Chef through Little Eaton till first Xrds. Turn L then R over railway crossing and take rd to Holbrook. Car parking in field at top of drive. ⅓-acre garden enclosed within old brick and stone walls. This garden is for plant enthusiasts. The wide range of herbaceous plants incl hardy geraniums, penstemons, silver plants, campanulas, delphiniums, English roses and pond. Private nursery adjacent. TEA. *Adm £1.50 Chd free. Sun June 23 (2-5.30) Private visits also welcome, please* **Tel 01332 880685**

Bluebell Nursery & Woodland Garden &✿❀ (Robert & Suzette Vernon) Smisby. From the A50 Burton on Trent to Ashby-de-la-Zouch Rd, turn for Smisby by the Mother Hubbard Inn, 1m NW of Ashby. Arboretum is on L after ½m Annwell Lane. 5-acre embryo Arboretum planted in the last 4 yrs incl many young specimens of rare trees and shrubs. Wide range of interesting plants for sale. Bring wellingtons in wet weather. TEA. *Adm £1 Chd 50p (Share to MENCAP®). Suns March 31, June 9, July 14, Aug 11, Oct 20; Weds April 3, 24; May 5, June 12, July 17, Aug 14, Sept 11, Oct 16 (10-5). Private visits welcome, please* **Tel 01283 222091**

¶**Bowbridge House** &✿ (Richard & Jennifer Wood) Mackworth. On A52 Derby to Ashbourne Rd 3m W of Derby Ring Rd, on S side, just past the Little Chef. 4½-acre garden originally laid out in 1762 by William Eames. Extensively replanted since 1978 by present owners with rare and unusual trees, shrubs, climbers and herbaceous plants. Flowering sized magnolia campbelli; paulownia; numerous rhododendrons, shrub roses, 3 conservatories, ponds and vegetable garden. TEA *Adm £1.50 Chd free. Suns March 31, April 28, May 26, June 30, Sept 29 (2-6)*

Broomfield College &✿❀ Morley on A608, 4m N of Derby and 6m S of Heanor. Landscaped garden of 10 ha; shrubs, trees, rose collection, herbaceous borders; glasshouses; walled garden under restoration; garden tours and advice; demonstrations. Crafts, carvery lunches, refreshments. *Adm £1 Chd free. Sats, Suns May 11, 12, Sept 14, 15 (10.30-4.30)*

Calke Abbey ✿ (The National Trust) Ticknall. 9m S of Derby on A514 between Swadlincote and Melbourne. Extensive walled gardens constructed in 1773. Divided into flower garden, kitchen garden and physic garden. Restoration commenced in 1987. Surrounding the walled garden the pleasure ground has been re-fenced and replanting is underway. Phase 1 of orangery restoration just completed. Phase 2 subject to further fundraising. Lunches and TEAS. *Adm £2 Chd £1. Wed July 24 (11-5)*

Cashel ❀ (Anita & Jeremy Butt) Kirk Ireton. Turn off B5023 (Duffield-Wirksworth rd). 2m S of Wirksworth. Follow rd to Kirk Ireton take sharp R turn at church corner. Follow lane for 200 metres. Garden on R, car parking at top of garden, 100 metres beyond the house. 2½ acres of gradually developing garden situated on a sloping site with views of the Ecclesbourne Valley. Many interesting trees, plants and shrubs. TEAS in aid of local church. *Adm £1 Chd free. Sun June 23 (2-5). Private visits welcome, please* **Tel 01335 370495**

Cherry Tree Cottage ✿❀ (Mr & Mrs R Hamblin) Hilton. 7m W of Derby, turn off the A516 opp The Old Talbot Inn in village centre. Parking - small public car park in Main St. A plant lover's C18 garden, about ⅓-acre with herbaceous borders; herb garden; scree garden. Many unusual and interesting plants; specie aquilegias, old dianthus. Featured in several gardening magazines, 'Gardeners World' and Good Garden Guide. *Adm £1 Chd free. Suns May 5, June 9, 30, Mon May 6 (2-5). Groups welcome by appt. weekdays April, May, June only. Visitors also welcome to see snowdrops and hellebores early spring. Please* **Tel 01283 733778**

¶**Corner Cottage** ⚭🌸 (Alan & Lynn Poulter) Osmaston-by-Ashbourne. 2½m SE of Ashbourne in centre of village ½m off A52. Country garden of ½acre in unspoiled Victorian estate village. Started from scratch in 1990 and aimed at providing seasonal variety and colour around every corner. Pond and bog garden, rockery, formal walled garden, shrubs, herbaceous borders and annuals. Cream TEAS in village hall in aid of Look to the Future. *Adm £1 Chd free. Suns June 9, July 21 (1.30-5.30)*

Daisy Hill Cottage 🌸 (Peter and Joy Beales) On the edge of Longford, approx 9m due W of Derby. Cottage is situated on the lane from Longford to Sutton-on-the-Hill. Simple flower garden and vegetable and herb garden in about ⅓ of an acre. TEAS in aid of The Ashbourne Animal Welfare. *Adm £1 Chd free. Sun July 21 (2-5)*

Dam Farm House ♿⚭🌸 (Mrs J M Player) Yeldersley Lane, Ednaston, 5m SE of Ashbourne on A52, opp Ednaston Village turn, gate on right 500yds. 2-acre garden beautifully situated contains mixed borders, scree. Unusual plants have been collected many are propagated for sale. TEAS (some Suns). *Adm £2 Chd free. Suns June 2, July 14, Aug 11 (1.30-4). For NGS Suns May 19, June 16 (1.30-4). Private visits and groups welcome April 1 to Oct 31, please* **Tel 01335 360291**

Darley House ♿⚭🌸 (Mr & Mrs G H Briscoe) Darley Dale, 2m N of Matlock. On A6 to Bakewell. 1½ acres; originally set out by Sir Joseph Paxton in 1845; being restored by present owners; many rare plants, trees; balustrade and steps separating upper and lower garden, a replica of Haddon Hall. As featured on BBC 'Gardeners World'. Picture Gallery. Plants and extensive range of seeds available. TEA. *Adm £1.50 Chd free. Suns May 26, June 9, 23, July 14 (2-5). Private visits welcome for parties not more than 12, any other Sun May 19 to July 21 and Sept 8 to Oct 6, please* **Tel 01629 733341**

Dove Cottage ⚭🌸 (Anne and Stephen Liverman) Clifton. 1½m SW of Ashbourne. ¾-acre garden by R Dove extensively replanted and developed since 1979. Emphasis on establishing collections of hardy plants and shrubs incl alchemillas, alliums, berberis, geraniums, euphorbias, hostas, lilies, variegated and silver foliage plants inc astrantias. Plantsmans garden featured on Channel 4 'Garden Club', 'Good Garden Guide' and 'Gardeners World Cottage Garden 1995'. TEA. *Adm £1.50 Chd free (Share to British Heart Foundation®). Suns May 26, June 23, July 14, 28, Aug 18 (1-5). Private visits welcome, please* **Tel 01335 343545**

Fanshawe Gate Hall ⚭🌸 (Mr & Mrs John Ramsden) Holmesfield. Situated on the edge of the Peak National Park. 1m E of Holmesfield Village. Follow B6054 towards Owler Bar. 1st R turn after Robin Hood Inn. Marked Old Hall on OS map. C13 seat of the Fanshawe family. Old-fashioned cottage-style garden approx 2 acres. Many stone features, fine C16 dovecote. Upper walled garden with mixed borders, shrubs, climbers, herb plantings, water features, rose beds, terracing and lawns. Lower courtyard enhanced by small formal knot garden and herb border. The garden continues to develop with particular emphasis on plantings of old-fashioned unusual varieties with interest in variegated subjects. TEAS. *Adm £1.50*

Chd free (Share to Derbyshire Wildlife Trust®). Sat, Sun, Wed July 7, 10, 13 (11-5). Also private visits welcome; written application please **Tel 0114 2890391**

¶**Field Farm** 🌸 (Graham & Irene Dougan) Kirk Ireton. Leave B5023 Duffield-Wirksworth Rd 2m S of Wirksworth and follow rd to Kirk Ireton. Continue up Main St, turn L past 'Barley Mow' towards Hulland, and on sharp R-hand bend find a farm track (Field Lane) ahead. Field Farm 300m on L. Parking in field. 1½-acre hilltop garden, planted since 1981 by present owners. Herbaceous borders, shrubs and trees in informal planting, alpines and dwarf conifers, shrub and old-fashioned roses make a garden for yr-round interest. Many plants grown for their perfume and foliage. Colourful display of containers in yard during summer months. TEA in aid of local WI. *Adm £1 Chd free. Suns June 9, July 14 (2-5) Private visits welcome by appt, please* **Tel 01335 370958**

Field House Farm ♿⚭🌸 (Keith & Judy Thompson) Rosliston. From junction 11 (M42) take A444 NW to Castle Gresley. Turn L to Linton and Rosliston. From A38 turn E at Barton Turns fly-over on to Walton-on-Trent Rd (width restriction). From Walton follow signs to Rosliston. Farm is signposted up drive between Rosliston and Coton-in-the-Elms. An artistic plant collector's ¾-acre farmhouse garden with some unusual features. 2 ponds, mature shrubs, spring bulbs, 'dry' bog garden, secret garden, stone garden, wildlife garden and herbaceous borders. Incl many hardy geraniums, hostas and penstemons. TEAS. *Adm £1 Chd free. Suns, Weds, April 21, 24, May 19, 22, June 16, 19, July 14, 17 (2-6). Private visits of 10 & over welcome, please* **Tel 01283 761472**

Fir Croft ⚭🌸 (Dr & Mrs S B Furness) Froggatt Rd, Calver, Via Sheffield. 4m N of Bakewell; between Q8 filling station and junction of B6001 with B6054. Plantsman's garden; rockeries; water garden and nursery; extensive collection (over 2000 varieties) of alpines, conifers. New tufa and scree beds. *Collection box. Nursery opens every Sat, Sun, Mon (1-6) March to Dec. Adjacent garden for NGS Suns April 28, May 12, June 2, 16 (2-6)*

Gamesley Fold Cottage ⚭🌸 (Mr & Mrs G Carr) Glossop. Off Glossop-Marple Rd nr Charlesworth, turn down the lane directly opp St Margaret's School, Gamesley. White cottage at the bottom. Old-fashioned cottage garden down a country lane with lovely views of surrounding countryside. A spring garden planted with herbaceous borders, wild flowers and herbs in profusion to attract butterflies and wildlife. Featured in Good Housekeeping and Good Gardens Guide. TEAS. *Adm £1 Chd free. Private visits and groups May and June daily, please* **Tel 014578 67856**

The National Gardens Scheme is a charity which traces its origins back to 1927. Since then it has raised a total of over £14 million for charitable purposes.

Regular Openers. Too many days to include in diary. Usually there is a wide range of plants giving year-round interest. See end of county section for the name and garden description for times etc.

Green Farm Cottage ✿❀ (Mr & Mrs Peter Bussell) Off-cote nr Ashbourne. 1½m NE of Ashbourne on T-junction Bradley-Kniveton-Ashbourne. Take Wirksworth Rd out of Ashbourne (B5035) and follow Offcote signpost (approx 1¼m from main rd). ⅓-acre plantsman's garden designed, constructed and maintained from a wilderness in 1978 by the present owners. Flower-filled terraces, lush lawns, and an impressive variety of perennials, shrubs and trees; greenhouse, vegetable plot and small orchard area. Beautiful rural views. TEA and plants in aid of Ashbourne Animal Welfare. *Adm £1 Acc chd free. Sun June 2 (2-5). Private visits welcome April to Aug, please* **Tel 01335 343803**

Hardwick Hall ♿✿❀ (The National Trust) Doe Lea, 8m SE of Chesterfield. S of A617. Grass walks between yew and hornbeam hedges; cedar trees; herb garden; herbaceous and rose borders. Finest example of Elizabethan house in the country. Restaurant in Old Kitchens. TEAS on days the Hall is open. *Adm hall and garden £5.50 Chd £2.70 garden only £2.50 Chd £1. Sun July 14 (12-5.30 last entry 4.30)*

32 Heanor Road ♿✿❀ (Mr & Mrs Eyre) 300yds from Codnor Market Place on A6007 towards Heanor. Down lane at side of Hunt's shop, last bungalow on L. Parking in adjacent field. 1-acre garden with lawns, variety of trees, shrubs, mixed borders, rockery, scree; 2 ponds, pergola. Prize winning garden. TEA. *Adm £1 Chd free (Share to Multiple Sclerosis Research®). Suns April 14, June 16, 30, July 7, 21 Aug 4 (2-5). Private visits welcome, please* **Tel 01773 746626**

Kedleston Hall ♿✿ (The National Trust) 3m NW of Derby. Signposted from junction of A38/A52. 12-acre garden. A broad open lawn, bounded by a ha-ha, marks the C18 informal garden. A formal layout to the W was introduced early this century when the summerhouse and orangery, both designed by George Richardson late C18, were moved to their present position. The gardens are seen at their best during May and June when the azaleas and rhododendrons are one mass of colour. The Long Walk, a woodland walk of some 3m, is bright with spring flowers. Guided walk of gardens and Long Walk at 2pm. TEA. *Adm £1.50 Chd 75p. Thurs June 6 (11-5)*

● **Lea Gardens** ♿❀ (Mr & Mrs Tye) Lea, 5m SE of Matlock off A6. A rare collection of rhododendrons, azaleas, kalmias, alpines and conifers in a delightful woodland setting. Light lunches, TEAS, home-baking. Coaches by appt. *Adm £2.50 Chd 50p daily, season ticket £3.50. Daily March 20 to July 7 (10-7)*

Lea Hurst (Residential Home) ✿❀ (Royal Surgical Aid Society) Holloway. 6m SE of Matlock off A6, nr Yew Tree Inn, Holloway. Former home (not open) of Florence Nightingale. Large garden consisting of rose beds, herbaceous borders, new shrubbery incl varieties, ornamental pond, all set in beautiful countryside. New wildlife garden 1994. TEAS in aid of RSAS. *Adm £1 Chd under 16 free. Sun July 14 (2-5)*

The Limes ♿❀ (Mr & Mrs W Belton) Crow Lane, Apperknowle, 6m N of Chesterfield; from A61 at Unstone turn E for 1m to Apperknowle; 1st house past Unstone Grange. Bus: Chesterfield or Sheffield to Apperknowle. 2½ acres

with herbaceous borders, lily ponds, roses and flowering shrubs, scree beds & rockeries; hundreds of naturalised daffodils and formal bedding with massed bedding of pansies in the spring, geraniums and bedding plants in summer. Putting green and large natural pond with ducks and geese. Nature trail over 5 acres. Home-made TEAS. *Adm £1 Chd 25p. Suns May 12, 19, 26; June 2, July 7, 21, 28 (2-6). Coach, private parties and evening visits of 10 and over, welcome, please* **Tel 01246 412338**

Locko Park ❀ Spondon, 6m NE of Derby. From A52 Borrowash bypass, 2m N➤via B6001, turn to Spondon. Large garden; pleasure gardens; rose gardens. House by Smith of Warwick with Victorian additions. Chapel, Charles II, with original ceiling. TEA. *Adm £1 Chd 30p. Sun May 19 (2-5)*

159 Longfield Lane ♿✿❀ (David & Diane Bennett) Ilkeston (Stanton side) off Quarry Hill, opp Hallam Fields Junior School. A house in a garden, a large, informal over-flowing garden that works for its owners with fruit, shrubs, flowers, two small fish ponds and a conservatory. A strong emphasis on texture, colour and lots of unexpected corners. 'Beautiful Erewash' commended 1994/5. Home-made TEAS. *Adm £1 Chd free. Sun July 7 (2-5.30). Private visits of 6 and under welcome, May to July, please* **Tel 01159 325238**

Meynell Langley ♿❀ (Godfrey Meynell Esq) Between Mackworth and Kirk Langley on A52 Derby-Ashbourne rd. Turn in at green iron gate by grey stone lodge on N side of road. Trees, lawns, daffodils, lake, views. TEAS in Regency country house. *Adm £1.50 Chd 50p. (Share to St Michael's Church®). Sun April 14 (2-6)*

23 Mill Lane ♿✿❀ (Mrs S Jackson) Codnor. 12m NW of Nottingham. A610 Ripley 10m N of Derby, A38 Ripley. 2 car parks nearby. Lawns, herbaceous borders, small pond, waterfall; fruit trees; clematis. Amber Valley 'Best Kept Garden' competition 2nd 1994. TEA. *Adm £1 Chd free. Suns July 7, Aug 4 (11-6). Private visits also welcome June to Sept, please* **Tel 01773 745707**

Mount Cottage ✿❀ (Mr & Mrs J T Oliver) 52 Main Street, Ticknall, 9m S Derby, adjacent entrance Calke Abbey NT. Medium-sized cottage garden, herbaceous borders, shrubs, lawns, small pool area, numerous roses, surrounding C18 cottage. TEAS outdoors weather permitting. *Adm £1 Chd free. Sat, Sun June 29, 30 (1-5)*

210 Nottingham Rd (Mr & Mrs R Brown) Woodlinkin, nr Codnor; A610. ½-acre; collections of old, modern shrub and climbing roses; geraniums; shrubs; trees. TEA. *Adm £1 Chd free. Sun June 16 (2-5)*

Oaks Lane Farm ✿❀ (Mr & Mrs J R Hunter) Brockhurst, Ashover nr Chesterfield. At Kelstedge 4m from Matlock on A632 Chesterfield Rd, just above Kelstedge Inn, turn L up narrow rd, then turn R ½m, garden is 150yds on R. Partly suitable for wheelchairs. ¾-acre informal plantsman's garden in beautiful situation with herbaceous borders, natural streams and pond. Small bog garden. Many varieties of hostas, euphorbia and old-fashioned roses. Partially suitable for wheelchairs. TEA. *Adm £1.50 Chd free. Wed May 15, Sun June 30, Wed July 10 (1-5). Open by appt May 1 to Aug 31, please* **Tel 01246 590324**

The Old Slaughterhouse &❀ (Robert & Joyce Peck) Shipley Gate. 1m S of Eastwood, take Church St from Sun Inn traffic lights, and over A610, L to narrow rd to Shipley Boat Inn; parking near Shipley Lock (Erewash Canal) and Inn. ¾-acre long, narrow garden, restored from overgrown ash tip since 1984; 200-yrs-old stone aqueduct over river; over 400 trees planted; hidden pond; pleasant extra walks in Erewash Valley (canal and river sides). TEA. *Adm £1 Chd free. Sun June 16 (2-6). Private visits welcome, please* **Tel 01773 768625**

57 Portland Close &❀ (Mr & Mrs A L Ritchie) Mickleover. Approx 3m W of Derby, turn R off B5020 Cavendish Way then 2nd L into Portland Close. Small plantsman's garden, wide variety of unusual bulbs, alpines and herbaceous plants. Special interest in sink gardens, hostas, named varieties of primulas (single and double); auriculas (show, border, alpine and doubles), violas and hardy geraniums. Featured in 'Good Garden Guide'. *Adm £1 Chd free under 16. Suns, May 19, June 16 (2-5.30). Private visits also welcome of 10 and over, please* **Tel 01332 515450**

Radburne Hall ❀ (Mrs J W Chandos-Pole) Radburne, Kirk Langley, 5m W of Derby. W of A52 Derby-Ashbourne rd; off Radburne Lane. Large landscape garden; large display of daffodils; shrubs; formal rose terraces; fine trees and view. Hall (not open) is 7-bay Palladian mansion built c1734 by Smith of Warwick. Ice-house in garden. *Adm £1 Chd 50p. Sun April 14 (2.30-6)*

Renishaw Hall &❀ (Sir Reresby & Lady Sitwell) Renishaw. Renishaw Hall is situated equidistant 6m from both Sheffield and Old Chesterfield on A616 2m from its junction with M1 at exit 30. Italian style garden with terraces, old ponds, yew hedges and pyramids laid out by Sir George Sitwell c1900. Interesting collection of herbaceous plants and shrubs; nature trail; museum; lakeside walk. Shop provides wine, souvenirs, antiques; also a musuem. TEAS. *Adm £3 OAPs £2 Chd £1. Every Fri, Sat, Sun and Bank Hol Mons April 5 to Sept 15. Mons April 8, May 6, 27, Aug 26 (10.30-4.30). Private parties of 20 and over welcome, please* **Tel 01246 432042**

The Riddings Farm ❀❀ (The Spencer Family) Kirk Ireton between Ashbourne and Wirksworth. Leave Kirk Ireton via Gorsey Lane (close to Barley Mow). Turn L at T-junction onto Broom Lane. 1st R into Hays Lane. Alternatively, a pleasant ½m lakeside walk from Severn - Trents Millfields Car Park. Informal hillside garden, about ¾ acre, created since 1979 and still developing, with lovely views over Carsington Water. Emphasis on foliage, yr-round colour and wildlife habitats. Unusual plants propagated for adjacent nursery. TEA. *Adm £1 Chd free. Sun April 28 (2-5). Private visits welcome, please* **Tel 01335 370331**

¶**42b Shop Lane** ❀ (Mrs P Longley) Nether Heage. 200yds from Village PO towards 'Guide Post'. Village is near Ambergate by A6. Young trees, shrubs, rhododendrons, camellias and herbaceous plants. Selection of ferns, grasses and herbs. Climbers incl roses and clematis, with water features and items of local interest. TEAS *Adm £1.50 Chd free. Sun June 23 (2-5) Private visits welcome, please* **Tel 01773 856900**

Shottle Hall Guest House ❀ (Mr & Mrs P Matthews) Belper. Off B5023 Duffield to Wirksworth Rd. 200yds N of Xrds (Railway Inn) with A517 Ashbourne to Belper Rd. 2½ acres natural garden featuring shrubs; roses; bedding plants; bulbs; small herbaceous border and lawns. Cream TEAS. *Adm £1 Chd under 12 free. Suns April 14, July 21 (2-5)*

Stainsborough Hall &❀ (Mr & Mrs Twogood) Wirksworth. On B5035 Wirksworth to Ashbourne Rd. 1½m W of Wirksworth take L turning to Kirk Ireton, house ¼m on R. Set in a wide valley to the N of Carsington Water, this country garden abounds with flowers and birds. The stone house and buildings merge delightfully with lawns, shrubs, roses and flower beds designed informally on different levels to provide meandering walks and pleasantly sited resting places. Covering some 2 acres, the garden incl many young trees, shrubs, herbaceous borders and rose beds. A duck pond with a variety of domestic ducks adds to the tranquillity of the scene. Cream TEAS. *Adm £1 Chd free. Sat June 29 (2-6)*

Thatched Farm &❀❀ (Mr & Mrs R A Pegram) Radbourne. Exit A52 Derby-Ashbourne road. 2m N of Derby Ring Road. A 2-acre plant lover's garden created from meadowland since 1987 and still being developed. The garden and courtyard surround a C17 listed farmhouse set in tranquil parkland. Many rare and unusual plants grown from seed collected from around the world. Mediterranean and island beds, troughs and alpines in raised beds, wild garden. Trees, shrubs and herbaceous perennials, extensive collection of tender perennials. 2 ponds and bog garden. As featured in Country Homes Magazine Aug 95. Home-made cream TEAS. *Adm £1.50 Chd free (Share to RELATE® June 2 & Parkinson's Disease Soc®June 23). Suns June 2, 23 (2-6). Private parties also welcome, please* **Tel 01332 824507**

Tissington Hall ❀❀ (Sir Richard FitzHerbert, Bt) N of Ashbourne. E of A515. Large garden; roses, herbaceous borders. Tea available in village. Please park considerately. *Adm £1 Chd free. Sat July 20, Mon Aug 26 (2-5). Parties by written appt only on other days*

Tudor House Farm ❀❀ (Mr & Mrs G Spencer) Kirk Langley. 4½m N of Derby on A52 Ashbourne Rd. Take turning towards Dalbury Lees and Longford, garden 400yds on R. ¼-acre garden on two levels. Mixed beds of shrubs and perennials; small fish and lily pond; heathers and alpine troughs. TEAS. *Adm £1 Chd free. Sun June 30 (2-5)*

Valezina Hillside ❀❀ (Mr & Mrs P Bowler) Heage. Between Ripley and Belper, further details on arranging appt. A butterfly/wildlife garden of ½ acre adjacent to open countryside. In parts steeply sloping, can be slippery. Mini-habitats incl a buddleia wilderness and wildlife pond. A small hillside meadow and woodland garden are overlooked by a cottage garden rich in butterfly nectar plants. Essentially kept wild (but controlled) in order to maintain a permanent breeding habitat for over 20 species of butterfly who have been encouraged to stay since 1985. Totally informal with a profusion of wild flowers. TEA. *Adm £1 Chd free (Share to Hedgehog Rescue Soc®). Private visits welcome May to Sept. Butterflies most numerous in July and Aug but numbers vary greatly with weather trends. Please* **Tel 01773 853099**

¶**White Gate** ⚥ (Mrs Judy Beba-Thompson) Arleston Meadows, Derby. From A5111 (Ring Rd) turn off S at Forester's Leisure Park onto Sinfin Lane and follow signs for Arleston for 2½m. At Xrds turn L into Wragley Way from A38, turn off at Findern through village for 3m, turn L at Littleover turn, over new by-pass then 1m and R into Wragley Way. Please park in Wragley Way. Garden signed through cutting by bus stop after Hobkirk Drive. Very small colour-themed garden, recently created by owners, with around 80 clematis and over 70 varieties of rose; hardy geraniums; spring and summer bulbs; tiny white garden; 2 ponds; lots of pots. TEAS in aid of WI. *Adm £1 Acc chd free. Suns June 23, 30, Aug 18 (1.30-5.30) Private visits and groups welcome by appt May to August, please* **Tel 01332 763653**

Devon

Hon County Organiser:	Mervyn T Feesey Esq., Woodside, Higher Raleigh Rd, Barnstaple EX31 4JA Tel 01271 43095
Assistant County Organisers:	
Exeter & E Devon	Mrs Ruth Charter, Ravenhill, Long Dogs Lane, Ottery St Mary EX11 1HX Tel 01404 814798
Tiverton & N E Devon	Mrs Diane Rowe, Little Southey, Northcott, Nr Cullompton EX15 3LT Tel 01884 840545
Bovey Tracey & Central Devon	Miss Elizabeth Hebditch, Bibbery, Higher Bibbery, Bovey Tracey TQ13 9RT Tel 01626 833344
Torbay & Dartmouth	Major David Molloy, Mulberry House, Kingswear TQ6 OBY Tel 01803 752307
Kingsbridge & South Devon	Mrs Sheila Blake, Higher Homefield, Sherford, Kingsbridge TQ7 2AT Tel 01548 531229
Plymouth & SW Devon	Mrs Sharin Court, Westpark, Yealmpton, Nr Plymouth PL8 2HP Tel 01752 880236

DATES OF OPENING

February 25 Sunday
Yonder Hill, Colaton Raleigh
March 10 Sunday
The Pines, Salcombe
March 17 Sunday
Bickham House, Kenn, nr Exeter
The Pines, Salcombe
Yonder Hill, Colaton Raleigh
March 23 Saturday
The Pines, Salcombe
March 24 Sunday
Higher Knowle, nr Bovey Tracey
38 Phillipps Avenue, Exmouth
The Pines, Salcombe
March 27 Wednesday
Westpark, Yealmpton
March 31 Sunday
Fast Rabbit Farm, Ash, Dartmouth
Gorwell House, nr Barnstaple
Higher Knowle, nr Bovey Tracey
Metcombe Brake, Higher
   Metcombe
Penrose, Crediton
Westpark, Yealmpton
April 5 Friday
Wylmington Hayes, nr Honiton
April 6 Saturday
Wylmington Hayes, nr Honiton

April 7 Sunday
Bickham Barton, Roborough
Bundels, Sidbury
Fast Rabbit Farm, Ash, Dartmouth
Higher Knowle, nr Bovey Tracey
38 Phillipps Avenue, Exmouth
The Pines, Salcombe
Wylmington Hayes, nr Honiton
Yonder Hill, Colaton Raleigh
April 8 Monday
Bickham Barton, Roborough
Fast Rabbit Farm, Ash, Dartmouth
1 Feebers Cottage, Westwood
Higher Knowle, nr Bovey Tracey
The Pines, Salcombe
Wylmington Hayes, nr Honiton
Yonder Hill, Colaton Raleigh
April 11 Thursday
Whitmore, nr Chittlehamholt
April 14 Sunday
Ash Thomas & Brithem Bottom
   Gardens
Bickham Barton, Roborough
Dippers, Shaugh Prior, nr
   Plymouth
Higher Knowle, nr Bovey Tracey
Meadowcroft, Plympton
8 Phillipps Avenue, Exmouth
Saltram House, Plymouth
Wylmington Hayes, nr Honiton

April 18 Thursday
Little Cumbre, Exeter
April 21 Sunday
Andrew's Corner, nr Okehampton
Bickham Barton, Roborough
Bickham House, Kenn, nr Exeter
Coleton Fishacre, Kingswear
Fast Rabbit Farm, Ash, Dartmouth
1 Feebers Cottage, Westwood
Higher Knowle, nr Bovey Tracey
Killerton Garden, Broadclyst
Wylmington Hayes, nr Honiton
April 24 Wednesday
Meadowcroft, Plympton
April 25 Thursday
Greenway Gardens, Churston
   Ferrers
April 28 Sunday
Bickham Barton, Roborough
Castle Drogo, Drewsteignton
Gorwell House, nr Barnstaple
Hartland Abbey, nr Bideford
Higher Knowle, nr Bovey Tracey
Knightshayes Gardens,
   nr Tiverton
Membland Villa, Newton Ferrers
Metcombe Brake, Higher
   Metcombe
Wylmington Hayes, nr Honiton
Yonder Hill, Colaton Raleigh

May 1 Wednesday
St Olaves, nr Chagford
May 2 Thursday
Greenway Gardens, Churston
  Ferrers
May 4 Saturday
Cleave House, Sticklepath
Mothecombe House, Holbeton
May 5 Sunday
Andrew's Corner, nr Okehampton
Bickham Barton, Roborough
Bundels, Sidbury
Cleave House, Sticklepath
Fast Rabbit Farm, Ash, Dartmouth
Hamblyn's Coombe, Dittisham
Higher Knowle, nr Bovey Tracey
The Lodge, Mannamead
Meadowcroft, Plympton
Mothecombe House, Holbeton
The Old Glebe, Eggesford
38 Phillipps Avenue, Exmouth
Starveacre, nr Axminster
Wylmington Hayes, nr Honiton
Yonder Hill, Colaton Raleigh
May 6 Monday
Bickham Barton, Roborough
Broadhembury House,
  Broadhembury
Fast Rabbit Farm, Ash, Dartmouth
Hamblyn's Coombe, Dittisham
Higher Knowle, nr Bovey Tracey
Little Upcott Gardens, Marsh
  Green
Meadowcroft, Plympton
Membland Villa, Newton
  Ferrers
The Old Glebe, Eggesford
Shobrooke Park Gardens, Crediton
Wylmington Hayes, nr Honiton
Yonder Hill, Colaton Raleigh
May 8 Wednesday
Lukesland, Ivybridge
St Olaves, nr Chagford
May 12 Sunday
Arlington Court, nr Barnstaple
Bickham Barton, Roborough
Broadhembury House,
  Broadhembury
Dippers, Shaugh Prior,
  nr Plymouth
Higher Knowle, nr Bovey Tracey
Higher Warcombe, Kingsbridge
Ivy Cottage, Heanton, nr Braunton
Lukesland, Ivybridge
Membland Villa, Newton Ferrers
The Old Mill, Blakewell
The Rectory, East Portlemouth
Saltram House, Plymouth
Wylmington Hayes, nr Honiton
May 15 Wednesday
Little Upcott Gardens, Marsh
  Green
May 16 Thursday
Little Cumbre, Exeter

May 18 Saturday
Ottery St Mary Gardens
Wolford Lodge, nr Honiton
Wood Barton, Kentisbeare
May 19 Sunday
Bickham Barton, Roborough
Bickham House, Kenn, nr Exeter
Broadhembury House,
  Broadhembury
The Cider House, Yelverton
Coleton Fishacre, Kingswear
Fast Rabbit Farm, Ash, Dartmouth
1 Feebers Cottage, Westwood
The Glebe House, Whitestone,
  nr Exeter
Higher Knowle, nr Bovey Tracey
Ottery St Mary Gardens
38 Phillipps Avenue, Exmouth
Wood Barton, Kentisbeare
Woodside, Barnstaple
Wylmington Hayes, nr Honiton
May 25 Saturday
Dartington Hall Gardens,
  nr Totnes
Little Upcott Gardens, Marsh
  Green
Monks Aish, South Brent
Sunrise Hill, Withleigh
Withleigh Farm, nr Tiverton
May 26 Sunday
Addisford Cottage, nr Dolton
Andrew's Corner, nr Okehampton
Bickham Barton, Roborough
Broadhembury House,
  Broadhembury
Bundels, Sidbury
Chevithorne Barton, nr Tiverton
Crosspark, Northlew
Dartington Hall Gardens,
  nr Totnes
Fast Rabbit Farm, Ash, Dartmouth
The Glebe House, Whitestone,
  nr Exeter
Gorwell House, nr Barnstaple
Higher Knowle, nr Bovey Tracey
Lee Ford, Budleigh Salterton
Little Upcott Gardens, Marsh
  Green
Metcombe Brake, Higher
  Metcombe
Monks Aish, South Brent
The Old Glebe, Eggesford
The Old Parsonage, Warkleigh
38 Phillipps Avenue, Exmouth
Purple Hayes, Halberton
Starveacre, nr Axminster
Topsham Gardens, nr Exeter
Twitchen Mill, nr South Molton
Withleigh Farm, nr Tiverton
Wylmington Hayes, nr Honiton
May 27 Monday
Alswood, George Nympton
Ash Thomas & Brithem Bottom
  Gardens

Bickham Barton, Roborough
Broadhembury House,
  Broadhembury
Crosspark, Northlew
Fast Rabbit Farm, Ash, Dartmouth
Higher Knowle, nr Bovey Tracey
Little Upcott Gardens, Marsh
  Green
Meadow Court, Slapton
Membland Villa, Newton Ferrers
The Old Glebe, Eggesford
Topsham Gardens, nr Exeter
Wylmington Hayes, nr Honiton
Yonder Hill, Colaton Raleigh
May 29 Wednesday
Little Upcott Gardens, Marsh
  Green
Stone Lane Gardens, nr Chagford
June 1 Saturday
Dicot, nr Chardstock
Hayne Old Manor,
  Moretonhampstead
Pleasant View Nursery, nr
  Newton Abbott
June 2 Sunday
Addisford Cottage, nr Dolton
Andrew's Corner, nr Okehampton
Beatlands Farm, Metcombe
Bickham Barton, Roborough
Bicton College of Agriculture
Broadhembury House,
  Broadhembury
Crosspark, Northlew
Dicot, nr Chardstock
Glebe Cottage, nr Warkleigh
The Glebe House, Whitestone,
  nr Exeter
Hayne Old Manor,
  Moretonhampstead
Ivy Cottage, Heanton,
  nr Braunton
Overbecks, Salcombe
38 Phillipps Avenue, Exmouth
Pleasant View Nursery,
  nr Newton Abbot
Vicar's Mead, East Budleigh
Wylmington Hayes, nr Honiton
June 3 Monday
Vicar's Mead, East Budleigh
June 4 Tuesday
Addisford Cottage, nr Dolton
Vicar's Mead, East Budleigh
June 5 Wednesday
Little Upcott Gardens, Marsh
  Green
Vicar's Mead, East Budleigh
June 6 Thursday
Vicar's Mead, East Budleigh
June 7 Friday
Vicar's Mead, East Budleigh
June 8 Saturday
Little Upcott Gardens, Marsh
  Green
Otterton Gardens

Vicar's Mead, East Budleigh
June 9 Sunday
  Addisford Cottage, nr Dolton
  Beatlands Farm, Metcombe
  Bicton College of Agriculture
  Broadhembury House,
    Broadhembury
  The Croft, Yarnscombe
  Crosspark, Northlew
  Fast Rabbit Farm, Ash, Dartmouth
  1 Feebers Cottage, Westwood
  Gidleigh Gardens, nr Chagford
  The Glebe House, Whitestone,
    nr Exeter
  Little Upcott Gardens, Marsh
    Green
  Meadowcroft, Plympton
  Otterton Gardens
  Vicar's Mead, East Budleigh
  Wylmington Hayes, nr Honiton
June 11 Tuesday
  Addisford Cottage, nr Dolton
June 12 Wednesday
  Little Upcott Gardens, Marsh
    Green
June 14 Friday
  Dippers, Shaugh Prior,
    nr Plymouth
June 15 Saturday
  Bovey Tracey Gardens
June 16 Sunday
  Andrew's Corner, nr Okehampton
  Bickham Barton, Roborough
  Bickham House, Kenn, nr Exeter
  Bicton College of Agriculture
  Bovey Tracey Gardens
  Broadhembury House,
    Broadhembury
  Castle Drogo, Drewsteignton
  Croftdene, Ham nr Dalwood
  Crosspark, Northlew
  Dippers, Shaugh Prior,
    nr Plymouth
  The Glebe House, Whitestone,
    nr Exeter
  The Lodge, Mannamead
  The Old Mill, Blakewell
  38 Phillipps Avenue, Exmouth
  Riversbridge, nr Dartmouth
  Wylmington Hayes, nr Honiton
  Yonder Hill, Colaton Raleigh
June 18 Tuesday
  Addisford Cottage, nr Dolton
June 19 Wednesday
  Cleave House, Sticklepath
  Little Upcott Gardens, Marsh
    Green
  Stone Lane Gardens, nr Chagford
  Winkfield, Colyford
June 22 Saturday
  Brixham Gardens
  Bundels, Sidbury
  Little Upcott Gardens, Marsh
    Green

Little Webbery, Alverdiscott
June 23 Sunday
  Addisford Cottage, nr Dolton
  Ash Thomas & Brithem Bottom
    Gardens
  Bundels, Sidbury
  Cleave House, Sticklepath
  The Croft, Yarnscombe
  Crosspark, Northlew
  Fast Rabbit Farm, Ash, Dartmouth
  The Glebe House, Whitestone,
    nr Exeter
  Kingston House, Staverton,
    nr Totnes
  Little Upcott Gardens, Marsh
    Green
  Little Webbery, Alverdiscott
  Membland Villa, Newton Ferrers
  The Old Parsonage, Warkleigh
  Overbecks, Salcombe
  Priors, Abbotskerswell
  Riversbridge, nr Dartmouth
  Wylmington Hayes, nr Honiton
June 25 Tuesday
  Addisford Cottage, nr Dolton
June 26 Wednesday
  Bundels, Sidbury
  Little Upcott Gardens, Marsh
    Green
June 27 Wednesday
  Scypen, Ringmore
June 29 Saturday
  Bundels, Sidbury
  Little Upcott Gardens, Marsh
    Green
  Penrose, Crediton
June 30 Sunday
  Addisford Cottage, nr Dolton
  Bundels, Sidbury
  Court Hall, North Molton
  Crosspark, Northlew
  1 Feebers Cottage, Westwood
  Flete, Ermington, Ivybridge
  Glebe Cottage, nr Warkleigh
  The Glebe House, Whitestone,
    nr Exeter
  Gorwell House, nr Barnstaple
  Ivy Cottage, Heanton, nr Braunton
  Knightshayes Gardens, nr Tiverton
  Little Southey, Culm Valley,
    nr Culmstock
  Little Upcott Gardens, Marsh
    Green
  Penrose, Crediton
  38 Phillipps Avenue, Exmouth
  Priors, Abbotskerswell
  Purple Hayes, Halberton
  Scypen, Ringmore
  Sowton Mill, Dunsford
  Wylmington Hayes, nr Honiton
July 1 Monday
  Fardel Manor, nr Ivybridge
  Little Southey, Culm Valley,
    nr Culmstock

July 2 Tuesday
  Addisford Cottage, nr Dolton
July 3 Wednesday
  Little Upcott Gardens, Marsh
    Green
July 5 Friday
  Court Hall, North Molton
July 7 Sunday
  Addisford Cottage, nr Dolton
  Alswood, George Nympton
  Arlington Court, nr Barnstaple
  The Croft, Yarnscombe
  Fast Rabbit Farm, Ash, Dartmouth
  The Glebe House, Whitestone,
    nr Exeter
  Heddon Hall, Parracombe
  Kerscott House, nr Swimbridge
  Killerton Garden, Broadclyst
  Kingston House, Staverton,
    nr Totnes
  Portington, nr Lamerton
  Priors, Abbotskerswell
  Sampford Peverell Gardens
  Winkfield, Colyford
  Yonder Hill, Colaton Raleigh
July 9 Tuesday
  Addisford Cottage, nr Dolton
July 10 Wednesday
  Stone Lane Gardens, nr Chagford
July 13 Saturday
  Little Upcott Gardens, Marsh
    Green
  Whitmore, nr Chittlehamholt
July 14 Sunday
  Andrew's Corner, nr Okehampton
  The Cider House, Yelverton
  The Glebe House, Whitestone,
    nr Exeter
  Little Upcott Gardens, Marsh
    Green
  The Old Mill, Blakewell
  38 Phillipps Avenue, Exmouth
  Portington, nr Lamerton
  The Rectory, East Portlemouth
  Sowton Mill, Dunsford
  Woodside, Barnstaple
July 16 Tuesday
  Addisford Cottage, nr Dolton
July 17 Wednesday
  The Garden House, Yelverton
  Heddon Hall, Parracombe
  Little Upcott Gardens, Marsh
    Green
July 21 Sunday
  Addisford Cottage, nr Dolton
  Bickham House, Kenn, nr Exeter
  1 Feebers Cottage, Westwood
  Heddon Hall, Parracombe
  The Lodge, Mannamead
  Membland Villa, Newton
    Ferrers
  Oare Manor Cottage, Oare,
    nr Brendon
  Sampford Peverell Gardens

Twitchen Mill, nr South Molton
Woodside, Whimple, nr Exeter
July 23 Tuesday
Addisford Cottage, nr Dolton
July 24 Wednesday
Sunrise Hill, Withleigh
July 27 Saturday
Dicot, nr Chardstock
Little Upcott Gardens, Marsh
Green
July 28 Sunday
Addisford Cottage, nr Dolton
The Croft, Yarnscombe
Dicot, nr Chardstock
Glebe Cottage, nr Warkleigh
Gorwell House, nr Barnstaple
Little Upcott Gardens, Marsh
Green
Longham, nr Lydford Gorge
38 Phillipps Avenue, Exmouth
Yonder Hill, Colaton Raleigh
July 30 Tuesday
Addisford Cottage, nr Dolton
July 31 Wednesday
Little Upcott Gardens, Marsh
Green
Sunrise Hill, Withleigh
August 4 Sunday
Addisford Cottage, nr Dolton
Longham, nr Lydford Gorge
August 7 Wednesday
Kerscott House, nr Swimbridge
August 10 Saturday
Little Upcott Gardens, Marsh
Green
Penrose, Crediton
August 11 Sunday
Addisford Cottage, nr Dolton
Glebe Cottage, nr Warkleigh
Little Upcott Gardens, Marsh
Green
The Old Parsonage, Warkleigh
38 Phillipps Avenue, Exmouth
Yonder Hill, Colaton Raleigh
August 14 Wednesday
The Garden House, Yelverton
Little Upcott Gardens, Marsh
Green

August 18 Sunday
Bickham House, Kenn, nr Exeter
Purple Hayes, Halberton
96 Wasdale Gardens, Plymouth
Woodside, Whimple, nr Exeter
August 21 Wednesday
Little Upcott Gardens, Marsh
Green
August 25 Sunday
Alswood, George Nympton
Fast Rabbit Farm, Ash, Dartmouth
96 Wasdale Gardens, Plymouth
Whitmore, nr Chittlehamholt
Yonder Hill, Colaton Raleigh
August 26 Monday
Membland Villa, Newton Ferrers
96 Wasdale Gardens, Plymouth
Yonder Hill, Colaton Raleigh
August 31 Saturday
Pleasant View Nursery,
nr Newton Abbot
September 1 Sunday
1 Feebers Cottage, Westwood
Gorwell House, nr Barnstaple
Kerscott House, nr Swimbridge
38 Phillipps Avenue, Exmouth
Pleasant View Nursery,
nr Newton Abbot
September 8 Sunday
Glebe Cottage, nr Warkleigh
September 15 Sunday
Bickham House, Kenn, nr Exeter
Yonder Hill, Colaton Raleigh
September 22 Sunday
1 Feebers Cottage, Westwood
September 29 Sunday
Gidleigh Gardens, nr Chagford
Glebe Cottage, nr Warkleigh
October 6 Sunday
1 Feebers Cottage, Westwood
Gorwell House, nr Barnstaple
Yonder Hill, Colaton Raleigh
October 13 Sunday
The Old Parsonage, Warkleigh
October 20 Sunday
Starveacre, nr Axminster
October 27 Sunday
Yonder Hill, Colaton Raleigh

1997
February 23
Yonder Hill, Colaton Raleigh

Regular openings
For details see garden description

Avenue Cottage
Burrow Farm Garden, Dalwood
Docton Mill, nr Hartland
The Downes, Monkleigh
The Garden House, Yelverton
Hill House, nr Ashburton
Lukesland, Ivybridge
Marwood Hill, nr Barnstaple
Plant World, nr Newton Abbot
Pleasant View Nursery, nr Newton
Abbot
The Rectory, East Portlemouth
Rosemoor Garden, Great Torrington
Tapeley Park & Gardens, Instow

By appointment only
*For telephone numbers and other
details see garden descriptions.
Private visits welcomed*

Barton House, Nymet Rowland
Castle Tor, Torquay
Clovelly Court
The Gate House, Lee, Ilfracombe
Higher Spriddlestone, Brixton,
nr Plymouth
Holywell, Bratton Fleming
The Moorings, nr Lyme Regis
The Old Rectory, Woodleigh
The Orchard, Kenn
Orchard Cottage, Exmouth
Quakers, Membury
Robin Hill, Exeter
Spillifords, nr Tiverton
Sweet Chestnut, Bovey Tracey
Weetwood, Offwell nr Honiton

DESCRIPTIONS OF GARDENS

Addisford Cottage *✷✿* (Mr & Mrs R J Taylor) West Lane, Dolton. ½m W of Dolton. From village centre past Royal Oak for ½m to bottom of valley, gate on R across ford. 1½-acre garden surrounding picturesque thatched cottage in secluded wooded valley. Natural stream, large pond and water garden with hardy moisture loving and woodland plants. Extensive herbaceous borders, densely planted for sun and shade alongside many wild species. Large collection of geraniums. TEAS Suns only. *Adm £1 Chd free. Suns May 26, June 2, 9, 23, 30, July 7, 21, 28, Aug 4, 11 (12-5); also every Tues June, July (2-5). Parties welcome by appt, please* **Tel 01805 804365**

Alswood &✿ (Bob & Marjorie Radford) George Nympton. 2m S of S Molton, halfway between the villages of George Nympton and Alswear. Ample parking, 2-acre developing garden, enthusiastically designed and maintained by owners; set in rural area with panoramic views of the Crooked Oak Valley. Many unusual specimen trees and shrubs. Well established spectacular herbaceous, erica and aquatic areas, pond and stream, unique architectural features. TEAS. *Adm £1 Chd free (Share to St George's Church®). Bank Hol Mon May 27, Suns July 7, Aug 25 (2-5.30)*

General Information. For general information on the use of this book see Page 15.

Andrew's Corner ৬๕๑ (H J & Mr & Mrs R J Hill) Belstone, 3m E of Okehampton signed to Belstone. Parking restricted but may be left on nearby common. Plantsman's garden 1,000ft up on Dartmoor, overlooking Taw Valley; wide range unusual trees, shrubs, herbaceous plants for year round effect inc alpines, rhododendrons, bulbs, dwarf conifers; well labelled. TEAS. *Adm £1 Chd free. Suns April 21; May 5, 26; June 2, 16; July 14; (2.30-6); also private visits welcome, please* Tel 01837 840332

Arlington Court ৬๕ (The National Trust) Shirwell, nr Barnstaple. 7m NE of Barnstaple on A39. Rolling parkland and woods with lake. Rhododendrons and azaleas; fine specimen trees; small terraced Victorian garden with herbaceous borders and conservatory. Regency house containing fascinating collections of objet d'art. Carriage collection in the stables, carriage rides. Restaurant. *Adm garden only £2.50 Chd £1.20. Suns May 12, July 7 (11-5.30)*

Ash Thomas and Brithem Bottom Gardens ๕ 5m SE of Tiverton, 2m S of Halberton. Take A361 from junction 27 on M5 signposted Tiverton but leave in ½m signposted Halberton. In 3m turn L signposted Ash Thomas. 1st garden 1m. A route map to each garden will be available on open days. TEAS at Greenlands. *Combined adm £1.50 Chd 25p. Sun April 14; Bank Hol Mon May 27; Sun June 23 (2-6)*

   Greenlands ৬๕ (Dr & Mrs J P Anderson) Ash Thomas. ⅓-acre garden in open rural setting with far-reaching views. Alpine beds and troughs, herbaceous borders, roses and rustic screening, spring bulbs, annuals, herbs, fruit garden, vegetable plot, pond and wild areas. Parking in surrounding lanes, except disabled. Plants for sale in adjacent nursery. TEAS. *(Share to St Francis Hospital, Katete, Zambia®). Private visits also welcome March to Sept, please* Tel 01884 821257

   Lower Beers ৬ (Mr & Mrs G Nicholls) Brithem Bottom. Listed C16 longhouse fronts a developing 3-acre hidden garden, incl ornamental herb and vegetable garden, herbaceous beds, woodland dell and large open area leading to stream. Parking in adjoining yard

   Lower Coombe Farm (Mr & Mrs M Weekes) Brithem Bottom. Large cottage garden with an interesting selection of plants, old roses and a ditch garden situated behind C17 farmhouse. Parking in farmyard

Avenue Cottage ৬ (Mr R J Pitts & Mr R C H Soans) Ashprington. A381 from Totnes to Kingsbridge. 3m SE Totnes, from centre of village uphill past church for 400yds, drive on R. 11 acres of garden with woodland. Part of listed C18 landscape. Secluded valley site undergoing re-creation. Large collection of young and mature planting. *Adm £1.50 Chd 25p. Collecting box. Tues to Sat April 2 to Sept 28 (11-5). Private visits welcome, please* Tel 01803 732769. *No coaches*

Barton House ๕๑ (Mr and Mrs A T Littlewood) Nymet Rowland. 9m NW of Crediton. Follow signs to Nymet Rowland from A377 at Lapford or B3220 at Aller Bridge. Garden opposite C15 church. 1-acre garden designed and maintained by owners. Beautiful views to Dartmoor. Individual areas developed with varied character. Herbs; pond; herbaceous; yew garden; ferns, grotto, roses and fountain pool. *Adm £1 Chd 50p. Private visits welcome, please* Tel 01363 83534

¶Beatlands Farm ৬๕๑ (Mr & Mrs D E Pounce) Metcombe, nr Tipton St John. 2½m S of Ottery St Mary. [SYO892]. 50yds N of Tipton Church take LH turn up Metcombe Vale for ½m. Instead of sharp R at Z bend, bear L up private rd. Care needed on ¼m narrow lane. Secluded 2-acre garden surrounding C17 farmhouse. Streams, waterways, large wildlife pond and wide variety of planting for colour and foliage effect. Streamside walk through woodland. Productive vegetable garden. *Adm £1.50 Chd 25p. Suns June 2, 9 (2-6)*

Bickham Barton ๕๑ (Helen Lady Roborough) Roborough, 8m N of Plymouth. Take Maristow turn on Roborough Down, ½-way between Plymouth and Tavistock, then follow poster directions. Bus stop: Maristow sign on Roborough Down; posters at Maristow turning 1m from house. Shrub garden; camellias; rhododendrons; azaleas; cherries; bulbs; trees. Lovely views. *Adm £1 Chd 50p. Every Sun April 7 to June 2 and 16, Mons April 8, May 6, Bank Hol Mon 27 (2-5.30); also private visits welcome until end of June, please* Tel 01822 852478

Bickham House ৬๕๑ (Mr & Mrs John Tremlett) Kenn. 6m W of Exeter 1m off A38. Plymouth-Torquay rd leave dual carriage-way at Kennford Services, follow signs to Kenn. 1st R in village, follow lane for ¾m to end of no-through rd. Ample parking. No shade for dogs. 5-acre garden in peaceful wooded valley. Lawns, mature trees and shrubs; naturalised bulbs, mixed borders. Conservatory, small parterre, pond garden; 1-acre walled kitchen garden; lake. Cream TEAS. *Adm £1.50 Chd 50p. Suns March 17, April 21, May 19, June 16, July 21, Aug 18, Sept 15 (2-5). Private visits also welcome, please* Tel 01392 832671

Bicton College of Agriculture ৬๕๑ Entrance to the College is by Sidmouth Lodge, half-way between Budleigh Salterton and Newton Poppleford on B3178. Proceed up famous monkey puzzle avenue with fine views of the parkland and trees. From the top of the drive follow signs to garden car park. The gardens are linked to the old Georgian mansion and extend via the arboretum to the old walled garden and glasshouses, being the centre of the Horticultural Dept. Rich variety of plants in beds and borders, laid out for teaching and effect; including NCCPG national collections of agapanthus & pittosporum; arboretum extends for ½m with various trees and shrubs incl magnolia, camellia and flowering cherries. Parking in gardens car park, short walk to gardens. Entrance tickets obtainable at Plant Centre. When plant centre closed please use box by gate. Plant centre closes 4.30pm. Garden and arboretum guides available. TEAS. *Adm £2 Chd free (Share to Bicton Overseas Agricultural Trust®). Suns, June 2, 9, 16 (10.30-4.30). Gardens also open daily throughout year, except Christmas day (10.30-5). Private parties welcome following written application using booking forms available, please* Tel 01395 568353

Bovey Tracey Gardens Gateway to Dartmoor. A382 midway Newton Abbot to Moretonhampstead. Teas locally. *Combined adm £1.75 Chd 25p. Sat, Sun June 15, 16 (2-6)*

   ¶Beavers Lea (Mr & Mrs D A Pook) Higher Bibbery. Cul-de-sac behind Coombe Cross Hotel. B3344 to Chudleigh Knighton. A very small garden on a sloping site. Shrubs, evergreens and herbaceous plants

Bibbery ❀ (Misses E & A Hebditch) Higher Bibbery. B3344 to Chudleigh Knighton. Cul-de-sac behind Coombe Cross Hotel. Plantspersons small garden, sheltered corners harbouring interesting shrubs and tender plants. *Also private visits welcome, please* **Tel 01626 833344**

Church View ❀ (Mr & Mrs R Humphreys) East Street. B3344 opp St Peter & St Paul's Church. Small garden, but many unusual plants, incl secluded vegetable area. Disabled parking

¶**Pineholm** (Dr & Mrs A A Baker) High Close. B3344 to Chudleigh Knighton. 1st L past Coombe Cross Hotel. Limited parking (not beyond brick pillars). 2-terraced garden on a very steep sloping site. Wide variety of fruit grown by expert

Smithays Cottage ❀ (Mr & Mrs Arthur Mann) Fore Street. Small traditional walled cottage garden

Sunnyside (Mr & Mrs Green) Hind Street. Nr town centre off A382. Opp Baptist Church. Well established enclosed garden; trees and shrubs; herbaceous and colourful conservatory; productive vegetable area. Parking nearby

Thuja ❀ (Mr & Mrs Bowman) Hind Street. Experienced plantswomen started new garden in small enclosed space with mediterranean feel, spot plantings in chippings

¶**Brixham Gardens** ✄❀ *Combined adm £2 Chd free. Sat June 22 (2-5)*

¶**Rosemarie Cottage** (Howard & Rosemary East) 42 Rea Barn Rd. From Brixham Town Centre take Dartmouth rd, in approx ¼m turn L at t-lights (or R if coming from Dartmouth). Garden is 150yds on L. Small secluded walled garden. Rose arbour; clematis; herbaceous borders. Beekeeping demonstration

¶**Southdown Farm** (Col & Mrs Stephen Love), Southdown Hill Rd. Take Dartmouth - Brixham rd. In Milton St, approx 1m from Brixham Town Centre follow NGS sign into Southdown Hill Rd. Farm is at end of rd in approx ½m. 1-acre garden of a working farm. Shrubs, roses and herbaceous perennials. Magnificent country views to sea

Broadhembury House ✄❀ (Mr & Mrs W Drewe) Broadhembury. 5m equidistant on A373 from Honiton-Cullompton signed Broadhembury. 2-acre informal garden in C16 picturesque thatched village. A spring garden with rhododendrons and azaleas, daffodils and bluebells. Ample parking in village square. TEAS. *Adm £1.25 Chd 50p (Share to Muscular Dystrophy Group®). Suns May 12, 19, 26; June 2, 9, 16 Bank Hol Mons May 6, 27 (2-5). Larger groups welcome by appt during May and June, please* **Tel 0140484 1326**

Bundels ৬❀ (Mr & Mrs A Softly) Ridgway, Sidbury. From Sidmouth B3175 turn left at free Car Park in Sidbury. From Honiton A375, turn right. Garden 100yds up Ridgway on left. 1½-acre organic garden inc small wood and pond set round C16 thatched cottage (not open); over 100 varieties of old-fashioned and other shrub roses. Typical cottage garden with accent on preservation of wild life. GRBS Gift stall. Teas in village. *Adm £1 Chd 20p. Wed June 26 (2-6), Sats June 22, 29 (10-12) & (2-6), Suns April 7, May 5, 26 (2-6), June 23, 30 (10-12) & (2-6). Private visits also welcome May to July for parties of 4 and over, please* **Tel 01395 597312**

Burrow Farm Garden ৬❀ (Mr & Mrs John Benger) Dalwood, 4m W of Axminster. A35 Axminster-Honiton rd; 3½m from Axminster turn N near Shute Garage on to Stockland Rd; ½m on right. Secluded 5-acre garden with magnificent views has been planned for foliage effect and includes woodland garden in a dell with rhododendrons, azaleas etc; large bog garden; pergola walk with rose-herbaceous borders. Nursery adjoining. Cream TEAS (Suns, Weds & Bank Hols). *Adm £2 Chd 50p. April 1 to Sept 30 daily (2-7). Private visits also welcome in the morning, please* **Tel 01404 831285**

Castle Drogo ৬✄❀ (The National Trust) Drewsteignton. W of Exeter, S of A30. Medium-sized garden with formal beds and herbaceous borders; shrubs, woodland walk overlooking Fingle Gorge. Wheelchair available. Plant centre. Restaurant. Tea room. *Adm gardens only £2.20 Chd £1.10. For NGS Suns April 28, June 16 (10.30-5.30)*

Castle Tor (Leonard Stocks) Wellswood, Torquay. From Higher Lincombe Rd turn E into Oxlea Rd. 200yds on right, entrance identified by eagles on gate pillars. Spectacular scenic listed garden superbly designed and laid out under the influence of Lutyens in the mid-30s. Stepped terraces, orangery, paved work and ornamental water. *Adm £1 Chd 25p. Private visits welcome for parties less than 5, please* **Tel 01803 214858**

Chevithorne Barton ❀ (Michael Heathcoat Amory) Chevithorne. 3m NE of Tiverton. A terraced walled garden and further informal planting in woodland of trees and shrubs incl NCCPG National Oak Collection. In spring the garden features magnolias, rhododendrons and azaleas. *Adm £1 Chd 50p (Share to CPRE®). Sun May 26 (2-6)*

The Cider House ৬✄❀ (Mr & Mrs M J Stone) Buckland Abbey, Yelverton. From A386 Plymouth-Tavistock, follow NT signs to Buckland Abbey. At Xrds before Abbey entrance turn N signed Buckland Monachorum. Drive 200yds on L, or short walk for visitors to Abbey. Peaceful and secluded garden with restrained planting complementing mediaeval house, part of a Cistercian monastery. Terrace borders and herbs, former Abbey walled kitchen garden with fruit, vegetables and flowers. Unspoilt aspect over wooded valley surrounded by NT land. Cream TEAS. *Adm £1 Chd 50p. Suns May 19, July 14 (2-6)*

Cleave House ✄❀ (Ann & Roger Bowden) Sticklepath, 3½m E of Okehampton on old A30 towards Exeter. Cleave House on left in village, on main road just past small right turn for Skaigh. ½-acre garden with mixed planting for all season interest. National Collection of hostas with 500 varieties, 150 of these are for sale. Partially suitable for wheelchairs. *Adm 50p Chd free (Share to NCCPG). Wed June 19; Sat May 4; Suns May 5, June 23 (10.30-5.30). Private visits also welcome April to Oct, please* **Tel 0183784 0481**

1996 Special Events. For information on special National Gardens Scheme events in 1996 see Pages 18-19.

Regular Openers. See end of county section.

Clovelly Court ⚬♿❀ (The Hon Mrs Rous) Clovelly. 11m W of Bideford. A39 Bideford to Bude turn at Clovelly Cross Filling Station, 1m lodge gates and drive straight ahead; also 'Long Walk' pedestrian entrance 200yds from top of village (back rd) at large green gate shared with entrance to coastal footpath. 25 acres parkland with beautiful open views through woodlands towards sea. 1-acre walled garden with borders, fruit and vegetables. 500yds walk from village (through green gate) along path lined with ancient trees and rhododendrons. Medieval Manor adjacent C14 Church nr coastline. Free parking in drive. Directions at Garden entrance, blue doors in Church Path. *Adm £1 Chd 20p (Share to NSPCC®). Private visits and coach parties welcome May 1 to Sept 30, please* Tel 01237 431215

Coleton Fishacre ♿❀ (The National Trust) 2m NE of Kingswear. 20-acre garden planted and developed according to personal taste of the D'Oyly Carte family during 1926-1947 and unaltered by subsequent owners, now under restoration; wide range of tender and uncommon trees and shrubs in spectacular coastal setting. TEAS weather permitting. Unusual plants sale. *Adm £3.10 Chd £1.50. Suns April 21, May 19 (10.30-5.30)*

Court Hall ♿❀ (Mr & Mrs C Worthington) North Molton. 2½m N from A361 Barnstaple-Tiverton rd. In N Molton drive up the hill into the square with church on your L take the only drive beside the old school buildings and Court Hall is just round the bend. A very small south facing walled garden; large conservatory; rose, clematis, honeysuckle arbours surround a swimming pool garden with tender plants, rock wall and table. *Adm £1 Chd 20p. Sun June 30, Fri July 5 (2-5.30)*

The Croft ⚬♿❀ (Mr & Mrs Jewell) Yarnscombe. From A377, 5m S of Barnstaple turning W opposite Chapelton Railway Stn. for 3m. Drive on L at village sign. From B3232 ¼m N of Huntshaw TV mast Xrds, turn E for 2m. 1-acre plantswoman's garden on edge of village with unspoilt distant views to West. Alpine area and wide selection of unusual plants and shrubs. Island beds, much herbaceous material, ponds and bog area. No toilets. Cream TEAS (Suns). *Adm £1 Chd free (Share to St. Andrews Church). Suns June 9, 23, July 7, 28 (2-6). Tues in June and July (2-5). Also by appt other times please* Tel 01769 560535

Croftdene ♿❀ (Joy and Phil Knox) Ham Dalwood. Between Axminster and Honiton. From A35 3½m W of Axminster turn N nr Shute Garage signed Dalwood and Stockland. Keep L up Stockland Hill until just past television mast. Turn R signed Ham. 1½m to Ham Cross. Park by telephone box. From A30 5m E of Honiton turn R signed Axminster and Stockland 3m to televsion mast turn L to Ham. 1½-acre garden in the making since 1988 with further 1 acre of natural woodland. Wide range of shrubs; herbaceous; ericaceous; alpines; woodland and water plants. Island beds; rock garden; peat beds; stream-side and pond. Featured on TV 'Gardens For All 1991'. TEAS at **Burrow Farm**. *Adm £1 Chd free. Sun June 16 (2-6). Private visits also welcome, please* Tel 01404 831271

Crosspark ⚬♿❀ (Mrs G West) Northlew. From Okehampton follow A30 for 1m turn R to Holsworthy, drive for 6m past Flare Garage turn R signposted Northlew, over bridge, turn L to Kimber, we are 3m along this rd on L, or 2½m from Highampton on the Northlew Rd. 1-acre plantswoman's garden by colour theme; herbaceous borders; ponds, incl wildlife pond; bog garden; rockery heathers and conifers. Wide range of plants. Featured on BBC Gardeners World and ITV. Large variety of unusual plants for sale. TEA. *Adm 75p Chd 20p. Suns May 26; June 2, 9, 16, 23, 30; Bank Hol Mon May 27 (2-5). Coaches welcome*

Dartington Hall Gardens ⚬♿❀ (Dartington Hall Trust) Approx 1½m NW of Totnes. From Totnes take A384, turn R at Dartington Parish Church. 28-acre garden surrounds C14 Hall and Tiltyard. Plant sales shop and nursery. *Adm (donation) £2.00 recommended. ▲Sat, Sun May 25, 26 (dawn to dusk)*

Dicot ♿❀ (Mr & Mrs F Clarkson) Chardstock. Axminster to Chard A358 at Tytherleigh to Chardstock. R at George Inn, L fork to Hook, R to Burridge, 2nd house on L. 3-acre enthusiasts garden, trees unusual shrubs and conifers, bog orchids in June. Stream, mixed borders, fish pool, features. TEAS. *Adm £1 Chd 50p. Sats, Suns June 1, 2, July 27, 28 (2-5.30) Private visits welcome, please* Tel 01460 220364

Dippers ♿❀ (Mr & Mrs R J Hubble) Shaugh Prior. 8m NE of Plymouth. From A38 take Ivybridge exit and follow signs to Cornwood, continue on same rd to Shaugh Prior. Garden 100yds down lane opp church near top of village. Park in village or at White Thorn public house. No parking in lane. ¾-acre informal garden. Emphasis on foliage contrast with collection of dwarf rhododendrons, dwarf conifers and shrubs together with herbaceous and heathers. Extensive collection of alpines, in raised beds and troughs. Special interest in pinks; scented pink walk. NCCPG National collection of dianthus. Choice alpines and unusual herbaceous for sale. Cream TEAS at Village Hall. *Adm £1 Chd free (Share to CPRE). Suns April 14, May 12, June 16, Fri June 14 (11-5). Opening in March 1997 Mons (2-4.30) for collection of hellebore cultivars and spring bulbs with hellebores for sale*

Docton Mill and Garden ❀ (Mr & Mrs M G Bourcier) Spekes Valley nr. Hartland. Off A39: From N Devon via Clovelly Cross & Hartland to Stoke, or from N Cornwall via Kilkhampton to the West Country Inn. On either route turn L and follow Elmscott signs towards Lymebridge in Spekes Valley for 3½m. A garden for all seasons (depicted BBC TV spring, summer and autumn) with working water mill dated 1249, 8 acres of sheltered wooded valley in one of Devon's outstanding beauty spots 1500yds from Spekes Mill Mouth coastal waterfalls and beach. Mill pond, leats, trout stream with footbridges and smaller streams. Cultivated areas incl bog garden, rockery, outcrops, woodland, and orchard. Displays of narcissi, primulas, shrub roses, specimen trees, shrubs and herbaceous plants, wild primroses, bluebells, foxgloves and ferns. Devon cream TEAS at mill. *Adm £2.50 Chd 50p. Daily March 1 to Oct 31 (10-5). For NGS every Tues. Parties by prior arrangement* Tel 01237 441369

The Downes ఈ❀ (Mr & Mrs R C Stanley-Baker) 4½m S of Bideford; 3m NW of Torrington. On A386 to Bideford turn left (W) up drive, ¼m beyond layby. 15 acres with landscaped lawns; fine views overlooking fields and woodlands in Torridge Valley; many unusual trees and shrubs; small arboretum; woodland walks. Featured in Homes and Gardens June 1993. TEA Sats, Suns only. *Adm £1 Chd 20p. Daily April 7 to June 9 (all day); private visits also welcome June to Sept, please* Tel **01805 622244**

Fardel Manor ఉఈ❀ (Dr A G Stevens) 1¼m NW of Ivybridge; 2m SE of Cornwood; 200yds S of railway bridge. 5-acre, all organic garden, maintained with conservation and wildlife in mind. Partly reticulated. 2½ acres developed over past 10 years with stream, pond and lake. Also, small courts and walled gardens around C14 Manor, with orangery, herbaceous borders, formal pond and shrub garden. TEAS. *Adm £1.50 Chd 50p (Share to Frame®). Mon July 1 (11-4.30). Parties welcome by appt, please* Tel **01752 892353**

Fast Rabbit Farm ఉఈ❀ (Mr & Mrs Mort) Ash Cross. 1½m from Dartmouth off the Dartmouth-Totnes rd pass park and ride. Turn L at Rose Cottage. Opp direction, from Totnes or Kingsbridge, pass Woodland Park on R, drive past Norton Park on L turn R at Rose Cottage. Newly created garden in sheltered valley with natural stream. Several ponds and lake; partially wooded; rockery; extensively planted; extends 8 acres with new woodland planting and walks being created through woodland at head of valley. Small specialist nursery open daily. Car park. Some level walks. 'Invalids' please phone prior to visit. TEAS. *Adm £1.50 Chd 50p. Suns March 31, April 7, 21, May 5, 19, 26, June 9, 23, July 7, Aug 25 Mons April 8, May 6, 27 (11-5). Parties welcome by appt, please* Tel **01803 712437**

1 Feebers Cottage ఉఈ❀ (Mr & Mrs M J Squires) Westwood. 2m NE of Broadclyst from B3181 (formerly A38) Exeter-Taunton, at Dog Village bear E to Whimple, after 1½m fork left for Westwood. A modern cottage garden, a little of everything set in ¾ of an acre, with a maze of pathways; specialising in plants which tolerate heavy clay soil (alpines are in raised beds) and with a section of plants introduced by Amos Perry. Nursery. Cream TEAS Sun June 30 only, tea and biscuits on other days. *Adm £1 Chd free. Mon April 8 and Suns April 21, May 19, June 9, 30 (Cream TEAS), July 21, Sept 1, 22, Oct 6 (2-6). Private visits of 30 and over also welcome, please* Tel **01404 822118**

Flete ❀ (Country Houses Association) Ermington, 2m W of Modbury on A379 Plymouth-Kingsbridge rd. Entrance adjacent to Sequers Bridge. 5 acres of gardens overlooking R Erme and valley. Landscaped in 1920's by Russell Paige and incl an Italian garden and water garden which Lawrence of Arabia helped to construct. Many fine trees and shrubs. Interesting cobbled terrace to W face of original Tudor manor. *Adm £2 Chd £1 (Share to Country Houses Assoc®). House and gardens open every Weds, Thurs pm May to end Sept. For NGS Sun June 30 (2.30-5) when TEAS will be available (2.30-5).* Tel **01752 830308**

The Garden House ఉఈ❀ (The Fortescue Garden Trust) Buckland Monachorum, Yelverton. W of A386, 10m N of Plymouth. 8-acre garden, incl a romantic, terraced walled garden surrounding the ruins of a C16 vicarage. Also incl an acer glade, spring garden, rhododendron walk, herbaceous glade, cottage garden and quarry garden. Coaches and parties by appt only. TEAS. *Adm £3 Chd £1 (Share to NGS®). March 1 to Oct 31 daily. For NGS Weds July 17, Aug 14 (10.30-5)*

The Gate House (Mr & Mrs D Booker) Lee Coastal Village. 3m W of Ilfracombe. Park in village car park. Take lane alongside The Grampus public house. Garden is 50yds past inn buildings. Peaceful streamside garden with a range of habitats; bog garden (National Collection of Rodgersia), woodland, herbaceous borders, patio garden with hardy 'exotics'. 2¼ acres, where no chemicals are used, only a few minutes walk from the sea and dramatic coastal scenery. Good food at the Grampus. *Collecting box. Open most days (9-12) (2-4). Please* Tel **01271 862409** *to check*

¶**Gidleigh Gardens** From A30 take A382 for Mortonhampstead via Whiddon Down. In 100yds R to Gidleigh for 4m. Entrances adjacent C15 Church. Home made TEAS at Castle Farm. *Combined adm £2 Chd £1. Suns June 9, Sept 29 (2-5.30)*

  ¶**Castle House** ❀ (Mr & Mrs M Hardy) 2 acres of hillside gardens around remains of mediaeval castle. New plantings amongst granite stones and water cascades link the gardens to the landscape

  ¶**Castle Farm** ఈ❀ (Mr & Mrs M Bell) A natural garden in one of Dartmoor's sheltered combes; stream, waterfalls and pools. Streamside walk in 6 acre wild valley. Views to deer forest and Castle Drogo

Glebe Cottage ఈ❀ (Mrs Carol Klein) Warkleigh. From N Devon link rd or A377. Halfway between S Molton and Umberleigh on B3227 at Homedown Cross. S for Chittlehamolt, straight on for 2m entrance 100yds beyond Xrds. Garden featured on BBC 'Gardeners World', 'Garden Club' and ITV West Country. Chelsea Gold Medal Winners 1992, 93, 94, 95. 1-acre cottage garden. recently redesigned with new features and exciting new plantings. S sloping, terraced. Wide collection of plants in different situations. Stumpery with ferns to sheltered formal beds and cottage garden plantings. Wide variety of unusual plants available from adjoining nursery open Tuesday to Friday. Cream TEAS on fine days. *Adm £1.50 Chd free. Suns June 2, 30, July 28, Aug 11, Sept 8, 29 (2-5)*

The Glebe House ❀ (Mr & Mrs John West) Whitestone. 2½-acre mature garden at 650ft S facing with outstanding views ranging from Exe estuary to Dartmoor. Garden on 3 levels; lower level with extensive lawns, mature trees and lge heather garden; middle level where house walls and buildings covered by climbing roses, clematis, honeysuckles and jasmines; upper level, given over to lawns with families of trees, acer, birch and eucalyptus underplanted with species and shrub roses. Over 300 varieties of rose most notable being Rosa filipes 'Kiftsgate', probably largest rose in UK, stretching over 150ft along C14 Tithe Barn (Ancient Monument) in courtyard. Former Rectory part C14 with Georgian frontage (not open). C13/14 Church adjoins. Parking in lanes around Church,

Frogmore is one of the Royal gardens HM The Queen graciously opens under the National Gardens Scheme. *Photograph The National Gardens Scheme.*

From town gardens to gracious parks, the gardens in the Scheme encompass all sizes. **23 Beech Croft Road, Oxford** measures only 23yd by 7yd but is a plant lover's paradise. *Photograph by John Glover.*

Right Frost adds a new dimension to the garden at **The Old Rectory, Burghfield** in **Berkshire**. Some of the gardens in the Scheme open during the winter months.
Photograph by Clive Nichols.

Below Many gardens in close proximity to each other combine to open on the same day. One of these group gardens is **Alwalton Gardens** in **Cambridgeshire.**
Photograph by Brian Chapple.

Right The Cancer Relief Macmillan Fund is the main beneficiary of the National Gardens Scheme. Here a Macmillan nurse enjoys a joke with one of her patients in his garden. *Photograph by courtesy of CRMF.*

Below The National Gardens Scheme benefits from one of its beneficiaries! The Gardeners' Royal Benevolent Society opens the gardens of **Gardeners Way**, a group of ten bungalows it provides for retired gardeners in **Gloucestershire**. *Photograph The National Gardens Scheme.*

Left This garden, **Nunwell House** on the **Isle of Wight**, includes exceptional views of the Solent amongst its attractions. *Photograph The National Gardens Scheme.*

Below **40 Osler Road, Oxford** is a 'secret garden' hidden in a built-up area. *Photograph by Clive Nichols.*

This is the arbour at **Conderton Manor, Worcestershire**. Other glorious features of the garden are the 100yd long mixed borders. *Photograph The National Gardens Scheme.*

Mrs Elizabeth Anton, Vice-Chairman of Council, presenting Mr John Berkeley of **Spetchley Park** with a tree in recognition of the garden opening for 60 years under the National Gardens Scheme. *Photograph by Mike Pollard.*

unsuitable for large coaches. *Adm £1.50 Chd free (Share to Whitestone Church®). Suns May 19, 26, June 2, 9, 16, 23, 30, July 7, 14 (2-6). Private visits also welcome, please* **Tel 01392 811200**

Gorwell House &❀ (Dr J A Marston) 1m E of Barnstaple centre, on Bratton Fleming rd, drive entrance between two lodges on left. 4 acres of trees and shrubs, walled garden; mostly created since 1982; small temple; summer house with views across estuary to Lundy and Hartland Point. TEAS (except March 31, April 28, Oct 6). *Adm £1 Acc chd free. Suns March 31 April 28, May 26, June 30, July 28, Sept 1, Oct 6 (2-6)*

Greenway Gardens ❀ (Mr & Mrs A A Hicks) Churston Ferrers, 4m W of Brixham. From B3203, Paignton-Brixham, take rd to Galmpton, thence towards Greenway Ferry. Partly suitable for wheelchairs; 30 acres; old-established garden with mature trees; shrubs; rhododendrons, magnolias and camellias. Recent plantings; commercial shrub nursery. Woodland walks by R Dart. Limited parking, partly suitable for wheelchairs. TEA and biscuits. *Adm £1 Chd 50p.* Thurs April 25, May 2 (2-6). **Tel 01803 842382**

Hamblyn's Coombe (Robert & Bridget McCrum) Dittisham. From Red Lion Inn follow the Level until it forks R up steep private road. Car park at top. 10 min pretty walk to 7-acre garden sloping steeply to R Dart. Extensive planting with unusual design features accompanying Bridget McCrum's stone carvings and bronzes. Bluebell meadow with stunning views. TEA. *Adm £1.50 Chd free (Share to National Hospital for Neurology & Neurosurgery®). Sun, Mon May 5, 6 (2-6). Private visits welcome by appt, please* **Tel 01803 722228**

Hartland Abbey ❀ (Sir Hugh Stucley & the Hon Lady Stucley) Hartland. Turn off A39 W of Clovelly Cross. Follow signs to Hartland through town on rd to Stoke and Quay. Abbey 1m from town on right. 2 woodland shrubberies with camellias, rhododendrons; wildflower walk through bluebell woods to remote Atlantic cove (Private walled gardens also open for NGS). TEAS. *Adm £1.50 Chd 50p (Share to St Nectan's Church, Hartland®).* ▲ *Sun April 28 (2-5.30). Tel The Administrator* **01237 441264**

Hayne Old Manor (Mr & Mrs R L Constantine) Moretonhampstead. ¼m S of Moretonhampstead on A382. 5 acres with lake and walled garden, shrubs and herbaceous borders. Recent landscaping and new plantings, extensive views. Cream TEAS. *Adm £1.50 Chd free. Sat, Sun June 1, 2 (2-5.30)*

Heddon Hall ❀ (Mr & Mrs W H Keatley) Parracombe. 10m NE of Barnstaple off A39. 400yds N up hill from village centre. Entrance to drive on R. Ample parking 200yds. Garden of former rectory on edge of Exmoor under restoration extending to 3 acres. Walled garden with formal layout and herbaceous beds; sheltered flower garden; semi shaded S sloping shrubbery with paths leading down to natural stream and water garden. Cream TEAS and plants Suns only. *Adm £1 Chd 50p. Suns July 7, 21; Wed July 17 (2-6)*

Higher Knowle (Mr & Mrs D R A Quicke) Lustleigh, 3m NW of Bovey Tracey A382 towards Moretonhampstead; in 2½m L at Kelly Cross for Lustleigh; in ¼m L/R at Brookfield along Knowle Rd; in ½m steep drive on left. 3-acre steep woodland garden; rhododendrons, camellias, magnolias on a carpet of primroses, bluebells; water garden and good Dartmoor views. Teas in village. *Adm £2 Chd free. Suns March 24, 31; April 7, 14, 21, 28; May 5, 12, 19, 26; Mons April 8, May 6, Bank Hol Mon 27 (2-6). Private visits welcome, please* **Tel 01647 277275**

Higher Spriddlestone & (Mr & Mrs David Willis) Brixton, nr Plymouth. A379 5m E from Plymouth, S at Martin's Garden Centre sign, ¾m to top of hill, R opp Spriddlestone sign, entrance 50yds on L. 1½-acre developing garden in rural setting. Level area around house, with borders, informal wildlife and kitchen gardens and ponds. *Adm £1 Chd free. Private visits and refreshments by arrangement, please* **Tel 01752 401184**

Higher Warcombe ✄❀ (Mr & Mrs A Treverton) Nr Kingsbridge. 2m N of Kingsbridge on the B3194 between Sorley Green Cross and Stumpy Post Cross. Take 1st turning L signposted Warcombe, house and garden approx ½m down lane. 1-acre garden on SW facing slope started in 1982 incl lawns, trees, rhododendrons, shrubs and herbaceous. Two steep banks planted for ground cover are a special feature and there is a pretty courtyard with container planting and a small walled garden. TEAS. *Adm £1 Chd 50p. Suns May 12 (2-5.30)*

Hill House Nursery & Gardens &❀ (Mr & Mrs R Hubbard) Landscove. Between Dartington & Ashburton signed A38 or A384 Buckfastleigh-Totnes. Old Vicarage beside church both designed by John Loughborough Pearson, architect of Truro Cathedral. The 3 acre garden was the subject of 'An Englishman's Garden' by Edward Hyams, a previous owner. Also featured in 'English Vicarages and Their Gardens' and several times on TV. A fine collection of plants. TEAS. *Adm - collection box. Open all year. Tea Room Mar 1 to Oct 1 (11-5)*

Holywell ✄❀ (Mr & Mrs R Steele) Bratton Fleming. 7m NE of Barnstaple. Turn W beside White Hart Inn (opp White Hart Garage) signed Village Hall. At 300yds fork L for Rye Park. Entrance drive ¼m at sharp L. Parking at house. Garden on edge of Exmoor in woodland setting of mature trees, in all about 25 acres. Stream, ponds and borders. Woodland walk to Lower River meadow and old Lynton Railway Track. Many unusual plants for sale. *Adm £1 Chd free. Private visits welcome, please* **Tel 01598 710213**

Ivy Cottage ✄ (John Turner) Heanton Punchardon. 4m W of Barnstaple off A361 to Ilfracombe at Chivenor Roundabout. Head for church clearly visible on brow of hill. Garden adjacent. Parking in church car park. C17 thatched cottage with small typical cottage garden with wind tolerant planting giving shelter from exposure to coastal winds. Mixed tender shrubs, ornamental trees, wall climbers and small secret courtyard. Filtered view over estuary of R Taw. TEA. *Adm £1 Chd free (Share to St Augustines Church, Heanton®). Suns May 12, June 2, 30 (12-5)*

Kerscott House &&& (Mrs J Duncan) Swimbridge. Barnstaple-South Molton (former A361) 1m E of Swimbridge, R at top of hill, immediate fork L, 100yds on L, 1st gate past house. Developing 6-acre garden surrounding C16 farmhouse in peaceful rural setting. Ornamental trees, wide selection of shrubs, herbaceous and tender perennials, ponds and bog garden. Living willow constructions. 2½ acres new woodland planted 1995. *Adm £1 Chd free. Suns July 7, Sept 1, Wed Aug 7 (2-6). Private visits also welcome during July, please* **Tel 01271 830943**

Killerton Garden &&& (The National Trust) 8m N of Exeter. Via B3181 Cullompton Rd (formerly A38), fork left in 7m on B3185. Garden 1m follow NT signs. 15 acres of spectacular hillside gardens with naturalised bulbs sweeping down to large open lawns. Delightful walks through fine collection of rare trees and shrubs; herbaceous borders. Wheelchair and 'golf' buggy with driver available. Restaurant. Tea room, plant centre. *Adm gardens only £3.10 Chd £1.50. For NGS Suns April 21, July 7 (10.30-5.30)*

¶ **Kingston House** &&& (Mr & Mrs M R Corfield) Staverton. 4m NE of Totnes. A384 Totnes to Buckfastleigh, from Staverton, 1m due N of Sea Trout Inn, follow signs to Kingston. George II 1735 house grade II. Gardens are being restored in keeping with the period. Walled garden, rose garden, herbaceous borders, pleached limes and hornbeams, vegetable garden. Unusual formal garden with santolinas, lavender and camomile. Cream TEAS. *Adm £1 Chd 50p. Suns June 23, July 7. Private parties over 20 welcome by arrangement, please* **Tel 01803 762235.** No coaches

Knightshayes Gardens &&& (The National Trust) 2m N of Tiverton. Via A396 Tiverton-Bampton; turn E in Bolham, signed Knightshayes Court; entrance ½m on left. Large 'Garden in the Wood', 50 acres of landscaped gardens with pleasant walks and views over the Exe valley. Choice collections of unusual plants, incl acers, birches, rhododendrons, azaleas, camellias, magnolias, roses, spring bulbs, alpines and herbaceous borders; formal gardens; Wheelchair available. Restaurant. *Adm garden only £3.10 Chd £1.50. Suns April 28, June 30 (10.30-5.30)*

Lee Ford &&& (Mr & Mrs N Lindsay-Fynn) Budleigh Salterton. Bus:DG, frequent service between Exmouth railway station (3½m) and Budleigh Salterton, alight Lansdowne corner. 40 acres parkland, formal and woodland gardens with extensive display of spring bulbs, camellias, rhododendrons, azaleas and magnolias. Adam pavilion. Picnic area. Car park free. Home made cream TEAS (3-5.30) and charity stalls. *Adm £1.50 OAPs £1.20 Chd 70p Special rate for groups 20 or more £1.20 (Share to the Lindsay Fynn Trust®). Sun May 26 (1.30-5.30); also by prior appt for parties of 20 or more* **Tel 01395 445894**

By Appointment Gardens. These owners do not have a fixed opening day usually because they do not like crowds or have insufficient parking space. Owner will often give guided tour.

The National Gardens Scheme is a charity which traces its origins back to 1927. Since then it has raised a total of over £14 million for charitable purposes.

Little Cumbre &&& (Dr & Mrs John Lloyd) Exeter. At top of Pennsylvania Rd, 50yds below telephone kiosk on same side. Extensive views of Dartmoor and the Exe Estuary. ½-acre mixed shrub and herbaceous garden. Galanthus, hellebores, clematis and small ornamental trees chosen for bark. Ample parking in rd. *Adm £1 Chd 50p. Thurs April 18, May 16 (2-5.30). Private visits also welcome for parties of 5 and over, please* **Tel 01392 58315**

Little Southey &&& (Mr & Mrs S J Rowe) Northcott, Nr Culmstock. Uffculme to Culmstock rd, through Craddock then turn R at 6'6 restriction sign, Little Southey ½m on L. Culmstock to Uffculme turn L at restriction sign to Blackborough, right at Xrds to Northcott. House on R. Garden surrounding C17 farmhouse. Wide variety of plants grown for round the year interest. Limited parking if wet. Plant sale partly in aid of NCCPG. TEAS (June 30 only). *Adm £1 Chd free. Sun June 30 (2-6); Mon July 1 (2-4)*

Little Upcott Gardens &&& (Mr & Mrs M Jones) Marsh Green, signposted off A30 Exeter to Honiton rd 4m E of M5 junction 29. Also signposted off B3180. Garden signposted from Marsh Green. Informal 2-acre garden with many features of visual interest on different levels, featured on TV in 1992. Sensitive combination of plant styles and colour and unusual varieties of conifers, shrubs, perennials and alpines, some of which are available for sale. The original cottage garden is also open and there is a newly landscaped water feature with ornamental ducks. Plenty of seats available and assistance given to disabled incl partially sighted, by prior arrangement. Parties welcomed with cream teas, available by appt. TEAS. *Adm £1.50 Chd 50p (Share to Cats Protection League, Ottery Branch). Mons, Weds, Sat, Sun May 15, 25, 26, 29, Weds, Sats, Suns June 5, 8, 9, 12, 19, 22, 23, 26, 29 30; Weds, Sat, Sun July 3, 13, 14, 17, 27, 28, 31; Sat, Sun, Weds Aug 10, 11, 14, 21 (Weds 11-3, other days 1.30-5.30). Private visits also welcome, please* **Tel 01404 822797**

Little Webbery &&& (Mr & Mrs J A Yewdall) Webbery Cross, Alverdiscott. Approx 2½m E of Bideford. Either from Bideford (E The Water) along the Alverdiscott Rd or from the Barnstaple to Torrington Rd B3232. Take the rd to Bideford at Alverdiscott and pass through Stoney Cross. Parking next door field. Approx 3-acre garden with two large borders near the house with lawns running down a valley; pond, mature trees on either side and fields below, separated by a Ha Ha. Walled garden with box hedging, partly used for fruit, vegetables, and incl a greenhouse; lawns; rose garden and trellises; shrubs and climbing plants. A tennis court below and a lake beyond. TEA 70p. *Adm £1.50 Chd free. Sat, Sun June 22, 23 (2-6)*

The Lodge &&& (Mr & Mrs M H Tregaskis) Hartley Ave, Mannamead, Plymouth. 1½m from City Centre via Mutley Plain. Turn right at Henders Corner into Eggbuckland Rd, 3rd right at Tel kiosk to end of cul de sac. ½-acre S sloping aspect with variety of citrus fruits, olives, unusual shrubs, conifers, camellias and ground cover plants. Former L.A. Nursery with range of lean-to glasshouses for fruit and tender subjects. Featured on TV, 'Gardens for All'. TEA. *Adm £1.25 Chd 20p (Share to St. Luke's Hospice®). Suns May 5, June 16, July 21, (2-5.30). Private visits also welcome, please* **Tel 01752 220849**

Longham ✲❀ (Jennie Hale & Andrew Osborne) Coryton. Nr Lydford Gorge. A30, turn onto A386 Tavistock. 5m to Dartmoor Inn, signed to Lyford, past Lydford Gorge (NT). 3m R for Chillaton, 500yds R to Liddaton, downhill to Liddaton Cross, sharp R, 400yds over railway bridge, immed R into T sign rd, ½m downhill, L over small bridge, signed Longham Farm. Follow short track to the cottage. Ample parking. Small cottage garden with colourful mass herbaceous planting, ornamental grasses, shrubs, unusual perennials and climbers, vegetable garden, raised beds and polytunnel. Beautiful rural setting in wooded valley. TEAS. *Adm £1 Chd 50p. Suns July 28, Aug 4 (2-6)*

Lower Ware, Lyme Regis See Dorset

Lukesland (Mr & Mrs B N Howell) Ivybridge. 1½m N of Ivybridge on Harford Rd, E side of Erme valley. 15 acres of flowering shrubs, wild flowers and fine and rare trees with pinetum in Dartmoor National Park. Beautiful setting of small valley around Addicombe Brook with small lakes, numerous waterfalls and pools. Extensive and unusual collection of large and small leaved rhododendrons and one of the largest Magnolia Campbellii in the country. Partially suitable for wheelchairs. TEAS. *Adm £2 Chd 50p (Share to Harford Church® and Wixenford House©). Suns, Weds April 21 to June 16 incl. Bank Hol Mons May 6, 27. For NGS Wed May 8, Sun 12 (2-6). Coaches on application only,* **Tel 01752 893390**

Marwood Hill ❀ (Dr J A Smart) Marwood, 4m N of Barnstaple signed from A361 Barnstaple-Braunton rd and B3230 Barnstaple to Ilfracombe Rd. In Marwood village, opp church. 20-acre garden with 3 small lakes. Extensive collection of camellias under glass and in open; daffodils, rhododendrons, rare flowering shrubs, rock and alpine scree; waterside planting; bog garden; many clematis; Australian native plants. National Collection astilbe, iris ensata, tulbaghia. Partially suitable for wheelchairs. Plants for sale between 11-1 and 2-5. Teas in Church Room (Suns & Bank Hols or by prior arrangement for parties). *Adm £2 Acc chd under 12 free. Daily except Christmas Day (dawn-dusk)*

Meadow Court ♿ (Ken & Heather Davey) Slapton. Entering the village of Slapton from the A379 at the Memorial on the beach. Take 2nd R and 1st L to house and garden in middle of village. Large free parking area. Level garden of 1 acre created in the last 12 yrs and maintained by the owner. Large pond with waterfall; Gunnera and marginals, water hens nest here. Large lawned area with trees and shrubs; heathers and shrub roses. TEAS. *Adm £1 Chd 50p. Sun May 27 (2-6)*

Meadowcroft ♿❀ (Mrs G Thompson) 1 Downfield Way, Plympton. From Plymouth left at St Mary's Church roundabout, along Glen Rd, 3rd right into Downfield Drive; garden on right. From A38, Plympton turn-off L at 1st roundabout, R at 2nd down Hillcrest Drive and Glen Rd, L at bottom of hill. Opp Dillons into Downfield Drive. Downfield Way on R. Medium size; stream; rhododendrons, azaleas, trees, flowering shrub borders. TEAS. *Adm 80p Chd 10p. Suns April 14, May 5, June 9,;Wed April 24; Bank Hol Mon May 6 (2-5)*

Membland Villa ✲❀ (Mr & Mrs Jack Hockaday) Newton Ferrers. 10m E of Plymouth. A374 Plymouth-Kingsbridge. At Yealmpton, S to Newton Ferrers. Sharp L at Widey Cross to Bridgend, then L to Membland. 2nd house on L from top of Membland Hill. Small house on the former Membland Estate built 1882 by Edward Baring (Lord Revelstoke) set in country garden. Laid out and planted over 23yrs by present owner. Ornamental pond. Old roses, shrubs, climbers. Many unusual plants. Steep bluebell woods spectacular in season. TEAS. *Adm £1.25 Chd 25p. Suns April 28, May 12, June 23, July 21, Bank Hol Mons May 6, 27, Aug 26 (2-5). Private visits also welcome for parties of 10 and over, please* **Tel 01752 872626**

¶Metcombe Brake ✲ (John & Valerie Fielden) Higher Metcombe. 3m SW of Ottery St Mary. From A30 S signed Exmouth or from A3052 N signed Ottery St Mary onto B3180 for approx 2m from either direction. Turn E at Tipton X, signed Tipton St John for ¾m. Entrance in wood on R. 6 acres, especially spring bulbs, in a true woodland and shrub setting. Teas in Ottery St Mary. Collecting box. *Suns March 31, April 28, May 26 (10-6)*

Monks Aish ✲❀ (Capt & Mrs M J Garnett) 1m W of South Brent, near the hamlet of Aish, off B3372 W of village. Follow signposts to Aish. After going under Aish railway bridge up hill, 3rd house on L next to Great Aish. [Grid Ref 688603.] A very attractive 1-acre garden with stream, a little different from most with varieties of shrubs, trees, flowers, fruit and vegetables. TEAS. *Adm £1.50 Chd under 12 50p (Share to The Missions to Seamen®). Sat, Sun May 25, 26 (2-5). Private visits of 8 or over welcome, please* **Tel 01364 73102**

The Moorings ❀ (Mr & Mrs A Marriage) Rocombe, Uplyme, 2m NW of Lyme Regis. From Lyme Regis, about 1m on A3070, turn R signposted Rocombe, over Xrds, take narrow lane signposted Rocombe 4th house on R, drive beyond house. From Axminster, straight at Hunters Lodge then fork R twice, straight at Xrds and R again. ¾m on L. 3-acre peaceful woodland garden, developed since 1965, on hillside with terraced paths, overlooking unspoilt countryside. Fine trees inc many species eucalyptus, unusual pines, nothofagus; flowering shrubs inc some rare; daffodils and other spring flowers, ground cover, many ferns, autumn colour. *Adm 75p Chd free. Private visits welcome, please* **Tel 01297 443295**

Mothecombe House ♿✲❀ (Mr & Mrs A Mildmay-White) Holbeton, SE of Plymouth 4m. From A379, between Yealmpton and Modbury, turn S for Holbeton. Queen Anne house (not open). Walled gardens, herbaceous borders. Orchard with spring bulbs; camellia walk and flowering shrubs. Newly planted bog garden; streams and pond; bluebell woods leading to private beach. Walk through picturesque thatched cottages to the Old School Teahouse and along the coastal footpath to the stunning Erme Estuary. TEAS. *Adm garden £2 Chd free (Share to Holbeton Church®). Sat, Sun May 4, 5 (2-5.30). Parties welcome by appt, please* **Tel 01752 830444**

Oare Manor Cottage ✲❀ (Mr & Mrs J Greenaway) Oare. 6m E of Lynton off A39. R after county gate to Oare. 50yds from Oare Church immortalized, in R D Blackmore's 'Lorna Doone'. Sheltered cottage garden in the romantic Oare Valley. Old-fashioned herbaceous borders, unusual shade plants, alpines, roses, Mediterranean pot plants. Fine views of the moor. Parking in lower field or opp church. TEAS. *Adm £1 Chd 50p. Sun July 21 (2-6). Also private visits and coach parties welcome, please* **Tel 01598 741242**

The Old Glebe &*❀* (Mr & Mrs Nigel Wright) Eggesford, 4m SW of Chulmleigh. Turn S off A377 at Eggesford Station (½-way between Exeter & Barnstaple), cross railway and River Taw, drive straight uphill (signed Brushford) for ¾m; turn right into bridle path. 5-acre garden of former Georgian rectory with mature trees and several lawns, courtyard, walled herbaceous borders and a bog garden; emphasis on species and hybrid rhododendrons and azaleas, 750 varieties. Specialist rhododendron nursery open daily by appt. TEAS. *Adm £1.50 Chd 50p (Share to The Abbeyfield Chulmleigh®). Suns, Mon Bank Hols May 5, 6, 26, 27 (2-6). Parties welcome by appt, please* **Tel 01769 580632**

The Old Mill *❀* (Mr & Mrs Shapland) Blakewell Muddiford, nr Barnstaple. ½m past hospital off B3230 to Ilfracombe at Blakewell Fisheries. Follow signs to Mill (grade II) at end of lane. A 3-acre south facing garden partly on slope at the rear surrounded by beautiful countryside views. Many varieties of shrubs, herbaceous, conifers and trees. Vegetable, herbs, an orchard, wildlife ponds. A young lime avenue leading to new folly. Parking in field. *Adm £1 Chd free. Suns May 12, June 16, July 14 (11-5). Private visits also welcome, please* **Tel 01271 75002**

The Old Parsonage *❀❀* (Mr & Mrs Alex Hill) Warkleigh. 4m SW South Molton on B3226 past Clapworthy Mill (Hancocks Cider) R at stone barn signs to Warkleigh. From S through Chittlehamholt then 2nd R at War Memorial. Telephone kiosk marked on OS landranger sheet 180. 1-acre garden around former C16 Parsonage. Herbaceous border at entrance; enclosed stepped terraced garden behind house with wide range of plants and raised beds. Hillside above planted with trees and shrubs for autumn colour. Cream TEAS. *Adm £1 Chd 50p (Share to NCCPG®). Suns May 26, June 23, Aug 11, Oct 13 (2-5.30)*

The Old Rectory &*❀* (Mr & Mrs H E Morton) Woodleigh nr Loddiswell. 3½m N of Kingsbridge E off Kingsbridge-Wrangaton Rd at Rake Cross (1m S of Loddiswell). 1½m to Woodleigh. Garden on R in hamlet. C19 Clergyman's garden partly enclosed by stone walls; restored and added to by present owners; mature trees with collection of rhododendrons, camellias and magnolias and other shrubs; large numbers of naturalised bulbs especially crocus and daffodils in early March. *Adm £1 Chd 10p. Private visits usually welcome at any time, please* **Tel 01548 550387**

The Orchard ❀ (Mrs Hilda M Montgomery) Kenn. 5m S of Exeter off A38. ¾ acre; mostly trees; variety of conifers, azaleas, camellias, rhododendrons, many shrubs; fishponds and flowerbeds. Masses of spring bulbs. Ample parking nr Church. *Adm £1 OAPs/Chd 50p (Share to Redgate Bird Sanctuary, Exmouth©). By appointment only, please* **Tel 01392 832530**

Orchard Cottage &❀ (Mr & Mrs W K Bradridge) 30, Hulham Rd, Exmouth, From Exeter A376 L into Hulham Road, just before first set of traffic lights. Entrance lane between Nos 26 and 32 Hulham Rd, opp lower end of Phillips Avenue. ¼-acre typical cottage garden. Parking in Hulham Road or Phillips Avenue. *Adm £1 Chd free. By appt only, please* **Tel 01395 278605** *(2.30-5.30)*

¶**Otterton Gardens** *❀* 3 Gardens situated in the main street of the picturesque village of Otterton between Sidmouth and Budleigh Salterton. Teas available at Otterton Mill. *Combined adm £1.50 Chd 50p Sat, Sun June 8, 9 (2.30-6)*

¶**Basclose** (Barbara & Clem Pointer) Fore St. S facing ½-acre cottage garden around C16 cob farmhouse, linhay, a small apiary and a mixed orchard and vegetable garden on a hill looking over the village

¶**Houstern Farmhouse** (Nan & Mike Dickens) Fore St. Converted walled farmyard on 2 levels at rear of thatched cob farmhouse - mainly lawn and herbaceous beds - cottage perennials and climbing plants: very sheltered. Also orchard, vegetable garden and fruit cage

¶**April Cottage** (Nora Butler) Fore St. Medium-sized cottage garden behind C15 cottage

Ottery St Mary Gardens Maps available at each garden. *Combined adm £1.50 Chd 50p. Sat, Sun May 18, 19 (2-6)*

Ernespie & (Dr & Mrs G Ward) Longdogs Lane. Next to Ravenhill, connected by garden gate. S facing hot, dry garden, planted for easy care, cutting and continuous colour; rhododendrons, heathers, roses, level terrace. TEAS

¶**Little Ash Farm** & (Sadie & Robert Reid) Fenny Bridges. Situated on A30, next to Esso Garage at Fenny Bridges. Park in layby. Developing ½-acre garden, trees, shrubs, large pond and borders with integrated vegetables. Handmade furniture workshop

Ravenhill &*❀* (Ruth & Guy Charter) Longdogs Lane. Take Sidmouth Rd from town square, 200yds up Tip Hill turn L up narrow Longdogs Lane, 5th house on R. Medium-sized garden with a wide variety of unusual plants. South aspect, country views; pond; keen NCCPG propagator. Unusual plants for sale (Share to NCCPG®)

10 Slade Close *❀* (Betty & Jenny Newell) From town centre take rd towards Seaton. Turn R into Slade Rd, then L into Slade Close and R again. Small garden, mixed shrubs, spring flowers, small pond, scree garden

Overbecks *❀* (The National Trust) Sharpitor 1½m SW of Salcombe. From Salcombe or Malborough follow NT signs. 6-acre garden with rare plants and shrubs; spectacular views over Salcombe Estuary. Tea room same days as museum 12-4.15. *Adm garden only £2.30 Chd £1.10. Suns June 2, 23 (10-8 sunset if earlier)*

Penrose *❀❀* (Mr & Mrs A Jewell) Crediton. A377 main Exeter to Barnstaple road, turn into Park Rd by Hillbrow Residential Home. Garden opp third turning on L. ⅓-acre town garden with small lawns, shrubs and herbaceous borders, pond with waterfall and wishing well, areas for fruit and veg and for growing produce for exhibition. Spring bulbs and summer annuals. TEA. *Adm £1 Chd free. Suns March 31, June 30, Aug 10, Sat June 29 (2-6). Private visits of 10 or over welcome, please* **Tel 01363 773587**

General Information. For general information on the use of this book see Page 15.

38 Phillipps Avenue ⚘❀ (Mr & Mrs R G Stuckey) Exmouth. From Exeter, turn L into Hulham rd just before 1st set of traffic lights, 1st L into Phillipps Avenue (ample parking). Small, highly specialised alpine and rock garden containing extensive collection of rock plants and minature shrubs, many rare and unusual; peat bed; scree bed; troughs; New Zealand collection. National NCCPG Helichrysum collection. Small alpine nursery. Teashops Exmouth. *Adm 50p Chd free. Suns March 24, April 7, 14, May 5, 19, 26; June 2, 16, 30 (Shore to NCCPG (Helichrysum Day)®) July 14, 28; Aug 11, Sept 1 (2-6). Private visits also welcome, please* **Tel 01395 273636**

The Pines ⚘ (R A Bitmead) Main Rd, Salcombe. At junction of Devon and Sandhills rds; lower entrance and parking Sandhills rd. All seasons ¾-acre S facing garden; fine coastal views to Sharpitor Headland and N Sands Valley. Informal garden of surprises; many interesting and unusual shrubs, trees; water gardens; bulbs, camellias, azaleas, heathers. *Adm £2 Chd free. Sat, Sun March 10, 17, 23, 24, April 7, Bank Hol Mon April 8 (11-5). Private visits also welcome all year, please* **Tel 01548 842198**

Plant World ❀ (Ray & Lin Brown) St. Mary Church Rd Newton Abbot. Follow brown signs from A380 Penn Inn Roundabout. Car park on L past Water Gardens. 4-acre Hillside Garden, laid out as a map of the world with native plants. Alpines, especially primulas and gentians, shrubs, herbaceous. Himalayan and Japanese gardens. Comprehensive cottage garden with double primroses, auriculas etc. 3 National Primula Collections. Seen on BBC Gardeners World June 1993. Rare and unusual plants sold in adjacent nursery. Picnic area, viewpoint over Dartmoor and Lyme Bay. Collecting box. *Adm £1 Chd under 12 free. Open daily March to Oct (9.30-5)*

Pleasant View Nursery ⚘❀ (Mr & Mrs B D Yeo) Two Mile Oak, nr Denbury. 2m from Newton Abbot on A381 to Totnes. R opp 2m Oak Garage signed Denbury. ¾m on L. Large car park. 2-acre plantsman's garden with a wide range of choice and uncommon shrubs giving colour all season. Additional 2-acre field recently planted with individual specimen shrubs. National Collections of Abelia and Salvia. Plants for sale in adjoining nursery (see advert). Guided tours of salvias Weds, Fris, July, Aug 3pm. *Adm £1.20 Chd 25p. Sats, Suns June 1, 2, Aug 31, Sept 1 (2-6) Every Wed and Fri, May to Sept (2-5). Parties welcome by appt, please* **Tel 01803 813388**

Portington (Mr & Mrs I A Dingle) nr Lamerton. From Tavistock B3362 to Launceston. ¼m beyond Blacksmiths Arms, Lamerton, fork L (signed Chipshop). Over Xrds (signed Horsebridge) first L then L again (signed Portington). From Launceston R at Carrs Garage and R again (signed Horsebridge), then as above. Small garden in peaceful rural setting with fine views over surrounding countryside. Mixed planting with shrubs and borders; woodland walk to small lake. TEAS. *Adm £1 Chd 20p (Share to St Luke's Hospice®). Suns July 7, 14 (2-5.30)*

Priors ⚘ (Mrs Hunloke) Abbotskerswell. 1½m SW of Newton Abbot on Totnes-Newton Rd, signposted Abbotskerswell. Garden at bottom of village. ⅔-acre enclosed colourful garden, long herbaceous borders, old shrub roses; unusual plants. *Adm £1 Chd 50p. Suns June 23, 30, July 7 (2-5.30). Private visits welcome June to July, please* **Tel 01626 53506**

Purple Hayes ⚘❀ (Kim & Bruce Thomas) Lake Farm, Halberton. B3391 ¼m SE of Halberton. Plantaholic's garden of 1 acre, started in 1987. Bold herbaceous planting, unusual plants, ornamental grasses, ponds, bog and herb garden. Pigmy goats and ducks. Cream Teas in adjoining farmhouse. *Adm 75p Chd free (Share to Cats Protection League®). Suns May 26, June 30, Aug 18 (11-5). Private visits welcome, please* **Tel 01884 821295**

Quakers ⚘❀ (Mr & Mrs T J Wallace) Membury. 3m NW of Axminster. A35 to Honiton, ½m W of Axminster turn N signed Membury. In village go 1m S of the church take sharp L turn. 100yds on L a red front door. Interesting small terraced flower garden around old Quaker Meeting House. 3 acres across lane, more a plantsman's whimsical collection than a garden. Mixed unusual tree and shrub plantings leading down to and over a wooded stream. *Adm £1 Chd 50p. Private visits welcome April to Nov, please* **Tel 01404 881312**

¶**The Rectory** ⚘⚘❀ (Mr & Mrs T A Rhodes) East Portlemouth (Opp Salcombe). From A379 Kingsbridge to Dartmouth, at Frogmore S over bridge towards E Portlemouth for 5 m, through village to estuary, R for 200yds, entrance on L. Or from Salcombe passenger ferry to E Portlemouth, L for ½m. Parking in field adjacent. Former rectory in 4-acre garden on Salcombe Estuary with lovely views to South Pool Creek. Springtime with camellias, magnolias, viburnums, bluebells and primroses. Summertime with herbaceous and mixed borders. Many unusual shrubs. Sheltered walled garden with glasshouse, roses and tender plants. TEAS. *Adm £1 Chd free (Share to Portlemouth Church®). Suns May 12, July 14 (2-5) Also every Thurs & Sat May 9 to Sept 14 with Collecting Box for NGS. Private visits (incl plant sales) welcome, please* **Tel 01548 842670**

Riversbridge ⚘❀ (Mr & Mrs Sutton-Scott-Tucker) ½m inland from Blackpool sands and signed from A3122. Small walled gardens adjoining farmyard in lovely unspoilt valley with ponds and stream; herbaceous plants, roses and some unusual shrubs. TEAS. *Adm £1.50 Chd free. Suns June 16, 23 (2-6)*

Robin Hill ⚘ (Dr G Steele-Perkins) Deepdene Park, Exeter. From Barrack Rd turn W into Wonford Rd; entry to drive on left beyond Orthopaedic Hospital. ½-acre around house on level ground with variety of ornamental trees and shrubs; wall plants, ground cover and small pond. *Adm £1 Chd free. Private visits welcome on Suns May 5 to July 28, please* **Tel 01392 72861**

Scotland's Gardens Scheme. The National Gardens Scheme has a similar but quite separate counterpart in Scotland. Called Scotland's Gardens Scheme, it raises money for the Queen's Nursing Institute (Scotland), the Gardens Fund of the National Trust for Scotland and over 160 registered charities nominated by garden owners. The Handbook is available (£3.25 incl p&p) from Scotland's Gardens Scheme, 31 Castle Terrace, Edinburgh EH1 2EL. Telephone 0131-229-1870, Fax 0131-229-0443

Rosemoor Garden &&& (The Royal Horticultural Society) Great Torrington. 1m SE of Great Torrington on B3220 to Exeter. Original plantsman's garden started in 1959 now recognised as a garden of national importance; rhododendrons (species and hybrid), ornamental trees and shrubs; dwarf conifer collection, species and old-fashioned roses, scree and raised beds with alpine plants, arboretum. The Society has expanded the Garden from 8 acres to 40. The new Garden already contains 2000 roses in 200 varieties, two colour theme gardens, herb garden, potager, 200 metres of herbaceous border, a large stream and bog garden, cottage garden, foliage and plantsman's garden and a fruit and vegetable garden. The Visitors Centre contains a restaurant, shop, and plant centre. Facilities for the disabled. Guide dogs only. *Adm £3 Chd £1 Groups £2.50 per person. Open daily all year (10-6 April to Sept. 10-5 Oct to March) (Share to NGS).* **Tel 01805 624067**

¶**St Olaves** ✄ (Mr & Mrs R Padley) Murchington. 1m W of Chagford. A382 1m S of Whiddon Down signed Throwleigh and Gidleigh, then signs to Murchington. From village centre, entrance to driveway adjacent house with iron railings, follow drive past cottage to open gate on L, then 50 yds for parking area. Converted by a Victorian clergyman from a row of cottages into a country house sometime after 1840, subsequently divided into 3 in 1961. Aim for section farthest from rd. 10-acre garden neglected after the war, restored and replanted since 1971. Romantic landscape views over the Upper Teign Valley. Fine old trees and a large number of younger ones from round the world. Massive granite retaining walls. Most of garden is on a S-facing slope down which a cascade falls to the river. *Adm £1.50 Chd 50p (Share to Devon Gardens Trust®). Weds May 1, 8 (2-5.30). Also private visits welcome for magnolias and camellias mid March to May, please* **Tel 01647 433415**

Saltram House &✄ (The National Trust) Plympton, 3m E of Plymouth, S of A38, 2m W of Plympton. 8 acres with fine specimen trees; spring garden; rhododendrons and azaleas. C18 orangery and octagonal garden house. George II mansion with magnificent plasterwork and decorations, incl 2 rooms designed by Robert Adam. Wheelchair available. Restaurant. *Adm gardens only £2.40 Chd £1.20. For NGS Suns April 14, May 12 (10.30-5.30)*

Sampford Peverell Gardens 6m from Tiverton on A373, 1m from junction 27 on M5. Canal walks. TEAS at Challis. *Combined adm £1.50 Chd 50p. Suns July 7, 21*

¶**7 Blackdown View** (Mr & Mrs Smith) Higher Town. Small garden in a quiet setting with extensive views over the countryside. Mixed planting with lawn, shrubs and bedding, greenhouse

Challis ❀ (Mr & Mrs G Issac) Next to Globe Inn in the centre of the village. A well established garden with trees and shrubs. Large lawned area with flower beds, fish ponds and rockery. Some interesting outbuildings with many hanging baskets in the courtyard. The garden leads directly to the tow path of the Grand Western Canal. TEAS

High Cross House ✄❀ (Mr &Mrs Bowers) Higher Town. Adjacent to Church. ¾-acre garden in sections comprising walled garden, courtyard garden, lawns with beds containing specimen shrubs and herbaceous plants. Large vegetable plot. Garden extends to the canal

Scypen ✄❀ (Mr & Mrs John Bracey) Ringmore. From A379 Plymouth-Kingsbridge S at Harraton Cross on B3392. R at Pickwick Inn. Park in Journey's End car park on L opp church. ½-acre coastal garden, integrating design, landscaping and mixed planting for year-round effect and to take advantage of lovely views. Salt and wind tolerant plants; silver garden; chamomile and thyme lawns. Featured on BBC 'Gardener's World'. TEAS. *Adm £1 Chd 25p. Wed June 27, Sun June 30 (2-5)*

¶**Shobrooke Park Gardens** &✄ (Dr & Mrs J R Shelley) Crediton. 1m NE Crediton on A3072. 15-acre woodland gardens with old rhododendrons. Laid out in mid C19 with extensive Portland Stone terraces with views over the park and ponds. Restoration in an early stage with help from The Countryside Commission. *Adm £2 Chd free. Mon May 6 (2-5)*

Sowton Mill &❀ (A Cooke and S Newton) nr Dunsford. From Dunsford take B3193 S for ½m. Entrance straight ahead off sharp R bend by bridge. From A38 N along Teign Valley for 8m. Sharp R after humpback bridge. 4 acres laid out around former mill, leat and river. Part woodland, ornamental trees and shrubs, mixed borders and scree. Year round interest. TEAS. *Adm £1.50 Chd free (Share to Cygnet Training Theatre®). Suns June 30, July 14 (2-6). Private visits also welcome, please* **Tel 01647 52347**

Spillifords (Dr Gavin Haig) Lower Washfield. Tiverton can be reached on A396 Tiverton to Bampton. Turn L over iron bridge signposted Stoodleigh and Ravenswood. L again after crossing bridge marked Washfield and L again on hill following Washfield sign. The bridge is approx 2m from link rd roundabout. Spillifords is 1st house on L after Hatswell. Parking for 25 cars by annexe on same side as house. 1½-acre wildlife and wild flower garden, ideal for those interested in natural history. On steeply sloping bank of R Exe (unsuitable for disabled) in which a wide range of wild flowers, butterflies, birds and other wildlife abound in an ideal arboreal and riverside environment. Frequently featured in media on various wildlife programmes. TEAS. *Adm £2 Chd £1. Maximum benefit for visitors would be derived from direct guidance from owner, hence garden open by appointment only. Weds, Sats April to Aug (3-6). Please* **Tel 01884 252422**

Starveacre ❀ (Mr and Mrs Bruce Archibold) Dalwood. Leave Axminster on A35 travelling W. After 3m (Shute Xrds) turn R at staggered Xrds signposted Dalwood. Follow signs to Dalwood and go through village, over stream, round sharp L bend. Follow road, ignoring left turn, up steep hill and at top turn L. Under pylons and up hill. Car park on L. A plantsman's garden of 5 acres on a hillside facing S and W with superb views. Mixed plantings of rhododendrons, camellias, conifers, acers, magnolias and much more. TEAS. *Adm £1 Chd under 14 free. Suns May 5, 26, Oct 20 (2-5)*

By Appointment Gardens. These owners do not have a fixed opening day usually because they do not like crowds or have insufficient parking space. Owner will often give guided tour.

Stone Lane Gardens ❀ (Kenneth & June Ashburner) Stone Farm Chagford. On NE edge of Dartmoor National park. From A30 signed Moretonhampstead, through Whiddon Down (A382) for ¼m, then signed Drewsteignton. After 1½m, 2nd R into Stone Lane. Parking in farmyards on L. 5-acres informally landscaped specialist arboretum with emphasis on foliage and bark and featuring national collections of wild-origin birch and alder; natural streams and ponds. Open views of Dartmoor. Exhibition of work within garden by sculptors and designers inspired by nature, myth and folklore June-Sept. Partially suitable for wheelchairs. No coaches. TEA. *Adm £2 Chd £1. Gardens open daily mid-June to mid-Nov (2-6). For NGS Weds May 29, June 19, July 10 (2-6). Private visits also welcome, please* Tel 01647 231311

Sunrise Hill ✿❀ (Chris & Sharon Britton) Withleigh. 3m W of Tiverton on B3137 rd to Witheridge and South Molton. Garden reached through Withleigh Nurseries, situated at E end of village. Approx 1 acre of colourful garden incl 100ft 'Rainbow' herbaceous border, unusual plants, shrubs, lawns and vegetable area. New plantings. Plants for sale in adjacent nursery (on open days 10% of plant sales for NGS). TEAS. *Adm £1 Chd free. Sat May 25, Weds July 24, 31 (2-5.30). Parties welcome by appt, please* Tel 01884 253351

¶**Sweet Chestnut** (P Thompson) Whisselwell Lane, Bovey Tracey. From Bovey Tracy, follow Haytor Rd to Edgemoor Hotel. Sharp L opp hotel, then 1st R, signed Whisselwell Farm. Last house on R. 1-acre woodland garden. Rhododendrons and camellias in abundance and other ericaceous plants and ground cover. Good yr-round planting and autumn colour with list available on request. Partially suitable for wheelchairs. *Adm £1.50 Chd 25p. Private visits welcome, please* Tel 01626 833280

Tapeley Park & Gardens ✿❀ (NDCI Ltd) Instow. Off A39 Barnstaple-Bideford rd 1m S of Instow. Italian garden of horticultural interest with many tender plants. Walled kitchen garden; woodland walk to lily pond. Putting, bowls, croquet, picnic area. Lunches & cream TEAS. *Adm £2.50 OAP, Chd £2. Collecting Box for NGS Easter to end Sept daily except Sats (10-6), please* Tel 01271 860528

Topsham Gardens 4m from Exeter. Free parking in Holman Way car park. Teas at 20 Monmouth Ave. *Adm 50p each garden Chd free. Suns, Mon May 26, 27 (2-6)*

4 Grove Hill ✿❀ (Margaret and Arthur Boyce) Off Elm Grove Rd, opp junction with Station Rd. A small town garden with some rare plants, troughs and screes with alpine plants and unusual bulbs

20 Monmouth Avenue ✿❀ (Anne & Harold Lock) Access to Monmouth Ave by footpath on the L after leaving Holman Way car park. ⅓-acre level garden, wide range of unusual plants and shrubs giving year round effect, mixed curved borders, herbaceous, shrubs and bulbs incl a collection of hardy geraniums and alliums. Some old fashioned roses. Featured on TV 'Gardens For All'. TEAS. *Private visits also welcome, please* Tel 01392 873734

Twitchen Mill ✿✿❀ (Geoffrey & Wyn Haydon) 6m NE of South Molton. B3227 S Molton to Taunton, 400yds past caravan site on outskirts of town, at top of hill L for 5m. Signposted from thereon. Parking on roadside and field. Wheelchairs if dry. 1½-acre level garden in the foothills of Exmoor. Ponds, bog plants, shrubs and mixed borders maintained by owners. Cream TEAS. *Adm £1.20 Chd free. Suns May 26, July 21 (2-6)*

Vicar's Mead ✿✿❀ (Mr & Mrs H F J Read) Hayes Lane, East Budleigh, 2m N of Budleigh Salterton. From B3178. Newton Poppleford-Budleigh Salterton, turn off W for East Budleigh; Hayes Lane is opp 'Sir Walter Raleigh'; garden 100yds W of public car park. 3½ acres of informal plantings around a 500yr-old historic former vicarage; wide range of unusual and rare shrubs, trees, bulbs and perennials etc, displayed on a steep terraced escarpment. Hostas and 4 National Collections a feature. Tea in village. *Adm £1 Chd free. Sun June 2 to Sun June 9 incl (2-6)*

96 Wasdale Gardens ✿ (David & Colleen Fenwick) Estover, Plymouth. Outskirts of city. From A38 Forder Valley Junction, follow Forder Valley Rd (old A38), R into Novorossisk Rd, L into Miller Way, 3rd L into Keswick Crescent, 1st L into Wasdale Gardens. Car park next to 102 Wasdale Gardens, follow path along top of car park past nos 95 and 94. Garden in front of 93, recognisable by 2 dovecotes. Small council house garden 15m × 11m. Large diversity of unusual plants, mostly herbaceous. Specialist collection of over 140 Crocosmia hybrids. Most landscaping and recyling demonstration garden features constructed using recycled materials. *Adm £1 Chd 25p. Suns Aug 18, 25, Mon Aug 26 (10-5). Private visits also welcome at other times, please* Tel 01752 785147

Weetwood ✿ (Mr & Mrs J V R Birchall) Offwell, 2m from Honiton. Turn S off A35 (signed Offwell), at E end of Offwell. 1-acre all seasons garden; rhododendrons, azaleas, shrubs, ornamental pools, rock gardens, collection of dwarf conifers. Teashops Honiton. *Adm 50p Chd 10p (Share to The Forces Help Society, Lord Roberts Workshops). Private visits usually welcome spring, summer & autumn, please* Tel 01404 831363

Westpark ✿❀ (Mr & Mrs D Court) Yealmpton, 7m E of Plymouth; on Kingsbridge Rd (A379) Xrds centre of village, turn S on Newton Ferrers rd; park end of Torr Lane. An old-fashioned rambling 2-acre garden in peaceful country setting. Year round colour and variety. Old roses, pergola, mulberry (1907), wood with cyclamen, ferns, bulbs, fruit cage, vegetable garden. Interesting C19 narcissi March/April. TEAS. *Adm £1.50 Chd 30p. Wed, Sun March 27, 31 (2-5). Private visits also welcome mid Feb to mid Oct, please* Tel 01752 880236

Whitmore ✿❀ (Mr & Mrs Cyril Morgan) Chittlehamholt. 12m SE Barnstaple, house marked on O.S. Landranger 180. From the village take rd S past Exeter Inn and High Bullen Hotel; Whitmore is ¼m further on L down long tree-lined drive. 3-acre garden with ponds, stream and herbaceous borders. An interesting collection of trees and shrubs. Further 3 acres of woodland garden mainly ferns with pleasant sylvan walks, amongst wood warblers and box breeding pied flycatchers and nuthatches. Red and roe deer often present. A secluded peaceful garden. TEAS. *Adm £1 Chd 50p. Thurs April 11, Sat July 13, Sun Aug 25 (2-5)*

Winkfield ✳❀ (Mr & Mrs R W Ramsdale) Colyford. On A3052 at Colyford. Next to St Michael's Chapel of Ease. Ample parking at Memorial Hall opp. Seaton 1½m. Garden approx 1 acre. Wide variety of hardy herbaceous plants, with iris, grasses and agapanthus a feature. Victorian pond. National Reference Collection of Heuchera. TEAS. *Adm £1 Chd free (Share to Friends of Seaton Hospital®). Wed June 19, Sun July 7 (2-5.30)*

Withleigh Farm ❀ (T Matheson) Withleigh village. 3m W of Tiverton on B3137, 10yds W of 'Withleigh' sign, entrance to drive at white gate. Peaceful undisturbed rural setting with valley garden, 14 years in making; stream, pond and waterside plantings; bluebell wood walk under canopy of mature oak and beech; wild flower meadow, primroses and daffodils in spring, wild orchids. TEA. *Adm £1 Chd 50p (Share to Cancer & Arthritis Research®). Sat, Sun May 25, 26 (2-5). Private visits also welcome, please* **Tel 01884 253853**

Wolford Lodge ৬ (The Very Rev. the Dean of Windsor and Mrs Patrick Mitchell) Dunkeswell. Take Honiton to Dunkeswell rd. L at Limer's Cross. Drive ½m on L at white entrance gate and lodge. 4 acres semi-woodland with massed rhododendrons, azaleas and camellias. Distant views to S over unspoilt Devon countryside. Woodland walks. *Adm £1 OAP/Chd 50p. Sat May 18 (2-6)*

Wood Barton ৬✳❀ (Mr & Mrs Richard Horton) Kentisbeare. 3m from M5 exit 28. A373 Cullompton to Honiton rd. 2m turn L signed Goodiford for 1m and turn L again at White Cottages. Farm drive, 100yds R. Bull on sign. [Landranger 192. Lat 09 Long 05/06.] 2 acres woodland garden planted 45yrs with species trees on S facing slope. Magnolias, azaleas, camellias, rhododendrons, acers; several ponds and water feature. Autumn colour. TEAS. *Adm £1 Chd 50p (Share to Action Research®). Sat, Sun May 18, 19 (2-6). Also private visits by appt Tel* **01884 266285**

Woodside ✳ (Mr & Mrs Mervyn Feesey) Higher Raleigh Rd, Barnstaple. On outskirts of Barnstaple, A39 to Hospital and Lynton, turn R 300yds above fire station. Semiwoodland, 2 acres S sloping in suburban area with intensive planting incl many ornamental grasses, sedges, bamboos and monocots (Author of RHS Handbook on Ornamental Grasses). Many parts of the garden are shaded and peaceful, offering protection to unusual and tender shrubs. Special interest in New Zealand flora. Raised beds and troughs, variegated, acid loving shrubs, ornamental trees and conifers, all with emphasis on form and colour of foliage, makes this a garden with a difference. *Adm £1 Chd 50p. Suns May 19, July 14 (2-5.30)*

Woodside ✳ (Mrs L L Braund) Whimple. Just off A30 rd between Honiton and Exeter. Turn N opp the B3180 turning for Exmouth. 1st L, house 1st on L, signposted Exeter 9m. Honiton 7m. ¾-acre garden 500' above sea level. Large variety of herbaceous plants, shrubs and roses. Colourful throughout the summer and an excellent example of what can be achieved in late season. TEA. *Adm £1 Chd free. Suns July 21, Aug 18 (2-5.30). Private visits welcome June to end Sept, please Tel* **01404 822340**

Wylmington Hayes ✳❀ (Mr and Mrs P Saunders) Wilmington. 5½m NE of Honiton on A30, turn R. Signposted Stockland 3m/Axminster 10m, after 3½m entrance gates on R (before Stockland TV Station) or from A35 3½m W of Axminster turn N nr Shute Garage on to Stockland Road for 3m, entrance on L nr TV mast. Reclaimed gardens, created in 1911. 83 acres of gardens and woodlands with spectacular hybrid rhododendrons, azaleas, magnolias, camellias, acers. Lakes, ponds, topiary, arboretum, woodland walks with abundant wildlife. Interesting collection of ornamental and domestic waterfowl including black swans. Scottish Country Dancing June 2, 16. TEAS. *Adm £2.50 Chd £1. Easter Fri, Sat, Sun, Mon April 5, 6, 7, 8; Suns April 14, 21, 28; May 5, 12, 19, 26 June 2, 9, 16, 23, 30; Bank Hol Mons May 6, 27 (2-5). Coaches & parties by appt please Tel* **01404 831751**

Yonder Hill ৬✳❀ (Mrs M H Herbert) Colaton Radleigh. A3052 at Newton Poppleford. B3178 towards Budleigh Salterton 1m 1st L signposted to Dotton then immed R into small lane. ¼m 1st house on R. Car parking. Part of a 4-acre smallholding set in peaceful countryside with panoramic views. Approx 2 acres with some 2000 different varieties for all-yr interest. Several unusual features. Variety of animals incl Rheas. Access to all parts for wheelchairs. Toilet facilities. Wheelchair available. DIY TEA. *Adm £1 Chd 50p. Suns Feb 25, March 17, Apr 7, 28, May 5, June 16, July 7, 28, Aug 11, 25, Sept 15, Oct 6, 27. Bank Hol Mons April 8, May 6, 27, Aug 26 (11-5). Visitors welcome on other days. Please, Tel* **01395 567541**. *Also open Sun Feb 23 1997*

Dorset

Hon County Organiser:	Mrs Hugh Lindsay, The Old Rectory, Litton Cheney, Dorchester DT2 9AH
	Tel 01308 482383
Assistant Hon County Organisers:	Mrs Raymond Boileau, Rampisham Manor, Dorchester DT2 0PT
	Tel 01935 83612
	Stanley Cherry Esq., Highbury, Woodside Rd, West Moors, Ferndown BH22 0LY
	Tel 01202 874372
	Miss Jane Bennett, The Maples, Fontmell Magna, Shaftesbury, Dorset SP7 0PF
	Tel 01747 811766
	Mr & Mrs W E Ninniss, 52 Rossmore Road, Parkstone, Poole BH12 3NL
	Tel 01202 740913
Publicity:	Mrs S Henwood, The Old Rectory, West Compton, Dorchester DT2 0EY
	Tel 01300 320007
Hon County Treasurer:	Michael Gallagher Esq, 6 West Street, Chickerell, Weymouth DT3 4DY

DATES OF OPENING

March 10 Sunday
Mews Cottage, Portland ‡
Witchcroft, Southwell, Portland ‡

March 17 Sunday
Langebride House, Long Bredy

March 31 Sunday
Chiffchaffs, Bourton
Domineys Yard, Buckland Newton
Langebride House, Long Bredy
Stour House, Blandford
Welcome Thatch, Witchampton

April 3 Wednesday
Cranborne Manor Garden,
Cranborne ‡
Edmondsham House, Cranborne ‡

April 6 Saturday
Ashley Park Farm, Damerham

April 7 Sunday
Chiffchaffs, Bourton ‡
Horn Park, Beaminster
Manor Orchard, Stratton ‡‡
1 Manor Close, Stratton ‡‡
The Old Rectory, Litton Cheney
Snape Cottage, Bourton ‡
Thistledown, Alweston

April 8 Monday
Broadlands, Hazelbury Bryan
Edmondsham House, Cranborne
Thistledown, Alweston

April 10 Wednesday
Edmondsham House, Cranborne
Manor Orchard, Stratton ‡
1 Manor Close, Stratton ‡

April 14 Sunday
Bexington, Lytchett Matravers
Boveridge Farm, Cranborne
Cartref, Stalbridge
Fernhill Cottage, Witchampton ‡
Fernhill House, Witchampton ‡
Frith House, Stalbridge

April 17 Wednesday
Edmondsham House,
Cranborne

April 18 Thursday
Knitson Old Farmhouse,
nr Swanage

April 24 Wednesday
Edmondsham House, Cranborne

April 28 Sunday
Chiffchaffs, Bourton
Corfe Barn, Broadstone
Fernhill Cottage, Witchampton
Thistledown, Alweston
Welcome Thatch, Witchampton

May 2 Thursday
Rampisham Manor, Rampisham

May 4 Saturday
Ashley Park Farm, Damerham
Lamorna, Chedington

May 5 Sunday
Chiffchaffs, Bourton
Lamorna, Chedington
Pumphouse Cottage, Alweston ‡
46 Roslin Road South,
Bournemouth
Thistledown, Alweston ‡

May 6 Monday
Pumphouse Cottage, Alweston ‡
Thistledown, Alweston ‡

May 11 Saturday
Lamorna, Chedington

May 12 Sunday
Bexington, Lytchett Matravers
Domineys Yard, Buckland Newton
Eurocentre Language School,
Bournemouth
Friars Way, Upwey
Glebe House, East Lulworth
7 Highfield Close, Corfe Mullen
Hilltop Cottage, Woodville
Lamorna, Chedington
Mews Cottage, Portland
North Leigh House, nr Wimborne

May 15 Wednesday
Chedington Court, Chedington ‡
Hilltop Cottage, Woodville
Lamorna, Chedington ‡
Wincombe Park, nr Shaftesbury

May 16 Thursday
Kingston Maurward Gardens,
Dorchester
Knitson Old Farmhouse,
nr Swanage
Melbury House, nr Yeovil

May 18 Saturday
Studland Bay House, nr Swanage

May 19 Sunday
Aller Green, Ansty ‡
Boveridge Farm, Cranborne
Cartref, Stalbridge
2 Curlew Road, Bournemouth
Fernhill Cottage, Witchampton ‡‡
The Friary, Hilfield, nr Cerne
Abbas
Ivy Cottage, Ansty ‡
Langebride House, Long Bredy
Lower Ware, Lyme Regis
Moigne Combe, nr Dorchester
52 Rossmore Road, Parkstone
Slape Manor, Netherbury
Smedmore, Kimmeridge
Star Cottage, Wimborne
Studland Bay House, nr Swanage
Welcome Thatch,
Witchampton ‡‡

May 21 Tuesday
The Friary, Hilfield, nr Cerne
Abbas

May 22 Wednesday
Friars Way, Upwey
The Friary, Hilfield, nr Cerne
Abbas

May 25 Saturday
Ashley Park Farm, Damerham

May 26 Sunday
Chiffchaffs, Bourton
Corfe Barn, Broadstone
Deans Court, Wimborne
Minster
Edgeways, Poole
Glebe House, East Lulworth
Highwood Garden, Wareham
Moigne Combe, nr Dorchester

Pumphouse Cottage, Alweston ‡
46 Roslin Road South,
Bournemouth
Thistledown, Alweston ‡

May 27 Monday
Broadlands, Hazelbury Bryan
Horn Park, Beaminster
Pumphouse Cottage, Alweston ‡
Thistledown, Alweston ‡

May 30 Thursday
Melbury House, nr Yeovil

June 1 Saturday
Lamorna, Chedington
The Manor House, Abbotsbury

June 2 Sunday
7 Church Street, Upwey
2 Greenwood Avenue, Ferndown
Highwood Garden, Wareham
Kingston Lacy, nr Wimborne
Minster ‡
Lamorna, Chedington
The Manor House, Abbotsbury
Mews Cottage, Portland ‡‡‡
52 Rossmore Road, Parkstone ‡‡
Waterfalls, Bournemouth ‡‡
Wimborne Minster Model Town &
Gardens ‡
Witchcroft, Southwell,
Portland ‡‡‡

June 4 Tuesday
7 Church Street, Upwey

June 8 Saturday
Lamorna, Chedington

June 9 Sunday
Bexington, Lytchett Matravers
Boveridge Farm, Cranborne ‡
Cranborne Manor Garden,
Cranborne ‡
Friars Way, Upwey
High Hollow, Corfe Mullen
Lamorna, Chedington
26 Milestone Road, Poole
The Old Rectory, Fifehead
Magdalen
Weston House, Buckhorn Weston

June 12 Wednesday
Friars Way, Upwey
The Orchard, Blynfield Gate,
nr Shaftesbury

June 13 Thursday
Melbury House, nr Yeovil
Red House Museum & Gardens,
Christchurch

June 16 Sunday
Ashley Park Farm, Damerham
The Cobbles, Shillingstone
Edgeways, Poole
Holworth Farmhouse, Holworth
The Manor Farmhouse, Little
Windsor
The Manor House, Hinton-St-Mary
Portesham House, Portesham
Snape Cottage, Bourton
Star Cottage, Wimborne

Sturminster Newton Gardens
Thornhill Park, Stalbridge

June 19 Wednesday
26 Milestone Road, Poole
The Orchard, Blynfield Gate,
nr Shaftesbury

June 22 Saturday
Higher Melcombe, Melcombe
Bingham
Knitson Old Farmhouse,
nr Swanage

June 23 Sunday
The Cobbles, Shillingstone ‡
Coombe Cottage, Shillingstone ‡
Corfe Barn, Broadstone
Farriers, Puddletown ‡‡
Fernhill Cottage,
Witchampton ‡‡‡
Fernhill House, Witchampton ‡‡‡
4 Flower Cottage, Lower
Waterston ‡
2 Greenwood Avenue, Ferndown
Hambledon Cottage, Child
Okeford
Litton Cheney Gardens
The Manor House, Hinton-St-Mary
The Old Vicarage, Stinsford ‡‡
Portesham House, Portesham
The Priests's House Museum &
Garden, Wimborne
46 Roslin Road South,
Bournemouth
Sticky Wicket, Buckland Newton
Welcome Thatch, Witchampton ‡‡‡
Weston House, Buckhorn
Weston

June 26 Wednesday
The Orchard, Blynfield Gate,
nr Shaftesbury

June 27 Thursday
Melbury House, nr Yeovil

June 30 Sunday
Chiffchaffs, Bourton
7 Church Street, Upwey
The Cobbles, Shillingstone ‡
Coombe Cottage, Shillingstone ‡
Edgeways, Poole
Frith House, Stalbridge
High Hollow, Corfe Mullen
The Manor Farmhouse, Little
Windsor
Pumphouse Cottage, Alweston ‡‡
Steeple Manor, nr Wareham
Thistledown, Alweston ‡‡

July 2 Tuesday
7 Church Street, Upwey

July 3 Wednesday
Manor Orchard, Stratton ‡
1 Manor Close, Stratton ‡

July 6 Saturday
Bowhay, Iwerne Minster ‡
Lamorna, Chedington
Stepleton House, Iwerne
Stepleton ‡

July 7 Sunday
2 Curlew Road, Bournemouth
7 Highfield Close, Corfe
Mullen ‡
Lamorna, Chedington
Manor Orchard, Stratton ‡‡
1 Manor Close, Stratton ‡‡
Mews Cottage, Portland ‡‡‡
26 Milestone Road, Poole
Portland House, Weymouth
Rampisham Gardens,
Rampisham
Three Bays, Beacon Hill ‡
24a Western Avenue, Poole
Wimborne Minster Model Town
& Gardens
Witchcroft, Southwell,
Portland ‡‡‡

July 10 Wednesday
The Orchard, Blynfield Gate,
nr Shaftesbury
Pumphouse Cottage, Alweston ‡
Thistledown, Alweston ‡

July 11 Thursday
Flowery Bottom, Loscombe ‡
Kingston Maurward Gardens,
Dorchester
Melbury House, nr Yeovil
Pear Tree Farm, Loscombe ‡

July 13 Saturday
Lamorna, Chedington

July 14 Sunday
Bexington, Lytchett Matravers
Edgeways, Poole
Flowery Bottom, Loscombe ‡
Friars Way, Upwey
2 Greenwood Avenue, Ferndown
7 Highfield Close, Corfe
Mullen ‡‡
Holworth Farmhouse, Holworth
Lamorna, Chedington
Loscombe House, nr Bridport ‡
The Old Mill, Spetisbury
Pear Tree Farm, Loscombe ‡
Portesham Gardens, Portesham
Snape Cottage, Bourton
Stour House, Blandford
Three Bays, Beacon Hill ‡‡

July 17 Wednesday
Chedington Court, Chedington ‡
Lamorna, Chedington ‡
The Orchard, Blynfield Gate,
nr Shaftesbury

July 21 Sunday
Hilltop Cottage, Woodville
Melplash Court, nr Bridport
North Leigh House, nr Wimborne
46 Roslin Road South,
Bournemouth
Thornhill Park, Stalbridge

July 24 Wednesday
Hilltop Cottage, Woodville
The Orchard, Blynfield Gate,
nr Shaftesbury

July 28 Sunday
Chiffchaffs, Bourton
7 Church Street, Upwey
Edgeways, Poole
Farriers, Puddletown
2 Greenwood Avenue, Ferndown
High Hollow, Corfe Mullen
Hilltop Cottage, Woodville

July 30 Tuesday
7 Church Street, Upwey

August 1 Thursday
Melbury House, nr Yeovil

August 3 Saturday
Knitson Old Farmhouse,
  nr Swanage
Lamorna, Chedington

August 4 Sunday
Lamorna, Chedington

August 10 Saturday
Lamorna, Chedington

August 11 Sunday
Bexington, Lytchett Matravers
Domineys Yard, Buckland Newton
Lamorna, Chedington
Stour House, Blandford

August 14 Wednesday
Hilltop Cottage, Woodville

August 18 Sunday
Frith House, Stalbridge
High Hollow, Corfe Mullen
Hilltop Cottage, Woodville
Mews Cottage, Portland
Thornhill Park, Stalbridge

August 25 Sunday
Chiffchaffs, Bourton
7 Church Street, Upwey
Sticky Wicket, Buckland Newton

August 26 Monday
7 Church Street, Upwey

September 1 Sunday
Aller Green, Ansty ‡

Ivy Cottage, Ansty ‡
Wimborne Minster Model Town &
  Gardens

September 7 Saturday
Bowhay, Iwerne Minster

September 8 Sunday
Bexington, Lytchett Matravers
Eurocentre Language School,
  Bournemouth

September 18 Wednesday
Chedington Court, Chedington ‡
Lamorna, Chedington ‡

September 22 Sunday
Cartref, Stalbridge
Snape Cottage, Bourton

September 29 Sunday
Chiffchaffs, Bourton
Deans Court, Wimborne Minster

October 2 Wednesday
Edmondsham House, Cranborne

October 6 Sunday
Fernhill Cottage, Witchampton ‡
Mews Cottage, Portland
Welcome Thatch, Witchampton ‡

October 9 Wednesday
Edmondsham House, Cranborne

October 16 Wednesday
Edmondsham House, Cranborne

October 23 Wednesday
Edmondsham House, Cranborne

October 27 Sunday
Domineys Yard, Buckland Newton

Regular openings
For details see garden description

Abbotsbury Gardens, nr Weymouth
Athelhampton House and Gardens
Aurelia Gardens, West Moors
Broadlands, Hazelbury Bryan

Cartref, Stalbridge
Chiffchaffs, Bourton
Compton Acres Gardens, Poole
Cranborne Manor Garden, Cranborne
Deans Court, Wimborne Minster
Forde Abbey, nr Chard
Heatherwood, Ashington, Wimborne
Horn Park, Beaminster
Ivy Cottage, Ansty
Kingston Maurward Gardens,
  Dorchester
Knoll Gardens, Hampreston
Loscombe House, nr Bridport
Mapperton Gardens, nr Beaminster
Minterne, nr Cerne Abbas
The Old Mill, Spetisbury
Parnham, Beaminster
Snape Cottage, Bourton
Stapehill Abbey, Wimborne
Star Cottage, Wimborne
Sticky Wicket, Buckland Newton
Thornhill Park, Stalbridge

By appointment only
*For telephone numbers and other
details see garden descriptions.
Private visits welcomed*

Highbury, West Moors
Little Platt, Plush
Moulin Huet, West Moors
Oakmead, nr Beaminster
The Old Rectory, Seaborough

DESCRIPTIONS OF GARDENS

● **Abbotsbury Gardens** ❀ (Ilchester Estates) 9m NW of Weymouth. 9m SW of Dorchester. From B3157 Weymouth-Bridport, turn off 200yds W of Abbotsbury village, at foot of hill. 20 acres; uniquely mild Mediterranean-type climate, started in 1760 and considerably extended in C19; much replanting during past few years; very fine collection of rhododendrons, camellias, azaleas; wide variety of unusual and tender trees and shrubs. Peacocks. Children's play area, woodland trail, aviaries and plant centre. Partly suitable for wheelchairs. TEAS. *Adm £4 OAPs £3.50 Chd £1.25, Family £9 Reduced rate in winter (For party rate Tel 01305 871387). Easter to Oct 31 (10-6), Nov to Feb (10-dusk)*

Aller Green ✄ (A J Thomas Esq) Aller Lane, Ansty, 12m N of Dorchester. From Puddletown take A354 to Blandford; After public house, take 1st L down Long Lane signed Dewlish-Cheselbourne; through Cheselbourne to

Ansty then 1st R before Fox Inn down Aller Lane. 1-acre typical Dorset cottage garden; unusual trees, shrubs and perennials in old orchard setting and many perennials grown for Autumn Colour. Teas at **Ivy Cottage**. *Combined adm with Ivy Cottage £2.50 Chd 50p. Suns May 19 (Share to the Samaritans®); Sept 1 (Share to the Red Cross®) (2-5.30)*

Ashley Park Farm ♿❀ (David Dampney Esq) Damerham. Follow yellow signs off B3078, immediately W of village, 5m from Fordingbridge. Newly created gardens of 5 acres with farm and woodland walks. With many interesting trees, an arboretum in the making although now mature enough for visiting; eucalyptus grove; wild flower meadow. Many exciting plants for south facing walls, borders. TEAS, also every Sun. *Adm £1.50 Chd free (Share to Damerham Church®). ▲For NGS Sats April 6; May 4, 25, Sun June 16 (2-5.30). (See also Boveridge Farm). Private visits welcome, please Tel 01725 518 200*

● ¶**Athelhampton House & Gardens** &⚘☸ (Patrick Cooke Esq) Dorchester. 5m E of Dorchester on A35(T). The Gardens date from 1891. The Great Court includes 12 yew pyramids approx 30ft in height. From the terrace, flanked by 2 pavilions, there are views over the gardens which include collections of tulips, magnolias, roses, clematis and lilies in season. The lion's mouth shelters sub tropical plants collected from the Abbey Gardens, Tresco. The lime cloister was later copied at New Palace Yard at the Palace of Westminster. This glorious Grade I garden is full of vistas and surprises and gains much from the fountains and River Piddle flowing through. The C15 Manor house is also open. Restaurant serving lunches, cream teas and refreshments. *Adm House & Gardens £4.50, OAPs £4.20, Chd £1.50. Gardens only adults & OAPs £2.80 Chd free. Reduced rates for groups available. Open March 31 to Oct 27 (11-5) except Saturdays*

Aurelia Gardens &⚘☸ (Mr & Mrs Robert Knight) Newman's Lane, West Moors. N of the village off B3072 Bournemouth-Verwood rd. Heathers, conifers, grasses, variegated and golden foliage plants have been used to create a garden for year round colour. 5-acre level site, incl nursery and an acre of free parking. *Adm 50p. Weds, Thurs, Fris, Sats and Suns all year (9-5)*

Bexington &⚘☸ (Mr & Mrs Robin Crumpler) Lytchett Matravers. In Lime Kiln Rd, opp old School at W end of village. Colourful garden of ½-acre maintained by owners, with mixed borders of many interesting and unusual plants, shrubs and trees. Bog garden of primulas and hostas etc. Four rockeries of alpines, with walkways over bog area connecting two lawns, making a garden of interest from spring bulbs to autumn colour. Cream TEAS & plant stall for Alzheimer Disease Society & gardening charities. *Adm 80p Chd 20p. Suns April 14, May 12, June 9, July 14, Aug 11, Sept 8 (2-6). Group visits welcome by appt, please* **Tel 01202 622068**

Boveridge Farm ⚘ (Mr & Mrs Michael Yarrow) Cranborne. Leave Cranborne on Martin Rd unclass, thence take 2nd R Boveridge Farm. A plantsman's garden of 2 acres on 3 levels, part chalk and part acid; with lawns around old farmhouse, formerly manor house of the Hooper family; in rural surroundings with fine views. Fountain, fern bank and many rare and interesting trees and shrubs. Specimen acer 'Brilliantissimum', prunus 'Shidare Yoshino', prunus 'Pendula Rubra', Paulownia tomentosa. Teas at **Ashley Park**, Damerham (next village 3m). *Adm £1 Chd free (Share to Cranborne Church®). Suns April 14, May 19, June 9 (2-5). (See also **Ashley Park Farm**). Group visits welcome by appt, please* **Tel 01725 517241**

Bowhay &⚘☸ (Stephen Ford Esq) Iwerne Minster. Iwerne Minster is connected by two roads to Shaftesbury, 6m to the N; and to Blandford, 6m to the S. Either turn up from the lower A350 rd at the village war memorial, or down from the higher rd at the signed Xrds, to the house or garden sign. Parking bottom of lane below house. Interesting and exciting 1-acre garden on hill above village, re-designed and re-built in last 4 years. Roses, rockery; pergola, ponds; cascades, terraces and sitting areas with wonderful views. 'Peaceful'. Exhibition of paintings and TEAS in aid of church lighting. *Adm*

£1.50 Chd 40p. Sats July 6, Sept 7 (9-12, 3.30-7.30). Visits by appt, please **Tel 01747 811289**

Broadlands &⚘☸ (Mr & Mrs M J Smith) Hazelbury Bryan. 4m S of Sturminster Newton. From A357 Blandford to Sherborne rd, take turning signed Hazelbury Bryan, garden ½m beyond Antelope public house. An outstanding 2-acre plantsman's garden begun in 1975, designed to give beautiful views at every turn. Woodland, water, courtyard, rose and cottage gardens, mixed beds by colour theme etc contain a remarkable range of the choicest foliage and flowering plants. TEA. *Adm £2 Acc chd free. Sun April 28, every Weds June, July and Aug (2-5.30) (Share to NGS®). For NGS Easter Mon April 8, Bank Hol Mon May 27 (2-5.30) (Share to Dorset Wildlife Trust®). Private visits by appt, please* **Tel 01258 817374**

Cartref ⚘☸ (Nesta Ann Smith) Station Rd, Stalbridge. From A30, S at Henstridge for 1m. Turn L opp Stalbridge PO, House 80yds on R. Free car park nearby. A plantsman's garden approx ¼-acre, cottage garden and unusual plants. Small woodland area with choice shade-loving plants. Small potager, organically grown. TEA. *Adm £1.50 Chd free. Tues (2-6), Fris (10-6) April to end of May and July to Sept 30. For NGS Suns April 14, May 19, Sept 22 (10-5).* **Tel 01963 363705**

Chedington Court (Mr & Mrs J P H Chapman) Chedington, Beaminster. 4½m SE of Crewkerne off the A356. Turn at Winyard's Gap Inn, or 4½m NE from Beaminster via A3066. Turn R past Admiral Hood Inn in Mosterton. 10 acres. Mature Victorian garden. Magnificent situation, extensive views. Interesting trees and shrubs. Herbaceous borders, water garden and grotto, giant yew topiary, wild flowers, spring bulbs, mixture of the well-tended and the wild. TEA. *Adm £2 Chd 50p. Weds May 15, July 17, Sept 18 (11-4.30)*

Chiffchaffs ⚘☸ (Mr & Mrs K R Potts) Chaffeymoor. Leave A303 (Bourton by pass) at junction signposted Gillingham, Blandford and Bourton at W end of Bourton village. A garden for all seasons with many interesting plants, bulbs, shrubs, herbaceous border, shrub roses. Attractive walk to woodland garden with far-reaching views across the Blackmore Vale. Nursery open Tues-Sat and on garden open days. TEAS last Sun and Spring Bank Hol weekends. *Adm £2 Chd 50p (Share to St Michael's Church, Penselwood®). Open March 31 to Sept 29 every Sun and Bank Holiday weekend, Weds & Thurs (except for 2nd Sun every month and 1st Sun July and Aug). For NGS last Sunday of each month and Suns of Bank Holiday weekends plus 10% of all receipts (2-5.30). Private visits by appt please* **Tel 01747 840841**

7 Church Street &⚘☸ (Ann & Gordon Powell) Upwey, nr Weymouth. ½m from bottom of Ridgeway Hill on A354 Dorchester—Weymouth rd turn R B3159 (Bridport rd) L turn at bottom of hill. Limited parking for disabled only. 3 acres of mixed planting. Main trees planted 1972 with recent additions of shrubs and perennials. Woodland planted early 50's. Teas at Wishing Well. *Adm £1 Chd free. Suns June 2, 30 July 28; Aug 25; Tues June 4, July 2, 30; Mon Aug 26 (2-6)*

The Cobbles ◊❀ (Mr & Mrs A P Baker) Shillingstone. 5m NW of Blandford. In middle of village opp Old Ox Inn, Shillingstone. Plantsman's 1½-acre chalk garden round C17 cottage. Borders thickly planted with a mixture of shrubs, herbs, wild flowers, old roses, foliage plants and perennials incl many hardy geraniums. Small lake, stream and ditch garden. TEAS in aid of Shillingstone Parish Church. *Adm £1 Chd free. Suns June 16, 23, 30 (2.30-5.30)*

● **Compton Acres Gardens** ◊❀❀ Canford Cliffs Road, Poole. Sign from Bournemouth and Poole. Wilts & Dorset Buses 147, 150, 151. Yellow Buses nos 11 & 12 stop at entrance. Reputed to be the finest gardens in Europe incl Japanese, Italian, Rock and Water, Heather Dell, Woodland Walk and Sub-Tropical Glen. Magnificent bronze and marble statuary. Large selection of plants and stoneware garden ornaments. Refreshments available. Large free car/coach park. *Adm £4.20, OAPs £3.20, Chd £1. March 1 to Oct 31 daily. 10.30-6.30 last admission 5.45pm.* **Tel 01202 700778**

¶**Coombe Cottage** ❀ (Mike & Jennie Adams) Blandford Rd, Shillingstone. 5m NW of Blandford on A357 next to PO Stores on main rd. Parking advised in Gunn Lane. ¼-acre plantsman's cottage garden, enclosed by walls and hedges, with a catholic mix of herbaceous and woody perennials, climbers, bulbs and self-seeding annuals (many unusual), in broad, mostly rectangular borders, some of them colour co-ordinated. Small formal vegetable plot. TEAS. *Adm £1 Chd free. Suns June 23, 30 (2-6)*

Corfe Barn ◊❀ (John & Kathleen McDavid) Corfe Lodge Rd, Broadstone. From main roundabout in Broadstone W along Clarendon Rd, ¾m N into Roman Rd, after 50yds W into Corfe Lodge Rd. ⅔ acre on three levels on site of C19 lavender farm. Informal country garden with much to interest both gardeners and flower arrangers. Parts of the original farm have been incorporated in the design. A particular feature of the garden is the use made of old walls. TEAS. *Adm 50p Chd 25p. Suns April 28, May 26, June 23 (2-5)*

Cranborne Manor Garden ◊❀❀ (The Viscount & Viscountess Cranborne) Cranborne. 10m N of Wimborne on B3078. Beautiful and historic garden laid out in C17 by John Tradescant and enlarged in C20, featuring several gardens surrounded by walls and yew hedges: white garden, herb and mount gardens, water and wild garden. Many interesting plants, with fine trees and avenues. *Adm £3 OAPs £2 (Share to NSPCC®). Weds March to Sept incl (9-5). For NGS Wed April 3, (9-5), Sun June 9 (10-5)*

2 Curlew Road ◊❀❀ (Mr & Mrs Gerald Alford) Strouden Park, Bournemouth. From Castle Lane West turn S into East Way, thence E into Curlew Rd. Small town garden 200' × 30' divided into rooms and linked by arches. Conifers, acers, rhododendrons, clematis; spring and summer bedding; three water features. Seen on Pebble Mill '94 and Grass Roots '95. The owners are seriously disabled and their garden is thus of especial interest to other disabled people. *Adm £1 Chd 30p. Suns May 19, July 7 (2-6). Private visits welcome of 2 or more please* **Tel 01202 512627**

Deans Court ◊❀❀ (Sir Michael & Lady Hanham) Wimborne. Just off B3073 in centre of Wimborne. 13 acres; partly wild garden; water, specimen trees, free roaming peacocks. House (open by written appt) originally the Deanery to the Minster. Herb garden with about 200 species chemical free plants for sale. Walled vegetable garden with chemical free produce for sale as available. Free car parking. Morning coffee/TEAS. *Adm £1.50 Chd 70p. Daffodil weekends with teas Sat, Sun March 16, 17, 23, 24 (2-5). Easter Sun (2-6) Bank Hol Mons (10-6). 1st and last Suns May to Oct 6 (2-6). Organic Gardens weekend June 22, 23 (2-6). For NGS Suns May 26, Sept 29 (2-6)*

Domineys Yard ◊❀❀ (Mr & Mrs W Gueterbock) Buckland Newton, 11m from Dorchester and Sherborne 2m E of A352 or take B3143 from Sturminster Newton. Take 'no through rd' between church and 'Gaggle of Geese' public house next to phone box. Entrance 200 metres on L. Park and picnic in field with alder lined stream and recent tree planting, or in lane if wet. 2½-acre garden on chalk, clay and greensand surrounding C17 thatched cottage with adjacent kitchen garden and terraced cottages with gardens. Developed since 1961 with many unusual plants, shrubs and trees justifying their space in a garden for all seasons. Heated pool for summer opening. TEAS. *Adm £1.50 Chd 50p (Share to Leonard Cheshire Foundation Dorset Care at Home Service®). Suns March 31, May 12, Aug 11 (2-6), Oct 27 (12.30-4.30). Private visits welcome, please* **Tel 01300 345295**

Edgeways ◊❀❀ (Mr & Mrs Gerald Andrew) 4 Greenwood Ave, Poole. From Lilliput Rd nr Compton Acres turn N into Compton Ave, W into Fairway Rd, thence L into Greenwood Ave. Please do not park by roundabout or cul-de-sac. Delightful ⅓-acre garden designed informally on a gentle slope in a setting of mature trees. Extensive range of choice perennials grouped for colour and foliage effect to provide a succession of seasonal pictures. Mixed and herbaceous borders, lawn, grass paths, arbour and a pond reaching into a steep rock area contibute to a variety of interesting vistas. Several seats. 'Lots to admire and inspire.' Dorset Garden Guide. Shown on ITV's Grass Roots. TEA. *Adm 80p Acc chd free. Suns May 26, June 16, 30, July 14, 28 (11.30-5)*

Edmondsham House ◊❀❀ (Mrs Julia Smith) Edmondsham, nr Cranborne. B3081, turn at Sixpenny Handley Xrds to Ringwood and Cranborne; thereafter follow signs to Edmondsham. Large garden; spring bulbs, trees, shrubs; walled garden with herbaceous border; vegetables and fruit; grass cockpit. Early church nearby. TEAS. *Adm £1 Chd 50p under 5 free (Share to PRAMA®). Mon April 8, Weds April 3, 10, 17, 24; Oct 2, 9, 16, 23 (2-5); also private visits and parties welcome, please* **Tel 01725 517207**

Eurocentre Language School ◊◊ (Eurocentres (UK)) 22-28 Dean Park Rd, Bournemouth. Off Wimborne Rd (A347) ¼m N of Richmond Hill roundabout. Series of 4 linked gardens, now being restored to reflect the original surroundings of the late Victorian houses. Mature specimen trees and lawns; rhododendrons, small trees and flowering shrubs; spring and summer bedding, climbers, dahlia borders and small fernery. TEA. *Adm 80p Chd 40p (Share to Bournemouth General Hospital Scanner Appeal®). Suns May 12, Sept 8 (2.30-5)*

Farriers ᏝᏜ (Mr & Mrs P S Eady) 16 The Moor, Puddletown. On the A354 Puddletown-Blandford rd opp the rd to Piddlehinton, close to the Blue Vinney public house, Dorchester 5m. ⅓-acre informal country garden with much to interest gardeners and flower arrangers, designed and maintained by owners; shrubs, herbaceous, dahlias, sweet peas, vegetable plot, greenhouse with collection of begonias and streptocarpus, pond. *Joint opening with* **4 Flower Cottage** *on June 23. Adm £1 each garden Chd free also July 28 (2-5.30). Private visits welcome, please* Tel 01305 848634

Fernhill Cottage ᏜᏜ (Miss Shirley Forwood) Witchampton. Next to Fernhill House, directions as below. Small thatched cottage garden, interesting perennials, pulmonarias, old roses, michaelmas daisies and cottage plants. *Joint opening with* **Fernhill House.** *Combined adm £1.50, Chd free (Share to Witchampton Village Hall®). Suns April 14, June 23 (2-5). Also Adm 50p Chd free. Suns April 28, May 19, Oct 6 (2-5)*

Fernhill House ᏝᏜᏜ (Mrs Henry Hildyard) Witchampton. 3½m E of Wimborne B3078 L to Witchampton then L up Lower St. (Blandford rd,) house on R 200yds. Spring bulbs and blossom, roses and herbaceous borders, woodland walk with water garden and shrubs. Teas in Village Hall, June 23. *Joint opening with* **Fernhill Cottage.** *Combined adm £1.50 Chd free (Share to Joseph Weld Hospice Trust®). Suns April 14, June 23 (2-5)*

4 Flower Cottage ᏝᏜᏜ (Audrey Penniston) Lower Waterston. From Puddletown on the B3142 take the rd between Blue Vinney public house and Old's Garage on way to Piddletrenthide. ⅓-acre cottage garden, with herbaceous borders, scree and vegetables. TEAS. *Joint opening with* **Farriers** *Adm £1 (each garden) Chd free (Share to Dewlish Parish Church®). Sun June 23 (2-6). Private visits welcome, please* Tel 01305 848694

¶Flowery Bottom Ꮬ (Peter Mugliston) Loscombe. N of Bridport S of Beaminster. Approx 1½m E of A3066. One way traffic as signed from B3163 via Mapperton and A3066 at Melplash (opp Half Moon Inn). (Leave Loscombe via West Milton. Do not approach from this direction), after ½m turn R at Loscombe signpost; continue to bottom of lane (2m). 2½ acres reclaimed field in a tranquil setting surrounded by hills. Garden with lake, native trees and meadow area left for wild flowers. *Combined adm with* **Loscombe House** *and* **Pear Tree Farm** *£2 Chd free. Sun July 14. Combined adm with* **Pear Tree Farm** *£1.50 Chd free. Thurs July 11 (2-6)*

● Forde Abbey ᏝᏜ (M Roper Esq) 4m SE of Chard. 7m W of Crewkerne; well signed off A30. 'Christies Garden of the Year 1993'. 30 acres; many fine shrubs and some magnificent specimen trees incl post-war arboretum; herbaceous borders, rock and kitchen gardens; in bog garden one of larger collections Asiatic primulas in SW. Refreshments 11-4.30 April 1 to Oct 31. *Adm £3.25 OAPs £3 Chd under 15 and wheelchairs free. Open daily all year (10-4.30)*

Friars Way ᏜᏜ (Les & Christina Scott) 190 Church Street, Upwey. Twixt Weymouth and Dorchester on B3159, Martinstown rd. C17 thatched cottage is opp church car park. ¾-acre plantsman's garden developed by owners since 1991. Idyllic situation, sloping, S facing partially terraced site. Newly created scented inner garden. Small nursery of garden propagated plants. TEAS. *Adm £1 Chd free. Suns May 12, June 9, July 14, Wed May 22, June 12 (2.30-6). Private visits and parties welcome, please* Tel 01305 813243

¶The Friary (The Society of St Francis) Hilfield, Dorchester. A352 from Dorchester to Minterne Magna, go through village and take 1st turning on L. The rd winds up a hill followed by a sharp bend to the L, take the 1st turning on R. At this point it is signposted to The Friary which lies at the bottom of the hill. Approaching from Yeovil turn off the A37 at the sign marked Batcombe and take 3rd turning on L. A small woodland garden on the Batcombe side of the Friary grounds that was begun in the late 1950's. It was then neglected for a number of years. In 1984 a start was made in the continuation of earlier work. The Secret Garden, oblong in shape, incl a number of mature trees, rhododendrons, azaleas, magnolias, camellias and other choice shrubs with a narrow stream running along its 4 sides (stout shoes recommended). TEA. *Adm £1 Chd free. Sun, Tue, Wed, May 19, 21, 22 (2-5). The Friary is happy to receive visitors every day apart from Monday*

Frith House ᏝᏜ (Urban Stephenson Esq) Stalbridge. Between Milborne Port & Stalbridge, 1m S of A30. Turn W nr PO in Stalbridge. 4 acres; self-contained hamlet: lawns; 2 small lakes; woodland walks. Terrace in front of Edwardian house, mature cedars; flower borders, excellent kitchen garden. TEAS. *Adm £1.50 Chd free. Suns April 14, June 30, Aug 18 (2-6). Groups welcome by appt, please* Tel 01963 250 232

Glebe House ᏝᏜ (Mr & Mrs J G Thompson) East Lulworth. 4m S of Wool 6m W of Wareham. Take Coombe Keynes Rd to East Lulworth. Glebe House just to E of Weld Arms and War Memorial. Shrub garden with lawns; walks and terrace, 2 acres with interesting and varied planting. TEAS. *Adm £1 Chd free (Share to Wool & Bovington Cancer Relief®). Suns May 12, 26 (2-6)*

2 Greenwood Avenue Ꮬ (Mr & Mrs P D Stogden) Ferndown. Off Woodside Rd which is between Ringwood Rd (A348) and Wimborne Rd (C50 ex-A31), E of town centre. ⅓-acre designed and maintained by owners. An interesting and informal garden, with accent on herbaceous plants; many rare and unusual. Hostas, sempervivums and plants for flower arranging are a special interest of the owners. Soft fruits and vegetable garden. Arbour and pergola. Dogs must be kept on leads. TEAS. *Adm £1 Acc chd free. Suns June 2, 23; July 14, 28 (11-5)*

Hambledon Cottage ᏝᏜ (Mr & Mrs D W Schwier) Child Okeford. 6m W of Blandford Forum take L turn at sign for Child Okeford. Drive through village and take the R fork after passing the church. This is Shaftesbury Rd. Hambledon Cottage is ¼m on L. It is white with a red brick wall surrounded by a white picket fence. The garden was started in Oct 89 and nearly 2 acres of docks and thistles have been transformed into a series of rooms. These rooms contain 700 old English roses and modern roses, sweet pea walks, fishponds, lawns, shrubs, perennials and annuals. The garden is bounded on three sides by an ancient nut hedge and uses Hambledon Hill as a natural backdrop. *Adm £1.50 Chd free. Sun June 23 (2-6)*

Heatherwood ✿❀ (Mr & Mrs Ronald Squires) 1m S of Wimborne. Leave A349 Wimborne-Poole rd at Merley Bridge, signed Ashington, into Merley Park Rd. Thence garden is ¾m on L. ½-acre garden created by present owners from original woodland. Main theme of the garden is heathers (800 in 50 varieties), conifers (300 in 30 varieties), azaleas and acers. Large lawn with ornamental pool and rockery. Featured on TVs 'That's Gardening' and 'Grass Roots'. Large car park at adjacent nursery. *Collection box. Daily except Dec 24 to Jan 1 (9-5, Suns 9.30-12)*

High Hollow ✿❀ (Paul & Valerie Guppy) 15 Chapel Close, Corfe Mullen. From Wareham Rd W end of village at Naked Cross turn N into Waterloo Rd; after 1m turn E into Chapel Lane. Please park nearby and not in Chapel Close. Beautiful and colourful exotic garden of ¼ acre surrounding bungalow, full of spiky and unusual plants from many countries. Herbaceous border and ferns. The use of water is a special feature. TEAS. *Adm 50p Chd 25p (Share to the Cats Protection League®). Suns June 9, 30 July 28, Aug 18 (2-5)*

Highbury ♿✿❀ (Stanley Cherry Esq) West Moors, 8m N of Bournemouth. In Woodside Rd, off B3072 Bournemouth-Verwood rd; last rd at N end of West Moors village. Woodland garden of ½ acre in mature setting surrounding interesting Edwardian house (1909 listed). Unusual plants and shrubs with ground cover. Weather station. Seen on T.V. TEAS in orchard when fine. *House and garden, organised parties Adm £1 (incl TEA); Otherwise by appt. Garden only 75p (2-6). April to Sept* **Tel 01202 874372**

Higher Melcombe ❀ (Lt Col and Mrs J M Woodhouse) Melcombe Bingham. 11m NE of Dorchester. From Puddletown A354 to Blandford. After ½m follow signs to Cheselbourne then to Melcombe. At Xrds in Melcombe Bingham follow signpost 'Private rd to Higher Melcombe'. From Sturminster Newton signs to Hazelbury Bryan, Ansty, past Fox Inn to Melcombe Bingham Xrds. 1½-acre garden, many annuals. Fine views and setting outside Elizabethan house. Parking adjoining field. TEAS in chapel. *Adm £1 per car (Share to Parish Church®). Combined with village fete. Sun June 22 (2-5). Parties by appt in July, please* **Tel 01258 880251**

7 Highfield Close ✿❀ (Mr & Mrs Malcolm Bright) Corfe Mullen. From Wareham Rd turn E in Hanham Rd, thence ahead into Highfield Close. Colourful ⅓-acre summer garden designed and made by owners over 15yrs. Bedding plants, fuchsias and pelargoniums interplanted with shrubs; fish pond and ornamental pool. Much to interest gardeners in a small area. TEAS. *Adm 50p Chd 25p. Suns May 12, July 7, 14 (2-5)*

Hightown Farm, nr Ringwood See Hampshire

Highwood Garden ✿ (H W Drax Esq) Charborough Park, Wareham, 6m E of Bere Regis behind long wall. Enter park by any lodge on A31; follow signpost to Estate Office, then Highwood Garden. Large garden with rhododendrons and azaleas in woodland setting. TEAS. *Adm £2 Chd £1 (7-16 yrs) (Share to Red Post Parish©). Suns May 26, June 2 (2.30-6)*

Hilltop Cottage ✿❀ (Mr & Mrs Emerson) approx 5m N Sturminster Newton on B3092 turn R at Stour Provost Xrds, signed Woodville. After 1¼m a thatched cottage on the RH-side. Parking in lane outside. Old cottage garden with a wealth of different and interesting perennials. Very colourful. An inspiration to those with smaller gardens. Includes a small nursery. TEAS. *Adm 50p Chd free. Weds May 15, July 24, Aug 14; Suns May 12, July 21, 28, Aug 18 (2-6)*

Holworth Farmhouse ✿❀ (Anthony & Philippa Bush) Holworth. 7m E of Dorchester, 1m S of A352. Follow signs to Holworth up the hill, through the farmyard, past duck pond on R. After 300yds turn L to the farmhouse. 3 acres of garden surrounding C16 grade II farmhouse on side of hill with lovely views. Main planting from 1980; considerable use of hedges as protection from exposed windy conditions; partially walled garden terraced and re-planted in 1990 with a wide variety of herbaceous plants, shrubs and old roses. Also small wood, orchard, vegetable garden and recently excavated pond. Home-made TEAS in aid of Joseph Weld Hospice & 'Fight for Sight'. *Adm £1.50 Chd free. Suns June 16, July 14 (2-7)*

Horn Park ♿✿❀ (Mr & Mrs John Kirkpatrick) Beaminster. On A3066 1½m N of Beaminster on L before tunnel. Ample parking, toilet. Large garden; magnificent view to sea; listed house built by pupil of Lutyens in 1910 (not open). Plantsman's garden worth visiting at all seasons; many rare plants and shrubs in terraced, herbaceous, rock and water gardens. Woodland garden and walks in bluebell woods. Wild flower meadow and orchids. TEAS. *Adm £2.50 Chd under 16 free. Open every Tues, Weds, Suns, also Bank Hol Mons April to Oct 31. For NGS Sun April 7, Bank Hol Mon May 27 (2-6)* **Tel 01308 862212**

Ivy Cottage ✿❀ (Anne & Alan Stevens) Aller Lane, Ansty, 12m N of Dorchester. A354 from Puddletown to Blandford; After pub take 1st L down Long Lane signed Dewlish-Cheselbourne, through Cheselbourne to Ansty then 1st R before Fox Inn, down Aller Lane. 1½-acre excellent plantsman's garden specialising in unusual perennials, moisture-loving plants; specimen trees and shrubs; well laid out vegetable garden. Featured in the book 'The New Englishwoman's Garden'. Meridian TV 'Grass Roots' 1994. TEAS Suns only. *Combined adm with* **Aller Green** *£2.50 Chd 50p. Also every Thurs April to Oct incl (10-5). For NGS Sun May 19 (Share to Samaritans®); Sun Sept 1 (Share to Red Cross®) (2-5.30).* **Tel 01258 880053**

Kingston Lacy ♿✿ (The National Trust) 1½m W of Wimborne Minster on the Wimborne-Blandford rd B3082. The setting landscaped in the C18, to W J Bankes's Kingston Lacy House. Magnificent trees planted over 175 years by Royal and famous visitors; avenue of limes and cedars; 9 acres of lawn; Dutch garden; sunken garden laid out to 1906 plans. TEAS and lunches. *Adm House & Garden £5.50, Gardens £2.20, Chd half price. For NGS Sun June 2 (11.30-6)*

> The National Gardens Scheme is a charity which traces its origins back to 1927. Since then it has raised a total of over £14 million for charitable purposes.

Kingston Maurward Gardens &&& E of Dorchester turn off the roundabout at end of Dorchester by-pass A35. Bus alight Stinsford ¼m. Follow brown Tourist Information signs. Classical Georgian mansion set in gardens laid out in the C18 incl a 5-acre lake and overlooks the Dorchester watermeadows. Restoration programme is nearing completion in the Edwardian gardens which are divided by hedges and stone balustrading. Stone features and interesting plants, including the National Collection of salvias and penstemons. An original Elizabethan walled garden is laid out as a demonstration of plants suitable for Dorset. Restaurant, full menu. *Adm £3 Chd £1.50. Open Easter to Oct 31. For NGS Thurs May 16, July 11 (10-6). Private visits welcome, please* **Tel 01305 264 738** *(Mike Hancock)*

Knitson Old Farmhouse && (Rachel & Mark Helfer) Knitson. Signposted L off A351 Knitson, approx 1m W of Swanage 3m E of Corfe Castle. Ample parking in yard or in adjacent level field. Approx 1 acre of mature cottage garden. Herbaceous borders, rockeries, climbers, shrubs – many interesting cultivars. Large organic kitchen garden, orchard. TEAS in aid of F.A.R.M. Africa. *Adm £1.50 Chd 50p. Thurs April 18, May 16, Sats June 22, Aug 3 (2-5). Private visits and parties welcome, please* **Tel 01929 422836**

●**Knoll Gardens** &&& (Neil Lucas, Esq) Hampreston. 2½m W of Ferndown, ETB brown signs from A31. Gardens on a 6-acre site. Wide collections of trees, shrubs and herbaceous plants, continually being expanded. Under new ownership since 1994. Water gardens with waterfalls, pools and streams; mixed borders and woodland setting. NCCPG collections of phygelius and ceanothus. Tea rooms and visitor centre, to which entry is free. Large car park. Many plants shown are available in adjacent nursery. TEAS. *Adm £3.45 OAP's £2.90 Students £2.40 Chd £1.70. Group rates on application. Daily, Easter to end Oct (10-5.30). Nov to Easter, Weds to Sats, reduced prices (10-4)*

Lamorna && (Mr & Mrs R Hewitt) Chedington. 5m N of Beaminster. Off A356 Dorchester-Crewkerne rd at Winyards Gap Inn. Drive ½m into village, Lamorna is next to village hall on L, off layby. Nearby is a National Trust woodland walk and the Wessex Division memorial. Approx 1-acre garden in conservation village with extensive views over Axe valley. Mixture of the formal and informal with many shrubs and plants incl pond, bog garden, dry shade garden, pergola, banks and other features. TEA. *Adm £1 Chd free. Weds May 15, July 17 Sept 18 (11-4.30) with* **Chedington Court**. *Sats, Suns May 4, 5; 11, 12; June 1, 2; 8, 9; July 6, 7; 13, 14; Aug 3, 4; 10, 11 (11-5). Private visits welcome, please* **Tel 01935 891410**

Langebride House & (Mrs John Greener) Long Bredy. ½-way between Bridport and Dorchester, S off A35, well signed. Substantial old rectory garden with many designs for easier management. 200-yr-old beech trees, bi-colour beech hedge, pleached limes, yew hedges, extensive collections of spring bulbs, herbaceous plants, flowering trees and shrubs. Special cake and plant stall in aid of hospice May 19. TEA in aid of Joseph Weld House March 17, 31. *Adm £1.50 Chd free. Suns March 17, 31 (2-5) May 19 (2.30-5). Private visits welcome March to end July* **Tel 01308 482 257**

Little Platt & (Sir Robert Williams) Plush, 9m N of Dorchester by B3143 to Piddletrenthide, then 1½m NE by rd signed Plush & Mappowder, 1st house on L entering Plush. 1-acre garden created from a wilderness since 1969; interesting collection of ornamental trees and flowering shrubs, incl several daphnes, spiraeas and viburnums; spring bulbs, hellebores, numerous hardy geraniums and unusual perennials. *Adm £1 Chd free. Private visits welcome March to Aug* **Tel 01300 348320**

¶**Litton Cheney Gardens** 1m S of A35, 10m Dorchester, 6m Bridport. Small village in the beautiful Bride Valley. TEAS in Church Hall in aid of the Church. *Combined adm £2.50 Chd 50p. Sun June 23 (2-6)*

  ¶**Faith House** && (Commander & Mrs Larry Herrick) Small unusual walled garden of ⅔ acre, surrounded by tall mature trees. Beds of shrubs interplanted with herbaceous plants and roses. Upper reaches of the Bride river flows through one corner

  ¶**2 Litton Hill** && (Patricia & Malcolm Munro) New garden on difficult site; ⅕ acre; shallow soil overlying chalk. S facing with steep slopes. Showing some plants that flourish on chalk; plants of interest to dyers

  The Old Rectory & (Mr & Mrs Hugh Lindsay) Small walled garden, partly paved and with a prolific quince tree. A steep path leads to 4 acres of natural woodland with many springs, streams and 2 small lakes; mostly native plants, also primulas. Wild flower lawn; (stout shoes recommended) TEAS in aid of Red Cross on 7 April. *Adm £1.50 Chd 20p. Also open Easter Sun April 7 (2-5.30). Private visits welcome April to June, please* **Tel 01308 482383**

  ¶**Paddock House** (Mr & Mrs G C Teychenne) Attractive and interesting cottage style garden with some unusual plants started from scratch 1991

  ¶**Skep House** & (John & Lorna Perrin) A 'new' garden (5yrs) of approx 1 acre, on several levels. Set into hillside with small copse of native trees. Roses and shrubs

Loscombe House & (Mr & Mrs Andrewes) Loscombe. N of Bridport. Take Loscombe turning opp Half Moon Inn in Melpash; after ½m turn R at Loscombe signpost; continue to bottom of lane (2m). 4-acre woodland garden in a hidden valley with stream, trees, shrubs, herbaceous plants and old-fashioned roses planted on a SE facing slope. *Adm Donation. Open every Sat, Sun, Bank Hol April 1 to Oct 31 (2-6). For NGS combined adm with* **Pear Tree Farm** *and* **Flowery Bottom** *£2 Chd free. Sun July 14 (2-6). Private visits welcome, please* **Tel 01308 488361**

Lower Ware & (Mr & Mrs J Bones) Ware Lane, Lyme Regis. Outskirts of Lyme Regis, off A3052 Sidmouth Rd. From the town E 2nd L after Holmbush Carpark; from W, app Lyme Regis, R at Xrds signposted to 'Ware'. Narrow lane, considerate parking please. Attractive 1-acre hillside garden overlooking Lyme Bay, mainly planted since 1989. Individual small gardens on three levels; mixed planting. TEAS. *Adm £1. Sun May 19 (2-6)*

Macpenny Woodland Garden & Nurseries, Bransgore
See Hampshire

1 Manor Close & (Mr & Mrs W A Butcher) Stratton. 3m NW of Dorchester off A37 to Yeovil, turn into village, gardens signed at church. ⅓-acre with alpine garden at front. To the rear interesting shrubs, perennials, grasses, conservatory and vegetable garden. *Combined adm with* **Manor Orchard** *£1.50 Chd free. Suns, Weds, April 7, 10; July 3, 7 (2.30-5.30)*

¶The Manor Farmhouse ✿✿ (Mr & Mrs E Hornsby) Little Windsor. 4m NW of Beaminstser; 1m from Broadwindsor. From A3066 turn off at Mosterton, signed Drimpton. 3 acres landscaped gardens; pond and water garden; unusual trees and shrubs. TEA. *Adm £1 Chd free. Suns June 16, 30 (2-6)*

The Manor House, Abbotsbury ✿✿ (Mr D Nabarro) Equidistant (9m) from Dorchester, Weymouth and Bridport. The Manor House is in Church St opp St Nicholas Church. Park in the public carpark by the Swan Inn. No parking by The Manor House. The gardens extending to 2½ acres were designed in 1988 by Ian Teh. They feature 4 inter-connecting ponds surrounded by herbaceous borders and a herb garden. The gardens lie below St Catherine's chapel and are in sight of the sea. TEAS. *Adm £1.50 Chd free. Sat, Sun June 1, 2 (2.30-6)*

The Manor House, Hinton St Mary & ✿ (Mr & Mrs A Pitt-Rivers) 1m NW of Sturminster Newton on B3092. Next to Church in Hinton St Mary. 5-acre garden with views over Blackmore Vale. Host to a Meridian TV Grass Roots programme in 1995. Trees and shrubs, yew and box hedges, pleached lime walk, lots of roses. Reopening following major alterations in 1992. C15 tithe barn. TEA. *Adm £2 Chd 50p. Suns June 16, 23 (2-6)*

Manor Orchard & ✿ (Mr & Mrs G B David) Stratton. 3m NW of Dorchester off A37 to Yeovil, turn into village, gardens signed at church. 1-acre enthusiast's garden overlooking water meadows. Lawns with spring bulbs, herbaceous and shrub borders planted for yr-round interest, pond, roses, vine. Kitchen garden with fruit arch and topiary. Cream TEAS in aid of Stratton Village Hall & Church (Suns only). DIY teas on Weds. *Combined adm with* **1 Manor Close** *£1.50 Chd free. Suns, Weds, April 7, 10; July 3, 7 (2.30-5.30)*

● **Mapperton Gardens** & ✿✿ (Montagu Family) nr Beaminster. 6m N of Bridport off A35. 2m SE of Beaminster off B3163. Descending valley gardens beside one of Dorset's finest manor houses (C16-C17) House and garden listed Grade I. Featured in current film version of Jane Austen's 'Emma'. Magnificent walks and views. Fish ponds, orangery, formal Italian-style borders and topiary; specimen trees and shrubs; car park. Upper levels only suitable for wheelchairs. House open to group tours by appt **Tel 01308 862645**. *Adm garden £2.50 Chd £1.50, under 5 free. March to Oct daily (2-6)*

Melbury House ✿✿ 6m S of Yeovil. Signed on Dorchester-Yeovil rd. 13m N of Dorchester. Large garden; very fine arboretum; shrubs and lakeside walk; beautiful deer park. Garden only. TEAS. *Adm £2 OAPs/Chd £1 (Share to CRMF®). Thurs May 16, 30, June 13, 27; July 11, Aug 1 (2-5). Private visits welcome for parties of 15 min, please* **Tel 01935 83699** (*Andrew Clark*)

Melplash Court & ✿ Melplash. On the A3066 between Beaminster and Bridport, just N of Melplash. Turn W and enter between field gates next to big gates and long ave of chestnut trees. While the gardens as they exist today were originally designed by Lady Diana Tiarks they continue to evolve and consist of park planting, bog garden, croquet lawn and adjacent borders. Formal kitchen garden and herb garden, ponds, streams and lake; new borders and areas of interest are added and opened up each year. TEAS in aid of Melplash Church. *Adm £2 Chd free. Sun July 21 (2-6)*

Mews Cottage ✿✿ (Mr & Mrs P J Pitman) 34 Easton Street, Portland. Situated in the 1st village on the top of the Island of Portland, Mews Cottage is in the main street of Easton, 50yds past the Punchbowl Inn on the L. Park in the main street and follow signs. Cottage style garden, with a pond and a good mix of herbaceous plants and unusual shrubs, particularly in Spring a good collection of hellebore and spring bulbs (National Collection holder). In the summer some 140 named varieties of Penstemon incl many alpine varieties, a large crinodendron hookerianum and callestemon. Autumn colour is achieved with a large collection of nerine bowdenii in various shades of pink. TEAS in aid of St Georges Church. *Adm £1 Chd free. Suns March 10, May 12, June 2, July 7, Aug 18, Oct 6 (2-5)*

26 Milestone Road ✿✿ (Mr & Mrs P M Fraser) Oakdale. At Oakdale, Poole traffic lights on Wimborne Rd, turn S into Vicarage Rd then 1st L into Milestone Rd. ¼-acre town garden, divided into three rooms. Features include ornamental ponds and waterfall, pergola with roses and other climbing plants, natural wooded area with wild flowers and ferns and many interesting shrubs. TEAS. *Adm 75p Chd 25p. Suns June 9, July 7, Wed June 19 (1-5)*

● **Minterne** (The Lord Digby) Minterne Magna. On A352 Dorchester-Sherborne rd. 2m N Cerne Abbas; woodland garden set in a valley landscaped in the C18 with small lakes, cascades and rare trees; many species and hybrid rhododendrons and magnolias tower over streams and water plants. *Adm £2 Acc chd and parking free. Open daily April 1 to Nov 10 (10-7)*

Moigne Combe (Maj-Gen H M G Bond) 6m E of Dorchester. 1½m N of Owermoigne turn off A352 Dorchester-Wareham Rd. Medium-sized garden; wild garden and shrubbery; heathers, azaleas, rhododendrons etc; woodland paths and lake walk. Tea Wyevale Garden Centre, Owermoigne. *Adm £1. 1st chd 25p thereafter 10p. Suns May 19, 26 (2-5.30)*

Moulin Huet & ✿✿ (Harold Judd Esq) 15 Heatherdown Rd, West Moors. 7m N of Bournemouth. Leave A31 at West Moors Garage into Pinehurst Rd, take 1st R into Uplands Rd, then 3rd L into Heatherdown Rd. thence into cul-de-sac. ⅓-acre garden made by owner from virgin heathland after retirement. Considerable botanical interest; collections of 90 dwarf conifers and bonsai; many rare plants and shrubs; alpines, sink gardens, rockeries, wood sculpture. *Adm 75p Chd free. Private visits and parties welcome April to July, please* **Tel 01202 875760**

North Leigh House ✿ (Mr & Mrs Stanley Walker) Cole-hill, 1m NE of Wimborne. Leave B3073 (formerly A31) nr Sir Winston Churchill public house into North Leigh Lane, thence ¾m. 5 acres of informal parkland with fine trees, small lake, rhododendrons; ornamental shrubs; specimen magnolia grandiflora and Green Brunswick fig; colony of orchis morio and naturalised spring bulbs in lawns; Victorian features include balustraded terrace, fountain pool, walled garden and superb conservatory, all being restored and maintained by owners. Dogs on leads welcome. Suitable wheelchairs in parts. NCCPG plant stalls May. Teas in Bothy Cottage. *Adm £1 Chd 20p (Share to Animal Aid®, May; Bournemouth & District Animal Ambulance Service© July). Suns May 12, July 21 (2-6). House open only to parties by appt, please* **Tel 01202 882592**

Oakdene, Sandleheath See Hampshire

Oakmead ㅅ (Mr & Mrs P D Priest) Mosterton. On A3066 N of Beaminster in centre of village. Roadside parking. ⅔-acre 'all seasons' garden. The skilful design incorporates traditional herbaceous border, fine heather bed, azaleas, camellias, shrub rose border, modern roses with lawns and gravel beds. 'A model of modern gardening' (Anna Pavord in The Independent) and 'should be high on anyone's visiting list' (The Dorset Garden Guide). *Private visits welcome, please* **Tel 01308 868466**

The Old Mill ㅅ✿ (The Rev & Mrs J Hamilton-Brown) Spetisbury, Spetisbury Village opposite school on A350 3m SE of Blandford. 2 acres mainly water garden by R Stour; rockery; choice trees and plants. TEAS on Sun in aid of Spetisbury Church. *Adm £2 Chd free. TEA every Wed May to Aug (2-5). For NGS Sun July 14.* **Tel 01258 453939**

The Old Rectory, Fifehead Magdalen ㅅ✿ (Mrs Patricia Lidsey) 5m S of Gillingham just S of the A30. Small garden with interesting shrubs and perennials; pond; grandchildren's garden; plant stall. *Adm 80p Chd free. Sun June 9 (2-6) also private visits welcome, please* **Tel 01258 820293**

Old Rectory, Seaborough ✿ (Mr & Mrs C W Wright) 3m S of Crewkerne. Take B3165, after derestriction sign 2nd L, ¾m 1st R, then after 2½m 2nd L in village. 2-acre garden constructed since 1967; splendid views; rare trees, conifers, magnolias, flowering shrubs, roses, Himalayan plants, bulbs throughout the year, ferns; over 1000 species and cultivars. *Adm £1 Chd 20p. Private visits welcome all year, please* **Tel 01308 868426**

The Old Vicarage, Stinsford ㅅ✿ (Mr & Mrs Antony Longland) Off roundabout at E end of Dorchester bypass A35. Follow signs for Stinsford Church 400yds. 1¼ acres incl an Italianate garden, herbaceous and mixed borders with unusual plants and shrubs, nearly 200 roses, lawns, terraces with exuberant pots, and fruit. Thomas Hardy, C Day Lewis and Cecil Hanbury, creator of gardens at La Mortola and Kingston Maurward, commemorated in church next door. TEAS. *Adm £1.50 Chd 50p. Sun June 23 (2-6). Private visits welcome for parties of 6 or more, please* **Tel 01305 265 827**

The Orchard ㅅ✿ (Mr & Mrs K S Ferguson) Blynfield Gate. 2m W of Shaftesbury on the rd to Stour Row. From Shaftesbury take B3091 to St James's Church then onto the Stour Row rd. A 3-acre country garden, orchard and native meadow developed since 1981. Lawns and paths link formal, informal and wild areas. Colourful mixed borders and island beds with a wide variety of plants, several chosen for their intermingling qualities and lengthy flowering period. Hedgebanks of hardy geraniums, interesting trees and shrubs, small natural pond and plenty of seats. Home-made TEAS. *Adm £1.50 to incl descriptive guide Chd free (Share to Red Cross®). Weds June 12, 19, 26; July 10, 17, 24 (2-6)*

● **Parnham** ㅅ (Mr & Mrs John Makepeace) ½m S of Beaminster on A3066, 5m N of Bridport. 14 acres extensively reconstructed early this century; much variety of form and interest, topiary; terraces; gazebos; spring fed water rills; small lake; fine old trees; grand herbaceous borders featured in Discovering Gardens (1990/91). Old roses in formal front courtyard; riverside walk and woodland; many unusual plants. House (Grade 1 listed, dating from 1540) exhibitions of contemporary craftsmanship, also John Makepeace furniture workshops. Restaurant, coffee, lunches. TEAS. *Adm to whole site £4 Chd 10-15 £2 under 10 free. April 5 to Oct 30 every Sun, Wed & Bank Hol incl. Good Friday (10-5).* **Tel 01308 862204**

Pear Tree Farm ⚘ (Major & Mrs John Poe) Loscombe. N of Bridport. S of Beaminster. Approx 1½m E of A3066. One way traffic (narrow lanes) as signed from B3163 via Mapperton and A3066 at Melplash (opp Half Moon Inn). Leave Loscombe via West Milton. You are requested not to approach from this direction. ½ acre garden started in 1989 making best use of limited space with sub dividing into different areas. Wide and interesting variety of shrubs, herbaceous plants, shrub roses with wild flowers and bulbs in long grass area. Conservatory with exotic plants. New developments and plants added every year. TEAS. *Combined adm with* **Loscombe House** *and* **Flowery Bottom** *£2 Chd free Sun July 14. Combined adm with* **Flowery Bottom** *£1.50 Chd free, Thurs July 11 (2-6)*

Portesham Gardens 7m W of Weymouth on coast rd, B3157 to Bridport. From Dorchester take A35 W, turn L in Winterborne Abbas and follow signs to Portesham; parking in village. TEAS at **Orchard House** in aid of Possum FEZ WIK. *Combined adm £1.50. Sun July 14 (2-6)*
    Orchard House ㅅ✿ (Mr & Mrs F J Mentern) ⅓-acre walled cottage garden; organic and wild garden, ground cover, herbs; unusual old-fashioned perennials; rockeries and water garden; fruitful veg area, working greenhouses run as a small nursery open daily for charity. *Also private visits and parties welcome June and July, please* **Tel 01305 871611**
    2 Winters Lane ㅅ✿ (Mr & Mrs K Draper) Portesham. Winters Lane is signposted in village to Coryates. ¼-acre garden with ponds and water features. Many ideas for smaller gardens such as small herb garden; container garden. 50 varieties of clematis, wishing well and miniature village; most plants labelled. Featured in 'The Water Garden' May 95. *Private visits and parties welcome June and July, please* **Tel 01305 871316**

Portesham House &&& (Mrs G J Romanes) Portesham. 7m W of Weymouth on coast rd, B3157 to Bridport. From Dorchester take A35 W, turn L in Winterborne Abbas and follow signs to Portesham; parking in village. Home of Admiral Sir Thomas Masterman Hardy with 300-yr-old mulberry tree; over an acre of family garden with modern dry stone walling, old walls and stream. Paeonies and unusual trees and shrubs. Teas at Millmead Country Hotel. *Adm £1 Chd free. Suns June 16, 23 (2-5.30)*

Portland House (Mr & Mrs A Phillipson) (National Trust) 24 Belle Vue Rd. 1m from Weymouth town centre. Take Portland Rd from town centre; turn L from Rodwell Rd into Bincleaves Rd then into Belle Vue Rd on R. Park in Belle Vue Rd. Over 4 acres of mature trees, lawns, hydrangeas and fuchsias, avenue of palm trees; superb views over Portland harbour (weather permitting). TEAS. *Adm £1 Chd free. Sun July 7 (2-6)*

The Priest's House Museum and Garden && (The Priest's House Museum Trust) 23 High St, Wimborne. Public car parks nearby. Old 'borough plot' garden of ½ acres, at rear of local museum, in historic town house. Extending to mill stream and containing many unusual plants, trees and exhibits. Tea-room daily. *Adm £1.95 Family £4.75 OAP/Students £1.50 Chd 75p. ▲Sun June 23 (2-5).* **Tel 01202 882533**

Pumphouse Cottage & (Mr & Mrs R A Pugh) Mundens Lane. Alweston 3m SE of Sherborne on A3030. Take L turning 50yds after PO. 1st cottage on L. ½-acre cottage garden with erratic stream, collection of old roses, herbaceous borders, and spring bulbs. *Adm £1 Chd free. Suns, Mons May 5, 6, 26, 27; Sun June 30, Wed July 10 (2-6). Private visits very welcome throughout the year, please* **Tel 01963 23535**

Rampisham Gardens && Dorchester. 9m S of Yeovil take A37 to Dorchester. 7m turn R signed Evershot follow signs to Rampisham. 11m NW Dorchester take A37 to Yeovil, 4m turn L A356 signed Crewkerne; at start of wireless masts R to Rampisham. Cream TEAS. Plant and cake stalls in aid of Church and Village Hall at Manor. *Combined adm £2 Chd 50p. Sun July 7 (2-6)*
   Broomhill & (Mr & Mrs D Parry) A family garden of 1 acre with trellised entrance leading to mixed borders and island beds with a great variety of plants. The lawns slope down to a large wild life pond
   Leigh Hill (Mr & Mrs P Thomas) Approx ½-acre Countryman's garden using large local stones to form sculptured rockeries, a raised 'wild' pond complex and scented garden
   Rampisham Manor (Mr & Mrs Boileau) 2½ acres of spacious lawns, formal white rose beds, hedged walks, shrubs mixed with English roses and herbaceous planting. new pond and grasses bed. Ornamental kitchen garden. TEAS. *Also open Thurs May 2 (2-5). Adm £1.50 Chd 50p*

Regular Openers. Too many days to include in diary. Usually there is a wide range of plants giving year-round interest. See head of county section for the name and garden description for times etc.

Red House Museum and Gardens &&& (The Hampshire Museum Service) Quay Road, Christchurch. Tranquil setting in heart of town's conservation area. Gardens of ½ acre developed from early 1950's to complement Museum; plants of historic interest; herb garden with sunken lawn, south garden with lawns, herbaceous and woodland plants; old rose border. Gardens used as gallery display area for sculpture exhibitions. Admission to Museum and Art Gallery included. TEAS. *Adm £1 OAP/Chd 60p (under 5 free) (Share to the Mayor of Christchurch's Appeal of the Year©). ▲For NGS Thurs June 13 (10-5)*

46 Roslin Road South && (Dr & Mrs Malcolm Slade) Bournemouth. W of N end of Glenferness Ave in Talbot Woods area of Bournemouth. ⅓-acre walled town garden of yr-round interest with unusual plants in attractive settings. Features include rose pergola, 2 pools, newly planted gravel garden with many colourful and mature herbaceous and shrub plantings. Carefully tended fruit and vegetable garden. *Adm 60p Chd 20p. Suns May 5, 26, June 23, July 21 (1.30-5). Also private visits welcome from May to July, please* **Tel 01202 510243**

52 Rossmore Road && (Mr & Mrs W E Ninniss) Parkstone, Poole. From A348 Poole-Ringwood rd turn SE into Rossmore Rd, thence ¼m. ⅓-acre interesting country garden in a town designed in rooms; containing many rare and unusual plants; small knot garden; scree garden; herb garden. TEAS. *Adm 80p Chd 25p. Suns May 19, June 2 (2-6). Parties welcome, please* **Tel 01202 740913**

Slape Manor && (Mr & Mrs Antony Hichens) Netherbury. 1m S of Beaminster turn W off A3066 to village of Netherbury. House ⅓m S of Netherbury on back road to Bridport. River valley garden — extensive lawns and lake. Azaleas, rhododendrons; specimen trees. TEAS in aid of Netherbury Village Hall. *Adm £1.50 Chd 50p under 5 free. Sun May 19 (2-6)*

Smedmore && (Dr Philip Mansel) Kimmeridge, 7m S of Wareham. Turn W off A351 (Wareham-Swanage) at sign to Kimmeridge. 2 acres of colourful herbaceous borders; display of hydrangeas; interesting plants and shrubs; walled flower gardens; herb courtyard. *Adm £2 Chd £1. Sun May 19 (2.15-5). Private visits welcome, please Tel* **01929 480 719** *(Mr T Gargett)*

Snape Cottage && (Ian & Angela Whinfield) Chaffeymoor at W end of Bourton. Opp Chiffchaffs. ½-acre plantsman's country garden full of old-fashioned and uncommon perennials, most labelled. Organically managed and planted for yr-round interest with large collection of snowdrops, hellebores, pulmonarias, auriculas, geraniums, dianthus, iris, penstemon and asters. Special emphasis on plant history and nature conservation. Beautiful views, wildlife pond. *Adm £1.50 Chd free. Every Sun in May to July and Wed in April to Sept (closed Aug). For NGS Suns April 7, June 16, July 14, Sept 22 (2-5). Parties welcome by appt, please* **Tel 01747 840330** *(evenings only)*

Spinners Boldre See Hampshire

● **Stapehill Abbey** &♨❀ Wimborne Rd West, Ferndown. 2½m W of Ferndown on the old A31, towards Wimborne, ½m E of Canford Bottom roundabout. Early C19 Abbey, its gardens and estate restored and renovated to lawns, herbaceous borders; rose and water gardens; Victorian cottage garden; lake and Victorian greenhouse. Mature trees. Busy working Craft Centre; Countryside Museum featuring the National Tractor Collection, all under cover. Refreshments available in former refectory throughout the day. Licensed coffee shop. Large free car/coach park. *Adm £4.50 OAPs £4 Chd £2.50. Open daily April to Oct (10-5); Nov to Easter (10-4); except Mons and Easter. Closed Christmas Eve to Feb 1.* Tel **01202 861686**

Star Cottage ❀❀ (Lys de Bray) 8 Roman Way, Cowgrove, Wimborne. Leave B3082 at Wimborne Hospital, along Cowgrove Rd for approx 1½m to Roman Way on R. Created in 1992 from a field, the garden is rapidly becoming another 'living library' of botanical artist and author Lys de Bray, lately of Turnpike Cottage, Wimborne. An opportunity to meet Miss de Bray and see a specialised garden in the making. The owner is a RHS gold medallist whose botanical drawings and paintings are on permanent exhibition in her working studios which are open throughout the year at weekends and bank holidays. *Adm £1 Chd 60p. Garden and Studio open Sats and Suns all year. Easter to end Oct (2-6). End Oct to end March (2-4). For NGS Suns May 19, June 16 (2-6). Private visits and parties welcome, please* Tel **01202 885130**

Steeple Manor &❀❀ (Mr Julian & the Hon Mrs Cotterell) Steeple, 5m SW of Wareham in Isle of Purbeck. Take Swanage rd from Wareham, or bypass, R in Stoborough. A beautiful garden designed by Brenda Colvin 1920's round C16/17 Purbeck stone manor house (not open); lovely setting in folds of Purbeck hills in small hamlet of Steeple next to ancient church, specially decorated for the occasion. Approx 5 acres, the garden includes walls, hedges, enclosed gardens, ponds, stream, bog garden and meadow, collection old roses; many interesting and tender plants and shrubs for the plantsman. Parts garden suitable for wheelchairs. Free parking. Cream TEAS. *Adm £2.50 (to include written guide) Chd under 16 free. Sun June 30 (1.30-6)*

Stepleton House &❀❀ (Mr & Mrs Derek Coombs) Iwerne Stepleton. Stepleton House is situated 4m N of Blandford Forum on the A350. Approx 1m N of Stourpaine. Grade I park and garden on English Heritage register undergoing extensive restoration. 27 acres incl C18 lake; river walk; walled garden; rose pergola; interesting shrubs and perennials. The park was replanted in 1987 under the guidance of Alan Mitchell VMH. TEAS in aid of St Mary's Shroton Organ Fund. *Adm £1.50 Chd 50p. Sat July 6 (2-5)*

Sticky Wicket &❀❀ (Peter & Pam Lewis) Buckland Newton. 11m from Dorchester and Sherborne. 2m E of A352 or take B3143 from Sturminster Newton. T-junction midway Church, School and Gaggle of Geese public house. 1½-acre garden created since 1987, unusual designs, well documented, showing wild life interest; fragrant cottage garden planting with many perennials and herbs. TEAS. *Adm £2 Chd £1. Every Thurs June to Sept incl (10.30-8). For NGS Suns June 23, Aug 25 (2-6).* Tel **01300 345476**

Stour House &❀❀ (T S B Card Esq) East St, Blandford. On 1-way system, 100yds short of market place. 2½-acre town garden, half on a romantic island in R Stour reached by a remarkable bridge; bulbs; borders well planted with perennials and many rare shrubs; river views. TEAS. (Teas in aid of Blandford Parish Church, July). *Adm £1 Chd 20p. Suns March 31 (2-5) July 14, Aug 11 (2-6)*

Studland Bay House &❀ (Mrs Pauline Ferguson) Studland. On B3351 5m E of Corfe Castle. Through village, entrance on R after Studland Bay House. Ample parking (no coaches). From Bournemouth, take Sandbanks ferry, 2½m, garden on L after Knoll House Hotel. 6-acre spring garden overlooking Studland Bay. Planted in 1930's on heathland; magnificent rhododendrons, azalea walk, camellias, magnolias, ferns and stream; recent drainage and replanting, garden suitable for wheelchairs. Cream TEAS in aid of Joseph Weld Hospice. *Adm £2 Chd free. Sat, Sun May 18, 19 (2-5)*

Sturminster Newton Gardens &❀ Off A357 between Blandford and Sherborne take turn opp Nat West Bank. Park in car park or behind Stourcastle Lodge. Walk down Penny St for **Ham Gate** and Goughs Close for **Stourcastle Lodge**. TEAS at **Ham Gate**. *Combined adm £2 Chd free. Sun June 16 (2-6). Parties by appt, please* Tel **01258 472462** or **01258 472320**

    Ham Gate (Mr & Mrs H E M Barnes) Informal 2-acre garden with shrubs, trees, lawns running down to R Stour, pleasant woodland views across water meadows, over the last few years Pam Lewis has helped redesign the garden

    Stourcastle Lodge (Jill & Ken Hookham-Bassett) A S facing secluded cottage garden, with a wide selection of interesting herbs, perennials and shrubs, a dovecote and water features

Thistledown &❀❀ (Mr & Mrs E G Gillingham) Alweston 3m SE of Sherborne. From main A3030, turn into Mundens Lane by Oxfords Bakery. Garden 100yds along lane on R; park in drive/lane, 1-acre plant enthusiast's garden with views to Bulbarrow Hill; garden planted for yr-round interest with spring bulbs, rhododendrons, shrubs, herbaceous borders, conifers, old-fashioned and modern roses, clematis, ornamental trees and ponds. *Adm £1 Chd free. Suns, Mons April 7, 8, 28, May 5, 6, 26, 27, June 30 (1.30-5), Wed July 10 (10-5)*

¶**Thornhill Park** ❀❀ (Richard and Cary Goode) Stalbridge. 1m S of Stalbridge on A357. Gates opposite T junction. Go down drive for ¾m. 6-acre garden surrounding C18 house built by Sir James Thornhill. Garden currently being re-established and extended by Cary Goode, a professional Garden Designer. Incl formal area with small parterre, 2 ponds, willow garden, potager, rose garden, several areas planted in colour themes and woodland. TEAS. *Adm £1.50 Chd 50p. Fris May to Sept (10-5) (Share to NGS®). For NGS (Share to Dorset Gardens Trust®) Suns June 16, July 21, Aug 18 (2-6)*

Three Bays ⚹❀ (Mr & Mrs Christopher Garrett) 8 Old Wareham Rd, Beacon Hill, (nr Limberlost junction with A350) 1½m SW of Corfe Mullen. Garden of ½ acre made and maintained by owners. There is a Japanese flavour to the garden, with stone lanterns, dovecot and water features. Fuchsias are a special interest with a covered garden. New rose garden 1993. Shrubs and herbaceous borders with much use of sloping site. TEAS. *Adm £1 Chd 50p (Share to Cancer Research Campaign®). Suns July 7, 14 (2-5). Private visits welcome for parties of 40 and over, please* **Tel 01202 623352**

Waterfalls ⚹ (Roger Butler Esq) 59 Branksome Wood Rd, Bournemouth. 1m W from Bournemouth Square, nr Coy Pond Rd. ⅓-acre redesigned garden. Made by owner over past 11 years utilising a steeply inclined site and featuring a series of waterfalls and koi pond. Mature trees provide a setting for ericaceous plants and ferns against a woodland background. *Adm 75p Chd 25p. Sun June 2 (2-6)*

Welcome Thatch ⚹❀ (Mrs Diana Guy) Witchampton. 3½m E of Wimborne, B3078 L to Witchampton, thence through village past church & shop to last but one on R. Please avoid parking close village centre. ⅔-acre plantsperson's garden surrounding a listed thatched cottage. Timber decking with exotic and tender plants, pond, summerhouse, potager, meadow, poultry and mixed borders. Recent additions include a silver garden, pumped stream and a small gravel garden with an oriental theme. Over 100 named varieties of hardy geraniums. Elderly, infirm or very young children need to take great care. TEAS except June when in village hall. *Adm £1 Chd free. Suns March 31, April 28, May 19, June 23, Oct 6 (2-5.30). Private visits also welcome by appt, please* **Tel 01258 840776**

¶**24a Western Avenue** (Mr & Mrs Peter Jackson) Poole. Central in Branksome Park, ½m from Compton Acres. Award winning 1-acre part Mediterranean, part English garden close to sea. Formal areas incl lawns, cherry tree walk, rose garden, herbaceous beds, topiary and courtyard with tender wall plants. Tree ferns, drimys, bamboo and camellias flourish. Sunny banks are planted with eucalyptus, acacias, and a collection of callistemons,

agaves, yuccas and other drought resistant plants. *Adm £1 Chd free. Sun July 7 (2-6)*

Weston House ⌖❀ (Mr & Mrs E A W Bullock) Buckhorn Weston. 4m W of Gillingham and 4m SE of Wincanton. From A30 turn N to Kington Magna, continue towards Buckhorn Weston and after railway bridge take L turn towards Wincanton. 2nd on L is Weston House. 1 acre plus fields; old and English roses; herbaceous and mixed borders backed by old walls with climbers. Small woodland and wild flower areas; wild-life pond; lawns and view of Blackmore Vale. TEAS in aid of Buckhorn Weston Parish Church. *Adm £1.50 Chd free. Suns June 9, 23 (2-6)*

Wimborne Minster Model Town & Gardens ⌖⚹❀ (The Wimborne Minster Model Town Trust). King St 200yds W of Minster, opp public car park. 1½-acre grounds with ⅒ scale models of the town in early fifties, surrounded by landscaped gardens. Herbaceous borders, alpines, herbs, heather and rose gardens, with many rare and unusual plants, with pools and fountain, making a colourful pleasure garden. Many seats and views over Stour valley. Refreshments daily. *Adm £2.25 OAPs £1.75 Chd £1 (3-15) under 3 free.* ▲*For NGS Suns June 2, July 7, Sept 1 (10-5).* **Tel 01202 881924**

Wincombe Park ❀ (The Hon M D Fortescue) 2m from Shaftesbury. Off A350 to Warminster signed to Wincombe and Donhead St Mary. Plantsman's garden surrounding house set in parkland; raised beds, shrubs, perennials; walled kitchen garden; view of valley with lake and woods. Unusual plants for sale. TEA. *Adm £1.50 Chd free. Weds May 15 (2-5.30), also private visits and groups by appt* **Tel 01747 852161**

Witchcroft ⚹❀ (Mr & Mrs Rowland & Pamela Reynolds) 1 Sweet Hill Rd, Southwell, Portland. Follow the signs for Portland Bill (A354). 'Witchcroft' is the bungalow 300yds on L, past Eight Kings Public House in the village of Southwell. Small cottage garden with pond, shrubs, and herbaceous borders and open rural views. In spring there are bulbs and hellebores, in summer new and old-fashioned roses. Park in main st. TEAS in aid of Cancer and Leukaemia in Childhood Trust. *Adm 60p Chd free. Suns March 10, June 2, July 7 (2-5.30)*

SYMBOLS USED IN THIS BOOK (See also Page 15)

‡   Following a garden name in the Dates of Opening list indicates that those gardens sharing the same symbol are nearby and open on the same day.

‡‡   Indicates a second series of nearby gardens open on the same day.

¶   Opening for the first time.

❀   Plants/produce for sale if available.

⌖   Gardens with at least the main features accessible by wheelchair.

⚹   No dogs except guide dogs but otherwise dogs are usually admitted, provided they are kept on a lead. Dogs are not admitted to houses.

●   Gardens marked thus do not necessarily give all their takings to the National Gardens Scheme. Instead they give a guaranteed contribution.

▲   Where this sign appears alongside dates in the descriptive entry for a garden it denotes that this garden is also open regularly to the public on days other than those for the NGS.

County Durham

Hon County Organiser: Mrs Ian Bonas, Bedburn Hall, Hamsterley, Bishop Auckland DL13 3NN
Tel 01388 488231

DATES OF OPENING

May 6 Monday
Birkheads Cottage Garden & Nursery

May 26 Sunday
Barningham Park, nr Barnard Castle
Westholme Hall, Winston

May 27 Monday
Birkheads Cottage Garden & Nursery

June 9 Sunday
Eggleston Hall Gardens, nr Barnard Castle

June 16 Sunday
17 The General's Wood, Harraton

June 30 Sunday
The Gainford Gardens ‡

Low Walworth Hall, nr Darlington ‡

July 7 Sunday
Croft Hall, Croft
Westholme Hall, Winston

July 14 Sunday
Bedburn Hall, Hamsterley
Birkheads Cottage Garden & Nursery
10 The Chesters, Ebchester

July 28 Sunday
Ravensford Farm, Hamsterley

August 25 Sunday
Westholme Hall, Winston

August 26 Monday
Birkheads Cottage Garden & Nursery

Regular openings
For details see garden description

Raby Castle, Staindrop
University of Durham Botanic Garden, Durham

By appointment only
For telephone numbers and other details see garden descriptions. Private visits welcomed

173 Gilesgate, Durham
St Aidan's College, Durham

DESCRIPTIONS OF GARDENS

Barningham Park ❀ (Sir Anthony Milbank) 6m S of Barnard Castle. Turn S off A66 at Greta Bridge or A66 Motel via Newsham. Woodland walks, trees and rock garden. House (not open) built 1650. Home-made cream TEAS. *Adm £2 Chd 50p (under 14). Sun May 26 (2-6). Also by appt for parties, please* **Tel 01833 621202**

Bedburn Hall ⬥❀ (Ian Bonas Esq) Hamsterley, 9m NW of Bishop Auckland. From A68 at Witton-le-Wear, turn off W to Hamsterley; turn N out of Hamsterley-Bedburn and down 1m to valley. From Wolsingham on B6293 turn off SE for 3m. Medium-sized garden; terraced garden on S facing hillside with streams; lake; woodland; lawns; rhododendrons; herbaceous borders; roses. TEAS. *Adm £2 Chd 50p. Sun July 14 (2-6)*

Birkheads Cottage Garden & Nursery ⬥❀ (Christine Liddle) Nr Sunniside. From A1M N or S take A692 or A693 on to A6076 rd between Sunniside and Stanley. Birkheads Nursery is signposted 1m S of Tanfield Steam Railway. It is exactly 1m from signed junction to Nursery. Look out for the beehive! Over 4,000 different hardy plants in garden of 1½ acres incl pond, formal topiary garden, rockeries, gravel garden, herbaceous borders. Set in S facing open countryside. Beautiful views. Small specialist nursery featured on TV 3 yrs ago. *Adm £1.50 Chd 50p. Mons May 6, 27, Aug 26, Sun July 14 (10-5). Parties welcome, at other times by appt, please* **Tel 01207 232262**

10 The Chesters ⬥❀ (Dianne Allison) Ebchester, Nr Consett. S end of village on A694, signposted, 2m from Consett. Small 'cottage-style' garden, with the National Collection of Polemoniums among a wide variety of plants. National Trust woodland walk nearby for dog walking etc. Lectures and group visits by appointment. TEAS. *Adm £1 Chd free/donation. Sun July 14 (2-5)*

¶Croft Hall ⬥❀❀ (W D Chaytor) Darlington. Croft Village lies 3m S of Darlington on A167 to Northallerton and 6m from Scotch Corner. Croft Hall is 1st house on R as you enter the village from Scotch Corner. Square yellow Georgian. 3 acres incl lawn with avenue of red may, water garden with temple, shrubbery bank, herb and knot gardens, long herbaceous border sheltered by magnificent yew hedge. TEAS. *Adm £2 Chd 50p. Sun July 7 (2-6)*

Eggleston Hall Gardens ⬥❀❀ (Sir William Gray) Eggleston, NW of Barnard Castle. Route B6278. Large garden with many unusual plants; large lawns, rhododendrons, greenhouses, mixed borders, fine trees, large extension of kitchen garden (all organically grown). Garden centre open. Homemade TEAS. *Adm £2 Chd free. Sun June 9 (2-5). Private visits welcome, please* **Tel 01833 650553**

The Gainford Gardens ⬥❀ On A67, 8m W of Darlington; 8m E of Barnard Castle. One of the loveliest villages in the county, lying around a large tranquil green between A67 and R Tees. Georgian flavour predominates. TEAS. *Combined adm £2 Chd free (Share to St Mary's Parish Church®). Sun June 30 (2-6)*

   1 Balmer Hill (Mr & Mrs R Holmes)
   2 Balmer Hill (Mr & Mrs A Best)
   3 Balmer Hill (Mr & Mrs Pennell)
   1 Academy Gardens (Dr & Mrs A G Leishman)
   14 Academy Gardens (Mr & Mrs G Taylor)
   35 Academy Gardens (Mr & Mrs M Metcalf)
   7 High Row (Peter & Merope)
   24 Low Green (Mrs M R Ferens)
   2 Piggy Lane (Mr & Mrs J G Ormston)

17 The General's Wood ✿ (Bob & Doreen Wigham) Harraton. From A1M at Chester-Le-Street take rd signposted Picktree. In 1m turn R into Bonemill Lane; after lm turn R into The General's Wood. ⅓rd acre mature garden in woodland setting with large pond area. Refreshments. *Adm 50p Chd free. Sun June 16 (2-5)*

173 Gilesgate & (Dr Anne Sullivan) Durham. Leave Durham Market Place to roundabout at top of Claypath. 3rd exit (marked Hild & Bede College) then immed 1st L. 173 is first house - phonebox outside. ½-acre garden of lawns, mixed herbaceous borders, with small formal herb garden, quiet 'cottage' garden, and small area of formal boxed beds, shade borders. *Adm £1. Private visits welcome, please* **Tel 0191 3866402**

Low Walworth Hall & ✿ (Mr & Mrs Worrall) 3½m W of Darlington, on Staindrop Rd. B6279 (½m drive). Old walled garden; herbaceous borders, shrubs, roses; trout rearing pond. Small Japanese garden. Interesting and varied shrubs and greenhouse plants for sale. Homemade cream TEAS. *Adm £2 Chd 50p. Sun June 30 (2-5.30)*

● **Raby Castle** & ✿ (The Rt Hon The Lord Barnard) Staindrop, NW of Darlington. 1m N of Staindrop on A688 Barnard Castle-Bishop Auckland. Buses: 75, 77 Darlington-Barnard Castle; 8 Bishop Auckland-Barnard Castle; alight Staindrop, North Lodge, ¼m. Large walled garden; informal garden with ericas; old yew hedges; shrub and herbaceous borders; roses. Castle also open, principally C14 with alterations made 1765 and mid-C19; fine pictures and furniture. Collection of horse-drawn carriages and fire engines. Garden only suitable wheelchairs. TEAS at Stables. Special terms for parties on application. *Adm Castle Gardens and carriages £3.50 OAPs £3.20 Chd £1.50. Family ticket £9 (2 adults, 2-3 Chd) Gardens & carriages only £1 OAPs/Chd 75p. Fri to Wed April 5-10, May 1 to June 30, Weds, Suns only; July 1 to Sept 30 daily (except Sats); also Bank Hol weekends, Sat to Tues (Castle 1-5; garden and park 11-5.30, last adm 4.30); also by appt for parties* **Tel 01833 660202**

¶**Ravensford Farm** ✿ (Mr & Mrs J Peacock) 9m NW of Bishop Auckland. From A68 at Witton-le-Wear turn off W to Hamsterley. Go through village and turn L just before tennis courts. 2½-acre, 10-yr-old garden, created from a field containing a mass of nettles and thistles, and 1 ancient apple tree. There is now a small wood, 2 ponds, a sunken garden, a rhododendron walk and mixed borders containing flowering shrubs, roses and herbaceous perennials. TEAS. *Adm £1.50 Chd 50p. Sun July 28 (2-6)*

St Aidan's College (By kind permission of the Principal) Durham. 1m from City centre. A1050 N towards Durham City; turn W at South End House, where St Aidan's College signposted. St Aidan's College was designed by Sir Basil Spence and the grounds laid out according to a plan by Prof Brian Hackett about 1966. The maturing garden (2 acres) includes shrub planting, rose beds and raised beds; several specimen trees of interest incl cedrus libani, have been planted. From the garden there are unequalled views of Durham Cathedral, Durham City and Durham University Observatory, designed by Anthony Salvin. Booklets 50p and postcards 20p available on request. *Gardens open all year except Christmas and Easter. Please arrange with Bursar* **Tel 0191 374 3269.** *Donations to NGS*

University of Durham Botanic Garden & ✿ 1m from centre of Druham. Turn off A167 (old A1) at Cock O'The North roundabout, direction Durham for 1m; turn R into Hollingside Lane which is between Grey and Collingwood Colleges; gardens 600yds on R. 18 acres on a beautiful SW facing hillside features 15-yr-old North American Arboretum planted 1980, woodland and ornamental bog garden, winter heather beds and tropical and desert display glasshouses. The Prince Bishop's garden contains 6 statues. TEAS in Visitor Centre. *Adm £1 Chd 50p. March 1 to Oct 31 (10-5), Nov 1 to Feb 28 every afternoon weather permitting. Private parties welcome, please* **Tel 0191 374 7971**

Westholme Hall & ✿ (Mr & Mrs J H McBain) Winston. 11m W of Darlington. From A67 Darlington-Barnard Castle, nr Winston turn N onto B6274. 5 acres of gardens and grounds laid out in 1892 surround the Jacobean house (not open). Rhododendrons, flowering shrubs, mixed borders, old-fashioned rose garden. The croquet lawn leads on to an orchard, stream and woodland. Home made TEAS. *Adm £2 Chd 50p. Suns May 26, July 7, Aug 25 (2-6)*

Dyfed

See separate Welsh section beginning on page 310

Essex

Hon County Organiser: Mrs Judy Johnson, Saling Hall, Great Saling, Braintree CM7 5DT
Tel 01371 850243
Assistant Hon County Organisers: Mrs Jill Cowley, Park Farm, Great Waltham, Chelmsford CM3 1BZ (Publicity)
Tel 01245 360871
Mrs Rosemary Kenrick, The Bailey House, Saffron Walden CB10 2EA
Hon County Treasurer: Eric Brown Esq, 19 Chichester Road, Saffron Walden CB11 3EW

DATES OF OPENING

March 30 Saturday
Olivers, nr Colchester
March 31 Sunday
The Magnolias, Brentwood
Olivers, nr Colchester
April 6 Saturday
Lower Dairy House, Nayland
April 7 Sunday
Glen Chantry, Wickham Bishops
Lower Dairy House, Nayland
The Magnolias, Brentwood
Park Farm, Great Waltham
April 8 Monday
Lower Dairy House, Nayland
Park Farm, Great Waltham
April 11 Thursday
Woodpeckers,
Burnham-on-Crouch
April 14 Sunday
Lower Dairy House, Nayland
April 21 Sunday
Deers, Clavering
Glen Chantry, Wickham Bishops
Lower Dairy House, Nayland
The Magnolias, Brentwood
Park Farm, Great Waltham
April 22 Monday
Park Farm, Great Waltham
April 28 Sunday
Lower Dairy House, Nayland
The Magnolias, Brentwood
Saling Hall Lodge, Great Saling
May 1 Wednesday
Saling Hall, Great Saling
May 3 Friday
Perrymans, Boxted
May 4 Saturday
Lower Dairy House, Nayland
Olivers, nr Colchester
May 5 Sunday
6 Fanners Green, Great
Waltham ‡
Glen Chantry, Wickham Bishops
Lower Dairy House, Nayland
Olivers, nr Colchester
Park Farm, Great Waltham ‡
Rose Cottage, Theydon Bois
May 6 Monday
Carters House, Sible Hedingham
6 Fanners Green, Great
Waltham ‡

Glen Chantry, Wickham Bishops
Lower Dairy House, Nayland
Olivers, nr Colchester
Park Farm, Great Waltham ‡
May 8 Wednesday
Saling Hall, Great Saling
May 10 Friday
Perrymans, Boxted
May 12 Sunday
Lower Dairy House, Nayland
The Magnolias, Brentwood
Park Farm, Great Waltham
Rose Cottage, Theydon Bois
May 13 Monday
Park Farm, Great Waltham
May 15 Wednesday
Horkesley Hall, Colchester
Saling Hall, Great Saling
May 17 Friday
Perrymans, Boxted
May 19 Sunday
1 Coronation Villa, Feering ‡
Feeringbury Manor, Feering ‡
Lower Dairy House, Nayland
The Magnolias, Brentwood
Park Farm, Great Waltham
Shore Hall, Cornish Hall End
May 20 Monday
Park Farm, Great Waltham
May 22 Wednesday
Saling Hall, Great Saling
May 24 Friday
Perrymans, Boxted
May 25 Saturday
Lower Dairy House, Nayland
May 26 Sunday
Glen Chantry, Wickham Bishops
Lower Dairy House, Nayland
Park Farm, Great Waltham
Rose Cottage, Theydon Bois
Saling Hall Lodge,
Great Saling
May 27 Monday
Edelweiss, Hornchurch
Glen Chantry, Wickham Bishops
Lower Dairy House, Nayland
Park Farm, Great Waltham
May 29 Wednesday
Saling Hall, Great Saling
May 31 Friday
Perrymans, Boxted
June 1 Saturday
Lower Dairy House, Nayland

June 2 Sunday
8 Dene Court, Chelmsford
Lower Dairy House, Nayland
The Magnolias, Brentwood
Park Farm, Great Waltham
June 3 Monday
Park Farm, Great Waltham
June 5 Wednesday
Saling Hall, Great Saling
June 9 Sunday
Carters House, Sible
Hedingham ‡
The Dower House, Castle
Hedingham ‡
The Fens, Langham
Lofts Hall, Elmdon, nr Saffron
Walden
The Old Rectory, Boreham
Park Farm, Great Waltham
June 10 Monday
Park Farm, Great Waltham
June 12 Wednesday
Horkesley Hall, Colchester
Park Farm, Great Waltham
Saling Hall, Great Saling
June 13 Thursday
Woodpeckers,
Burnham-on-Crouch
June 15 Saturday
Amberden Hall, Widdington
Lower Dairy House, Nayland
Stamps & Crows, Layer Breton
Heath
June 16 Sunday
Amberden Hall, Widdington
Barnards, Sible Hedingham
1 Coronation Villa, Feering
8 Dene Court, Chelmsford
6 Fanners Green, Great
Waltham ‡
Lower Dairy House, Nayland
Park Farm, Great Waltham ‡
Rose Cottage, Theydon Bois
Stamps & Crows, Layer Breton
Heath
June 17 Monday
6 Fanners Green, Great
Waltham ‡
Park Farm, Great Waltham ‡
June 19 Wednesday
Saling Hall, Great Saling
Stamps & Crows, Layer Breton
Heath

June 20 Thursday
Woodpeckers, Burnham-on-Crouch
June 23 Sunday
Clavering Gardens, nr Saffron Walden
Lower Dairy House, Nayland
The Magnolias, Brentwood
Park Farm, Great Waltham
Shore Hall, Cornish Hall End
June 24 Monday
Park Farm, Great Waltham
June 26 Wednesday
Saling Hall, Great Saling
June 29 Saturday
Lower Dairy House, Nayland
Olivers, nr Colchester
June 30 Sunday
8 Dene Court, Chelmsford
Edelweiss, Hornchurch
Glen Chantry, Wickham Bishops
Lower Dairy House, Nayland
The Old Vicarage, Rickling
Olivers, nr Colchester
Park Farm, Great Waltham
Rose Cottage, Theydon Bois
Saling Hall, Great Saling ‡
Saling Hall Lodge, Great Saling ‡
July 1 Monday
Park Farm, Great Waltham
July 3 Wednesday
Saling Hall, Great Saling
July 6 Saturday
Lower Dairy House, Nayland
July 7 Sunday
Littlebury Gardens
Lower Dairy House, Nayland
Park Farm, Great Waltham
Rose Cottage, Theydon Bois
July 8 Monday
Park Farm, Great Waltham
July 10 Wednesday
Saling Hall, Great Saling
July 14 Sunday
1 Coronation Villa, Feering
8 Dene Court, Chelmsford
Fanners Farm, Great Waltham ‡
6 Fanners Green, Great Waltham ‡
The Magnolias, Brentwood
Woodpeckers, Burnham-on-Crouch
July 15 Monday
Fanners Farm, Great Waltham ‡
6 Fanners Green, Great Waltham ‡
July 17 Wednesday
Horkesley Hall, Colchester
Saling Hall, Great Saling
July 24 Wednesday
Saling Hall, Great Saling
July 28 Sunday
8 Dene Court, Chelmsford
Edelweiss, Hornchurch
The Magnolias, Brentwood
July 31 Wednesday
Saling Hall, Great Saling
August 4 Sunday
Wickets, Langley Upper Green
August 11 Sunday
8 Dene Court, Chelmsford
August 18 Sunday
The Magnolias, Brentwood
August 25 Sunday
Edelweiss, Hornchurch
September 1 Sunday
Deers, Clavering
Glen Chantry, Wickham Bishops
September 8 Sunday
Folly Faunts House, Goldhanger
September 12 Thursday
Woodpeckers, Burnham-on-Crouch
September 15 Sunday
Glen Chantry, Wickham Bishops
The Magnolias, Brentwood
October 20 Sunday
The Magnolias, Brentwood
Writtle College, Writtle

Regular openings
For details see garden description

Beth Chatto Gardens, Elmstead Market
The Gardens of Easton Lodge, Great Dunmow
Feeringbury Manor, Feering
The Fens, Langham
Glen Chantry, Wickham Bishops
Hyde Hall, RHS Garden, Rettendon
Volpaia, Hockley

By appointment only
For telephone numbers and other details see garden descriptions. Private visits welcomed

Reed House, Great Chesterford

DESCRIPTIONS OF GARDENS

Amberden Hall ♿✿❀ (Mr & Mrs D Lloyd) Widdington. 6m from Saffron Walden. E off B1383 nr Newport. Follow signs to Mole Hall Wildlife Park. Drive ½m beyond park on R. Medium-sized walled garden with collection of unusual hardy plants, shrubs and ivy allée. Raised vegetable garden. TEAS on Sun. *Adm £2 Chd free (Share to St Mary's Church, Widdington®). Sat, Sun June 15, 16 (2-6)*

¶Barnards ♿✿❀ (Mr & Mrs Leonard Ratcliff) Sible Hedingham. 1½m from A604, on Hedingham-Wethersfield rd. Garden on L. Formal plantsman's garden of 2 acres, created since 1994 with Elizabethan 'forthright'; parterre; Mediterranean edible garden; lime walk; evergreen 'Mondrian' garden. Rough area of old-fashioned shrub roses and grasses and walk to belts of newly-planted English trees. TEA. *Adm £1 Chd free. Sun June 16 (2-5.30)*

●Beth Chatto Gardens ✿❀ (Mrs Beth Chatto) On A133, ¼m E of Elmstead Market. 5 acres of attractively landscaped garden with many unusual plants, shown in wide range of conditions from hot and dry to water garden. The recently made gravel garden, converted from the original car park, has been planted with drought-tolerant plants to help gardeners who have hose-pipe watering bans. Books available by Beth Chatto The Dry Garden, The Damp Garden, Beth Chatto's Garden Notebook, The Green Tapestry. Adjacent nursery open. *Adm £2 Chd free. March 1 to Oct 31, every Mon to Sat but closed Bank Hols (9-5); Nov 1 to end of Feb every Mon to Fri but closed Bank Hols (9-4). Parties by appt*

By Appointment Gardens. These owners do not have a fixed opening day usually because they do not like crowds or have insufficient parking space. Owner will often give guided tour.

¶**Carters House** ᴅ&ᴥ❀ (Mrs Michael Gosling) High Street Green, Sible Hedingham. Well-marked off A604 from Sible Hedingham. Hedingham to Wethersfield Rd. ¾-acre garden, created since 1990. Many bulbs, especially tulips. Malus, cherries, lilacs, clematis and roses; white border, gold and blue border; other interesting and species plants of yr-round interest. TEAS. *Adm £1.50 Chd free. Mon May 6; Sun June 9 (2-6)*

Clavering Gardens ᴅ&❀ Clavering. On B1038 7m N of Bishops Stortford. Turn W off B1383 (old A11) at Newport. TEAS in Cricket Pavilion on village green in aid of Clavering Cricket Club. *Adm £2.50 Chd free. Sun June 23 (1-5.30)*
> **Brooklands** (Mr & Mrs John Noble) Walled garden, herbaceous and shrub borders, rustic rose trellis. 15-yr-old arboretum. Newly planted orchard area 1½ acres
> **Clavering Court** (Mr & Mrs S R Elvidge) Approx 1½ acres fine trees, shrubs and borders. Walled garden, Edwardian greenhouse
> **Deers** (Mr & Mrs S Cooke) Shrub and herbaceous borders; ponds; old roses in formal garden; walled vegetable garden; flower meadow; trees. 4 acres. Parking in yard next to house. Runner-up in large garden competition 1994
> **Piercewebbs** (Mr & Mrs B R William-Powlett) Includes old walled garden, shrubs, lawns, ha ha, yew and stilt hedges, pond and trellised rose garden. Extensive views. Best amateur garden in Country Gardens Competition. Plant stall
> **Shovellers** (Miss J & Miss E Ludgate) Stickling Green. 3-acre extended cottage garden, orchard and meadow

1 Coronation Villa ❀ (Mr Colin Smith) Feering. 9m W of Colchester. 4m E of Witham, signposted off the A12 ½m NE from The Bell Inn on R-hand side towards The Teys. ⅓-acre informal garden consisting of a variety of trees, shrubs, climbing plants and perennials; also pond, gazebo, pergola and sink gardens. TEAS. *Adm £1 Chd free. Suns May 19, June 16, July 14 (2-5)*

Deers (Mr & Mrs S Cooke) Clavering. On B1038 7m N of Bishop's Stortford. Turn W off B1383 (old A11) at Newport; close to Fox & Hound Inn, centre of village. Follow signs to Langley, 2nd L on bend, sign to Ford End. Shrub and herbaceous borders; ponds; old roses in formal garden; walled vegetable garden; flower meadow; trees. 4 acres. Parking in yard next to house. Runner-up in large gardens competition 1994. *Combined adm with Clavering Gardens £2.50 Chd free. Sun June 23 (1-5.30). Adm £2 Chd free. Suns April 21, Sept 1 (2-5)*

8 Dene Court ❀❀ (Mrs Sheila Chapman) Chelmsford. W of Chelmsford (Parkway). Take A1060 Roxwell Rd for 1m. Turn R at traffic lights into Chignall Rd, Dene Court 3rd exit on R. Parking in Chignall Rd. Well maintained and designed compact garden (250 sq yds) circular lawn surrounded by many unusual plants incl wide variety of clematis, roses, ferns and grasses; ornamental well; three pergolas; rose-covered perimeter wall. Featured in Essex Homes and Living, Garden News and Daily Mirror. *Adm £1 Chd 50p (Share to Audrey Appleton Trust for the Terminally Ill®). Suns June 2, 16, 30, July 14, 28, Aug 11 (2-5.30)*

The Dower House ❀❀ (Mr & Mrs John Allfrey) Castle Hedingham on B1058. 5m from Halstead A604. 1m NE of Sible Hedingham. Follow signs to Hedingham Castle. Garden 50yds from entrance. Terraced plantsman's garden of 1½ acres overlooking Tudor church and village. Mixed borders developed since 1987 with flower arranging in mind. TEAS. *Adm £1.50 Chd free (Share to St Nicholas Church, Castle Hedingham®). Sun June 9 (2-6)*

●**The Gardens of Easton Lodge** formerly **Warwick House** ᴅ&❀❀ (Mr & Mrs B Creasey) Easton Lodge. 1m N of Great Dunmow on B184, take rd to Lt Easton, ½m turn L to Easton Lodge, 1¼m to white gates marked Easton Lodge, pass through these; gardens ½m on R. Originally wing of Easton Lodge, home of Countess of Warwick; old house now demolished and gardens of 6 acres created since 1972 on much of old house site. Includes recently acquired 4.5 acres of the abandoned gardens designed by Harold Peto at the turn of the century, now under restoration. Features incl C18 dovecote; conservatory; cobbled, herringbone courtyard with fountain; ponds with koi and water fowl. History of Easton Lodge and occasionally American Air Force Exhibits. Cream TEAS. *Adm £2 Chd free (Share to Five Parishes®). Sats, Suns, Bank Hols April 5 to Oct 27 (2-6). Private visits welcome, please* Tel 01371 876979

Edelweiss ❀❀ (Joan H Hogg, Pat F Lowery) 20 Hartland Road, Hornchurch. From Romford head in an easterly direction along the A124 past Tesco on L, turn R into Albany Rd opp church on corner of Park Lane on the L. Go to the bottom of Albany Rd, humps all the way down, turn L at the end into Hartland Rd. A small town garden approx 200′ × 25′ very colourful and maintained to a high standard. Laid out to maximise use of small narrow plot and featuring many containers, baskets, seasonal bedding and mixed borders. Tiny prize-winning garden to the front of the property. Owners sell home-made produce, eggs etc. Narrow access and steps at side and rear not really suitable for push-chairs. TEAS. *Adm £1 Chd free. Mon May 27, Suns June 30, July 28, Aug 25 (3-6). Private visits welcome, June - Aug please* Tel 01708 454610

Fanners Farm ᴅ&❀ (Mr & Mrs P G Lee) 4m N of Chelmsford. In Great Waltham turn into South Street opp One Step Beyond restaurant (Six Bells Inn). Garden 1¼m on R. Informal garden of approx 2 acres surrounding C14 house (not open). Conservatory featured in The Garden, Feb 1990. Small collection of vintage cars. TEAS Sun only. *Adm £1 Chd free. Sun, Mon July 14, 15 (2-6)*

6 Fanners Green ❀❀ (Dr & Mrs T M Pickard) 4m N of Chelmsford. In Great Waltham turn into South Street opp One Step Beyond restaurant (Six Bells Inn). Garden 1¼m on the R. A 15-yr-old small country garden of ⅓ acre divided into different formal areas with informal planting. Herb garden and conservatory. *Adm £1 Chd free. Suns, Mons May 5, 6; June 16, 17, July 14, 15 (2-6). Parties by appt May to July, please* Tel 01245 360035

Regular Openers. See end of county section.

Feeringbury Manor & (Mr & Mrs G Coode-Adams) Coggeshall Rd, Feering, on rd between Coggeshall and Feering. 7-acre garden bordering R Blackwater. Many unusual plants including wide variety of honeysuckles, clematis, old-fashioned roses; rare bog-loving plants, border, ponds and stream; small Victorian water wheel. Contemporary sculpture exhibition during June. Featured in Country Life 1994 and The Passionate Gardener. Plants in aid of All Saints Church, Feering and cream TEAS May 19 only. *Adm £2 Chd free. Sun May 19 (2-6). Weekday mornings April 29 to Aug 2 (8-1) closed weekends and Bank Hols. Private visits welcome, please* **Tel 01376 561946**

The Fens & ✿❀ (Mrs Ann Lunn) Old Mill Rd, Langham. 5m N of Colchester off A12. From Shepherd and Dog pub take High St. Turn R into Old Mill Rd starts at T-junction with High St and is an extension of Chapel Rd, leading to Boxted-Dedham Rd. Undulating 2-acre cottage garden maintained by owners. Pond, shade and ditch gardens. TEA for charity. *Adm £1 Chd 50p. Thurs April to Aug, Sun June 9 (2-5). Private visits welcome for groups, please* **Tel 01206 272259**

Folly Faunts House & ✿ (Mr & Mrs J C Jenkinson) Goldhanger. On B1026 between Colchester and Maldon. Winner best large garden in Essex award 1994. 5-acre garden around an C18 manor house (not open) created since 1963. Garden is divided into 7 different compartments each with a wide variety of unusual plants, shrubs and trees. Formal and informal water gardens. 20 acres of park and woodland, planted in 1988, is divided into 5 double avenues. Large car park. Unusual and interesting plants for sale. TEAS. *Adm £1.50 Chd £1. Sun Sept 8 (2-5). Private visits welcome, please* **Tel 01621 788213**

Glen Chantry & ✿❀ (Mr & Mrs W G Staines) Wickham Bishops 1½m SE of Witham. Take Maldon Rd from Witham and 1st L to Wickham Bishops. Pass Benton Hall Golf Course: cross narrow bridge over R Blackwater and turn immediately L up track by side of Blue Mills. 3-acre garden, emphasis on mixed borders, unusual perennials and shrub roses. Limestone rock gardens with associated ponds form a dominant feature, formal specialist white garden and foliage beds with grasses and hostas; range of plants for sale. TEAS in aid of local charities. *Adm £1 Chd 50p. Suns April 7, 21; May 5, 26; June 30; Sept 1, 15; Mons May 6, 27 (2-5). Fris, Sats June, July and August (10-4) (no TEAS). Also parties by appt, please* **Tel 01621 891342**

Horkesley Hall & (Mr & Mrs Richard Eddis) Little Horkesley, , Colchester. Little Horkesley is W of A134, 3m N of Colchester. House marked on map just beyond church. A young garden of approx 5 acres within the setting of a classical house, 2 old fishponds and some fine old trees around the perimeter. Its creation began in 1990/91 and the emphasis is on shrubs and trees chosen for colour and effect and incl some which are unusual and rare. Total area about 4-5 acres. *Adm £2 Chd £1 (Share to Co-workers of Mother Theresa®). Weds May 15, June 12, July 17 (2-5). Parties by appt on weekdays, please* **Tel 01206 272067**

●**Hyde Hall Garden** & ✿❀ (Royal Horticultural Society) Rettendon. 7m SE of Chelmsford; 6m NE of Wickford. Signed from A130. Flowering trees, shrubs, perennials, roses, bulbs, ornamental greenhouses and ponds; all-yr-round colour. Restaurant. *Adm £2.70 Chd 70p 6-14. Parties 20+ £2.20. Every Wed, Thurs, Fri, Sat, Sun and Bank Hols March 24 to Oct 27 (11-6), Sept, Oct (11-5)*

Littlebury Gardens ✿❀ 2m from Saffron Walden, opp Littlebury church on B1383 1m N of Audley End House, entrance in Littlebury Green Rd. TEAS. *Combined adm £1.25 Chd free. Sun July 7 (2-5.30)*
  Granta House & (Mr & Mrs R A Lloyd). Old walled garden of 1 acre; unusual shrubs, herbaceous plants and roses
  North House (Mr & Mrs B G Sanders) opp Granta House. Mixed borders, herb garden and roses

Lofts Hall & ✿ (Maj & Mrs C R Philipson) Elmdon. 8m E of Royston. 5m W of Saffron Walden off B1039. Large garden, 6 acres; roses; herbaceous and shrub borders; kitchen garden; lake and C16 carp pond. Early C17 dovecote (reputedly 2nd largest in England), stud farm. TEAS. *Adm £2 Chd 50p. Sun June 9 (2-6)*

Lower Dairy House & ✿❀ (Mr & Mrs D J Burnett) 7m N of Colchester off A134. Turn L at bottom of hill before Nayland village into Water Lane, signed to Little Horkesley. Garden ½m on L past farm buildings. Plantsman's garden approx 1½ acres. Natural stream with waterside plantings; rockery and raised beds; lawns; herbaceous borders; roses. Many varieties of shrubs and ground cover plants. Garden made and maintained by owners for yr-round colour and variety. Good spring bulbs and blossom. Tudor House (not open). TEAS. *Adm £1.50 Chd 50p. Sats, Suns, Mons April 6, 7, 8, 14, 21, 28; May 4, 5, 6, 12, 19, 25, 26, 27; June 1, 2, 15, 16, 23, 29, 30; July 6, 7 (2-6). Also private visits welcome, please* **Tel 01206 262220**

The Magnolias ✿❀ (Mr & Mrs R A Hammond) 18 St John's Ave, Brentwood. From A1023 turn S on A128; after 300yds R at traffic lights; over railway bridge; St John's Ave 3rd on R. ½-acre well-designed informal garden with particular appeal to plantsmen; good collection spring bulbs; ground-cover; trees and shrubs incl maples, rhododendrons, camellias, magnolias and pieris. Koi ponds and other water interests. Featured on Garden Club in 93. TEA. *Adm £1 Chd 50p. Suns March 31; April 7, 21, 28; May 12, 19; June 2, 23; July 14, 28; Aug 18; Sept 15; Oct 20 (10-5). Parties by appt March to Oct incl, please* **Tel 01277 220019**

The Old Rectory & ✿❀ (Sir Jeffery & Lady Bowman) Boreham. 4m NE of Chelmsford. Take 1137 to Boreham Village, turn into Church Rd at Red Lion Public House. ½m along on R opp church. 2½-acre garden with ponds, stream, interesting trees and shrubs, herbaceous borders and kitchen garden. TEAS. *Adm £1 Chd free. Sun June 9 (2-6)*

General Information. For general information on the use of this book see Page 15.

The Old Vicarage &⚘❀ (Mr & Mrs James Jowitt) Rickling. 7m S from Saffron Walden: from Newport take B1038 W to Wicken Bonhunt. In village turn L to Rickling, The Old Vicarage is on the L after 1m. 2-acre garden divided by mature yew hedges, interesting 'hot' borders, herbaceous and mixed borders; rose garden, shrubbery, all largely created by present owners. TEAS in aid of Rickling Church. *Adm £1.50 Chd free. Sun June 30 (2-6)*

Olivers &⚘❀ (Mr & Mrs D Edwards) 3m SW of Colchester, between B1022 & B1026. Follow signs to zoo and continue 1m towards Colchester. Turn R at roundabout (Cunobelin Drive) and R into Olivers Lane. From Colchester via Maldon Rd turn L at roundabout, R into Olivers Lane (signposted Roman River Centre). C18 house (not open) overlooks Roman River valley, surrounded by terrace and yew-backed borders; closely planted with wide variety of plants, many unusual and for varying conditions. Lawns; 3 lakes; meadow; woodland with fine trees underplanted with shrubs including rhododendrons and old roses; spring bulbs and bluebells. TEA. *Adm £1.50 Chd free. Sat, Sun March 30, 31, May 4, 5, June 29, 30; Mon May 6; Weds April 1 to June 30 (11-5). Also private visits welcome, please* Tel 01206 330575

Park Farm ⚘❀ (Mrs J E M Cowley & Mr D Bracey) Great Waltham. Take B1008 N from Chelmsford through Broomfield Village. On Little Waltham bypass turn L into Chatham Hall Lane signposted Howe Street; Park Farm ½m on L. 2 acres of garden in separate 'rooms' formed by yew hedges with climber-obscured old farmhouse and dairy in centre. Many different species of bulbs; shrubs; roses and herbaceous perennials; designing still proceeding with new projects underway. Featured in magazines and on TV. TEAS. *Adm £1 Chd 50p. Suns, Mons April 7, 8, 21, 22; May 5, 6, 12, 13, 19, 20, 26, 27; June 2, 3, 9, 10, 16, 17, 23, 24, 30; July 1, 7, 8, (2-6). Parties by appt, please* Tel 01245 360871

Perrymans &⚘❀ (Mr & Mrs H R J Human) Boxted. 4m NE from Colchester Station to Boxted Cross. Follow Dedham Rd, drive entrance on R 200yds past village shop. 7-acre undulating garden created from scratch since 1970, lakes, rose garden, holly collection, and borders, spring bulbs and selection of old and new trees. Teas by special arrangement. *Adm £1.50 Chd 50p. Fri mornings in May (8.30-12.30). Private visits welcome, any number, please* Tel 01206 272297

Reed House &⚘ (Mrs W H Mason) Great Chesterford. 4m N of Saffron Walden and 1m S of Stump Cross, M 11. On B184 turn into Great Chesterford High Street. Then L at Crown & Thistle public house into Manor Lane. ¾-acre garden developed in the last 6 years with collection of unusual plants. Featured in Essex Homes and Living. *Adm £1.50 Chd 50p. Private visits welcome, please* Tel 01799 530312

¶**Rose Cottage** ⚘❀ (Anne & Jack Barnard) 42 Blackacre Rd, Theydon Bois. 2m S of Epping on B172. At pedestrian crossing turn into Poplar Row (opp Bull inn). Pass village pond, turn 2nd R. Garden at top of hill on R. Small romantic garden 35′ × 130′, on a sloping site on verges of Epping Forest. Designed in compartments incl woodland, sundial, cottage and fountain gardens. Luxuriant

planting; small collection of old-fashioned and new English roses; cottage garden; unusual plants, herbs and bulbs. TEAS. *Adm £1 Chd free. Suns May 5, 12, 26; June 16, 30; July 7 (2-6). Private visits welcome by appt May to July, please* Tel 01992 814619

Saling Hall &⚘ (Mr & Mrs H Johnson) Great Saling, 6m NW of Braintree. A120; midway between Braintree-Dunmow turn off N at the Saling Oak. 12 acres; walled garden dated 1698; small park with fine trees; extensive new collection of unusual plants with emphasis on trees; water gardens. Hugh Johnson is 'Tradescant' of the RHS. TEAS Sun only. *Adm £2 Chd free (Share to St James's Church, Great Saling®). Weds in May, June, July (2-5). Sun June 30 with* **Saling Hall Lodge** *Combined adm £2.50 (2-6). Parties by appt on weekdays. Written application, please*

Saling Hall Lodge &⚘❀ (Mr & Mrs K Akers) Great Saling. 6m from Braintree. Turn N off A120 between Braintree and Dunmow at the Saling Oak. Drive at end of village on L, please park in village. Well-designed and maintained ½-acre garden with pond, limestone rock garden, small peat garden, tufa bed and sinks. As seen on Channel 4 and Anglia TV. TEAS. *Adm £1 Chd free. Suns April 28, May 26, (2-5). Combined adm with* **Saling Hall** *£2.50 Sun June 30 (2-6). Also parties by appt please,* Tel 01371 850683

Shore Hall ⚘❀ (Mr & Mrs Peter Swete) Cornish Hall End, nr Braintree. 2½m NE of Finchingfield. ½m W of Cornish Hall End on Gt Sampford Rd. Long drive with poplars. 3½-acre garden surrounding C17 house (not open) with several enclosed formal areas and interesting shrubs. 100-yr-old box hedges enclose formal beds planted with herbaceous and old roses; rose garden surrounding lily ponds; newly planted ornamental vegetable and fruit garden and many young rare trees. TEAS in aid of local charity. *Adm £2 Chd free. Suns May 19, June 23 (2-5). Parties by appt weekdays, May to July, please* Tel 017995 86411

Stamps and Crows &⚘ (Mr & Mrs E G Billington) Layer Breton Heath. 5½m S of Colchester on B1022 take L fork signposted Birch and Layer Breton. Garden on R side of Layer Breton Heath. 2½ acres of moated garden surrounding C15 farmhouse (not open). Herbaceous borders, mixed shrubs, old roses and good ground cover. Recently created bog garden and dovecote. Highly commended in Essex Country Garden Competition. Fine views towards Layer Marney Tower. TEAS (Sun only). *Adm £1.50 Chd free (Share to St. Mary's Church, Layer Breton®). Sat, Sun, Wed June 15, 16, 19 (2-6). Parties by appt, please* Tel 01206 330220

●**Volpaia** ⚘❀ (Mr & Mrs D Fox) 54 Woodlands Rd, Hockley. 2¾m NE of Rayleigh. B1013 Rayleigh-Rochford, turn S from Spa Hotel into Woodlands Rd. On E side of Hockley Woods. 1-acre containing many exotic trees, rhododendrons, camellias and other shrubs. Carpets of wood anemones and bluebells in spring, underplanting is very diverse, especially with woodland, liliaceous plants and ferns. Home of Bullwood Nursery. TEA. *Adm £1 Chd 30p (Share to Essex Group of NCCPG®). All Thurs & Suns from April 7 to June 2 (2.30-6). Also private visits welcome, please* Tel 01702 203761

¶**Wickets** ﾟ (Mr & Mrs D Copeland) Langley Upper Green. 11m N of Bishops Stortford. Turn W off B1383 (old A11) at Newport. After 5m turn R off B1038 at Clavering, signed Langley. Drive over ford and Upper Green is 3m further on. Last house on R of cricket green. Cottage garden and paddock with long views. 1½ acres. Newly planted in 1990. Island beds; herbaceous borders; rose borders; hanging baskets; pond. Highest village in Essex, windy site. TEAS. *Adm £1 Chd free. Sun Aug 4 (2-5.30)*

¶**Woodpeckers** ﾟ (Mr & Mrs N J Holdaway & Mrs L M Burton) Mangapp Chase, Burnham-on-Crouch. B1010 to Burnham-on-Crouch. Just beyond town sign turn L into Green Lane. Turn L after ½m. Garden 200yds on R. 1½ acres redeveloped since 1991. Planted for long season of interest using old 'cottage' favourites as well as newer varieties of roses, shrubs and herbaceous perennials. 'Potager', rose walk, new pond all set amongst mature trees. TEAS. *Adm £1 Chd 50p. Thurs April 11; June 13, 20; Sept 12. Sun July 14 (2-6). Parties welcome by appt, please* **Tel 01621 782137**

¶**Writtle College** ﾟ Lordship Rd, Writtle. On A414 W of Chelmsford, nr Writtle village, clearly signed. Approx 15 acres; informal lawns, tree collection, good autumn tints, mixed borders, alpines, formal 'Victorian' garden, aromatic garden. Small gardens designed and built by students undergoing training, bedding trial area, heather garden, ornamental and landscaped glasshouses. TEAS. *Adm £2 Chd free. Sun Oct 20 (10-4)*

Glamorgan

See separate Welsh section beginning on page 310

Gloucestershire

Hon County Organiser:	Mrs Heather Wondrausch, The New Inn, Poulton, Cirencester GL7 5JE Tel 01285 850226
Assistant Hon County Organisers:	Mr Guy Acloque, Alderley Grange, Wotton-under-Edge GL12 7QT
	Mrs Wendy Dare, Old Mill Dene, Blockley, Moreton-in-Marsh GL56 9HU
	Mrs Jennie Davies, Applegarth, Alstone, nr Tewkesbury GL20 8JD
	Mrs Sally Gough, Trevi, Over Old Road, Hartpury GL19 3BJ
	Mr Tony Marlow, Greenedge, 32 Dr Browns Road, Minchinhampton GL6 9BT
	Mrs Elizabeth-Ann Pile, Ampney Knowle, nr Cirencester GL7 5ED
Hon County Auditor:	Mr H J Shave, ACCA (Bradings) 31 Castle Street, Cirencester GL7 1QD

DATES OF OPENING

February
Tin Penny Cottage, Whiteway,
   nr Stroud. Every Wed
February 4 Sunday
Home Farm, Huntley, nr Newent
February 5 Monday
The Old Rectory, Duntisbourne
   Rous, nr Cirencester
February 8 Thursday
Cinderdine Cottage, Dymock,
   nr Newent
February 13 Tuesday
Cinderdine Cottage, Dymock,
   nr Newent
February 15 Thursday
Cinderdine Cottage, Dymock,
   nr Newent
February 18 Sunday
Cinderdine Cottage, Dymock,
   nr Newent

Minchinhampton Gardens
February 20 Tuesday
Cinderdine Cottage, Dymock,
   nr Newent
February 22 Thursday
Cinderdine Cottage, Dymock,
   nr Newent
February 25 Sunday
Camp Cottage, Highleadon,
   nr Newent
March
Camp Cottage, Highleadon,
   nr Newent. Every Sun
Grove Cottage, Lower Lydbrook,
   Cinderford. Every Thurs
The Old Manor, Twyning. Every
   Mon
Tin Penny Cottage, Whiteway,
   nr Stroud. Every Wed
March 3 Sunday
Green Cottage, Lydney
Home Farm, Huntley, nr Newent

March 10 Sunday
Green Cottage, Lydney
March 14 Thursday
Trevi Garden, Hartpury,
   nr Gloucester
March 17 Sunday
Green Cottage, Lydney
Tin Penny Cottage, Whiteway,
   nr Miserden
March 21 Thursday
Trevi Garden, Hartpury,
   nr Gloucester
March 24 Sunday
Cinderdine Cottage, Dymock,
   nr Newent
Green Cottage, Lydney
March 28 Thursday
Trevi Garden, Hartpury,
   nr Gloucester
March 31 Sunday
Brockweir Gardens,
   nr Chepstow

Misarden Park, Miserden,
nr Cirencester
North Rye House, Broadwell,
nr Moreton-in-Marsh
Painswick Rococo Garden,
Painswick

April

Camp Cottage, Highleadon,
nr Newent. Every Suns & Tues
Grove Cottage, Lower Lydbrook,
Cinderford. Every Thurs
The Old Manor, Twyning. Every
Mon
Tin Penny Cottage, Whiteway,
nr Stroud. Every Wed

April 6 Saturday
Ashley Manor, nr Tetbury

April 7 Sunday
Beverston Castle, Beverston
Gardens, nr Tetbury
Bredon Manor, nr Tewkesbury
Cinderdine Cottage, Dymock,
nr Newent
Pinbury Park, nr Cirencester
Trevi Garden, Hartpury,
nr Gloucester
Westonbirt Gardens at
Westonbirt School

April 8 Monday
Ashley Manor, nr Tetbury
Beverston Castle, Beverston
Gardens, nr Tetbury
Camp Cottage, Highleadon,
nr Newent
Cinderdine Cottage, Dymock,
nr Newent
Tin Penny Cottage, Whiteway,
nr Miserden
Trevi Garden, Hartpury,
nr Gloucester

April 11 Thursday
Trevi Garden, Hartpury,
nr Gloucester

April 14 Sunday
Home Farm, Huntley, nr Newent
Minchinhampton Gardens
Stanway House, nr Winchcombe

April 16 Tuesday
Cinderdine Cottage, Dymock,
nr Newent

April 18 Thursday
Trevi Garden, Hartpury,
nr Gloucester

April 21 Sunday
Clover House, Winson,
nr Cirencester
Old Mill Dene, Blockley
Pigeon House, Southam
Sudeley Castle Gardens,
Winchcombe
Tin Penny Cottage, Whiteway,
nr Miserden
Trevi Garden, Hartpury,
nr Gloucester

Upton Wold, nr Moreton-in-Marsh

April 25 Thursday
Trevi Garden, Hartpury,
nr Gloucester

April 28 Sunday
Blockley Gardens,
Moreton-in-the-Marsh
Brockweir Gardens, nr Chepstow
Nympsfield Gardens,
nr Nailsworth

May

Camp Cottage, Highleadon,
nr Newent. Every Sun, Mon &
Tues
Grove Cottage, Lower Lydbrook,
Cinderford. Every Thurs
Tin Penny Cottage, Whiteway,
nr Stroud. Every Wed
The Old Manor, Twyning. Every
Mon

May 1 Wednesday
Daylesford House,
nr Stow-on-the-Wold

May 4 Saturday
Barnsley House, nr Cirencester

May 5 Sunday
Abbotswood, Stow-on-the-Wold
Ampney Knowle, Barnsley,
nr Cirencester
Cinderdine Cottage, Dymock,
nr Newent
Eastcombe, Bussage & Brownshill
Gardens
Ewen Manor, nr Cirencester
Green Cottage, Lydney
Hidcote Manor Garden, Chipping
Campden
Lydney Park Gardens, Lydney
Millend House, nr Newland,
Coleford
Tin Penny Cottage, Whiteway,
nr Miserden
Trevi Garden, Hartpury,
nr Gloucester

May 6 Monday
Cinderdine Cottage, Dymock,
nr Newent
Eastcombe, Bussage & Brownshill
Gardens
Millend House, nr Newland,
Coleford
Trevi Garden, Hartpury,
nr Gloucester

May 9 Thursday
Trevi Garden, Hartpury,
nr Gloucester

May 11 Saturday
Kiftsgate Court, nr Chipping
Campden

May 12 Sunday
Batsford Arboretum,
nr Moreton-in-Marsh
Cerney House, North Cerney
Green Cottage, Lydney

Home Farm, Huntley, nr Newent
Rodmarton Manor, nr Cirencester
Snowshill Manor, nr Broadway
Stowell Park, nr Northleach

May 13 Monday
The Old Rectory, Duntisbourne
Rous, nr Cirencester

May 16 Thursday
Rockcliffe, Lower Swell
Trevi Garden, Hartpury,
nr Gloucester

May 19 Sunday
Abbotswood, Stow-on-the-Wold
Green Cottage, Lydney
Millend House, nr Newland,
Coleford
Old Mill Dene, Blockley
Trevi Garden, Hartpury,
nr Gloucester

May 20 Monday
Church Cottage, Stinchcombe,
nr Dursley

May 21 Tuesday
Cinderdine Cottage, Dymock,
nr Newent

May 22 Wednesday
Lydney Park Gardens, Lydney

May 23 Thursday
Trevi Garden, Hartpury,
nr Gloucester

May 26 Sunday
Bourton-on-the-Hill Gardens
Brockweir Gardens, nr Chepstow
Eastington Gardens,
nr Northleach
Millend House, nr Newland, Coleford
Nympsfield Gardens, nr Nailsworth
The Red House, Staunton,
nr Gloucester
Trevi Garden, Hartpury,
nr Gloucester
Willow Lodge, nr Longhope,
Gloucester

May 27 Monday
Brackenbury, Coombe,
nr Wotton-under-Edge
Brockweir Gardens, nr Chepstow
Eastington Gardens,
nr Northleach
Millend House, nr Newland,
Coleford
The Red House, Staunton,
nr Gloucester
Tin Penny Cottage, Whiteway,
nr Miserden
Trevi Garden, Hartpury,
nr Gloucester
Willow Lodge, nr Longhope,
Gloucester

May 30 Thursday
Bourton House Garden,
Bourton-on-the-Hill
Trevi Garden, Hartpury,
nr Gloucester

June
Camp Cottage, Highleadon,
  nr Newent. Every Sun, Mon &
  Tues
Grove Cottage, Lower Lydbrook,
  Cinderford, Every Thurs
The Old Manor, Twyning. Every
  Wed
Tin Penny Cottage, Whiteway,
  nr Stroud. Every Wed

June 1 Saturday
Barnsley House, nr Cirencester

June 2 Sunday
Boddington Manor, nr Cheltenham
The Chestnuts, Minchinhampton
Cinderdine Cottage, Dymock,
  nr Newent
Green Cottage, Lydney
Pigeon House, Southam
Stanway House, nr Winchcombe

June 3 Monday
The Old Rectory, Duntisbourne
  Rous, nr Cirencester

June 5 Wednesday
Green Cottage, Lydney

June 9 Sunday
25 Bowling Green Road,
  Cirencester
Green Cottage, Lydney
High Bank, 59 Bourne Drive,
  Brimscombe
Hillesley House, Hillesley,
  nr Wotton-under-Edge
Home Farm, Huntley, nr Newent
Hunts Court, North Nibley,
  nr Dursley
Icomb Place, nr Stow-on-the-Wold
Millend House, nr Newland,
  Coleford
Pitt Court, North Nibley, Dursley
Tetbury Gardens
Willow Lodge, nr Longhope,
  Gloucester

June 10 Monday
Willow Lodge, nr Longhope,
  Gloucester

June 12 Wednesday
Green Cottage, Lydney

June 13 Thursday
Old Mill Dene, Blockley
Trevi Garden, Hartpury,
  nr Gloucester

June 15 Saturday
Old Chapel, Chalford
Tin Penny Cottage, Whiteway,
  nr Miserden

June 16 Sunday
Adlestrop Gardens,
  Stow-on-the-Wold
25 Bowling Green Road,
  Cirencester
Chalford Gardens, nr Stroud
Green Cottage, Lydney
Hunts Court, North Nibley,

nr Dursley
13 Merestones Drive, Cheltenham
Pitt Court, North Nibley, Dursley
Randwick Gardens, nr Stroud
The Red House, Staunton,
  nr Gloucester
Trevi Garden, Hartpury,
  nr Gloucester
Willow Lodge, nr Longhope,
  Gloucester

June 17 Monday
Church Cottage, Stinchombe,
  nr Dursley
Old Chapel, Chalford
Willow Lodge, nr Longhope,
  Gloucester

June 18 Tuesday
Cinderdine Cottage, Dymock,
  nr Newent
Old Chapel, Chalford

June 19 Wednesday
Daylesford House,
  nr Stow-on-the-Wold
Green Cottage, Lydney
Old Chapel, Chalford

June 20 Thursday
Old Chapel, Chalford
Old Mill Dene, Blockley
Trevi Garden, Hartpury,
  nr Gloucester

June 21 Friday
Old Chapel, Chalford

June 22 Saturday
Hartpury College, nr Gloucester

June 23 Sunday
Cotswold Farm, nr Cirencester
Ewen Manor, nr Cirencester
Grange Farm, Evenlode,
  nr Moreton-in-Marsh
Green Cottage, Lydney
Hunts Court, North Nibley,
  nr Dursley
Millend House, nr Newland,
  Coleford
The Old Rectory, Great
  Rissington
Pitt Court, North Nibley, Dursley
Poulton Gardens, nr Cirencester
Trevi Garden, Hartpury,
  nr Gloucester
Upton Wold, nr Moreton-in-Marsh
Willow Lodge, nr Longhope,
  Gloucester
Witcombe Gardens, nr Gloucester

June 24 Monday
The Old Rectory, Duntisbourne
  Rous, nr Cirencester
Willow Lodge, nr Longhope,
  Gloucester

June 26 Wednesday
Moor Wood, Woodmancote,
  nr Cirencester
North Rye House, Broadwell,
  nr Moreton-in-Marsh

June 27 Thursday
Bourton House Garden,
  Bourton-on-the-Hill
Old Mill Dene, Blockley
Trevi Garden, Hartpury,
  nr Gloucester

June 30 Sunday
Beverston Gardens, nr Tetbury
Blockley Gardens,
  Moreton-in-the-Marsh
25 Bowling Green Road,
  Cirencester
Brackenbury, Coombe,
  nr Wotton-under-Edge
Brockweir Gardens, nr Chepstow
Hunts Court, North Nibley,
  nr Dursley
13 Merestones Drive,
  Cheltenham
Misarden Park, Miserden,
  nr Cirencester
Pinbury Park, nr Cirencester
Quenington Gardens, nr Fairford
20 St Peters Road, Cirencester
Stanton Gardens, nr Broadway
Stowell Park, nr Northleach
Trevi Garden, Hartpury,
  nr Gloucester

July
Camp Cottage, Highleadon,
  nr Newent. Every Sun, & Tues
Grove Cottage, Lower Lydbrook,
  Cinderford. Every Thurs
The Old Manor, Twyning. Every
  Mon
Tin Penny Cottage, Whiteway,
  nr Stroud. Every Wed

July 1 Monday
Beverston Gardens, nr Tetbury
Camp Cottage, Highleadon,
  nr Newent

July 3 Wednesday
Rookwoods, Waterlane, nr Bisley

July 4 Thursday
Old Mill Dene, Blockley

July 6 Saturday
Rockcliffe, Lower Swell

July 7 Sunday
Broad Campden Gardens,
  nr Chipping Campden
Cinderdine Cottage, Dymock,
  nr Newent
Combend Manor, Elkstone,
  nr Cheltenham
Gardeners Way, Kings Stanley,
  nr Stroud
Hullasey House, Tarlton,
  nr Cirencester
Hunts Court, North Nibley,
  nr Dursley
Rockcliffe, Lower Swell
Sezincote, nr Moreton-in-Marsh
Withington Gardens,
  nr Cheltenham

July 8 Monday
Camp Cottage, Highleadon,
nr Newent
Church Cottage, Stinchcombe,
nr Dursley
July 10 Wednesday
Rookwoods, Waterlane, nr Bisley
July 11 Thursday
Millend House, nr Newland,
Coleford
Old Mill Dene, Blockley
Trevi Garden, Hartpury,
nr Gloucester
July 14 Sunday
25 Bowling Green Road,
Cirencester
Campden House, nr Chipping
Campden
Cirencester Gardens
The Red House, Staunton,
nr Gloucester
20 St Peters Road, Cirencester
Tin Penny Cottage, Whiteway,
nr Miserden
Willow Lodge, nr Longhope,
Gloucester
July 15 Monday
The Old Rectory, Duntisbourne
Rous, nr Cirencester
Willow Lodge, nr Longhope,
Gloucester
July 16 Tuesday
Cinderdine Cottage, Dymock,
nr Newent
July 18 Thursday
Trevi Garden, Hartpury,
nr Gloucester
July 21 Sunday
25 Bowling Green Road,
Cirencester
Cowley Manor, nr Cheltenham
Willow Lodge, nr Longhope,
Gloucester
July 22 Monday
Willow Lodge, nr Longhope,
Gloucester
July 25 Thursday
Bourton House Garden,
Bourton-on-the-Hill
Trevi Garden, Hartpury,
nr Gloucester
July 28 Sunday
25 Bowling Green Road,
Cirencester
Brackenbury, Coombe,
nr Wotton-under-Edge
Brockweir Gardens, nr Chepstow
Millend House, nr Newland,
Coleford
St Francis, Minchinhampton
Willow Lodge, nr Longhope,
Gloucester
July 29 Monday
St Francis, Minchinhampton

Willow Lodge, nr Longhope, Gloucester
August
Camp Cottage, Highleadon,
nr Newent. Every Sun, & Tues
Grove Cottage, Lower Lydbrook,
Cinderford. Every Thurs
The Old Manor, Twyning. Every Mon
Tin Penny Cottage, Whiteway,
nr Stroud. Every Wed
August 4 Sunday
25 Bowling Green Road,
Cirencester
Cinderdine Cottage, Dymock,
nr Newent
Tin Penny Cottage, Whiteway,
nr Miserden
Trevi Garden, Hartpury,
nr Gloucester
Willow Lodge, nr Longhope,
Gloucester
August 5 Monday
Willow Lodge, nr Longhope,
Gloucester
August 7 Wednesday
Cowley Manor, nr Cheltenham
August 8 Thursday
Trevi Garden, Hartpury,
nr Gloucester
August 11 Sunday
25 Bowling Green Road,
Cirencester
Willow Lodge, nr Longhope,
Gloucester
August 12 Monday
Willow Lodge, nr Longhope,
Gloucester
August 15 Thursday
Trevi Garden, Hartpury,
nr Gloucester
August 17 Saturday
Kiftsgate Court, nr Chipping
Campden
August 18 Sunday
Cowley Manor, nr Cheltenham
Millend House, nr Newland,
Coleford
Westonbirt Gardens at
Westonbirt School
August 20 Tuesday
Cinderdine Cottage, Dymock,
nr Newent
August 22 Thursday
Trevi Garden, Hartpury,
nr Gloucester
August 25 Sunday
Bourton-on-the-Hill Gardens
Brockweir Gardens, nr Chepstow
Eastington Gardens, nr Northleach
Millend House, nr Newland,
Coleford
Trevi Garden, Hartpury,
nr Gloucester
August 26 Monday
Brackenbury, Coombe,

nr Wotton-under-Edge
Brockweir Gardens, nr Chepstow
Camp Cottage, Highleadon,
nr Newent
Eastington Gardens, nr Northleach
Millend House, nr Newland,
Coleford
Tin Penny Cottage, Whiteway,
nr Miserden
Trevi Garden, Hartpury,
nr Gloucester
August 29 Thursday
Bourton House Garden,
Bourton-on-the-Hill
Trevi Garden, Hartpury,
nr Gloucester
September
Grove Cottage, Lower Lydbrook,
Cinderford. Every Thurs
The Old Manor, Twyning. Every
Mon
Tin Penny Cottage, Whiteway,
nr Stroud. Every Wed
September 1 Sunday
Camp Cottage, Highleadon,
nr Newent
Cinderdine Cottage, Dymock,
nr Newent
Green Cottage, Lydney
Park Farm, Alderley
Westbury Court Garden,
Westbury-on-Severn
September 8 Sunday
Green Cottage, Lydney
Westonbirt Gardens at
Westonbirt School
September 12 Thursday
Trevi Garden, Hartpury,
nr Gloucester
September 15 Sunday
Sudeley Castle Gardens,
Winchcombe
September 17 Tuesday
Cinderdine Cottage, Dymock,
nr Newent
September 19 Thursday
Trevi Garden, Hartpury,
nr Gloucester
September 22 Sunday
Tin Penny Cottage, Whiteway,
nr Miserden
September 27 Thursday
Bourton House Garden,
Bourton-on-the-Hill
September 29 Sunday
Laurel Cottage, Brockweir Gardens
October
The Old Manor, Twyning. Every Mon
October 6 Sunday
Painswick Rococo Garden,
Painswick
October 14 Monday
The Old Rectory, Duntisbourne
Rous, nr Cirencester

February 1997
Cinderdine Cottage, Dymock,
   nr Newent, Thurs 6, 13, 20 Tues,
   11, 18, Sun 16 (12-4)

Regular openings
For details see garden description

Barnsley House, nr Cirencester
Batsford Arboretum,
   nr Moreton-in-Marsh
Bourton House Garden,
   Bourton-on-the-Hill
Camp Cottage, Highleadon,
   nr Newent
Cerney House, North Cerney

Cowley Manor, nr Cheltenham
Ewen Manor, nr Cirencester
Grove Cottage, Lower Lydbrook,
   Cinderford
Hunts Court, North Nibley, nr Dursley
Kiftsgate Court, nr Chipping
   Campden
Lydney Park Gardens, Lydney
Misarden Park, Miserden,
   nr Cirencester
The Old Manor, Twyning
Painswick Rococo Garden, Painswick
Rodmarton Manor, nr Cirencester
Seizincote, nr Moreton-in-Marsh
Stanway House, nr Winchcombe
Sudeley Castle Gardens,
   Winchcombe

Tin Penny Cottage, Whiteway,
   nr Miserden
Trevi Garden, Hartpury,
   nr Gloucester

By appointment only
*For telephone numbers and other
details see garden descriptions.
Private visits welcomed*

Amai Yume Teien, Blockley
Jasmine House, Bream, nr Lydney
Orchard Cottage, Gretton,
   nr Winchcombe

DESCRIPTIONS OF GARDENS

Abbotswood (Dikler Farming Co) 1m W of Stow-on-the-Wold, nr Lower Swell. Several acres of massed plantings of spring bulbs, heathers, flowering shrubs and rhododendrons in dramatic, landscaped hillside stream gardens; fine herbaceous planting in elegant formal gardens with lily pond, terraced lawn and fountain created by Sir Edwin Lutyens. TEAS. Car park free. *Adm £2 Chd free. Suns May 5, 19 (1.30-6)*

Adlestrop Gardens ✿ 3m E of Stow-on-the-Wold, off A436. A delightful small village made famous by Jane Austen and the poet Edward Thomas. 7 or more gardens incl several of traditional cottage character, will be on show at this village festival. Produce and plant stalls. TEAS in aid of Village Hall. *Adm £1.50 Chd free. Sun June 16 (2-6)*

Amai Yume Teien (Garden of Sweet Dreams) ✗ (Mr Tim Brown) Blockley. On the Chipping Campden rd almost opp St Georges Hall and the School. A unique example of a Japanese kare sansui teien (dry landscape garden) set in the improbable context of an old Cotswold village. The garden is a small rectangle within a 25sq metre space bounded by two interesting types of Japanese fencing. It is crossed by rectilinear paths (an example of mino ishi) which create five sub-rectangles. Looks interesting in all weathers. *Adm £1 Chd 50p (Share to London Lesbian and Gay Switchboard®) Private visits welcome usually last Sun of each month, please Tel 01386 701026*

Ampney Knowle ✿ (Mr & Mrs Richard Pile) nr Cirencester. 4m NE Cirencester B4425 ¼m S of Barnsley on Ampney Crucis rd. Medium-sized garden around C18 farmhouse with plant packed terrace; walled gardens, mixed borders with choice and less known plants and old shrub roses. Atmospheric woodland garden with indigenous wild flowers and 40-acre bluebell wood. Picnic site. TEAS in aid of Corinium Nursing Home Appeal. *Adm £2 Chd free. Sun May 5 (12-6). Private visits welcome, please Tel 01285 740230*

Ashley Manor ✿ (Mr & Mrs M J Hoskins) 3m NE of Tetbury on A433, turn R through Culkerton to Ashley. Old garden next to church redesigned by present owners and imaginatively planted. Mature yew hedges divide 4 separate gardens and are the backdrop to a collection of clematis, shrub roses and herbaceous plants. Sweet-smelling herb terrace and kitchen garden. TEA. *Adm £1.50 Chd free (Share to Ashley Church®). Sat April 6, Mon April 8 (2-5)*

Barnsley House ⑊✗✿ (Mrs Rosemary Verey) Barnsley 4m NE of Cirencester on B4425. Mature garden with interesting collection of shrubs and trees; ground cover; herbaceous borders; pond garden; laburnum walk; knot and herb gardens; formal kitchen garden; C18 summer houses. C17 house (not open). *Adm £2.50 OAPs £1.50 Chd free (no charge Dec and Jan). Mons, Weds, Thurs & Sats (10-6). Parties by appt only Tel 01285 740281. For NGS (Share to Barnsley Church®). Sats May 4, June 1 (2-6)*

Batsford Arboretum ⑊✿ (The Batsford Foundation Registered Charity No 286712) 1½m NW of Moreton-in-Marsh, off A44. Arboretum & wild gardens; over 1500 named trees (many rare) and shrubs; magnolias, flowering cherries, bulbs; beautiful views from Cotswold escarpment. House not open. TEAS at Garden Centre. *Adm £2.50 OAPs and parties of 12 and over £2 Chd 5-15 £2 under 5 free. Open daily, March 1 to Nov 5 (10-5). For NGS Sun May 12 (2-5)*

Beverston Gardens ⑊✿ 2m W of Tetbury on A4135 rd to Dursley
   Beverston Castle (Mrs L Rook) Overlooked by romantic C12-C15 castle ruin, the overflowingly planted paved terrace leads from C17 house across moat to sloping lawn with spring bulbs in abundance and full herbaceous and shrub borders. Large walled kitchen garden and greenhouses. TEAS June 30. *Adm £1.50 OAPs £1 Chd (under 12) 50p (Share to Beth Meredith Laser Fund®). Suns, Mons April 7 (2-6) 8 (11-6), June 30 (2-6) July 1 (11-6)*

Orchard Cottage ✕ (Mr & Mrs H L Pierce) On corner by memorial garden. ⅔-acre space used to the full with mixed borders, trees, shrubs, climbers, ferns and other shady plants, together with kitchen garden, wall and cordon fruit and herb interest in sheltered back garden. *Adm £1 Chd free. Sun, Mon June 30, July 1 (2-6)*

Blockley Gardens ✕❀ NW of Moreton-in-Marsh. A44 Moreton-Broadway; turning E. Some gardens not safe for small children. TEAS at St George's Hall in aid of Blockley WI and Blockley Ladies Choir. *Combined adm £3 Chd free. Suns April 28, June 30 (2-6)*

¶**Colebrook House** Old silk mill garden undergoing restoration. 2¾-acres with 2 streams, herbaceous borders and 400yr-old yew

Elm Barns (Sir Thomas & Lady Skyrme) Shrubs; lawns; pool; beautiful views. *Sun April 28 only*

The Garage Garden (Mrs M Stuart-Turner) Unusual garden making the best of a difficult slope; varied plantings. *Sun June 30 only*

Grange Cottage (Mrs J Moore) Small garden with unusual plants

Holly House (Simon Ford & Robert Ashby) Secluded garden 'rooms', lovely views, unusual trees, small formal kitchen garden

Malvern Mill (Mr & Mrs J Bourne) Converted mill with pond and stream; 1-acre incl orchard

Old Mill Dene (Mr & Mrs B S Dare) 2½-acre garden with terraced slopes and mill pool. *For additional openings and full desc see main entry*

¶**The Old Silk Mill** (Mr & Mrs A Goodrick-Clarke) Secret places and tiny streams decorate this 2½-acre mill garden. (Very dangerous for children)

Paxton House (Mr & Mrs P Cator) Walled garden on different levels; unusual plants

Pear Trees (Mrs J Beckwith) Small secluded, walled cottage garden with unusual plants

Rodneys (Mr & Mrs T Q Abell) Formal walled garden. *Sun April 28 only*

Boddington Manor ♿❀ (Robert Hitchins Ltd) Boddington 3m W of Cheltenham off the A4019 Cheltenham to Tewkesbury rd. After crossing the M5 motorway take first turning L which is signed to Boddington. Old garden sympathetically restored since 1985 incl wild flower woodland walk, mature specimen trees, extensive lawns and lakes; established Pinetum and bog garden. New planting of acers, birches, liquidambars, in meadow setting. Neogothic manor house (not open). Rare plant sale. Cream TEAS in aid of Glos Macmillan Nurses. *Adm £1.50 Chd free. Sun June 2 (11-5)*

Bourton House Garden ✕❀ (Mr & Mrs R Paice) Bourton-on-the-Hill 2m W of Moreton-in-Marsh on A44. Intensively planted 3 acres with topiary, knot garden, potager, colour and herbaceous borders, water features and C16 Tithe Barn. Imaginative containers, vast range of unusual plants incl tender and half hardy; a plantsman's paradise. *Adm £2.50 Chd free. Every Thurs & Fri May 23 to Sept 27. Also Bank hols Mon May 27, Sun Mon Aug 25, 26 (12-5). For NGS last Thurs of every month. May to Sept (12-5). Also in conjunction with* **Bourton-on-the-Hill Gardens**. *Parties welcome, please* **Tel 01386 700121**

Bourton-on-the-Hill Gardens ✕❀ 2m NW Moreton-in-Marsh A44 to Broadway. Wide selection of gardens of varied character in charming hillside village. Plant stall. TEAS (2-5). *Gardens adm £3 (including* **Bourton House** *as above) Chd free (Share to The Old School, Bourton®). Suns May 26, Aug 25 (1-6)*

¶**Fenhill Close** (Mr A Evans) Prizewinning begonias, sweet williams and fuschias in minuscule estate garden

Glebe House (Sir Peter & Lady Herbert) Ex rectory garden. Mixed borders. Views

Hillcrest (Mr & Mrs M Gaden) Small garden, mixed borders

Porch House (Mr & Mrs A Firth) Established terraced garden next to Churchyard

Springwood (Mr & Mrs D Storey) Cottage garden. Mixed borders

Tawnies (Mr & Mrs P Hayes) Raised beds with ericaceous plants. Long lawn

25 Bowling Green Road ❀ (Fr John & Susan Beck) Cirencester. Take A417 to Gloucester just to traffic lights, cross or turn R into The Whiteway then 1st L to no 25 on R of rd bend. Please respect neighbours' driveways, no pavement parking. Fast developing edge of town smaller garden to which its plant-dedicated owners recently moved from well-known garden in Cecily Hill. Wide range of perennials, especially geraniums, daylilies and delphiniums, roses and clematis. *Adm £1 Chd under 16 free Suns June 9, 16, 30 (2-5), July 21, 28 Aug 4, 11 (2-5). Combined adm £2 chd under 16 free. Sun July 14 (2-6) with* **Cirencester Gardens**. *Private visits welcome June to Aug, please* **Tel 01285 653778**

Brackenbury ❀ (Mr & Mrs Peter Heaton) Coombe, 1m NE of Wotton-under-Edge. From Wotton Church ½m on Stroud rd B4058 turn R (signed Coombe); from Stroud on B4058, 300yds past Wotton-under-Edge sign turn L, (signed Coombe). Garden on R. ⅔-acre terraced plantsman's and flower arranger's garden; foliage a special feature. Well stocked mixed borders, cottage garden, pool; 800 different hardy perennials and 200 different shrubs. Fruitcage, vegetables on deep-bed system. National Collection of Erigeron cultivars on show in June and July. Home-made TEAS. *Adm £1.50 Chd free (Share to Cotswold Care Hospice®). Mon May 27, Suns June 30, July 28, Mon Aug 26 (2-6)*

Bredon Manor ✕ (Mr & Mrs Richard George) 3m from Tewkesbury on the B4080. The house is next to the NT Tithe Barn in Bredon. 5 acres of well stocked formal gardens incl a ½-acre walled kitchen garden, a walled rose garden, sunken garden of various shrub roses and hostas, water garden with C17 monks fishpond and riverside meadows. TEAS in aid of Save the Children. *Adm £2 Chd free. Sun April 7 (2-5)*

Broad Campden Gardens ♿❀ 5m E of Broadway 1m SE of Chipping Campden. Big group of gardens of wide appeal and expertise: large and small, old and new, formal and informal, within picturesque popular village with meandering stream. Teas in aid of Village Hall. *Combined adm £2.50 or 60p each garden Chd free. Sun July 7 (2-6). Free car park. Coaches by appt only* **Tel 01386 840467**

The Angel House (Mr & Mrs Bill Boddington) Angel Lane

Briar Hill House (Sir Geoffrey and Lady Ellerton)

Cherry Orchard Cottage (Mr & Mrs David Brook)

The Farthings (Mr & Mrs John Astbury)

¶**Halfpenny Cottage** (Mr & Mrs Kenneth Jones)

Hillside (Mr John Wilkinson)

The Malt House (Mr & Mrs Nick Brown)

Manor Barn (Mr Michael Miles & Mr Christopher Gurney) Angel Lane

Oldstones (Mr & Mrs H R Rolfe) Angel Lane

Pinders (Mr & Mrs Ian Dunnett)

Sharcomb Furlong (Mr & Mrs Basil Hasberry)

Vine Cottage (J Murray)

¶**Wyldlands** (Mr & Mrs John Wadey)

Brockweir Gardens ❀ (2m Tintern Abbey) From A466 Chepstow to Monmouth rd, cross R Wye to Brockweir, ¾m uphill take L turning to Coldharbour. TEAS in aid of Marie Curie Cancer Care and RSPCA at Laurel Cottage. *Adm £1 each garden. Suns March 31, April 28, May 26, June 30, July 28, Aug 25, Mons May 27, Aug 26 (2-6)*

Laurel Cottage ৬✗ (David & Jean Taylor) Informal 1-acre cottage garden with lovely views over Offas Dyke. Dry stone walling creates gardens within a garden with lawns, herbaceous flowers and spring bulbs. Interesting selection of unusual shrubs and plants. *Also open Sept 29. Private visits welcome all year, please* Tel 01291 689565

Threeways (Iorrie & Gwen Williams) Follow signs from A466 Brockweir Bridge or from B4228 at Hewelsfield Xrds: also on foot from Laurel Cottage. 2-acre garden with unusual shrubs and trees. Small woodland area, bog garden and stream. Formal area with water feature and well stocked herbaceous borders. *Private visits welcome, please* Tel 01291 689686

Camp Cottage ✗❀ (Les Holmes & Sean O'Neill) Highleadon, nr Newent. 6m NW of Gloucester. From Glos take A40 Ross rd, turn R onto B4215 Newent rd, 2½m along turn R at sign for Upleadon. The cottage is about 100yds up lane on L hand side. A much publicised plant lover's garden around C17 thatched cottage. About 1 acre overflowing with old roses, climbing plants, snowdrops, hellebores and many unusual plants from all over the world mostly grown from seed and cuttings. Pergola, arches and short shrubland walk to bog garden. TEA on Suns and some weekdays. *Adm £1 Chd 50p. Suns Feb 25 to March 31 (11-3) April 7 to Sept 1, Mons May 6 to July 8, Tues April 2 to Aug 27. Bank Hol Mons April 8, May 6, 27, Aug 26 (2-6). Private visits welcome all year, please* Tel 01452 790352

Campden House ৬❀ (Mr & Mrs Philip Smith) Chipping Campden. Drive entrance on Chipping Campden to Weston Subedge rd, about ¼m SW of Campden. 2-acre garden featuring mixed borders of plant and colour interest around Manor House and C17 Tithe Barn. Set in fine parkland in hidden valley. TEAS and plant stall in aid of the Glos Macmillan Nurses. *Adm £1.50 Chd free. Sun July 14 (2-6)*

Cerney House Gardens ৬✗❀ (Sir Michael & Lady Angus) North Cerney. 4m N of Cirencester on A435 Chel-

tenham rd. Turn L opp Bathurst Arms, past church to top of hill, pillared gates on R. Romantic walled garden filled with old-fashioned roses and herbaceous borders. There is a working kitchen garden with a scented garden and well-labelled herb garden. Spring bulbs in abundance all around the wooded grounds. TEAS. *Adm £2 Chd free. Tues, Weds, Fris, Feb to Oct (2-6). For NGS Sun May 12 (2-6). Private visits welcome, please* Tel 01285 831300

Chalford Gardens ✗ 4m E of Stroud on A419 to Cirencester. Gardens are high above the Chalford Vale and reached on foot by steep climb from car park on main rd or from High St. Cream TEAS at Marle Hill House. *Combined adm £2.50 Chd free. Sun June 16 (2-6)*

¶**Marle Hill House** (Mike & Leslie Doyle-Davidson) 1-acre newly reclaimed Victorian woodland garden, containing a number of interlinked secret, formal and natural areas on terraced hillside

The Old Chapel (F J & F Owen) Artists' 1-acre Victorian chapel garden on precipitous hillside. A tiered tapestry of herbaceous borders, formal potager, small orchard, pond and summer house, old roses. Gothic pergola and rose tunnel, many unusual plants all laid out on terraced S-facing Marle Cliff. *Garden also open with Art Exhibition in studio Sat June 15 to Fri June 21 (10-5) Adm £1*

The Rock House (Mr & Mrs George Edwards) 1-acre, S facing old garden, recently reconstructed. Dramatic 40' cliff and cave provide backdrop for climbing roses, clematis, shrubbery, rockery, lawn and herbaceous borders. *Private visits welcome (May to July), please* Tel 01453 886363

The Chestnuts ✗❀ (Mr & Mrs E H Gwynn) Minchinhampton. From Nailsworth by Avening rd (B4014) L Weighbridge Inn ¼m up hill. From Minchinhampton 1m via New Rd or Well Hill. Celebrating 21 yrs of opening for the NGS, this peaceful ⅔-acre walled garden with lovely views offers an interesting mix of shrubs, bulbs, roses, clematis, rock garden, pool garden and wildflower lawn. ⅔-acre arboretum, with wide variety of unusual trees and shrubs. *Adm £1.50 Chd free (Share to Glos Wildlife Trust®). Sun June 2 (2-6)*

¶**Church Cottage** ✗❀ (Mr & Mrs David Leach) Stinchcombe. Off A38, 5m NW of Dursley. Peacefully situated next to the church. A plant lover's cottage garden of about ¼-acre planted since 1992 and still evolving. Good variety of hardy plants. *Adm £1 Chd free. Mons May 20, June 17, July 8 (11-5.30). Private visits welcome, May and June, please* Tel 01453 542116

By Appointment Gardens. These owners do not have a fixed opening day usually because they do not like crowds or have insufficient parking space. Owner will often give guided tour.

Regular Openers. Too many days to include in diary. Usually there is a wide range of plants giving year-round interest. See end of county section for the name and garden description for times etc.

Cinderdine Cottage &⚘ (John & Daphne Chappell) Dymock. 3m NE of Newent. Off the B4215 just S of Dymock village signed Ryton/Ketford. Cottage ¾m on R of lane. ½-acre garden in the heart of daffodil country belonging to 2 plant-aholics. Combining the formal and informal in a white garden and single-colour borders for summer and early autumn and sheltered spots for woodland plants in winter and early spring, incl our huge collection of species and hybrid snowdrops. TEA at Cinderdine Cottage Mons, Tues only. Refreshments Three Choirs Vineyard 5 minutes away March to Sept only. *Adm £1 Chd free (Share to St Mary's Church, Dymock®). Tues, Thurs, Suns, Feb 8, 13, 15, 18, 20, 22 (12-4). Suns, Tues March 24, April 7, 16, May 5, 21, June 2, 18, July 7, 16, Aug 4, 20, Sept 1, 17. Bank Hol Mons, April 8, May 6, (2-6). Feb 1997 Thurs 6, 13, 20, Tues 11, 18, Sun 16 (12-4). Private parties welcome Feb to Sept, please* **Tel 01531 890265**

Cirencester Gardens of contrasting charms in and around a town of historic interest. *Combined adm £2 Chd under 16 free. Sun July 14 (2-6)*
   25 Bowling Green Road ⚘ (Fr John and Susan Beck) From Cirencester take A417 to Gloucester just to traffic lights, cross or turn R into The Whiteway then 1st L to no 25 on R of rd bend. New edge of town smaller garden of owners recently moved from well-known garden in Cecily Hill. For additional openings and full description see main entry
   40 Cecily Hill Exhibition of botanical pictures and china by Annette Firth, NDD, SBA
   Cecily Hill House & (Mr & Mrs Rupert de Zoete) On W side of Cirencester near gates into Park and open air swimming pool. Walled town garden with tranquil atmosphere; herbaceous and shrub borders; small ornamental kitchen garden. *Private visits also welcome mid June to July 31, please* **Tel 01285 653766**
   20 St Peters Road ⚘⚘ (Meg and Jeff Blumsom) Off Cricklade St. turn R into Ashcroft Rd then L then R. For additional openings and full description see main entry

Clover House (Mrs Kenneth Kemble) Winson B4425 6½m from Cirencester. Take Cirencester-Burford rd, then N to Winson just W of Bibury. 4-acres; spring blossom and bulbs; lawns, mixed borders and roses. R Coln flows alongside the garden. *Adm £1.50 Chd 50p. Sun April 21 (2-6)*

Combend Manor ⚘ (Mr & Mrs Noel Gibbs) Elkstone. On A417 halfway between Cirencester and Cheltenham turn R signed Elkstone immed R through pillars 1m on R. 3-acre mature garden in beautiful setting, partly laid out by Gertrude Jekyll: a variety of gardens within the main garden incl an arboretum, water garden, old-fashioned roses, heather garden. TEAS. *Adm £2 Chd free (Share to Elkstone Parish Church®). Sun July 7 (2-6)*

Cotswold Farm ⚘ (Major & Mrs P D Birchall) 5m N of Cirencester on A417; signed immediately W of Five Mile House Inn. Cotswold garden in lovely position on different levels with a terrace designed by Norman Jewson in 1938; shrubs, mixed borders, alpine border, spring flowers, shrub roses; walled kitchen garden. TEAS. *Adm £2 Chd free. Sun June 23 (2-5.30). Private visits welcome May, June and July, by written application*

¶Cowley Manor &⚘ Cowley, nr Cheltenham. SE of Cheltenham off A435. 50 acres of Victorian landscaped grounds with lakes and Italianate terraces and cascade (awaiting restoration) provide a setting for innovatory herbaceous planting inspired by contemporary German and Dutch design. Lakeside walk. 1st yr of a garden returning to life after a period of neglect. No dogs at weekends. TEAS in aid of Alzheimers Disease Society. *Adm £2.50 Chd free. Every day except Mon & Fri from March 1 to Oct 30. For NGS Suns July 21, Aug 18, Wed Aug 7 (2-6)*

Daylesford House &⚘⚘ (Sir Anthony & Lady Bamford) Daylesford. Between Stow-on-the-Wold and Chipping Norton off A436. Magnificent lakeside and woodland walks amidst unusual shrubs and trees and massed bluebells. Large decorative formal fruit and vegetable walled garden with orchid house, peach house and working glasshouses. Trellised rose garden on raised terrace. Grounds immed around Grade 1 house not open. *Adm £2 Chd free (Share to Marie Curie Cancer Care® and Katharine House Hospice®). Weds May 1, June 19 (2-6). Coaches by appt,* **Tel 01608 659777**

Eastcombe, Bussage & Brownshill Gardens 3m E Stroud. 2m N of A419 Stroud to Cirencester on turning signposted to Bisley and Eastcombe. Cream Teas at Eastcombe Village Hall. *Combined adm £2.50 Chd free (Share to Glos Macmillan Nurses®, and Cotswold Care Day Hospice®). Sun, Mon May 5, 6 (2-6)*
Eastcombe:
   Ashcroft (Mr & Mrs H T Cornell) Small garden with many bulbs, primulas and year-round colour
   Brewers Cottage & (Mr & Mrs T G N Carter) Easily managed hillside garden with laburnum covered pergola, shady & sunny borders and a small hidden courtyard
   ¶18 Farmcote Close & (Mr & Mrs K Chalmers) Small garden planned for retirement, giving scope to potter and enjoy without major maintenance
   21 Farmcote Close &⚘ (Mr & Mrs R Bryant) A housing estate garden, designed with curved beds to soften appearance. Nearly 350 varieties of interesting perennials, bulbs, shrubs and old roses on various colour themes. Espalier fruit
   Fidges Hill House (Mr & Mrs R Lewis) Transformed from building site with knee high weeds to cottage garden; secluded and lovely view. No car access, please park in village. Steep descent
   Highlands (Mr & Mrs J Page) Small, tranquil and colourful cottage garden with views across the Toadsmoor Valley
   Jasmine Cottage (Mr & Mrs K Hopkins) Very colourful cottage garden with view of the beautiful Toadsmoor valley
   Vatch Rise &⚘ (Mr & Mrs R G Abbott) Extensive and interesting collection of bulbous plants, alpines and unusual perennials. A real plantsman's garden. Beautiful view
Brownshill:
   Beechcroft & (Mr & Mrs R H Salt) Garden surrounds Edwardian house bounded by meadow. Mature trees, shrubs, borders, vegetables, fruit, conservatory and wild area

Bovey End (Sir Norman & Lady Wakefield) A large, informal garden sloping steeply with beautiful views across the Golden and Toadsmoor Valleys; many trees and shrubs

Bussage:

Pine Corner (Mr & Mrs W Burns-Brown) ¾-acre terraced garden overlooking Toadsmoor Valley. Spring bulbs, shrubs, alpines; kitchen & herb garden

Redwood ❀ (Mr & Mrs D F Collins) Terraced garden with 3 small ponds and many unusual trees, shrubs, bulbs, alpines and herbaceous plants. Vegetables and cordon fruit trees. Nearly 1000 plants for sale. *Private visits welcome April to July, please* **Tel 01453 882595**

Spindrift, The Ridge ♿ (Mr & Mrs B Wilson) Small garden on housing estate devoted largely to plant breeding experiments incl a foxglove mutation

Eastington Gardens 1m SE of Northleach (A40). Charming Cotswold village with lovely views. TEAS at **Middle End**. *Combined adm £1.50 Chd free (Share to Northleach Church Fund®). Suns, Mons May 26, 27, Aug 25, 26 (2-6)*

Bank Cottage (Mr & Mrs E S Holland) Lower End. Colourful cottage garden

Middle End ❀ (Mr & Mrs Owen Slatter) Medium-sized garden of general interest

Yew Tree Cottage (Mr M Bottone) Hardy plants for sun and shade

Ewen Manor ♿❀ (Lady Gibbs) 4m S of Cirencester via A429 3m from Cirencester turn at signpost Ewen 1m. Profusely planted series of gardens with architectural features, yew hedges, pattern mown lawn, terrace and containers, lily pool, cedar trees over 200yrs old and woodland area all around. Georgian Cotswold manor (not open). TEAS Sun only. *Adm £2 Chd free. Weds, Thurs, Fris May 8 to July 5 (11-4.30) Suns May 5, June 23 (Share to Cotswold Care Hospice®) (2-6). Private visits welcome, please* **Tel 01285 770206**

Gardeners Way ✲❀ (GRBS) Kings Stanley, 3m W of Stroud off A419, 2nd turn R after church in village. The ten bungalows provided by the Gardeners' Royal Benevolent Society for retired gardeners are a colourful showpiece of gardening skills. The gardens are all of individual design and character and contain many interesting plants and ideas. Gardening questions gladly answered. TEA. *Adm £2 OAP's £1 Chd free (Share to the GRBS®). Sun July 7 (2-6)*

Grange Farm ✲ (Lady Aird) Evenlode, nr Moreton in Marsh. Evenlode 3m from Moreton-in-Marsh and Stow-on-the-Wold. E of the A429 Fosseway and 1½m from Broadwell. The medium sized garden has been considerably developed over the past few yrs but the old rose-covered house and apple trees provide a delightful setting for the newer water and sunken gardens while mature shrubs conceal hidden corners. TEAS. *Adm £2 Chd free (Share to Evenlode Church®). Sun June 23 (2-6)*

Green Cottage ♿❀ (Mr & Mrs F Baber) At far end of Lydney from Gloucester on A48 turn R into narrow lane just after derestriction sign. Garden 50yds on R. Shady car park. Informal country garden of approx 1 acre with planted stream bank, hostas, hellebores, iris and cottage garden. Many herbaceous paeonies, incl National Reference Collection of pre and early post 1900 cultivars in June. Hellebores at their best in March, paeonies May, June. Large clematis montana rubens in May. Cream TEAS Suns only. *Adm £1.50 Chd free. Suns March 3, 10, 17, 24 (1-4), May 5, 12, 19, June 2, 9, 16, 23, Sept 1, 8, (2-6) Weds June 5, 12, 19 (11-5). Private visits for parties in June, please* **Tel 01594 841918**

Grove Cottage ✲❀ (Graham Birkin & Allan Thomas) Forge Hill, Lower Lydbrook. 5m NW of Cinderford. From Upper Lydbrook follow sign to Joys Green; after ¾m turn L into Forge Hill. Very steep 2-acre garden with glorious views over Wye valley. Packed with woodland and shade tolerant plants growing in raised beds, peat beds, shrub and herbaceous borders; large rockery. Extensive collections of rare N American woodland plants, irises and over 1000 hellebores. Many steps and steep paths. Not suitable for small children. TEA. *Adm £1 Chd 50p. Thurs March 7 to Sept 26 (2-6). Private visits welcome, please* **Tel 01594 860544**

Hartpury College ❀ Hartpury House, 5m N of Gloucester on A417 Gloucester-Ledbury. An extensive and historically important garden still retaining many of the original features created by its designers, notably Alfred Parsons and, later, Thomas Mawson. 17 acres of landscaped grounds incl a Victorian walled garden, terraced borders, glasshouses, herbaceous and alpine borders, and a collection of old apple and pear varieties as well as an extensive tree and shrub collection. TEA. *Adm £2 Chd free. Sat June 22 (2-5). Private visits welcome by arrangement, please* **Tel 01452 700283**

Hidcote Manor Garden ✲❀ (The National Trust) 4m NE of Chipping Campden. Series of formal gardens, many enclosed within superb hedges, incl hornbeam on stems. Many rare trees, shrubs, plants. Coffee, lunches and teas. *Adm £5.20 Chd £2.60. ▲For NGS Sun May 5 (11-6)*

High Bank, 59 Bourne Drive ✲❀ (Mr & Mrs Malcolm Buckenham) Brimscombe. 2m E of Stroud on A419 on L, opp Golden Valley Cars sales showroom, up short footpath to 2nd gate on L. Intensely planted ¼-acre terraced hillside garden with herbaceous beds hosting a variety of interesting plants and offering fine views across the Golden Valley. Featuring sunken dell, pergolas, formal pool, enclosed rose garden, small gazebo, rockery and many unusual containers; also roses and clematis. TEAS. *Adm £1.50 Chd free. Sun June 9 (2-6). Private visits welcome July, please* **Tel 01453 731169**

Hillesley House ❀ (Mr & Mrs J Walsh) Hillesley. 3m from Wotton-under-Edge on rd to Hawkesbury Upton and the A46. Newly revived garden in 4 acres surrounding Tudor house (not open); walled garden, borders in sun and shade, roses. Innovative perennial plantings by Noël Kingsbury offer interesting ideas. TEAS. *Adm £1.50 Chd free. Sun June 9 (2-6)*

Home Farm (Mrs T Freeman) Huntley. On the B4216 ½m from the A40 in Huntley travelling towards Newent. Set in elevated position with exceptional views. 1m walk through woods and fields to show carpets of spring flowers. Waterproof footwear advisable. *Adm £1.50 Chd free. Suns Feb 4, March 3, April 14, May 12, June 9 (2-5). Private visits welcome for parties of 2 and over, please* **Tel 01452 830209**

¶**Hullasey House** ✿✿ (Jonathan & Gail Taylor) Tarlton. Midway between Cirencester and Tetbury off A433. Newly created 2½-acre garden with exceptional views. Stone walls, many old roses, gravel gardens round the house. Walled herb and fruit potager; walled mixed shrub/herbaceous garden. *Adm £2 Chd free (Share to Tarlton Church ®). Sun July 7 (2-6)*

Hunts Court ♿✿✿ (Mr & Mrs T K Marshall) North Nibley, Dursley. 2m NW of Wotton-under-Edge. From Wotton B4060 Dursley rd turn R in Nibley at Black Horse; fork L after ¼m. Unusual shrubs, 450 varieties old roses, large collection of penstemons in peaceful 2½-acre garden with lawns set against tree clad hills and Tyndale monument. Superb views. House (not open) possible birth place of William Tyndale. Picnic area. Home-made TEAS (Suns only). *Adm £1.50 Chd free. Garden and Nursery open Tues-Sat all year ex Aug; also Bank Hol Mons, May 6, 27. For NGS Suns June 9, 16, 23, 30; July 7, (2-6); Private visits welcome, please* **Tel 01453 547440**

Icomb Place ✿ (Mr & Mrs T L F Royle) 4m S of Stow-on-the-Wold; after 2m on A424 Burford rd turn L to Icomb village. 100-year-old sizeable garden extensively restored. Featuring woodland walk through mature & young trees in arboretum; rhododendrons & azaleas; grotto; pools, stream and water garden; parterre; lawned garden with extensive views. C14 manor house (not open). TEAS. *Adm £2 Chd £1 (Share to Deus Laudamus Trust®). Sun June 9 (2-6)*

Jasmine House ♿✿✿ (Mr & Mrs V M Bond) Bream. 3m N of Lydney in centre of Forest of Dean village. Approx 1 acre informal country garden, planted for yr-round interest. Many old-fashioned and unusual plants to discover. TEAS by arrangement. *Adm £1 Chd free. A sincere welcome to individuals or groups (even at short notice) from Easter to Oct, please* **Tel 01594 563688**

Kiftsgate Court ✿✿ (Mr & Mrs J G Chambers) 3m NE of Chipping Campden, adjacent to Hidcote Nat Trust Garden. 1m E of A46 and B4081. Magnificent situation and views; many unusual plants and shrubs; tree paeonies, hydrangeas, abutilons, species and old-fashioned roses, inc largest rose in England, R.filipes Kiftsgate. TEAS (April 28 to Sept 1). Lunches June and July. Buses by appt. *Adm £3 Chd £1. Suns, Weds, Thurs & Bank Hols Mons April 3 to Sept 29 (2-6). Also Suns, Weds, Thurs, Sats in June & July (12-6). For NGS (Share to Sue Ryder Home, Leckhampton Court®) Sats May 11, Aug 17, (2-6). Tel* **01386 438777**

Lydney Park Gardens ✿ (Viscount Bledisloe) Lydney. On A48 Gloucester-Chepstow rd between Lydney & Aylburton. Drive is directly off A48. 8 acres of extensive valley garden with many varieties of rhododendron, azaleas and other flowering shrubs; trees and lakes. Garden round house; magnolias and daffodils (April). Roman Temple Site and Museum. Deer park with fine trees. TEAS; also picnic area (in park). *Adm £2 Weds £1 (Acc chd & cars free). Easter Sun & Mon; Every Sun, Wed & Bank Hol from Sun April 7 to June 9. Every day Sun May 26 to June 2 (11-6). For NGS Sun May 5, Wed May 22 (11-6). Tel* **01594 842844**

13 Merestones Drive ✿ (Mr Dennis Moorcraft) Cheltenham. Merestones Drive is a turning off The Park reached by following signs to Gloscat (a technical college). Nearest main rd is A46 from Stroud. Small town garden shaded by large trees; hostas and ferns a speciality; many unusual plants; scree garden; small brook. Limited parking. TEAS. *Adm £1.50 Chd 50p. Suns June 16, 30 (2-6). Private visits welcome, please* **Tel 01242 578678**

Millend House ✿✿ (Mr & Mrs J D'A Tremlett) Coleford. 1½m SW out of Coleford on the Newland rd, centre of Coleford clocktower signposted (Newland 2m). Magnificently located with beautiful valley views, the 2-acre hillside garden contains many unusual herbaceous plants and shrubs, both shade and sun loving, many of which are for sale. There are also scree and fern beds, a gazebo, ornamental pond, small vegetable and soft fruit garden, and a walk round a 200yr-old wood. TEAS in aid of Glos Macmillan Nurses. *Adm £1.50 Chd free. Suns, Mons, May 5, 6, 19, 26, 27; Suns, Thurs, June 9, 23, July 11, 28; Aug 18; Sun, Mon, Aug 25, 26 (2-6). Private groups welcome May 1 to Sept 30, please* **Tel 01594 832128**

Minchinhampton Gardens ✿✿ Minchinhampton 4m SE Stroud. From Market Sq down High St 100yds; then R at Xrds; 300yds turn L. Cream TEAS except Feb TEA. *Combined adm £2 Chd free (Share to Minchinhampton Centre for the Elderly®). Suns Feb 18, April 14, (11-4.30)*

    Lammas Park (Mr & Mrs P Grover) Lawns, herbaceous borders, wild garden, restored 'hanging gardens'. Superb views

    St Francis (Mr & Mrs Peter Falconer) Garden made in old park round modern Cotswold stone house. Fine beech avenue; terraced garden; trough gardens; bonsai trees; unusual plants; giant snowdrops (spring); C18 ice-house. Picnickers welcome. *Also open July 28, Mon July 29 (11-5) Also private visits welcome, please* **Tel 01453 882188**

Misarden Park ♿✿✿ (Maj M T N H Wills) Miserden 6m NW of Circencester. Follow the signs off the A417 or B4070 from Stroud. Spring flowers, shrubs, fine topiary (some designed by Sir Edwin Lutyens) and herbaceous borders within a walled garden; roses; fine specimen trees; C17 manor house (not open) standing high overlooking Golden Valley. Garden Nurseries open daily except Mons. *Adm £2.50 Chd free. April 2 to Sept 26 every Tues, Wed & Thurs (9.30-4.30). For NGS (Share to Cobalt Unit Appeal Fund®). TEAS in aid of Miserden School PTA. Suns March 31, June 30 (2-6). Tel* **01285 821303**

Moor Wood ✿ (Mr & Mrs Henry Robinson) Woodmancote. 3½m from Cirencester turn L off A435 to Cheltenham at North Cerney signed 'Woodmancote 1¼m': entrance in village on L beside lodge with white gates. 2 acres of shrub, orchard and wildflower gardens in isolated valley setting. Holder of the National Collection of rambler roses. TEA. *Adm £2 Chd free. Wed June 26 (2-6). Private visits, please* **Tel 01285 831397**

By Appointment Gardens. See end of county section

North Rye House ♿❀ (Mr & Mrs Peter Stoddart) nr Broadwell, Moreton-in-Marsh. On A429 Fosseway halfway between Moreton-in-Marsh and Stow-on-the-Wold. Also signed from Broadwell village. Recently established 3-acre garden with modern ha-ha designed to blend scenically into its surrounding parkland setting with mature trees. Spring bulbs, mixed borders, shrub roses, alpines, small vegetable garden and gardener's cottage garden provide continuous colour and interest. TEAS in aid of Glos Macmillan Nurses. *Adm £2 Chd free. Sun March 31, Wed June 26 (2-5)*

Nympsfield Gardens ✲❀ 3m NW of Nailsworth. Signed from B4066 Stroud-Dursley rd. A group of 10 or more gardens mostly modest cottage-size but ranging up to 1 acre and incl 2 of plantsman interest in isolated and sometimes windswept hillside situation. Teas and plants in Village Hall. *Combined adm £2.50 Chd free (Share to St Bartholomew's Church® and Nympsfield Village Hall®). Suns April 28, May 26 (2-6)*

- **¶Amaranth** ❀ (Mr & Mrs G Wood)
- **Bath Road Farm** (Mr & Mrs K Wright)
- **Bell Cottage** (Mr & Mrs P Mack) *April 28 only*
- **Candle Cottage** (Mr & Mrs A N Pearce) *May 26 only*
- **The Coach House** (Mr & Mrs R F Overton)
- **Four Wells** (Mr J Price) *May 26 only*
- **¶Four Winds** (Mr & Mrs C Marshall)
- **Highlands** (Mr & Mrs R Easton)
- **¶Loom Cottage** (Mr & Mrs C Webber)
- **The Post Office** (Mr & Mrs B Westwood)
- **¶Stone Court** (Mr & Mrs D Jackson)
- **¶Vale View** (Mr & Mrs B Freeman)

The Old Manor ♿✲❀ (Mrs Joan Wilder) Twyning. 3m N of Tewkesbury via A38 to Worcester; follow sign to Twyning; garden opposite T-junction at top end of village. 2-acre walled garden full of interest. Unusual shrubs, trees, herbaceous, alpines; two areas of developing arboretum; sunken garden; terrace plantings; troughs. Field walks for picnics. Small nursery, all stock from garden (catalogue 30p and large SAE). TEA on Bank Hol Mons only. *Adm £1.50 Acc chd free (Share to GRBS® & RGOF®). Every Mon March to Oct (2-5, or dusk if earlier) Private visits welcome by appt except Suns incl winter months, please* **Tel 01684 293516** *evenings*

Old Mill Dene, Blockley ✲❀ (Mr & Mrs B S Dare) School Lane. Limited parking. From A44, Bourton-on-the-Hill, take the turn to Blockley. 1m down hill turn L behind 30mph sign, labelled cul de sac. 2½-acre garden with steep lawned terraces and mill-pool in a frost pocket with stream. Vegetable garden parterre. New grotto and trompe l'oeil. Dangerous for young children. TEAS. *Adm £2 Chd 50p (Share to Glos Historic Churches Trust®). Suns April 21, May 19, Thurs June 13, 20, 27; July 4, 11 (2-5.30). Also open with* **Blockley Gardens***: combined adm £3 chd free. Suns April 28, June 30. Private visits welcome (not August) please* **Tel 01386 700457**

The Old Rectory, Duntisbourne Rous ✲ (Charles & Mary Keen) NW of Cirencester at Daglingworth take valley rd for the Duntisbournes. After ½m no through rd joins from R at entrance to Old Rectory. Writer and designer's own 1½-acre Cotswold family garden in the making, now in its 4th yr. Beautiful setting nr Saxon church. Planted for atmosphere and all-yr-interest, this small garden has ten distinct areas and moods. Winter flowers, tender plants and unusual pelargoniums a speciality. *Adm £2 Chd free. Mons Feb 5, (10-3) May 13, June 3, 24, July 15 (10-6) Oct 14 (10-3). Private visits by written appt welcome. Charges negotiable*

The Old Rectory, Great Rissington ♿ (Captain & Mrs Richard Turner). Off A429 through Bourton-on-the-Water. At village green, Lamb Inn, turn R downhill towards church. 1½-acre garden, with large borders, incl a yellow border. Secluded white, blue and pink garden. Roses, shrubs, vegetable garden leading to 2-acre woodland walk through 4,500 newly planted trees. (Woodland walk is not suitable for wheelchairs.) Cream TEAS. *Adm £2 Chd free. Sun June 23 (2-6)*

Orchard Cottage, Gretton ♿✲ (Mr Rory Stuart) 2m N of Winchcombe. Up Duglinch Lane beside Bugatti Inn in the middle of Gretton. Approx 300yds up lane turn R after Magnolia Grandiflora and opp black railings. Approx 1½-acres. Romantically overplanted, owner-maintained garden, created largely by the late Mrs Nancy Saunders. Always some interest. Teas in Winchcombe. *Adm £1.50 Open all year. By appt only, please* **Tel 01242 602491**

Painswick Rococo Garden ❀ (Painswick Rococo Garden Trust Reg No 299792) ½m outside village on B4073. Unique C18 garden restoration from the brief Rococo period combining contemporary buildings, vistas, ponds and winding woodland walks. Coach House restaurant for coffee, lunches. 'Present Collection' shop. *Adm £2.75 OAP £2.35 Chd £1.50. Jan 10 to Nov 30. Weds to Suns and Bank Hol July and Aug daily. Restaurant open Weds to Suns (11-5). For NGS Suns March 31, Oct 6 (11-5)* **Tel 01452 813 204**

¶Park Farm ♿ (Mr & Mrs A J V Shepherd) Alderley. 1½m S from Wotton-under-Edge on R by stream just before village. The lake with its waterside plants and large Koi carp is the pivotal attraction in a scenically designed 2½-acre garden also offering maturing herbaceous borders, young trees and a new rose garden. TEAS in aid of Alderley Church Fund. *Adm £1.50 Chd 50p. Sun Sept 1 (2-6)*

Pigeon House ✲ (Mr & Mrs Julian Taylor) Southam Lane, Southam. 3m from Cheltenham off B4632 toward Winchombe. Revitalised 2-acre garden surrounding C14 manor house. Small lake and bubbling water garden with fish and bog plants. Wide range of flowering shrubs and borders designed to create multitude of vistas and plant interest. TEAS in aid of Southam Church of the Ascension. *Adm £1.50 Chd free. Suns April 21, June 2 (2-6)*

Pinbury Park ❀ (Mr & Mrs John Mullings) Cirencester 6½m. Signed off Sapperton-Winstone rd between A419 and A417. 5-acre garden in a hidden and almost secret valley; with topiary, yew avenue, spring bulbs incl shoals of daffodils and anemones, and gazebo. Rose garden and many varieties of clematis. Tudor Manor house (not open) former Royal residence of King Penda. TEAS. *Adm £1.50 Chd 50p. Suns April 7, June 30 (2-5)*

Pitt Court &&&& (Mr & Mrs M W Hall) North Nibley. Turn off the B4060 at North Nibley past the Black Horse Inn into Barrs Lane. Continue for approx ¾m. A small garden of about ⅓ acre, making interesting and ingenious use of paving, stones and brick for walls, steps and beds as settings for increasing collection of smaller trees, conifers, shrubs and herbaceous plants. Separate lawn and alpine area. Limited car parking. Teas at **Hunts Court** open nearby with plenty of parking (½m). *Adm £1 Chd free. Suns June 9, 16, July 23 (2-6)*

Poulton Gardens & 5m E of Cirencester on A417. Cream TEAS at **Poulton Manor**. *Combined adm £2.50 Chd free. Sun June 23 (2-6)*

    Almas Cottage (Mr & Mrs G Lavin) Tiny garden overflowing with traditional cottage plants

    The New Inn ❀ (Mrs Heather Wondrausch) An acre behind erstwhile pub transformed into idiosyncratically meandering garden

    The Old School (Mr & Mrs Derek Chalk) Small walled garden with interesting shrubs, clematis, roses, herbaceous plants

    Poulton House (Mr & Mrs Tom Boyd) 1½-acre Cotswold garden; herbaceous border, rose border, pond, shrubs, kitchen garden and specimen trees

    Poulton Manor ❀ (Mrs Anthony Sanford) 2 acres reconstructed for minimal maintenance; old yew hedges, hornbeam avenue, mixed borders, herb parterre, walled kitchen garden, natural area with trees, pond and bog garden. Charles II house (not open)

    Sarnia (Mr & Mrs W M Young) ½-acre garden with shrubs and perennials to give colour and interest throughout the year

Quenington Gardens &❀ 2m N of Fairford, E of Cirencester. Peaceful Cotswold riverside village with church renowned for Norman doorways. TEAS in aid of The Home Farm Trust at **The Old Rectory**. *Combined adm £2.50 Chd free. Sun June 30 (2-6)*

    Apple Tree Cottage (Mrs P Butler-Henderson) Interesting small cottage garden protected by its own 'micro-climate'. Conservatory with unusual plants

    Court Farm (Mr & Mrs Frank Gollins) Natural riverside landscape; part of historic grounds of Knights Hospitallers with dovecote, woodland walk and water garden

    Mawley Field (Mr & Mrs N Collins) Secluded 1-acre Cotswold garden; orchard, mixed herbaceous borders, rose garden, kitchen garden

    ¶**Old Post House** (Mrs D Blackwood). A small terraced garden, plant-filled and colourful, only recently created from old orchard

    The Old Rectory (Mr & Mrs David Abel-Smith) Picturesque and varied riverside garden with herbaceous border and wilderness; extensive organic vegetable garden

    Pool Hay (Mr & Mrs A W Morris) Small is beautiful. Picturesque riverside cottage garden

¶**Randwick Gardens** ✿ 2m W of Stroud, signed at Cainscross off A419 toward M6 junction 13. TEAS at **Blenheim House**. *Combined adm £1.50 Chd free. Sun June 16 (2-6)*

    ¶**Blenheim House** (Mr & Mrs B P Stanley) Mixed borders of shrubs, trees and annuals in ⅓-acre garden surrounding C18 house and newly-restored coach house. Small pond

¶**Humphreys End House** (Mr & Mrs J W A Hutton) Different areas of contrasting mood and interesting planting in 1-acre garden surrounding C16 farmhouse. Wildlife pond, herbs, old roses, grasses. *Private visits welcome on Fris in May, June, July, please,* **Tel 01453 765401**

¶**The Old Bakehouse** (Mr & Mrs F C Holmes) ⅓-acre cottage garden on exposed S-facing slope featuring vegetables, fruit, alpines and hardy perennials

The Red House &&& (Mr & Mrs W K Turner) Pillows Green, Staunton, 8m NW of Gloucester on A417; from Staunton Xrds ½m off B4208. Split level 2 acre organic garden and wildlife garden with herbaceous borders; rockery and terrace with containers; parterre; also flower meadow. C17 House (part open). Garden designed & maintained by owners. All plants for sale grown from garden stock. TEA. *Adm £1.50 Chd free (Share to Glos Wildlife Trust®). Sun, Mon May 26, 27; Suns June 16, July 14 (2-6). Private visits welcome, please* **Tel 01452 840505**

Rockcliffe &&& (Mr & Mrs Simon Keswick) nr Lower Swell. On B4068. From Stow-on-the-Wold turn R into drive 1½m from Lower Swell. 5-acre garden incl herbaceous borders, pink and white and blue gardens, rose terrace, walled kitchen garden and orchard. TEAS in aid of St Peters Church, Upper Slaughter. *Adm £1.50 Chd under 15 free. Thurs May 16 (10-5), Sat July 6, Sun July 7 (10-6)*

Rodmarton Manor && (Mr & Mrs Simon Biddulph) Between Cirencester and Tetbury off A433. The 8-acre garden of this fine Arts and Crafts house is a series of 'outdoor rooms' each with its own distinctive character. Leisure garden, winter garden, troughery, topiary, hedges, lawns, rockery, containers, wild garden, kitchen garden; recently replanted herbaceous borders. *Adm £2 Sats, £2.50 any other time Acc chd free. Every Sat May 11 to Aug 31 (2-5). For NGS (Share to Rodmarton PCC®) Sat May 12 (2-6). Private visits welcome, please* **Tel 01285 841253**

Rookwoods ✿ (Mr & Mrs R Luard) Waterlane, 5m E of Stroud. Between Sapperton and Bisley. Turn down 'No Through Rd' in Waterlane then follow signs. 3-acre well structured garden with herbaceous borders to colour themes. Pleached Whitebeam around pool area. Wide variety of old-fashioned and modern climbing and shrub roses (labelled), water gardens and outstanding views. TEAS. *Adm £1.50 Chd free. Weds July 3, 10 (2-6). Coaches by appt. Private visits welcome May and July, please* **Tel 01452 770747**

20 St Peters Road ✿❀ (Meg & Jeff Blumson) Cirencester. Off Cricklade St. turn R into Ashcroft Rd then L then R. Small town garden entirely remade without grass; herbaceous, clematis, rockery, pond. *Adm 50p Chd free. Suns June 30. Combined adm £2 Chd under 16 free July 14 with* **Cirencester Gardens** *(2-6). Private visits welcome, please* **Tel 01285 657696**

The National Gardens Scheme is a charity which traces its origins back to 1927. Since then it has raised a total of over £14 million for charitable purposes.

Sezincote ⚔ (Mr & Mrs David Peake) 1½m SW of Moreton-in-Marsh. Turn W along A44 towards Evesham; after 1½m (just before Bourton-on-the-Hill) take turn L, by stone lodge with white gate. Exotic oriental water garden by Repton and Daniell with lake, pools and meandering stream, banked with massed perennial plants of interest. Large semi-circular orangery, formal Indian garden, fountain, temple and unusual trees of vast size in lawn and wooded park setting. House in Indian manner designed by Samuel Pepys Cockerell was insipiration for Brighton Pavilion. TEAS (NGS day only). *Adm £3 Chd £1 under 5 free. Open every Thurs Fri & Bank Hols (except Dec) (2-6). For NGS Sun July 7 (2-6)*

Snowshill Manor ⚔ (The National Trust) 3m SW of Broadway. Small terraced garden in which organic and natural methods only are used. Highlights include tranquil ponds, old roses, old-fashioned flowers and herbaceous borders rich in plants of special interest. House contains collections of fine craftmanship incl musical instruments, clocks, toys, bicycles. Ticket office, restaurant and shop open 12 noon. *Adm house & gdn £5.20 Chd £2.60. Family ticket £13.* ▲ *For NGS Sun May 12 (1-6)*

Stanton ⚊⚘ Broadway. One of the most picturesque and unspoilt C17 Cotswold villages with many gardens to explore (23 open in 1995) ranging from charming cottage to large formal gardens of appeal to visitors of all tastes. Plant stall. Car park £1. TEAS from 3-5.30. *Adm £2 Chd free (Share to Stanton Burland Hall®). Sun June 30 (2-6)*

Stanway House (Lord Neidpath) 1m E of B4632 Cheltenham-Broadway rd on B4077 Toddington to Stow-on-the-Wold rd. 20 acres of planted landscape in early C18 formal landscape setting. Arboretum, historic pleasure grounds with specimen trees incl pinetum; remains of ornamental canal and cascade; chestnut and oak avenue; folly. Striking C16 manor with gatehouse, tithe barn and church. Tea at The Bakehouse, Stanway. *Adm grounds only £1 Chd 50p; House and grounds £3 OAPs £2.50 Chd £1. Also house open Tues & Thurs June to Aug (2-5). For NGS (Share to The Garden History Society®) Suns April 14, June 2 (2-5)* Tel 01386 584469

Stowell Park ⚊⚔ (The Lord & Lady Vestey) 2m SW of Northleach. Off Fosseway A429. Large garden, lawned terraces with magnificent views over the Coln Valley. Fine collection of old-fashioned roses and herbaceous plants, with a pleached lime app to the House. Two large walled gardens contain vegetables, fruit, cut flowers and ranges of greenhouses, also a long rose pergola and wide, plant-filled borders divided into colour sections. House (not open) originally C14 with later additions. TEAS. *Adm £2 Chd free (Share to St Johns Ambulance Brigade® and Royal British Legion®). Suns May 12, June 30 (2-5)*

Sudeley Castle Gardens ⚔⚘ (Lord and Lady Ashcombe) Winchcombe. The seven individual gardens around C15 Castle incl the Queen's Garden, with old-fashioned roses, perennials, herbs and the recently opened Tudor Knot Garden with water features. Also formal pools, spring bulbs and fine trees in extensive grounds. Specialist plant centre. Restaurant. *Adm gardens and Emma Dent exhibition £4 OAPs £3.20 Chd £1.80. Open daily March 1 to 31 (11-4.30) April 1 to Oct 31 (10.30-*

5.30). For NGS Suns April 21, Sept 15 (10.30-5.30). TEAS. Group tours of gardens can be booked Tel 01242 602308

Tetbury Gardens, Tetbury. *Combined adm £2.50 Chd free. Sun June 9 (2-6)*

  The Chipping Croft ⚘ (Dr & Mrs P W Taylor) At bottom of Chipping Hill approached from market place. 2-acre, secluded, walled town garden on three levels, with mature trees, shrubs, herbaceous borders, rose beds and unusual plants; spring blossom and bulbs. A series of formal gardens, incl fruit and vegetable/flower potager all informally planted; also a water garden. C17 Cotswold house (not open). TEAS in aid of Action Research for the Crippled Child. *Private visits by arrangment welcome, please* Tel 01666 503570

  The Old Stables (Brigadier and Mrs J M Neilson) Enter New Church St B3124 from Long St at Xrds signed to Stroud and Dursley. Turn L at Fire station into Close Gardens. Small walled garden on two levels in old stable yard of a town house. Flowering shrubs; clematis; bonsai; water garden; paved area with alpines in troughs

Tin Penny Cottage ⚔⚘ (E S Horton) Whiteway, near Miserden, 6m NE Stroud between Birdlip & Stroud on B4070. At Fostons Ash Public House take rd signed Bisley then immediately L to Whiteway ½m; 300yd walk to garden. Enthusiast's medium-sized garden on cold clay. Designed to be visually attractive and grow a wide variety of hardy plants, many unusual and rarely seen, and incl a collection of Sempervivum. TEAS in Village Hall Mon April 8, Sun May 5, Mon May 27, Suns July 14, Aug 4, Mon Aug 26. *Adm £1 Chd free. Weds until end Sept. Bank Hol Mons April 8, May 27, Aug 26, Sat June 15. Suns March 17, April 21, May 5, July 14, Aug 4, Sept 22 (2-6). Private visits welcome all year, please* Tel 01285 821482. *After Sept 30, please* Tel 01453 835864

Trevi Garden ⚊⚔⚘ (Gilbert & Sally Gough) Hartpury 5m NW of Gloucester via A417. In village sharp back R into Over Old Road before War Memorial. 1 acre of gardens within a garden; winding water garden; laburnum/clematis walk, shrubberies, herbaceous borders, collection of hardy geraniums/penstemons; redesigned vegetable/flower garden. Garden completely designed by owners. TEAS. *Adm £1.50 Chd free. Suns, Mons April 7, 8, 21; May 5, 6, 19, 26, 27; Suns June 16, 23, 30; Suns, Mon Aug 4, 25, 26; also open every 2nd, 3rd, 4th (5th) Thurs March 14 to Sept 19 (2-6); coaches/groups by appt on other dates* Tel 01452 700370

Upton Wold ⚔⚘ (Mr & Mrs I R S Bond) 5m W of Moreton-in-Marsh, on A44 1m past A424 junction at Troopers Lodge Garage. Ever developing and changing garden architecturally and imaginatively laid out around C17 house with commanding views. Yew hedges; old shrub roses; herbaceous walk; some unusual plants and trees; vegetable garden; pond garden and woodland garden. Cream TEAS. *Adm £2 Chd free (Share to Chipping Norton Theatre Trust®). Suns April 21, June 23 (10-6). Private visits welcome May to July, please* Tel 01386 700667

Westbury Court Garden &⚹ (The National Trust) Westbury-on-Severn 9m SW of Gloucester on A48. Formal Dutch style water garden, earliest remaining in England; canals, summer house, walled garden; over 100 species of plants grown in England before 1700. *Adm £2.50 Chd £1.25.* ▲ *For NGS Sun Sept 1 (11-6)*

Westonbirt Gardens at Westonbirt School & 3m S of Tetbury. A433 Tetbury-Bristol. 22 acres. Formal Victorian Italian garden, terraced pleasure garden, rustic walks, lake redredged & stocked with carp. Rare, exotic trees and shrubs. Tea at Hare & Hounds Hotel, Westonbirt ½m, (to book tea room for parties **Tel 01666 880233**). *Adm £1.50 Chd 25p (Share to Westonbirt Church Organ Appeal®). Suns April 7, Aug 18, Sept 8 (2-5.30)*

Willow Lodge &⚹❀ (Mr & Mrs John H Wood) on A40 between May Hill & Longhope 10m W of Gloucester, 6m E of Ross-on-Wye. Plantsman's garden with unusual and rare plants incl colour themed herbaceous borders, shrubs, an alpine walk, stream and pools with water features, several greenhouses, organic vegetable garden, newly planted small arboretum with over 200 trees and shrubs from around the world, and wild flowers in the 4-acre grounds. Plants labelled. Ample parking. TEAS. *Adm £1 Chd free. Suns, Mons, May 26, 27; June 9, 10, 16, 17, 23, 24; July 14, 15, 21, 22, 28, 29; Aug 4, 5, 11, 12 (2-6). Groups and private visits especially welcome between May and Aug, please* **Tel 01452 831211**

Witcombe Gardens & 4m E of Gloucester on A417 turn R at 12 Bells Inn for Church Cottage and Witcombe Park; ½m up A417 from Inn turn L signed **Court Farm House.** Strawberry cream TEAS at Court Farm House in aid of Witcombe and Bentham Flower Show. *Combined adm £2 Chd free. Sun June 23 (2-6)*

Church Cottage ⚹❀ (Sir Christopher & Lady Lawson) Great Witcombe. More than 2 acres of country garden with shrubs, trees and lawns. Stream and two ponds. Rose arbour. Old clipped yews. Further beds of roses, herbaceous borders, and several seats for resting. Soft drinks

Court Farm House ❀ (Mr & Mrs Andrew Hope) Little Witcombe. An informal family garden of 1 acre. Shrubs, roses, herbaceous perennials and self-seeding annuals; pond, pergola; wild garden, rock garden, herb garden, scree bed, play area; children welcome

Witcombe Park ⚹ (Mrs W W Hicks Beach) Great Witcombe. A plant connoisseur's medium-sized garden set in beautiful Cotswold scenery. Richly planted borders, flowering shrubs, roses; walled garden, cottage garden area and sunken water garden; C17 gazebo

¶**Withington Gardens** 8m E of Cheltenham, S of A40 in hidden Cotswold valley. TEAS at Halewell. *Combined adm £2.50 Chd free (Share to St Michael's and All Angels Church®). Sun July 7 (2-6)*

Halewell (Mrs Elizabeth Carey-Wilson) Grade II listed part C15 house (not open) with 4 acres of terraced garden, incl topiary, leading down to lakeside walk

¶**Keepers Cottage** (Mr E C Housego) ¾-acre cottage garden on edge of village with lovely views

¶**The Old House** (Mr & Mrs John Holmes-Smith) Plantsman's Cotswold stone terraced garden of 1 acre with shrubbery; small pond; herbaceous borders and an abundance of roses. Secret garden in yellow and white

¶**Withington Court** (Mr & Mrs Jonathan Carr) Elegant setting with fine C18 listed house (not open). 5 acres incl paddock running down to R Colne. Trees, old clipped yew. Borders being gradually replanted

Gwent & Gwynedd

See separate Welsh section beginning on page 310

SYMBOLS USED IN THIS BOOK (See also Page 15)

‡   Following a garden name in the Dates of Opening list indicates that those gardens sharing the same symbol are nearby and open on the same day.

‡‡   Indicates a second series of nearby gardens open on the same day.

¶   Opening for the first time.

❀   Plants/produce for sale if available.

&   Gardens with at least the main features accessible by wheelchair.

⚹   No dogs except guide dogs but otherwise dogs are usually admitted, provided they are kept on a lead. Dogs are not admitted to houses.

●   Gardens marked thus do not necessarily give all their takings to the National Gardens Scheme. Instead they give a guaranteed contribution.

▲   Where this sign appears alongside dates in the descriptive entry for a garden it denotes that this garden is also open regularly to the public on days other than those for the NGS.

Hampshire

Hon County Organiser:	Central West: Mrs A R Elkington, Little Court, Crawley nr Winchester SO21 2PU Tel 01962 776365
Assistant Hon County Organisers:	South-East: Mrs R J Gould, Ewell House, 44 Belmore Lane, Lymington SO41 3NN
	East: Mrs D Hart Dyke, Hambledon House, Hambledon PO7 4RU
	South: Mrs J S M Jones, Durford Mill House, Petersfield GU31 5AZ
	North: J J Morris Esq, The Ricks, Rotherwick, Hook RG27 9BL
	North-East: Mrs E Powell, Broadhatch House, Bentley, Nr Farnham GU10 5JJ
	Central-East: Mrs W F Richardson, Hill House, Old Alresford SO24 9DY
	South-West: C K Thornton Esq, Merrie Cottage, Woodgreen, Nr Fordingbridge SP6 2AT
	North-West: M H Walford Esq, Little Acre, Down Farm Lane, Headbourne Worthy, Winchester SO23 7LA
Hon County Treasurer:	S Every Esq, The White House, Crawley, Winchester SO21 2PR

DATES OF OPENING

February 10 Saturday
Brandy Mount House, Alresford
February 25 Sunday
Little Court, Crawley,
nr Winchester
February 26 Monday
Little Court, Crawley,
nr Winchester
March 3 Sunday
Longthatch, Warnford
The White Cottage, Beech, Alton
March 10 Sunday
Longthatch, Warnford
March 17 Sunday
Bramdean House, Bramdean
Brandy Mount House, Alresford
Longthatch, Warnford
Pennington Chase, Lymington
March 20 Wednesday
Hayden Barn Cottage, Warnford
March 24 Sunday
Little Court, Crawley,
nr Winchester
Sowley House, Sowley, Lymington
March 25 Monday
Little Court, Crawley,
nr Winchester
March 31 Sunday
Abbey Cottage, Itchen Abbas
Bramley Lodge, Fyfield
Durmast House, Burley
The Old House, Silchester
April 5 Friday
Greatham Mill, nr Liss
April 7 Sunday
Bramdean House, Bramdean
April 8 Monday
Bramdean House, Bramdean
April 10 Wednesday
Hayden Barn Cottage, Warnford
April 14 Sunday
Beechenwood Farm, nr Odiham ‡

Cheriton Cottage, nr Alresford
Copperfield, Dogmersfield ‡
The Cottage, Chandlers Ford
Court Lodge, West Meon ‡‡
Crawley Gardens,
nr Winchester
East Lane, Ovington
Fairfield House, Hambledon
Hall Place, West Meon ‡‡
Jervis Lodge, Upper Swanmore
Little Court, Crawley
Norsebury Gardens, Stoke Charity
The Old House, Silchester
April 15 Monday
The Cottage, Chandlers Ford
Crawley Gardens, nr Winchester
Norsebury Gardens, Stoke Charity
April 21 Sunday
Bramdean House, Bramdean ‡
Hinton Ampner, nr Alresford ‡
60 Lealand Road, Drayton
Longthatch, Warnford
Rowans Wood, Ampfield
White Windows, nr Andover
April 22 Monday
White Windows, nr Andover
April 27 Saturday
Coles, Privett, nr Alton
April 28 Sunday
Abbey Road Gardens, Fareham
Brandy Mount House, Alresford
Coles, Privett, nr Alton
Fernlea, Chilworth, Southampton
North Ecchinswell Farm,
nr Newbury
The Old House, Silchester
Rowans Wood, Ampfield
Shalden Park House, Shalden
May 5 Sunday
Abbey Cottage, Itchen Abbas
Coles, Privett, nr Alton
The Cottage, Chandlers Ford
Ewell House, Lymington
Greatham Mill, Greatham, nr Liss

Rumsey Gardens, Clanfield
South End House, Lymington
Vernon Hill House, Bishop's
Waltham
May 6 Monday
Abbey Cottage, Itchen Abbas
Coles, Privett, nr Alton
The Cottage, Chandlers Ford
House-in-the-Wood, Beaulieu
Rookley Manor, Up Somborne
Stratfield Saye House
Vernon Hill House, Bishop's
Waltham
May 7 Tuesday
Hambledon House, Hambledon
May 8 Wednesday
Exbury Gardens, nr Southampton
May 11 Saturday
Coles, Privett, nr Alton
May 12 Sunday
Brandy Mount House, Alresford
Coles, Privett, nr Alton
The Dower House, Dogmersfield
Heathlands, Locks Heath
53 Ladywood, Eastleigh
Lithend, Crawley
Little Court, Crawley,
nr Winchester
Pennington Chase, Lymington
Pylewell Park, Lymington
May 13 Monday
Lithend, Crawley ‡
Little Court, Crawley,
nr Winchester ‡
May 15 Wednesday
Hayden Barn Cottage, Warnford
May 18 Saturday
Coles, Privett, nr Alton
Littlewood, Hayling Island ‡
Mill Court, Binsted
3 St Helens Road, Hayling
Island ‡
Verona Cottage, Hayling
Island ‡

May 19 Sunday
Bramdean House, Bramdean
Bramshaw Lodge, Bramshaw ‡
Coles, Privett, nr Alton
The Dower House, Dogmersfield
Hightown Farm, nr Ringwood
Little Barn Garden & Barnhawk
  Nursery, Fordingbridge
Littlewood, Hayling Island ‡‡
Mill Court, Binsted
The Old House, Silchester
Paddocks Way, Brook ‡
Pylewell Park, Lymington
Rowans Wood, Ampfield
3 St Helens Road, Hayling
  Island ‡‡
Tylney Hall Hotel, Rotherwick
Verona Cottage, Hayling
  Island ‡‡
The Vyne, Sherborne St John
Waldrons, Brook ‡
Walhampton, Lymington
May 20 Monday
Hightown Farm, nr Ringwood
May 21 Tuesday
Hambledon House, Hambledon
May 23 Thursday
Maurys Mount, West Wellow
May 26 Sunday
Coles, Privett, nr Alton
Hambledon House, Hambledon
Longthatch, Warnford
Monxton Gardens, nr Andover
Pumpkin Patch, Ringwood
Rowans Wood, Ampfield
May 27 Monday
Coles, Privett, nr Alton
Longthatch, Warnford
Monxton Gardens, nr Andover
Pumpkin Patch, Ringwood
Rowans Wood, Ampfield
May 29 Monday
Chilland, Martyr Worthy
June 2 Sunday
Cheriton Cottage, nr Alresford
Jenkyn Place, Bentley
Maurys Mount, West Wellow
North Ecchinswell Farm,
  nr Newbury
Pumpkin Patch, Ringwood
Rosewood Farm, West Tytherley ‡
2 Warren Farm Cottages, West
  Tytherley ‡
June 4 Tuesday
Hambledon House, Hambledon
June 5 Wednesday
Warwick House, Wickham
June 8 Saturday
Pumpkin Patch, Ringwood
June 9 Sunday
Beechenwood Farm, nr Odiham
Croft Mews, Botley
The Garden House, Lymington
Robins Return, Tiptoe

Tylney Hall Hotel, Rotherwick
Vernon Hill House, Bishop's
  Waltham
West Silchester Hall, nr Reading
The White Cottage, Beech, Alton
June 10 Monday
Croft Mews, Botley
The White Cottage, Beech, Alton
June 12 Wednesday
Robins Return, Tiptoe
June 15 Saturday
Springfield, Hayling Island
June 16 Sunday
Applecroft, Woodgreen ‡
Bramdean House, Bramdean ‡‡‡
Bramdean Lodge, Bramdean ‡‡‡
Closewood House, Denmead ‡‡
Cranbury Park, Otterbourne
Crookley Pool, Horndean ‡‡
Droxford Gardens
Durmast House, Burley
Longstock Park & Water Gardens,
  Stockbridge
Merrie Cottage, Woodgreen ‡
Pumpkin Patch, Ringwood
Southview, Eversley Cross
Upham Gardens, nr Bishops
  Waltham
June 17 Monday
Applecroft, Woodgreen ‡
Merrie Cottage, Woodgreen ‡
June 18 Tuesday
Hambledon House, Hambledon
June 19 Wednesday
Closewood House, Denmead ‡
Crookley Pool, Horndean ‡
Upham Gardens, nr Bishops
  Waltham
June 22 Saturday
Pumpkin Patch, Ringwood
June 23 Sunday
Brandy Mount House, Alresford
Chilland, Martyr Worthy ‡
Chilland Ford, Martyr Worthy ‡
Cliddesden Gardens, Nr
  Basingstoke
Crossways, Woodgreen Common
Fairfield House, Hambledon
Hambledon House, Hambledon
Jervis Lodge, Upper Swanmore
60 Lealand Road, Drayton
Longthatch, Warnford
Mottisfont Abbey, nr Romsey
Oakdene, Sandleheath
The Old Vicarage, Appleshaw
Warwick House, Wickham
Westbrook House, Holybourne
June 24 Monday
Chilland, Martyr Worthy ‡
Chilland Ford, Martyr Worthy ‡
Crossways, Woodgreen Common
Jervis Lodge, Upper Swanmore
June 25 Tuesday
Oakdene, Sandleheath

June 29 Saturday
Hinton Ampner, Bramdean
John Hine Studios, Aldershot
June 30 Sunday
Abbey Road Gardens, Fareham
Brocas Farm, Lower Froyle, nr Alton
Manor Lodge, Crawley,
  nr Winchester
Fritham Lodge, Fritham ‡
Hinton Ampner, Bramdean
Holt End House, Ashford Hill
Kempshott Junior & Infant
  Schools, Basingstoke
Manor Lodge, Crawley
Marycourt, Odiham ‡
Moth House, nr Alresford
Old Meadows, Silchester
The Old Rectory, West
  Tytherley ‡‡
Paddocks Way, Brook ‡
Pumpkin Patch, Ringwood
Tunworth Old Rectory,
  nr Basingstoke
Tylney Hall Hotel, Rotherwick
Vernon Hill House, Bishop's
  Waltham
Waldrons, Brook ‡
2 Warren Farm Cottages, West
  Tytherley ‡‡
July 1 Monday
The Old Rectory, West Tytherley
July 2 Tuesday
Hambledon House, Hambledon
July 3 Wednesday
Greatham Mill, Greatham, nr Liss
July 5 Friday
Manor Lodge, Crawley
July 6 Saturday
Pumpkin Patch, Ringwood
July 7 Sunday
Abbey Cottage, Itchen Abbas
Jenkyn Place, Bentley
John Hine Studios, Aldershot
Lake House, Northington ‡
Manor Lodge, Crawley,
  nr Winchester
Marycourt, Odiham
Moundsmere Manor, Preston
  Candover ‡
Valentine Cottage, Newnham
July 10 Wednesday
Marycourt, Odiham
July 13 Saturday
Merebimur, Mockbeggar
July 14 Sunday
Broadhatch House, Bentley
1 Brook Cottages, East Meon
Fernlea, Chilworth, Southampton
Heathlands, Locks Heath
53 Ladywood, Eastleigh
Longparish Gardens, nr Andover
Longthatch, Warnford
Malt Cottage, Upper Clatford
Merdon Manor, Hursley

Merebimur, Mockbeggar ‡
Pumpkin Patch, Ringwood ‡
Robins Return, Tiptoe
12 Rozelle Close, Littleton
Swarraton Gardens, Alresford
The White Cottage, Beech, Alton
July 15 Monday
Broadhatch House, Bentley
The White Cottage, Beech, Alton
July 16 Tuesday
Hambledon House, Hambledon
Swarraton Gardens, Alresford
July 17 Wednesday
Robins Return, Tiptoe
July 20 Saturday
Pumpkin Patch, Ringwood
July 21 Sunday
Bramdean House, Bramdean ‡
Bramdean Lodge, Bramdean ‡
Crookley Pool, Horndean
Empshott Grange, nr Selborne
Jasmine Lodge, Basingstoke
Little Court, Crawley,
  nr Winchester
The Vyne, Sherborne St John
July 22 Monday
Little Court, Crawley,
  nr Winchester
July 23 Tuesday
22 Springvale Road, Kingsworthy
July 27 Saturday
12 Rozelle Close, Littleton
July 28 Sunday
Cheriton Cottage, nr Alresford
Chilland, Martyr Worthy ‡
Jasmine Lodge, Basingstoke
John Hine Studios, Aldershot
Martyr Worthy Gardens,
  nr Winchester ‡
Paddocks Way, Brook
Pumpkin Patch, Ringwood
12 Rozelle Close, Littleton
July 29 Monday
Chilland, Martyr Worthy
August 4 Sunday
The Barn House, Oakley ‡
Bohunt Manor, Liphook
Hill House, Old Alresford
Oakley Manor, Oakley ‡
West Silchester Hall, nr Reading
August 5 Monday
West Silchester Hall, nr Reading

August 10 Saturday
Pumpkin Patch, Ringwood
August 11 Sunday
The White Cottage, Beech, Alton
August 12 Monday
The White Cottage, Beech, Alton
August 18 Sunday
Bramdean House, Bramdean ‡
Bramdean Lodge, Bramdean ‡
Little Court, Crawley, nr
  Winchester
60 Lealand Road, Drayton
August 19 Monday
Little Court, Crawley,
  nr Winchester
August 25 Sunday
Abbey Cottage, Itchen Abbas
Longthatch, Warnford
Norsebury House Stoke Charity
Wonston Lodge, Wonston
August 26 Monday
Abbey Cottage, Itchen Abbas
Norsebury House, Stoke Charity
Pumpkin Patch, Ringwood
Wonston Lodge, Wonston
September 1 Sunday
Hambledon House, Hambledon
September 3 Tuesday
Hambledon House, Hambledon
September 14 Saturday
Hinton Ampner, Alresford
September 15 Sunday
Little Court, Crawley,
  nr Winchester
Hinton Ampner, Alresford
Pumpkin Patch, Ringwood
September 16 Monday
Little Court, Crawley,
  nr Winchester
September 17 Tuesday
Hambledon House,
  Hambledon
September 22 Sunday
White Windows, Longparish
September 25 Wednesday
Greatham Mill, Greatham, nr Liss
September 29 Sunday
53 Ladywood, Eastleigh
Paddocks Way, Brook
October 6 Sunday
Abbey Cottage, Itchen Abbas
Coles, Privett, nr Alton

October 13 Sunday
Coles, Privett, nr Alton

1997
February 8 Saturday
Brandy Mount House, Alresford
February 17 Monday
Little Court, Crawley,
  nr Winchester
February 18 Tuesday
Little Court, Crawley,
  nr Winchester

Regular openings
For details see garden description

Apple Court & Apple Court Cottage,
  nr Lymington
Exbury Gardens
Furzey Gardens Charitable Trust,
  Minstead
Hambledon House, Hambledon
Sir Harold Hillier Arboretum,
  nr Romsey
Jenkyn Place, Bentley
53 Ladywood, Eastleigh
Longthatch, Warnford
Lymore Valley Herbs,
  Milford-on-Sea
Macpenny Woodland Garden &
  Nurseries, Bransgore
Pumpkin Patch, Ringwood
Spinners, Boldre
Stratfield Saye
The Vyne, Sherbourne St John
2 Warren Farm Cottages, West
  Tytherley

By appointment only
For telephone numbers and other details see garden descriptions. Private visits welcomed

Bracken Cottage, nr Liss
The Little Cottage, Lymington
Little Mead, Hambledon

DESCRIPTIONS OF GARDENS

Abbey Cottage ⅍⚘ (Colonel P J Daniell) Rectory Lane, Itchen Abbas. Turn off B3047 Alresford-Kingsworthy Rd, 1m E of Itchen Abbas. Interesting and inspiring walled garden and meadow of 1½ acres with trees, designed, created and maintained by owner. *Adm £1.50 Chd free (Share to Winchester Cathedral®). Suns March 31, July 7, Oct 6; Suns, Mons May 5, 6, Aug 25, 26 (12-5.30). Private visits welcome, please* **Tel 01962 779575**

Abbey Road Gardens From M27 Junction 9 travel on A27 towards Fareham. At top of hill past Titchfield Gyratory, turn L at traffic lights into Highland Rd. Take 4th turning R into Blackbrook Rd. Abbey Rd is 4th turning on L. *Combined adm £1.50 Chd free. Suns April 28, June 30 (11-5)*

80 Abbey Road ⚘⚘ (Brian & Vivienne Garford) Very small garden with developing collection of herbs and plants of botanical and historical interest. 2 small ponds, miniscule meadow area, but no lawn

86 Abbey Road ✿✱ (Tricia & Don Purseglove) Small developing garden started in 1991. Mixed planting and trellis work for breezy position. Small vegetable plot and Japanese garden. TEA

● **Apple Court & Apple Court Cottage** ❧✿✱ (Mrs D Grenfell, Mr R Grounds & Mrs M Roberts) Lymington. From the A337 between Lymington and New Milton turn N into Hordle Lane at the Royal Oak at Downton Xrds. Formal 1½-acre garden created by designer-owners within the walls of former Victorian kitchen garden. 3 National Reference Collections incl small leafed hosta. Theatrical white garden, daylily display borders, collection of ferns and grasses. Small specialist nursery. Adjoining small cottage garden with variegated catalpa. *Adm £1.50 Chd 25p. Thurs to Mons Feb 1 to Thurs Oct 31; every day July to Aug (9.30-1) (2-5.30)*

Applecroft (Mr & Mrs J B Milne) Brook Lane, Woodgreen. 3m N of Fordingbridge on A338 turn E to Woodgreen. Turn R at Horse and Groom and R again along the edge of the common. Park on common and walk down through 5-barred gate. Small garden created over 9 yrs with distant view to the SW over the Avon Valley. Mixed planting incl annuals and vegetables in the cottage style. Shady arbour and pond. TEA (Mon). *Adm £1 Chd free Sun, Mon June 16, 17 (2-5.30)*

Ashley Park Farm. See Dorset

The Barn House ✿✱ (Brigadier & Mrs H R W Vernon) Rectory Rd, Oakley. 5m W of Basingstoke. From Basingstoke towards Whitchurch on B3400. Turn L at Station Rd ½m W of Newfound and follow signs. Bus No 55a, 55b Basingstoke to Oakley. Small garden, with view of church. Borders, alpines and uncommon plants, large collection of clematis, informal planting in cottage style. Tea at Oakley Manor. *Combined adm with Oakley Manor £2 Chd free. Free parking at Manor. Sun Aug 4 (2-5.30) also private visits welcome, please Tel 01256 780271*

Beechenwood Farm ❧✿✱ (Mr & Mrs M Heber-Percy) Hillside, Odiham; turn S into King St. from Odiham High St. Turn L after cricket ground for Hillside. Take 2nd turn R for Roke after 1m. Modern house ½m. Garden in many parts incl woodland garden, rock garden, pergola, conservatory, herb garden with exuberant planting, belvedere with spectacular views over Odiham. Newly planted 8 acre wood, open from 1pm for picnics. WI TEAS. *Adm £1.50 Chd free. Sun April 14 (2-5); Sun June 9 (2-6); also private visits welcome April to July, please Tel 01256 702300*

Bohunt Manor ❧✿ (Lady Holman) Liphook. On old A3 in 30m area in Liphook nr station. Flowering shrubs, herbaceous borders, lakeside and woodland walks, rhododendrons, bulbs, wild flowers and vegetable garden. Tame waterfowl will eat out of children's hands. Specimen trees. About ¾hr to walk round, lake 3½ acres. *Adm £1.50 OAP £1 Chd free. Sun Aug 4 (10-6)*

¶**Bracken Cottage** ✿ (Mr & Mrs Day) Petersfield Rd, Greatham. On A325 halfway between Petersfield and Farnham. On the RH-side 100yds S of the village PO and store. ⅓-acre cottage garden on 3 levels. Redeveloped since 1987 for foliage and variety. Small pond and vegetable area. *Adm £1.50 Chd free. Private visits welcome weekends only May 18 to July 28, please Tel 01420 538680*

Bramdean House ✿ (Mr & Mrs H Wakefield) In Bramdean village on A272. 6½ acres carpets of spring bulbs. Walled garden with famous herbaceous borders, 1-acre working kitchen garden, large collection of unusual plants. TEAS. *Adm £1.50 Chd free (Share to Bramdean Parish Church®). Mon April 8; Suns March 17, April 7, 21, May 19, June 16, July 21, Aug 18, (2-5); also private parties welcome, please Tel 01962 771214*

Bramdean Lodge ❧ (Hon Peter & Mrs Dickinson) Bramdean village, on A272 (car park and TEAS as for Bramdean House). 1¾ acres around Victorian Gothic house. Walled garden. Borders densely planted. Style evolved rather than planned. Many oddities. Over 100 varieties of clematis, and 300 of roses, all labelled. *Adm £1.50 Chd free. Suns June 16, July 21, Aug 18 (2-5)*

Bramley Lodge ❧✿✱ (Mrs J D Ward) Fyfield. From Weyhill roundabout take Thruxton Rd. In 150yds turn R signed Fyfield. Continue ¾m under bridge 100yds on R. Long 1-acre garden framed and sheltered by old railway embankment, with many shrubs in curving beds, underplanted with drifts of spring bulbs; pond and bog garden, lime tolerant heathers and conifers. Plants in aid of Stroke Assoc. TEAS. *Adm £1.50 Chd free. Sun March 31 (2-5)*

¶**Bramshaw Lodge** ❧✿ (Dr, Mrs & Miss Couchman) Bramshaw, Lyndhurst. 2m from junction 1 on M27 on B3079. On L past Bramshaw Village Hall. Victorian garden of 1½ acres, circa 1850, with mature trees, rhododendrons and azaleas and expanding shrub and herbaceous planting surrounded by natural forest. Dressage manège. *Adm £1.50 Chd free. Sun May 19 (11.30-5.30)*

Brandy Mount House ❧✱ (Mr & Mrs M Baron) Alresford centre, first R in East St before Sun Lane. Please leave cars in Broad St. 1-acre informal plantsman's garden, spring bulbs, hellebores, species geraniums, snowdrop collection, daphne collection, clematis, herbaceous and woodland plants. Featured in Gardeners World Feb 1993. TEAS April 28, May 12, June 23. *Adm £1.50 Chd free. Sat Feb 10 (11-4); Suns March 17, April 28, May 12, June 23 (2-5), Sat Feb 8 1997. Also private visits welcome on Sats, please Tel 01962 732189*

Broadhatch House ❧✿✱ (Bruce & Lizzie Powell) Bentley; 4m NE of Alton; off A31 between Farnham/Alton; go up School Lane. 3½ acres formal garden, double herbaceous borders; rose gardens, old-fashioned roses; unusual flowering shrubs. Included and illustrated in 'Rose Gardens of England'. TEA. *Adm £1.50 Chd free (Share to Killoran Trust®). Sun, Mon July 14 (2-6); July 15 (11-6). Also private visits welcome in June/July, please Tel 01420 23185*

Brocas Farm ✿✱ (Mrs A A Robertson) Lower Froyle. ½m up road to Lower Froyle from A31 turning just W of Bentley; C18 House (not open) and old timber barn. 2-acre garden surrounded by open country views. Large yew hedges, roses, herbaceous. Interesting ground cover planting. Maturing arboretum. TEAS. *Adm £1.50 Chd 75p (Share to CRMF®). Sun June 30 (2-6)*

¶**1 Brook Cottages** ❀ (Mr & Mrs D Stapley) East Meon, Petersfield. Off A272 at Langrish turn L for East Meon. Turn L in front of church. Follow rd round L into the High Street. Brook Cottage is just past Izaak Walton Public House. ⅓-acre with over 300 herbs. Small areas with herbs for wines and liqueurs. Open knot of culinary and physic herbs. Chamomile seat and covered way of scented climbers. Medical astrology garden; herbs for homeopathic medicine and essential oils. Raw materials for dyes, flowercrafts, basketry etc. *Adm £1.50. Sun July 14 (2-6). Private visits welcome for parties of 10-15, May 19 to July 31, please* Tel **01730 823376**

Cheriton Cottage ❀❀ (Mrs I Garnett-Orme) Cheriton. 3m S of New Alresford on B3046 on R behind brick wall. Garden created over 44 yrs with chalk streams of R Itchen, and small plantations of specimen trees 4 to 5 acres. Home-made teas in Village Hall. *Adm £1.50 Chd 50p. Suns April 14, June 2, July 28 (2-5)*

Chilland ❀ (Mr & Mrs John Impey) Martyr Worthy. Midway between Winchester and Alresford on B3047. 4-acre garden with stream at bottom overlooking R Itchen watermeadows with woods and farmland beyond. Large collection of mature shrubs planned for their yr-round colour effects. Many fine trees incl huge plane and ancient mulberry, nutwalk, spring bulbs, clematis and herbaceous borders. *Adm £1.50 Chd free. Sun, Mon June 23, 24 (2-5.30) with* **Chilland Ford,** *Mon July 29 (2-6). Also Sun July 28 with* **Martyr Worthy Gardens**

¶**Chilland Ford** ❀ (Mrs D R Cooper) Martyr Worthy. Midway between Winchester and Alresford on B3047. A small, romantic, riverside garden with many climbing plants. *Adm £1 Chd free. Sun, Mon June 23, 24 (2-5.30) with* **Chilland**

Cliddesden Gardens ❀❀ 2m S of Basingstoke. Take A339 (Basingstoke to Alton Rd) Turn R into Farleigh Rd (B3046) Gardens situated about 1m on L. TEAS. *Combined adm £1.50 Chd free. Sun June 23 (2-5.30)*
    Yew Tree Cottage ❀ (Jean & Peter Matthews) Cottage garden in ⅓-acre. Areas of different character. Thatched well-head with roses, white garden, stream and pool. *(Share to Local Primary School Garden Project)*
    Sussex House ❀ (Molly & Bob Jones) ⅓-acre garden with herbaceous borders and rose beds. Pond stocked with Koi and Orfe bordered by a small rock garden partly enclosed with dwarf conifers. *(Share to St Michael's Hospice, Basingstoke®)*

Closewood House ❀ (Mr & Mrs Peter Clowes) Denmead. Take Closewood Rd to the W of the B2150 between Waterlooville and Denmead. L at T-junction after ½m. Signs to car park after 300 metres. 1½ acres, surrounded by farmland, looking towards Portsdown Hill. Good collection of scented roses and flowering shrubs. Unusual trees. Car park. TEAS (Sun) TEA (Wed). *Adm £1.50 Chd free. Sun June 16, Wed June 19 (2-6)*

Coles ❀❀ (W B S Walker) Privett, nr Alton and Petersfield. Approx 6m NW of Petersfield betweeen the hamlets of Privett and High Cross. From A3 take A272 at Petersfield to Winchester, turn N after 5m signposted to Privett; turn 1st R, continue past the church, 1m to entrance. From A32, S of Alton between East Tisted and West Meon Hut, turn E to Froxfield at Pig and Whistle/Lawns public house, after ½m turn L at T-junction and continue for ¾m, entrance on L. 26 acres of spectacular gardens specialising in rhododendrons and azaleas, set amongst mixed woodland with rare specimens. Undulating ground with walks and clearings opening onto views of decorative ponds and other unusual features. Spring bluebells and wide variety of acid loving plants. Wonderful Autumn leaf colours. TEAS in aid of Privett Village Hall. *Adm £2.75, OAP £2.50 Chd 50p. Sats Suns, April 27, 28, May 11, 12, 18, 19, Suns, Mons May 5, 6, 26, 27, Suns Oct 6, 13.(2-5.30) Private visits welcome, please* Tel **0171 493 2008**

Copperfield ❀❀ (John Selfe) Dogmersfield. Turn N off Odiham-Farnham A287 to Dogmersfield. Turn L by Queens Public House. Set in 1½ acres, 'Copperfield' is a true plantsman's garden; with vast beds displaying a wide range of plants and ornamental trees incl many rare and unusual varieties. Designed by nurseryman owner to provide spectacular yr-round colour and a stunning water feature. A camomile lawn and woodland walk. TEAS. *Adm £1.50 Chd free. Sun April 14 (2-5.30)*

The Cottage ❀❀ (Mr & Mrs H Sykes) 16 Lakewood Rd, Chandler's Ford. Leave M3 at junction 12, follow signs to Chandler's Ford. At Hanrahans on Winchester Rd, turn R into Merdon Ave, then 3rd rd on L. ¾-acre garden planted for yr-round interest with spring colour from bulbs, camellias, rhododendrons, azaleas and magnolias. Woodland, conifers, herbaceous borders, bog garden, ponds, fruit and vegetable garden; bantams. TEAS. *Adm £1.50 Chd 10p (Share to British Heart Foundation®). Suns, Mons April 14, 15; May 5, 6 (2-6)*

Court Lodge ❀❀ (Patricia Dale) West Meon, 8m W of Petersfield, S on A32. ¼-acre specialist cottage garden, home of botanical artist Patricia Dale and her husband. Rich in small spring plants, anemones, erythroniums, hellebores, narcissi, primulas, etc. Many used as subjects for paintings and cards, which may be seen in the Studio. Also miniature gardens in sinks, small pond, and gravel paths with interesting edge plants. Regret not suitable for small children. Teas at church. *Adm £1.50 Chd free. Sun April 14 (12-6) Private visits welcome, please* Tel **01730 829473**

Cranbury Park ❀❀ (Mr & Mrs Chamberlayne-Macdonald) Otterbourne, 5m S of Winchester. 2m N of Eastleigh; main entrance on old A33 between Winchester-Southampton, by bus stop at top of Otterbourne Hill. Entrance also in Hocombe Rd, Chandlers Ford. Extensive pleasure grounds laid out in late C18 and early C19; fountains; rose garden; specimen trees; lakeside walk. Family carriages and collection of prams will be on view. TEAS. *Adm £1.50 Chd 50p. Sun June 16 (2-5)*

Crawley Gardens 5m NW of Winchester, off A272 Winchester-Stockbridge Rd. Gardens signed from centre of village. Parking at top of village nr the church. Please do not obstruct access drives. TEA Sun only. *Combined adm £3 Chd free. Sun, Mon April 14, 15 (2-5.30)*

Glebe House ㅿ (Lt-Col & Mrs John Andrews) 1½-acres. Bulbs, shrubs and herbaceous borders

Lithend ㅿ⚘❀ (Mrs F L Gunner) Small cottage garden. *Also open Sun May 12 (2-5.30) Mon May 13 (2-7). Combined adm £2 Chd free with Little Court*

Little Court ㅿ⚘❀ (Professor & Mrs A R Elkington) See separate entry. *Also open on Sun, Mon, Feb 25, 26, March 24, 25, April 14, 15, May 12, 13, July 21, 22, Aug 18, 19, Sept 15, 16, Feb 17, 18 (1997)*

Manor Lodge ㅿ⚘❀ (Mr & Mrs K Wren) See separate entry. Cream Teas in aid of Crawley Recreation Ground. *Also open June 30, July 7*

Paige Cottage ⚘ (Mr & Mrs T W Parker) 1 acre of traditional English country garden with large shrub and herbaceous borders and incl grass tennis court and walled Italian style swimming pool; roses climbing into apple trees. *Sun April 14 (2-5)*

Croft Mews ㅿ⚘❀ (Captain & Mrs W T T Pakenham) Botley. 2m N of Botley on B3354, on L under trees (M27 exit 7). A recently created garden about 2 acres with much older buildings and walls, in grounds of old country house. Walled garden, lawns and mixed borders, woodland area, kitchen garden. Many interesting ideas and features incl new ha ha with views over meadows. TEAS in aid of NSPCC (Sun only). *Adm £1.50 Chd free. Sun June 9 (2-6) Mon June 10 (11-5). Private visits welcome May to Aug (no coaches), please Tel 01703 692425*

Crookley Pool ㅿ⚘❀ (Mr & Mrs F S K Privett) Horndean. Turn up Blendworth Lane by the main bakery from the centre of Horndean. House 200yds before church on L. Off the A3 5m S of Petersfield. 1-acre garden surrounded by parkland. Mixed borders with unusual plants, with a special interest in colour and plants for hot dry situations. Wisteria covered walls and terraces overlooking pool garden. Walled kitchen garden. TEAS. *Adm £1.50 Chd free. Sun June 16 (2-6); Wed June 19, Sun July 21 (2-6)*

Crossways ⚘❀ (J Egerton-Warburton) Woodgreen Common. 3m N of Fordingbridge on A338 turn E to Woodgreen, bear L in village and R immediately after the Horse and Groom, on to the common turn R. Parking on the common. Colourful spring garden with bulbs and azaleas. TEAS in aid of Age Concern. *Adm £1 Chd free. Sun, Mon June 23, 24 (2-6)*

The Dower House (Mr Michael Hoare) Dogmersfield. Turn N off A287. 6-acre garden including bluebell wood with large and spectacular collection of rhododendrons, azaleas, magnolias and other flowering trees and shrubs; set in parkland with fine views over 20-acre lake. TEAS. *Adm £1.50 Chd free. Suns May 12, 19 (2-6)*

Droxford Gardens 4½m N of Wickham on A32 approx mid-way between Alton-Portsmouth. *Combined adm £3 Chd 50p 1 garden £1. Sun June 16 (2-6)*

　Fir Hill ❀ (Mrs Derek Schreiber) 4½ acres; roses, shrubs, herbaceous and shrub borders. Home-made TEAS. Car park

　The Mill House ㅿ❀ (Mrs C MacPherson) Garden of 2 acres; shrubs, flower beds, orchard, mill stream, roses, pond. Car park

Mylor Cottage ㅿ❀ (Dr & Mrs Martin ffrench Constant) ½m S of Droxford on the Swanmore Rd. Car park. Mature beeches set off colourful herbaceous borders, fine lawns and foliage beds. A much loved and cherished chalk garden. *Parties welcome, please Tel 01489 877462*

Park View ㅿ (Mrs F V D Aubert) Small town garden, flowers, shrubs and very small wooded walk

Durmast House ㅿ❀ (Mr & Mrs P E G Daubeney) 1m SE of Burley, nr White Buck Hotel. 4-acre garden designed by Gertrude Jekyll in 1907 in the process of being restored from the original plans. Formal rose garden edged with lavender, 130-yr-old Monterey pine, 100-yr-old cut leaf beech and large choisya. Victorian rockery, lily pond, coach-house, large wisteria and herbaceous border. *Adm £1 Chd 50p (Share to Delhi Commonwealth Women's Assoc Clinic®). Suns March 31, June 16 (2.30-5.30). Private parties welcome, please Tel 01425 403527*

East Lane (Sir Peter & Lady Ramsbotham) Ovington A31 from Winchester towards Alresford. Immediately after roundabout 1m west of Alresford, small sign to Ovington turn sharp L up incline, down small country rd to Ovington. East Lane is the only house on left, 500yds before Bush Inn. 4 acres, spring bulbs, mixed herbaceous and shrubs; woodland plantings; walled rose garden. Terraced water garden. Ample parking. *Adm £1.50 OAPs £1 Chd 50p. Sun April 14 (1.30-5.30)*

Empshott Grange ⚘ (Mr & Mrs Hamish Burton) Nr Selborne. Take B3006 from Alton. Turn R 2m out of Selborne towards Empshott Green entrance 600m on L. Or from A3 head N from roundabout at West Liss towards Farnham. L onto B3006. 2m L as above. Close to Greatham Mill. Restored victorian garden on upper greensand laid out in 1860. Next to C12 church. 3 acre garden surrounded by 30 acres magnificent hanger of mixed woodland and park with large pond fed by stream from Noar Hill. (Open) Good trees and shrubs, magnolia grandiflora, liquidamber, judas, myrtle, loquat, medlar and acers, formal yew hedges. The walled garden contains a traditionally managed kitchen garden, mature fig, espalier apples backing a double mixed border, fruit and vegetables interspersed with flowers and the original greenhouse with large vine and walled trained fruit. Gates open noon for picnicking. TEAS in aid of Empshott Church. *Adm £1.50 Chd free. Sun July 21 (2-5)*

Ewell House ㅿ❀ (Mr & Mrs R J Gould) 44 Belmore Lane, Lymington. 100yds downhill on R from exit off Waitrose car park. Town garden of ⅓ acre completely replanned and replanted in 1986. New planting still taking place but has acquired maturity. Large variety of interesting shrubs include camellias and small rhododendrons. TEAS at **South End House** (q.v.). Plants at Ewell House. *Combined adm £2 Chd free. Sun May 5 (2-5.30)*

● **Exbury Gardens** ㅿ❀ (Exbury Gardens Trust) Exbury, 2½m SE of Beaulieu; 15m SW of Southampton. Via B3054 SE of Beaulieu; after 1m turn sharp R for Exbury. 200 acres of woodland garden incorporating the Rothschild Collection of azaleas, rhododendrons, magnolias, maples and camellias. Luncheons and teas. Plant Centre and Gift Shop. *Spring Season: Sat Feb 17 to mid April*

Adm £3 OAPs £2.50. Parties of 15 or more £2.50 Chd 10-16 £2. Adm mid April-early June £4.50 OAPs & groups £4 (OAPs reduced 50p Weds and Thurs) Chd 10-16 £3.50. Mid June to July 7 Adm £3 OAPs £2.50. Parties £2.50 Chd £2. Gardens N of Gilbury Lane Bridge open Summer July 8 to Sept 13 Adm adults & parties £2 OAPs & Chd 10-16 £1.50. Autumn Sept 14 to Oct 27. Adm £2.50 OAPs & groups £2 Chd 10-16 £1.50. Open daily 10-5.30/dusk. Share to NGS Wed May 8 (10-6.30)

Fairfield House ⚘⚘ (Mrs Peter Wake) Hambledon. 10m SW of Petersfield. Hambledon village. 5-acre informal garden on chalk, with extensive walls, fine mature trees; large collection of shrubs and climbing roses mixed with wide variety of small trees and interesting perennials. Adjacent car park and wild flower meadow. Featured in 'A Heritage of Roses' by Hazel Le Rougetel, 'The Rose Gardens of England' by Michael Gibson, 'The Latest Country Gardens' by George Plumptre. TEAS. Adm £2 Chd free. Suns, April 14, June 23 (2-6). Also private visits welcome anytime by appt; suitable for groups, please Tel **01705 632431**

Fernlea ⚘⚘ (Mr & Mrs P G Philip) Chilworth. From Winchester on M27. After Eastleigh turn off, take fork marked A33 to Southampton. At roundabout follow rd sign marked Romsey A27 and Chilworth rd. Turn L at Clump Inn (Lunches available). Follow Manor rd. To cross the M27 immed turn R into Chilworth Dr. 15-acre organic garden created to encourage wild life, with many birds and butterflies, and woodland, meadow and heathland habitats. Many Mediterranean plants, specially Cistus with informal planting. Views to the Isle of Wight and large specimen trees. Garden merges into woodland. 15 acres in all. Picnics welcome. TEAS. Adm £1.50 Chd free. Suns April 28, July 14 (12-5)

Fritham Lodge ⚘⚘ (Christopher and Rosie Powell) Fritham, nr Lyndhurst. 3m NW of Cadnam junction 1 on M27. Follow signs to Fritham, after approx 3m at turning into Fritham village, turn down gravel track low sign Fritham Lodge only; parking in field. Set in heart of New Forest. Approx 1-acre; old walled garden surrounding C17 listed house (not open) originally one of Charles II's hunting lodges. Parterre of old roses, potager with wide variety of vegetables, herbs and fruit trees, pergola, herbaceous and blue and white mixed borders, ponds, walk across hay meadows to woodland and stream. TEAS. Adm £1.50 Chd free. Sun June 30 (2-5)

● **Furzey Gardens** ⚘⚘ (Furzey Gardens Charitable Trust) Minstead, 8m SW of Southampton. 1m S of A31; 2m W of Cadnam and end of M27; 3½m NW of Lyndhurst. 8 acres of informal shrub garden; comprehensive collections of azaleas and heathers; water garden; fernery; summer and winter flowering shrubs. Botanical interest at all seasons. Also open (limited in winter) Will Selwood Gallery and ancient cottage (AD 1560). High quality arts and crafts by many local craftsmen. Adm £3 OAPs £2.50 Chd £1.50 Families £7 March to Oct. £1.50 OAPs £1 Chd 75p Families £3.50 winter (Share to Minstead Training Project and other charities). Daily except Dec 25 & 26 (10-5; dusk in winter). Tel **01703 812464**

The Garden House ⚘ (Mr & Mrs C Kirkman) Lymington. Off Lymington High St opp Woolworths. An explosion of unusual herbaceous, roses, grasses, house leeks agaves and shrubs, interspersed with a riot of annuals, punctuated by 2 ponds in ¾ acre. Prime example of close boscage. TEAS with extravagant portions of clotted cream. Adm £2 Chd free (Share to Alzheimers Disease Society®). Sun June 9 (2-6)

Greatham Mill ⚘⚘⚘ (Mr & Mrs E Groves) Greatham, nr Liss. 5m N of Petersfield. From A325, at Greatham turn onto B3006 towards Alton; after 600yds L into 'No Through Rd' lane to garden. Interesting garden with large variety of plants surrounding mill house, with mill stream and nursery. Home-made TEAS. Adm £1 Chd free. Fri April 5, Weds July 3, Sept 25 (2-6). Private visits welcome, please Tel **01420 538245**

Hall Place ⚘ (Mr & Mrs Dru Montagu) West Meon. 7m W of Petersfield. From A32 in West Meon, take rd to East Meon, garden on R. Parking in drive. Large collection of rare and unusual daffodils in 8 acres of garden designed by Lanning Roper 30 years ago. Grass walks, spring bulbs, many varieties of trees and shrubs; walled kitchen garden. Adm £1.50 Chd free. Sun April 14 (2-6)

Hambledon House ⚘⚘ (Capt & Mrs David Hart Dyke) Hambledon. 8m SW of Petersfield. In village centre behind George Hotel. Approx 2 acres partly walled garden with unusual plants, shrubs suited to chalk soil and to give colour and interest through the seasons. Centred around 150-yr-old copper beech. Special interest in grasses, salvias, penstemons. TEAS (Suns). Adm £1.50 Chd free. 1st, 3rd Tues, May, June, July, Sept (2-5). Suns May 26, June 23, Sept 1 (2-6); also private visits welcome, please Tel **01705 632380**

¶**Hayden Barn Cottage** ⚘⚘⚘ (Captain & Mrs Broadbent) Take A32 to Warnford. Opp George and Falcon public house take single track rd signposted to Clanfield. Go ¾m. Red brick cottage on L. 1-acre garden on several levels developed entirely by owners. Herbaceous and mixed borders, rockery, shrubberies and good spring colour set off by extensive brick and flint walling, terraces and grassy banks. No coaches. Parking through garden not in lane. TEA. Adm £1.50 Chd free. Weds March 20, April 10, May 15 (1-5)

Heathlands ⚘ (Dr & Mrs John Burwell) 47 Locks Rd, Locks Heath. Locks Rd runs due S from Park Gate into Locks Heath. No 47 is 1m down on the R hand side [Grid Ref 513 069]. 1-acre garden designed & developed by the owner since 1967. An attempt has been made to give yr-round interest against a background of evergreens and mature trees. Spring bulbs, rhododendrons, paulownias. cyclamen, ferns and some less usual plants. Topiary, small herbaceous border and scree bed. National Collection of Japanese anemones. 'A treat for garden visitors' Stefan Buczacki TVS. TEAS. Adm £1.50 Chd free. Suns May 12, July 14 (2-5.30). Private visits welcome, please Tel **01489 573598**

> **By Appointment Gardens.** See foot of county section

Hightown Farm ❀ (Oliver and Margaret Ziegler) Hightown Hill, Ringwood. A31 ¼m W of Picket Post, turn L at Hightown and Crow sign. Cross 2 cattle grids, garden 100yds further. If going E return from Picket Post via underpass. Parking in field. Disabled may drive to house. Approx 3 acres of formal and informal areas, wide variety of plants and shrubs, many unusual. Brilliant display of rhododendrons and azaleas from huge to miniature. A dry and stony garden. New planting going on in basically mature garden. Owner maintained. Lovely view over field to forest. TEA (Sun only). *Adm £2 Chd free (Share to Oak-haven Hospice, Lymington®) Sun, Mon May 19, 20 (2-5.30) Private visits and coaches welcome by appt, please* **Tel 01425 474278**

Hill House, Old Alresford ❀ (Maj & Mrs W F Richardson) From Alresford 1m along B3046 towards Basingstoke, then R by church. 2 acres with large old-fashioned herbaceous border and shrub beds, set around large lawn; kitchen garden. TEAS. *Adm £1.50 Chd free. Sun Aug 4 (2-5.30)*

● **Sir Harold Hillier Arboretum** ❀❀❀ Jermyns Lane, Ampfield. Situated between Ampfield and Braishfield, 3m NE of Romsey. Signposted from A31 and A3057. 166-acres containing the finest collection of hardy trees and shrubs in the UK. Home to 11 national collections quercus, carpinus, cornus, cotoneaster, ligustrum, lithocarpus, corylus, photinia, pinus hamamelis and Hillier plants. Pond, scree beds, heather garden, peat garden, centenary border and acer valley. Wonderful spring and autumn colour with guided tours at 2pm every Suns and Weds in May and Oct. Fine collections of magnolias, azaleas and rhododendrons. TEAS. *Adm April to Nov £4 OAP £3.50 Chd £1 (Group rate 30+ £3.50); Dec to Feb £3, OAP £2.50 Chd £1. Daily April 1 to Oct 31 (10.30-6); Nov 1 to March 31 (10.30-5 or dusk)*

Hinton Ampner ❀❀ (The National Trust) S of Alresford. On Petersfield-Winchester Rd A272. 1m W of Bramdean village. 12-acre C20 shrub garden designed by Ralph Dutton. Strong architectural elements using yew and box topiary, with spectacular views. Bold effects using simple plants, restrained and dramatic bedding. Orchard with spring wild flowers and bulbs within formal box hedges; magnolia and philadephus walks. Dell garden made from chalk pit, now restored and maturing. Shrub rose border dating from 1950s. Special interest viburnum, buddleia, cotinus, foxgloves. Chosen for 'Alan Titchmarsh's favourite gardens' 1995. TEAS. *Adm £2.50 Chd £1.25. Sats, Suns, Tues, Weds & Bank Hol Mons March 30 to Sept 29.* ▲*For NGS Sats, Suns April 21, June 29, 30; Sept 14, 15 (1.30-5)*

Holt End House ❀❀ (Maj & Mrs J B B Cockcroft) Ashford Hill, Newbury. Ashford Hill is on B3051 between Kingsclere and Tadley. The garden is in the village on the R going E. 3-acre garden with extensive collection of labelled roses, with many climbers on unusual tree hosts. Substantial mature shrub planting. Large ginkgo biloba. Area of SSI woodland. TEAS. *Adm £2 Chd free (Share to St Paul's Church, Ashford Hill®). Sun June 30 (2-6)*

House-in-the-Wood ❀ (Countess Michalowska) Well signed 1½m from Beaulieu; signed from Motor Car Museum, Beaulieu. R on B3056 Beaulieu-Lyndhurst Rd. 13-acre woodland garden; rhododendrons and azaleas. *Adm £2 Chd 50p. Mon May 6 (2.30-6.30). Parties by appt.* **Tel 01590 612346**

¶**Jasmine Lodge** ❀ (Mr & Mrs N B Murgatroyd) Jasmine Rd, Basingstoke. From M3, junction 7, follow Basingstoke signs. Straight over next roundabout. At Kempshott roundabout turn L into Heather Way, then immed R into Jasmine Rd. 2nd house on L, with brick wall. Park on rd away from bend. Front and back gardens each approx 30' × 70'. Basingstoke in Bloom large front garden winner 1995; floral containers 1994. Approx 3,500 summer bedding plants, carpet bedding and over 70 tubs, containers and hanging baskets, fuschias, small conifers, pond and rockery. TEA. *Adm £1 Chd 50p. Suns July 21, 28 (11-5)*

Jenkyn Place ❀❀❀ (Trustees of Jenkyn Place Garden Trust) Bentley. 400yds N of Xrds in Bentley. Heritage sign on A31. Bus: Guildford-Winchester, alight Bentley village, 400yds. Well designed plantsman's garden, many interesting shrubs and perennials, double herbaceous borders. Featured in NGS video 1. Car park free. Disabled may set down at gates (Coaches only by prior appt). *Adm £2 Chd 75p. Thurs, Fris, Sats, Suns & Bank Hol Mons April 11 to Sept 8 (2-6). For NGS Suns June 2, July 7 plus 5 per cent of other receipts*

Jervis Lodge ❀❀❀ (Mrs Nicholas Haydon) Upper Swanmore. Take Swanmore Rd from Bishops Waltham for 2m turning L into Hampton Hill, ½m further on, turn 1st L to Jervis Lodge. A mature 3½-acre garden still evolving surrounding Regency house. Spring bulbs, large mixed borders, walled garden with box parterres. Conservatory and greenhouse. TEA. *Adm £2 Chd free. Suns April 14, June 23, Mon June 24 (2-6). Private visits welcome, by written application*

John Hine's Studios ❀❀ (Mr John Hine) 2 Hillside Rd, Aldershot. From A31 take exit off large roundabout on E side of Farnham signed Farnborough A325 and Basingstoke A30. At next roundabout take 3rd exit signed Aldershot B3007. After 1m, with railway bridge ahead, rd bends sharply L and becomes Eggars Hill. Hillside Rd is 400yds on L. Garden is 2nd entrance on R. A small newly created courtyard garden (approx 50' × 60') surrounded by a restored C17 barn (open). Garden is planted with a wide range of climbers & herbaceous plants to give maximum colour and interest over a long season. Garden also includes hanging baskets, window boxes, containers and a dovecote. TEAS in traditional English tea room. *Adm £1 Chd 50p. Suns June 29, July 7, 28 (10.30-4.30). Private visits welcome, please* **Tel 01252 307200**

¶**Kempshott Junior & Infant Schools** ❀❀❀ (Hampshire County Council). Kempshott is SW of Basingstoke. From Basingstoke on A30 find Kempshott Roundabout. Take 3rd exit into Heather Way and then 1st R into Jasmine Rd, then into Homesteads Rd. Take 2nd L into Old Down Close. Planting started in 1985. Gradually designed and extended by the children. Chequerboard garden, herbaceous borders, butterfly garden, herb wheel. Large nature pond. New hedging and young trees to enhance the environment. Developed as a learning resource. Winner of the schools' section of Basingstoke in Bloom and Southern England in Bloom. TEA. *Adm £1 Chd free (Share to Kempshott Schools PTA®). Sun June 30 (2-6)*

53 Ladywood ♿❀ (Mr & Mrs D Ward) Eastleigh. Leave M3 at junction 12, signed A335 Eastleigh N and follow A335 towards Eastleigh. R at roundabout into Woodside Ave, 2nd R into Bosville. Ladywood is 5th R off Bosville, please park in Bosville. A plant lover's very small garden, 45' × 45', developed by the owners over the last 6 yrs, giving many ideas for the small garden featured on Gardener's World 1994. Over 1000 different plants labelled. Rustic fences have been built to give vertical space for clematis and climbing roses. A secluded shade garden, a pond garden and a tiny lawn; collections of hardy geraniums, pulmonarias, asters for the small garden and many foliage plants. TEAS. *Adm £1.50 Chd 75p. Suns May 12, July 14, Sept 29 (11-5.30). Private visits welcome April 1 to Sept 30 Tuesday afternoons, please* Tel 01703 615389

Lake House ♿❀ (Lord & Lady Ashburton) Northington, Alresford. 4m N of Alresford off B3046. Follow English heritage signs to The Grange. From Winchester take A33 N turning R at Lunway Inn follow signs to Northington and The Grange. 20 acres in Candover Valley. 2 large lakes set off by mature woodland with waterfalls, abundant bird life, long landscape vistas. 1½ acre walled garden divided into a series of garden rooms with rose garden, exotic border, long herbaceous border, rose pergola leading to moon gate. Formal kitchen garden, featured in 'The Garden Show'. Numerous flowering pots, conservatory and greenhouses. Experts to answer questions. Visit can be conveniently extended by seeing The Grange, an English heritage property in the Greek revival style. Picnicking by lakes. TEAS. *Adm £2 Chd free. Sun July 7 (11-5) (Share to Winchester Hospital Radio®). Group visits welcome, please* Tel 01962 734426

Landford Lodge Landford see Wiltshire

60 Lealand Road ♿❀❀ (Mr F G Jacob) Drayton. 2m from Cosham E side of Portsmouth. Old A27 (Havant Rd) between Cosham and Bedhampton. Small prize winning garden created and designed by owner since 1969. Featured in National Gardening Magazines. Exotic plants with rockery, ponds, dwarf conifers and collection of grasses, cacti and other exotics in greenhouse. TEAS. *Adm £1 Chd free. Suns April 21, June 23, Aug 18 (11-5). Also private visits welcome, please* Tel 01705 370030

Lithend ♿❀❀ (Mrs F L Gunner) For directions see under **Crawley Gardens** *open April 14, 15. Also open with* **Little Court, Crawley** *Combined adm £1.50 Chd free. Sun, Mon May 12, 13 (2-5.30)*

Little Barn Garden & Barnhawk Nursery ♿❀ (Drs R & V A Crawford) Woodgreen. 3m NE of Fordingbridge via A338. Turn E to Woodgreen; bear L in village; R immediately past Horse and Groom, continue for 1¼m; 2½ acres of mature informal garden with all-yr interest in form, colour and texture; rhododendron; azalea; camellia; magnolia; acer and collector's plants with peat, scree, rock, woodland, bog and water area. TEAS. *Adm £1 Chd 25p. Sun May 19 (2-6). Also private visits welcome, please* Tel 01725 512213

The Little Cottage ♿❀ (Lyn & Peter Prior) On N fringe of Lymington A337, opp Toll House Inn. Small formal town garden arranged as rooms closely planted in harmonious colour schemes with box edges and topiary. Each room has arbours, seats, pots and urns used to form focal points. Featured in Practical Gardening Jan 1996 and other publications. *Adm £2. Private visits welcome on Tues for NGS from June to August (10-1 & 2-6), please* Tel Lymington 01590 679395. *Tours with lunch by arrangement on Thursdays*

Little Court ♿❀❀ (Prof & Mrs A R Elkington) Crawley 5m NW of Winchester off A272 in Crawley village; 300yds from either village pond or church. 1½ acres, a very peaceful and sheltered garden. Prolific bulbs; new spring woodland walk. Harmonious informal planting incl drought-tolerant plants. Euphorbia, geraniums and eryngiums. Victorian walled kitchen garden. Bantams and Geese. Beautiful view. TEAS Suns only. *Adm £1.50 (Combined with* **Lithend** *£2; with* **Crawley Gardens** *£3). Sun, Mon, Feb 25, 26, March 24, 25; April 14, 15; May 12, 13. Suns, Mons, July 21, 22; Aug 18, 19; Sept 15, 16 (Suns 2-5.30, Mons 11-7). (Feb 17, 18 (1997). Also private visits welcome, please* Tel 01962 776365

Little Mead ♿❀ (Mr & Mrs K C Moon) Old Barn Cres. Hambledon 8m SW of Petersfield on B2150 opp Hartridges. Plantsman and flower arrangers intensively planted garden of ⅓ acre with wide range of plants and areas divided by many climbers featured on TV twice and in Garden News. *Adm £1.50 Chd free. Private visits welcome by parties of up to 10 between July 10 and Aug 30, please* Tel 01705 632758

Littlewood ♿❀❀ (Steven and Sheila Schrier) 163 West Lane, Hayling Island. From A27 Havant/Hayling Island roundabout, travel S 2m, turn R into West Lane. Travel 1m and Littlewood is on R in a wood. 2½-acre woodland garden protected from the sea winds by multi barrier hedge. Woodland walk and access to Hayling Billy harbour trail. Rhododendrons, azaleas, camellias and many other shrubs. Features incl pond, bog garden watered from roof of comfortable conservatory with many house plants. Picnickers welcome. Easy access for elderly and wheelchair bound. TEAS. *Donations. Sat, Sun May 18, 19 (11-6)*

Longparish Gardens ♿❀ 5m E of Andover off A303 to village centre on B3048. *Combined adm £2.50 Chd free. Sun July 14 (12-5)*

  Longmead House ♿❀ (Mr & Mrs J H Ellicock) 2½-acre organic garden. Large hedged vegetable garden with deep beds, polytunnel, fruit cage and composting display. A fishpond and wildlife pond, wildflower meadow, herbaceous and shrub borders, trees. Angora goats, dairy goat and chickens. TEAS. *Private visits welcome, please* Tel 01264 720386

  ¶**Longparish House** ❀ (Mr & Mrs R C Kelton) Period house set in parkland. Newly planted roses in formal beds. Est shrubs and trees in lawns sweeping down to banks of the Test. Long and short riverside walks along mown paths with wonderful natural flora and fauna (Bring wellies if wet) Park and picnic in the grounds

Longstock Park Gardens &⚘❀ (Leckford Estate Ltd; Part of John Lewis Partnership) 3m N of Stockbridge. From A30 turn N on to A3057; follow signs to Longstock. A famous water garden with extensive collection of aquatic and bog plants set in 7 acres of woodland with rhododendrons and azaleas. A walk through the park leads to an arboretum, herbaceous border and nursery. Featured in several TV programmes and gardening books. Plants and Teas at nearby garden centre. *Adm £2 Chd 50p. 1st and 3rd Sunday in month April to Sept. For NGS Sun June 16 (2-5)*

Longthatch &⚘❀ (Mr & Mrs P Short) Warnford. 1m S of West Meon on A32 turn R from N or L from S at George & Falcon, 100yds turn R at T-junction, continue for ¼m; thatched C17th house on R, follow signs for parking. 2-acre plantsman's garden rolling down to R. Meon. Good selection of rare trees and shrubs. Part of the National Collection of Helleborus, alpine bog gardens, ponds and riverside plantings with fine lawns and herbaceous borders, always being added to by the enthusiastic owners. *Adm £1.50 Chd free. Open for NGS Suns March 3, 10, 17, April 21; Sun, Mon May 26, 27; Suns June 23, July 14, Aug 25 (2-5). Also private visits by Societies and individuals welcome. We also open Weds Mar 6 to Aug 28 (10-5) please* **Tel 01730 829285**

Lymore Valley Herbs &⚘❀ (N M Aldridge) Braxton Farm. 3m W of Lymington. From A337 at Everton take turning to Milford-on-Sea, 70yds on L is Lymore Lane. Turn into Lane and gardens are at Braxton courtyard on L. Attractive courtyard with raised lily pool and dovecote. Restored C19 barn leading into formal walled garden. Lake and parkland walks; knot garden and lawns. Horticultural societies welcome. Special evening visits. TEA. Shop, nursery, no dogs in courtyard or walled garden (dog rings & water provided). *Donations. Open 9-5 all year round except Dec 25 to March 1st.* **Tel 01590 642008**

Macpenny Woodland Garden & Nurseries ❀ (Mr & Mrs T M Lowndes) Burley Road, Bransgore. Midway between Christchurch and Burley. From Christchurch via A35, at Cat and Fiddle turn left; at Xrds by The Crown, Bransgore turn R and on ¼m. From A31 (travelling towards Bournemouth) L at Picket Post, signed Burley; through Burley to Green Triangle then R for Bransgore and on 1m beyond Thorney Hill Xrds. 17 acres; 4-acre gravel pit converted into woodland garden; many choice, rare plants incl camellias, rhododendrons, azaleas, heathers. Large selection shrubs and herbaceous plants available. Tea Burley (Forest Tearooms) or Holmsley (Old Station Tea Rooms). *Collecting box. Daily except Dec 25 & 26 and Jan 1. (Mons-Sats 9-5; Suns 2-5)*

Malt Cottage ⚘ (Mr & Mrs Richard Mason) Turn into Upper Clatford off the Andover-Stockbridge or Andover-Salisbury Rd. Park behind village hall. Garden is down short lane, opposite Crook & Shears Public House, 6 acres developed by designer owners. Formal garden blending into natural water meadows with ¼m chalk stream. Lakes, bog garden; uncommon trees and shrubs. TEA available in aid of another charity. *Adm £2 Chd free. Sun July 14 (2-5)*

Manor Lodge &⚘❀ (Mr & Mrs K Wren) Crawley, nr Winchester. Signposted from A272 and near the village pond. Extensively planted drive with shrubs and specie roses, incl white roses climbing through yew trees. Low maintenance border. Walled garden with many scented roses and clematis collection. Thatched summerhouse. Extensive lawns. Ancient walnut tree. Cream TEAS in garden room in aid of Crawley recreation ground (June) WWF (July). Parking outside House only. *Adm £1.50. Sun June 30; July 7 (2-5.30) Wed July 5 (2-7). Also open with* **Crawley Gardens** *April 14 (2-5.30); also private visits welcome, please* **Tel 01962 776372**

Martyr Worthy Gardens Midway between Winchester and Alresford on B3047. Gardens joined by Pilgrims Way through Itchen Valley, approx ½m. TEAS in Village Hall in aid of village hall committee. *Adm £1.50 per garden Chd free. Sun July 28 only (2-5.30)*

    Chilland & (Mr & Mrs John Impey) See separate entry. *Also open Sun, Mon June 23, 24, July 29*

    Manor House & (Cdr & Mrs M J Rivett-Carnac) Large garden, roses, mixed borders, lawns, shrubs and fine trees, next to C12 church

Marycourt & (Mr & Mrs M Conville) Odiham 2m S of Hartley Wintney on A30 or Exit 5 on M3; In Odiham High St. 1-acre garden and paddocks. Old garden roses; shrubs; ramblers dripping from trees. Silver/pink border, long shrubaceous and colourful herbaceous borders; hosta beds and delphinium planting. Dry stone wall/alpines thriving. Grade II starred house. *Adm £2 Chd free. Suns June 30, July 7 (2-6); Wed July 10 (all day) also group visits welcome, please* **Tel 01256 702100**

Meadow House, nr Newbury See Berkshire

Maurys Mount &⚘❀ (Dr & Mrs P Burrows) Slab Lane, West Wellow. On A 36 midway between Salisbury and Southampton, Slab Lane is a turning between the roundabout and Red Rover Inn on A36 in West Wellow. An Edwardian style garden created over 3 generations of family. 10-acres of woodland, garden and paddocks incl young arboretum, conservatory, formal herb and kitchen gardens and mature trees incl 300yr old oak. Woodland walk with pond, orchard and wild-flower meadow. Jacob sheep, ducks, geese, hens and horses. TEAS in aid of Imperial Cancer Research Fund. *Adm £1.50 Chd 50p. Thurs May 23, (2-7.30) Sun June 2 (2-5)*

Merdon Manor &⚘❀ (Mr & Mrs J C Smith) Hursley, SW of Winchester. From A3090 Winchester-Romsey, at Standon turn on to rd to Slackstead; on 2m. 5 acres with panoramic views; herbaceous and rose borders; small secret walled water garden as seen on TV. Ha-ha and sheep. TEAS. *Adm £1.50 Chd 25p. Sun July 14 (2-6); also private visits welcome, please* **Tel 01962 775215 or 775281**

Merebimur &❀ (Mr & Mrs C Snelling) Mockbeggar. 3m N of Ringwood on the A338, turn E to Mockbeggar at The Old Beams Inn. Turn L at the next small Xrds and next L into New Rd. Limited parking at garden but parking on verge opp the end of New Rd via very short walk. ½-acre owner maintained garden with pond, lawns, pergola and mixed borders with many unusual plants. TEA. *Adm £1 Chd free. Sat, Sun July 13, 14 (10-5). Private visits welcome, please* **Tel 01425 473116**

Merrie Cottage &⚘ (Mr & Mrs C K Thornton) Woodgreen 3m N of Fordingbridge on A338 turn E to Woodgreen. Fork R at PO towards Godshill. Entrance 200 yds on L. Limited parking for disabled or park on common and walk down footpath. The irregular sloping shape offers vistas with a profusion of iris and primulas in May and June, followed by seed-grown lilies and wide variety of moisture lovers. There is no hard landscape or colour theme but interest is held throughout year. TEAS (Sun) TEA (Mon) at Applecroft. *Adm £1.50 Chd free. Sun, Mon June 16, 17 (2-5.30). Private visits welcome, please* **Tel 01725 512273**

Mill Court &⚘ (Leila Viscountess Hampden) Binsted, nr Alton. 2m E of Alton on A31. Signpost opp Hen & Chicken. 24 acres with 3 acres garden, woodland and river walk. Walled herbaceous border, rhododendrons, bulbs. Mixed shrubbery, vegetable garden and greenhouses. All surrounding Tudor barn. TEA. *Adm £2 Chd free. Sat, Sun May 18, 19 (2-6)*

Monxton Gardens &⚘⚘ 3m W of Andover, between A303 and A343; parking and teas at Field House. TEAS in aid of Church. *Combined adm £2 Chd free. Sun, Mon May 26, 27 (2-5.30)*
> **Bec House** &⚘ (Mr & Mrs Anthony Rushworth-Lund) Old rectory garden with spring bulbs and mature trees; rose garden, croquet lawn, orchard and new water garden. Ticket holders are welcome to picnic in paddock by stream. No cars
> **Field House** (Dr & Mrs Pratt) 2-acre garden made by owners with an air of tranquility, winding paths, 2 ponds one with frogs, herbaceous borders, foliage and kitchen garden
> **Hutchens Cottage** (Mr & Mrs R A Crick) ¾-acre cottage garden with old roses, clematis, shrubs, mature trees, small orchard; mixed thyme patch and kitchen garden
> **White Gables** (Mrs & Mrs D Eaglesham) Cottage style garden of ⅓ acre, leading down to Pill Hill Brook. Interesting shrubs, old roses and herbaceous plants

Moth House (Mrs I R B Perkins) Brown Candover. On B3046 from Alresford toBasingstoke in Brown Candover Village. 5m from Alresford, just past village green on L. 2-acre garden. Gold and silver garden. Herbaceous borders and shrub walk. Speciality -roses. TEAS. *Adm £1.50 Chd free. Sun June 30 (2-5.30)*

Mottisfont Abbey & Garden &⚘⚘ (The National Trust) Mottisfont, 4½m NW of Romsey. From A3057 Romsey-Stockbridge turn W at sign to Mottisfont. 4 wheelchairs and battery car service available at garden. 30 acres; originally a C12 Priory; landscaped grounds with spacious lawns bordering R Test; magnificent trees; remarkable ancient spring pre-dating the Priory; walled garden contains NT's famous collection of old-fashioned roses. Lunch and tea available in the Abbey. *Adm £4 Chd £2. March 31 to Oct 30 Sat to Wed (12-6) June only daily (12-8.30). For NGS Sun June 23 (12-8.30), last adm 7.30 pm*

Moundsmere Manor ⚘ (Mr & Mrs Andreae) 6m S of Basingstoke on B3046. Drive gates on L just after Preston Candover sign. Authentic Edwardian garden designed by Reginald Blomfield incl period greenhouse in full use. Formal rose garden and long herbaceous borders, unusual mature specimen trees and superb views over the Candover Valley. Coaches by appt. *Adm £2 Chd £1. Sun July 7 (2-6)*

¶Norsebury Gardens ⚘ Stoke Charity, nr Winchester. Just S of A30 and W of A34 2m from Sutton Scotney. Follow signs to Stoke Charity and Hunton. TEAS in aid of Stoke Charity Church. *Adm £2.50 Chd free. Sun, Mon April 14, 15 (2-5.30)*
> **¶Lower Norsebury** & (Mrs F Hughes-Onslow) Spring woodland walk
> **¶Norsebury House** ⚘⚘ (Mr & Mrs M Goranson) 16-acres incl paddocks. Fine views, garden in many sections incl topiary, rose garden, sunken garden. Pony rides. *Adm £2 Chd free. Sun, Mon Aug 25, 26 (2-5.30)*

North Ecchinswell Farm &⚘⚘ (Mr & Mrs Robert Henderson) Nr Newbury. Turn S off A339 Newbury-Basingstoke rd. House 1m from turning (sign-posted Ecchinswell and Bishops Green) on L-hand side. Approx 6-acre garden. Extensive woodland walks with stream and small lake; planting still being extended; carpets of wild flowers incl bluebells; bog plants and many shrubs, fine trees and small arboretum. TEA. *Adm £2 Chd free. Suns April 28, June 2 (Share to Ecchinswell Village Hall Appeal®). (2.30-5.30)*

Oakdene &⚘⚘ (Mr & Mrs Christopher Stanford) Sandleheath. Just into Sandleheath on the B3078, 1 from Fordingbridge on the RH-side immed beyond small church. Garden of nearly 2 acres with roses of all types incl rambler covered long pergola, 'white' and 'red' herbaceous beds, orchard with free-range hens, flower-bordered productive organic vegetable garden, dovecote with resident doves. TEAS in aid of St George's Church Damerham. *Adm £1.50 Chd 50p. Sun June 23, Tue June 25 (2-5.30). Private visits welcome, please* **Tel 01425 652133**

Oakley Manor &⚘⚘ (Mr & Mrs Priestley) Rectory Rd, Oakley. 5m W of Basingstoke. From Basingstoke towards Whitchurch on B3400 turn L Station Rd and follow signs. Bus 55a, 55b Basingstoke to Oakley. Large 5-acre garden surrounded by open farmland with comprehensive planting incl a conservation area. Mature trees, shrubs, perennials and annuals. Thatched Wendy House. TEA. Free parking at the Manor. *Combined adm with* **The Barn House** *£2 Chd free. Sun Aug 4 (2-5.30)*

The Old House &⚘ (Mr & Mrs M Jurgens) Bramley Road, Silchester; next to Roman Museum. Queen Anne rectory with large garden dating from 1920s with pergola, dell, ponds, spring bulbs, woodland carpeted with bluebells, well labelled collection of rhododendrons, camellias, azaleas, specimen trees and shrubs; easy walk to Roman town and medieval church. TEAS in aid of St Mary the Virgin Church, Silchester. *Adm £1.50 Chd 50p. Suns March 31, April 14, 28 May 19. Private parties welcome March to May, please* **Tel 01734 700240**

Old Meadows &✿❀ (Dr & Mrs J M Fowler) Silchester. Off A340 between Reading and Basingstoke. 1m S of Silchester on rd to Bramley, signposted at Xrds. 5 acres including walled potager. Herbaceous borders, meadow walk. TEAS. *Adm £1.50 Chd free (Share to Basingstoke North Hampshire Medical Fund®). Sun June 30 (11-6). Private visits welcome, July to Aug, please* Tel 01256 881450

¶**The Old Rectory** (Mr & Mrs Charles Vincent) West Tytherley. 10m E of Salisbury; 10m NW of Romsey; from A30 4½m W of Stockbridge take turn signed W Tytherley/Norman Court. In village take turning signed to Northaw School. Queen Anne house, Grade II listed (not open). Very extensive developments incl lake and rockery, waterfall with bridges. Gazebo, rope pergola walk. Traditional walled kitchen garden with full range of vegetables and fruit. In all 120 acres, incl thoroughbred stud with mares and foals. TEAS. *Adm £2 Chd 50p (Share to Jonathan Conville Memorial Trust®). Sun, Mon June 30, July 1 (2-6)*

The Old Vicarage ✿ (Sir Dermot & Lady De Trafford) Appleshaw. Take A342 Andover to Marlborough Rd, turn to Appleshaw 1m W of Weyhill, fork L at playing field, on L in village by clock. 2-acre walled garden mature trees, bush and rambler roses, shrub borders, shrubs and trees in grass; fruit and herb garden with box hedges. TEAS. *Adm £1.50 Chd free (Share to St Peter in the Wood Church, Appleshaw®). Sun June 23 (2-5)*

Paddocks Way &✿❀ (Mr & Mrs K Elcock) Brook. 1m W from junction 1 M27 on B3079 turn L into Canterton Manor Drive before Green Dragon. Country garden of ¾ acre. Maintained solely by plant loving owners. Mixed borders and island beds containing many interesting and unusual herbaceous perennials, grasses and shrubs grown for flower and foliage effect. Kitchen garden containing vegetables, fruit, greenhouse and frames. TEAS. *Adm £1.50 Chd 50p. Suns May 19, June 30, July 28, Sept 29 (11-5.30). Private visits welcome, please* Tel 01703 813297

Pennington Chase &✿❀ (Mrs V E Coates) 2m SW Lymington L off A337, at Pennington Cross roundabout. 2 acres, spring bulbs, flowering shrubs, azaleas, rhododendrons and a variety of trees. TEAS 50p. *Adm £1 Chd 50p. Suns March 17, May 12 (2-7)*

¶**Pumpkin Patch** ✿❀ (Richard & Jenny Henry) Leave A31 1m N Ringwood signed Poulner. 600yds toward town centre turn R by mobile garage into Seymour Rd. ½-acre garden positively invites you up the garden path! Densely planted mixed shrubs, climbers and herbaceous. Glass houses hold varied collections of plants incl succulents, orchids and other exotics. TEA. *Adm £1 Chd free (Share to Cystic Fibrosis Trust®). Sun, Mon May 26, 27, Sats June 8, 22 July 6, 20, Aug 10, Suns June 2, 16, 30, July 14, 28, Sept 15, Mon Aug 26 (10-5)*

Pylewell Park &✿ (The Lord Teynham) 2½ m E of Lymington beyond IOW car ferry. Large garden of botanical interest; good trees, flowering shrubs, rhododendrons, lake, woodland garden. *Adm £2.50 Chd 50p (Share to*

Wessex Regional Medical Oncology Unit®). Suns May 12, 19 (2-6). Private visits welcome, please Tel 01590 673010

Robins Return &✿❀ (John & Marjorie Ingrem) Tiptoe. 2m NE of New Milton. Take B3055, at Xrds by Tiptoe Church. Turn into Wootton Rd (signposted to Wootton). Garden 400yds on L. ⅔-acre garden. Wisteria pergola (35 yds long). An abundance of miniature roses and box edgings; ornamental pool and rock gardens; newish fern garden, greenhouses, organic kitchen garden. TEAS. *Adm £1 Chd free (Share to the Evangelical Aid Relief Tear Fund®). Sun, Wed June 9, 12, July 14, 17 (2-5)*

Rookley Manor &✿ (Lord & Lady Inchyra) Up Somborne. 6m W of Winchester. From A272 Winchester-Stockbridge Rd. At Rack and Manger turn L towards Kings Somborne. 2m on R. 2 acres; spring bulbs, flowers and blossom; herbaceous, shrub roses, kitchen garden. TEAS. *Adm £1.50 Chd 20p. Mon May 6 (2-6)*

Rosewood Farm &✿❀ (Mr & Mrs D Bowman) Frenchmoor, West Tytherley. 10m E of Salisbury, 10m NW of Romsey. From A30 4½m W of Stockbridge take turn S signed West Tytherley - Norman Court. Continue through village on rd to West Dean after ½m L signed to Frenchmoor. Flower arrangers garden of 1 acre created since 1990 with extensive views in noise free setting, large range of foliage plants and trees, waterfall and lily pond. Cream TEAS. *Adm £1.50 Chd free. Sun June 2 (2-6)*

Rowans Wood &✿❀ (Mrs D C Rowan) Straight Mile, Ampfield, on A31 (S side); 2m E of Romsey. 2m W of Potters Heron Hotel. Parking on service Rd. Woodland garden planted for yr-round interest. Camellias, rhododendrons, flowering trees, spring bulbs followed by azaleas, hostas and other perennials. Views. TEAS. *Adm £1.50 Chd free (Share to Winchester & Romsey Branch RSPCA®). Suns April 21, 28 (2-5), May 19, 26, Mon May 27 (2-6). Parties welcome, mid April to end May, please* Tel 01794 513072

12 Rozelle Close ✿ (Margaret & Tom Hyatt) Littleton. Turn E off A272 Winchester to Stockbridge Rd. Just inside Winchester 40 mph zone. 1m Hookers Nursery on R. Rozelle Close 150yds on L just short of Running Horse public house. ⅓-acre spectacular display of herbaceous and 10,000 bedding plants; tubs; troughs; hanging baskets; 2 ponds; 3 greenhouses; vegetables. *Donations. (Share to Littleton and Haverstock New Memorial Hall®). Suns July 14, 28, Sat July 27 (9.30-5.30)*

Rumsey Gardens &✿❀ (Mr & Mrs N R Giles) 117 Drift Rd, Clanfield, 6m S of Petersfield. Turn off A3 N of Horndean, signed Clanfield. Planting of garden from a cornfield began during 1956 in poor shallow chalk soil. Acid beds have been constructed enabling lime hating shrubs and plants to be grown. Rock garden, heather beds, pools and bog gardens have been laid out. Collection of cotoneasters. TROBI/NCCPG. *Adm £1 Chd 50p. Sun May 5 (11-5). Private visits by societies welcome, please* Tel 01705 593367

3 St Helens Road &❀ (Mr & Mrs Norman Vaughan) Hayling Island. From Beachlands on seafront, turn R 3rd turning on R into Staunton Avenue, then 1st L. Parking in drive. ⅓-acre ornamental garden with conifers in variety. Interesting trees and shrubs; water garden; old roses; fine lawns. Prizewinning garden featured in 'Amateur Gardening'. TEAS. *Adm by donation. Sat, Sun May 18, 19 (11-5)*

Shalden Park House &❀ (Mr & Mrs Michael Campbell) Shalden. Take B3349 from either Alton or M3 intersection 5. Turn W at Xrds by The Golden Pot Public House marked Herriard, Lasham, Shalden. Garden is ¼m on L. 4-acre woodland garden with extensive views. Pond with duckhouse. Walled kitchen garden. Herbaceous borders. Beds of annuals. Glasshouses. Embryonic arboretum with wild flower walk. Lunchtime picnickers welcome. TEAS. *Adm £1.50 Chd free (Share to The Red Cross®). Sun April 28 (12-5)*

South End House &❀ (Mr & Mrs Peter Watson) Lymington. At town centre, turn S opp St Thomas Church 70yds, or park free behind Waitrose and use walkway. Walled town garden to Queen Anne house. ¼-acre, architecturally designed as philosophers' garden. Pergolas, trellises and colonnade attractively planted with vines, clematis, wisteria and roses, combine with sculpted awnings to form 'outdoor rooms', enhanced by fountains, music and lights. Featured on TV 'That's Gardening' and NGS video 2. TEAS. Opening with **Ewell House, 44 Belmore Lane, q.v.** Plants for sale at Ewell House. *Combined adm £2 Chd free. Sun May 5 (2-5.30). Private visits welcome, please* **Tel 01590 676848**

Southview ❀❀ (Mr & Mrs Mark Trenear) Chequers Lane, Eversley Cross. Signposted from A30 (W of Blackbush Airport) and from B3272 2m W of Yateley. Turn up Chequers Lane alongside the Chequers Inn. Car park signposted. A plantsman's garden with well designed areas incl old pinks, Roman garden, white garden, herbaceous areas and many unusual plants. Featured on TV twice in 1993. TEAS in aid of St Mary's Church Extension Fund. *Adm £1 Chd 50p. Sun June 16 (2-6)*

Sowley House &❀❀ (Mr & Mrs O Van Der Vorm) Sowley. At Lymington follow signs to I.O.W. ferry. Continue E on this rd past the ferry nearest to the Solent for 3m until Sowley pond on L. Sowley House is opp the pond. Beautiful setting overlooking Solent and I.O.W. of 19 acres at high tide and 52 acres at low tide, stream walk, wild garden with drifts of primroses and violets. Helleborus collection is a feature, woodland and walled herb garden with varied planting; roses, clematis. TEAS. *Adm £2 Chd free (Share to Oakhaven Hospice Lymington®). Sat March 23 (2-5). Private visits welcome, please* **Tel 01590 626231**

Spinners ❀❀ (Mr & Mrs P G G Chappell) Boldre. Signed off the A337 Brockenhurst-Lymington Rd (do not take sign to Boldre Church). Azaleas, rhododendrons, magnolias, hydrangeas, maples etc interplanted with a wide range of choice herbaceous plants and bulbs. Nursery specialises in the less common and rare hardy shrubs and plants. *Adm £1.50 Chd under six free. April 14 to Sept 14 daily (10-5) except Suns and Mons (but open Suns in*

May). Nursery and part of garden open at the same times over the winter. **Tel 01590 673347)**

Springfield ❀ (Vice-Adm Sir John & Lady Lea) 27 Brights Lane, Hayling Island. From Havant take main rd over Hayling bridge, 3m fork R at roundabout into Manor Rd, Brights Lane ¼m on R. Bus: from Havant, ask for Manor Rd, Hayling Island, alight at Manor Rd PO. This medium sized walled Victorian cottage garden, seen several times on TV, has been gradually altered over the years to produce borders massed with unusual as well as traditional plants surrounding the central lawn and young mulberry tree. The productive vegetable areas and greenhouses keep some of the cottage garden feel. Plants for sale depending on stocks. Partially suited for wheelchairs. *Adm by donation Sat June 15 (11-5). Private visits welcome, please* **Tel 01705 463801**

22 Springvale Road ❀ (Mr & Mrs Fry) Kingsworthy. N end of Springwell Rd. Kingsworthy almost opp Dairiall's shop. ¾ acre. End March, early April for magnolias, snowdrops, crocuses and daffodils. From late June: a large and comprehensive display of Agapanthus Headbourne Hybrids being Lewis Palmer's stock: he lived nearby. Sept for drifts of cyclamen, heathers and fine display of foliage. *Adm by Donation. Tues July 23. Private visits welcome, please* **Tel 01962 882288**

● **Stratfield Saye House** &❀ (Home of the Dukes of Wellington) Off A33, equidistant between Reading and Basingstoke. House built 1630; presented to the Great Duke in 1817; unique collection of paintings, prints, furniture, china, silver and personal mementoes of the Great Duke. Special Wellington Exhibition; Great Duke's funeral carriage. 3½-acre walled garden with fruit, vegetables, herbs and greenhouses. Large rose garden. Early C19 garden created by the 1st Duke with many plants of American origin: leading to Park with magnificent specimen trees incl Wellingtonia, and riverside walk with wild fowl. Refreshments. Also, nearby, Wellington Country Park with woodlands, meadowlands and lake. TEAS. *Adm £4.50 Chd £2.25 special rates for 20 or more.* **Tel 01256 882882.** *Open daily (except Fri) May 1 until the last Sun in Sept. House (12-4), grounds (11.30-6). For NGS Mon May 6. Adm to grounds £2 Chd £1 (11.30-6)*

Swallowfield Park, nr Reading see Berkshire

¶**Swarraton Gardens** &❀❀ 3½m N of Alresford off B3046 close to the main entrance to The Grange. Follow English Heritage signs to The Grange. From Winchester, take A33 turning N at Roman Post (formerly Lunways Inn), follow signs to Northington and The Grange. TEAS. *Combined adm £2.50 Chd free (Share to The Friends of St John's Church, Northington®). Sun, Tues July 14, 16 (2-6)*

  ¶**The Clock House** (Mr & Mrs Michael Brodrick) Colourful garden of about 1¼ acres which is still being developed with mixed borders, many clematis, roses and hardy geraniums. Large vegetable garden and trained fruit

  ¶**Meadow Lodge** (Mr & Mrs D W Hardy) Small cottage garden, many varieties of fuchsias; hanging baskets, pergola, hens, horses and sheep

Tunworth Old Rectory &✿ (The Hon Mrs Julian Berry) 5m SE of Basingstoke. 3m from Basingstoke turn S off A30 at sign to Tunworth. Garden laid out with yew hedges, enclosing different aspects of the garden i.e. swimming pool, double rose and mixed border; ruby wedding garden; pleached hornbeam walk; lime avenue, ornamental pond, interesting trees incl beech lined walk to church. TEAS. *Adm £2 OAP £1 Chd free (Share to All Saints Church Tunworth®). Sun June 30 (2-5.30)*

Tylney Hall Hotel &✿✿ From M3 Exit 5 Via A287 and Newnham, M4 Exit 11 via B3349 and Rotherwick. Large garden. 67 acres surrounding Tylney Hall Hotel with extensive Woodlands and fine vistas now being fully restored with new plantings; fine avenues of Wellingtonias; rhododendron and azaleas; Italian Garden; lakes; large water and rock garden and dry stone walls originally designed with assistance of Gertrude Jekyll. TEA. *Adm £2 Chd free. Suns May 19, June 9, 30 (2-6)*

Upham Gardens 3m Bishops Waltham on A333, small R turn to Upham by Woodmans Public House. TEAS. *Combined adm £2 or £1 per garden Chd free. Sun, Wed June 16, 19 (11-5)*

  The Old Rectory (Mr & Mrs J R Vail) beside church. Enclosed village garden, small woodland area, kitchen parterre, mixed borders, knot garden
  Upham Farm (Mr & Mrs J Walker) Garden made over last 10 yrs; herbaceous, trellis garden of old roses. Walk to small lake with ornamental ducks, wild fowl

¶**Valentine Cottage** &✿✿ (Gill Brown) Newnham Rd. From Hook follow A30 towards Basingstoke. After approx 1m at The Dorchester Arms public house turn R into School Lane signposted Newnham. At the end of School Lane turn L into Newnham Rd and 200yds on the R is the car park at Village Hall. 25yd walk along Newnham Rd to Valentine Cottage. Approx ⅓-acre developed over the last 4yrs into a cottage garden divided into individual compartments specialising in clematis and roses. TEAS. *Adm £1.50 Chd 50p. Sun July 7 (2-6)*

Vernon Hill House ✿ (Mr & Mrs F C Fryer) ½m N of Bishop's Waltham roundabout, turn off B3035 into Beeches Hill and follow garden signs. Attractive 6-acre spring and summer garden; wild garden with bulbs growing informally; fine trees, roses, unusual shrubs; kitchen garden. Picnickers welcome. TEA. *Adm £1.25 Chd 25p. Sun, Mon May 5, 6; Suns June 9, 30 (2-7); also private parties welcome May to early July, please* **Tel 01489 892301**

Verona Cottage ✿✿ (David J Dickinson Esq) 6 Webb Lane, Mengham. Entrance opp the Rose in June public house. Arranged on 3 levels; 3 contrasting but linked gardens with ideas for everyone with a small garden. Wide range of shrubs, spring bulbs and flowers, paved areas, iris, all within a walled garden 500 metres from the sea. It is an oasis by a main road. TEA (Sun). *Adm £1 Chd free. Sat, Sun May 18, 19 (11-5.30)*

The Vyne &✿✿ (The National Trust) Sherborne St John, 4m N of Basingstoke. Between Sherborne St John and Bramley. From A340 turn E at NT signs. 17 acres with extensive lawns, lake, fine trees, herbaceous border. Garden tours will incl developments made possible by NGS funding. Gardeners available to answer questions. TEAS. *Adm house & garden £4 Chd £2; garden only £2 Chd £1.* ▲*For NGS Suns May 19, July 21 (12.30-5.30)*

Waldrons &✿✿ (Major & Mrs J Robinson) Brook, Lyndhurst. 1m W from exit 1 M27 (on A3079). 1st house L past the Green Dragon public house and directly opp the Bell Inn. A C18 listed cottage with a conservatory, in a garden of 1 acre, containing lawns; a herbaceous border, shrubs and flower beds created around old orchard trees. Small duck pond (free roaming call ducks); fruit cage, herb garden, arbour, rose trellis, raised alpine garden and a small stable yard. TEAS. *Adm £1.50 Chd free. Suns May 19 June 30 (11-5.30)*

Walhampton &✿ (Walhampton School Trust) Lymington. 1m along B3054 to Beaulieu. 90 acres with azaleas; rhododendrons; lakes; shell grotto. TEAS. *Adm £1 Chd 50p. Sun May 19 (2-6)*

¶**2 Warren Farm Cottages** ✿✿ (Dr & Mrs J G Mitchell) West Tytherley, 10m E of Salisbury, 10m NW of Romsey. From A30 4½m W of Stockbridge take turn S signed West Tytherley - Norman Court. 3rd house on R, approx 1.9m. Park along rd. A working cottage garden of ⅓ acre in remote location. 100 plus labelled hardy geraniums, cottage plants, pots of vegetables. Shade area for ferns and hostas, good late season interest interspersed by lounging cats and busy wildlife. *Adm £1 Chd 50p. Suns June 2, 30 (10-6), Fris May 1 to Sept 30 (10-6)* **Tel 01980 863101**

Warwick House ✿✿ (Mrs Lucy Marson) Wickham. 2½m N of Fareham on A32. Park in square or signed car park. Warwick House is in Bridge St. Turn R at the end of the square furthest from the Winchester Rd. Teas available in the Square. ⅛-acre intimate walled town garden with interesting and contrasting planting. Paved courtyard, troughs. Ornamental vegetable and herb garden. *Adm £1 Chd free. Wed, Sun June 5, 23 (11-6). Private visits welcome between June 1 and 30, please* **Tel 01329 832313**

West Silchester Hall &✿ (Mrs Jenny Jowett) Bramley Rd, Silchester. Off A340 between Reading and Basingstoke. 1½ acres, plantsman's garden, a good collection of herbaceous plants, rose and shrub borders, rhododendrons and many acid loving plants, small pond and bog garden, and interesting display of half hardies, kitchen garden, and owner maintained. Exhibition of Jenny Jowett's botanical paintings. TEAS. *Adm £1.50 Chd 50p. Suns June 9, Aug 4, Mon Aug 5 (2-6). Parties by appt March-Sept, please* **Tel 01734 700278**

Westbrook House ✿✿ (Andrew Lyndon-Skeggs) Howards Lane, Holybourne. Turn off A31 at roundabout immed to NE of Alton towards Holybourne/Alton 1st R to Holybourne. 1st L up towards Lane on R. 2½ acres with continuing design and development. Mature trees and impressive formal planting of shrubs and herbaceous with 'maze' garden leading to orchard, woodland, stream and unexpected view. CREAM TEAS. *Adm £1.50 Chd free. Sun June 23 (2.30-5.30)*

¶The White Cottage ఉ⚹❀ (Mr & Mrs P Conyers) 35 Wellhouse Rd. Beech, nr Alton. Leave Alton on Basingstoke Rd A339. After approx 1m turn L to Medstead and Beech. Wellhouse Rd is 2nd turning on R. Parking at village hall at bottom of rd, limited parking outside house. 1-acre chalk garden with a wide range of unusual shrubs and plants; many hardy geraniums, and in the spring hellebores and bulbs. Conservatory with exotics, large collection of carnivorous plants, pond and scree bed. TEA. *Adm £1.50 Chd free. Sun March 3 (11-6) Suns, Mons June 9, 10, July 14, 15, Aug 11, 12 (Suns 11-6, Mons 2- 6). Private visits welcome, please* Tel 01420 89355

White Windows ఉ⚹❀ (Mr & Mrs B Sterndale-Bennett) Longparish, Nr Andover. E of Andover off A303 to village centre on B3048. ⅔-acre with unusual range of hardy perennials, trees and shrubs planted for yr-round foliage interest and colour blendings in garden rooms, incl many hellebores, hardy geraniums and euphorbias. Garden featured on TV and in books and magazines. TEAS except Mon April 22. *Adm £1.50 Chd free. Sun, Mon April 21, 22 (1-5) Sun Sept 22 (2-6). Private visits welcome Weds April to Sept, please* Tel 01264 720222

Wonston Lodge ఉ (Mr & Mrs N J A Wood) Wonston. A34 or A30 to Sutton Scotney. At War Memorial turn to Wonston-Stoke Charity; ¾m in Wonston centre. 3 acres, owner maintained. Pond with aquatic plants and ornamental ducks; shrub roses; clematis; topiary. TEAS in barn. *Adm £1.50 Chd free. Sun, Mon Aug 25, 26 (2-6)*

Hereford & Worcester

Hon County Organisers:	(Hereford) Lady Curtis, Tarrington Court, nr Hereford HR1 4EX
	(Worcester) Mrs Barbara Andrews, Cedar Lodge, Blakeshall, Wolverley, nr Kidderminster DY11 5XR Tel 01562 850238
Assistant County Organisers	(Worcester) Mrs Jeanie Neil, Viewlands, Blakeshall, Wolverley, nr Kidderminster DY11 5XL Tel 01562 850360
	(Worcester) Mrs Jane Carr, Conderton Manor, nr Tewkesbury, Glos GL20 7PR
	(Hereford) Mr & Mrs Roger Norman, Marley Bank, Whitbourne, Worcester WR6 5RU
	(Hereford) Dr J A F Evans, The Lawns, Nunnington, Hereford HR1 3NJ Tel 01432 850664
Hon County Treasurer	(Worcester) Mrs Elizabeth Anton, Summerway, Torton, nr Kidderminster Tel 01299 250388
	(Hereford) Mr M Robins, Bursar, Royal National College for the Blind, College Road, Hereford HR8 2AN

DATES OF OPENING

February 22 Thursday
Dial Park, Chaddesley Corbett
March 17 Sunday
Holland House, Cropthorne
March 21 Thursday
The Cottage, Broughton Green
March 24 Sunday
Kyre Park, Tenbury Wells
Little Malvern Court, nr Malvern
March 31 Sunday
Ripple Hall, nr Tewkesbury
Witley Park House, Great Witley
April
Eastgrove Cottage Garden
Nursery, Shrawley

Thurs to Mon
April 5 Friday
Arrow Cottage,
nr Weobley
Spetchley Park, nr Worcester
White Cottage, Stock Green,
nr Inkberrow
April 6 Saturday
Arrow Cottage, nr Weobley
White Cottage, Stock Green,
nr Inkberrow
April 7 Sunday
Arrow Cottage, nr Weobley
White Cottage, Stock Green,
nr Inkberrow
Whitlenge House Cottage,
Hartlebury

April 8 Monday
Stone House Cottage Gardens,
Stone
White Cottage, Stock Green,
nr Inkberrow
Whitlenge House Cottage,
Hartlebury
April 14 Sunday
Garnons, nr Hereford
Lower Hope, Ullingswick
April 17 Wednesday
Arrow Cottage, nr Weobley
April 18 Thursday
The Cottage, Broughton Green
April 21 Sunday
Arrow Cottage, nr Weobley
Barbers, Martley, nr Worcester

April 27 Saturday
Eastgrove Cottage Garden
 Nursery, Shrawley
April 28 Sunday
Barnard's Green House, Malvern
Stone House, Scotland,
 Wellington
May
Eastgrove Cottage Garden
 Nursery, Shrawley
 Thurs to Mon
May 2 Thursday
The Manor House, Birlingham,
 nr Pershore
May 4 Saturday
White Cottage, Stock Green,
 nr Inkberrow
May 5 Sunday
Arley House, Upper Arley,
 nr Bewdley
Arrow Cottage, nr Weobley
Brilley Court, nr Whitney on Wye
Staunton Park, Staunton on Arrow
Stone House Cottage Gardens,
 Stone ‡
Strawberry Cottage, Hamnish
White Cottage, Stock Green,
 nr Inkberrow
Windyridge, Kidderminster ‡
May 6 Monday
The Manor House, Birlingham,
 nr Pershore
Stone House Cottage Gardens,
 Stone
White Cottage, Stock Green,
 nr Inkberrow
May 8 Wednesday
Monsieur's Hall, Bromsgrove
May 10 Friday
The Manor House, Birlingham,
 nr Pershore
May 12 Sunday
The Coach House, Eckington
Priors Court, Long Green
Spetchley Park, nr Worcester
Windyridge, Kidderminster
May 16 Thursday
The Cottage, Broughton Green
The Manor House, Birlingham,
 nr Pershore
May 19 Sunday
Astley Horticultural Society,
 Astley Cross
Bodenham Arboretum, Wolverley
Bryan's Ground, Stapleton
The Coach House, Eckington
Elmbury, 98 Aylestone Hill.
 Hereford
Lingen Nursery & Garden,
 Lingen
Nafford House, Eckington
Strawberry Cottage, Hamnish
May 20 Monday
Ivytree House, Clent

May 22 Wednesday
Ivytree House, Clent
May 23 Thursday
The Manor House, Birlingham,
 nr Pershore
Torwood, Whitchurch
May 25 Saturday
White Cottage, Stock Green,
 nr Inkberrow
May 26 Sunday
Arrow Cottage, nr Weobley
The Priory, Kemerton
Red House Farm, Bradley Green
Stone House, Scotland,
 Wellington
Stone House Cottage Gardens,
 Stone ‡
White Cottage, Stock Green,
 nr Inkberrow
Whitlenge House Cottage,
 Hartlebury ‡
May 27 Monday
The Manor House, Birlingham,
 nr Pershore
Stone House Cottage Gardens,
 Stone ‡
White Cottage, Stock Green,
 nr Inkberrow
Whitlenge House Cottage,
 Hartlebury ‡
May 29 Wednesday
Arrow Cottage, nr Weobley
St Egwins Cottage, Norton,
 Evesham
May 30 Thursday
The Manor House, Birlingham,
 nr Pershore
21 Swinton Lane, Worcester
Strawberry Cottage, Hamnish
June
Eastgrove Cottage Garden
 Nursery, Shrawley
 Thurs to Mon
June 1 Saturday
White Cottage, Stock Green,
 nr Inkberrow
June 2 Sunday
Arrow Cottage, nr Weobley
Ash Farm, Much Birch
Caves Folly Nusery, Colwall
 Green ‡
Frogmore, nr Ross on Wye
Hartlebury Castle, nr
 Kidderminster
Lingen Nursery & Garden, Lingen
Longacre, Colwall Green ‡
Lower Hope, Ullingswick
St Egwins Cottage, Norton,
 Evesham
Strawberry Cottage, Hamnish
21 Swinton Lane, Worcester
White Cottage, Stock Green,
 nr Inkberrow
Woodmancote, Wadborough

June 5 Wednesday
St Egwins Cottage, Norton,
 Evesham
June 9 Sunday
How Caple Court, Ross on Wye
Pershore College of Horticulture
Staunton Park, Staunton on
 Arrow
Stone House Cottage Gardens,
 Stone
Torwood, Whitchurch
Whitfield, Wormbridge
June 12 Wednesday
The Manor House, Birlingham,
 nr Pershore
June 13 Thursday
Red House Farm, Bradley Green
Torwood, Whitchurch
June 15 Saturday
White Cottage, Stock Green,
 nr Inkberrow
June 16 Sunday
Bell's Castle, Kemerton ‡
Birtsmorton Court, nr Malvern ‡
Brook House, Colwall
Cedar Lodge, Blakeshall,
 nr Wolverley
Moccas Court, nr Hereford
Orchard Bungalow, Bishops Frome
Overcourt Garden Nursery,
 Sutton St Nicholas
Pershore Gardens, Pershore
Upper Court, Kemerton ‡
White Cottage, Stock Green,
 nr Inkberrow
June 17 Monday
Ivytree House, Clent
June 19 Wednesday
Ivytree House, Clent
The Manor House, Birlingham,
 nr Pershore
St Egwins Cottage, Norton,
 Evesham
June 20 Thursday
The Cottage, Broughton Green
The Cottage Herbery, Boraston,
 Tenbury Wells
Strawberry Cottage, Hamnish
June 21 Friday
Bryan's Ground, Stapleton
June 22 Saturday
Abberley Gardens, nr Worcester
Hergest Croft Gardens, Kington
June 23 Sunday
Abberley Gardens, nr Worcester
The Bannut, Bringsty, Bromyard
Coddington Vineyard, nr Ledbury
The Elms, Lower Broadheath
Grantsfield, nr Leominster
Holland House, Cropthorne
Linton Hall, Gorsley
The Priory, Kemerton
Stone House, Scotland,
 Wellington

Stone House Cottage Gardens,
Stone
Strawberry Cottage, Hamnish
Torwood, Whitchurch
June 24 Monday
Linton hall, Gorsley
June 25 Tuesday
Croft Castle, Kingsland
June 26 Wednesday
The Manor House, Birlingham,
nr Pershore
June 27 Thursday
The Cottage Herbery, Boraston,
Tenbury Wells
Dial Park, Chaddesley Corbett
Monsieur's Hall, Bromsgrove
21 Swinton Lane, Worcester
June 30 Sunday
Arrow Cottage, nr Weobley
Astley Horticultural Society,
Astley Cross
Berrington Hall, Leominster
Brilley Court, nr Whitney on Wye
Brook Cottage, Lingen
Lingen Nursery & Garden, Lingen
21 Swinton Lane, Worcester
Well Cottage, Lingen
Woodmancote, Wadborough
July
Eastgrove Cottage Garden
Nursery, Shrawley
Thurs to Mon
July 3 Wednesday
The Manor House, Birlingham,
nr Pershore
July 4 Thursday
The Cottage Herbery, Boraston,
Tenbury Wells
July 6 Saturday
28 Cornmeadow Lane, Claines,
Worcester
July 7 Sunday
Arrow Cottage, nr Weobley
Bredenbury Court (St Richards),
Bredenbury
Broadway, Snowshill Road
Gardens
Hanbury Hall, nr Droitwich
Lakeside, Whitbourne
Lower Hope, Ullingswick
St Egwins Cottage, Norton,
Evesham
Spetchley Park, nr Worcester ‡
Strawberry Cottage, Hamnish
Torwood, Whitchurch
Yew Tree House, Ombersley ‡
July 10 Wednesday
The Manor House, Birlingham,
nr Pershore
Monsieur's Hall, Bromsgrove
St Egwins Cottage, Norton,
Evesham
July 11 Thursday
Strawberry Cottage, Hamnish

Torwood, Whitchurch
July 13 Saturday
Barnard's Green House, Malvern
Eastgrove Cottage Garden
Nursery, Shrawley
July 14 Sunday
Arley Cottage, Upper Arley,
nr Bewdley
Arrow Cottage, nr Weobley
The Bannut, Bringsty, Bromyard
Orchard Bungalow, Bishops Frome
Pedwardine Cottage, Brampton
Bryan
The Priory, Kemerton
Stone House, Scotland,
Wellington
Witley Park House, Great Witley
July 15 Monday
Ivytree House, Clent
July 17 Wednesday
Ivytree House, Clent
July 19 Thursday
The Cottage, Broughton Green
July 21 Sunday
Arrow Cottage, nr Weobley
Caves Folly Nusery, Colwall Green
Lingen Nursery & Garden, Lingen
Torwood, Whitchurch
July 24 Wednesday
Arrow Cottage, nr Weobley
July 25 Thursday
21 Swinton Lane, Worcester
July 27 Saturday
Wych & Colwall Horticulture
Society Show
July 28 Sunday
Arrow Cottage, nr Weobley
Eastgrove Cottage Garden
Nursery, Shrawley
Red House Farm, Bradley Green
Strawberry Cottage, Hamnish
21 Swinton Lane, Worcester
July 31 Wednesday
Arrow Cottage, nr Weobley
August 4 Sunday
The Priory, Kemerton
Torwood, Whitchurch
August 11 Sunday
The Bannut, Bringsty, Bromyard ‡
Brookside, Bringsty ‡
St Egwins Cottage, Norton,
Evesham
Strawberry Cottage, Hamnish
August 14 Wednesday
St Egwins Cottage, Norton,
Evesham
August 15 Thursday
Arrow Cottage, nr Weobley
The Cottage, Broughton Green
August 18 Sunday
Coddington Vineyard, nr Ledbury
August 22 Thursday
Arrow Cottage, nr Weobley
Strawberry Cottage, Hamnish

August 24 Saturday
Monnington Court, Monnington
on Wye
August 25 Sunday
Barnard's Green House,
Malvern
Monnington Court, Monnington
on Wye
Orchard Bungalow, Bishops
Frome
The Priory, Kemerton
Stone House Cottage Gardens,
Stone ‡
Strawberry Cottage,
Hamnish
Whitlenge House Cottage,
Hartlebury ‡
August 26 Monday
Monnington Court, Monnington
on Wye
Stone House Cottage Gardens,
Stone ‡
Whitlenge House Cottage,
Hartlebury ‡
September
Eastgrove Cottage Garden
Nursery, Shrawley
Thurs to Sats
September 1 Sunday
Arrow Cottage, nr Weobley
September 5 Thursday
The Manor House, Birlingham,
nr Pershore
September 8 Sunday
The Priory, Kemerton
September 12 Thursday
The Manor House, Birlingham,
nr Pershore
September 14 Saturday
White Cottage, Stock Green,
nr Inkberrow
September 15 Sunday
White Cottage, Stock Green,
nr Inkberrow
September 19 Thursday
The Cottage, Broughton Green
The Manor House, Birlingham,
nr Pershore
September 22 Sunday
Lingen Nursery & Garden,
Lingen
September 26 Thursday
Dial Park, Chaddesley Corbett
The Manor House, Birlingham,
nr Pershore
September 29 Sunday
Kyre Park, Tenbury Wells
October 13 Sunday
Nerine Nursery, Welland
October 20 Sunday
The Coach House, Eckington
October 27 Sunday
The Coach House, Eckington

1997
February 21 Thursday
Dial Park, Chaddesley Corbett

Regular openings
For details see garden description

Abbey Dore Court, nr Hereford
Barnard's Green House, Malvern
Bryan's Ground, Stapleton
The Cottage Herbery, Boraston,
  Tenbury Wells
Eastgrove Cottage Garden Nursery,
  Shrawley
The Elms, Lower Broadheath
Hergest Croft Gardens, Kington

How Capel Court, Ross on Wye
Kingstone Cottages, Ross on Wye
Kyre Park, Tenbury Wells
Lingen Nursery and Garden, Lingen
The Manor House, Birlingham, nr
  Pershore
The Marsh Country Hotel, Eyton
The Picton Garden, Colwall
The Priory, Kemerton
Staunton Park, Staunton on Arrow
Stone House Cottage Gardens, Stone
Strawberry Cottage, Hamnish
White Cottage, Stock Green, nr
  Inkberrow
Whitlenge House Cottage, Hartlebury

By appointment only
*For telephone numbers and other
details see garden descriptions.
Private visits welcomed*

Bredon Pound, Ashton under Hill
Conderton Manor, nr Tewkesbury
Keepers Cottage, Alvechurch
Overbury Court, nr Tewkesbury
Well Cottage, Blakemere

> The National Gardens Scheme is
> a charity which traces its origins
> back to 1927. Since then it has
> raised a total of over £14 million
> for charitable purposes.

DESCRIPTIONS OF GARDENS

Abberley Gardens ✗❀ 12m NW of Worcester on A443. Collection of gardens in and around the village of Abberley. Many with interesting plants and fine views of area. Individual details of gardens and maps provided. Flower festival in Church. TEAS. *Combined adm £2 OAP's 50p Chd free (Share to Abberley PCC®). Sat June 22 (11-6) Sun June 23 (12-5)*

● **Abbey Dore Court** &✗❀ (Mrs C L Ward) 11m SW of Hereford. From A465 midway between Hereford-Abergavenny turn W, signed Abbey Dore; then 2½m. 5 acres bordered by R Dore of rambling and semi formal garden with unusual shrubs, perennials and many clematis in large borders. Pond and rock garden made in a field recently enlarged. River walk with ferns and hellebores leading to a fairly new area, on the site of an old barn and roadway, planted for foliage colour. Large collection of late summer anemones. NCCPG Euphorbia collection. Featured in NGS video 1. Many unusual plants for sale. Out of the ordinary gift gallery. Coffee, lunch and TEAS (11-5). *Adm £1.75 Chd 50p (Share to Mother Theresa®). Sat March 2 to Sun Oct 20 daily except Weds (11-6). Earlier visits for hellebores welcome, please* **Tel 01981 240419**

Arley Cottage & (Woodward family) Upper Arley, nr Bewdley. 5m N of Kidderminster off A442. Small country garden with lawns bordered by interesting shrubs and collection of rare trees. Cream TEAS. *Adm £1 Chd free (Share to Lane-Fox Unit, St Thomas' Hospital, London®). Sun July 14 (2-5)*

Arley House ✗ (R D Turner Esq) Upper Arley, 5m N of Kidderminster. A442. Arboretum containing specimen conifers and hardwoods, rhododendrons, camellias, magnolias, heathers; Italianate garden; greenhouses with orchids, alpines. Aviary with ornamental pheasants, budgerigars. TEA. *Adm £1.50 Chd free (Share to St Peter's, Upper Arley®). Sun May 5 (2-7)*

Arrow Cottage ✗❀ (Mr & Mrs L Hattatt) nr Weobley. From Weobley take unclassified rd direction Wormsley (Kings Pyon/Canon Pyon). After 1m, turn L signposted Ledgemoor. 2nd R (no through rd). 1st house on L. Formal design elements link a series of carefully planted garden rooms in this 2-acre plantsman's garden. A newly developed gothic garden is in addition to C19 shrub roses, white and green gardens, kitchen garden, herbaceous borders and natural stream, all maintained to a high standard. Featured on Channel 4 TV 1991 and Central TV 1993 and incl in the Good Gardens Guide. Rare and beautiful hardy plants are propagated for sale. The garden is unsuitable for children. TEAS if fine. *Adm £2. Weds, Fri, Sats, Suns April 5, 6, 7, 17, 21; May 5, 26, 29, June 2, 30, July 7, 14, 21, 24, 28, 31, Sept 1 (2-5). Thurs Aug 15, 22, (4-8). Private visits welcome, please* **Tel 01544 318468**

Ash Farm ✗ (David & Alison Lewis) Much Birch. From Hereford take A49 S to Much Birch (approx 7m). After the Pilgrim Hotel take 1st turning R at Xrds into Tump Lane. Garden is on L. Ample parking. Small walled farmhouse garden and ½-acre new garden created from old fold yard for all-yr interest over past 5 yrs. Small trees, herbaceous borders, blue and white borders. *Adm £1 Chd free. Sun June 2 (2-6)*

Astley Horticultural Society &❀ 3m W of Stourport on Severn on the B4196 to Worcester. Start the trail around the 3 villages from the Parish Room. Map provided **Spring opening** *Combined adm £1.50 Chd free (Share to Kemp House Hospice®). Sun May 19 (1-6)*
   The Sytch Terraced garden leading down to a ha-ha. Good vegetable garden and orchard to the rear
   6 Elm Grove ❀ Plantsman's garden with borders for all seasons and a raised pool. Small area for show vegetables
   The White House An attempt on a small scale (and small budget) to create a classical garden, follies and architectural features, long herbaceous border, pools and pergolas

Pool House Beautiful Strawberry Hill style house, surrounded by extensive grass with bulbs and wild flowers, which lead down to 3 large, well stocked pools. Old walled garden with rare climbers

Astley Town House A pretty black and white cottage. The garden has been created over the last 3yrs to a very ambitious design, and is now reaching maturity. Formal kitchen garden with central fountain, grass paths winding through shrub and herbaceous borders

Woodstock Fine collection of rhododendrons and other shrubs surrounding Scandinavian bungalow in an old orchard

Summer opening *Combined adm £2 Chd free. Sun June 30 (1-6)*

The Sytch (For details see above)

6 Elm Grove (For details see above)

Astley Town House (For details see above)

Swevenings & A developing garden on a series of terraces on a steep slope, leading down to a small pool

The White House (for details see above)

Koi Cottage A superb collection of Koi carp in a Japanese garden

Little Yarhampton Black and white with extensive formal gardens. Small arboretum and a lovely woodland walk. Magnificent views

Yarronbridge Old farmhouse above a restored water mill. Fine collection of old roses and other shrubs

The Conifers Magnificent display of hanging baskets and patio plants in a garden full of summer colour

Woodlands Farm Delicious cream TEAS on the lawn of an old farm house

The Bannut &❀ (Mr Maurice & Mrs Daphne Everett) Bringsty. 3m E of Bromyard on A44 Worcester Rd. (½m E of entrance to National Trust, Brockhampton). A 1-acre garden, planted with all-yr colour in mind; mainly established by the present owners since 1984. Mixed borders and island beds of trees, shrubs and herbaceous plants and a small 'damp' garden. Walls, pergola, and terraces around the house are used to display unusual climbers and colourful pots and urns. The heather garden designed around a Herefordshire cider mill and an unusual heather knot garden with water feature has appeared in several gardening magazines. Plants for sale. TEAS. *Adm £1.50 Chd free. Suns June 23, July 14, Aug 11 (2-5). Also groups by appt, please Tel 01885 482206*

Barbers &❀❀ (Mr & the Hon Mrs Richard Webb) Martley 7m NW of Worcester on B4204. Medium-sized garden with lawns, trees, shrubs, pools and wild garden. Cowslip and fritillary lawn. Home-made TEAS. *Adm £1.50 Chd free (Share to Martley Church®). Sun April 21 (2-6)*

Barnard's Green House &❀❀ (Mr & Mrs Philip Nicholls) 10 Poolbrook Rd, Malvern. On E side of Malvern at junction of B4211 and B4208. 3-acre cultivated garden; herbaceous, rockeries, heather beds, woodland/water garden, vegetable plot; several unusual plants and shrubs; 2 fine cedars, lawns. Mrs Nicholls is a specialist on dried flowers, on which she has written a book. Half-timbered house (not open) dates from 1635; home of Sir Charles Hastings, founder of BMA. Coach parties by appt. TEAS. *Adm £1.50 Acc chd free (Share to Save the Children Fund®). Sat July 13, Suns April 28, Aug 25 and every*

Thursday April to Sept incl. (2-6). Also private visits welcome, please Tel 01684 574446

Bell's Castle &❀ (Lady Holland-Martin) Kemerton, NE of Tewkesbury. 3 small terraces with battlements; wild garden outside wall. The small Gothic castellated folly was built by Edmund Bell (Smuggler) c1820; very fine views. TEAS. *Adm £1 Chd free. Sun June 16 (2-6). Parties welcome, please Tel 01386 725333*

Berrington Hall &❀ (The National Trust) 3m N of Leominster on A49. Signposted. Bus Midland Red (W) x 92, 292 alight Luston, 2m. Extensive views over Capability Brown Park; formal garden; wall plants, unusual trees, camellia collection, herbaceous plants, wisteria. Woodland walk, rhododendrons, walled garden with apple collection. Light lunches and TEAS. *Adm house & garden £3.80 Chd £1.90. Grounds only £1.70. ▲For NGS Sun June 30 (12.30-6)*

Birtsmorton Court &❀ (Mr & Mrs N G K Dawes) nr Malvern. 7m E of Ledbury on A438. Fortified manor house (not open) dating from C12; moat; Westminster pool, laid down in Henry V11's reign at time of consecration of Westminster Abbey; large tree under which Cardinal Wolsey reputedly slept in shadow of ragged stone. Topiary. Motor Museum extra. Featured in NGS video 1. TEAS. *Adm £2 Chd 50p. Sun June 16 (2-6)*

Bodenham Arboretum (Mr & Mrs J D Binnian) 2m N of Wolverley; 5m N of Kidderminster. From Wolverley Church follow signs. 134 acres landscaped and planted during the past 21 years; 2 chains of lakes and pools; woods and glades with over 1600 species and shrubs; Laburnum tunnel; Grove and Swamp Cypress in shallows of 3-acre lake. Bring wellingtons or strong boots. Partly suitable for wheelchairs. TEA. NO COACHES. *Adm £1.50 Chd free (Share to The Kemp House Hospice®). Sun May 19 (2-6). Private visits welcome for parties of 10 and over at other times of the year Tel 01562 850382*

Bredenbury Court (St Richards) &❀ (Headmaster: R E H Coghlan Esq) Bredenbury, 3m W of Bromyard. On A44 Bromyard-Leominster rd; entrance on R (N) side of rd. 5-acre garden; 15 acres parkland with fine views. Simple rose garden and herbaceous borders. Picnics allowed. Use of swimming pool 30p extra. TEA. *Adm £1.50 Chd 50p (Share to St Richards Hospice®). Sun July 7 (12-6)*

Bredon Pound (Mr & Mrs David King) Ashton under Hill. 6m down the Cheltenham Rd from Evesham. A recently landscaped garden at the foot of Bredon Hill with fine views over the Vale of Evesham to the Cotswold Hills. Shrub roses, heathers and an interesting collection of trees and shrubs. TEAS. *Adm £1 Chd free (Share to St Richard's Hospice®). Private visits welcome May to Sept, please Tel 01386 881209*

Brilley Court &❀ (Mr & Mrs D Bulmer) nr Whitney-on-Wye 6m E Hay-on-Wye. 1½m off main A438 Hereford to Brecon Rd signposted to Brilley. Medium-sized walled garden spring and herbaceous. Valley stream garden; spring colour. Ornamental kitchen garden. Large quantity of roses. Wonderful views. TEAS. *Adm £1.50 Chd 50p (Share to CRMF®). Suns May 5, June 30 (2-6). Also by appt, please Tel 01497 831467*

Broadway, Snowshill Road Gardens ⚘✿ All six gardens are on Snowshill Rd. TEAS at **Far Bunchers.** *Combined adm £2 Chd free (Share to Lifford Hall, Broadway®). Sun July 7 (2-6)*

Far Bunchers (Mrs A Pallant) A recently developed mixed garden of about 1 acre. Emphasis on shrub roses and organic vegetable growing

Meadowside (Mrs P Bomford) A very pleasing and compact cottage garden that slopes down to the stream

The Old Orchard (Major & Mrs I Gregory) A cottage garden that slopes down to the stream together with an old orchard and shrub rose garden adjacent to the rd

Mill Hay Cottage (Dr & Mrs W J A Payne) The 2-acre garden is of relatively recent origin and is still being developed. A special feature is the number of unusual trees, incl many fruiting species

The Mill (Mr & Mrs H Verney) A 2½-acre paddock, bounded by 2 streams has been transformed since 1975 into an attractive garden that will support a variety of wildlife. Informal planting of trees, shrub roses and other shrubs, moisture loving plants and bulbs. Minimal annual maintenance required

Mill Hay House (Mr & Mrs H Will) The large mill pond is a centre for attention in a well laid out and interesting garden

Brook Cottage ⚘ (Dorothy Phillips) Lingen. 5m NE of Presteigne. 15m SW of Ludlow. 15m NE of Leominster. On B4362 (Mortimers Cross to Presteigne) take N turn 2m from Presteigne centre marked Kinsham and Lingen. Garden in centre of Lingen village at top of lane opp the Royal George. 1¾ acres woodland and field garden with brook developed over 10 yrs by owner for yr-round interest and low maintenance. Old apple trees draped in roses; shrubs and trees for foliage colour and shape plus herbaceous plants of the more robust type suitable for a sheltered, frost pocket garden. Parking at Lingen Nursery Garden. TEAS. *Combined adm with **Lingen Nursery Garden** and **Well Cottage** £2 Chd under 10 free (Share to Lingen Village Hall©). Sun June 30 (2-6)*

Brook House ♿ (Mr J Milne) Colwall. 3m SW Malvern and 3m E of Ledbury on B2048. ½-way between Malvern/Ledbury via Wyche Cutting; opp Oddfellows Hotel. Water garden; flowering trees and shrubs; walled garden. Old Herefordshire farmhouse with mill stream. TEAS. *Adm £1.50 Chd 50p. Sun June 16 (2-6). Private visits welcome, please Tel 01684 540283*

Brookside ⚘✿ (Mr & Mrs John Dodd) Bringsty; 3m E of Bromyard via A44 10m W of Worcester; Bringsty Common turn down track to 'Live & Let Live'; at PH carpark bear L to Brookside. C16 cottage with 1½-acre garden designed by Denis Hoddy; specimen trees and shrubs in grass sloping to lake; mixed beds with all year interest. Unusual plants. Small alpine collection. TEAS on terrace. *Adm £1 Chd 20p (Share to Save the Children Fund®). Sun Aug 11 (2-5.30). Parties and private visits welcome, please Tel 01886 821835*

¶**Bryan's Ground** ⚘✿ (David Wheeler & Simon Dorrell) Stapleton, nr Presteigne. 12m NW of Leominster. At Mortimers Cross take B4362 signposted Presteigne. After 6m, at Combe, turn R signposted Kinsham and Lingen. After

½m turn L signposted Stapleton. After 1m turn L into garden. An Edwardian garden of approx 3 acres undergoing extensive restoration and development. Edwardian house (not open). Home of Hortus The International Garden Journal. Yew and box topiary, parterres, formal herb garden, large partly walled kitchen garden, newly planted flower and shrub borders incl 'Gothic' garden with 'Sulking House', rose, black and white and grey gardens etc. Shrubbery with spring bulbs, recently created 'Heritage' apple orchard, lighthouse and Edwardian greenhouse. Featured in New York Times and The Observer. Fine views of the Lugg valley. TEAS. *Adm £1.50 Chd 50p. Fris, Suns, Bank Hol Mons April 5 to Sept 15. For NGS Sun, Fri May 19, June 21 (2-5)*

Caves Folly Nursery ♿⚘ (Mr Leaper & Mrs Evans) Evendine Lane, off Colwall Green. 3m SW Malvern and 3m E of Ledbury on B2048. Car parking at Caves Folly. Small nursery established 11 yrs. Specialising in herbaceous and alpine plants, some unusual. All plants are grown organically in peat-free compost. Recently planted herbaceous borders and a wildflower meadow. TEAS. *Combined adm with **Longacre** £1.50 Chd free. Sun June 2 (2-6). Also open Sun July 21. Adm £1 Chd free (2-5). Private visits welcome, clubs, societies etc, please Tel 01684 540631*

Cedar Lodge ⚘✿ (Mrs Barbara Andrews) Blakeshall. 4m N of Kidderminster off B4189. 1½m from Wolverley village. ¾-acre prize-winning garden with extensive range of trees, shrubs and plants. Shade borders, gravel garden, small pool and large mixed borders. Beautiful rural setting adjoining Kinver Edge. Featured in NGS Video 3. TEAS. *Adm £1.50 Chd free. Sun June 16 (2-5.30)*

¶**The Coach House** ⚘ (Mr & Mrs Maurice Juggins) Woollas Hall, Eckington. Half way up Bredon Hill off B4080 Bredon to Pershore rd, follow signs to The Combertons and Woollas Hall. Drive past the farm over cattle grid up private rd (marked). Park on adjacent field next to Woollas Hall. An unusual 2-acre collection of conifers, Japanese maples, bamboos and camellias. Splendid views towards the Malverns. Remarkable autumn and spring colour. TEA. *Adm £2 Chd free (Share to Vale Wildlife Rescue Centre®). Suns May 12, 19, Oct 20, 27 (2-6)*

¶**Coddington Vineyard** ♿ (Drs Denis & Ann Savage) Coddington, nr Ledbury. From Ledbury take Bromyard rd, 1st R after railway bridge signposted Wellington Heath, turn R at next T-junction (oak tree on island) and follow signs to Coddington. Vineyard signposted. 5 acres incl 2-acre vineyard, listed cruck barn and cider mill. Garden and vineyard planted 1985 with terraces, woodland, pond and stream. Interesting trees and shrubs. Wine tasting incl in *Adm £2 Chd free. Suns June 23, Aug 18 (2-6)*

Conderton Manor ♿⚘ (Mr & Mrs William Carr) 5½m NE of Tewkesbury. 7-acre garden with magnificent views of Cotswolds; many trees and shrubs of botanical interest. 100yd long mixed borders, rose walks and formal terrace. Teas available at the Silk Shop in the village. *Adm £2 (Share to Soil Assoc®). Private visits by appt not mid July to end Aug, please Tel 01386 725389*

28 Cornmeadow Lane ✠✿ (Rev P J Wedgwood) Claines is a northern suburb of Worcester; follow signpost Claines at roundabout junction of A449 and M/way link rd; R at church. House beside 3rd hall on L about ½m down Cornmeadow Lane. Parking in Church Hall grounds. Small town garden packed with rare and tropical plants with plenty of colour. Plants in aid of Claines Church Choir Fund. TEAS. *Adm £1 Chd free. Sat July 6 (2-6)*

¶**The Cottage** ✿✿ (Mr Terry Dagley) Broughton Green. 4½m E of Droitwich. 3½m via B4090, turn S at sign 1m. Park on side of rd. The Cottage 250yds up farm track. Approx ½-acre plantsman's country garden, stocked with extensive range of hardy perennials, bulbs, shrubs and trees to give yr-round interest. The quiet rural setting encourages abundant wildlife. *Adm £1 Chd free. Thurs March 21, April 18, May 16, June 20, July 19, Aug 15, Sept 19 (11-5) Private visits welcome, please* Tel 01905 391670

The Cottage Herbery ✿✿ (Mr & Mrs R E Hurst) 1m E of Tenbury Wells on A456, turn for Boraston at Peacock Inn, turn R in village, signposted to garden. Half timbered C16 farmhouse with fast-flowing Cornbrook running close to its side and over ford at the bottom of garden. 1-acre garden specializing in a wide range of herbs, aromatic and scented foliage plants, planted on a cottage garden theme; also unusual hardy perennial and variegated plants; early interest bulbs, pulmonarias, euphorbias, symphytums. Nursery sells large selection of herbs. Organic garden. Chelsea Medallists. Featured in Central TV Gardening Time. Gold Medal Winners '94 and '95. TEAS (served in garden and barn). *Adm £1 Chd free. Every Sun May 5 to Aug 25. Thurs June 20, 27, July 4 (11-5) please* Tel 01584 781575

Croft Castle ൠ✿✿ (The National Trust) 5m NW of Leominster. On B4362 (off B4361, Leominster-Ludlow). Large garden; borders; walled garden; landscaped park and walks in Fishpool Valley; fine old avenues. Special garden open for NGS (Castle closed). *Adm £1 Chd 50p. Tues June 25 (1.30-4.30)*

Dial Park ✿✿ (Mr & Mrs David Mason) Chaddesley Corbett. 4½m from Kidderminster, 4½m from Bromsgrove on A448. 150yds towards Kidderminster from turn into Chaddesley Corbett village. Approx ¾-acre garden developed since 1990 containing interesting and unusual plants with yr-round interest. Incl collections of snowdrops, sambucus and hardy ferns. Also small collection of country bygones. TEA. *Adm £1 Chd free. Thurs Feb 22 (1-5) June 27, Sept 26 (2-6). Thurs Feb 21 1997 (1-5). Private visits welcome, please* Tel 01562 777451

●**Eastgrove Cottage Garden Nursery** ൠ✿✿ (Mr & Mrs J Malcolm Skinner) Sankyns Green, Shrawley. 8m NW of Worcester on rd between Shrawley (on B4196) and Great Witley (on A443). Set in 5 acres unspoilt meadow and woodland, this unique 1-acre garden and nursery is of particular interest to the plantsman. Very fine collection of hardy and tender perennial plants in old world country flower garden with much thought given to planting combinations both of colour and form. Garden and nursery

maintained since 1970 by owners who give help and advice. Featured in The Times, The Telegraph and BBC TV. Wide range of well grown less usual plants for sale, all grown at Nursery. *Adm £2 Chd 20p. April 1 to July 29 Thurs, Fri, Sat, Sun, Mon. Sept 5 to Oct 19; Thurs, Fris, Sats (2-5). Closed throughout August*

¶**Elmbury** ✿ (Mrs E Haines) 98 Aylestone Hill, Hereford. ¾m NE of city centre on A4103 Worcester rd. ½-acre garden on sloping site containing alpine and scree beds, herbaceous borders, 2 pools with small stream and water plants, several raised peat beds containing meconopsis, camellias and rhododendrons are a special feature. TEAS in aid of Save the Children Fund®. *Adm £1 Chd free. Sun May 19 (2-5.30)*

¶**The Elms** ✿✿ (Mr & Mrs Marshall Stewart) Lower Broadheath. 4m W of Worcester, turn off B4204 opp school into Frenchlands Lane. After ½m (drive with care) through farm gate, lane becomes a track. Isolated setting, lovely views in Elgar country. 1½-acre garden surrounding late Georgian farmhouse (not open). Range of listed buildings. Begun by present owners in 1988. Cool mixed borders, hot trellis borders, blue and white cider house garden, lily pool, rose walk, small pond with waterfall. Nursery specialising in unusual hardy plants and cottage garden favourites set in ornamental kitchen garden created from old fold yard. Rare breed Shropshire sheep. Agricultural artifacts. TEAS (Sun), TEA (Tues, Wed). *Adm £1.50 Chd free (Share to Christchurch, Lower Broadheath®). Sun June 23 (2-6). Tues, Weds June 25 to Oct 31 (10-4)*

The Elms School see Wych & Colwall Horticultural Society Show

Frogmore ൠ✿✿ (Sir Jonathan & Lady North) Pontshill. 4m SE of Ross-on-Wye. 1m S of A40 through Pontshill. 2-acre garden with fine mature trees and many unusual young trees and shrubs. Mixed borders specialising in hardy geraniums. Nut walk and ha ha. Mown walk along stream and to spinney. TEAS in aid of Hope Mansel Church. *Adm £2 Chd free. Sun June 2 (2-6)*

Garnons ൠ✿ (Sir John & Lady Cotterell) 7m W of Hereford on A438; lodge gates on R; then fork L over cattle grid. Large park landscaped by Repton; attractive spring garden. House is remaining wing (1860) of house pulled down in 1957. TEA. *Adm £2 Chd 50p (Share to Byford Church®). Sun April 14 (2-5)*

Grantsfield ൠ✿✿ (Col & Mrs J G T Polley) nr Kimbolton, 3m NE of Leominster. A49 N from Leominster, turn right to Grantsfield. Car parking in field; not coaches which must drop and collect visitors at gate. Contrasting styles in gardens of old stone farmhouse; wide variety of unusual plants and shrubs, old roses, climbers; herbaceous borders; superb views. 2-acre orchard and kitchen garden with flowering and specimen trees. Spring bulbs. TEAS. *Adm £1.20 Chd free (Share to St John Ambulance®). Sun June 23 (2-5.30). Private visits welcome April to end Aug, please* Tel 01568 613338

Hanbury Hall ♿ ✻ (The National Trust) Hanbury, 3m NE of Droitwich, 6m S of Bromsgrove. Signed off B4090. Recreation of C18 formal garden by George London. Victorian forecourt with detailed planting. William & Mary style brick house of 1701 with murals by Thornhill; contemporary Orangery and Ice House. TEAS. *Adm garden only £2.50 Chd £1. ▲For NGS Sun July 7 (2-6)*

Hartlebury Castle ♿ ✻ (The Rt Revd The Lord Bishop of Worcester) Medieval moated castle reconstructed 1675, restored 1964. Many Tudor and Hanoverian Royal connections. Herbaceous borders, terraced garden. Wheelchairs ground floor. *Adm gardens & state rooms 75p OAPs 50p Chd 25p. Sun June 2 (2-5). Private visits welcome for parties of 30, please* **Tel 01299 250410**

Hergest Croft Gardens ♿ ❀ (W L Banks Esq & R A Banks Esq) ½m off A44 on Welsh side of Kington, 20m NW of Hereford: Turn L at Rhayader end of bypass; then 1st R; gardens ¼m on L. 50 acres of garden owned by Banks' family for 4 generations. Edwardian garden surrounding house; Park wood with rhododendrons up to 30ft tall; old-fashioned kitchen garden with spring and herbaceous borders. One of finest private collections of trees and shrubs; now selected to hold National Collections Maples and Birches. Hergest Croft celebrates is centenary in 1996. TEAS. *Adm £2.50 Chd under 15 free (Share to NCCPG®). Fri April 5 to Sun Oct 30 daily. For NGS Sat June 22 (1.30-6.30).* **Tel 01544 230160**

Holland House ✻ (Warden: Mr Peter Middlemiss) Main St, Cropthorne, Pershore. Between Pershore and Evesham, off A44. Car park at rear of house. Gardens laid out by Lutyens in 1904; thatched house dating back to 1636 (not open). TEAS. *Adm £1 Chd free (Share to USPG®). Suns March 17, June 23 (2.30-5)*

How Caple Court ❀ (Mr & Mrs Peter Lee) How Caple, 5m N of Ross on Wye 10m S of Hereford on B4224; turn R at How Caple Xrds, garden 400 yds on L. 11 acres; Edwardian gardens set high above R Wye in park and woodland; formal terraces: yew hedges, statues and pools; sunken florentine water garden under restoration; woodland walks; herbaceous and shrub borders, shrub roses, mature trees: Mediaeval Church with newly restored C16 Diptych. Nursery specialising in old rose varieties and apple varieties, unusual herbaceous plants and herbs. Shop open for gifts, fabric and menswear. TEAS. *Adm £2.50 Chd £1.25. Open Mon to Sat all yr. Also Suns April 1 to Oct 31 (10-5). For NGS Sun June 9 (10-5).* **Tel 01989 740612**

Ivytree House (Mrs L Eggins) [OS139 91.79] Bromsgrove Rd, Clent. 3m SE of Stourbridge and 5m NW of Bromsgrove, off A491 Stourbridge to Bromsgrove dual carriageway. Car parking next door at Woodman Hotel. Over 1,000 varieties of small trees, shrubs and herbaceous plants in approx ½-acre plantsman's cottage garden; tree ivies and ivytrees, collection of aucubas, small conservatory with fuchsia trees, pond garden, fruit and vegetables, bantams and bees. *Adm £1 Chd free. Mons, Weds May 20, 22, June 17, 19, July 15, 17 (2-5). Also private visits welcome, please* **Tel 01562 884171**

Keepers Cottage ✻ ❀ (Mrs Diana Scott) Alvechurch. Take main A441 rd through Alvechurch towards Redditch. Turn opp sign to Cobley Hill and Bromsgrove for 1m over 2 humpback bridges. 3-acre garden at 600ft with fine views towards the Cotswolds; rhododendrons, camellias; old-fashioned roses; unusual trees and shrubs; rock garden; 2 alpine houses; paddock with donkeys. *Adm £1.50 Chd 80p. Private visits welcome in May, please* **Tel 01214 455885**

Kingstone Cottages ✻ ❀ (Michael & Sophie Hughes) A40 Ross-Gloucester, turn L at Weston Cross to Bollitree Castle, then L to Rudhall. Informal 1½-acre cottage garden containing National Collection of old pinks and carnations and other unusual plants. Terraced beds, ponds, grotto, summerhouse, lovely views. Some areas now replanted incl a new parterre containing the Collection. Dianthus and other plants for sale, also garden furniture designed and made on premises. The garden has featured in several magazines and Channel 4 programmes. *Adm £1 Chd free. Mons to Fris May 7 to July 12 (except Bank Hols) (9-4). Private visits welcome, please* **Tel 01989 565267**

Kyre Park ♿ ❀ (Mr & Mrs M H Rickard & Mr & Mrs J N Sellers) Kyre. 4m S of Tenbury Wells or 7m N of Bromyard. Follow signs to Kyre Church off B4214. Approx 29 acres, shrubbery walk, 5 lakes, waterfalls, hermitage, picturesque views, mature trees, Norman dovecote and Jacobean tithe barn. Landscaped in 1754 but neglected for several decades, now in early stages of restoration. A rare example of a Georgian shrubbery hardly touched for 240yrs. Stout shoes advised. Ferns for sale at Rickards Hardy Fern Nursery. TEAS. *Adm £1.50 Chd 50p. Open daily Easter to Oct. For NGS Suns March 24, Sept 29 (11-6). Coach parties by appt, please* **Tel 01885 410282**

Lakeside ✻ ❀ (Mr D Gueroult & Mr C Philip) Gaines Rd, Whitbourne. 9m W of Worcester off A44 at County boundary sign (ignore sign to Whitbourne Village). 6-acres, large walled garden with many mixed beds and borders; spring bulbs, climbers, unusual shrubs and plants, heather garden, bog garden, medieval carp lake with fountain. Uncommon plants for sale. Steep steps and slopes. TEAS in aid of Red Cross. *Adm £2 Chd free. Sun July 7 (2-6). Parties of 10 or more by appt, please* **Tel 01886 821119**

Lingen Nursery and Garden ♿ ✻ ❀ (Mr Kim Davis) Lingen. 5m NE of Presteigne take B4362 E from Presteigne, 2m turn L for Lingen, 3m opposite Chapel in village. 2 acres of specialist alpine and herbaceous nursery and general garden intensively planted giving a long period of interest having large areas of rock garden and herbaceous borders, a peat bed, raised screes and an Alpine House and stock beds, together with 2 acres of developing garden where picnics are welcome. Many unusual plants with comprehensive labelling. Wide range of plants for sale from the nursery frames. Catalogue available. National collection of iris sibirica held for NCCPG. TEAS (NGS days only). *Adm £1 Chd free. Feb-Oct every day (10-6). For NGS Suns May 19; June 2; July 21 Sept 22 (2-6). Combined adm with* **Brook Cottage** *and* **Well Cottage** *£2 Sun June 30 (2-6). Coach parties by appt* **Tel 01544 267720**

Linton Hall ❀ (Mr & Mrs Sanders & Mr & Mrs Berrington) Gorsley. 5m E of Ross-on-Wye, junction 3 off M50 toward Newent. Entrance ½m on RH-side on county boundary. Ample parking. 8½ acres of woodland and gardens, mature trees, interesting and varied borders with old-fashioned roses. TEAS. *Adm £1.50 Chd 50p. Sun, Mon June 23, 24 (2-6)*

Little Malvern Court ❀❀ (Mrs T M Berington) 4m S of Malvern on A4104 S of junction with A449. 10 acres attached to former Benedictine Priory, magnificent views over Severn valley. An intriguing layout of garden rooms, and terrace round house. Newly made and planted water garden below, feeding into chain of lakes. Wide variety of spring bulbs, flowering trees and shrubs. Notable collection of old-fashioned roses. TEAS. *Adm £2.50 Chd 50p (5-14) (Share to SSAFA®). Sun March 24 (2-6)*

Longacre ❀❀ (Mr D Pudsey & Mrs H Pudsey) Evendine Lane, off Colwall Green. 3m SW Malvern and 3m E of Ledbury on B2048. 1-acre garden developed since 1970 with ½-acre extension being developed from field in 1995. Emphasis on multi-season trees and shrubs planted to create vistas across lawns, down paths and along avenues. TEAS at Caves Folly Nursery. *Combined odm with **Caves Folly Nursery** £1.50 Chd free. Sun June 2 (2-5)*

Lower Hope ❀❀❀ (Mr & Mrs Clive Richards) Ullingswick. From Hereford take the A465 N to Bromyard. After 6m this road meets the A417 at Burley Gate roundabout. Turn L on the A417 signposted Leominster. After approx 2m take the 3rd turning on the R signposted Lower Hope and Pencombe. Lower Hope is 0.6m on the LH-side. 5-acre garden facing S and W constitutes principally herbaceous borders, rose borders, water gardens, woodland walks; in addition other features include a Laburnum Walk, conservatories and greenhouses, a small fruit and vegetable garden. Surrounding the gardens are paddocks in which the prize-winning Herd of Pedigree Poll Hereford cattle and flock of Pedigree Suffolk sheep are grazed. TEAS. *Adm £2 Chd £1 (Share to St John Ambulance®). Suns April 14, June 2, July 7 (2-6). Also private visits welcome, following written application*

The Manor House ❀ (Mr & Mrs David Williams Thomas) Birlingham, nr Pershore off A4104. Very fine views of Bredon Hill with short walk to R Avon for picnics. Walled white and silver garden, gazebo and many herbaceous borders of special interest to the plantsman. A large selection of plants propagated from the garden on sale. Featured in 'House & Garden' 1994 and 'Sunday Express' 1995. TEAS. *Adm £1.50 Chd free. Every Thurs May 2 to May 30. Every Wed, Thurs June 5 to July 25. Closed Aug. Every Thurs Sept 5 to Sept 26. Also Mons May 6, 27, Fri May 10 (11-5.30) Private visits welcome, please **Tel 01386 750005***

The Marsh Country Hotel ❀❀ (Mr & Mrs Martin Gilleland) Eyton. 2m NW of Leominster. Signed Eyton and Lucton off B4361 Richard Castle Rd. A 1½-acre garden created over the past 7 years. Herbaceous borders, small orchard, lily pond, herb garden and stream with planted banks and rose walk. Vegetable plot. Landscaped reed bed sewage treatment system. Featured in 'The Gardener' 1994. C14 timbered Great Hall listed grade II* (not open). TEAS. *Adm £1.50 Chd 50p. Suns May 5 to Oct 27 (2-5)*

Moccas Court ❀ (Trustees of Baunton Trust) 10m W of Hereford. 1m off B4352. 7-acres; Capability Brown parkland on S bank of R. Wye. House designed by Adam and built by Keck in 1775. Teas in village hall. *Adm house & garden £1.95 Chd £1 (Share to Moccas Church®). Sun June 16 (2-6). By appt for groups of 20 or over, please **Tel 01981 500381***

Monnington Court ❀ (Mr & Mrs John Bulmer) Monnington. The ¾m lane to Monnington on Wye to Monnington Court is on the A438 between Hereford and Hay 9m from either. Approx 20 acres. Lake, pond and river walk. Sculpture garden (Mrs Bulmer is the sculptor Angela Conner); various tree lined avenues including Monnington Walk, one of Britain's oldest, still complete mile long avenues of Scots pines and yews, made famous by Kilvert's Diary; collection of swans and ducks; Foundation Farm of the British Morgan Horse - a living replica of ancient horses seen in statues in Trafalgar Square, etc; working cider press; FREE horse and carriage display at 3.30 each of open days. The C13, C15, C17 house including Mediaeval Moot Hall is also open. Carriage display (3.30). Barbecue on fine days, lunches. TEA 10.30-6.30. Indoor horse display and films on rainy days. *Adm house, garden and display £4 Chd £2.50, garden and display only £3.50 Chd £1.50 (Share to British Morgan Horse Foundation Farm©). Sat, Sun, Mon Aug 24, 25, 26 (10.30-7). Private visits for 10 or over welcome, please **Tel 01981 500264***

¶**Monsieur's Hall** ❀❀ (Dr & Mrs A Cowan) Bromsgrove. A448 1½m W Bromsgrove. L into Monsieurs Hall Lane. 400yds on L. Hilltop acre with extensive views. Formal garden around C16 farmhouse (not open). Informal mixed borders, pool and rockeries leading to wilder area and recently planted spinney. Conservatory. *Adm £1 Chd free. Wed May 8, Thurs June 27, Wed July 10 (2-6) Private visits welcome, please **Tel 01527 831747***

¶**Nafford House** ❀ (Mr & Mrs John Wheatley) Eckington. On entering Eckington from A4104 take 1st L, follow lane for ¾m. Nafford House on sharp R-hand bend. Georgian house set in elevated position overlooking R Avon. Features incl extensive lawns, well established herbaceous borders, many young specimen trees, small formal rose garden and copse recently replanted. TEA. *Adm £2 Chd free. Sun May 19 (2-6)*

Nerine Nursery ❀ (Mr & Mrs I L Carmichael) Brookend House, Welland, ½m towards Upton-on-Severn from Welland Xrds (A4104 × B4208). Internationally famous National Collection of Nerines, 30 species and some 800 named varieties in 5 greenhouses and traditional walled garden with raised beds, hardy nerines. Coaches by appt only. TEAS. *Adm £1.50 Chd free. Sun Oct 13 (2-5). Private visits welcome, please **Tel 01684 594005***

The National Gardens Scheme is a charity which traces its origins back to 1927. Since then it has raised a total of over £14 million for charitable purposes.

1996 Special Events. For information on special National Gardens Scheme events in 1996 see Pages 18-19.

Orchard Bungalow ✤❀ (Mr & Mrs Robert Humphries) Bishops Frome. 14m W of Worcester. A4103 turn R at bottom of Fromes Hill, through village of Bishops Frome on B4214. Turn R immediately after de-regulation signs along narrow track for 250yds. Ample parking in field 200yds from garden. ½-acre garden with conifers, trees, shrubs and herbaceous borders. Over 200 roses incl many old varieties, 4 ponds, small stream, 3 aviaries and dovecote. 1993 winner of Garden News water garden competition. TEAS. *Adm £1 Chd free. Suns June 16, July 14, Aug 25 (2-6). Private visits welcome, please* **Tel 01885 490273**

Overbury Court & (Mr & Mrs Bruce Bossom) nr Tewkesbury, Glos GL20 7NP. 5m NE of Tewkesbury, 2½m N of Teddington Hands Roundabout, where A438 crosses A435. Georgian house 1740 (not open); landscape gardening of same date with stream and pools. Daffodil bank and grotto. Plane trees, yew hedges. Shrub, cut flower, coloured foliage, gold and silver, shrub rose borders. Norman church adjoins garden. *Adm £1.50 Chd free. Private visits welcome by parties of 10 or more following written application or* **Fax 01386 725528**

¶Overcourt Garden Nursery &✤❀ (Mr & Mrs Peter Harper) Sutton St Nicholas. 3m N of Hereford. Turn L at Xrds in village on rd to Marden for ¼m. A Grade II C16 house once used as a vicarage and schoolhouse, with connections dating back to the Crusader Knights of St John. Delightful views to the Black Mountains. A 1½-acre plant enthusiast's developing country garden planted over last 3yrs for yr-round interest. Large shrub and herbaceous perennial borders, ponds and small copse. Well maintained vegetable garden. Wide range of unusual herbaceous plants propagated from the garden for sale in the nursery. TEAS. *Adm £1 Chd free (Share to CRMF®). Sun June 16 (2-6). Private visits welcome, please* **Tel 01432 880845**

Pedwardine Cottage ✤ (Robert Milne) On rd to Lingen, 1m S of Brampton Bryan which is 12m W of Ludlow. ⅛-acre organic kitchen garden. Efficient design. 18th yr of intensive cropping. Informative written guide and plan. *Adm £1.20 Chd free. Sun July 14 (10-6). Please* **Tel 01568 770489**

Pershore College of Horticulture &✤❀ 1m S of Pershore on A44, 7m from M5 junction 7. 180-acre estate; ornamental grounds; arboretum; fruit, vegetables; amenity glasshouses; wholesale hardy stock nursery. Plant Centre open for sales. West Midlands Regional Centre for RHS. Plant Centre open for gardening advice. TEA. *Adm £1 Chd 50p. Sun June 9 (2-4)*

Pershore Gardens &✤ Variety of town gardens all within easy walking distance. Free parking nr Abbey. TEAS. *Combined adm £2 Chd free. Sun June 16 (2-6)*

The Picton Garden &✤❀ (Mr & Mrs Paul Picton) Walwyn Rd, Colwall. 3m W of Malvern on B4218. 1½ acres W of Malvern Hills. A plantsman's garden extensively renovated in recent yrs. Rock garden using Tufa. Moist garden. Rose garden with scented old and modern varieties. Mature interesting shrubs. Large herbaceous borders full of colour from early summer. NCCPG National Reference collection of asters, michaelmas daisies, occupies its own vast borders and gives a tapestry of colour from late Aug through Sept and Oct. If wet there will be a small display of Asters under cover. *Adm £1.50 Chd free. Open Wed to Sun April 3 to Oct 31 incl, Mon, Tues Sept 1 to Oct 15 (10-1; 2.15-5.30). Private parties of 10 or over welcome, please* **Tel 01684 540416**

Priors Court ✤❀ (Robert Philipson-Stow) Long Green. From Tewkesbury take A438 to Ledbury. Exactly 5m pass under M50. Garden on hill on L of A438. From Ledbury, Worcester or Gloucester aim for Rye Cross (A438 and B4208) then take A438 for Tewkesbury. Priors Court is approx 3m from Rye Cross on R. 3-acre garden established in 1920s by owner's parents surrounding C15 house (not open). Rock, herb and vegetable gardens, also mature trees and shrubs, herbaceous and rose borders; stunning views. Norman church 250yds over field will be open. TEAS. *Adm £1.50 Chd 50p (Share to Berrow & Pendock Parish Church®). Sun May 12 (2-6). Private visits by appt for parties of less than 20, please* **Tel 01684 833221**

The Priory &❀ (The Hon Mrs Peter Healing) Kemerton, NE of Tewkesbury B4080. Main features of this 4-acre garden are long herbaceous borders planned in colour groups; stream, fern and sunken gardens. Many unusual plants, shrubs and trees. Featured in BBC2 'Gardeners' World' and 'The Garden magazine'. Small nursery. TEAS Suns only. *Adm £1.50 May and June, £2 July to Sept Chd free. (Share to St Richard's Hospice® Aug 25, SSAFA® Sept 8, Tewkesbury Wheelchair Bus Assoc© Aug 4). Every Fri May 31 to Sept 28 also Suns May 26, June 23, July 14, Aug 4, 25, Sept 8 (2-6). Private visits welcome for 20 and over, please* **Tel 01386 725258**

Red House Farm ✤❀ (Mrs M M Weaver) Flying Horse Lane, Bradley Green. 7m W of Redditch on B4090 Alcester to Droitwich. Turn opp The Red Lion. Approx ½-acre plant enthusiast's cottage garden containing wide range of interesting herbaceous perennials; roses; shrubs; alpines. Garden and small nursery open daily offering wide variety of plants mainly propogated from garden. *Adm £1 Chd free. Suns May 26, July 28, Thurs June 13 (11-5). Private visits welcome, please,* **Tel 01527 821269**

Ripple Hall & (Sir Hugo Huntington-Whiteley) 4m N of Tewkesbury. Off A38 Worcester-Tewkesbury (nr junction with motorway); Ripple village well signed. 6 acres; lawns and paddocks with donkeys; walled vegetable garden; cork tree and orangery. TEAS. *Adm £1.50 Acc chd free (Share to St John Ambulance®). Sun March 31 (2-5)*

St Egwins Cottage ✤❀ (Mr & Mrs Brian Dudley) Norton. 2m N of Evesham on A435. Park in St Egwins Church car park. Walk through churchyard to Church Lane (50yds). Please do not park in Church Lane. ⅕-acre plantsman's garden, many unusual plants; mainly perennials incl hardy geraniums, campanulas and salvias. Small thatched cottage next to C12 church (open). TEAS Suns only. TEA Weds only. *Adm £1 Chd free. Suns, June 2, July 7, Aug 11; Weds May 29, June 5, 19, July 10; Aug 14 (2-5). Also private visits welcome April to September, please* **Tel 01386 870486**

Spetchley Park ໒ & (R J Berkeley Esq) 2m E of Worcester on A422. 30-acre garden containing large collection of trees, shrubs and plants, many rare and unusual. New garden within kitchen garden open for first time 1996. Red and fallow deer in nearby park. TEAS. *Adm £2.50 Chd £1.20. Good Fri April 5 (11-5) Suns May 12, July 7 (2-5)*

Staunton Park ໒ & (Mr E J L & Miss A Savage) Staunton-on-Arrow. 3m from Pembridge; 6m from Kington on the Titley road. 18m from Hereford; 11m from Leominster; 16m from Ludlow. Signposted. 14-acres of garden, specimen trees, herbaceous borders, herb garden, rock garden, hosta border, lake, lakeside garden, woodland walk, spring bulbs. New scented border. TEAS. *Adm £1.50 Chd free. Thurs, Suns April to end Sept. Easter and Bank Holidays. For NGS Suns May 5, June 9 (2-5.30)*

Stone House ※ (Peter & Sheila Smellie) Scotland, Wellington. A49 6m N of Hereford, end of dual carriageway, turn L for Westhope. ¾m turn R up narrow track. Parking ¼m. Parking difficult in wet conditions. 1-acre S sloping garden with magnificent views over countryside. Winding paths traverse the bank and terraced areas which contain a wide selection of unusual shrubs and herbaceous plants. Children welcome. *Adm £1.50 Chd 50p. Suns April 28, May 26, June 23, July 14 (12-6). Private visits welcome, please* **Tel 01432 830470**

● **Stone House Cottage Gardens** ໒ & ※ (Maj & the Hon Mrs Arbuthnott) Stone, 2m SE of Kidderminster via A448 towards Bromsgrove next to church, turn up drive. 1-acre sheltered walled plantsman's garden with towers; rare wall shrubs, climbers and interesting herbaceous plants. In adjacent nursery large selection of unusual shrubs and climbers for sale. Featured in The Garden, Country Life and Hortus. Coaches by appt only. *Adm £2 Chd free. Suns May 5, 26; June 9, 23; Aug 25; Mons April 8, May 6, 27; Aug 26; also open March to Sept every Wed, Thurs, Fri, Sat (10-5.30). Private visits welcome Oct to Feb, please* **Tel 01562 69902**

Strawberry Cottage & ※ (Mr & Mrs M R Philpott) Hamnish. 3m E of Leominster. A44 E from Leominster, turn L at 1st Xrds to Hamnish. A 2-acre cottage garden created by the present owners since 1988. Part of garden on steep slope with large rockeries. Wide variety of plants and shrubs, many unusual. Over 250 roses. Mixed and herbaceous borders. Beds with single colour themes. Pond and rock garden area, herb and large kitchen garden. Superb position with spectacular views. TEAS. *Adm £1.50 Chd free Garden and nursery open every Thurs, Suns and Bank Hol Mons April 28 to Sept 12. For NGS Suns, Thurs May 5, 19, 30, June 2, 20, 23, July 7, 11, 28, Aug 11, 22, 25 (11-5). Private visits welcome, please* **Tel 01568 760319**

21 Swinton Lane & ※ (Mr A Poulton & Mr B Stenlake) Worcester. 1½m W of City Centre off A4103 Hereford Rd turning into Swinton Lane between Portabello public house and Worcester Golf Course. ⅓-acre town garden featuring a wide variety of plants in colour theme borders and containers. The intimate silver and white garden is surrounded by old roses on trellis work. Interesting and rare tender plants are a delight during the summer

months. The garden holds the NCCPG National Collection of lobelia. *Adm £1.50 Chd free. Thurs, Suns May 30, June 2, 27, 30, July 25, 28 (11-6). Parties welcome by appt, please* **Tel 01905 422265**

Torwood & ※ (Mr & Mrs S G Woodward) Whitchurch, Ross-on-Wye. A40 turn to Symonds Yat W. Garden adjacent village school and roundabout. Interesting and colourful shrubs, conifers, herbaceous plants, bulbs, etc. Featured by Central TV 'My Secret Garden'. TEAS. *Adm £1 Chd free. Thurs, Suns May 23 June 9, 13, 23, July 7, 11, 21 Aug 4 (2-6). Private visits welcome all year, please* **Tel 01600 890306**

Upper Court & (Mr & Mrs W Herford) Kemerton, NE of Tewkesbury B4080. Take turning to Parish Church from War Memorial; Manor behind church. Approx 13 acres of garden and grounds incl a 2-acre lake where visitors would be welcome to bring picnics. The garden was mostly landscaped and planted in 1930s. TEAS. *Adm £1.50 Chd free. Sun June 16 (2-6)*

Well Cottage, Blakemere & ※ (R S Edwards Esq) 10m due W of Hereford. Leave Hereford on A465 (Abergavenny) rd. After 3m turn R towards Hay B4349 (B4348). At Clehonger keep straight on the B4352 towards Bredwardine. Well Cottage is on L by phone box. ¾-acre garden of mixed planting plus ½ acre of wild flower meadow suitable for picnics. There is a natural pool with gunnera and primulae. Good views over local hills and fields. Featured in Diana Saville's book 'Gardens for Small Country Houses' and Jane Taylor's 'The English Cottage Garden'. *Adm £1.50 OAPS £1 Chd free. Private visits welcome May to Aug, please* **Tel 01981 500475**

Well Cottage, Lingen ※ (Mrs A Turnbull) 5m NE of Presteigne. 15m SW of Ludlow. 15m NE of Leominster. On B4362 (Mortimers Cross to Presteigne), take N turn 2m from Presteigne Centre marked Kinsham and Lingen. Garden is next to Lingen Alpine Nursery. Approx ½-acre cottage garden with stream. Entirely managed by OAP! *Combined adm with* **Brook Cottage** *and* **Lingen Nursery** *£2 Chd under 10 free (Share to Lingen Village Hall®). Sun June 30 (2-6)*

White Cottage & ※ (Mr & Mrs S M Bates) Earls Common Rd, Stock Green. A422 Worcester-Alcester; turn L at Red Hart public house (Dormston) 1½m to junction in Stock Green. Turn L. 2-acre garden, developed since 1981; large herbaceous and shrub borders, many unusual varieties; specialist collection of hardy geraniums; stream and natural garden carpeted with primroses, cowslips and other wild flowers; nursery; featuring plants propagated from the garden. When fine teas at Coneybury Plant Centre. *Adm £1 OAPs 75p Chd free. Garden and nursery open daily April 5 to Sept 22 except Weds, Thurs and 2nd and 4th Suns each month. For NGS Fri, Sats, Suns, Mons April 5, 6, 7, 8, May 4, 5, 6, 25, 26, 27, June 1, 2, 15, 16, Sept 14, 15 (10-5). Private visits welcome by prior appt only, please* **Tel 01386 792414**

Whitfield & (G M Clive Esq) Wormbridge, 8m SW of Hereford on A465 Hereford-Abergavenny Rd. Parkland, large garden, ponds, walled kitchen garden, 1780 gingko tree, 1½m woodland walk with 1851 Redwood grove. Picnic parties welcome. TEAS. *Adm £2 Chd £1 (Share to St John Ambulance®). Sun June 9 (2-6). Private visits welcome, please* Tel 0198 121 202

Whitlenge House Cottage &✿❀ (Mr & Mrs K J Southall) Whitlenge Lane, Hartlebury. S of Kidderminster on A449. Take A442 (signposted Droitwich) over small island, ¼m, 1st R into Whitlenge Lane. Follow signs. Home of Creative Landscapes, RHS medal winners. Professional landscaper's demonstration garden with over 400 varieties of trees, shrubs, conifers, herbaceous, heathers and alpines, giving year-round interest. Water features, rustic work, twisted pillar pergola, gravel gardens rockeries and stone walls. Evolved over 11 years. 2 acres of informal plantsman's garden incorporating adjacent nursery specialising in large specimen shrubs. TEAS. *Adm £1.50 Chd free. Suns, Mons April 7, 8, May 26, 27, Aug 25, 26 (10-5). Nursery not open Mondays. Private visits welcome for parties of 10 and over, please* Tel 01299 250720

Windyridge ✿❀ (Mr P Brazier) Kidderminster. Turn off Chester Rd N (A449) into Hurcott Rd, then into Imperial Avenue. 1-acre spring garden containing azaleas, magnolias, camellias, rhododendrons, mature flowering cherries and davidia. Please wear sensible shoes. *Adm £1 Chd free. Suns May 5, 12 (2-6). Private visits welcome, please* Tel 01562 824994

Witley Park House &❀ (Mr & Mrs W A M Edwards) Great Witley. 9m NW of Worcester. On A443 1m W of Little Witley. Garage on L coming from Worcester and Droitwich. 18 acres incl pool, lakeside and woodland walk, water fowl, many varieties trees, shrubs and roses. TEAS. *Adm £1.50 Chd 25p (Share to Worcester Swan Rescue Service®). Suns March 31 (2-5), July 14 (2-6)*

Woodmancote &❀ (Ila & Ian Walmsley) Wadborough. 1½ m S of Stoulton, which is on A44 between Worcester and Pershore. A garden of approx ¾ acre acquired and developed in stages since 1986 by the present owners. 2 ponds, wide variety of shrubs and herbaceous plants in mixed borders, to give interest for most of the yr. Please park considerately at The Mason Arms 400yds. TEAS in aid of St Peter's Church. *Adm £1 Chd free. Suns June 2, 30 (2-6). Private visits welcome, please* Tel 01905 840391

●**Wych & Colwall Horticultural Society Show**. The Elms School &❀ (L A C Ashley, Headmaster) Colwall Green. Medium-sized garden, herbaceous borders, fine views of Malvern Hills. Interesting exhibits of perennials, shrubs and crafts. Classes for flowers, vegetables, art & handicrafts. Professional Horticultural displays. TEAS. *Adm to show and garden 80p Chd 10p (Share to NGS®). Sat July 27 (2-5.30)*

Yew Tree House & (Mr & Mrs W D Moyle) Ombersley. Turn off A449 up Woodfield Lane R at T-junction. 2½-acre garden with many rare herbaceous plants and shrubs. Pretty walled garden with alpines and lily pond, numerous old-fashioned roses. Mature plantings of blue, pink and white borders around tennis court and other yellow and white beds. Orchard, copse and lawns with lovely views set around c1640 timber framed house. TEA. *Adm £2 Chd free. Sun July 7 (2-6)*

Hertfordshire

Hon County Organiser: Mrs Edward Harvey, Wickham Hall, Bishop's Stortford CM23 1JQ
Assistant Hon County Organisers: Mrs Hedley Newton, Moat Farm House Much Hadham SG10 6AE
                                   Mrs Leone Ayres, Patmore Corner, Albury, Ware, Herts SG11 2LY
Hon County Treasurer: Mrs Rösli Lancaster, Manor Cottage, Aspenden, Nr Buntingford SG9 9PB

DATES OF OPENING

April 7 Sunday
  Pelham House, Brent Pelham
April 8 Monday
  Holwell Manor, nr Hatfield
  23 Wroxham Way, Harpenden
April 21 Sunday
  The Abbots House, Abbots
    Langley
  Odsey Park, nr Baldock
  St Paul's Walden Bury, Hitchin

April 28 Sunday
  Great Munden House, nr Ware
  Hunton Park, Kings Langley
May 2 Thursday
  23 Wroxham Way, Harpenden
May 5 Sunday
  St Paul's Walden Bury, Hitchin
May 12 Sunday
  Hunton Park, Kings Langley
  Pelham House, Brent Pelham
May 18 Saturday
  Cockhamsted, Braughing

May 19 Sunday
  The Abbots House, Abbots
    Langley
  Bovingdon Gardens
  Cockhamsted, Braughing
  Hipkins, Broxbourne
  West Lodge Park, Hadley Wood
May 26 Sunday
  Great Sarratt Hall, Rickmansworth
  Queenswood School, Hatfield
May 27 Monday
  Queenswood School, Hatfield

June 8 Saturday
Cockhamsted, Braughing
June 9 Sunday
Cockhamsted, Braughing
Hill House, Stanstead Abbots
Hunton Park, Kings Langley
Moor Place, Much Hadham
St Paul's Walden Bury, Hitchin
23 Wroxham Way, Harpenden
June 16 Sunday
Forge Cottage, Childwick Green ‡
6 High Elms, Harpenden ‡
Little Gaddesden Gardens
The Gardens of Mackerye End,
    Harpenden
June 23 Sunday
The Abbots House, Abbots
    Langley ‡
The Barn, Abbots Langley ‡
Rushmead, Abbots Langley ‡
Serge Hill, Abbots Langley ‡
June 25 Tuesday
The Abbots House, Abbots
    Langley
June 29 Saturday
Benington Lordship, nr Stevenage
June 30 Sunday
Bayford Village Gardens

Benington Lordship, nr Stevenage
Odsey Park, nr Baldock
Old Hammers, Rushden ‡
The Old Rectory, Walkern, nr
    Stevenage ‡
Putteridge Bury, Luton ‡
St Paul's Walden Bury, Hitchin ‡
Waterdell House, Croxley Green
July 4 Thursday
23 Wroxham Way, Harpenden
July 7 Sunday
The Manor House, Ayot St
    Lawrence
The Mill House, Tewin,
    nr Welwyn
July 14 Sunday
Rothamsted Manor, Harpenden
Rushmead, Abbots Langley
July 20 Saturday
23 Wroxham Way, Harpenden
July 21 Sunday
Putteridge Bury, Luton ‡
Temple Dinsley Garden, Preston ‡
23 Wroxham Way, Harpenden
August 25 Sunday
The Abbots House, Abbots
    Langley
23 Wroxham Way, Harpenden

September 29 Sunday
Knebworth House, Stevenage
October 13 Sunday
Capel Manor Gardens, Enfield
October 20 Sunday
West Lodge Park, Hadley Wood

Regular openings
For details see garden description

Benington Lordship, nr Stevenage
Capel Manor Gardens, Enfield
West Lodge Park, Hadley Wood

By appointment only
For telephone numbers and other details see garden descriptions. Private visits welcomed

207 East Barnet Road
Garden Cottage, Abbots Langley
1 Gernon Walk, Letchworth

DESCRIPTIONS OF GARDENS

The Abbots House &⚘ (Dr & Mrs Peter Tomson) 10 High Street, Abbots Langley NW of Watford (5m from Watford). Junction 20 M25, junction 6 M1. Parking in free village car park. 1¾-acre garden with interesting trees; shrubs; mixed borders; sunken garden; ponds; conservatory. Nursery featuring plants propagated from the garden. TEAS. *Adm £1.50 Chd free (Share to Friends of St Lawrence Church®). Suns, April 21, May 19, June 23; Aug 25, Tues June 25 (2-5). Also at other times by appt Tel 01923 264946*

The Barn &⚘❀ (Tom Stuart-Smith and family) Abbots Langley. ½m E of Bedmond in Serge Hill Lane. 1-acre plantsman's garden. Small sheltered courtyard planted with unusual shrubs and perennials, contrasts with more open formal garden with views over wild flower meadow. Teas at Serge Hill. *Combined adm £3 with Serge Hill (Share to Tibet Relief Fund UK®). Sun June 23 (2-5)*

¶**Bayford Village Gardens** &⚘❀ Off B158 between Hatfield and Hertford. Bayford won 1995 Herts Best Kept Small Village Competition. 14 very interesting large and small gardens. Marked walks; bands playing. Ploughman's lunches, bars, home-made TEAS. *Combined adm £3.50 Chd 50p (Share to St Mary's Church and Village School®). Sun June 30 (11.30-5) Gardens include*
    ¶**Bayford Hall** (Mr & Mrs George Rowley) Rose garden, ornamental pond, 1-acre of wild garden, peacocks, guinea fowl
    ¶**Bayford House** (Mr & Mrs Robert Wilson Stephens) Extensive lawns, old cedars and other specimen trees, shrubs and herbaceous borders. Walled kitchen garden

¶**The Manor House** (Mr & Mrs David Latham) Ancient garden with ornamental lake, many specimen trees, walled garden, John of Gaunt 900-year-old oak tree
¶**The Warren House** (Mr & Mrs Neville Hudson) Mature garden with extensive views, ornamental lake with island and cascade

Benington Lordship ⚘❀ (Mr & Mrs C H A Bott) Benington. 5m E of Stevenage, in Benington Village. Hilltop garden on castle ruins overlooking lakes. Amazing April display of scillas, scented rose garden, hidden rock/water garden, spectacular borders, ornamental kitchen garden, nursery. *Adm £2.50 Chd free (Share to St Peters Church®). Spring and Summer Bank Hol Mons, Weds April to Sept 25 (12-5). Suns April to Aug 25, Sun Oct 20 (2-5). For NGS TEAS and Floral Festival in Church adjoining garden. Sat, Sun June 29, 30 (12-6). Private visits of 20 and over, please Tel 01438 869668*

¶**Bovingdon Gardens** &⚘❀ Half way along B4505 Hemel Hempstead/Chesham Rd, take turning marked Bovingdon Green. 1st L into Green Lane. TEAS. *Adm £2 Chd free. Sun May 19 (1.30-5)*
    ¶**Westwinds** (Mr & Mrs D Wright) 2-acre garden with mature trees, wild garden with bluebells, extensive pergola and rockery. TEAS
    ¶**7 Green View Close** ❀ (Mr & Mrs F Miller) ¼-acre garden designed and planted for yr-round interest

Regular Openers. Too many days to include in diary. Usually there is a wide range of plants giving year-round interest. See end of county section for the name and garden description for times etc.

Capel Manor Gardens & (Horticultural & Environmental Centre) Bullsmoor Lane, Enfield, Middx. 3 mins from M25 junction M25/A10. Nearest station Turkey Street - Liverpool Street line (not Suns). 30 acres of historical and modern theme gardens, Japanese garden, large Italian style maze, rock and water features. 5 acre demonstration garden run by Gardening Which? Walled garden with rose collection and woodland walks. TEAS. *Adm £3 OAP £2 Chd £1.50. Open daily (10-5.30 - check for winter opening times). For NGS (Share to Horticultural Therapy©) Sun Oct 13 (10-5.30). For other details* Tel 0181 3664442

Cockhamsted & *&* (Mr & Mrs David Marques) Braughing. 2m E of village towards Braughing Friars (7m N of Ware). 2 acres; informal garden; shrub roses surrounded by open country. Island with trees surrounded by water-filled C14 moat. TEAS in aid of Leukaemia Research. *Adm £2 Chd free. Sat, Sun May 18, 19; June 8, 9 (2-6)*

¶207 East Barnet Road *&&* (Margaret Arnold) New Barnet. M25 junction 24 then A111 to Cockfosters. Underground stations High Barnet or Cockfosters. On bus route 84A and 307. This is a delightful example of a minute courtyard garden. High fences are covered with clematis, honeysuckle and passion flowers, roses and vines scramble over an arch above a seat. Small pond with goldfish and water plants. Many interesting and unusual plants mainly in pots. TEA. *Adm £1 Chd 50p. Private visits welcome, please* Tel 0181 440 0377

¶Forge Cottage *&* (Mr & Mrs S Andrews) Childwick Green. Midway between St Albans and Harpenden on A1081. Entrance through wrought iron gates signposted St Mary's Church. Garden diagonally opp church. ⅓-acre plantsman's garden. Informal with rockery and pond, troughs and containers, mixed herbaceous and shrub beds, pergolas with roses and clematis. The garden has been developed to compliment a cottage dating from C17. TEAS. *Adm £1.25 Chd 50p (Share to The National Autistic Society®). Sun June 16 (2-6)*

Garden Cottage & *&* (Anthony House) 85 Furtherfield, Abbots Langley. NW of Watford 5m from Watford junction 20 M25 junction 6 M1. A small plantsman's garden in total 100' long by 20' wide; planted in 1991, filled with unusual perennials and interesting features all year. TEA. *Adm £1 Chd 50p. Private visits welcome, please* Tel 01923 260571

1 Gernon Walk *&* (Miss Rachel Crawshay) Letchworth (First Garden City). Tiny town garden (100ft long but only 8ft wide in middle) planned and planted since 1984 for yr-round and horticultural interest. *Collecting box. Private visits only, please* Tel 01462 686399

Great Munden House *&&* (Mr & Mrs D Wentworth-Stanley) 7m N of Ware. Off A10 on Puckeridge by-pass turn W; or turning off A602 via Dane End. 3½-acre informal garden with lawns, mixed shrub and herbaceous borders; variety shrub roses, trees; kitchen and herb garden. Plant stall. TEAS in aid of NE Herts NSPCC. *Adm £2 Chd 50p. Sun April 28 (2-5). Private visits welcome, please* Tel 01920 438244

Great Sarratt Hall & *&&* (H M Neal Esq) Sarratt, N of Rickmansworth. From Watford N via A41 (or M1 Exit 5) to Kings Langley; and left (W) to Sarratt; garden is 1st on R after village sign. 4 acres; herbaceous and mixed shrub borders; pond, moisture-loving plants and trees; walled kitchen garden; rhododendrons, magnolias, camellias; new planting of specialist conifers and rare trees. TEAS. *Adm £2 Chd free (Share to Courtauld Institute of Art Fund®). Sun May 26 (2-6)*

¶High Elms Gardens & *&* Harpenden. On B487 (Redbourne Lane) off A1081 St Albans to Harpenden Rd. TEAS. *Adm £1.50 Chd 50p (Share to Multiple Sclerosis Society®). Sun June 16 (2-6)*
  ¶4 High Elms (Prof & Mrs Logan) ½-acre garden featuring an extensive herbaceous border
  ¶The Spinney, 6 High Elms (Tina & Michael Belderbos) ½-acre garden planted since 1980 with many special trees and shrubs and a recently designed herb garden

Hill House *&* (Mr & Mrs R Pilkington) Stanstead Abbotts, near Ware. From A10 turn E on to A414; then B181 for Stanstead Abbotts; left at end of High St, garden 1st R past Church. Ample car parking. 8 acres incl wood; species roses, herbaceous border, water garden, conservatory, aviary, woodland walk. Lovely view over Lea Valley. Modern Art Exhibition in loft gallery (20p extra). Unusual plants for sale. Home-made TEAS. *Adm £2 Chd 50p (Share to St Andrews Parish Church of Stanstead Abbotts®). Sun June 9 (2-5.30). Private visits and parties welcome, please* Tel 0192 0870013

Hipkins & *&&* (Michael Goulding Esq) Broxbourne. From A10 to Broxbourne turn up Bell or Park Lane into Baas Lane, opposite Graham Avenue. 3-acre informal garden with spring fed ponds; azaleas and rhododendrons; shrub and herbaceous borders specialising in plants for flower arrangers; many unusual plants; fine trees and well kept kitchen garden. TEAS. *Adm £1.50 Chd 50p. Sun May 19 (2-6)*

Holwell Manor *&&* (Mr & Mrs J Gillum) Nr Hatfield. On W side of B1455, short lane linking A414 with B158 between Hatfield (3m) and Hertford (4m). B1455 joins the A414 roundabout and is signposted Essendon. Holwell is 500yds from this roundabout. Natural garden with large pond fed by hydraulic ram powered fountain, mature trees, river walks; approx 2-3 acres. Island in pond covered with daffodils and narcissi in spring. TEA. *Adm £1.50 Chd 50p. Mon April 8 (2-5)*

Hunton Park *&* Kings Langley. 1m S of Junction 20 off M25 and 3m N of Watford. On exiting from Junction 20 follow signs to Watford (A41), turn L at traffic lights after ½m signposted Abbots Langley. Follow Bridge Rd for ½m up hill and Hunton Park is to be found on the RH-side. 22 acres of terraced lawns, gardens, pond and woodlands incl mature trees and ancient yews. First established in the 1840s the present grounds staff are working to return the gardens to their original setting comprising herbaceous borders, heather gardens, woodland plants and rose garden. A picnic area is provided for lunches. TEAS. *Adm £1.50 Chd free. Suns April 28, May 12, June 9 (12-5). Private visits welcome following tel/written application, please* Tel 01923 261511

Knebworth House &% (The Lord Cobbold) Knebworth. 28m N of London; direct access from A1(M) at Stevenage. Station and Bus stop: Stevenage 3m. Historic house, home of Bulwer Lytton; Victorian novelist and statesman. Lutyens garden designed for his brother-in-law, the Earl of Lytton, comprising pleached lime avenues, rose beds, herbaceous borders, yew hedges, restored maze and various small gardens in process of restoration; Gertrude Jekyll herb garden. Restaurant and TEAS. *Adm £1.50 Chd £1.* ▲*For NGS Sun Sept 29 (12-5)*

Little Gaddesden Gardens ❀ Approach from Hemel Hempstead along Leighton Buzzard Rd or from centre of Berkhamsted N of Station. The village hall is in Church Rd in centre of village, which is 2m N of Berkhamsted or 3½m W of Hemel Hempstead. Plants and Teas at village hall in aid of ARC. *Combined adm £2.50 Chd 50p. Sun June 16 (11-5)*

> **Ashridge Management College** & From hall down Church Rd to Village Rd and straight over to Ashridge Rd. Through gates into Ashridge College. 180 acreage approx/features as on map. The pleasure gardens were planned by Capability's disciple Humphry Repton (1813). Mount garden, circular rose garden and grotto. A new rock and water garden rhododendron walk
>
> **1 Home Farm** % (Mr & Mrs D E A Tucker) From village hall, down to main village rd L SE towards Nettleden ¾m to Home Farm Cottage and Shepherds Cottage on L. 4yr old garden with some mature trees, herbaceous borders, roses, clematis, water feature; a cottage garden
>
> **Nettleden Lodge** & (Mr & Mrs Allsop) From village hall down main Village Rd to Nettleden 1½m on R. Approx 4 acres comprising extensive lawns, herbaceous borders, ornamental lake and cascade, rhododendrons, magnolias, acers and many unusual plants. A plantsman's garden
>
> **Shepherds Cottage** % (Mr & Mrs G A B Ward) Small walled garden of interesting design. Unusual plants, water feature

The Gardens of Mackerye End %❀ A1 junction 4, follow signs for Wheathampstead then Luton. Gardens ½m from Wheathampstead on R. M1 junction 10 follow Lower Luton Rd (B653) to Cherry Tree Inn. Turn L to Wheathampstead. Lunches and TEAS. *Adm £2.50 Chd £1 (Share to MacIntyre®). Sun June 16 (12-5)*

> **Mackerye End House** (Mr & Mrs David Laing) A 1550 Grade 1 manor house set in 11 acres of gardens and park. Front garden set in framework of formal yew hedges with a long border and a fine C17 tulip tree. Victorian walled garden now divided into smaller sections; path maze; cutting garden; quiet garden; vegetables. Newly created W garden enclosed by pergola walk of old English roses and vines. Partially suitable for wheelchairs as flat but with gravel paths
>
> **Hollybush Cottage** (Mr & Mrs John Coaton) Delightful cottage garden around this listed house
>
> ¶**Eightacre** (Mr J Walker) 2-acre garden incl shrub and herbaceous beds, wild life pond, raised vegetable beds, greenhouse and orchards

The Manor House &% (Mrs Andrew Duncan) Ayot St Lawrence. Bear R into village from Bride Hall Lane, ruined Church on L and the Brocket Arms on R. On bend there is a pair of brick piers leading to drive - go through green iron gates. The Manor house is on your L. New garden, with formal garden, mixed borders and nut grove, large walled garden and orchard. TEAS NGS day only. *Adm £2 OAP/Chd £1 (under ten free). By appt for parties, please* **Tel 01438 820943**. *For NGS Sun July 7 (2-6)*

The Mill House &%❀ (Dr and Mrs R V Knight) Tewin, nr Archers Green. 3½m W of Hertford and 3½m E of Welwyn on B1000. Parking at Archers Green which is signposted on B1000. On the banks of the R Mimram. Approx 20 acres; mature gardens incl fine hedges, woodlands, many rare trees labelled, shrub and herbaceous borders, spring fed water gardens, with an abundance of wildlife in a lovely valley setting. Plants and TEAS in aid of Isabel Hospice. *Adm £2 Chd under 10 free. Sun July 7 (2-6)*

Moor Place &❀ (Mr & Mrs Bryan Norman) Much Hadham. Entrance either at war memorial or at Hadham Cross. 2 C18 walled gardens. Herbaceous borders. Large area of shrubbery, lawns, hedges and trees. 2 ponds. Approx 10 acres. TEAS. *Adm £2 Chd 50p. Sun June 9 (2-5.30)*

Myddelton House see London

Odsey Park &% (Mr & The Hon Mrs Jeremy Fordham) Situated equidistant between Royston and Baldock 4½m each way. On N carriageway of A505 enter by Lodge and drive into park as signposted. Recently re-made medium-sized garden originally dating from the 1860s with walled garden, set in park with mature trees, spring bulbs, tulips; small colourful herbaceous border, roses, shrubs and small herb garden. Car parking free. TEA April 21. TEAS June 30. *Adm £1.50 Chd free (Share to Ashwell Church Restoration Fund①). Suns April 21 (1-5); June 30 (2-6)*

¶**Old Hammers** %❀ (Mrs G D Chalk) Rushden. Off A507 Baldock/Buntingford Rd or from Royston A505. Turn L at Slip End. 1-acre garden on gentle slope with interesting trees, shrubs and herbaceous plants. Car park opp. Teas at Moon and Stars inn. *Adm £1 Chd 50p. Sun June 30 (2-5.30)*

¶**The Old Rectory** % (Mr & Mrs J M Dyson) Walkern. 3m E of Stevenage. N of village on B1037. 2-acre country garden with mixed herbaceous, old-fashioned rose and shrub borders. Large pond landscaped into meadow setting overlooking R Beane. Mown grass paths lead to spinney and adjacent St Mary's Church. TEAS in aid of St Mary's Church. *Adm £1.50 Chd 50p. Sun June 30 (2-5.30)*

Pelham House &%❀ (Mr David Haselgrove & Dr Sylvia Martinelli) Brent Pelham. On E side of Brent Pelham on B1038. When travelling from Clavering immed after the village sign. 3½-acre informal garden on alkaline clay started by present owners in 1986. Plenty of interest to the plantsman. Wide variety of trees and shrubs especially birches and oaks. Bulb frames, raised beds with alpines and acid-loving plants and small formal area with ponds. Many daffodils and tulips. TEAS. *Adm £1.50 Chd free (Share to Brent Pelham Church®). Suns April 7, May 12 (2-5)*

¶**Putteridge Bury** ❀ (University of Luton) On A505 Hitchin/Luton rd 2m NE of Luton on S side of dual carriageway. Gertrude Jekyll's plans for the rose garden and mixed border have been faithfully restored by the Herts Gardens Trust and are maintained by the University. Edwin Lutyens' reflecting pool and massive yew hedges are important features. Wide lawns, mature trees and new specimens make this an enjoyable garden to visit. Combined with nearby Temple Dinsley it provides an insight into garden design by Lutyens and Jekyll. TEAS. *Adm £3 OAP/Chd £1.50 (Share to Herts Gardens Trust®). Suns June 30, July 21 (10-5)*

Queenswood School ♿❀❀ Shepherds Way. From S: M25 junction 24 signposted Potters Bar. In ½m at lights turn R onto A1000 signposted Hatfield. In 2m turn R onto B157. School is ½m on the R. From N: A1000 from Hatfield. In 5m turn L onto B157. 120 acres informal gardens and woodlands. Rhododendrons, fine specimen trees, shrubs and herbaceous borders. Glasshouses; fine views to Chiltern Hills. Picnic area. Lunches and TEAS. *Adm £1.50 OAP's/Chd 75p. Sun, Mon May 26, 27 (11-6)*

¶**Rothamsted Manor** ♿❀❀ (Rothamsted Experimental Station) 5m N of St Albans, 1m from Harpenden. Turn off A1081 at roundabout. Junction with B487 toward Redbourn. Immed take R diagonal rd across Hatching Green. 6-acre formal gardens with fine topiary, rose garden and large herbaceous border surrounding C17 house, former home of Sir John Lawes, set in parkland. Concert band of Sir John Lawes School will play. TEA. *Adm £2 Chd £1 (Share to Lawes Agricultural Trust®). Sun July 14 (2-5)*

Rushmead ❀ (Mr & Mrs Brian Munnery) Abbots Langley. Garden sited midway between Abbots Langley and Bedmond on main Watford-Leverstock Green Rd. M25 junction 20 or M1 junction 6. A ¼-acre garden with variety of shrubs, trees and perennials; a lge, deep pond (care needed with children) with ornamental lilies and fish. *Adm £1.50 Chd free (Share to Abbots Langley Community Centre®). Suns June 23, July 14 (2-5)*

St Paul's Walden Bury ♿ (Simon Bowes Lyon and family) Whitwell, on B651 5m S of Hitchin; ½m N of Whitwell. Formal woodland garden listed Grade 1. Laid out about 1730, influenced by French tastes. Long rides and avenues span about 40 acres, leading to temples, statues, lake and ponds. Also more recent flower gardens and woodland garden with rhododendrons, azaleas and magnolias. Dogs on leads. TEAS. *Adm £2 Chd 50p (Share to St Pauls Walden Church®). Suns April 21, May 5, June 9, 30 (2-7) followed by lakeside concert 7pm. Also other times by appt* **Tel 01438 871218** *or* **871229**

Serge Hill ❀❀ (Murray & Joan Stuart-Smith) Abbots Langley. ½m E of Bedmond. The house is marked on the OS map. Regency house in parkland setting with fine kitchen garden of ½ acre. A range of unusual wall plants, mixed border of 100yds. New small courtyard garden and wall garden planted with hot coloured flowers. TEAS. *Combined adm £3 with* **The Barn** *(Share to Herts Garden Trust®). Sun June 23 (2-5)*

Tarn, Oxhey Drive South, Northwood *see* London.

¶**Temple Dinsley** (Princess Helena College) Preston, nr Hitchin. B656 Hitchin/Welwyn Garden City rd. Turn off just S of St Ippolits, signed Preston and Princess Helena College. The Herts Gardens Trust is restoring this important Edwin Lutyens garden which surrounds an altered Queen Anne house. Edwardian rose garden pergolas and architectural features are surrounded by lawns and trees. This evocative garden demonstrates the skill of Lutyens' designs and is an interesting counterpart to the gardens at Putteridge Bury. TEAS. *Adm £2.50 Chd £1 (Share to Princess Helena College®). Sun July 21 (10-5). Private visits welcome, please* **Tel 01462 432100**

Waterdell House ♿❀❀ (Mr & Mrs Peter Ward) Croxley Green. 1½m from Rickmansworth. Exit 18 from M25. Direction R'worth to join A412 towards Watford. From A412 turn left signed Sarratt, along Croxley Green, fork right past Coach & Horses, cross Baldwins Lane into Little Green Lane, then left at top. 1½-acre walled garden systematically developed over more than 40 years: mature and young trees, topiary holly hedge, herbaceous borders, modern island beds of shrubs, old-fashioned roses, vegetable, fruit and pond gardens. TEAS 80p. *Adm £1.50 OAPs/Chd £1. Sun June 30 (2-6) and private visits welcome by appt yr round, please* **Tel 01923 772775**

West Lodge Park ♿ (T Edward Beale Esq) Cockfosters Rd, Hadley Wood. On A111 between Potters Bar and Southgate. Exit 24 from M25 signed Cockfosters. The 10-acre Beale Arboretum consists of over 700 varieties of trees and shrubs, incl national plant collections of elaeaqnus and hornbeam cultivars, with a good selection of conifers, oaks, maples and mountain ash. A network of paths has been laid out, and most specimens are labelled. Lunch or teas can be booked in West Lodge Park hotel in the grounds. *Adm £1.50 Chd 30p. Suns May 19 (2-5.30); Oct 20 (12-4). Organised parties anytime by appt* **Tel 0181 4408311**

23 Wroxham Way ❀❀ (Mrs M G M Easter) Harpenden. NE Harpenden off Ox Lane. M1 Junction 6 + A1081 or Junction 10a + A1081. A1 Junction 4 or 5 and B653 Lower Luton Road. Plantsman's garden 70' × 35'. Sloping site with steps and walls. Large mixed border at front. Planted for yr round interest. Penstemon; alpine scree; herbs; national collection of thymus. *Adm £1 (Share to Gt Ormond St Children's Hospital®). Mon April 8, Thurs May 2, July 4, Suns June 9, July 21, Aug 25, Sat July 20 (2-5.30). Private visits welcome, please* **Tel 01582 768467**

Humberside

See Yorkshire

Isle of Wight

Hon County Organiser: Mrs John Harrison, North Court, Shorwell I.O.W. PO30 3JG
Hon County Treasurer: Mrs S Robak, 12 Cherry Tree Lane, Sherford Road, Taunton, Somerset, TA1 3RA

DATES OF OPENING

April 7 Sunday
Kings Manor, Freshwater

April 21 Sunday
Woolverton House, St Lawrence

April 28 Sunday
Badminton, Clatterford Shute, Carisbrooke

May 6 Sunday
Yaffles, Bonchurch

May 19 Sunday
Blackwater Mill, Newport ‡
Rock Cottage, Blackwater ‡

May 27 Monday
Waldeck, Brighstone

June 2 Sunday
North Court Gardens, Shorwell

June 9 Sunday
The Watch House, Bembridge

June 16 Sunday
Hamstead Grange, Yarmouth

June 19 Wednesday
Mottistone Manor Garden, Mottistone

June 30 Sunday
Nunwell House, Brading

July 6 Saturday
Pitt House, Bembridge

September 22 Sunday
North Court Gardens, Shorwell

Regular openings
For details see garden description

Yaffles, Bonchurch

By appointment only
For telephone numbers and other details see garden descriptions. Private visits welcomed

Highwood, Cranmore
Owl Cottage, Mottistone
Westport Cottage, Yarmouth

DESCRIPTIONS OF GARDENS

Badminton ❀ (Mr & Mrs G S Montrose) Clatterford Shute. Parking in Carisbrooke Castle car park. Public footpath in corner of car park leads down to the garden. ¾-acre garden with natural chalk stream. Mixed borders planted by owners during last 20 yrs, for all-yr interest. Lovely views. *Adm £1 Chd 25p. Sun April 28 (2.30-5)*

Blackwater Mill ♿✗❀ (Mrs Jacque Humphreys) Newport. Take the main Sandown rd from Newport, turn R at the junction to Blackwater. Pass the garage on your L and the garden open is approx 200yds on the R by the bus stop. Look for the Blackwater Mill Retirement Home sign. Garden set in 6 acres incl 2-acre lake with waterfowl; river walk and bridges; lge selection of shrubs; herbaceous, grasses, trees, conifers and heathers; scree bed, spring bulbs and many unusual plants. Easy walks around. TEAS. *Combined adm with* **Rock Cottage** *£1.50 Chd free. Sun May 19 (2.30-5.30). Private visits by parties of 6 and over welcome, please* **Tel 01983 526208**

Hamstead Grange ♿❀ (Mr & Mrs Tom Young) Yarmouth. Entrance to drive on A3054 between Shalfleet and Ningwood. Rose garden with shrubs, lawns and trees. 3 acres with superb views of Solent. Swimming pool. TEAS in aid of local charity. *Adm £1.50 Chd 20p. Sun June 16 (2.30-5.30)*

Highwood ✗❀ (Mr & Mrs Cooper) Cranmore Ave is approx halfway between the town of Yarmouth and the village of Shalfleet on the A3054. From Yarmouth the turning is on the L hand side, opp a bus shelter approx 3m out of Yarmouth on an unmade rd. 10-acre site with several acres under cultivation; pond with marginal planting, woodland area with hellebores and many spring flowers. Unusual shrubs, trees and perennials. *Private visits welcome March to Oct, please* **Tel 01983 760550**

Kings Manor ♿✗ (Mrs Jamie Sheldon) Freshwater. Head E out of Yarmouth over R Yar Bridge. Approx 1m turn L at top of Pixleys Hill. Entrance on L at top of next hill. 3-acre informal garden with shrubs and spring bulbs and frontage onto marshes. Special features - views of estuary and saltings - formal garden around lily pond. TEAS. *Adm £1.50 Chd free (Share to Jubilee Sailing Trust®). Sun April 7 (2.30-5)*

Mottistone Manor Garden ❀ (The National Trust) Mottistone. 8m SW Newport on B3399 between Brighstone and Brook. Medium-sized formal terraced garden, backing onto medieval and Elizabethan manor house, set in wooded valley with fine views of English Channel and coast between Needles and St. Catherine's Point. ▲*Adm £1.80 Chd 90p. Wed June 19 (2-5.30)*

North Court Gardens ♿✗❀ (Mrs C D Harrison, Mr & Mrs J Harrison, Mrs L Harrison) Shorwell 4m S of Newport on B3323, entrance on R after rustic bridge, opp thatched cottage. 14 acres; varied garden landscaped terraces, stream and water garden, woodland, walled garden, herbaceous borders, shrubs surrounding Jacobean Manor House. TEAS. *Combined adm £1.50 Chd 25p. Suns June 2, Sept 22 (2.30-5)*

Nunwell House ✗❀ (Col & Mrs J A Aylmer) Brading. 3m S of Ryde; signed off A3055 in Brading into Coach Lane. 5 acres beautifully set formal and shrub gardens with fountains. Exceptional view of Solent. House developed over 5 centuries, full of architectural interest. Coaches by appt only. TEAS. *Adm £1.50 Chd 20p incl Home Guard Museum; House £1.50 Chd 20p extra (Share to St Johns, Isle of Wight®). Sun June 30 (2-5)*

Owl Cottage &❀ (Mrs A L Hutchinson) Hoxall Lane, Mottistone. 9m SW of Newport, from B3399 at Mottistone turn down Hoxall Lane for 200yds. Interesting cottage garden, view of sea. Home-made TEAS. Plant sale. *Adm £1.50 Chd 20p. Visits by appointment everyday May until Aug, parties of 10 up to 30 (2.30-5.30), please* **Tel 01983 740433** *after 6pm*

Pitt House &✍ (L J Martin Esq) Bembridge. NE of Bembridge Harbour. Enter Bembridge Village, pass museum and take 1st L into Love Lane. Continue down lane (5 min walk) as far as the bend; Pitt House is on L. Enter tall wrought iron gates. If coming by car enter Ducie Ave 1st L before museum. Pitt House at bottom of ave, on the R. Parking in lane. Approx 4 acres with varied aspects and points of interest. A number of sculptures dotted around the garden; also victorian greenhouse, mini waterfall and 4 ponds. *Adm £1.20 Chd 50p. Sat July 6 (10.30-5)*

Rock Cottage ✍ (Mary & Cliff Pain) Blackwater. From Newport take main rd to Ventnor. Park in Blackwater on/off main rd **but not** in Sandy Lane. Short walk, approx 200yds, up Sandy Lane to Rock Cottage. ⅓-acre. Cottage garden. Some flowering shrubs, spring bulbs, numerous clematis and hardy perennials; fruit and vegetables. Lawn and numerous small plots divided by grass paths. Tea at Blackwater Mill. *Combined adm with* **Blackwater Mill** *£1.50 Chd free. Sun May 19 (2.30-5). Also private visits by appt for max 10, please* **Tel 01983 525845**

Waldeck ✍ (Mr & Mrs G R Williams) Brighstone. 8m SW of Newport. Take Carisbrooke-Shorwell rd, then B3399 to Brighstone. Through village centre, turn R off main rd into Moor Lane. Limited parking in lane. ¾-acre garden informally planted to provide some colour and interest from trees, shrubs and perennial plants throughout the year. Special emphasis placed on foliage and shade tolerant plants such as acers, ferns, hostas, etc. Teas available. *Adm £1 Chd free (Share to Society for the Blind®). Mon May 27 (2.30-5.30)*

The Watch House ✍ Bembridge. Most easterly part of I of W. St Helens-Bembridge. Before ascending hill by Pilot Inn turn L to Silver Beach Cafe. Last house on R. ¾-acre garden best known for its garden architecture and sea views (house built for the Admiralty). Formal garden at rear of house with fruit trees, rose arches and box hedges. TEA. *Adm £1 Chd 20p (Share to Bembridge Lifeboat®). Sun June 9 (2-5)*

Westport Cottage &❀ (M Fisher & K Sharp) Tennyson Close off Tennyson Rd. ½-acre walled garden, wildlife pond, orchard, vegetables, patio and greenhouse. Semi-hardy and unusual plants. TEA. *Adm £1.50 Chd 50p (Share to St Mary's Hospital League of Friends©). Private visits welcome, especially garden groups, flower arrangers. Talks and meals by arrangement, please* **Tel 01983 760751**

Woolverton House (Mr & Mrs S H G Twining) St Lawrence. 3m W of Ventnor; Bus 16 from Ryde, Sandown, Shanklin. Flowering shrubs, bulbs, fine position. Home-made TEAS. *Adm £1.50 Chd 20p (Share to St Lawrence Village Hall®). Sun April 21 (2-5)*

Yaffles ❀ (Mrs Wolfenden) The Pitts. The garden may be approached through Bonchurch Village, up the hill past the parish church 1st on L or from the top rd (Shanklin 2m to the E) turn L down the Bonchurch Shute, garden is immediately above St Boniface Church and next to the cul de sac The Pitts. Park in the rd. A 60′ flowering cliff sculptured into glades; it is full of interesting plants and commands excellent views of the Channel. Only suitable for wheelchairs on the top level where the teas and toilet are situated. Joan Wolfenden's book the Year from Yaffles is sold in aid of the NGS. Coffee and TEAS in aid of church. *Adm £1.50 Chd free. Open all year. For NGS May 6 (3-5.30). Private visits welcome. Parties of 10 or more preferred. Please* **Tel 01983 852193** *after 12 noon*

By Appointment Gardens. These owners do not have a fixed opening day usually because they do not like crowds or have insufficient parking space. Owner will often give guided tour.

Regular Openers. Too many days to include in diary. Usually there is a wide range of plants giving year-round interest. See end of county section for the name and garden description for times etc.

SYMBOLS USED IN THIS BOOK (See also Page 15)

‡   Following a garden name in the Dates of Opening list indicates that those gardens sharing the same symbol are nearby and open on the same day.

‡‡   Indicates a second series of nearby gardens open on the same day.

¶   Opening for the first time.

❀   Plants/produce for sale if available.

&   Gardens with at least the main features accessible by wheelchair.

✍   No dogs except guide dogs but otherwise dogs are usually admitted, provided they are kept on a lead. Dogs are not admitted to houses.

●   Gardens marked thus do not necessarily give all their takings to the National Gardens Scheme. Instead they give a guaranteed contribution.

▲   Where this sign appears alongside dates in the descriptive entry for a garden it denotes that this garden is also open regularly to the public on days other than those for the NGS.

Kent

Hon County Organiser:	Mrs Valentine Fleming, Stonewall Park, Edenbridge TN8 7DG
Assistant Hon County Organisers:	Mrs Jeremy Gibbs, Upper Kennards, Leigh, Tonbridge TN11 8RE
	Mrs Nicolas Irwin, Hoo Farmhouse, Minster, Ramsgate CT12 4JB
	Mrs Richard Latham, Stowting Hill House, nr Ashford TN25 6BE
	Miss E Napier, 447 Wateringbury Road, East Malling ME19 6JQ
	Mrs M R Streatfeild, Hoath House, Chiddingstone Hoath, Edenbridge TN8 7DB
	Mrs Simon Toynbee, Old Tong Farm, Brenchley TN12 7HT
Hon County Treasurer:	Valentine Fleming Esq, Stonewall Park, Edenbridge TN8 7DG

DATES OF OPENING

February 11 Sunday
Goodnestone Park, Wingham,
  nr Canterbury
190 Maidstone Road, Chatham
February 29 Thursday
Hadlow College, Hadlow
March 3 Sunday
Great Comp, Borough Green
March 10 Sunday
Goodnestone Park, Wingham,
  nr Canterbury
Great Comp, Borough Green
Owl House, Lamberhurst
Weeks Farm, Egerton Forstal
March 17 Sunday
Copton Ash, Faversham
Great Comp, Borough Green
March 24 Sunday
Church Hill Cottage, Charing
  Heath
Cobham Hall, Cobham
March 31 Sunday
Church Hill Cottage, Charing
  Heath
Crittenden House, Matfield
190 Maidstone Road, Chatham
Spilsill Court, Staplehurst
April 7 Easter Sunday
Church Hill Cottage, Charing
  Heath ‡
Copton Ash, Faversham
Godinton Park, Ashford
Hole Park, Rolvenden
Jessups, Mark Beech,
  nr Edenbridge
Longacre, Selling
The Pines Garden and Bay
  Museum, St Margaret's Bay
Sissinghurst Place, Sissinghurst
Weeks Farm, Egerton Forstal ‡
April 8 Easter Monday
Brewhouse, Boughton Aluph
Church Hill Cottage, Charing
  Heath
Copton Ash, Faversham
Crittenden House, Matfield
Horton Priory, Sellindge
Longacre, Selling
Mere House, Mereworth

Sissinghurst Place, Sissinghurst
April 14 Sunday
Church Hill Cottage, Charing
  Heath
Coldham, Little Chart Forstal
Edenbridge House, Edenbridge
Finchcocks, Goudhurst
Hole Park, Rolvenden
2 Thorndale Close, Chatham
Withersdane Hall, Wye
April 15 Monday
Groombridge Place, Groombridge
April 20 Saturday
Pett Place, Charing
April 21 Sunday
Longacre, Selling ‡
Luton House, Selling ‡
New Barns House, West Malling
Pett Place, Charing
Torry Hill, nr Sittingbourne
Yalding Gardens
April 24 Wednesday
Hole Park, Rolvenden
Sissinghurst Castle Garden,
  Sissinghurst
Westview, Hempstead, Gillingham
April 27 Saturday
Westview, Hempstead, Gillingham
April 28 Sunday
Beech Court Gardens, Challock
Bradbourne House, East Malling
Brewhouse, Boughton Aluph
Church Hill Cottage, Charing
  Heath
Coldharbour Oast, Tenterden
Hole Park, Rolvenden
Maurice House, Broadstairs
Mount Ephraim, Hernhill,
  Faversham
Stoneacre, Otham
Swan Oast, Stilebridge, Marden
2 Thorndale Close, Chatham
May 1 Wednesday
Rock Farm, Nettlestead
Stoneleigh House, Stone Street,
  nr Canterbury
May 3 Friday
Great Maytham Hall, Rolvenden
May 4 Saturday
Peddars Wood, St Michaels,
  Tenterden

Riverhill House, Sevenoaks
Rock Farm, Nettlestead
May 5 Sunday
Charts Edge, Westerham
Church Hill Cottage, Charing
  Heath
Copton Ash, Faversham
Doddington Place,
  nr Sittingbourne
Edenbridge House, Edenbridge ‡
Godmersham Park, nr Ashford
Hault Farm, Waltham,
  nr Canterbury
Hole Park, Rolvenden
Longacre, Selling
St Michael's House, Roydon,
  Peckham Bush
Stonewall Park Gardens,
  nr Edenbridge ‡
Swan Oast, Stilebridge, Marden
Thornham Friars, Thurnham
Turkey Court, Maidstone
Whitehurst, Chainhurst, Marden
May 6 Monday
Beech Court Gardens, Challock
Brewhouse, Boughton Aluph
Church Hill Cottage, Charing
  Heath
Copton Ash, Faversham
Crittenden House, Matfield
Longacre, Selling
Meadow Wood, Penshurst
May 8 Wednesday
Penshurst Place, Penshurst
Rock Farm, Nettlestead
Stoneleigh House, Stone Street,
  nr Canterbury
May 11 Saturday
Emmetts Garden, Ide Hill
Rock Farm, Nettlestead
May 12 Sunday
Charts Edge, Westerham
Church Hill Cottage, Charing
  Heath
Doddington Place,
  nr Sittingbourne
Larksfield, Crockham Hill ‡
Larksfield Cottage, Crockham
  Hill ‡
The Red House, Crockham Hill ‡
Sea Close, Hythe

Swan Oast, Stilebridge, Marden
2 Thorndale Close, Chatham
May 15 Wednesday
Hole Park, Rolvenden
Rock Farm, Nettlestead
Stoneleigh House, Stone Street,
  nr Canterbury
Westview, Hempstead, Gillingham
May 18 Saturday
Rock Farm, Nettlestead
Westview, Hempstead, Gillingham
May 19 Sunday
Bilting House, Ashford
Brenchley Gardens
Doddington Place,
  nr Sittingbourne ‡
Flint Cottage, Bourne Park,
  Bishopsbourne
Goudhurst Gardens
Hole Park, Rolvenden
Larksfield, Crockham Hill ‡‡
Larksfield Cottage, Crockham Hill ‡‡
Marle Place, Brenchley
Pevington Farm, Pluckley
Ramhurst Manor, Leigh,
  Tonbridge
The Red House, Crockham Hill ‡‡
Torry Hill, nr Sittingbourne ‡
Town Hill Cottage, West Malling
Walnut Tree Gardens, Little Chart
May 22 Wednesday
Edenbridge House, Edenbridge
Rock Farm, Nettlestead
Stoneleigh House, Stone Street,
  nr Canterbury
Waystrode Manor, Cowden
May 24 Friday
Kypp Cottage, Biddenden
May 25 Saturday
Kypp Cottage, Biddenden
Riverhill House, Sevenoaks
Rock Farm, Nettlestead
May 26 Sunday
The Beehive, Lydd ‡
Church Hill Cottage, Charing
  Heath
Hartlip Gardens
Hole Park, Rolvenden
Kypp Cottage, Biddenden
Ladham House, Goudhurst
Little Trafalgar, Selling ‡‡
Longacre, Selling ‡‡
Mill House, Hildenborough
Olantigh, Wye
Old Buckhurst, Mark Beech
Oxon Hoath, nr Hadlow
The Pines Garden & Bay
  Museum, St Margaret's Bay
St Michael's House, Roydon,
  Peckham Bush
2 Thorndale Close, Chatham
Vine House, Lydd ‡
Walnut Tree Gardens, Little Chart
Waystrode Manor, Cowden

May 27 Monday
Beech Court Gardens, Challock
The Beehive, Lydd ‡
Brewhouse, Boughton Aluph
Church Hill Cottage, Charing
  Heath
Forest Gate, Pluckley
Kypp Cottage, Biddenden
Little Trafalgar, Selling ‡‡
Longacre, Selling ‡‡
Scotney Castle, Lamberhurst
The Silver Spray, Sellindge
Stoneleigh House, Stone Street,
  nr Canterbury
Vine House, Lydd ‡
Walnut Tree Gardens, Little Chart
May 28 Tuesday
Kypp Cottage, Biddenden
May 29 Wednesday
Kypp Cottage, Biddenden
Rock Farm, Nettlestead
Stoneleigh House, Stone Street,
  nr Canterbury
Whitehurst, Chainhurst, Marden
June 1 Saturday
Peddars Wood, St Michaels,
  Tenterden
Rock Farm, Nettlestead
June 2 Sunday
Church Hill Cottage, Charing
  Heath
Copton Ash, Faversham
Flint Cottage, Bourne Park,
  Bishopsbourne
Kypp Cottage, Biddenden
Mere House, Mereworth
Northbourne Court, nr Deal
Owl House, Lamberhurst
Sea Close, Hythe
Walnut Tree Gardens, Little Chart
Whitehurst, Chainhurst, Marden
June 3 Monday
Kypp Cottage, Biddenden
June 4 Tuesday
Kypp Cottage, Biddenden
June 5 Wednesday
Hole Park, Rolvenden
Knole, Sevenoaks
Kypp Cottage, Biddenden
Rock Farm, Nettlestead
Sissinghurst Castle Garden,
  Sissinghurst
Stoneleigh House, Stone Street,
  nr Canterbury
Westview, Hempstead, Gillingham
June 6 Thursday
Penshurst Place, Penshurst
June 8 Saturday
Rock Farm, Nettlestead
Westview, Hempstead, Gillingham
June 9 Sunday
Abbotsmerry Barn, Penshurst
Amber Green Farmhouse, Chart
  Sutton ‡

Beech Court Gardens, Challock
Kypp Cottage, Biddenden
Little Trafalgar, Selling ‡‡
Longacre, Selling ‡‡
Nonington & Woodnesborough
  Gardens
Northbourne Court, nr Deal
Springhead, Loose ‡
2 Thorndale Close, Chatham
Walnut Tree Gardens, Little
  Chart
June 10 Monday
Kypp Cottage, Biddenden
June 11 Tuesday
Kypp Cottage, Biddenden
June 12 Wednesday
Kypp Cottage, Biddenden
Rock Farm, Nettlestead
Stoneleigh House, Stone Street,
  nr Canterbury
Upper Pryors, Cowden
June 15 Saturday
Downs Court, Boughton Aluph
Haydown, Great Buckland
The Old Parsonage, Sutton
  Valence
Rock Farm, Nettlestead
June 16 Sunday
Abbotsmerry Barn, Penshurst
Amber Green Farmhouse, Chart
  Sutton ‡
Brewhouse, Boughton Aluph
Downs Court, Boughton Aluph
Edenbridge House, Edenbridge
Goudhurst Gardens
Horton Priory, Sellindge
Kypp Cottage, Biddenden
Lullingstone Castle, Eynsford
Northbourne Court, nr Deal
Pevington Farm, Pluckley
St Michael's House, Roydon,
  Peckham Bush
Springhead, Loose ‡
Town Hill Cottage, West
  Malling ‡‡
Waystrode Manor, Cowden
Went House, West Malling ‡‡
Whitehill, Wrotham
June 17 Monday
Kypp Cottage, Biddenden
June 18 Tuesday
Kypp Cottage, Biddenden
The Old Parsonage, Sutton
  Valence
June 19 Wednesday
Ightham Mote, Ivy Hatch
Kypp Cottage, Biddenden
Rock Farm, Nettlestead
Stoneleigh House, Stone Street,
  nr Canterbury
Waystrode Manor, Cowden
June 21 Friday
The Old Parsonage, Sutton
  Valence

June 22 Saturday
Elham Gardens
Pett Place, Charing
Rock Farm, Nettlestead
The Silver Spray, Sellindge
June 23 Sunday
Battel Hall, Leeds
Egerton Gardens
Kypp Cottage, Biddenden
Lily Vale Farm, Smeeth, Ashford ‡
Little Trafalgar, Selling ‡‡
Lodge House, Smeeth, Ashford ‡
Long Barn, Weald, Sevenoaks
Longacre, Selling ‡‡
Northbourne Court, nr Deal
The Old Parsonage, Sutton
    Valence
Old Place Farm, High Halden
Pett Place, Charing
Plaxtol Gardens
Rogers Rough, Kilndown
St Clere, Kemsing
Sibton Park, Lyminge
The Silver Spray, Sellindge
2 Thorndale Close, Chatham
Walnut Tree Gardens, Little Chart
Whitehurst, Chainhurst, Marden
June 24 Monday
Kypp Cottage, Biddenden
June 25 Tuesday
Kypp Cottage, Biddenden
June 26 Wednesday
Kypp Cottage, Biddenden
Lily Vale Farm, Smeeth, Ashford ‡
Lodge House, Smeeth,
    Ashford ‡
Rock Farm, Nettlestead
Stoneleigh House, Stone Street,
    nr Canterbury
Wyckhurst, Aldington
June 28 Friday
Great Maytham Hall, Rolvenden
June 29 Saturday
Coach House, Sissinghurst Place ‡
Rock Farm, Nettlestead
Sissinghurst Place, Sissinghurst ‡
Street End Place, nr Canterbury
Womenswold Gardens
June 30 Sunday
Coach House, Sissinghurst Place ‡
Forest Gate, Pluckley
Kypp Cottage, Biddenden
Northbourne Court, nr Deal
Olantigh, Wye
Otham Gardens
Placketts Hole, Bicknor, nr
    Sittingbourne
Shipbourne Gardens
Sissinghurst Place, Sissinghurst ‡
Street Cottage, Bethersden
Swan Oast, Stilebridge, Marden
Walnut Tree Gardens, Little Chart
Waystrode Manor, Cowden
Went House, West Malling

Womenswold Gardens
Wyckhurst, Aldington
July 1 Monday
Kypp Cottage, Biddenden
July 2 Tuesday
Kypp Cottage, Biddenden
July 3 Wednesday
Chartwell, Westerham
Kypp Cottage, Biddenden
Rock Farm, Nettlestead
The Silver Spray, Sellindge
Stoneleigh House, Stone Street,
    nr Canterbury
July 6 Saturday
Beech Court Gardens, Challock
Rock Farm, Nettlestead
The Silver Spray, Sellindge
South Hill Farm, Hastingleigh
July 7 Sunday
Brewhouse, Boughton Aluph
Godinton Park, Ashford
Kypp Cottage, Biddenden
Little Trafalgar, Selling ‡
Longacre, Selling ‡
Nettlestead Place, Nettlestead
Northbourne Court, nr Deal
Old Tong Farm, Brenchley
Sea Close, Hythe
South Hill Farm, Hastingleigh
Walnut Tree Gardens, Little Chart
Waystrode Manor, Cowden
Withersdane Hall, Wye
Worth Gardens
July 8 Monday
Kypp Cottage, Biddenden
July 9 Tuesday
Kypp Cottage, Biddenden
July 10 Wednesday
Kypp Cottage, Biddenden
Rock Farm, Nettlestead
Sissinghurst Garden, Sissinghurst
Stoneleigh House, Stone Street,
    nr Canterbury
July 13 Saturday
Rock Farm, Nettlestead
July 14 Sunday
Bilting House, Ashford
Church Hill Cottage, Charing
    Heath
Coldham, Little Chart Forstal ‡
Copton Ash, Faversham
Edenbridge House, Edenbridge
Field House, Staplehurst
Goodnestone Park, Wingham,
    nr Canterbury
Groome Farm, Egerton
115 Hadlow Road, Tonbridge
Kypp Cottage, Biddenden
Long Barn, Weald, Sevenoaks
Northbourne Court, nr Deal
Old Buckhurst, Mark Beech
Old Tong Farm, Brenchley
Owl House, Lamberhurst
Rogers Rough, Kilndown

Squerryes Court, Westerham
Swan Oast, Stilebridge, Marden
Walnut Tree Gardens, Little
    Chart ‡
July 15 Monday
Kypp Cottage, Biddenden
July 16 Tuesday
Kypp Cottage, Biddenden
July 17 Wednesday
Cares Cross, Chiddingstone
    Hoath (evening opening)
Kypp Cottage, Biddenden
Rock Farm, Nettlestead
The Silver Spray, Sellindge
July 20 Saturday
Peddars Wood, St Michaels,
    Tenterden
Rock Farm, Nettlestead
The Silver Spray, Sellindge
July 21 Sunday
Little Trafalgar, Selling ‡
Longacre, Selling ‡
Northbourne Court, nr Deal
Walnut Tree Gardens, Little Chart
July 24 Wednesday
Rock Farm, Nettlestead
July 27 Saturday
Haydown, Great Buckland
Rock Farm, Nettlestead
July 28 Sunday
Copton Ash, Faversham
190 Maidstone Road, Chatham
Northbourne Court, nr Deal
Orchard Cottage, Bickley
Spilsill Court, Staplehurst
Swan Oast, Stilebridge, Marden
Walnut Tree Gardens, Little Chart
July 31 Wednesday
185 Borden Lane, Sittingbourne
Rock Farm, Nettlestead
August 3 Saturday
Beech Court Gardens, Challock
Peddars Wood, St Michaels
    Tenterden
Rock Farm, Nettlestead
August 4 Sunday
185 Borden Lane, Sittingbourne
Field House, Staplehurst
115 Hadlow Road, Tonbridge
Little Trafalgar, Selling ‡
Longacre, Selling ‡
Northbourne Court, nr Deal
Sea Close, Hythe
Walnut Tree Gardens, Little Chart
Withersdane Hall, Wye
August 7, Wednesday
Knole, Sevenoaks
Rock Farm, Nettlestead
Stoneleigh House, Stone Street,
    nr Canterbury
August 10 Saturday
Rock Farm, Nettlestead
August 11 Sunday
Chevening, Sevenoaks

Marle Place, Brenchley
Northbourne Court, nr Deal
Swan Oast, Stilebridge, Marden
Walnut Tree Gardens, Little Chart

August 18 Sunday
Church Hill Cottage, Charing
  Heath
Northbourne Court, nr Deal
Squerryes Court, Westerham
Walnut Tree Gardens, Little Chart
West Studdal Farm, nr Dover

August 21 Wednesday
The Silver Spray, Sellindge

August 25 Sunday
The Beehive, Lydd ‡
Church Hill Cottage, Charing
  Heath
Copton Ash, Faversham
115 Hadlow Road, Tonbridge
Little Trafalgar, Selling ‡‡
Longacre, Selling ‡‡
Northbourne Court, nr Deal
The Pines Garden & Bay
  Museum, St Margaret's Bay
Swan Oast, Stilebridge, Marden
Vine House, Lydd ‡

August 26 Monday
The Beehive, Lydd ‡
Church Hill Cottage, Charing
  Heath
Copton Ash, Faversham
Little Trafalgar, Selling ‡‡
Longacre, Selling ‡‡
The Silver Spray, Sellindge
Vine House, Lydd ‡

September 1 Sunday
185 Borden Lane, Sittingbourne
Cobham Hall, Cobham
Coldharbour Oast, Tenterden
Turkey Court, Maidstone
Withersdane Hall, Wye

September 7 Saturday
Beech Court Gardens, Challock

September 8 Sunday
Longacre, Selling
Swan Oast, Stilebridge, Marden

September 15 Sunday
Finchcocks, Goudhurst
Groome Farm, Egerton ‡
Hadlow College, Hadlow
Little Trafalgar, Selling
Weeks Farm, Egerton Forstal ‡

September 25 Wednesday
Edenbridge House, Edenbridge

September 27 Friday
Great Maytham Hall, Rolvenden

September 29 Sunday
Edenbridge House, Edenbridge
Nettlestead Place, Nettlestead
Sea Close, Hythe

October 2 Wednesday
Sissinghurst Garden, Sissinghurst

October 5 Saturday
Emmetts Garden, Ide Hill

October 6 Sunday
Everden Farmhouse, Alkham
Marle Place, Brenchley
Whitehurst, Chainhurst, Marden

October 13 Sunday
Beech Court Gardens, Challock
Hault Farm, Waltham,
  nr Canterbury
Hole Park, Rolvenden
Mere House, Mereworth
Mount Ephraim, Hernhill,
  Faversham
Stoneacre, Otham
Whitehurst, Chainhurst, Marden

October 14 Monday
Groombridge Place, Groombridge

October 20 Sunday
Copton Ash, Faversham
Hole Park, Rolvenden

November 3 Sunday
Great Comp, Borough Green

Regular openings
For details see garden description

Beech Court Gardens, Challock
Cobham Hall, Cobham
Doddington Hall, nr Sittingbourne
Finchcocks, Goudhurst
Godinton Park, Ashford
Goodnestone Park, nr Wingham,
  Canterbury
Great Comp, Borough Green
Groombridge Place, Groombridge
Hault Farm, Waltham, nr Canterbury
Hever Castle, nr Edenbridge
Marle Place, Brenchley
Mount Ephraim, Hernhill, Canterbury
Owl House, Lamberhurst
Penshurst Place, Penshurst
The Pines Garden and Bay Museum,
  St Margaret's Bay
Riverhill House, Sevenoaks
Squerryes Court, Westerham

By appointment only
*For telephone numbers and other
details see garden descriptions.
Private visits welcomed*

Greencroft, Hildenborough
Greenways, Single Street, nr Downe
43 Layhams Road, West Wickham
The Pear House, Sellindge
Saltwood Castle, nr Hythe
Tanners, Brasted
39 Warwick Crescent, Borstal,
  nr Rochester

DESCRIPTIONS OF GARDENS

Abbotsmerry Barn ✿ (Mr & Mrs K H Wallis) Salmans Lane, Penshurst. Between Penshurst and Leigh on B2176: 200yds N of Penshurst turn L, 1m down lane with speed ramps. 5-acre garden with widely varied planting on S-facing slope overlooking the Eden valley. Teas in Penshurst. *Adm £2 Acc chd free. Suns June 9, 16 (2-5.30)*

Amber Green Farmhouse ✿❀ (Mr & Mrs J Groves) Chart Sutton, 7m SE of Maidstone. Turn W off A274 onto B2163, in 1m turn L at Chart Corner, next R is Amber Lane, house ½m W. C17 listed weatherboarded farmhouse (not open) in 1-acre garden. Enchanting cottage garden with hardy perennials, old fashioned climbing and shrub roses, two old ponds, bog plants, shrub borders. **Springhead, Loose** also open both days. *Adm £1.50 Acc chd free. Suns June 9, 16 (2-5.30)*

Battel Hall ❀✿ (John D Money Esq) Leeds, Maidstone. From A20 Hollingbourne roundabouts take B2163 S (signed Leeds Castle), at top of hill take Burberry Lane, house 100yds on R. Garden of approx 1 acre created since 1954 around medieval house; roses, herbaceous plants, shrubs and ancient wisteria. TEAS. *Adm £2 Chd £1 (Share to Macmillan Fund for Cancer Relief®). Sun June 23 (2-6)*

Beech Court Gardens ❀✿❀ (Mr & Mrs Vyvyan Harmsworth) Challock, W of crossroads A251/A252, off the Lees. 10-acre woodland garden with many acers, rhododendrons, azaleas and viburnums giving spring colour; philadelphus, roses and hydrangeas follow on; autumn colour. Picnic area in paddock: refreshments available. *Adm £2 Chd £1. Open every day March 31-October 31 (10-5; Suns 12-5). For NGS Suns April 28, June 9, Oct 13 (12-5); Mons May 6, 27; Sats July 6, Aug 3, Sept 7 (10-5); also private visits welcome, please Tel 01233 740735*

The Beehive ⚸ (C G Brown Esq) 10 High Street, Lydd. S of New Romney on B2075, in centre of Lydd opp Church. Small walled garden, tucked behind village street house dating from 1550, with over 200 varieties of plants. There are paths and cosy corners in this cottage garden with pond and pergola; a pool of seclusion; the busy world outside unnoticed passes by. Teas usually available in the church. *Adm £1.50 Acc chd free (Share to Horder Centre for Arthritis, Crowborough®). Suns, Mons May 26, 27, Aug 25, 26 (2.30-5)*

Bilting House ♿⚸ (John Erle-Drax Esq) A28, 5m NE of Ashford, 9m from Canterbury. Wye 1½m. Old-fashioned garden with ha-ha; rhododendrons, azaleas; shrubs. In beautiful part of Stour Valley. TEAS. *Adm £1.50 Chd 50p (Share to BRCS®). Suns May 19, July 14 (2-6)*

185 Borden Lane ♿⚸❀ (Mr & Mrs P A Boyce) ½m S of Sittingbourne. 1m from Sittingbourne side of A2/A249 junction. Small informal garden with many varieties of fuchsia; hardy perennials; shrubs; pond; fruit, vegetable and herb garden. Home-made TEAS. *Adm £1 Acc chd free. Wed July 31, Suns Aug 4, Sept 1; (2-5.30); also private visits welcome, please* Tel 01795 472243

Bradbourne House Gardens ♿ (East Malling Trust for Horticultural Research & Horticulture Research International) East Malling, 4m W of Maidstone. Entrance is E of New Road, which runs from Larkfield on A20 S to E Malling. The Hatton Fruit Garden consists of demonstration fruit gardens of particular interest to amateurs, in a walled former kitchen garden and incl intensive forms of apples and pears. Members of staff available for questions. TEAS. *Adm £1.50 Acc chd free. Sun April 28 (2-5)*

Brenchley Gardens 6m SE of Tonbridge. From A21 1m S of Pembury turn N on to B2160, turn R at Xrds in Matfield signed Brenchley. *Combined adm £2.50 Acc chd free. Sun May 19 (2-6)*

    Holmbush ♿⚸ (Brian & Cathy Worden Hodge) 1½-acre informal garden, mainly lawns, trees and shrub borders, planted since 1960

    Portobello (Barry M Williams Esq) 1½ acres, lawn, trees, shrubs incl azaleas and shrub roses; walled garden. House (not open) built by Monckton family 1739

    Puxted House ♿❀ (P J Oliver-Smith Esq) 1½ acres with rare and coloured foliage shrubs, water and woodland plants. Alpine and rose garden all labelled. Present owner cleared 20yrs of brambles in 1981 before replanting. TEAS

Brewhouse ⚸❀ (Mrs R Nicholson) Malthouse Lane, Boughton Aluph, 3m N of Ashford, off Pilgrims Way. ¼m N and signed from Boughton Lees village green, on A251 Ashford-Faversham. 1-acre plantsman's garden. C16 farmhouse (not open) with fine views of open chalkland. Collections of old roses, other old-fashioned flowers, herbaceous and foliage plants. TEAS (in aid of All Saints Church; not April 8, 28, May 6). *Adm £1.50 Acc chd free. Mons April 8, May 6, 27; Suns April 28, June 16, July 7 (2-5.30); also by appt, please* Tel 01233 623748

Cares Cross ♿❀ (Mr & Mrs R L Wadsworth) Chiddingstone Hoath. [Ordnance Survey Grid ref. TQ 496 431.] Landscaped garden around C16 house (not open). Dramatic views to N Downs over fields with old oaks, restored hedgerows, wildfowl lake and **vineyard**. Garden features old roses; water garden; innovative ground cover; rare shrubs and trees; speciality American plants. Featured on BBC Gardeners World 1990. *Adm £3 (incl glass of Kentish wine) OAP £2.50 Acc chd free. Wed July 17 (5-8pm)* **NB EVENING OPENING;** *also by appt to groups of 5-20, weekdays only mid May to end July*

Charts Edge ♿ (Mr & Mrs John Bigwood) Westerham, ½m S of Westerham on B2026 towards Chartwell. 7-acre hillside garden being restored by present owners; large collection of rhododendrons, azaleas & magnolias; specimen trees & newly-planted mixed borders; Victorian folly; walled vegetable garden; rock garden. Fine views over N Downs. Dressage display, if riders available, at 3.30pm. TEAS. *Adm £1.50 Chd 25p (Share to BHS Dressage Group©). Suns May 5, 12 (2-5)*

Chartwell (The National Trust) 2m S of Westerham, fork L off B2026 after 1½m, well signed. 12-acre informal gardens on a hillside with glorious views over Weald of Kent. Fishpools and lakes together with red-brick wall built by Sir Winston Churchill, the former owner of Chartwell. The avenue of golden roses given by the family on Sir Winston's golden wedding anniversary will be at its best. Self-service restaurant serving coffee, lunches and teas. *Adm £2 Chd £1.* ▲*Wed July 3 (11-4.30)*

Chevening ♿ (By permission of the Board of Trustees of Chevening Estate and the Rt Hon Malcolm Rifkind) 4m NW of Sevenoaks. Turn N off A25 at Sundridge traffic lights on to B2211; at Chevening Xrds 1½m turn L. 27 acres with lawns and woodland garden, lake, maze, formal rides, parterre. Garden being restored. TEAS in aid of Kent Church Social Work and overseas charities. *Adm £1.50 Chd 50p. Sun Aug 11 (2-6)*

Church Hill Cottage ♿❀ (Mr & Mrs Michael Metianu) Charing Heath, 10m NW of Ashford. Leave M20 at junction 8 (Lenham) if Folkestone-bound or junction 9 (Ashford West) if London-bound: then leave A20 dual carriageway ½m W of Charing signed Charing Heath and Egerton. After 1m fork R at Red Lion, then R again; cottage 250yds on R. C16 cottage surrounded by garden of 1½ acres, developed & planted by present owners since 1981. Several separate connected areas each containing island beds & borders planted with extensive range of perennials, shrubs, spring bulbs, ferns and hostas. Gardens & nursery open every day except Mons. Picnic area. Lunches/snacks at Red Lion. *Adm £1.50 Chd 50p (Share to Paula Carr Trust®). For NGS Suns March 24, 31, April 7, 14, 28, May 5, 12, 26, June, 2, July 14, Aug 18, 25; Mons April 8, May 6, 27, Aug 26 (11-5): also private visits welcome, please* Tel 01233 712522

The Coach House ♿⚸❀ (Mr & Mrs Michael Sykes) Sissinghurst Place, E of Sissinghurst Village on A262. Designed by owners in 1983, and planted within established yew hedges. Many unusual trees, shrubs and plants. **Sissinghurst Place** (with TEAS) open same days. *Combined adm £2 Chd 25p Sat, Sun June 29, 30 (1.30-5.30)*

Cobham Hall &⚘ (Westwood Educational Trust), Cobham. next to A2/M2 8m E of junction 2 of M25, midway between Gravesend and Rochester. Beautiful Elizabethan mansion in 150 acres landscaped by Humphry Repton at end of C18. Acres of daffodils and flowering trees planted in 1930s; grounds now being restored by Cobham Hall Heritage Trust. TEAS. *Adm House £2.50 OAP/Chd £2 Garden £1 (Share to Cobham Hall Heritage Trust®).* ▲*For NGS Suns March 24, Sept 1 (2-5). For details of other open days, please* **Tel 01474 823371/824319**

Coldham &⚘⚘ (Dr & Mrs J G Elliott) Little Chart Forstal, 5m NW of Ashford. Leave M20 at junction 8 (Lenham) if Folkestone-bound or junction 9 (Ashford West) if London-bound: then leave A20 at Charing by road signposted to Little Chart, turn E in village, ¼m. 2-acre garden developed since 1970 in setting of old walls; good collection of rare plants, bulbs, alpines, mixed borders. C16 Kent farmhouse (not open). TEAS. *Adm £2 Chd 50p. Suns April 14, July 14 (2-5.30)*

Coldharbour Oast &⚘ (Mr & Mrs A J A Pearson) Tenterden. 300yds SW of Tenterden High St (A28), take lane signed West View Hospital, after 200yds bear R on to concrete lane signed Coldharbour, proceed for 600yds. Garden started in late 1987 from ¾-acre field in exposed position. Pond; dry stream; unusual shrubs and perennials; maintained by owners. TEA in aid of League of Friends of West View Hospital. *Adm £1.25 Acc chd free. Suns April 28, Sept 1 (1.30-5.30)*

Copton Ash &⚘⚘ (Mrs John Ingram & Drs Tim & Gillian Ingram) 105 Ashford Rd, Faversham, 1m. On A251 Faversham-Ashford rd opp E-bound junction with M2. 1½-acre plantsman's garden developed since 1978 on site of old cherry orchard. Wide range of plants in mixed borders and informal island beds; incl spring bulbs, alpine and herbaceous plants, shrubs, young trees and collection of fruit varieties. Special interest in plants from Mediterranean-type climates. Good autumn colour. TEAS. *Adm £1.50 Acc chd free (Share to National Schizophrenia Fellowship, East Kent Group®). Suns March 17, April 7, May 5, June 2, July 14, 28, Aug 25, Oct 20; Mons April 8, May 6, Aug 26 (2-6)*

Crittenden House ⚘ (B P Tompsett Esq) Matfield, 6m SE of Tonbridge. Bus: MD 6 or 297, alight Standings Cross, Matfield, 1m. Garden around early C17 house completely planned and planted since 1956 on labour-saving lines. Featuring spring shrubs (rhododendrons, magnolias), roses, lilies, foliage, waterside planting of ponds in old iron workings, of interest from early spring bulbs to autumn colour. *Adm £2 Chd (under 12) 25p. Sun March 31; Mons April 8, May 6 (2-6)*

Doddington Place &⚘ (Richard Oldfield Esq) 6m SE of Sittingbourne. From A20 turn N opp Lenham or from A2 turn S at Teynham or Ospringe (Faversham) (all 4m). Large garden, landscaped with wide views; trees and yew hedges; woodland garden with azaleas and rhododendrons, Edwardian rock garden; formal garden planted for late summer interest. TEAS, restaurant, shop. *Adm £2 Chd 25p (Share to Kent Assoc for the Blind and Doddington Church®). May to Sept: Suns 2-6; Weds and Bank Hol Mons 11-6. For NGS Suns May 5, 12, 19 (2-6)*

Downs Court &⚘⚘ (Mr & Mrs M J B Green) Boughton Aluph, 4m NE of Ashford off A28. Take lane on L signed Boughton Aluph church, fork R at pillar box, garden is next drive on R. Approx 3 acres with fine downland views, and some mature trees and yew hedges. Mixed borders largely replanted by owners in last 10 years; shrub roses. TEAS Sunday only in aid of National Hospital Development Foundation®. *Adm £1.50 Chd 50p. Sat, Sun June 15, 16 (2-6)*

Edenbridge House &⚘ (Mrs M T Lloyd) Crockham Hill Rd, 1½m N of Edenbridge, nr Marlpit Hill, on B2026. 5-acre garden of bulbs, spring shrubs, herbaceous borders, alpines, roses and water garden. House part C16 (not open). TEAS. *Adm £1.50 Chd 25p. Suns April 14, May 5, June 16, July 14, Sept 29 (2-6); Weds May 22, Sept 25 (1-5); also private visits welcome for groups, please* **Tel 01732 862122**

Egerton Gardens ⚘ 10m W of Ashford. From A20 at Charing Xrds take B2077 direction Biddenden; at Pluckley turn R to Egerton, then R at George Inn. Start at Glebe Cottage, next to church; maps available. A group of cottage gardens reflecting the owners' tastes and needs. TEAS. *Combined adm £2 Chd 25p (Share to St James's Church, Egerton). Sun June 23 (2-6)*

Elham Gardens ⚘⚘ 7m from Hythe, 11m from Canterbury. Enter Elham on B2065 from Lyminge or Barham (Hythe/Canterbury). Start at The Old School House, entrance on E side of High Street between Brown's (estate agent) and St Mary's Road. A collection of at least four small gardens, full of colour and all very different, within easy walking distance (maps available). Flower Festival and TEAS in church. *Combined adm £2 Chd 25p. Sat June 22 (2-6)*

Emmetts Garden &(in parts) (The National Trust) Ide Hill, 5m SW of Sevenoaks. 1½m S of A25 on Sundridge-Ide Hill Rd. 1½m N of Ide Hill off B2042. 5-acre hillside garden. One of the highest gardens in Kent, noted for its fine collection of rare trees and shrubs; lovely spring and autumn colour. TEAS. *Adm £3 Chd £1.50. March Sats, Suns; April to end Oct every Wed to Sun. Open Bank Hol Mons. For NGS Sats May 11, Oct 5 (1-6) last adm 5, or sunset if earlier*

Everden Farmhouse ⚘ (Martinez family) Alkham, 4m W of Dover. Follow signs to Alkham Valley, turn R opp Hoptons Manor to Everden, then follow 'Garden Open' signs. Designer's garden created from field since 1990, exposed hillside, alkaline soil. Many unusual plants combined with colour and form in mind. *Adm £1.50 Chd 50p. Sun Oct 6 (2-6); also private visits welcome, please* **Tel 01303 893462**

Field House &⚘⚘ (Mr & Mrs N J Hori) Clapper Lane, Staplehurst. W of A229, 9m S of Maidstone and 1½m N of Staplehurst village centre. A 'Garden of the Mind'. Approx 1½ acres designed in the tradition of contemplative and paradise gardens. Good plant collection on Wealden clay, also 1-acre, species-rich meadow with pond. TEAS. *Adm £1.50 Chd 50p. Suns July 14, Aug 4 (2-6)*

Finchcocks &.&❀ (Mr & Mrs Richard Burnett) Goudhurst. 2m W of Goudhurst, off A262. 4-acre garden surrounding early C18 manor, well-known for its collection of historical keyboard instruments. Spring bulbs; mixed borders; autumn garden with unusual trees & rare shrubs; recently restored walled garden on lines of C18 pleasure garden. TEAS. *Adm £4.80 House & garden, £1.50 Garden, Chd £3.20 & 50p. Suns Easter to Sept 24; Bank Hol Mons; Aug every Wed to Sun (2-6). For NGS Suns April 14, Sept 15 (2-6)*

Flint Cottage ❀❀ (Mr & Mrs P J Sinnock) Bourne Park, Bishopsbourne, 4m S of Canterbury turn off A2 to Bridge, through village turn W at church, follow garden signs. Small garden; alpines in gravel beds, sink gardens; water feature; mixed borders and small heather beds; herb garden. TEAS. *Adm £1.20 Chd 50p (Share to Foundation for the Study of Infant Death®). Suns May 19, June 2 (2-5.30); also private visits welcome, please* **Tel 01227 830691**

Forest Gate &.&❀ (Sir Robert & Lady Johnson) Pluckley, 8m W of Ashford. From A20 at Charing take B2077 to Pluckley village; turn L signed Bethersden, continue 1m to garden 100yds S of Pluckley station. 2-acre garden on heavy clay; well stocked mixed borders, laburnum tunnel, ponds and interesting herb collection. Many plants labelled. C17 house (not open). Picnics allowed in meadow. TEAS in aid of Cystic Fibrosis Trust. *Adm £1.40 Acc chd free. Mon May 27, Sun June 30 (1-6)*

Godinton Park ❀ (Alan Wyndham Green Esq) Entrance 1½m W of Ashford at Potter's Corner on A20. Bus: MD/EK 10, 10A, 10B Folkestone-Ashford-Maidstone, alight Hare & Hounds, Potter's Corner. Formal and wild gardens. Topiary. Jacobean mansion with elaborate woodwork. Unique frieze in drawing room depicting arms drill of Kent Halbardiers 1630. *Adm garden only £1, house & garden £2, Chd under 16 £1.* ▲*Suns April 7, July 7 (2-5)*

Godmersham Park (John B Sunley Esq) off A28 midway between Canterbury and Ashford. Associations with Jane Austen. Circular walk through bluebell woods in magnificent downland setting, less than 2m, uphill first ½m, not for infirm. TEAS in Godmersham Church. *Adm £2 Acc chd free (Share to Godmersham Church®). Sun May 5 (11-6)*

Goodnestone Park &.&❀ (The Lady FitzWalter) nr Wingham, Canterbury. Village lies S of B2046 rd from A2 to Wingham. Sign off B2046 says Goodnestone. Village St is 'No Through Rd', but house and garden at the terminus. Bus: EK13, 14 Canterbury-Deal; bus stop: Wingham, 2m. 5 to 6 acres; good trees; woodland garden, snowdrops, spring bulbs, walled garden with old-fashioned roses. Connections with Jane Austen who stayed here. Picnics allowed. TEAS available (not in Feb, Mar). *Adm £2.30 OAP £2 Chd under 12 20p (Disabled people in wheelchair £1). Suns March 31 to Oct 20 (12-6); Mons, Weds to Fris March 25 to Oct 25 (11-5). For NGS (Share to National Kidney Research Fund®) Suns Feb 11 (snowdrops), March 10 (spring bulbs and hellebores), July 14 (12-6). Closed Tues and Sats*

Goudhurst Gardens 4m W of Cranbrook on A262. TEAS. *Combined adm £2.50 Acc chd free. Suns May 19, June 16 (1-6)*

Crowbourne Farm House &.& (Mrs S Coleman) 2-acre farmhouse garden in which replanting started in 1989. Established cottage garden; shrub roses; vegetable garden; and areas newly planted with trees and shrubs. Former horse pond now stocked with ornamental fish

Garden Cottage &.❀ (Mr & Mrs Peter Sowerby) ¾-acre garden with small trees, shrubs, perennials and grass, to provide year-round softly coloured foreground to outstanding views of Teise valley. First laid out in 1930s with extensive planting since 1980s

Tara ❀❀ (Mr & Mrs Peter Coombs) 1¼ acres redesigned in 1982 into a number of linked garden areas, including a formal herb garden, each providing a different atmosphere, using an interesting range of plants and shrubs

Tulip Tree Cottage ❀❀ (Mr & Mrs K A Owen) 1½ acres with sweeping lawn, established trees in herbaceous and shrub borders; 90ft Liriodendron tulipifera, said to be one of finest in country, also fine Cedrus atlantica glauca. In May azalea garden of ½-acre, established 1902

Great Comp Charitable Trust &.&❀ (R Cameron Esq) 2m E of Borough Green. A20 at Wrotham Heath, take Seven Mile Lane, B2016; at 1st Xrds turn R; garden on L ½m. Delightful 7-acre garden skilfully designed by the Camerons since 1957 for low maintenance and yr-round interest. Spacious setting of well-maintained lawns and paths lead visitors through a plantsman's collection of trees, shrubs, heathers and herbaceous plants. From woodland planting to more formal terraces good use is made of views to plants, ornaments and ruins. Good autumn colour. Early C17 house (not shown). TEAS on Suns, Bank Hols and NGS days (2-5). *Adm £2.50 Chd £1. Open Suns in March and every day April 1 to Oct 31 (11-6). Openings for NGS (Share to Tradescant Trust®) Suns Mar 3, 10, 17 (for hellebores, heathers and snowflakes); Nov 3 (for autumn colour) (11-6)*

Great Maytham Hall ❀❀ (Country Houses Association) Rolvenden, 4m SW of Tenterden. On A28 in Rolvenden turn L at church towards Rolvenden Layne; Hall ½m on R. Lutyens house (not open) and garden, 18 acres of parkland with bluebells, daffodils and flowering trees in spring; formal gardens incl blue and silver border, roses, hydrangeas and autumn colour. Walled garden inspired Frances Hodgson Burnett to write her novel 'The Secret Garden'. TEAS. *Adm £1.50 Chd 75p (Share to Country Houses Association©). Fris May 3, June 28, Sept 27 (2-5)*

Greencroft ❀❀ (Dr & Mrs A Marr) Nizels Lane, Hildenborough, 3½m S of Sevenoaks. Take A225, at Riverhill roundabout take B245, Nizels Lane 1st R. 2-acre plantsman's garden. Trees, shrubs, mixed borders. Interesting planting to screen Tonbridge by-pass; water and woodland garden, being developed by owner-gardeners with view to easy maintenance. *Adm £1.50 Acc chd free. Private visits welcome on Weds, pm between April 24 and Sept 25, please* **Tel 01732 833236**

> **General Information.** For general information on the use of this book see Page 15.

Greenways ♿✂❀ (Mr & Mrs S Lord) Single Street, nr Downe. Gardener's garden; interesting design ideas and plant collections; willows, jasmines, buddleias, honeysuckles and alpines; bonsai miniature garden display; small pool, plant house and pottery. *Adm £1.50 (Share to Save the Children Fund®). Private visits welcome, anytime, please* **Tel 01959 574691**

Groombridge Place Gardens ✂❀ (Andrew de Candole Esq) 4m SW of Tunbridge Wells. Take A264 towards E. Grinstead, after 2m take B2110: Groombridge Place entrance on L, past the church. C17 formal walled gardens with medieval moat, ancient topiary and fountains. Canal boat rides to Enchanted Forest; children's garden and birds of prey displays. Restaurant. *Adm £5 OAPs £4.50 Chd £3.50. Open daily April 1 to Oct 31 (10-6). For NGS Mons April 15, Oct 14 (10-6)*

Groome Farm ♿✂❀ (Mr & Mrs Michael Swatland) Egerton, 10m W of Ashford. From A20 at Charing Xrds take B2077 Biddenden Rd. Past Pluckley turn R at Blacksmiths Tea Rooms; R again, until Newland Green sign on L, house 1st on L. 1½ acres around C15 farmhouse and oast. Interesting collection trees, shrubs, roses and herbaceous plants; also water, heather and rock gardens. Picnics welcome in field. TEAS. *Adm £1.50 Acc chd free. Suns July 14, Sept 15 (2-6). Private visits welcome, please* **Tel 01233 756260**

¶Hadlow College, Broadview Gardens ♿✂❀ Hadlow. On A26 9m SW of Maidstone and 4m NE of Tonbridge. 35 acres of ornamental planting in attractive landscape setting; island beds with mixed plantings, rock gardens, lake and water gardens; series of demonstration gardens including oriental, Italian and cottage gardens. TEAS in aid of local charities. *Adm £2 Acc chd free. Thurs Feb 29 (hellebores); Sun Sept 15 (10-4)*

115 Hadlow Road ✂ (Mr & Mrs Richard Esdale) in Tonbridge. Take A26 from N end of High St signed Maidstone, house 1m on L in service rd. ⅓-acre unusual terraced garden with roses, herbaceous border, clematis, hardy fuchsias, shrub borders, alpines, kitchen garden and pond; well labelled. TEA. *Adm £1.50 Acc chd free. Suns July 14, Aug 4, 25 (2-6); also private visits welcome, please* **Tel 01732 353738**

Hartlip Gardens 6m W of Sittingbourne, 1m S of A2 midway between Rainham and Newington. Parking for Craiglea in village hall car park and The Street. *Combined adm £2 Acc chd free. Sun May 26 (2-6)*

Craiglea ♿✂ (Mrs Ruth Bellord) The Street. Small cottage garden crammed with interesting shrubs and plants; vegetable garden; tiny pond

Hartlip Place ✂ (Lt-Col & Mrs J R Yerburgh) Secret garden concealed by rhododendrons, planted with old roses; shrub borders; wilderness walk; sloping lawns; pond. TEAS in aid of Kent Gardens Trust

Hault Farm ♿✂❀ (Mr & Mrs T D Willett) 7m S of Canterbury, between Petham and Waltham. From B2068 turn R signed Petham/Waltham; 2m on L. Victorian house on site of Knights Templar property once occupied by Crusader Sir Geofrey de Hautt. Plantaholic's 4 acres of woodland, bog, herbaceous, rose and scree areas. TEAS. *Adm £2 Chd £1. Suns from April 21 to June 30. For NGS Suns May 5, Oct 13 (2-5) Groups welcome at any time by appt, please* **Tel 01227 700263**

Haydown ✂❀ (Dr & Mrs I D Edeleanu) Great Buckland, nr Cobham, 4m S of A2. Take turning for Cobham, at war memorial straight ahead down hill, under railway bridge to T-junction, turn R, after 200yds take L fork, follow narrow lane for 1½m. Entrance on L after riding stables. North Downs 9-acre hillside garden developed since 1980, with woodland and meadowland, incl native and unusual trees, shrubs, small vineyard, orchard, ponds, bog garden; patio with terracing; roses. TEAS. *Adm £1.50 Acc chd free (Share to Rotary Charities). Sats June 15, July 27 (2-6)*

● **Hever Castle** ♿❀ (Broadland Properties Ltd) 3m SE of Edenbridge, between Sevenoaks and E. Grinstead. Signed from junctions 5 and 6 of M25, from A21 and from A264. Formal Italian gardens with statuary, sculpture and fountains; large lake; rose garden and Tudor style gardens with herb garden, topiary and maze. Romantic moated castle, the childhood home of Anne Boleyn, also open. No dogs in castle, on lead only in gardens. Refreshments available. *Open every day from March 1 to Nov 30 (11-6 last adm 5, March & Nov 11-4, Castle opens 12 noon). Adm Castle and gardens £6, OAP £5.30, Chd £3, Family (2 adults, 2 chd) £15; gardens only £4.40, OAP £3.90, Chd £2.60 Family (2 adults, 2 chd) £11.40*

Hole Park ♿✂ (D G W Barham Esq) Rolvenden-Cranbrook on B2086. Beautiful parkland; formal garden with mixed borders, roses, yew hedges and topiary a feature, many fine trees. Natural garden with daffodils, rhododendrons, azaleas, conifers, dell and water gardens; bluebell wood in spring. Autumn colour. *Adm £2.50 Chd under 12 50p (Share to St Mary's Church, Rolvenden©). Suns April 7, 14, 28, May 5, 19, 26, Oct 13, 20; Weds April 24, May 15, June 5 (2-6)*

Horton Priory ✂ (Mrs A C Gore) Sellindge, 6m SE of Ashford. From A20 Ashford-Folkestone, 1m from Sellindge, turn E along Moorstock Lane, signed Horton Priory. Bus: EK/MD 10, 10A, 10B Maidstone-Ashford-Folkestone; alight Sellindge, 1m. Herbaceous and rose border, lawn, pond and rock garden. Priory dates back to C12; church destroyed in reign of Henry VIII, but remains of W doorway and staircase to S aisle of nave can be seen by front door. Along W front Norman buttresses (all genuine) and C14 windows (some restored); one genuine small Norman window. Outer hall only open to visitors. TEAS. *Adm £1 Chd 50p (Share to Leonora Childrens Cancer Fund®). Mon April 8, Sun June 16 (2-6)*

The National Gardens Scheme is a charity which traces its origins back to 1927. Since then it has raised a total of over £14 million for charitable purposes.

1996 Special Events. For information on special National Gardens Scheme events in 1996 see Pages 18-19.

Ightham Mote &♦❀ (The National Trust) Ivy Hatch. 6m E of Sevenoaks, off A25 and 2½m S of Ightham [188: TQ584535] Buses: Maidstone & District 222/3 from BR Borough Green: NU-Venture 67/8 Sevenoaks to Plaxtol passing BR Sevenoaks: alight Ivy Hatch ½m walk to Ightham Mote. 14-acre garden and moated medieval manor c.1340. Mixed borders with many unusual plants; lawns; courtyard; newly-planted orchard; water features incl small lake, leading to woodland walk with rhododendrons and shrubs. TEAS. ▲*Adm £4 Chd £2. House and garden open as normal. Tours of garden 1.30pm, 2.30pm, 3.30pm. NT members £1 donation for tours. Wed June 19 (11.30-5.30 last admission 5pm)*

Jessups ❀ (The Hon Robin Denison-Pender) Mark Beech. 3m S of Edenbridge. From B2026 Edenbridge-Hartfield rd turn L opp Queens Arms signed Mark Beech, 100yds on L. Small established garden, spring bulbs and shrubs, fine views to Sevenoaks Weald. Small wood. Wildfowl pond (25 different breeds). TEA. *Adm £1.50 Acc chd free. Sun April 7 (2-5)*

Knole &♦ (The Lord Sackville; The National Trust) Sevenoaks. Station: Sevenoaks. Pleasance, deer park, landscape garden, herb garden. TEAS. *Adm Car park £2.50: garden 50p Chd 30p; house £4.50 Chd £2.25 Weds June 5, Aug 7 (11-4.30 last adm 4)*

Kypp Cottage ♦❀ (Mrs Zena Grant) Woolpack Corner, Biddenden. At Tenterden Rd A262 junction with Benenden Rd. Tiny woodland garden planted by owner on rough ground, now overflowing with interesting plants. Hundreds of roses and clematis intertwine, providing shady, scented nooks. Large variety of geraniums and other ground cover plants. Subject of Meridian TV programme. Morning coffee & TEAS. *Adm £1.50 Chd 30p (Share to NSPCC®). Suns May 26, June 2, 9, 16, 23, 30, July 7, 14 (2-6); Mons May 27, June 3, 10, 17, 24, July 1, 8, 15; Tues May 28, June 4, 11, 18, 25, July 2, 9, 16; Weds May 29, June 5, 12, 19, 26, July 3, 10, 17; Fri May 24; Sat May 25 (10.30-6); also private visits welcome all season please Tel 01580 291480*

Ladham House ❀ (Betty, Lady Jessel) Goudhurst. On NE of village, off A262. 10 acres with rolling lawns, fine specimen trees, rhododendrons, camellias, azaleas, shrubs and magnolias. Arboretum. Spectacular twin mixed borders; fountain and bog gardens. Fine view. Subject of many magazine articles. TEAS. *Adm £2 Chd under 12 50p. Sun May 26 (11-5.30)*

Larksfield &❀ (Mr & Mrs P Dickinson) Crockham Hill, 3m N of Edenbridge, on B269 (Limpsfield-Oxted). Octavia Hill, a founder of the NT, lived here and helped create the original garden; fine collection of azaleas, shrubs, herbaceous plants, rose beds and woodlands; views over Weald and Ashdown Forest. **The Red House** and **Larksfield Cottage** gardens open same days. TEAS at The Red House. *Combined adm £2.50 OAPs £2 Chd 50p (Share to the Schizophrenia Association of G.B.®). Suns May 12, 19 (2-6)*

Larksfield Cottage &❀ (Mr & Mrs J Mainwaring) Crockham Hill, 3m N of Edenbridge, on B269. An enchanting garden redesigned in 1981 with attractive lawns and shrubs. Views over the Weald and Ashdown Forest. **Larksfield** and **The Red House** gardens also open same days. *Combined adm £2.50 OAPs £2 Chd 50p (Share to The Schizophrenia Association of G.B.®). Suns May 12, 19 (2-6)*

43 Layhams Road &♦ (Mrs Dolly Robertson) West Wickham. Semi-detached house recognisable by small sunken flower garden in the front. Opp Wickham Court Farm. A raised vegetable garden, purpose-built for the disabled owner with easy access to wide terraced walkways. The owner, who maintains the entire 24ft × 70ft area herself, would be pleased to pass on her experiences as a disabled gardener so that others may share her joy and interest. *Collecting box. Private visits welcome all year, please Tel 0181-462 4196*

Lily Vale Farm &♦ (Mr & Mrs R H V Moorhead) Smeeth, 4m E of Ashford. Turn N off A20 at garage opp converter station W of Sellindge; follow lane to T-junc, turn L, entrance ½m on L. Family garden with trees and pastoral outlook; shrub roses, herbaceous borders and courtyard garden. **Lodge House** open same days. TEAS. *Adm £1.50 Acc chd free. Sun June 23; Wed June 26 (2-6)*

Little Trafalgar &♦❀ (Mr & Mrs R J Dunnett) Selling, 4m SE of Faversham. From A2 (M2) or A251 make for Selling Church, then follow signs to garden. ¾-acre garden of great interest both for its wealth of attractive and unusual plants, and its intimate, restful design. Emphasis is placed on the creative and artistic use of plants. TEAS. *Adm £1 Acc chd free. Suns May 26, June 9, 23, July 7, 21, Aug 4, 25, Sept 15; Mons May 27, Aug 26 (2-6); also private visits welcome, please Tel 01227 752219*

Lodge House &❀ (Mr & Mrs J Talbot) Smeeth, 4m E of Ashford. From A20 3m E of Ashford, turn N signed Smeeth, turn R at Woolpack, continue ½m to entrance. 2-acre garden, with sloping lawns; shrubs; herbaceous borders and ponds in lovely setting. Field walk to **Lily Vale Farm** open same days. Picnickers welcome. Informal live music June 23. TEAS. *Adm £1.50 Acc chd free (Share to Brabourne Church©). Sun June 23; Wed June 26 (2-6)*

Long Barn ♦ (Brandon & Sarah Gough) Weald, 3m S of Sevenoaks. Signed to Weald at junction of A21 & B245. Garden at W end of village. 1st garden of Harold Nicolson and Vita Sackville-West. 3 acres with terraces and slopes, giving considerable variety. Dutch garden designed by Lutyens, features mixed planting in raised beds. Teas in village. *Adm £2 OAP £1 Chd 50p under 5 free (Share to Hospice in the Weald®). Suns June 23, July 14 (2-5)*

General Information. For general information on the use of this book see Page 15.

Regular Openers. Too many days to include in diary. Usually there is a wide range of plants giving year-round interest. See end of county section for the name and garden description for times etc.

Longacre ♿✂❀ (Dr & Mrs G Thomas) Perry Wood, Selling, 5m SE of Faversham. From A2 (M2) or A251 follow signs for Selling, passing White Lion on L, 2nd R and immediately L, continue for ¼m. From A252 at Chilham, take turning signed Selling at Badgers Hill Fruit Farm. L at 2nd Xrds, next R, L and then R. Small, ¾-acre plantsman's garden with wide variety of interesting plants, created and maintained entirely by owners. Lovely walks in Perry Woods adjacent to garden. TEAS in aid of local charities. *Adm £1 Acc chd free (Share to Canterbury Pilgrims Hospice®). Suns April 7, 21, May 5, 26, June 9, 23, July 7, 21, Aug 4, 25, Sept 8; Mons April 8, May 6, 27, Aug 26 (2-5); also private visits welcome, please* **Tel 01227 752254**

Lullingstone Castle ♿✂❀ (Mr & Mrs Guy Hart Dyke) In the Darenth Valley via Eynsford on A225. Eynsford Station ½m. All cars and coaches via Roman Villa. Lawns, woodland and lake, mixed border, small herb garden. Henry VII gateway; Church on the lawn open. TEAS. *Adm garden £2 OAPs/Chd £1; house 50p extra. Sun June 16 (2-6)*

Luton House ✂ (Sir John & Lady Swire) Selling, 4m SE of Faversham. From A2 (M2) or A251 make for White Lion, entrance 30yds E on same side of rd. 4 acres; C19 landscaped garden; ornamental ponds; trees underplanted with azaleas, camellias, woodland plants. *Adm £1.50 Acc chd free. Sun April 21 (2-6)*

190 Maidstone Road ✂❀ (Dr M K Douglas) Chatham. On A230 Chatham-Maidstone, about 1m out of Chatham and 7m from Maidstone. Informal ¼-acre garden; herbaceous borders on either side of former tennis court; scree garden and pool; many snowdrops and other spring bulbs. TEAS (not Feb). *Adm £1.50 Acc chd free. Suns Feb 11 (snowdrops), March 31, July 28 (2-6)*

Marle Place ♿✂❀ (Mr & Mrs Gerald Williams) Brenchley, 8m SE of Tonbridge, signed from Brenchley. Victorian gazebo; plantsman's shrub borders; walled scented garden, large herb rockery; herbaceous borders and new bog garden. Woodland walk; collection of bantams. C17 listed house (not open). Specialist nursery. TEAS. *Adm £2.50 Chd £2. Every day April 1 to Oct 31 (11-6). For NGS Suns May 19, Aug 11, Oct 6 (11-6)*

Maurice House ♿ (The Royal British Legion Residential Home) Callis Court Rd, Broadstairs. From Broadstairs Broadway take St Peter's Park Rd; turn R under railway arch into Baird's Hill; join Callis Court Rd entrance on R, 100yds beyond Lanthorne Rd turning. Well-maintained 8-acre garden; lawns, flowering trees, shrubs; formal flower beds; rose and water gardens; orchard. Spring bedding displays of wallflowers, tulips, polyanthus; wide variety of herbaceous plants and shrubs especially suited to coastal conditions. TEAS. *Adm £1.50 Chd 25p (Share to the Royal British Legion®). Sun April 28 (2-5.30)*

Meadow Wood ♿ (Mr & Mrs James Lee) Penshurst. 1¼m SE of Penshurst on B2176 in direction of Bidborough. 1920s garden, on edge of wood with long southerly views over the Weald, and with interesting trees and shrubs; azaleas, rhododendrons and naturalised bulbs in woods with mown walks. TEAS. *Adm £2 Chd £1 (Share to Relate®). Mon May 6 (2-6)*

Mere House ♿❀ (Mr & Mrs Andrew Wells) Mereworth, midway between Tonbridge & Maidstone. From A26 turn N on to B2016 and then into Mereworth village. 6-acre garden with C18 lake; ornamental shrubs and trees with foliage contrast; lawns, daffodils; Kentish cobnut plat. Woodland walk. TEAS. *Adm £1.50 Acc chd free. Mon April 8; Suns June 2, Oct 13 (2.30-6)*

Mill House ♿✂❀ (Dr & Mrs Brian Glaisher) Mill Lane, ½m N of Hildenborough, 5m S of Sevenoaks. From B245 turn into Mill Lane at Mill garage. 3-acre garden laid out in 1906; herbaceous and mixed borders; new secluded herb garden; old shrub roses and climbers; clematis and many fine trees. Formal garden with topiary; ruins of windmill and conservatory with exotics. *Adm £1.50 Chd 25p. Sun May 26 (2-6)*

Mount Ephraim (Mrs M N Dawes and Mr & Mrs E S Dawes) Hernhill, Faversham. From M2 and A299 take Hernhill turning at Duke of Kent. Herbaceous border; topiary; daffodils and rhododendrons; rose terraces leading to a small lake; Japanese rock garden with pools; water garden; small vineyard. TEAS daily except Tues; lunches only Bank Hol Suns & Mons. *Adm £2 Chd 50p. Open April to Sept (1-6). For NGS Suns April 28 (Share to Karna Prayag Trust, Madras), Oct 13 (1-6)*

Nettlestead Place ♿✂ (Mr & Mrs Roy Tucker) Nettlestead, 6m W/SW of Maidstone. Turn S off A26 onto B2015 then 1m on L (next to Nettlestead Church). C13 manor house set in 11-acre plantsman's garden on different levels with fine views over open countryside; many plant collections incl herbaceous and shrub island beds; formal garden with shrub and species roses; hardy geranium border; sunken pond garden; 4 acres in course of development as pinetum and glen garden. TEAS. *Adm £1.50 Acc chd free (Share to St Mary's Church, Nettlestead®). Suns July 7, Sept 29 (2-5.30)*

New Barns House ♿✂❀ (Mr & Mrs P H Byam-Cook) West Malling. Leave M20 at Exit 4 to West Malling. In High Street turn E down Waters Lane, at T-junction turn R, take bridge over by-pass, follow lane 400yds to New Barns House. 1-acre garden with fine trees and flowering cherries. Walled garden, mixed borders and shrubs. TEAS. *Adm £1.50 Acc chd free. Sun April 21 (2-6)*

Nonington & Woodnesborough Gardens ♿✂ 6m & 3m from Sandwich respectively on Sandwich-Woodnesborough-Nonington Road. *Combined adm £2.50 Acc chd free (Share to Kent and Canterbury Macmillan Nurses Appeal®). Sun June 9 (2-6)*

Birnam (Mr & Mrs Douglas Miller) Hamill Road, ½m SW of Woodnesborough. ¾-acre garden on clay, designed in 1963 by Anthony du Gard Pasley for a windswept site. Interesting trees, shrubs, roses. TEA

Gooseberry Hall Cottage (Mr Edward & Dr Audrey Carey) Nonington. From A2 take B2046 at Barham, after 300yds turn R for Nonington, proceed for 3m, passing disused Snowdon Colliery through Nonington village to mini-roundabout, turn R, house further ¾m on L. Cottage garden, with special-interest hedges and croquet lawn

Gooseberry Hall Farm (Mr & Mrs F McL Hayward) Nonington. 400yds from **Gooseberry Hall Cottage** down Gooseberry Lane on R. ½-acre garden surrounding Grade II thatched hall house. Herbaceous borders, lawns, climbing and hybrid roses, mature English elms and small vegetable garden aimed at near self sufficiency

Northbourne Court ✗ (The Hon Charles James) W of Deal. Signs in village. Great brick terraces, belonging to an earlier Elizabethan mansion, provide a picturesque setting for a wide range of shrubs and plants on chalk soil; geraniums, fuchsias and grey-leaved plants. TEA. *Adm £2.50 OAPs/Chd £1.50 (Share to National Art Collections Fund®). All Suns in June, July, Aug (2-5)*

Olantigh ✗ (J R H Loudon Esq) Wye, 6m NE of Ashford. Turn off A28 either to Wye or at Godmersham; ¾m from Wye on rd to Godmersham. Edwardian garden in beautiful setting; water garden; rockery; shrubbery; herbaceous border; extensive lawns. *Adm £1.50 Chd 50p. Suns May 26, June 30 (2-5)*

Old Buckhurst ♿ (Mr & Mrs J Gladstone) Chiddingstone Hoath Road, Mark Beech. 4m E of Edenbridge via B2026, at Cowden Pond turn E to Mark Beech. First house on R after leaving Mark Beech on Penshurst Rd. 1-acre garden surrounding C15 farmhouse (not open). Part-walled ornamental and kitchen gardens; 'New English' roses; range of clematis, shrubs and herbaceous plants. *Adm £1.50 Acc chd free (Share to St Mary's Church, Chiddingstone©). Suns May 26, July 14 (2-5.30)*

The Old Parsonage ♿✗❀ (Dr & Mrs Richard Perks) Sutton Valence, 6m SE of Maidstone. A274 from Maidstone or Headcorn, turn E into village at King's Head Inn and proceed on upper rd through village; climb Tumblers Hill and entrance at top on R. 4-acre labour-saving garden planted since 1959 with emphasis on ground cover; trees, shrubs and mixed borders; cranesbills and shrub roses. Ancient nut plat now developed as a wild garden. Fine views over Low Weald. In grounds is Sutton castle, C12 ruined keep, permanently open to the public. *Adm £1.50 Chd 50p. Sat June 15, Tue June 18, Fri June 21, Sun June 23 (2-6); also private visits welcome, please* **Tel 01622 842286**

Old Place Farm ♿✗❀ (Mr & Mrs Jeffrey Eker) High Halden, 3m NE of Tenterden. From A28 take Woodchurch Rd (opp Chequers public house) in High Halden, and follow for ½m. 3½-acre garden, mainly designed by Anthony du Gard Pasley, surrounding period farmhouse & buildings with paved herb garden & parterres, small lake, ponds, lawns, mixed borders, cutting garden, old shrub roses, lilies & foliage plants; all created since 1969 & much new planting in 1995 and 1996. TEAS in aid of St Mary's Church, High Halden. *Adm £2 Chd 50p. Sun June 23 (2-6)*

Old Tong Farm ✗❀ (Mr & Mrs Simon Toynbee) 1¼m S of Brenchley. Follow Horsmonden rd from Brenchley, take first R. Medium-size garden made by owners around C15 farmhouse (not open); rose garden, pond, herb parterre, nut plat; wild woodland walk. Adj cottage with newly planted garden also open. TEAS. *Adm £1.50 Acc chd free. Suns July 7, 14 (2-6)*

Orchard Cottage ♿✗❀ (Professor & Mrs C G Wall) 3 Woodlands Road, Bickley, 1½m E of Bromley, about 400 yds from the A222. From Bickley Park Road turn into Pines Road, then 1st R into Woodlands Road, no 3 is 1st house on L. Attractive ⅓-acre garden in course of development; mixed borders with many interesting herbaceous plants and shrubs; scree beds and troughs with alpines and other small plants. TEAS. *Adm £1.50 Acc chd free (Share to Downs Syndrome Association: SE Branch®). Sun July 28 (2-5.30)*

Otham Gardens 4m SE of Maidstone. From A2020 or A274 follow signs for Otham 1m. Parking restricted to official car parks except for disabled people. TEAS. *Combined adm £2.50 Acc chd free (Share to Maidstone Mencap®). Sun June 30 (2-6)*

Bramley (Miss Ware) Interesting garden on different levels; water garden and new alpine garden (raised)

Greenhill House (Dr & Mrs Hugh Vaux) Established herbaceous and shrub borders; wild garden; new herb garden

Little Squerryes ♿ (Mr & Mrs Gerald Coomb) Established garden; herbaceous borders; interesting trees

The Limes ♿ (Mr & Mrs John Stephens) Well established garden with herbaceous borders, wisteria pergola and sculpture

Stoneacre Special opening; *NT members to pay.* For garden description see individual entry

Swallows ♿ (Mr & Mrs Eric Maidment) Cottage garden with colourful terrace

Tulip Cottage ♿ (Mrs Gloria Adams) Shows what can be done in a small space

Owl House ♿(in parts)❀ (Maureen, Marchioness of Dufferin and Ava) Lamberhurst. 1m W of A21, signposted from Lamberhurst. 16½-acre woodland garden surrounding C16 wool smuggler's cottage: water gardens, unusual roses climbing into woodland trees; daffodils, rhododendrons, azaleas, magnolias, camellias, roses, irises, good autumn colour. *Adm £3 Chd £1 (Share to Maureen's Oast House for Arthritics®). Open all year except Christmas Day and New Year's Day. For NGS Suns March 10, June 2, July 14 (11-6)*

Oxon Hoath ✗❀ (Mr & Mrs Henry Bayne-Powell) nr Hadlow, 5m NE of Tonbridge. *Car essential.* Via A20, turn off S at Wrotham Heath onto Seven Mile Lane (B2016); at Mereworth Xrds turn W, through West Peckham. Or via A26, in Hadlow turn off N along Carpenters Lane. 10 acres, landscaped with fine trees, rhododendrons and azaleas; woodland walk; replanted cedar avenue; formal parterre rose garden by Nesfield. Large Kentish ragstone house (not shown) principally Georgian but dating back to C14; Victorian additions by Salvin. Once owned by Culpeppers, grandparents of Catherine Howard. View over C18 lake to Hadlow Folly. TEAS in picnic area if fine. *Adm £1.50 Chd 50p (Share to W. Peckham Church©). Sun May 26 (2-6)*

By Appointment Gardens. See end of county section

The Pear House ✗❀ (Mrs Nicholas Snowden) Stone Hill, Sellindge, 6m E of Ashford. Turn L off A20 at Sellindge Church towards Brabourne into Stone Hill. ⅔ acre developed by present owner. Contains smaller gardens with informal planting; bulbs, roses (over 100 different, mostly old-fashioned), shrubs, small orchard with climbing roses, pond garden, shady areas. *Adm £1.50 Chd 50p. Due to limited parking, visits by appointment welcome anytime between April 28 to July 7, please* **Tel 01303 812147**

Peddars Wood ⅃✗❀ (Mr & Mrs B J Honeysett) 14 Orchard Rd, St Michaels, Tenterden. From A28, 1m N of Tenterden, turn W into Grange Rd at Crown Hotel, take 2nd R into Orchard Rd. Small plantsman's garden created by present owner since 1984. One of the best collections of rare and interesting plants in the area, incl over 100 clematis, 50 climbing roses, lilies and ferns. TEAS. *Adm £1 Chd 20p (Share to Baptist Minister's Help Society). Sats May 4, June 1, July 20, Aug 3 (2-6); also private visits welcome, please* **Tel 015806 3994**

Penshurst Place ⅃✗ (Viscount De L'Isle), S of Tonbridge on B2176, N of Tunbridge Wells on A26. 10 acres of garden dating back to C14; garden divided into series of 'rooms' by over a mile of clipped yew hedge; profusion of spring bulbs: herbaceous borders; formal rose garden; famous peony border. All yr interest. TEAS and light refreshments. *Adm House & Gardens £5.50 OAPs £5.10 Chd £3 Family Ticket £14.50: Gardens £4 OAPs £3.50 Chd £2.75 Family Ticket £10.50. Open daily April 1 to Sept 29. For NGS Wed May 8, Thurs June 6 (11-6)*

Pett Place ✗❀ (Mrs I Mills, C I Richmond-Watson Esq & A Rolla Esq) Charing, 6m NW of Ashford. From A20 turn N into Charing High St. At end turn R into Pett Lane towards Westwell. Four walled gardens covering nearly 4 acres. Within formal framework of old walls, much planting has been carried out since 1981 to make a garden of different, pleasing vistas and secret places. A ruined C13 chapel is a romantic feature beside the manor house (not open), which was re-fronted about 1700 and which Pevsner describes as 'presenting grandiloquently towards the road.' TEAS. *Adm £2 Chd 50p (Share to Kent Gardens Trust®). Sats, Suns April 20, 21, June 22, 23 (2.30-5)*

Pevington Farm ⅃❀ (Mr & Mrs David Mure) Pluckley, 3m SW of Charing. From Charing take B2077 towards Pluckley, before Pluckley turn R towards Egerton. Pevington Farm ½m on. From SW go through Pluckley, turn L for Egerton. ¾-acre garden with wonderful views over the Weald. Mixed borders with many interesting plants. Tours of garden with the owner at 12pm, 2pm and 3.30pm. TEAS on May 19 for Friends of St Nicholas Church, Pluckley: on June 16 for Pluckley School Building Fund. *Adm £1.50 Chd 50p. Suns May 19, June 16 (11-5); private visits welcome* **Tel 01233 840317**

The Pines Garden & The Bay Museum ⅃❀ (The St Margaret's Bay Trust) Beach Rd, St Margaret's Bay, 4½m NE of Dover. Beautiful 6-acre seaside garden. Water garden with waterfall and lake. Statue of Sir Winston Churchill complemented by the Bay Museum opposite. Fascinating maritime and local interest. TEASHOP. *Adm £1.25 Chd 30p. Gardens open daily except Christmas Day. Museum open May to end Aug (closed Mon and Fri). For NGS Suns April 7, May 26, Aug 25 (10-5)*

Placketts Hole ⅃✗❀ (Mr & Mrs D P Wainman) Bicknor 5m S of Sittingbourne, and W of B2163. Owners have designed and planted 2-acre garden around charming old house (C16 with Georgian additions); interesting mix of shrubs, large borders, rose garden, a formal herb garden and sweet-smelling plants. TEAS. *Adm £1.50 Acc chd free (Share to Bicknor Church®). Sun June 30 (2-6.30)*

Plaxtol Gardens 5m N of Tonbridge, 6m E of Sevenoaks, turn E off A227 to Plaxtol village. TEAS. Tickets and maps available at all gardens. Parking at Spoute Cottage. *Combined adm £2.50 Acc chd free (Share to Friends of Plaxtol Church©). Sun June 23 (2-6)*

    Ducks Farm ✗ (Mr & Mrs H Puleston Jones) Dux Lane. 2 acres, in course of restoration, surrounding medieval/Victorian farmhouse. Mixed herbaceous borders, walled garden, vegetable garden, herb garden

    ¶**The Retreat** ✗ (Mr & Mrs S Cartwright), Plaxtol Lane. Newly constructed, 2-acre garden with lake and pond, rock landscape, cottage garden; wide range of interesting trees and shrubs

    Spoute Cottage ⅃✗❀ (Mr & Mrs Donald Forbes) situated at the bottom of Plaxtol St on L side opp Hyders Wrought Iron Works. ¾ acre of mixed borders of contrasting flowering and foliage plants, especially for flower arranging; small pond & stream. New Japanese garden. Plant nursery attached. Large car park

    Watermead ✗❀ (Mr & Mrs Michael Scott) Long Mill Lane. Garden of ¼ acre with perennials for all year interest with flowers and foliage; fruit and vegetable plot; small pond

Ramhurst Manor ⅃ (The Lady Rosie Kindersley) Powder Mill Lane, Leigh, Tonbridge. Historic property once belonged to the Black Prince and Culpepper family. Formal gardens; roses, azaleas, rhododendrons, wild flowers. TEA. *Adm £1.50 Acc chd free. Sun May 19 (2.30-6)*

The Red House ⅃❀ (K C L Webb Esq) Crockham Hill, 3m N of Edenbridge. On Limpsfield-Oxted Rd, B269. Formal features of this large garden are kept to a minimum; rose walk leads on to 3 acres of rolling lawns flanked by fine trees and shrubs incl rhododendrons, azaleas and magnolias. Views over the Weald and Ashdown Forest. TEAS. **Larksfield** and **Larksfield Cottage** gardens also open same days. *Combined adm £2.50 OAPs £2 Chd 50p (Share to The Schizophrenia Association of Great Britain®). Suns May 12, 19 (2-6)*

Riverhill House ✗ (The Rogers family) 2m S of Sevenoaks on A225. Mature hillside garden with extensive views; specimen trees, sheltered terraces with roses and choice shrubs; bluebell wood with rhododendrons and azaleas; picnics allowed. TEAS. *Adm £2.50 Chd 50p (Share to Hospice at Home®). Every Sun in April, May & June and Bank Hol weekends in this period (12-6). For NGS Sats May 4, 25 (12-6)*

Rock Farm ⅃✗❀ (Mrs P A Corfe) Nettlestead. 6m W of Maidstone. Turn S off A26 onto B2015 then 1m S of Wateringbury turn R. 2-acre garden set around old Kentish farmhouse and farm buildings in beautiful setting with lovely views; created since 1968 with emphasis on all-year interest and ease of maintenance. Plantsman's collection of shrubs, trees and perennials for alkaline soil: extensive herbaceous border, vegetable area, bog garden and plantings around two large natural ponds. Plant nursery adjoining garden. *Adm £2 Chd 50p (Share to St Mary's Church, Nettlestead®). Every Wed & Sat from May 1 to Aug 10 (11-5)*

Rogers Rough &% (Richard and Hilary Bird) Kilndown, Cranbrook 10m S of Tonbridge. From A21 2m S of Lamberhurst turn E into Kilndown; take 1st R down Chick's Lane until rd divides. Garden writer's 1½-acre garden, mainly herbaceous borders, but also rock gardens, shrubs, a small wood and pond. Extensive views. TEAS in aid of Christ Church Kilndown Restoration Fund. *Adm £1.50 Chd 50p. Suns June 23, July 14 (2-5.30)*

St Clere &% (Mr & Mrs Ronnie Norman) Kemsing, 6m NE of Sevenoaks. Take A25 from Sevenoaks toward Ightham; 1m past Seal turn L signed Heaverham and Kemsing; in Heaverham take rd to R signed West Kingsdown; in 75yds straight ahead marked Private rd; 1st L and follow rd to house. 4-acre terraced garden with beautiful views; well laid-out herbaceous and gold-and-silver borders; crataegus arch; pergola; pond; rare trees; vegetable garden; walled vineyard. TEAS. *Adm £2 Chd 50p. Sun June 23 (2-6)*

St Michael's House &% (Brig & Mrs W Magan) Roydon Road, Seven Mile Lane, 5m NE Tonbridge, 5m SW Maidstone. On A26 at Mereworth roundabout take S exit (A228) signed Paddock Wood, after 1m turn L at top of rise (signed Roydon). Gardens ¼m up hill on L. Old vicarage garden of ¾ acre enclosed by shaped yew hedge; tulips; roses, climbing roses, irises; 6-acre meadow with extensive views. TEAS. *Adm £2 OAPs £1 Chd 50p. Suns May 5 (tulips), May 26 (irises), June 16 (roses) (2-6)*

● **Saltwood Castle** (The Hon Mrs Clark) 2m NW of Hythe, 4m W of Folkestone; from A20 turn S at sign to Saltwood. Medieval castle, subject of quarrel between Thomas a Becket and Henry II. C13 crypt and dungeons; armoury; battlement walks and watch towers. Lovely views; spacious lawns and borders; courtyard walls covered with roses. Picnics allowed. Saltwood Castle closed to the general public in 1995. *Private parties of 20 or more weekdays only, please write for appt*

Scotney Castle &% (Mrs Christopher Hussey; The National Trust) On A21 London-Hastings, 1¼m S of Lamberhurst. Bus: (Mon to Sat) Autopoint 256, Tunbridge Wells-Wadhurst; alight Lamberhurst Green. Famous picturesque landscape garden, created by the Hussey family in the 1840s surrounding moated C14 Castle. House (not open) by Salvin, 1837. Old Castle open May – mid-Sept (same times as garden). Gift Shop. Picnic area in car park. Tea Lamberhurst. *Adm £3.50 Chd £1.70; Family ticket £8.70; Pre-booked parties of 15 or more (Wed-Fri) £2.20 Chd £1.10; March 30-Nov 2, daily except Mons & Tues, but open Bank Hol Mons (closed Good Fri). Wed-Fri (11-6), Sats & Suns 2-6 or sunset if earlier; Bank Hol Mons & Suns preceeding (12-6). For NGS (Share to Trinity Hospice, Clapham Common®) Mon May 27 (12-6)*

Sea Close %% (Maj & Mrs R H Blizard) Cannongate Rd, Hythe. A259 Hythe-Folkestone; ½m from Hythe, signed. A plantsman's garden; 1¼ acres on steep slope overlooking the sea; designed, laid out & maintained by present owners since 1966. Approx 1000 named plants & shrubs, planted for visual effect in many varied style beds of individual character. Cold refreshments. Teas Hythe. *Adm £1.50 Acc chd free (Share to Royal Signals Benevolent Fund®). Suns May 12, June 2, July 7, Aug 4 (2-5), Sept 29 (2-4)*

Shipbourne Gardens 3m N of Tonbridge, 5m E of Sevenoaks on A227. TEAS in village hall. Maps available at gardens and village hall. Parking on village green. *Combined adm £2.50 Acc chd free. Sun June 30 (2-6)*
    1 Batey's Cottage &% (Mr & Mrs E Martin) Stumble Hill. Small cottage garden with vegetable patch, herbaceous borders, shrubs
    Brookers Cottage &%% (Ann & Peter Johnson) Back Lane. ⅔-acre garden with natural pond, herbaceous borders and island beds; large collection of hardy geraniums (cranesbills); small fruit and vegetable patch
    The Coach House %% (Mrs Ann Buckett) The Grange. Small informal garden, ⅓ acre, in former orchard; herbaceous and shrub borders with roses growing through apple trees; small pond; vegetable garden
    Plantation House ※ (Mr & Mrs A Primarolo) Reeds Lane. ¾-acre garden originally a Kent cobnut orchard, with island and herbaceous borders; conifers, heathers, roses, old apple trees, azaleas, small vegetable garden
    Yew Tree Cottage ※ (Susan & Ian Bowles) The Green. Small cottage garden, partially walled, with herbaceous border, small gravel garden and old roses. Studio of wild life artist Ian Bowles will be open

Sibton Park &% (Mrs Ridley-Day & Mr & Mrs C Blackwell) Lyminge, 8m NW of Folkestone. Off Elham Valley road, N of Lyminge, turn L for Rhodes Minnis, ¼m on L. Landscaped garden with spacious lawns, 30 feet high yew hedges and topiary; old walled garden; children's adventure playground (own risk). TEAS. *Adm £1.50 OAP £1 Chd 50p. Sun June 23 (2-6)*

The Silver Spray &%% (Mr & Mrs C T Orsbourne) Sellindge. 7m SE of Ashford on A20 opposite school. 1-acre garden developed and planted since 1983 and maintained by owners. Attractively laid out gardens and wild area combine a keen interest in conservation (especially butterflies) with a love of unusual hardy and tender plants. TEAS. *Adm £1 Acc chd free (Share to St Mary's Church, Sellindge®). Mons May 27, Aug 26; Weds July 3, 17, Aug 21; Sats June 22, July 6, 20; Sun June 23 (2-5)*

Sissinghurst Garden &%% (Nigel Nicolson Esq; The National Trust) Cranbrook. Station: Staplehurst. Bus: MD5 from Maidstone 14m; 297 Tunbridge Wells (not Suns) 15m. Garden created by the late V. Sackville-West and Sir Harold Nicolson. Spring garden, herb garden. Tudor building and tower, partly open to public. Moat. **Because of the limited capacity of the garden, daily visitor numbers are restricted; timed tickets are in operation and visitors may have to wait before entry.** Lunches and TEAS. *Adm £5 Chd £2.50 (Share to Charleston Farmhouse Trust®). Garden open April 2 to Oct 15. (Closed Mons incl Bank Hols). Tues to Fri 1-6.30 (last adm 6pm); Sats and Suns 10-5.30 (last adm 5pm). For NGS Weds April 24, June 5, July 10, Oct 2 (1-6.30)*

Sissinghurst Place & ✍ ❀ (Mr & Mrs Simon macLachlan) Sissinghurst, 2m NE of Cranbrook, E of Sissinghurst village on A262. Large garden of herbaceous beds, lawns, rhododendrons, fine trees, daffodils, shrubs and roses; herbs and climbers in ruin of original house, wild spring garden and pond. TEAS June openings only. **The Coach House** open on June days. *Adm £1 (April), Combined adm £2 (June), Chd 25p (Share to Hospice in the Weald, Tunbridge Wells). Sun, Mon April 7, 8; Sat, Sun June 29, 30 (1.30-5.30)*

South Hill Farm & ✍ ❀ (Sir Charles Jessel Bt) Hastingleigh, E of Ashford. Turn off A28 to Wye, go through village and ascend Wye Downs, in 2m turn R at Xrds marked Brabourne and South Hill, then first L. Or from Stone Street (B2068) turn W opp Stelling Minnis, follow signs to Hastingleigh, continue towards Wye and turn L at Xrds marked Brabourne and South Hill, then first L. 2 acres high up on N Downs, C17/18 house (not open); old walls; ha-ha; formal water garden; old and new roses; unusual shrubs, perennials and foliage plants. TEAS. *Adm £1.50 Chd 25p (Share to Kent Association for the Blind®). Sat, Sun July 6, 7 (2-6)*

Spilsill Court & ✍ ❀ (Mr & Mrs C G Marshall) Frittenden Road, Staplehurst. Proceed to Staplehurst on A229 (Maidstone-Hastings). From S enter village, turn R immediately after Elf garage on R & just before 30mph sign, into Frittenden Rd; garden ½m on, on L. From N go through village to 40mph sign, immediately turn L into Frittenden Rd. Approx 4 acres of garden, orchard and paddock; series of gardens including those in blue, white and silver; roses; lawns; shrubs, trees and ponds. Small private chapel. Jacob sheep & unusual poultry. TEA. *Adm £1.50 Chd under 16 50p (Share to Gardening for the Disabled Trust®). Suns March 31, July 28 (11-5)*

¶**Springhead** & (Mrs P Brice), Salts Lane, Loose, 3½m S of Maidstone. Turn W off A229 to Loose. Parking in village; proceed 300 yds on foot up Salts Lane. Peaceful garden of about an acre, at head of Loose Valley. Terraced and mixed beds; small pond and waterfall. **Amber Green Farmhouse** open same days. TEAS in aid of Loose Amenities Assoc. *Adm £1 Acc chd free. Suns June 9, 16 (2-5.30)*

Squerryes Court & (Mr & Mrs John Warde) ½m W of Westerham signed from A25. 15 acres of well-documented historic garden, C18 landscape. Part of the formal garden has been restored by the family using C17 plan. Lake, spring bulbs, azaleas, herbaceous borders, C18 dovecote, cenotaph commemorating Gen Wolfe; woodland walks. TEAS on NGS days for St Mary's Church, Westerham. *Adm £2.20 Chd £1.20 (House and garden £3.70 Chd £1.80). Weds, Sats, Suns from April 1 to Sept 30 (2-6). For NGS Suns July 14, Aug 18 (2-6)*

Stoneacre ❀ (Mrs Rosemary Alexander; The National Trust) Otham, 4m SE of Maidstone, between A2020 and A274. Old world garden recently replanted. Yew hedges; herbaceous borders; ginkgo tree. Timber-framed Hall House dated 1480. Subject of newspaper and magazine articles. (National Trust members please note that openings in aid of the NGS are on days when the property would not normally be open, therefore adm charges apply). TEAS. *Adm £2 Chd 50p (Share to Garden History Society®). Open Weds & Sats April-Oct 26 (2-5). For NGS Suns April 28, Oct 13 (2-5) and on June 30 with Otham gardens; private visits welcome, please* **Tel 01622 862871**

Stoneleigh House & ❀ (John Martin Esq) Stone Street, 6m S of Canterbury on B2068, 7m N of M20 junction 11. About 6 acres including 3 acres of 'ornamental' lawns, herbaceous borders, rose garden, specimen trees and shrubs, polytunnels, glasshouses and large vegetable garden incl top and soft fruit; computerised irrigation system throughout the garden. TEA. *Adm £2 Chd £1 (Share to Peter Allis: Powered Wheelchairs for Children). Mon May 27; Weds May 1, 8, 15, 22, 29, June 5, 12, 19, 26, July 3, 10, Aug 7 (10-5); also private visits welcome, please* **Tel 01227 700761**

Stonewall Park Gardens (Mr & Mrs V P Fleming) Chiddingstone Hoath, 5m SE of Edenbridge. ½-way between Mark Beech and Penshurst. Large walled garden with herbaceous borders. Extensive woodland garden, featuring species and hybrid rhododendrons, azaleas; wandering paths, lakes. **North Lodge** (Mrs Dorothy Michie) traditional cottage garden full of interest. TEA. *Adm £2 Acc chd free. Sun May 5 (2-5.30)*

Street Cottage (Mr & Mrs Timothy Stubbs) The Street, Bethersden. 6m SW of Ashford, 6m NE of Tenterden, turn off A28 to village centre. 1½-acre garden in lovely setting next to St Margaret's Church. Herbaceous, shrub and rose borders, vegetables and fruit with lawns and ponds. TEAS. *Adm £1.50 Acc chd free (Share to Bethersden Parish Records Society®). Sun June 30 (2-6)*

Street End Place & (Mr & Mrs R Baker White) Street End. 3m S of Canterbury-Hythe rd (Stone St). Drive gates at Granville Inn. Long established garden incl walled rose garden, in pleasant setting, fine trees. *Adm £1.50 Chd 50p. Sat June 29 (2-4.30)*

Swan Oast & (Mr & Mrs Bedford) Stilebridge, Marden, 6m S of Maidstone. On A229 (Maidstone-Hastings) ½m S of Stilebridge inn, 3m N of Staplehurst. 20-year-old 1¾-acre garden, incl ¼ acre of water, landscaped with shrubberies, rockeries, with dwarf conifers and heathers, raised beds of seasonal bedding, kitchen garden; ornamental fish and small collection of waterfowl. TEAS in aid of The Mike Colinwood Trust. *Adm £1.50 Acc chd free. Suns April 28, May 5, 12, June 30, July 14, 28, Aug 11, 25, Sept 8 (2-6)*

Tanners ✍ ❀ (Lord & Lady Nolan) Brasted, 2m E of Westerham, A25 to Brastead; in Brasted turn off alongside the Green and up the hill to the top; 1st drive on R opp Coles Lane. Bus stop Brasted Green and White Hart 200yds. 5 acres; mature trees and shrubs; magpies, magnolias, rhododendrons and foliage trees; water garden; interesting new planting. Plants mostly labelled. Teas in Village Tearoom, High Street, Brasted. *Adm £1.50 Chd 50p. By appointment, groups also welcome, please* **Tel 01959 563758**

2 Thorndale Close &⚘ (Mr & Mrs L O Miles) Chatham. From A229 Chatham-Maidstone rd turn E opp Forte Posthouse into Watson Ave, next R to Thorndale Close. Minute front and rear gardens of 11 × 18ft and 20 × 22ft. Plantsman's garden with alpines, pool, bog garden, rockery, peat and herbaceous beds. *Adm £1 Acc chd under 10 free. Suns April 14, 28, May 12, 26, June 9, 23 (2-5.30); also private visits welcome, please* Tel 01634 863329

Thornham Friars &⚘ (Geoffrey Fletcher Esq) Pilgrims Way, Thurnham, 4m NE of Maidstone. From M20 or M2 take A249, at bottom of Detling Hill turn into Detling and 1m along Pilgrims Way to garden. 2-acre garden on chalk. Distant views across parkland. Many unusual shrubs; trees; lawns with special beds for ericaceous shrubs. Tudor house. *Adm £1.50 Chd 25p. Sun May 5 (2-5.30)*

Torry Hill &⚘❀ (Lord & Lady Kingsdown) 5m S of Sittingbourne. Situated in triangle formed by Frinsted, Milstead and Doddington. Leave M 20 at junction 8 for A20, at Lenham turn N for Doddington; at Great Danes N for Hollingbourne and Frinsted (B2163). From M2 Intersection 5 via Bredgar and Milstead. From A2 and E turn S at Ospringe via Newnham and Doddington. 8 acres; large lawns, specimen trees, flowering cherries, rhododendrons, azaleas and naturalised daffodils; walled gardens with lawns, shrubs, roses, herbaceous borders, wild flower areas and vegetables. Extensive views to Medway and Thames estuaries. TEA. *Adm £1.50 Chd over 12 50p (Share to St Dunstan's Church, Frinsted©). Suns April 21, May 19 (2-5)*

Town Hill Cottage ⚘❀ (Mr & Mrs P Cosier) 58 Town Hill, West Malling. From A20 6m W of Maidstone, turn S onto A228. Top of Town Hill at N end of High St. Part walled small village garden of C16/C18 house, with many interesting plants. Hardy ferns for sale. TEAS. *Adm £1.50 Chd 75p. Suns May 19, June 16 (2-5)*

Turkey Court &⚘❀ (Mr & Mrs Peter Young) Ashford Road, Maidstone. Leave M20 at exit 7 to town centre, then A20 E for ½m. Large garden 1st established in early C17, now with lawns, lake, river and waterfall. Walled garden, beautiful trees, herbaceous borders and shrubs; yr-round interest. TEAS. *Adm £1.30 Chd 30p. Suns May 5, Sept 1 (2-6)*

Upper Pryors ⚘ (Mr & Mrs S G Smith) Cowden, 4½m SE of Edenbridge. From B2026 Edenbridge-Hartfield, turn R at Cowden Xrds and take 1st drive on R. 10 acres recently redesigned to incorporate parkland and a water garden. The terrace, with courtyard and wisteria walkway leads out onto large lawns, borders and open views. TEAS. *Adm £2 Chd 50p. Wed June 12 (2-5)*

Vine House &⚘❀ (Dr & Mrs Peter Huxley-Williams) 62 High St, Lydd. S of New Romney on B2075, past the church in High St on R-side. Informal gardens of about 1 acre surrounding C16 farmhouse; many unusual small trees & shrubs; ponds with waterfall; vineyard; new planting of old roses. Teas usually available in the church. *Adm £1.50 Acc chd free (Share to Iris Fund for the Blind®). Suns, Mons May 26, 27, Aug 25, 26 (2.30-5)*

Walnut Tree Gardens &⚘❀ (Mr & Mrs M Oldaker) Swan Lane, Little Chart. 6m NW of Ashford. Leave A20 at

Charing signed to Little Chart. At Swan public house turn W for Pluckley, gardens 500yds on L. Romantic 4-acre garden set within and around walls dating from early C18. Large collection of old roses; extensive range of unusual and interesting plants, shrubs and young trees. TEAS subject to weather. *Adm £1.50 Acc chd free (Share to Green Wicket Animal Sanctuary©). Suns May 19, 26, June 2, 9, 23, 30, July 7, 14, 21, 28, Aug 4, 11, 18; Mon May 27 (2-5) Coaches by appt, please* Tel 01233 840214

39 Warwick Crescent ⚘ (Mr & Mrs J G Sastre) Borstal, Rochester. From A229 Maidstone-Chatham at 2nd roundabout turn W into B2097 Borstal-Rochester rd; turn L at Priestfields, follow Borstal St to Wouldham Way, 3rd turning on R is Warwick Cres. Small front & rear plantsperson's gardens; most plants labelled; alpine terraces, peat & herbaceous beds; rockery with cascade & pool, bog garden, borders. Featured in NGS video 2. *Adm £1 Acc chd free. Private visits welcome by prior arrangement, please* Tel 01634 401636

Waystrode Manor &⚘❀ (Mr & Mrs Peter Wright) Cowden, 4½m S of Edenbridge. From B2026 Edenbridge-Hartfield, turn off at Cowden Pound. 8 acres; sweeping lawns, borders, ponds, bulbs, shrub roses, clematis and many tender plants. Orangery. All trees, plants and shrubs labelled. House C15 (not open). Last entry ½-hour before closing time. TEAS. Gift shop. *Adm £2 Chd 50p. Weds May 22, June 19 (1.30-5.30); Suns May 26, June 16, 30, July 7 (2-6); also open for groups of 15 or more by appt* Tel 01342 850695

Weeks Farm &⚘❀ (Robin & Monica de Garston) Bedlam Lane, Egerton, Forstal, 3½m E of Headcorn. Take Smarden Road out of Headcorn, Bedlam Lane is 3rd turning on L, Weeks Farm approx 1½m on R. 2-acre garden on Wealden clay, showing varied use of badly drained site; double herbaceous borders flanking gateway, vista a feature; orchard with crocus & fritillaria. New water garden, ponds with abundance of wild life. TEAS. *Adm £1.50 Acc chd free. Suns March 10 (12-5), April 7, Sept 15 (12-6). Private visits welcome* Tel (evenings) 01233 756252

Went House &❀ (Mrs Robin Baring) Swan Street, West Malling. From A20, 6m W of Maidstone turn S onto A228. Turn E off High Street in village towards station. Queen Anne house with secret garden surrounded by high wall. Interesting plants, water gardens, woodland, parterre and octagon potager. TEAS. *Adm £1.50 Acc chd free (Share to Lane-Fox Respiratory Patients Assoc, St Thomas's Hospital®). Suns June 16, 30 (2-6)*

West Studdal Farm &❀ (Mr & Mrs Peter Lumsden) West Studdal, N of Dover half-way between Eastry and Whitfield. From Eastry take A256, after 2½m pass Plough & Harrow, then 2nd L and 1st R, entrance ¼m on L. From Whitfield roundabout take A256, after 2½m pass High & Dry public house, ¼m fork R at 3-way junction, entrance ½m on R. Medium-sized garden around old farmhouse set by itself in small valley; herbaceous borders, roses and fine lawns protected by old walls and beech hedges. TEAS in Dodecagonal folly. *Adm £1.50 Chd 50p. Sun Aug 18 (2-6)*

Westview ❀ (Mr & Mrs J G Jackson) Spekes Rd, Hempstead. From M2 take A278 to Gillingham; at 1st roundabout follow sign to Wigmore, proceed to junction with Fairview Av, turn L & park on motorway link rd bridge, walk into Spekes Rd, Westview 3rd on L. ¼-acre town garden on very sloping site with many steps; good collection of plants & shrubs suitable for a chalk soil; designed by owners for all-year interest and low maintenance. Good autumn colour. TEAS. *Adm £1 Acc chd free. Weds April 24, May 15, June 5; Sats April 27, May 18, June 8 (2-5); also private visits welcome, please* **Tel 01634 230987**

Whitehill ✄ (Mrs Henderson) Wrotham. On A20 at Wrotham, between junctions 2A (M26) and 2 (M20). 3-acre garden, incl 1½ acres with design by Gertrude Jekyll in 1919, now carefully restored from original plans. *Adm £1.50 Chd 50p (Share to Kent Air Ambulance©). Sun June 16 (2-5.30); private visits welcome, please* **Tel 01732 882521**

Whitehurst ♿✄ (Mr & Mrs John Mercy) Chainhurst, 3m N of Marden. From Marden station turn R into Pattenden Lane and under railway bridge; at T-junction turn L; at next fork bear R to Chainhurst, then second turning on L. 1½ acres of trees, roses & water garden. Victorian spiral staircase leading to aerial walkway through the tree tops. Exhibition of root dwellings. TEAS. *Adm £2 Chd 50p (Share to Stroke Assoc®). Suns May 5, June 2, 23, Oct 6, 13; Wed May 29 (2-5.30)*

Withersdane Hall ✄ (University of London) Wye College, 3m NE of Ashford. A28 take fork signed Wye. Bus EK 601 Ashford-Canterbury via Wye. Well-labelled garden of educational and botanical interest, containing several small carefully designed gardens; flower and shrub borders; spring bulbs; herb garden. Rain-fed garden. Free guide book with map available. TEAS. *Adm £1.50 Chd 50p. Suns April 14, July 7, Aug 4, Sept 1 (2-5)*

Womenswold Gardens ♿✄❀ Midway between Canterbury and Dover, SE of A2, take B2046 signed Wingham at Barham crossover, after about ¼m turn R at Armada beacon, follow signs for gardens. Four diverse and colourful cottage gardens within easy walking distance. St Margaret's Church will be open, with craft exhibition. TEAS. *Combined adm £2 Acc chd free (Share to St Margaret's Church). Sat, Sun June 29, 30 (2-6)*

Worth Gardens ♿✄❀ 2m SE of Sandwich and 5m NW of Deal, from A258 signed Worth. A group of cottage gardens in wide variety in peaceful village setting. Maps and tickets available at each garden. TEA. *Combined adm £1.50 Chd 25p. Sun July 7 (2-5)*

Wyckhurst ♿✄❀ (Mr & Mrs C D Older) Mill Road, Aldington, 4m SE of Ashford. Leave M20 at junction 10, on A20 travel S to Aldington turning; proceed 1½m to Aldington village hall, 'Walnut Tree' take rd signed to Dymchurch, after ¼m turn R into Mill Road. C16 cottage (not open) surrounded by 1-acre cottage garden; old roses; herbaceous borders; unusual perennials. Extensive views across Romney Marsh. TEAS in aid of Bonnington Church. *Adm £2 Chd 50p. Wed June 26; Sun June 30 (11-6)*

Yalding Gardens ✄❀ 6m SW of Maidstone, three gardens S & W of village. *Combined adm £2 Chd £1. Sun April 21 (2-5.30)*

Long Acre (Mr & Mrs G P Fyson) is on L in Cheveney Farm Lane, just off Yalding-Hunton rd (Vicarage Road) ⅓m from Yalding War Memorial. Long, narrow garden comprising shrubberies, lawns, vegetable and fruit garden and paddock with young specimen trees. Shrubberies have been recently developed to eliminate the work in maintaining flower beds

Parsonage Oasts ✄❀ (Mr & the Hon Mrs Raikes) Between Yalding village and station turn off at Anchor public house over bridge over canal, continue 100yds up the lane. ¾-acre riverside garden with walls, shrubs, daffodils. TEAS in aid of The Fifth Trust for Mentally Handicapped Adults

Rugmer Farmhouse ✄❀ (Mr & Mrs R Lawrence) S of village, off Benover Rd (B2162), 440yds past Woolpack Inn. 2-acre garden, surrounding C16 cottage (not open), developed by present owners since 1975; spring bulbs, mixed borders and vegetables, on Wealden clay

---

SYMBOLS USED IN THIS BOOK (See also Page 15)

‡   Following a garden name in the Dates of Opening list indicates that those gardens sharing the same symbol are nearby and open on the same day.

‡‡ Indicates a second series of nearby gardens open on the same day.

¶   Opening for the first time.

❀   Plants/produce for sale if available.

♿   Gardens with at least the main features accessible by wheelchair.

✄   No dogs except guide dogs but otherwise dogs are usually admitted, provided they are kept on a lead. Dogs are not admitted to houses.

●   Gardens marked thus do not necessarily give all their takings to the National Gardens Scheme. Instead they give a guaranteed contribution.

▲   Where this sign appears alongside dates in the descriptive entry for a garden it denotes that this garden is also open regularly to the public on days other than those for the NGS.

Lancashire, Merseyside & Greater Manchester

Hon County Organisers: Mr & Mrs R Doldon, Old Barn Cottage, Greens Arms Road, Turton, Nr Bolton
BL7 OND Tel 01204 852139

Assistant Hon County Organiser: J Bowker Esq, Swiss Cottage, 8 Hammond Drive, Read, Burnley

DATES OF OPENING

April 14 Sunday
Lindeth Dene, Silverdale

May 5 Sunday
The Ridges, Limbrick, nr Chorley

May 6 Monday
The Ridges, Limbrick, nr Chorley

May 19 Sunday
191 Liverpool Rd South, Maghull
Loxley, Wrightington

May 24 Friday
Gresgarth Hall, Caton

May 26 Sunday
Catforth Gardens, Catforth
Cross Gaits Cottage, Blacko
Lindeth Dene, Silverdale
191 Liverpool Rd South, Maghull
Old Barn Cottage, Turton

May 27 Monday
Cross Gaits Cottage, Blacko
Old Barn Cottage, Turton

June 2 Sunday
Bank House, Borwick
Higher Parrock House, Barrowford
Rufford Old Hall, Rufford, nr
Ormskirk

June 5 Wednesday
Higher Parrock House, Barrowford

June 9 Sunday
Loxley, Wrightington
Mill Barn, Salmesbury Bottoms
Speke Hall, The Walk, Liverpool

June 22 Saturday
Linden Hall, Borwick

June 23 Sunday
Linden Hall, Borwick
Mill Barn, Salmesbury Bottoms

June 29 Saturday
The Mansion House, St Helens

June 30 Sunday
Catforth Gardens, Catforth
Clearbeck House, Higher
Tatham
Hesketh Bank Village Gardens
The Mansion House, St Helens ‡
The Ridges, Limbrick, nr Chorley
Windle Hall, St Helens ‡

July 7 Sunday
Bank House, Borwick
Clearbeck House, Higher Tatham
Frigham Cottage, Trawden
Swiss Cottage, Read
Weeping Ash, Glazebury

July 14 Sunday
Cross Gaits Cottage, Blacko

July 21 Sunday
Montford Cottage, Fence

July 28 Sunday
Catforth Gardens, Catforth
Greyfriars, Fulwood, Preston

August 4 Sunday
Bank House, Borwick

August 17 Saturday
The Mansion House, St Helens

August 18 Sunday
The Mansion House, St Helens

August 26 Monday
Old Barn Cottage, Turton

September 1 Sunday
Bank House, Borwick
Windle Hall, St Helens

September 8 Sunday
Weeping Ash, Glazebury

Regular openings
For details see garden description

Catforth Gardens, Catforth

DESCRIPTIONS OF GARDENS

Bank House ⚫✿ (Mr & Mrs R G McBurnie) Borwick. 2m NE of Carnforth off A6. Leave M6 at junction 35. Plantsman's garden of 2 acres designed to provide all year round shape, colour and form. Divided into different areas of interest including shady borders, sunny gravel area with old-fashioned roses, arboretum, fruit and vegetables. Island beds, silver and gold borders. Collection of carnivorous plants. TEAS. *Adm £1.50 Chd free. Suns June 2, July 7, Aug 4, Sept 1 (2-6)*

Catforth Gardens ♿⚫✿ Leave M6 at junction 32 turning N on A6. Turn L at 1st set of traffic lights; 2m to T-junction, turn R. Turn L at sign for Catforth, L at next T-junction, 1st R into Benson Lane. Bear L at church into Roots Lane. Incl adjoining gardens of **Willowbridge Farm** with access through **Catforth Gardens Nursery** as seen on Gardeners World 1993, featured in the Good Gardens Guide. TEAS NGS days only. *Combined adm £2 OAP £1.50 Chd 50p. Suns May 26, June 30, July 28 (12-5), adjacent nursery and gardens open March 16 to Sept 15 (10.30-5). Parties by appt, please* **Tel 01772 690561/690269**
   Catforth Gardens Nursery (Mr & Mrs T A Bradshaw) 1-acre informal country garden, planted for year round interest and colour. Wide variety of unusual shrubs; trees; rhododendrons, azaleas; rare herbaceous plants incl euphorbias, dicentras, pulmonarias; ground cover plants; national collection of hardy geraniums; 2 ponds with bog gardens, large rockery and woodland garden
   Willow Bridge Farm (Mr & Mrs W Moore) ¼-acre garden planted with a wide variety of herbaceous perennials (many rare). Planted with particular attention to colour from spring to autumn, giving a cottage garden effect, plus an acre garden in the making, large ponds, sunny banks and long herbaceous borders

Clearbeck House ♿✿ (Mr & Mrs P Osborne) Higher Tatham. Signed from Wray (M6 Junction 34, A683, B6480) and Low Bentham. Partly re-landscaped garden of about 1 acre focused on larger lake and wildlife area with increasing bird species. Traditional and formal borders near house lead out through vistas to distant views. Pyramid and symbolic garden; sculptures (some for sale); varied planting incl. old-fashioned roses and wet areas. A garden to walk in, with surprises. TEAS *Adm £1 Chd free. Suns June 30, July 7 (11.30-5.30) Private visits welcome, please* **Tel 015242 61029**

Cross Gaits Cottage ⚘❀ (Mr & Mrs S J Gude) Take M65 exit junction 13. Follow Barrowford signs then Barnoldswick signs. Garden 1½m on Barnoldswick Road opp Cross Gaits Inn. ⅔-acre walled cottage garden; shrub and herbaceous borders; 2 ornamental ponds. 700ft above sea level; fine view of Pennines. TEA. *Adm £1 Chd 50p. Sun, Mon May 26, 27; Sun July 14 (1-5). Private visits welcome, please* **Tel 01282 617163**

Frigham Cottage ❀ (Sue & Alec Rumbold) Trawden. 3m SE of Colne. From the A6068, follow the B6250 into Trawden. Turn L at church, then straight on for 1m. No parking at the house on open day - visitors have a 600yd walk. ⅓-acre of recently developed garden on the lower slopes of Boulsworth Hill at 850ft above sea level. Divided into several small gardens and secret corners; water features and a wide variety of shrubs and plants. TEAS. *Adm £1 Chd free. Sun July 7 (11-5). Private visits welcome May to July (with parking at the house), please* **Tel 01282 870581**

¶Gresgarth Hall ⚘ (Sir Mark & Lady Lennox-Boyd) Caton. Exit 34 on M6 and take Kirkby Lonsdale Road for 2m to Caton. Turn R signposted Quernmore and continue ½m to where road turns sharp R. The drive to Gresgarth is straight ahead. Large garden by banks of Artle Beck, extensively relandscaped and planted in recent yrs by Arabella Lennox-Boyd, a landscape designer. *Adm £2 Chd £1. Fri May 24 (2-6)*

Greyfriars ⚘⚘ (Mr & Mrs William Harrison) Walker Lane, Fulwood. 2m N of Preston. Junction 32 off M6 (M55); S to Preston; at Black Bull Xrds, R to Boys Lane Xrds, entrance ½m on R. 8 acres; lawns, rose beds, fuchsias; 4 greenhouses with hybrid begonias, geraniums and carnations; fountains and water display. TEAS. *Adm £1.50 Chd 50p. Sun July 28 (2-5)*

¶Hesketh Bank Village Gardens ⚘❀ Midway between Preston and Southport. From Preston take A59 towards Liverpool, then turn R at traffic lights for Tarleton village. Straight through Tarleton to Hesketh Bank. Tickets and maps at The Hawthornes, Marsh Road. TEAS in aid of Hedgehog Rescue Wildlife Hospital at **31 Becconsall Lane**. *Combined adm £2 Chd free. Sun June 30 (1-6)*
  31 Becconsall Lane (Mr & Mrs J Baxter) Cottage style garden with pond, white and green beds and semi-woodland walk. *Also open by appt please,* **Tel 01772 813018**
  74 Chapel Road (Mr & Mrs T Iddon) Compact colourful garden. Wide variety of plants. Pond, arbour and gazebo
  Hawthornes (Mr & Mrs R Hodson) Marsh Rd. 1-acre garden, mixed borders and beds. Shrubs, roses, clematis, many perennials. Pond. Nursery attached. *Also open by appt, please* **Tel 01772 812379**
  11 Shore Road (Mr A Taylor) Terraced garden with herbaceous plants, shrubs, roses and summer bedding
  Manor Farm (Mr & Mrs K Dickinson) Shore Rd. Informal cottage garden with herbs, shrub roses and woodland walk in a naturalistic setting. *Also open by appt, please* **Tel 01772 812530**
  155 Station Road (Mr & Mrs G Hale) Large, interesting garden. Features incl pond, mixed herbaceous, shrub borders and climbers

Higher Parrock House ⚘ (Mr & Mrs J S Thornton) Barrowford. M65 motorway. Take turning to Fence at junction 13, R after 600yds to top of Parrock Rd. 2 acres of mature gardens on S facing slope. Spring flowering trees and shrubs, mature conifers, gardens within gardens, ponds and water features, rambling roses. TEAS (Sun June 2) TEA (Wed June 5) in aid of St Thomas Church, Barrowford. *Adm £1. Sun June 2 (11-5), Wed June 5 (2-6)*

Linden Hall ⚘⚘ (Mr & Mrs E P Sharp) Borwick. 3m NE of Carnforth. Leave M6 exit 35; take A6 to Milnthorpe. House in centre of Borwick village. C19 garden of 5 acres, wide range of trees, shrubs and old-fashioned roses; ornamental lake with Chinese pagoda, herbaceous borders and knot garden. Victorian greenhouses and ornamental kitchen garden. TEAS. *Adm £1 Chd 50p. Sat, Sun June 22, 23 (2-5)*

Lindeth Dene ❀ (Mrs B M Kershaw) 38 Lindeth Rd, Silverdale. 13m N of Lancaster. Take M6 to junction 35, turn L (S) on A6 to Carnforth traffic lights. Turn R follow signs Silverdale. After level crossing ¼m uphill turn L down Hollins Lane. At T junction turn R into Lindeth Rd. Garden is 4th gateway on L, park in rd. 1¼ acres overlooking Morecambe Bay. Limestone rock garden; troughs; pools; heathers; veganic kitchen garden, saxifrages, geraniums, Elizabethan primroses, N.Z. plants and hardy perennials. Teas and toilets available in village. *Adm £1 Acc child free. Suns April 14, May 26 (2-5). Private visits welcome by appt, please* **Tel 01524 701314**

191 Liverpool Rd South ⚘❀ (Mr & Mrs D Cheetham) Maghull. From A59 take turning for Maghull Town Centre. Turn L at traffic lights and veer R over canal bridge. Garden ¼m on R. ½-acre suburban garden; rhododendrons, azaleas, camellias, rockery, pool, sink gardens, primulas, a variety of trees (some unusual), shrubs, bulbs and herbaceous plants for all year colour in the smaller garden. Featured in Lancashire Life 1995. TEAS. *Adm £1 Acc chd free. Suns May 19, 26 (1.30-5.30)*

Loxley ⚘❀ (Mr & Mrs D Robinson) Robin Hood Lane, Wrightington, nr Wigan. Situated 1m from junction 27 of the M6. Continue past Wrightington Hospital to Xrds, turn R by the garage ½m up the rd situated on the L. ¼-acre garden designed on 2 levels with water feature and ornamental fish pond. Variety of shrubs, conifers, rhododendrons, azaleas and perennials. Barbecue, weather permitting. TEA. *Adm £1 Acc chd free. Suns May 19, June 9 (12-5). Private visits welcome, please* **Tel 01257 254120**

¶The Mansion House ⚘⚘❀ (Age Concern) Victoria Park, St Helens. ½m S of Carr Mill exit of A580. ½-acre walled Victorian kitchen garden providing fruit, vegetables and flowers for this activity and leisure centre for frail older people, conservatory and formal walled garden. Feature: rose walk, herb garden, fruit and vegetables, fruit cordons. Not complete. Formerly derelict site, planting started in 1995. Of particular interest to aged and infirm. Bistro open to public. TEAS. *Adm £1.50 Chd 50p (Share to Age Concern, St Helens®). Sats, Suns June 29, 30, Aug 17, 18 (11-4)*

Mill Barn &❀ (Dr C J Mortimer) Goose Foot Close, Samlesbury Bottoms, Preston. 6m E of Preston. From M6 junction 31 2½m on A59/A677 B/burn. Turn S. Nabs Head Lane, then Goose Foot Lane 1m. 1½-acre tranquil, terraced garden on the site of C18 corn and cotton mills along the banks of the R Davwen. Varied planting with many uncommon herbaceous perennials. A maturing garden that is still being developed and extended. TEAS. *Adm £1 Chd free. Suns June 9, 23 (2-6). Private visits of 4 and over welcome, please* **Tel 01254 853300**

Montford Cottage &❀❀ (C Bullock & A P Morris) Fence, nr Burnley. Situated on the B6248 between Brierfield and Fence. From the M65 junction 13, take the A6068 (signs for Fence) and in 2m turn L onto the B6248 (signs for Brierfield). Proceed down the hill for ½m, entrance to garden is on L (near dangerous bend - drivers please take care). Walled garden ⅔-acre developed over last 11 yrs and now maturing, with many unusual plants of particular interest to flower arrangers and plantsmen. Particular emphasis on variety of foliage, with varied shrubs, trees, herbaceous plants, pools and featuring new oriental garden and further developments for 1996. No coaches. TEAS. *Adm £1.50 Chd 50p. Sun July 21 (2-6)*

Old Barn Cottage &❀ (Ray & Brenda Doldon) Greens Arms Rd, Turton. Midway between Bolton and Darwen on B6391 off A666, or through Chapeltown Village High St (B6391). 1-acre garden on moorland site. Spring flowering trees; shrubs; azaleas, rhododendrons; water gardens; heathers; conifers, herbaceous beds; moorland views. As seen on TV Garden Club 1993. TEAS in aid of St Ann's Church (May 26 and Aug 26), Beacon Counselling Service (May 27). *Adm £1 Chd free. Sun, Mon, May 26, 27, Mon Aug 26 (12-5). Private visits welcome by appt (May to Aug), please* **Tel 01204 852139**

The Ridges &❀ (Mr & Mrs J M Barlow) Limbrick, nr Chorley. Approx 2m SE of Chorley. M61 from Manchester Chorley S junction 6 approx 6m, passing through Adlington taking Long Lane to Limbrick. Passing Black Horse follow rd to L and up hill on L. From Preston and N, junction 8 M61, take Cowling Rd out of Chorley towards Rivington approx 1½m on R. C17 house with 2¼-acre gardens. Incl old walled kitchen garden, now cottage style garden with lawn, large well stocked herbaceous borders, and area for growing annuals to dry. Also fish pond with patio; laburnum arch leads to large formal lawn, surrounded by rhododendrons, and natural woodland. TEAS in aid of Chorley Stroke Club and the Diabetic Society. *Adm £1 Chd 50p. Sun, Mon May 5, 6, Sun June 30 (11-5). Private visits for 5 & over welcome, please* **Tel 01257 279981**

Rufford Old Hall & (The National Trust) Rufford. On A59 Liverpool to Preston rd in village of Rufford, 7m N of Ormskirk. Set in 14 acres of garden and woodland. Informal garden and walks. Spectacular in May and June for spring flowering rhododendrons and azaleas. TEAS. *Adm £1.60 Chd 80p (Garden only). Sun June 2 (12-4.30)*

Speke Hall &✄ (The National Trust) Liverpool. 8m SE of Liverpool adjacent to Liverpool Airport. Follow signs for Liverpool Airport. A formal garden with herbaceous border, rose garden; moated area with formal lawns. A stream garden now open this yr. A wild wood is included. Approx size of estate 35 acres. TEAS. *Adm £1.20 Chd 60p (Garden only). Sun June 9 (1-5.30). Parties of 20 or over welcome, please* **Tel 0151 4277231**

Swiss Cottage ✄❀ (James & Doreen Bowker) 8 Hammond Drive, Read. 3m SE of Whalley on A671 Whalley to Burnley Road, turn by Pollards Garage, up George Lane to T junction, L into Private Rd. 1½-acre hillside garden designed on 2 levels in mature woodland setting. Variety of shrubs, trees, rhododendrons, azaleas, perennials and alpines. Stream and bog garden feature. Featured in Lancashire Life. TEAS. *Adm £1.50 Chd free. Sun July 7 (1-5). Private visits welcome by appt, please* **Tel 01282 774853**

Weeping Ash &✄ (John Bent Esq) Glazebury. ¼m S A580 (East Lancs Rd Greyhound Motel roundabout, Leigh) on A574 Glazebury/Leigh Boundary. 2-acre garden of yr-round interest on heavy soil. A broad sweep of lawn with mixed borders of shrubs and herbaceous perennials gives way to secret areas with pools, roses and island beds, a rockery with alpines, a ruined Doric temple and elevated viewing points to enable one to see the garden, plus industrial Lancashire landscape. A hot area with mediterranean planting and a further extensive lawn. Teas 100yds N at Garden Centre. *Adm £1.50 Chd 50p (Share to Macmillan Leigh Home Care Unit®). Suns July 7, Sept 8 (1-5.30)*

Windle Hall &❀ (The Lady Pilkington) N of E Lancs Rd, St Helens. 5m W of M6 via E Lancs Rd, nr Southport junction. Entrance by bridge over E Lancs Rd. 200yr old walled garden surrounded by 5-acres of lawns, rock and water garden; thatched summer house. Tufa stone grotto; herbaceous borders, pergola and rose gardens containing exhibition blooms, miniature ornamental ponies, ducks; greenhouses. TEAS. *Adm £1 Chd 50p. Suns June 30, Sept 1 (2-5)*

Leicestershire & Rutland

Hon County Organisers: (Leicestershire) Mr John Oakland, Old School Cottage, Oaks-in-Charnwood, nr Loughborough LE12 9YD Tel 01509 502676 or 01509 890376
(Rutland) Mrs Jeffy Wood, Townsend House, Morcott Road, Wing, LE15 8SE Tel 01572 737465

Assistant Hon County Organiser: Mrs Rose Dejardin, Wingwell, Top Street, Wing LE15 8SE Tel 01572 737727
Hon County Treasurer (Rutland): A Whitamore Esq., The Stockyard, West Street, Easton-on-the-Hill, Stamford, Lincs PE9 3LS

DATES OF OPENING

April 4 Thursday
Burbage Gardens, Burbage
April 7 Sunday
Long Close, Woodhouse Eaves
April 9 Tuesday
Whatton House, Loughborough
April 13 Saturday
Paddocks, Shelbrook, Ashby-de-la-Zouch
April 14 Sunday
Paddocks, Shelbrook, Ashby-de-la-Zouch
April 21 Sunday
Gunthorpe, Oakham
April 28 Sunday
Ashwell Lodge, Oakham
May 2 Thursday
Burbage Gardens, Burbage
May 5 Sunday
Burrough House, Burrough on the Hill
Gaddesby Hall, Gaddesby
Long Close, Woodhouse Eaves
May 6 Monday
Burrough House, Burrough on the Hill
Gaddesby Hall, Gaddesby
May 7 Tuesday
Whatton House, Loughborough
May 12 Sunday
Burrough House, Burrough on the Hill
Glebe House, Hoby, nr Melton Mowbray
18 Park Road, Birstall
May 16 Thursday
1 Cumberland Road, Loughborough
May 19 Sunday
Burrough on the Hill Gardens
1 Cumberland Road, Loughborough
Owston Gardens, Oakham
18 Park Road, Birstall
Reservoir Cottage, Knipton
May 26 Sunday
Burrough House, Burrough on the Hill
Long Close, Woodhouse Eaves

May 27 Monday
Burrough House, Burrough on the Hill
May 28 Tuesday
Whatton House, Loughborough
June 2 Sunday
The Dairy, Coleorton ‡
The Gables, Thringstone ‡
Orchards, Walton, nr Lutterworth
Woodyton Farmhouse, Grace Dieu ‡
June 5 Wednesday
Arthingworth Manor, Market Harborough
June 8 Saturday
Paddocks, Shelbrook, Ashby-de-la-Zouch
June 9 Sunday
Burbage Gardens, Burbage
Paddocks, Shelbrook, Ashby-de-la-Zouch
Pine House, Gaddesby
Prebendal House, Empingham
June 12 Wednesday
Arthingworth Manor, Market Harborough
Pine House, Gaddesby
June 16 Sunday
Arthingworth Manor, Market Harborough
The Old Rectory, Teigh ‡
Shorne Hill, Brooke ‡
Wartnaby, nr Melton Mowbray
June 19 Wednesday
Arthingworth Manor, Market Harborough
June 22 Saturday
Sheepy Magna Gardens
June 23 Sunday
Clipsham House, nr Oakham
Gaddesby Hall, Gaddesby
Hill House, Dunton Bassett ‡
Langham Lodge, Oakham
Orchards, Walton, nr Lutterworth ‡
Queniborough Gardens
Sheepy Magna Gardens
June 26 Wednesday
Arthingworth Manor, Market Harborough ‡
Orchards, Walton, nr Lutterworth ‡

June 30 Sunday
Ashwell Gardens, Oakham
Brooksby Agricultural College, nr Melton Mowbray ‡
Glebe House, Hoby, nr Melton Mowbray ‡
Market Bosworth Gardens
Sutton Bonington Hall, Sutton Bonington
July 3 Wednesday
Arthingworth Manor, Market Harborough
July 4 Thursday
Burbage Gardens, Burbage
July 7 Sunday
Forge Cottage, Edith Weston
The Priory, Ketton
July 9 Tuesday
Stoke Albany House, Market Harborough
July 10 Wednesday
Arthingworth Manor, Market Harborough ‡
Stoke Albany House, Market Harborough ‡
July 14 Sunday
Burrough House, Burrough on the Hill
South Luffenham Hall, nr Stamford
Stoke Albany House, Market Harborough
Woodyton Farmhouse, Grace Dieu
July 16 Tuesday
Stoke Albany House, Market Harborough
July 17 Wednesday
Arthingworth Manor, Market Harborough
Stoke Albany House, Market Harborough
July 20 Saturday
Paddocks, Shelbrook, Ashby-de-la-Zouch
July 21 Sunday
Fenny Drayton Gardens
Paddocks, Shelbrook, Ashby-de-la-Zouch
Wartnby, nr Melton Mowbray
July 24 Wednesday
Arthingworth Manor, Market Harborough

July 28 Sunday
University of Leicester Botanic
Garden, Oadby
August 4 Sunday
The Dairy, Coleorton
Orchards, Walton, nr Lutterworth
August 10 Saturday
Paddocks, Shelbrook,
Ashby-de-la-Zouch
August 11 Sunday
Paddocks, Shelbrook,
Ashby-de-la-Zouch
August 18 Sunday
Woodyton Farmhouse,
Grace Dieu
August 26 Sunday
Burrough House, Burrough on the
Hill

August 27 Monday
Burrough House, Burrough on the
Hill
September 8 Sunday
Barnsdale Plants & Gardens,
Exton ‡
Hill House, Market Overton ‡
Little Frome, Fenny Drayton
September 15 Sunday
Whatton House, Loughborough
October 6 Sunday
1700 Melton Road, Rearsby
Whatton House, Loughborough

Regular openings
For details see garden description

Long Close, Woodhouse Eaves
1700 Melton Road, Rearsby
Whatton House

By appointment only
*For telephone numbers and other
details see garden descriptions.
Private visits welcomed*

Beeby Manor, Beeby
Stepping Stones, Old Farm, Little
Beeby

DESCRIPTIONS OF GARDENS

Arthingworth Manor ✤ (Mr & Mrs W Guinness) 5m S of Market Harborough. From Market Harborough via A508 at 4m L to Arthingworth; from Northampton via A508. At Kelmarsh turn R at bottom of hill for Arthingworth. In village turn R at church 1st L. 6 to 7-acre beautiful garden; collection shrub roses; white garden; delphiniums; herbaceous and mixed borders; greenhouses. Newly planted 3-acre arboretum. Original house now restored. Art gallery, British Modern Pictures. TEAS only on Sunday. *Adm £1.50 Chd 50p. Weds June 5, 12, 19, 26, July 3, 10, 17, 24; Sun June 16 (2-5)*

Ashwell Gardens ⚘ 3m N of Oakham, via B668 towards Cottesmore, turn L for Ashwell. TEAS at Ashwell House. *Combined adm £2 Chd 50p (Share to St Mary's Church®). Sun June 30 (2-6)*
   Ashwell House ↧✤ (Mr & Mrs S D Pettifer) 1½-acre vicarage garden, 1812; vegetable garden; almost original format partly given over to specialist flowers for drying. Pleasure garden with summer pavilion in classical style and architectural features by George Carter. TEAS. Home-made produce stall
   The Old Hall (Mrs N L McRoberts) Medium-sized garden, mixed borders, good variety of shrubs, climbers and herbaceous plants. Good trees and view of church
   Thistles ↧✤ (Mr & Mrs M Hope) Small plantsman's garden with over 280 named varieties (many unusual) in bog, pond, scree, shade and raised beds. Borders and climbers on pergolas and fences. Sale of rare and unusual plants

Ashwell Lodge ↧⚘✤ (Mrs B V Eve) Ashwell, 3m N of Oakham. From Al, 10m N of Stamford, turn W through Greetham and Cottesmore; then turn R for Ashwell. Park in village st. Medium-sized garden redesigned by Percy Cane c.1973; spring bulbs; herbaceous borders, paved rose garden, shrubs, greenhouse. As featured in 'Country Life' Nov 1990. TEAS. *Adm £1 Chd 25p (Share to Forces Help Soc & Lord Roberts Workshops®). Sun April 28 (2-6)*

Barnsdale Plants & Gardens ↧⚘✤ (Mr Geoff & Mr Nick Hamilton) The Avenue, Exton. Turn off Stamford/Oakham rd A606 at Barnsdale Lodge Hotel. 2-acres of small gardens laid out in the same style as the main television garden which is not open. A good mix of different types of gardens with the artisan's and gentleman's cottage gardens rebuilt for viewing. Also 2 gardens which have been constructed for forthcoming series in 1997. Geoff Hamilton will be on hand to answer any questions you may have. *Adm £1.50 Chd 25p (Share to Plant Life®). Sun Sept 8 (10-4)*

Beeby Manor ↧⚘✤ (Mr & Mrs Philip Bland) Beeby. 8m E of Leicester. Turn off A47 in Thurnby and follow signs through Scraptoft. 3-acre mature garden with venerable yew hedges, walled herbaceous border, lily ponds, rose towers and box parterre. Plus the start of a 1-acre arboretum. C16 and C18 house (not open). *Private visits welcome in June and July, please Tel 01162 595238*

Brooksby College ↧⚘✤ 6m SW of Melton Mowbray. From A607 (9m from Leicester or 6m from Melton Mowbray) turn at Brooksby; entrance 100yds. Bus: Leicester-Melton Mowbray; alight Brooksby turn, 100yds. Grounds incl extensive lawns, lake, ornamental brook, flowering shrub borders, heather bed, large collection young trees; other ornamental features; glasshouses, nursery. Church built 1220 open. *Adm £2 Chd free. Sun June 30 (1-5). Private visits welcome, please Tel 01664 434291*

Burbage Gardens ✤ From M69 junction 1, take B4109 signed Hinckley. TEA (Thurs only). *Combined adm £1.50 Chd free (Share to LOROS®). Thurs April 4, May 2, July 4 (2-5) Combined adm £2. Sun June 9 (11-5)*
   6 Denis Road ⚘✤ (Mr & Mrs D A Dawkins) Sketchley Manor Estate. From M69 junction 1 take 1409 signposted Hinkley then 1st L after roundabout. Small garden with wide range of plants, many unusual, incl plants grown for scent, alpines in sinks. Species clematis, scree area, hellebores, spring bulbs. *Private visits welcome, please Tel 01455 230509*
   7 Hall Road Burbage (Mr & Mrs D R Baker) Sketchley Manor Estate. 1st roundabout 1st L to Sketchley Lane; 1st R; 1st R; 1st R again; 1st L to Hall Rd. Medium-sized garden; mixed borders; alpines; sink gardens; scree area; collection of hellebores and hosta; unusual plants; foliage plants. Partially suitable for wheelchairs. *Private visits welcome, please Tel 01455 635616*

The Long Close Bullfurlong Lane & (Mr & Mrs A J Hopewell) Burbage. 1st R onto Coventry Road 2nd R onto Bullfurlong Lane, garden on L. Limited parking, park if poss on Coventry Rd. ½-acre family garden. Mixed borders; 'natural' ponds; vegetable plot; greenhouse and cool orchid house. Local orchid society in attendance. Cream TEAS, ploughman's lunches in aid of Childrens Society; toilets. *Open Sun June 9 only*

11 Primrose Drive (Mr & Mrs D Leach) Take 2nd turning on R into Sketchley Rd. 1st L into Azalea Drive, 1st R into Marigold Drive, 1st L Begonia Drive, 1st R into Primrose Drive. No 11 is on L on bend. Small cottage garden. Spring interest camellias, clematis and hellebores, summer interest paeonies, clematis and new English roses. *Private visits welcome April 13 to July 7, please* Tel 01455 250817

¶**Burrough on the Hill Gardens** ✕ 6m W of Oakham, 5m S of Melton Mowbray. From A606 at Langham, take rd signposted to Cold Overton and Somerby, continue through Somerby to Burrough on the Hill. TEAS at Burrough House. *Combined adm £2 Chd free (Share to St Mary's Church, Burrough on the Hill®). Sun May 19 (1-6)*

Burrough House &❀ (Mrs Barbara Keene) Approx 5½ acres of garden with special Spring interest with tulips, azaleas, rhododendrons and a unique wisteria wheel. A timber thatch-roofed bower house used by the Prince of Wales and Mrs Simpson; cascading water pools, peony and delphinium borders plus new herbaceous borders as well as a rose garden offer summer attraction. Featured in The Times in 1995. *Sun May 12 (tulips), Sun July 14 (delphinium & peony). Bank hols Suns & Mons May 5, 6, 26, 6, 27, Aug 26, 27 (1-6). Private visits welcome, please* Tel 01664 454226
¶**Cheseldyne House** (H & V J Blakebrough) Kings Lane. Garden approx ⅔-acre. Well established garden with pretty flower borders
¶**1 Gilson Greene** & (Mr & Mrs M Walton) Main Street. A very small cottage garden include a few vegetables, herbaceous area, annual borders and a few shrubs. Cared for by retired husband and disabled wife
¶**The Manor House** (M A Chamberlain & G E Palmer) 1½-acres mainly lawns with informal mixed shrubberies, evergreens, mature trees, a sunken pond garden, new woodland walk and outstanding views to Owston and Tilton
¶**The White House** (Mr & Mrs D Cooper) Main Street. ¾-acre garden created in the last 8 yrs from a paddock. Mixed borders containing many unusual and interesting plants; special features incl a small Japanese garden, a wild garden, a woodland walk and a rock garden, incl raised beds and an alpine house. Spectacular views of Burrough Hill and its Iron Age Fort

Clipsham House &❀ (Mr & Mrs Robert Wheatley) Clipsham. On B668 2m E of A1 NE of Oakham. 2 acres around early C19 former rectory; lawns, good trees, walled garden with summer house; herbaceous borders, roses, variety of shrubs, folly in small park. Featured in NGS video 1 and in The Gardener Magazine. TEAS. *Adm £1.50 Chd 25p (Share to St Mary's Church®). Sun June 23 (2-6)*

1 Cumberland Road &❀ (Mr & Mrs R Peddle) Loughborough. On A512 into Loughborough, 1m E of M1 junction 23, 1st L turn 300yds after Ring rd roundabout. Parking in Cumberland Rd and adjacent streets. Plant enthusiast's small walled town garden, herbaceous borders, scree, climbers, pots. Planted for sun and shade. TEAS. *Adm £1 Chd free (Share to NCCPG®). Thurs, Sun May 16, 19 (1-5)*

¶**The Dairy** &❀❀ (Mr & Mrs J B Moseley) Coleorton. Moor Lane off A512 W of Peggs Green Roundabout. A garden of approx ⅓-acre with mature trees and shrubs, herbaceous borders containing some unusual plants, herb garden and pergola leading to other interesting areas. TEAS. *Adm £1 Chd 50p. Suns June 2, Aug 4 (2-6)*

Fenny Drayton Gardens Situated approx 3m N of Nuneaton on the A444, crossing the A5 at The Royal Red Gate Inn and MSF Garage junction. Teas in St Michael's Church. *Combined adm £1.50 Chd free (Share to St Michael's and all Angels Church®). Sun July 21 (2-6)*
4 Drayton Lane ✕❀ (Mr & Mrs G Wright) ½ acres of lawn, with heather conifer beds, inlaid with bedding, plant areas, rockeries, pond and a wishing well
Little Froome &❀ (Mr & Mrs G J Cookes) Drayton Lane. 1½-acre garden, mature trees and wide variety of conifers. Landscaped with heathers at their best in Sept, large pond with bridge. *Adm £1 chd free. Also open Sun Sept 8 (2-6). TEAS*
4 Rookery Close ✕❀ (Mr & Mrs J Dowse) Average sized garden with pond and waterfall. Abundance of hanging baskets and tubs. Very good selection of perennials and shrubs
Crofters & (Mr & Mrs G M Heaton) 16 Rookery Close. Neat tidy garden front and rear, mostly lawns and flower beds. Open views of Leicestershire countryside at rear
19 Rookery Close & (Mr & Mrs Ratcliffe) Small garden lots of colour
Gem Cottage ✕ (Alan & Jane Priest) 4 Church Lane. ⅓-acre cottage side and rear gardens. Trees, shrubs and plants with pool and fish. Chimney pots and cart filled to brim with colour
12 Church Lane & (Mr & Mrs M Ambrose) ½-acre garden, ornamental walls and borders with rockeries, pond and waterfall. *Private visits of 6 and over welcome, please* Tel 01827 713257
Five Corners &❀ (Mr & Mrs Perrin) ¼-acre garden, mainly lawns with mixed shrubbery borders and evergreen hedges
¶**Tewlawny House** (Mr & Mrs C Outhwaite) Old Forge Road. A flower arranger's garden

¶**Forge Cottage** ✕❀ (Prof J Lindesay & Dr G Hall) Edith Weston. 5m E of Oakham off A6003. ¼-acre garden with an emphasis on drought-tolerant plants and vegetables. Collection of phlomis, euphorbia, cacti and succulents. Featured on Channel 4 Garden Club Sept 95. *Adm £1 Chd 25p. Sun 7 July (2-6)*

The Gables &❀❀ (Mr & Mrs P J Baker) Main St, Thringstone. Leave A512 Lougborough to Ashby de la Zouch rd at Bull's Head, signposted Thringstone. Main St is off the village green. ⅓-acre country garden. Herbaceous borders, many unusual plants, containers, clematis and old roses. Grade 11 listed cottage not open. TEAS. *Adm £1 Chd 25p. Sun June 2 (2-6)*

¶**Gaddesby Hall** ⌖❀ (Mr & Mrs David Jinks) Gaddesby. NE of Leicester. From A607 Leicester-Melton Mowbray, at Rearsby turn off for Gaddesby. A well structured 6-acre garden in the grand manner, completely restored over the last 11 yrs. Rare specimen trees, herbaceous borders, dingle walk spring garden, bulbs, formal lily pond with yew and box. TEAS. For May opening, flowers in C13 Church next door. TEAS. *Adm £2 Chd 50p (Share to Gaddesby Church®). Bank Hol Sun, Mon May 5, 6, Sun June 23 (2-6)*

Glebe House ⌖❀ (Mr & Mrs Horsfield) Church Lane, Hoby. 1m NW of A607 Leicester-Melton rd. turn at Brooksby Agricultural College. 1-acre of shrubs and herbaceous mixed borders, created since 1977, mainly within lovely C18 wall; paddock. Pleasing views over glebe land. TEAS. *Adm £1.50 Chd free (Share to Foundation for Study of Infant Death®). Suns May 12, June 30 (2-6)*

Gunthorpe ⌖ (A T C Haywood Esq) 2m S of Oakham. On Uppingham Rd; entrance by 3 cottages, on R going S. Medium-sized garden; spring flowers and flowering trees in good setting. TEAS. *Adm £1.50 Chd 50p (Share to CRMF®). Sun April 21 (2-5.30)*

Hill House ⌖❀ (Brian & Judith Taylor) Teigh Rd, Market Overton. 6m N of Oakham beyond Cottesmore, 5m from the A1 via Thistleton, 10m E from Melton Mowbray via Wymondham. ½-acre plant enthusiasts' garden consisting mainly of mixed beds designed for seasonal interest and comprising many unusual hardy and tender perennials; owner maintained. Featured on Channel 4 Garden Club Sept 95. TEAS. *Adm £1 Chd 25p. Sun Sept 8 (2-6)*

¶**Hill House** ⌖❀ (Mr & Mrs M J Rowe) The Mount, Dunton Bassett, nr Lutterworth. S of Leicester via A426 (between Leicester and Lutterworth) follow signs for Dunton Bassett, then to Lcirc. Small ½-acre family garden planted for yr-round interest and colour; pond, rockery, herbs, soft fruits, ferns and large mixed herbaceous beds. TEAS in aid of Dunton Bassett PTA. *Adm £1.20 Chd free. Sun June 23 (2-5)*

Langham Lodge ⌖❀ (Mr & Mrs H N Hemsley) Oakham. ½m out of Langham on Burley Rd. 1 acre; shrubs; interesting foliage; stone walls; shrub roses. Light lunches in aid of Langham Church. *Adm £1 Chd free. Sun June 23 (11-6). Private visits welcome, please Tel 01572 722912*

Long Close ❀ (Mrs George Johnson) 60 Main St, Woodhouse Eaves, S of Loughborough. From A6, W in Quorn B591. 5 acres rhododendrons (many varieties), azaleas, flowering shrubs, camelias, magnolias, many rare shrubs, trees, conifers, forest trees; lily ponds; terraced lawns, herbaceous borders, wild flower meadow walk. TEAS and specialist plant sale April 7, May 26. Tea and plant sale May 5. *Adm £2 Chd 20p. Suns April 7, (2-5), May 5, 26 (2-6). Daily Mons-Sats March-June (9.30-5.30). Tickets available at Pene Crafts shop opp. Also private parties welcome March to June, please Tel 01509 890616 business hrs*

Market Bosworth Gardens ⌖❀ 1m off A447 Coalville to Hinckley Rd, 3m off A444. Pay on Market Bosworth Market Place. Village plan available. Other gardens will also open. TEA. *Combined adm £2 Chd 50p. Sun June 30 (2-6)*

16 Northumberland Avenue (Mr & Mrs K McCarthy) Landscaped garden

24 Northumberland Avenue (Mr & Mrs E G Watkins) Flowers, shrubs and lawns

¶**The Rectory** (Rev J Plant) Rectory garden with flowers and shrubs

¶**4 Rectory Lane** (Mr & Mrs P Bonsell) Lawn, flowers and shrubs

273 Station Road (Mrs R J Baker) Flower garden and model village

8 Weston Drive (Mr & Mrs J Earl-Davies) Flower garden fuchsias a speciality

Witherstitch Farm (Ann Carter) Farm garden with rockery

1700 Melton Road ⌖❀ (Hazel Kaye) Rearsby, N of Leicester on A607. In Rearsby, on L.H. side from Leicester. 1-acre garden with wide range of interesting herbaceous plants; some shrubs and trees. Nursery. *Adm 50p Chd 10p. Daily March to Oct (Wed to Sat 10-5, Sun 10-12) Suns in May (2-5). Also SPECIAL OPEN DAY Sun Oct 6 (2-5). Adm £1 Chd 10p. TEAS Oct 6 only. Tel 01664 424578*

The Old Rectory ⌖❀ (Mr & Mrs D B Owen) Teigh. 5m N of Oakham. Between Wymondham and Ashwell; or from A1 via Thistleton and Market Overton. Medium-sized walled garden; mixed borders; good variety shrubs, herbaceous and climbing plants. House and garden featured in BBC's new production of 'Pride and Prejudice' as Mr Collin's Parsonage. Unusual C18 church next door. TEAS. *Adm £1 Chd under 12 free (Share to Holy Trinity Church, Teigh®). Sun June 16 (2-6)*

Orchards ❀❀ (Mr & Mrs G Cousins) Hall Lane, Walton, nr Lutterworth. 8m S of Leicester via the A50 take a R turn just after Shearsby (sign-posted Bruntingthorpe); thereafter follow signs for Walton. A garden of surprises. It is full of rare and unusual plants which are grown in colour-theme garden 'rooms'. Featured on TVs Garden Club. Views of countryside. TEAS. *Adm £1.20 Chd free. Suns June 2, 23, Aug 4, Wed June 26 (2-5). Also private visits welcome June to Sept, please Tel 01455 556958*

Owston Gardens ⌖❀ 6m W of Oakham via Knossington, 2m S of Somerby. From Leicester turn L 2m E of Tilton. TEAS. *Combined adm £1.50 Chd free. Sun May 19 (2-6)*

The Homestead (Mr & Mrs David Penny) ⅓ acre with lawn, clematis, ponds, borders, containers, alpine garden, views and photographs. Plants and sundries stalls

Rose Cottage (Mr & Mrs John Buchanan) Undulating 1¾ acres; shrub and flower borders; spring bulbs, roses, alpines, ponds, waterfall, fine views. *Private visits welcome by parties less than 5, please Tel 01664 454545*

By Appointment Gardens. These owners do not have a fixed opening day usually because they do not like crowds or have insufficient parking space. Owner will often give guided tour.

Paddocks &⚘❀ (Mrs Ailsa Jackson) Shelbrook. 1½m W of Ashby-de-la-Zouch on B5003 towards Moira. A plantaholic's garden with over 2000 varieties in 1 acre incl snowdrops, hellebores, astrantias and many less common herbaceous plants & shrubs. Plants propagated from garden for sale. NCCPG collection of old named double and single primulas. Silver medallist at Chelsea and Vincent Square. TEA. *Adm £1 Chd free. Sats and Suns April 13, 14, June 8, 9, July 20, 21; Aug 10, 11 (2-5). Also private visits of 10 or more welcome, please* **Tel 01530 412606**

18 Park Road &⚘ (Dr & Mrs D R Ives) Birstall. Turn off A6 into Park Rd at crown of the hill on Leicester side of Birstall. Local buses stop at end of Park Rd. Approx 1-acre of lawn, trees, shrubs and other mixed planting incl bluebells etc with emphasis on foliage and scent. TEAS. *Adm £1 Chd 25p (Share to LOROS®). Suns May 12, 19 (2-5.30). Private visits welcome mid April to mid June, please* **Tel 0116 2675118**

¶**Pine House** ⚘❀ (Mr & Mrs T Milward) Rearsby Rd, Gaddesby. From A607 Leicester-Melton Mowbray, at Rearsby turn off for Gaddesby. 2-acre garden with fine mature trees, woodland walk and pond. Herb and potager garden with a vinery. Pleached lime trees, mixed borders and rockery. TEA. *Adm £1.50 Chd free. Sun, Wed June 9, 12 (2-5)*

Prebendal House & (Mr & Mrs J Partridge) Empingham. Between Stamford & Oakham on A606. House built in 1688; summer palace for the Bishop of Lincoln. Recently improved old-fashioned gardens incl water garden, topiary and kitchen gardens. TEAS. *Adm £1.50 Chd 50p. Sun June 9 (2-6)*

The Priory &⚘❀ (Mr & Mrs J Acton) Ketton. 3m W of Stamford. Take A6121 to Ketton, turn at Xrds in Ketton, down Church Rd, opp the churchyard. Newly created 2-acre garden; herbaceous border; water garden; alpines. Over 100 different roses. 2 courtyard gardens with mixed planting and cottage garden. TEA. *Adm £1.50 Chd 50p (Share to Rutland Dyslexia Assoc®). Sun July 7 (2-6)*

Quenlborough Gardens ⚘❀ A607 N out of Leicester. 6m from Leicester. 9m from Melton Mowbray. *Combined adm £1 Chd free. Sun June 23 (11-5)*
    5 Barkby Road (Mr & Mrs A R B Wadd) Small cottage garden containing herbs, pond, herbaceous borders. Small orchard with greenhouse, collection of scented leaved pelargoniums
    21 Barkby Road (Mr & Mrs P Hemingray) Small, enclosed, organic, wildlife friendly garden. *Private visits welcome during July, please* **Tel 0116 2605824**
    40 The Ringway (Mr & Mrs W D Hall) Small garden with alpine scree, tufa bed, alpine house. Large pond and bog, herbaceous plants and greenhouse. *Private visits welcome, please* **Tel 0116 2605908**
    8 Syston Road (Mrs R A Smith) Plant enthusiasts cottage style garden; old and new English roses, small pond with frogs and newts; organic vegetable garden. *Private visits welcome during July, please* **Tel 0116 2605606**

Reservoir Cottage & (Lord & Lady John Manners) Knipton, 7m W of Grantham. W of A1; between A52 and A607; nr Belvoir Castle. Medium-sized country garden with lovely views over the lake. TEA. *Adm £1 Chd free. Sun May 19 (2-6)*

Sheepy Magna Gardens &⚘ B4116 2½m N of Atherstone on Atherstone to Twycross Rd. Cream TEAS in aid of Sheepy Magna Church. *Combined adm £2 Chd 30p. Sat, Sun June 22, 23 (2-6)*
    Gate Cottage ❀ (Mr & Mrs O P Hall) Church Lane. Opp church. Approx ½-acre cottage garden; mixed herbaceous borders; greenhouse; vegetable garden; several specimen trees; lawns, patio and pond
    The Grange (Mr & Mrs V Wetton) Main Rd. ¼m from shop towards Twycross opp entrance to trout ponds farm. Spacious Edwardian garden redeveloped since 1989. Extensive lawns; mature specimen trees; ponds; massed roses; heather beds; mixed borders
    Vine Cottage ❀ (Mr & Mrs T Clark) 26 Main Rd. Opp shop. Approx ¾-acre cottage garden; mixed herbaceous borders with many unusual plants; alpine gardens; ponds; vegetable plot with greenhouse. Cream TEAS. *Also private visits welcome Adm £1.50. May to Sept, please* **Tel 01827 880529**

¶**Shorne Hill** (Miss June Curwen) Brooke. 3m W of Oakham via Braunston on A47 Oakham to Leicester rd, 1m from Braunston on Uppingham Rd. House built in 1962, Elizabethan brick. 1½-acres, herbaceous and shrub border, mixed borders below terrace; interesting trees. Walled garden under construction with roses and perennials. Limited wheelchair access. TEAS. *Adm £1 Chd free (Share to Brooke Church®). Sun June 16 (2-6)*

South Luffenham Hall &⚘❀ (Dr & Mrs G Guy) South Luffenham on 6121 between Stamford and Uppingham. Turn off A47 at Morcott. 3-acre garden around 1630 house (not open), featured in 'The Perfect English Country House'. Shrubs, roses, herbaceous borders, lawns, pleached lime hedge and terrace with alpines and lilies. TEAS. *Adm £1.50 Chd 50p (Share to St Marys Church, S Luffenham®). Sun July 14 (2-6)*

Stepping Stones &⚘ (Mr Clem Adkin) Little Beeby. 8m NE of Leicester, through Scraptoft or Barkley, to Beeby Xrds, Hungarton Lane 500yds turn R (signed No Rd). 2-acre garden on site of deserted medieval village (part excavated). Stream, arboretum, shrub roses, spring bulbs in variety. Spring blossom, surprise features, autumn colour. More than 2000 additional bulbs this year. C14 church and medieval well in nearby village. Lovely countryside. TEA. *Adm £1.50 Chd free. Private visits only welcome Feb to Oct, please* **Tel 01162 595677** *or just arrive. Welcome assured*

Stoke Albany House &❀ (Mr & Mrs A M Vinton) 4m E of Market Harborough via A427 to Corby; turn to Stoke Albany; R at the White Horse (B669); garden ½m on L. Large garden with fine trees; shrubs; herbaceous borders and grey garden. TEAS on Sun only. *Adm £1.80 Chd free. Sun July 14 (2-5.30); Tues, Weds July 9, 10; 16, 17 (2-5). Private parties welcome May to July Mons to Thurs only, please* **Tel 01858 535227**

Sutton Bonington Hall &❀ (Anne, Lady Elton) Sutton Bonington, 5m NW of Loughborough; take A6 to Hathern; turn R (E) onto A6006; 1st L (N) for Sutton Bonington. Conservatory, formal white garden, variegated leaf borders. Queen Anne house (not open). Picnics. TEA. *Adm £1.50 Chd 50p (Share to St Michael's and St Ann's Church, Sutton Bonington®). Sun June 30 (12-5.30)*

University of Leicester Botanic Garden &✿❀ Stoughton Drive South, Oadby. SE outskirts of city opp race course. 16-acre garden incl grounds of Beaumont Hall, The Knoll, Southmeade and Hastings House. Wide variety of ornamental features and glasshouses laid out for educational purposes incl NCCPG collections of aubrieta, hardy fuchsia and skimmia. TEA. *Adm £1.50 Chd free. Sun July 28 (2-5)*

Wartnaby &❀ (Lord & Lady King) Wartnaby. 4m NW of Melton Mowbray. From A606 turn W in Ab Kettley, from A46 at Six Hills Hotel turn E on A676. Medium-sized garden, shrubs, herbaceous borders, a good collection of old-fashioned roses, small arboretum and vegetable garden. TEAS. *Adm £2 Chd 20p (Share to Wartnaby Church©). Suns June 16, July 21 (2-6). Private parties welcome, please* **Tel 01664 822296 business hours**

Whatton House &❀ (Lord Crawshaw) 4m NE of Loughborough on A6 between Hathern and Kegworth; 2½m SE of junc 24 on M1. 15 acres; shrub and herbaceous borders, lawns, rose and wild gardens, pools; arboretum. Nursery open. TEAS. Teas in Old Dining Room. Catering arrangements for pre-booked parties any day or evening. *Adm £2 OAP/Chd £1. Open Suns and Weds from Easter to end August. Also Bank Hol Mons. For NGS Tues April 9, May 7, 28 (2-6). Special plant sales Suns Sept 15, Oct 6. Also private visits welcome, please* **Tel 01509 842268**

Woodyton Farmhouse &✿❀ (Mr & Mrs F A Slater) Coalville. On A512, 6m E of Ashby de la Zouch, 6m W of Loughborough, 3m W of M1 junction 23. ¼-acre garden, herbaceous borders, shrub roses, hydrangeas, scree and shade. TEA. *Adm £1 Chd free. Suns June 2, July 14, Aug 18 (2-6)*

Lincolnshire

Hon County Organiser: Mrs Patrick Dean, East Mere House, Lincoln LN4 2JB Tel 01522 791371
Assistant Hon County Organisers: Lady Bruce-Gardyne, The Old Rectory, Aswardby, Spilsby, Lincs PE23 4JS Tel 01790 752652
Mrs Peter Sandberg, Croft House, Ulceby, N Lincs DN39 6SW Tel 01469 588330
Hon County Treasurer: Mrs Julian Gorst, Oxcombe Manor, Horncastle, Lincs LN9 6LU Tel 01507 533227

DATES OF OPENING

February 17 Saturday
21 Chapel Street, Hacconby ‡
Manor Farm, Keisby, Bourne ‡
Westcombe, Rippingale ‡
February 18 Sunday
21 Chapel Street, Hacconby ‡
Manor Farm, Keisby, Bourne ‡
Westcombe, Rippingale ‡
March 7 Thursday
21 Chapel Street, Hacconby
March 31 Sunday
Pinchbeck Hall, nr Spalding
April 7 Sunday
21 Chapel Street, Hacconby
April 8 Monday
Croft House, Ulceby, nr Brigg
April 14 Sunday
Little Ponton Hall, Grantham
April 21 Sunday
Doddington Hall, nr Lincoln
Grimsthorpe Castle Gardens, Bourne

April 28 Sunday
Holton-le-Moor Hall, Holton-le-Moor
May 2 Thursday
21 Chapel Street, Hacconby
May 4 Saturday
Belton House, Grantham
May 5 Sunday
83 Halton Road, Spilsby
May 19 Sunday
Grantham House, Grantham
Luskentyre, nr Holbeach
May 26 Sunday
Laburnum Cottage, Cadney
The Old Rectory, Welton le Wold ‡
Stenigot House, Louth ‡
Westcombe, Rippingale
June 2 Sunday
Croft House, Ulceby, nr Brigg
June 6 Thursday
21 Chapel Street, Hacconby
June 8 Saturday
Bishop's House, Lincoln

Westholme, Lincoln ‡
136 Yarborough Road, Lincoln ‡
June 9 Sunday
Holly House, Boston ‡
Holton-cum-Beckering Gardens
Springtyme, Sibsey, Boston ‡
Toft House, Old Leake ‡
June 16 Sunday
Auburn Hall, Auborn
83 Halton Road, Spilsby ‡
Marston Hall, nr Grantham
The Old Rectory, East Keal ‡
June 20 Thursday
Grimsthorpe Castle Gardens, Bourne
June 23 Sunday
Grange Cottage, Cadney
The Old Vicarage, Holbeach Hurn ‡
Old White House, Holbeach Hurn ‡
The Villa, South Somercotes, Louth
June 30 Sunday
Gunby Hall, Burgh-le-Marsh

Houlton Lodge, Goxhill
Laburnum Cottage, Cadney
Onslow House, Long Sutton
July 4 Thursday
21 Chapel Street, Hacconby
July 7 Sunday
Harrington Hall, Spilsby
Pinefields, Bigby,
nr Barnetby
July 13 Saturday
Belton House, Grantham
July 14 Sunday
Houlton Lodge, Goxhill
July 21 Sunday
Harlaxton Manor Gardens,
Grantham
August 1 Thursday
21 Chapel Street, Hacconby

August 18 Sunday
Luskentyre, nr Holbeach
September 1 Sunday
Hall Farm Harpswell
September 5 Thursday
21 Chapel Street, Hacconby
September 7 Saturday
Belton House, Grantham
September 29 Sunday
Harlaxton Manor Gardens,
Grantham
October 13 Sunday
21 Chapel Street, Hacconby

1997
February 15, 16 Sat, Sun
21 Chapel Street, Hacconby

Regular opening
(see text for dates)

Hall Farm, Harpswell

By appointment only
*For telephone numbers and other
details see garden descriptions.
Private visits welcomed*

The Manor House, Bitchfield
Park House Farm, Walcott
2 School House, Stixwould
Walnut Cottage, Careby

DESCRIPTIONS OF GARDENS

Aubourn Hall &⚅❀ (Sir Henry Nevile) Aubourn. 7m SW of Lincoln. Signposted off A606 at Harmston. Approx 3 acres. Lawns, mature trees, shrubs, roses, mixed borders. C11 church adjoining. Wheelchairs in dry weather only. TEAS. *Adm £1.50 Chd 50p (Share to St. Peters Church Aubourn - repairs®). Sun June 16 (2-6)*

Belton House &⚅ (The National Trust) 3m NE of Grantham on the A607 Grantham to Lincoln rd. Easily reached and signed from the A1 (Grantham N junction). 32 acres of garden incl formal Italian and Dutch gardens, and orangery by Sir Jeffrey Wyatville. TEAS. *Adm house & garden £4.50 Chd £2.10.* ▲*Sats May 4, July 13, Sept 7 (11-5.30)*

Bishop's House &⚅❀ (Bishop of Lincoln) Lincoln. Approaching Lincoln from N take A15 towards Cathedral. Enter Bailgate via Newport Arch, turn L into Eastgate. Bishop's House last on L before Eastgate Hotel. Various car parks in city. Approx 1½ acres walled town garden of lawns, trees, shrubs and herbaceous borders. Vegetable garden. *Adm £1 Chd 50p. Sat June 8 (2-5)*

The Chaff Barn see Nottinghamshire

21 Chapel Street ⚅❀ (Cliff & Joan Curtis) A15 3m N of Bourne, turn E at Xrds into Hacconby. Cottage garden overflowing with plants for yr-round interest, special interest alpines, bulbs, herbaceous. Early opening for hellebores and snowdrop collection. Asters for late opening. Featured on TV. TEAS. *Adm £1 Chd free (Share to Marie Curie Memorial Foundation®). Suns April 7, Oct 13 (11-5) Thurs March 7, May 2, June 6, July 4, Aug 1, Sept 5 (2-6). Sat, Sun Feb 15, 16, 1997 (11-4). Private visits and parties welcome, please Tel 01778 570314*

Croft House &❀ (Mr & Mrs Peter Sandberg) Ulceby near Brigg. At War Memorial turn into Front Street and then into Pitmoor Lane. 2 acres plantswoman's garden largely created and solely maintained by present owners. Mixed borders; gravel garden, bulbs; lawns, fine trees; hedging. Victorian vinery, many interesting plants. TEAS. *Adm £1.50 Chd free. Easter Mon April 8, Sun June 2 (2-5.30). Also by appt, please Tel 01469 588330*

Doddington Hall &⚅ (Antony Jarvis Esq) 5m SW of Lincoln. From Lincoln via A46, turn W on to B1190 for Doddington. Superb walled gardens; thousands of spring bulbs; wild gardens; mature trees; Elizabethan mansion. Free car park. Lunches and TEAS available from 12 noon in fully licensed garden restaurant. *Adm garden only £1.85 Chd 90p (Share to Lincolnshire Old Churches Trust© and St Peter's Church Doddington®).* ▲*Sun April 21 (2-6)*

Grange Cottage ⚅❀ (Mr & Mrs D Hoy) Cadney. 3m S of Brigg. In Brigg turn L into Elwes St; follow rd to Cadney. From Market Rasen to Brigg Rd, turn L in Howsham on to Cadney Rd. ⅓-acre cottage garden; many unusual and old-fashioned plants; old roses; pond; orchard; conservatory with interesting tender plants. *Adm £1 Chd free. Sun June 23 (2-5). Private visits also welcome May to July, please Tel 01652 678771*

Grantham House &⚅ (Lady Wyldbore-Smith) Castlegate, opp St Wulframs Church, Grantham. An old English garden of approx 5 acres of bulbs, many unusual shrubs and trees; river walk and water garden. TEAS. *Adm £1 Chd 50p. Sun May 19 (2-5)*

Grimsthorpe Castle Gardens &❀ (Grimsthorpe and Drummond Castle Trust) 8m E of A1 on the A151 from the Colsterworth junction, 4m W of Bourne. 15 acres of formal and woodland gardens which incl bulbs and wild flowers. The formal gardens encompass fine topiary, roses, herbaceous borders and an unusual ornamental kitchen garden. TEAS. *Adm £2 OAP/Chd £1. Combined adm castle and garden £4 OAP/Chd £2 (Share to Grimsthorpe and Drummond Castle Trust®).* ▲*Sun April 21, Thurs June 20 (11-6)*

Gunby Hall &❀ (Mr & Mrs J D Wrisdale; The National Trust) 2½m NW of Burgh-le-Marsh; S of A158. 7 acres of formal and walled gardens; old roses, herbaceous borders; herb garden; kitchen garden with fruit trees and vegetables. Tennyson's 'Haunt of Ancient Peace'. House built by Sir William Massingberd 1700. House unsuitable for wheelchairs. Plant centre, games. TEAS. *Adm House and gardens £3.20, gardens only £2.00 Chd half price (Share to St Barnabas Hospice (Lincoln)®).* ▲*For NGS Sun June 30 (2-6) NT membership cards not valid*

Hall Farm &✿❀ (Pam & Mark Tatam) Harpswell. 7m E of Gainsborough on A631. 1½m W of Caenby Corner. ¾-acre garden with mixed borders of trees, shrubs, roses and unusual perennials. Over 100 - mainly old - varieties of rose. Sunken garden, pond and recently constructed courtyard garden. Short walk to old moat and woodland. Free seed collecting in garden Sept 1. TEAS. *Adm £1 Chd 25p. Sun Sept 1 (2-6). Garden open daily with collecting box (10-5); by appt in the evenings* Tel 0142 7668412

83 Halton Road ✿❀ (Jack & Joan Gunson) Spilsby. In Spilsby take B1195 towards Wainfleet; garden on L. Limited parking on Halton Rd, free car park Post Office Lane, Spilsby. ¼-acre town garden and hardy plant nursery, divided into a series of smaller gardens featuring densely planted mixed borders, incl many unusual plants and hardy geranium collection of approx 130 varieties. Spring bulbs a feature, many unusual. Featured in 'The Times' and 'Practical Gardening'. TEAS. *Adm £1 Chd free. Suns May 5, June 16 (2-6)*

Harlaxton Manor Gardens (University of Evansville) Grantham. 1m W of Grantham off A607 Melton Mowbray rd. Historically important 110-acre formal gardens and woodland currently undergoing major restoration. Fascinating stonework and steps. 6-acre walled gardens, extremely ornate walls; potager and theme gardens. Harlaxton Manor was built by Gregory Gregory and the house and garden built to rival anything in Europe. Alan Mason is spearheading the restoration project. Formal gardens built as a walk around European styles, Dutch canal, Italian gardens, French terracing, views. Partially suitable for wheelchairs. TEAS. *Adm £2.50 Chd £1.25. April 1 to Oct closed Mons except Bank Hol Mons. For NGS Suns July 21, Sept 29 (11-5)*

Harrington Hall ✿❀ (Mr & Mrs David Price) Spilsby. 6m NW of Spilsby. Turn off A158 (Lincoln-Skegness) at Hag worthingham, 2m from Harrington. Approx 5-acre Tudor & C18 walled gardens, incl recently designed kitchen garden; herbaceous borders, roses and other flowering shrubs. High terrace mentioned in Tennyson's 'Maud'. TEAS. *Adm £1.50 Chd free. Sun July 7 (2-5)*

Holly House &✿❀ (Sally & David Grant) Fishtoft Drove, nr Frithville, Boston. Fishtoft Drove is an unclassified rd approx 3m N of Boston and 1m S of Frithville on the W side of the West Fen Drain. Approx 1-acre informal gardens with mixed borders, scree beds, old sinks with alpines and steps leading down to a large pond with cascade and stream. Softly curving beds are full of unusual and interesting herbaceous plants. TEAS. *Adm £1 Chd free (Share to Pilgrim Heart and Lung Fund®). Sun June 9 (2-6)*

Holton-Cum-Beckering Gardens Take A158 E from Lincoln. 2m past Langworth turn L on B1399. Village in 2m. TEAS at Grangemead in aid of Save the Children. *Combined adm £1.50 Chd free. Sun June 9 (12-5)*

    Amber Lea ✿❀ (Mr & Mrs W H Fehnert) Mature, country cottage style garden. Approx ⅓-acre, lawns, orchard, vegetable garden, variety of perennials, shrubs, trees, bulbs, palm tree, yucca tree, beech hedges. Small pond with fountain and fish. Environmentally friendly and natural

    ¶**Field House** & (Mrs Betty Grant) Trees, herbaceous borders, lawns, clematis

    Grangemead & (Mr Howard Crapp) 2-acre landscaped garden. Plantsman's collection of 130 conifers some 30yrs old. See how your conifers will look when they grow up! Alpine troughs and rock garden. Flowering shrubs, 2 ponds

    Upfield &❀ (Allan & Irene Wakeman) A new garden approx ⅕-acre. (1994). Herbaceous bed and shrub borders. Gravel area with alpines. Raised pond with fish and plants. Heather and conifer beds. One year on and now becoming established!

¶**Holton-le-Moor Hall** &✿❀ (Mr & Mrs P H Gibbons) Holton-le-Moor. From A46 Market Rasen to Caistor rd, take B1434 (Brigg). In Holton-le-Moor turn E by Church. 2nd driveway on R. 2½ acres well-established garden with spring bulbs and flowering trees and shrubs. Large kitchen garden and orchard. *Adm £1.50 Chd free. Sun April 28 (2-5.30)*

Houlton Lodge &✿❀ (Mr & Mrs M Dearden) Goxhill. 6m E of Barton-on-Humber. Follow signs to Goxhill, do not go into village centre but straight on over railway bridge and take 5th turning on R. Houlton Lodge is about 100yds from junction on LH-side. Park cars outside property. A well-established very neat garden approx ¾ acre. Shrub rose and mixed borders; large island bed and rockery and conifer bed. TEAS in aid of Goxhill Methodist Church. *Adm £1 Chd free. Suns June 30, July 14 (2-6). Private visits welcome, please* Tel 01469 531355

Laburnum Cottage &✿ (Colin & Jessie Lynn) Cadney. 3m S of Brigg. In Brigg turn L into Elwes St, follow rd to Cadney. From Market Rasen to Brigg Rd turn L in Howsham on to Cadney Rd. 1-acre, herbaceous and mature shrub borders; island beds; smaller separate gardens within the garden; rose covered walk leading to shrub roses; small orchard; wildlife and formal pond. TEAS in aid of Blue Cross Animal Hospital. *Adm £1 Chd free. Suns May 26, June 30 (1-5). Private parties of 10 and over welcome, please* Tel 01652 678725

Little Ponton Hall &❀ (Mr & Mrs Alastair McCorquodale) Grantham 3m. ½m E of A1 at S end of Grantham bypass. 3 to 4-acre garden. Spacious lawns with cedar tree over 200yrs old. Many varieties of old shrub roses; borders and young trees. Stream with spring garden; bulbs and river walk. Kitchen garden and listed dovecote. Adjacent to Little Ponton Hall is St Guthlacs Church which will be decorated and all visitors welcome. TEAS. *Adm £1.50 Chd under 12 free (Share to St Guthlacs Church, Little Ponton). Sun April 14 (2-6)*

Luskentyre ✿❀ (Mr & Mrs C Harris) 7m E of Spalding signed from A17 at Saracen's Head. Attractive small garden extensively planted with a wide range of interesting plants mainly chosen for their ability to withstand dry conditions and give yr-round interest. As seen in 'Inspirations'. *Adm £1 Chd free. Suns May 19, Aug 18 (1-5). Private visits welcome, please* Tel 01406 423987

Regular Openers. See end of county section.

Manor Farm &❀ (Mr & Mrs C A Richardson) Keisby. 9m NW of Bourne, 10m E of Grantham, signed to Keisby from Lenton and Hawthorpe. ½-acre plantsman's garden. Snowdrop collection and hellebores. *Adm £1 Chd free (Share to Stamford and Bourne CRMF®). Sat, Sun Feb 17, 18 (11-4)*

The Manor House & (John Richardson Esq) Bitchfield; 6m SE of Grantham, close to Irnham and Rippingale. A52 out of Grantham to Spital Gate Hill roundabout; take B1176 to Bitchfield; house on R after public house. 1½ acres re-created in 1972; essentially a shrub rose garden (96 varieties) with shrubs and other perennials; 50 by 40ft pond planted spring 1985; small box hedged formal garden; ha-ha, new large garden room with fountain and over 100 plants. *Adm £2. Parties of 20 or more welcome by appointment June 1 to mid-July; no bookings accepted before May 1. Please Tel 01476 85261*

Marston Hall &❀ (The Rev Henry Thorold) 6m N of Grantham. Turn off A1, 4½m N of Grantham; on 1½m to Marston. Station: Grantham. Notable trees; wych elm and laburnum of exceptional size. House C16 continuously owned by the Thorold family. Interesting pictures and furniture. TEAS. *Adm house & garden £2.50 Chd £1 (Share to Hougham Church Restoration Fund®).* ▲*Sun June 16 (2-6)*

The Old Rectory ❀ (John & Ruth Ward) East Keal. 2m SW of Spilsby on A16. Turn into Church Lane by PO. A rambling cottage garden with a variety of mixed borders, incl shrubs, roses, climbers, perennials and annuals. Ponds and rock garden. TEAS. *Adm £1.20 Chd free. Sun June 16 (2-6). Private visits welcome, please Tel 01790 752477*

¶**The Old Rectory** ❀ (Mr & Mrs Richard Dickinson) Welton le Wold. 3m W of Louth in the valley between A157 Lough-Wragby rd on the S and A631 Louth-Market Rasen rd on the N. The Old Rectory is on the approach rd from A157 halfway down the hill. Situated in charming valley. Garden has been developed from an 1853 Victorian garden into the present 4 acres of woodland, mixed shrub and herbaceous borders and a water garden of 4 pools linked by a small stream. A half-walled vegetable garden, divided by a brick and timber pergola leads to a small arboretum. The adjoining park has mature trees and a young 2 acre wood with woodland walk. The nearby church is open to visitors and there are fine views. TEAS. *Adm £1 Chd 50p. Sun May 26 (2-6)*

¶**The Old Vicarage** &❀❀ (Mrs Liz Dixon-Spain) Holbeach Hurn. Turn off A17 N to Holbeach Hurn, past PO in the middle of village, turn R into Low Rd. Old Vicarage on R approx 400 yds. 2 acres of gardens incl mature trees, formal and informal areas, a croquet lawn surrounded by borders of shrubs, roses, herbaceous plants; also pond, bog garden and wild flowers; shrub roses in old paddock area. *Combined adm with Old White House £1.50 Chd free (Share to Hovenden House Cheshire Home®). Sun June 23 (2-6)*

¶**Old White House** &❀ (Mr & Mrs A Worth) Holbeach Hurn. Turn off A17 N to Holbeach Hurn, follow signs to village, go straight through, turn R after the Rose and Crown at Baileys Lane. 1½ acres of mature garden, featuring herbaceous borders, roses, patterned garden, and wild garden with small pond. TEAS. *Combined adm with The Old Vicarage £1.50 Chd free (Share to Hovenden House, Cheshire Home®). Sun June 23 (2-6)*

Onslow House &❀❀ (Mr & Mrs Julian Proctor) ¾m S of Long Sutton A17 bypass, on B1390. Parking on L of B1390, garden on R. A 3-acre garden with topiary, lawns, lily pond, rose garden and herbaceous borders, C18 dovecote and mature trees. TEAS in aid of British Diabetic Assoc. *Adm £1.50 Chd 50p. Sun June 30 (2-6)*

Park House Farm &❀ (Mr & Mrs Geoffrey Grantham) Walcott. 16m S of Lincoln on B1189 between Billinghay and Metheringham. Traditional farm buildings adapted to make a series of garden rooms; half-hardy climbers, gravel. Winter and white garden. Featured in 'Living' magazine 1995 by Margot Bishop. *Adm £1.50 Chd free. Parties welcome by appt, May to July, please Tel 01526 860409*

¶**Pinchbeck Hall** &❀ (Mr & Mrs George Adams) Situated in centre of Pinchbeck on A16. Next door to Bull public house. 2m from Spalding. Informal country garden with some fine old-trees. Areas of bulbs in spring. Approx 6 acres. TEA. *Adm £1 Chd 50p. Sun March 31 (12-4)*

¶**Pinefields** &❀ (Reg & Madeleine Hill) Bigby. Off A1084 between Caistor 5m and Brigg 4m. At top of Smithy Lane - junction with Main St. 4th house from Church. ¾-acre plantsman's garden. Shrubs and herbaceous borders containing some unusual plants. Roses and clematis on pergolas and trellis. Gravelled alpine area with adjoining seating. An established wildlife pond with arches to an area of wild flowers. Filmed for TV programme Sept '95. TEAS. *Adm £1.20 Chd free. Sun July 7 (1.30-5.30)*

2 School House &❀❀ (Andrew & Sheila Sankey) Stixwould. 1½m N of Woodhall Spa. ¼-acre garden, redesigned in Oct 1994 and in process of being developed to incl front garden with unusual perennials and shrubs, herb garden, vegetable garden. Owners are garden designers. TEAS. *Adm £1 Chd free (Share to Sick Children's Trust®). Private visits welcome by appt only May to Sept, please Tel 01526 352453*

¶**Springtyme** &❀❀ (Mr & Mrs J W Lynn) Station Rd, Sibsey. 5m N of Boston. From A16 at Sibsey turn R onto B1184, towards Old Leake, garden on R in 400yds. Approx ¼-acre informal garden with alpine house, scree beds, alpine troughs, densely planted mixed borders and 2 ponds. TEA. *Adm £1 Chd free. Sun June 9 (2-6)*

Stenigot House &❀ (Mr & Mrs Peter Dennis) Louth. 6m S of Louth. Turn W off A153 at sign to Stenigot - 2m. Spacious lawns with lovely view over Wolds. Water garden with several varieties of astilbes; shrub roses and borders; kitchen garden. TEAS. *Adm £1.50 Chd 50p (Share to St Nicholas Church, Stenigot®). Sun May 26 (2-6)*

¶**Toft House** &❀❀ (Mr & Mrs Grant) Old Leake. 7m from Boston on A52 to Skegness, garden situated 1½m N of Church in Fold Hill. Also 4m from Sibsey on B1184. Approx 2-acre garden has evolved over 40 yrs. It has large informal beds with many unusual trees, shrubs and plants enhanced by a bowling green lawn. A formal potager is being established with rose arches and box hedging. TEA. *Adm £1 Chd 50p. Sun June 9 (2-6)*

The Villa ✿ (Michael & Judy Harry) South Somercotes. 8m E of Louth. Leave Louth by Eastfield Rd. Follow signs to S Cockerington. Take rd signposted to N & S Somercotes. House on L 100yds before church. ¼-acre densely planted in cottage style; large collection of herbs, old-fashioned and unusual perennials; orchard with interesting old varieties of fruit trees. Livestock incl flock of Lincoln Longwool Sheep. TEAS. *Adm £1 Chd free. Sun June 23 (2-6). Private visits welcome, preferably May and September, please* Tel 01507 358487

Walnut Cottage ৬✿ (Roy & Sue Grundy) Careby. 6m N of Stamford on B1176. 5m E of A1 at Stretton. Situated approx ⅓m at end of Main St on L. ½-acre developing garden with interesting herbaceous borders. Herb garden, small shade and gravel areas, water garden with S facing slope leading to small woodland feature with natural pond. Featured on Channel 4 'Garden Club'. TEA. *Adm £1 Chd free. Private visits welcome Tues and Sat, May to Sept, please* Tel 01780 410660

Westcombe ৬✕✿ (Mr & Mrs R Beddington) 25 High St, Rippingale. On A15 5m N of Bourne. Turn E at Xrds into Rippingale. No 25, Westcombe is 5th house on R. ½-acre village garden. Borders, island beds, ponds and vegetable garden. Yr-round interest. Hellebores and snowdrops in spring. TEA (Feb). TEAS in aid of Macmillan Nurses (May). *Adm £1 Acc chd free. Sat, Suns Feb 17, 18 (11-4) May 26 (2-6)*

¶**Westholme** ✕✿ (Ian Warden & Stewart Mackenzie) 10 Yarborough Rd, Lincoln. From bypass take A57 to City. At first major t-lights continue straight ahead. After 50yds continue ahead, uphill at t-lights, house 100yds from t-lights after L-hand bend. Free car park in Hampton St 300 yds past house on L. Tiny town garden planted to reflect owners' interest in unusual herbaceous perennials and shrubs. Ponds with natural plantings. Collection of hostas; plants in containers. Unusual plants for sale. TEAS. *Combined adm with* **136 Yarborough Road** *£1.50 Chd 50p. Sat June 8 (11-6). Private visits welcome by parties of less than 10, please* Tel 01522 568401

¶**136 Yarborough Road** ✕ (Mr & Mrs Colin Merry) Lincoln, 400yds uphill from Westholme. Family garden approx ⅕ acre on sloping site with wide views across West Common. Alpines, herbs, cordon fruit trees and vegetable. Bearded iris, clematis, herbaceous and mixed shrub borders. TEAS in aid of Lincoln and District Children in Need Fund. *Combined adm with* **Westholme** *£1.50 Chd 50p. Sat June 8 (11-6)*

London (Greater London Area)

Hon County Organiser:	Mrs Maurice Snell, Moleshill House, Fairmile, Cobham, Surrey KT11 1BG Tel 01932 864532
Assistant Hon County Organisers:	Mrs Stuart Pollard, 17 St Alban's Rd, Kingston-upon-Thames, Surrey Tel 0181 546 6657
	Mrs C G Wall, Orchard Cottage, 3 Woodlands Road, Bickley, Kent Tel 0181 467 4190
	Mrs V West, 11 Woodlands Rd, Barnes, SW13 0JZ Tel 0181 876 7030
	Miss Alanna Wilson, 38 Ornan Road, London NW3 4QB Tel 0171 794 4071

DATES OF OPENING

February 25 Sunday
Myddleton House Gardens, Enfield
March 9 Saturday
The Elms, Kingston-on-Thames
Lambeth Palace, SE1
March 10 Sunday
The Elms, Kingston-on-Thames
March 30 Saturday
Savoy Hotel Laundry, SW4
March 31 Sunday
Savoy Hotel Laundry, SW4
April 7 Sunday
Chelsea Physic Garden, SW3
April 14 Sunday
29 Deodar Road, SW15

Ham House, Richmond
April 20 Saturday
The Elms, Kingston-on-Thames
April 21 Sunday
The Elms, Kingston-on-Thames
7 The Grove, N6
St Mary's Convent & Nursing Home, W4
7 Upper Phillimore Garden, W8
7 Woodstock Road, W4
April 27 Saturday
Trinity Hospice, SW4
April 28 Sunday
Chiswick Mall, W4
51 Cholmeley Crescent N6
Eccleston Square, SW1
Trinity Hospice, SW4

47 Winn Road, Lee, SE12
May 5 Sunday
Elm Tree Cottage, 85 Croham Road, South Croydon
51 Gloucester Road, Kew
Southwood Lodge, N6
The Water Gardens, Kingston-on-Thames
May 6 Monday
26 Nassau Road, SW13
May 11 Saturday
The Elms, Kingston-on-Thames
Roots & Shoots, SE11
May 12 Sunday
5 Burbage Road, SE24
9 Eland Road, SW11
The Elms, Kingston-on-Thames

49 & 51 Etchingham Park Road,
N3
11 Hampstead Way, NW11
37 Heath Drive, NW3
64 Kings Road, Richmond
Malvern Terrace, N1
2 Millfield Place, N6
43 Penerley Road, SE26
Roots & Shoots, SE11
Savoy Hotel Laundry, SW4

May 15 Wednesday
12 Lansdowne Road, W11

May 18 Saturday
Highwood Ash, NW7

May 19 Sunday
10 Chiltern Road, Pinner
Chiswick Mall, W4
2 Cottesmore Gardens, W8
133 Crystal Palace Road, SE22
5 Greenaway Gardens, NW3
Hall Grange, Croydon
117 Hamilton Terrace, NW8
Highwood Ash, NW8
Osterley Park House, Isleworth
3 Radnor Gardens, Twickenham
South London Botanical
Institute, SE24
131 Upland Road, SE22
Wimbledon Gardens, SW19

May 26 Sunday
Elm Tree Cottage, 85 Croham
Road, South Croydon
22 Loudoun Road, NW8
Myddleton House Gardens, Enfield
Regents College, NW1

May 27 Monday
66 Wallingford Avenue, W10

June 2 Sunday
39 Boundary Road, NW8
66 Floriston Avenue,
Hillingdon
Museum of Garden History,
Tradescant Trust, SE1
15 Norcott Road, N16
2 Northbourne Road, SW4
Flat 1 1F Oval Road, NW1
7 St George's Road,
Twickenham
Trumpeters' House & Lodge
Garden, Richmond

June 7 Friday
Flat 1 1F Oval Road, NW1

June 8 Saturday
Lambeth Community Care
Centre, SE11
Flat 1 1F Oval Road, NW1
Trinity Hospice, SW4

June 9 Sunday
Barnes Gardens, SW13
43 Brodrick Road, SW17
5 Burbage Road, SE24
37 Creighton Avenue, N10
Eccleston Square, SW1
133 Haverstock Hill, NW3

Lambeth Community Care
Centre, SE11
10 Lawn Road, NW3
4 Macaulay Road, SW4
North Ruislip Gardens, Ruislip,
Middlesex
174 Peckham Rye, Rye Common,
SE22
13 Queen Elizabeth Walk, N16
Southwood Lodge, N6
103 Thurleigh Road, SW12
Trinity Hospice, SW4

June 16 Sunday
Albion Square Gardens, E8
5 Cecil Road, N10
101 Cheyne Walk, SW10
43 Dene Road, Northwood
Elm Tree Cottage, 85 Croham
Road, South Croydon
Fenton House, NW3
7 The Grove, N6
Highgate Village N6
Islington Gardens, N1
Leybourne Park Gardens, Kew
Little Lodge, Thames Ditton
17a Navarino Road, E8
78 Palace Road, SW2
43 Penerley Road, SE26
7 St George's Road,
Twickenham
South London Botanical Institute,
SE24
23 Woodville Road, W5

June 19 Wednesday
Little Lodge, Thames Ditton
12a Selwood Place, SW7
103 Thurleigh Road, SW12

June 20 Thursday
Southwood Lodge, N6

June 23 Sunday
15a Buckland Crescent, NW3
10 Chiltern Road, Pinner
133 Crystal Palace Road, SE22
De Beauvoir Gardens, N1
Elm Tree Cottage, 85 Croham
Road, South Croydon
5 Greenaway Gardens, NW3
5 Hillcrest Avenue, NW11
125 Honor Oak Park, SE23
13 Mercers Road, N19
Ormeley Lodge, Richmond
14 Sebright Road, High Barnet
103 Thurleigh Road, SW12
13 Trecastle Way, N7
Trumpeters' House & Lodge
Garden, Richmond
3 Wellgarth Road, NW11
35 Wincanton Road, SW18
47 Winn Road, Lee, SE12

June 29 Saturday
19 St Gabriel's Road, NW2
St Michael's Convent, Ham

June 30 Sunday
33 Balmuir Gardens, SW15

22 Cambridge Road, TW11
20 Eatonville Road, SW17
Goldsborough, Blackheath
125 Honor Oak Park, SE23
20 Lessingham Avenue, SW17
21a The Little Boltons, SW10
29 Mostyn Road, SW19
48 Rommany Road, SE27
5 St Regis Close, N10
Savoy Hotel Laundry, SW4
10 Wildwood Road, NW11
66 Woodbourne Avenue, SW16

July 7 Sunday
17 Fulham Park Gardens, SW6
15 Lawrence Street, SW3
3 Radnor Gardens, Twickenham
15 Upper Grotto Road,
Strawberry Hill

July 14 Sunday
7 Cloncurry Street, SW6
Elm Tree Cottage, 85 Croham
Road, South Croydon
37 Heath Drive, NW3
Horticultural Therapy
Demonstration Garden, SW11
15 Norcott Road, N16
10A The Pavement, Chapel Road,
SE27
9 Ranelagh Avenue, SW6
3 Radnor Gardens, Twickenham
15 Upper Grotto Road,
Strawberry Hill

July 20 Saturday
Trinity Hospice, SW4
27 Wood Vale, N10

July 21 Sunday
235 Eastcote Road, North Ruislip
70 Gloucester Crescent, NW1
5 Greenaway Gardens, NW3
· 2 Millfield Place, N6
13 Queen Elizabeth Walk, N16
Trinity Hospice, SW4
27 Wood Vale, N10

July 28 Sunday
29 Addison Avenue, W11
117 Hamilton Terrace, NW8
Myddleton House Gardens,
Enfield
48 Rommany Road, SE27
57 St Quintin Avenue, W10
5 St Regis Close, N10

August 4 Sunday
10 Chiltern Road, Pinner
57 St Quintin Avenue, W10

August 11 Sunday
1 Lister Road, E11

August 18 Sunday
73 Forest Drive East, E11
17a Navarino Road, E8
47 Winn Road, Lee, SE12

August 25 Sunday
2 Cottesmore Gardens, W8

August 26 Monday
66 Wallingford Avenue, W10

September 7 Saturday
Trinity Hospice, SW4
September 8 Sunday
43 Penerley Road, SE26
Trinity Hospice, SW4
September 14 Saturday
19 St Gabriel's Road, NW2
September 15 Sunday
17 Fulham Park Gardens, SW6
September 22 Sunday
7 Cloncurry Street, SW6
October 13 Sunday
The Water Gardens,
    Kingston-on-Thames

October 27 Sunday
Chelsea Physic Garden, SW3

1997
February 23
Myddleton House Gardens, Enfield

Regular openings
For details see garden description

Chelsea Physic Garden, SW3
Myddleton House Gardens, Enfield

SPECIAL EVENING OPENINGS

June 19 Wednesday
Little Lodge, Thames Ditton
June 20 Thursday
Southwood Lodge, N6
June 19 Wednesday
103 Thurleigh Road, SW12

DESCRIPTIONS OF GARDENS

29 Addison Avenue, W11 ✿❀ (Mr & Mrs D B Nicholson) No entry for cars from Holland Park Avenue; approach via Norland Square and Queensdale Rd. Station: Holland Park. Bus 94. Small garden packed with interesting plants, winner of many prizes and photographed over the last 10yrs for several gardening magazines. Featured in the Good Garden Guide 1996. Lots of unusual wall shrubs, variegated plants and colourful perennials. Phlox paniculata (over 25 varieties) a special favourite. *Adm £1 Chd 50p (Share to the Tradescant Trust®). Sun July 28 (2-6)*

The Anchorage See Kent

Albion Square Gardens, E8 ✿❀ 2m N of Liverpool St Station (BR & tube). 1m S of Dalston/Kingsland Station (BR). Buses 22, 67, 149, 243. By car approach from Queensbridge Rd northbound turning L into Albion Drive leading to Albion Square. TEAS. *Combined adm £3 for 4 or £1 each Chd £1 for 4 or 50p each. Sun June 16 (2-5.30)*
¶**12 Albion Square** (Ann Black & David Richardson) Victorian gothic church provides backdrop to this 70' × 60' L-shaped garden. Brick paved herb garden leads to lawns and a terrace. Ornamental trees, shrubs and flowers. Planting is 4 yrs old and is just beginning to take shape
24 Albion Square (Mr David French) 80' town garden designed to unfold as a series of views and focal points divided by a yew hedge. Emphasis on foliage plants rather than flowers. Secluded seating areas, fountain and through shared summer house to
25 Albion Square (Sandy Maclennan) 80' informal walled garden on two levels with pond beside camomile patch and features ornamental shrubs and trees creating interest in foliage, form and colour
¶**252 Haggerston Road** (Heather Wilson). 60' long, mid-terrace shady town garden. Informal, densely planted design with emphasis on unusual perennials and shrubs, incl peat bed, herbs, ferns, dry shade area, herbaceous border, soft fruit and (friendly) bee-hive. TEAS

33 Balmuir Gardens, SW15 ✿❀ (Mrs Gay Wilson) Putney. 5 mins walk from Putney SR Station. Off the Upper Richmond Rd on corner with Howards Lane. Bus 37, 74, 14. A designer's garden on a corner plot that is continually evolving with newly designed beds for 1996. Se-
cluded tiny mixed borders backed by stained beams. Pots, and a formal pond with a waterfall through moose antlers. A passionate plantswoman who tries out different colour combinations before using them on clients. All crammed into 80' × 38' at widest only 16' at narrowest. *Adm £2 Chd 50p (Share to The Berith Foundation®). Sun June 30 (2-6)*

Barnes Gardens Barnes, SW13. TEAS at 25 Castelnau. *Adm £5 for 5 gardens or £1.50 each garden, OAP £3 for 5 gardens or £1 each garden, Chd free. Sun June 9 (2-6)*
25 Castelnau ✿ (Dr & Mrs P W Adams) Castelnau is on the main route from Hammersmith Bridge. The garden is approx 120' × 40' designed in 1978 by Malcolm Hillier and the late Colin Hilton, well known for their books on flowers and garden design. The garden was planned for ease of maintenance and family living. There is a good variety of herbaceous plants, some attractive roses and a compact working vegetable area and screened swimming pool. TEAS
29 Lonsdale Road ✿ (Mrs R Morris) Over Hammersmith Bridge first R. Underground Hammersmith. Bus 9, 33, 72. ⅓-acre S facing walled garden with York terrace. Designed to give all yr interest. A plantsman's garden with herbaceous borders. Old English roses, clematis, peonies, iris, lilies and flowering shrubs, lavender walk with spring bulbs and hostas
26 Nassau Road ♿❀ (Mr & Mrs Anthony Hallett) 26 Nassau Road lies midway between the Thames and Barnes Pond and is approached via Lonsdale Rd or Church Rd in Barnes. Long, slim, terraced garden with tallest wisteria in Barnes, shrouded on all sides by weigela, philadelphus, pittosporum, chaemomeles, ceanothus with borders of hebe, cistus, rose, delphiniums, potentilla and spiraea. New borders of blue and yellow; white and red perennials; cool phlox; red hot lilies and campanula abound. 200ft of dense green and gold arranged in 'rooms', add to the excitement. Plants for sale. *Adm £1.50 OAP £1. Also open on Mon May 6 (2-6). Private visits welcome, please Tel 0181 748 5940*
8 Queen's Ride ♿ (His Honour Judge White & Mrs White) Train: Barnes Station, turn R down Rocks Lane, then L along Queen's Ride. Bus, 22 terminus at Putney Hospital; 3 minutes walk W along Queen's Ride. House is at the junction of Queen's Ride and St Mary's Grove. ⅔-acre garden facing Barnes Common. Croquet lawn with herbaceous and mixed borders and a small history of the rose garden. TEA

12 Westmoreland Road ⚘⚘ (Mr & Mrs Norman Moore) From Hammersmith take Bus 9, 33, or 72 to the Red Lion. Briefly retrace steps along Castelnau turn L into Ferry Rd then L at Xrds. Small garden with raised stone terrace planted with choisya, convolvulus, euonymus, honeysuckle and decorative herbs, leading to lower lawn. Borders densely planted with wide variety of flowering shrubs and pretty pool with fountain. Gravel garden with lilies, agapanthus, diascia and lady's mantle. *(Share to St Mary's Churchyard®)*

28 Barnsbury Square, N1 ⚘ (F T Gardner Esq) Islington. 1¾m N of King's Cross off Thornhill Rd. Bus stop: Islington Town Hall, Upper St or Offord Rd, Caledonian Rd. Tube Highbury and Islington. Small prize-winning Victorian garden; gazebo; pond; grotto; roses, shrubs, plants of interest throughout year. *Adm £1.50 Chd free (Share to CRMF®). Sun June 16 (2-6)*

39 Boundary Road, NW8 ⚘ (Hermoine Berton) Between Swiss Cottage and St John's Wood tube. Buses 13, 113, 82, 46, 139. Enjoy the surprises of a wild-life garden as seen on Gardeners World 1992. 'Inside Britain' 1993, London TV The Real Gardening Show 1995. *Adm £1.50 Chd 30p (Share to London Lighthouse Aids Centre®). Sun June 2 (2-6) Private visits welcome April - Sept. Please* **Tel 0171 624 3177**

43 Brodrick Road, SW17 ⚘ (Helen Yemm) Wandsworth Common. Approx 1m S of Wandsworth Bridge, off Trinity Rd. A long (110'), tranquil garden of a typical Victorian terrace house, surrounded by mature trees. Its length is broken by a bank of shrubs and a pond, overhung by an ancient rose-clad apple tree. Small gravel garden, herbaceous planting for semi-shade, clematis, roses - distinctly un-urban. Featured in Sainsbury's Magazine and Sunday Times. *Adm £1.50 Chd 50p (Share to Alzheimers Disease Soc®). Sun June 9 (2-6). Small groups (min 5, max 15) welcome by appt May and June.* **Tel 0181 672 1473**

15a Buckland Crescent, NW3 ⚘⚘⚘ (Lady Barbirolli) Swiss Cottage Tube. Bus: 46, 13 (6 mins) or Hampstead Hoppa (request stop nearby). ⅓-acre; interesting collection of shrubs and trees in well-designed garden featured in Country Life Nov 88, also in books 'Private Gardens of London' by Arabella Lennox Boyd and 'Town Gardens' by Caroline Boisset. *Adm £1.25 Chd over 12 50p (Share to RUKBA®). Sun June 23 (2.30-6.30). Private visits welcome for parties of 25 and over, please* **Tel 0171 586 2464**

5 Burbage Road, SE24 ⚘⚘ (Crawford & Rosemary Lindsay) Nr junction with Half Moon Lane. BR Station Herne Hill, 5 mins walk. Buses 2, 3, 37, 40, 68, 196. Garden of member of The Society of Botanical Artists. 150' × 40' with large and varied range of plants. Herb garden, herbaceous borders for sun and shade, terraces, climbing plants, collection of potters' plant containers, lawns. TEAS. *Adm £1 Chd free. Suns May 12, June 9 (2-5).* **Tel 0171 274 5610**

Regular Openers. Too many days to include in diary. Usually there is a wide range of plants giving year-round interest. See end of county section for the name and garden description for times etc.

---

22 Cambridge Road ♿⚘ (Sheila & Roger Storr) Teddington. S turning off Teddington High St. Buses 281, 285. A family garden of approx ⅙-acre. Designed to give the long garden a feeling of width. Many unusual shrubs and herbaceous perennials. A tree house has been built around an old pear tree incl a drawbridge and flying fox. The water feature allows children to paddle in it. At the end of the garden is a large vegetable and soft fruit plot. TEA. *Adm £1 Chd 50p. Sun June 30 (2-6)*

Capel Manor Farm and Gardens See Hertfordshire

5 Cecil Road, N10 ⚘ (Ben Loftus Esq) Just off Alexander Park Rd between Muswell Hill and the North Circular Rd. 70' × 20' garden designer's peaceful garden; old apple trees, roses, euphorbias, masses of lilies, paeonies, hellebores, ferns, bulbs and evergreens; many scented plants, rich and varied foliage; unusual plants in containers. *Adm 80p Chd free. Sun June 16 (2-5)*

Chelsea Physic Garden, SW3 ♿⚘⚘ (Trustees of the Garden) 66 Royal Hospital Rd, Chelsea. Bus 239 (Mon-Sat). Station: Sloane Square (10 mins). Cars: restricted parking nr garden weekdays; free Sundays, or in Battersea Park weekdays. Entrance in Swan Walk (except wheelchairs). Second oldest Botanic Garden in UK; 3.8 acres; medicinal and herb garden, incl an ethnobotanical 'Garden of World Medicine' perfumery border; family order beds; historical walk, glasshouses and over 5,000 trees, shrubs and herbaceous plants, many rare or unusual. TEAS. *Adm £3.50 Students/Chd £1.80. Suns April 2 to Oct 27 (2-6); Weds April 10 to Oct 23 (2-5); Winter Festival Suns Feb 4, 11 (11-3) also in Chelsea Flower Show week Mon-Fri May 20-24 and in Chelsea Festival Week Mon-Fri June 3-7 (12-5). For NGS Suns April 7, Oct 27 (2-6)*

101 Cheyne Walk, SW10 ⚘⚘ (Malcolm Hillier Esq) Situated to the W of Battersea Bridge. Long and narrow strongly layered with a structure of evergreen hedges and topiaries. A colonnaded Mediterranean terrace with many containers leads to a winding path set about with old roses and perennials. A romantic arbour surrounded and covered by perfumed plants surveys the whole length of the garden. TEAS. *Adm £1.50 Chd 50p. Sun June 16 (1-6). Private visits welcome for parties of 5 and over, please* **Tel 0171 352 9031**

10 Chiltern Road ⚘⚘ (Mrs G & Mr D Creswell) Eastcote, Pinner. Off Bridle Rd-Eastcote Rd between Francis Rd and Cheney St. Please park in Francis Rd. Plantswoman's garden ⅓-acre, mature trees, mixed shrubs and herbaceous plantings. Plants for sale propagated from the garden. TEAS. *Adm £1.50 Chd free. Suns May 19, June 23, Aug 4 (2-5)*

Chiswick Mall, W4 Station: Stamford Brook (District Line). Bus: 290 to Young's Corner from Hammersmith. By car A4 Westbound turn off at Eyot Gdns S, then R into Chiswick Mall. *Suns April 28 (2-6), May 19 (2-7)*

    16 Eyot Gardens ⚘ (Dianne Farris) Small town garden at end of terrace. Front has mostly yellow, blue and white flowers, a lot of pink in the back garden with raised beds and a terrace. Planting and design with the help of Anthony Noel. TEAS. *Adm £1.20 Chd free OAP £1*

Walpole House ✿❀ (Mr & Mrs Jeremy Benson) Plantsman's garden; specie and tree peonies; water garden; spring flowers. Features in 'The Englishman's Garden'. Mid C16 to early C18 house, once home of Barbara Villiers, Duchess of Cleveland. Seeds and some plants for sale. *Adm £1.50 OAP/Chd 50p (Share to Chiswick House Friends Cascade Appeal®)*

51 Cholmeley Crescent, N6 ✿❀ (Ernst & Janet Sondheimer) Highgate. Between Highgate Hill and Archway Rd, off Cholmeley Park. Nearest tube Highgate. Approx ⅙-acre garden with many alpines in screes, peat beds, tufa, troughs and greenhouse; shrubs, rhododendrons, camellias, magnolias, pieris, ceanothus etc. Clematis, bog plants, roses, primulas, treeferns. Alpines for sale. TEA. *Adm £1 Chd 50p. Sun April 28 (2-6). Private visits welcome, please* Tel 0181 340 6607

¶7 Cloncurry Street, SW6 ✿ (Mr & Mrs D Adams) Nearest tube Putney Bridge. Buses 74, 14, 220 off Fulham Palace Rd at Fulham End. 50' × 20' garden designed by Anthony Noel in partnership with owners. Formal, elegant, French style. Restrained colours - mainly white, silver and soft blue. Topiary; trellis; fine lawn; paving and pots. *Adm £2. Suns July 14, Sept 22 (2.30-6)*

2 Cottesmore Gardens, W8 ✿ (The Marchioness of Bute) From Kensington Rd turn into Victoria Rd. Cottesmore Gardens on R. A wide range of trees, shrubs and plants concentrating on foliage shapes, fragrance and unusual plant material; many spring bulbs. TEA. *Adm £2 Chd £1 (Share to Winter Garden Trust). Suns May 19, Aug 25 (2-5)*

37 Creighton Avenue, N10 ✿❀ (Tim Elkins & Margaret Weaver) Muswell Hill. Buses 43, 134, 243 from Highgate tube to Muswell Hill Broadway-Fortis Green Rd, along Tetherdown, turn R into Creighton Ave at mini-roundabout. Mature S facing rear garden 120' × 30'. Two alpine beds, well stocked mixed borders, evergreen shrubs, ornamental trees and patio with pots. TEAS. *Adm £1 Chd 50p (Share to CHICS Children with Cancer Support Group®). Sun June 9 (2-5)*

133 Crystal Palace Road, SE22 ✿❀ (Sue Hillwood-Harris) East Dulwich. Buses 176, 185, 12. Featured by Gay Search in Sainsbury's magazine, this inspirational Victorian town house garden packs winding charm into its 17' × 36'. Formality tempered by wilful indiscipline. Roses, wisteria, shrubs, herbs, shade loving plants. Original wall, a victim of gales, reborn as a central circular terrace. A garden of character and surprises. TEAS. *Adm £1 Chd 50p (Share to Crusaid®). Suns May 19, June 23 (2-6). Private visits welcome, please* Tel 0181 693 3710

De Beauvoir Gardens, N1 Islington-Hackney border. *Combined adm £2 Chd 50p. Sun June 23 (2-6)*
  51 Lawford Road ✿ (Mrs Carol Lee) Lawford Rd (formerly called Culford Rd) is a cul-de-sac with entrance for cars from Downham Rd. Parking fairly restricted. Downham Rd runs between Kingsland and Southgate Rd. Buses Kingsland Rd 149, 243, 22A/B and 67, Southgate Rd 141. A small garden 16' × 45' at rear of a typical Victorian terraced house. Bricked with different levels, lots of pots and a pond with waterfalls.

Hostas, ferns and fuchsias greatly favoured. TEAS. *(Share to National Deaf Children's Soc®). Sun June 11 (2-6)*

26 Northchurch Road ✿ (Mrs Kathy Lynam) Angel tube then Buses 38, 73, 56, 30, 171A down Essex Rd, alight bus stop after Essex Rd Station just before Northchurch Rd. Cross over and proceed down Northchurch Rd (petrol stn on corner) to lower end near church. House on L. By car from Angel down Essex Rd. R into Halliford St past lights at Southgate Rd. Turn L 1st rd Upton Rd, then R at bottom, house on L. Walled back garden, approx 70' × 30' with 2 old apple trees, greenhouse and lawn, mixed borders with clematis, roses and lots of perennials. Places to sit and ponder. TEA. *Private visits welcome, please* Tel 0171 254 8993

¶43 Dene Road ✿❀ (Mr & Mrs M Hillman) Northwood. 10 min walk from Northwood Station (Met line). Turn L into Green Lane 2nd R Dene Rd. Car park, RNIB Sunshine House next door. Access also from Rickmansworth Rd. ⅓-acre S facing garden yr-round interest, large lawn surrounded by wide borders; island beds filled with shrubs and perennials with a backdrop of colourful trees. Terrace with many containers. TEAS. *Adm £1 Chd free (Share to RNIB Sunshine House®). Sun June 16 (2-6)*

29 Deodar Road, SW15 ✿❀ (Peter & Marigold Assinder) Putney. Off Putney Bridge Rd Bus: 14, 22, 37, 74, 80, 85, 93, 220. Tubes: Putney Bridge and East Putney. Small garden 130ft × 25ft running down to Thames with lovely view. Camellias, wide range of variegated shrubs, hardy geraniums and hydrangeas. TEA. *Adm £1 Chd 50p (Share to All Saints Church Putney Restoration Appeal®). Suns April 14 (2-5). Cuttings and visits at other times by arrangement* Tel 0181 788 7976.

20 Eatonville Road, SW17 ❀ (Pamela Johnson & Gethyn Davies) Tooting. 400yds from Tooting Bec tube (Northern Line). Bus stop Trinity Rd nr Police Station. Nos. 249, 219, 349 or 155 and 355 on Balham High Rd at tube station. Garden designer's own 42' × 23' S facing garden. Interesting plant combinations and an imaginative use of containers shows just how much can fit into a small space. Tiny front garden. Excellent plant sale and delicious home-made cakes. TEAS. *Adm £1 Chd 50p. Sun June 30 (2-6)*

Eccleston Square, SW1 ♿❀ (Garden Manager Roger Phillips) Central London; just off Belgrave Rd near Victoria Station, parking allowed on Suns. 3-acre square was planned by Cubitt in 1828. The present Garden Committee have worked intensively over the last 16 years to see what can be created despite the inner city problems of drought, dust, fumes, shade and developers. Within the formal structure the garden is sub-divided into mini-gardens incl camellia, iris, rose, fern, and container gardens. A national collection of ceanothus incl more than 50 species and culitvers is held in the square. TEAS. *Adm £1.50 Chd 75p. Suns April 28, June 9 (2-5)*

1996 Special Events. For information on special National Gardens Scheme events in 1996 see Pages 18-19.

9 Eland Road, SW11 ✿ (Nancye Nosworthy) Battersea. Off Lavender Hill backing onto Battersea Arts Centre. 345, 77 and 77a bus stop at top of st. Clapham Junction Station and buses 19, 49, 319, 239, 249, 295, 137a nearby. 50' courtyard on slopes of Lavender Hill. Terraces with unusual shrubs, a pergola covered in vitis coignetiai and pink and white jasmine. Pool with fountain designed by Christopher Masson. *Adm £1 Chd free. Sun May 12 (1-6)*

Elm Tree Cottage ✿ (Wendy Witherick & Michael Wilkinson) 85 Croham Rd, S Croydon, off B275 from Croydon, off A2022 from Selsdon 64 Bus Route. A gently sloping plantsperson's garden with fine views of Croham Hurst and Valley. Cottage garden full of rare and unusual roses, perennials, climbers and shrubs. Pond and bog garden in pots. *Adm £1.50 Chd free. Suns May 5, 26 June 16, 23, July 14 (10-4). Private visits welcome, please* **Tel 0181 681 8622**

The Elms ✿✿ (Prof & MRs R Rawlings) Kingston-on-Thames entry via Manorgate Rd. Im E Kingston on A308. Buses to Kingston Hospital: LT 213, 85, 57, K3, K5, K6, K8, K10, 718: BR Norbiton Station 100yds. Enter via garages in Manorgate Rd which is off A308 at foot of Kingston Hill. Wheelcharis limited to the tea area. 55' × 25' garden owned by 'plantaholic!' Trees, shrubs, climbers, herbaceous and ground cover plants, some rare and unusual. Pool with geyser; fruit trees and soft fruits. In Good Garden Guide, and on radio. Seed and plants. TEAS. *Adm £1 Chd 50p (Share to Princess Alice Hospice/Home Farm Trust®). Sats, Suns March 9, 10 April 20, 21; May 11, 12 (2-5). Private groups welcome, please* **Tel 0181 546 7624**

49 & 51 Etchingham Park Rd, N3 ♿✿✿ (Robert Double, Gilbert Cook and Diane & Alan Langleben) Finchley. Off Ballards Lane overlooking Victoria Park. Station: Finchley Central. 2 rear gardens. ⅝-acre; lawn, small orchard, shrubs, large selection of hostas. Sculpture by Wm Mitchell, new ornamental vegetable garden as seen on TV. Exhibition and sale of water colour paintings by Robert Double. TEAS. Live music. *Adm £1 Chd free. Sun May 12 (2-6)*

Fenton House, NW3 ✿ (The National Trust) 300yds from Hampstead Underground. Entrances: top of Holly Hill and Hamstead Grove. 1½-acre walled garden in its first decade of development. It is on three levels with compartments concealed by yew hedges and containing different plantings, some still in the experimental stage. The herbaceous borders are being planned to give yr-round interest while the recently brick paved sunken rose garden is already donning the patina of age. The formal lawn area contrasts agreeably with the rustic charm of the orchard and kitchen garden. *Adm £1.50 Chd 50p. For NGS Sun June 16 (11-6)*

¶66 Floriston Avenue ✿✿ (Jean Goodall) Hillingdon. From A40 at Master Brewer Motel into Long Lane (to Hillingdon) 2nd L by church (Ryefield Ave), L after shops. Pedestrian entrance to garden by lane rear of shops. Plantswoman's long narrow garden (90' × 17') with many design features, Auricular theatre, species iris and alliums, herbs, colour themed borders. TEAS. *Adm £1 Chd 50p. Sun June 2 (2-6). Private visits welcome, please* **Tel 01895 251036**

Frogmore Gardens See Berkshire

73 Forest Drive East, E11 ✿✿ (A J Wyllie) Leytonstone. Into Whipps Cross Rd, then SW into James Lane. 1st L into Clare Rd, 1st R into Forest Drive East. By bus to Whipps Cross Hospital or tube to Leytonstone and bus to James Lane. 20' × 65' country garden in miniature, but with full-sized plants, behind a terraced house. Small lawn with mixed borders leading to a shrub and woodland area. Two fountains and various unusual plants. Also 20' front garden informally planted round formal paths and centre piece. TEA. *Adm £1 Chd 50p (Share to The Margaret Centre, Whipps Cross Hospital®). Sun Aug 18 (11-5)*

17 Fulham Park Gardens, SW6 ✿ (A Noel Esq) Putney Bridge Tube. Refer to A-Z. Up Kings Road L at Threshers Off-licence, (Elysium St.) into Fulham Park Gardens. Turn R, on RH-side. 40ft × 17ft romantic silver and white garden, with interesting variety of plants in harmoniously designed form. An oasis of peace in a hostile environment. Featured in Sunday Times and on ITV. *Adm £3 OAPs £1.50. Suns July 7, Sept 15 (2.30-6)*

70 Gloucester Crescent, NW1 ✿ (Lucy Gent & Malcolm Turner) Nr junction Gloucester Crescent and Oval Rd 600yds SW of Camden Town Tube Station. A square in front; plants growing into shingle. A triangle at the side, a circle has evolved. A wedge at the back. Maybe a fernery by July 1996, maybe not. *Adm £1.50 Chd 50p. Sun July 21 (11-3). Private visits welcome, please* **Tel 0171 485 6906**

51 Gloucester Road ♿✿ (Mrs Lindsay Smith) Kew. 10 mins walk from Kew Gardens Tube Station. Travel towards S Circular along Leybourne Park Rd, cross main rd, down Forest Rd 1st L into Gloucester Rd. House ½-way down on R. A small square cottage garden. Many interesting plants and shrubs. Wallflowers and bulbs in spring. TEA. *Adm £1.50 Chd 75p. Sun May 5 (2-6)*

Goldsborough, SE3 ♿✿ 112 Westcombe Park Rd, Blackheath. Nearest BR Westcombe Park (10 mins walk) or Maze Hill (15 mins walk). Buses to the Standard from Central London and surrounding areas. Car parking available. Community garden for close care and nursing home residents. Approx ½ acre of landscaped gardens, incl walkways of rose-covered pergolas; fish ponds; herbaceous borders and colourful annuals. A very sheltered and peaceful garden. TEAS. *Adm £1 Chd 50p. Sun June 30 (2-5)*

5 Greenaway Gardens, NW3 ✿ (Mrs Marcus) Tube (½ mile) Hampstead or Finchley Road Stations. Buses: Finchley Road, West End Lane stop, nos. 13, 82, 113, off Frognal Lane. Large and varied garden landscaped on three levels with yr-round interest. Terrace with variety of climbing plants; water feature and swimming pool; large lawn surrounded by herbaceous borders, wide variety of trees and shrubs, decorative urns and furniture. Partially suitable for wheelchairs. TEAS July 21 only. *Adm £1 Chd free. Suns May 19, June 23, July 21 (2-6)*

7 The Grove, N6 &% (Thomas Lyttelton Esq) The Grove is between Highgate West Hill & Hampstead Lane. Stations: Archway or Highgate (Northern Line, Barnet trains) Bus: 210, 271 to Highgate Village. ½-acre designed for maximum all-yr interest with minimum upkeep. TEAS on June 16 only at No. 5. *Adm £1 per garden or £2.50 for 3 gardens OAPs/Chd 50p per garden or £1 for 3 gardens. Suns April 21, June 16 (2-5.30). Private visits welcome, please* **Tel 0181 340 7205**

Hall Grange &% (Methodist Homes) Croydon. Situated in Shirley Church Rd near to junction with Upper Shirley Rd. From N leave A232 at junction of Shirley Rd and Wickham Rd. From S leave A212 at junction of Gravel Hill and Shirley Hills Rd. The garden was laid out circa 1913 by Rev W Wilkes secretary to RHS comprises 5 acres of natural heathland planted with azaleas, rhododendrons, heathers and shrubs and is unchanged. Parking nearby. TEA. *Adm £1.20 Chd free. Sun May 19 (2-5)*

Ham House &%❀ (The National Trust) Richmond. Midway between Richmond and Kingston W of A307 on the Surrey bank of the R Thames. Signposted with Tourism brown signs. Restored C17 garden, gravel terrace, paths dividing eight large grass plats; wilderness; parterre. TEAS. *Adm House £4 Chd £2 Garden free. For NGS Sun April 14 (10.30-6)*

117 Hamilton Terrace, NW8 &% (Mrs K Herbert and the Tenants Association) Hamilton Terrace, where there is room for parking, is parallel with Maida Vale. Buses from Marble Arch 16, 16a, 98 go to Elgin Avenue which is near. This is a large garden, part of the back is kept wild and there is a tiny garden in memory of Dame Anna Neagle, who lived in the house. TEA. *Adm £1 Chd 20p (Share to the Spastics Society®). Suns May 19, July 28 (2-6)*

11 Hampstead Way, NW11 %❀ (Mr & Mrs R L Bristow) Nearest tube station Golders Green, 10 minute walk up North End Road, L into Wellgarth Road, R up Hampstead Way. ¼-acre prize winning garden, water features. unusual plants around lawns in the front and patio at the back. TEAS. *Adm £1.50 Chd 50p. Sun May 12 (2-6)*

133 Haverstock Hill, NW3 %❀ (Mrs Catherine Horwood) Belsize Park Tube Station turn L out of station. Buses C11, C12, 168 (Haverstock Arms stop). Prizewinning 120ft long narrow garden divided into rooms. Packed planting of old and English roses, clematis, cottage garden perennials from balconied terrace to mini-orchard. Many unusual tender perennials and scented plants. Featured in Country Life and Wonderful Windowboxes. *Adm £1 Chd 50p. Sun June 9 (2-5.30). Private visits welcome, please* **Tel 0171 586 0908**

37 Heath Drive, NW3 &%❀ (Mr & Mrs C Caplin) Station: Finchley Rd; buses: 82, 13 & 113 Heath Drive. Many uncommon plants; lawn; pond; rockery; ferns. Unusual treatment of fruit trees, greenhouse and conservatory. 1982, 1983, 1987, 1988, 1989, 1991, 1993 winner of Frankland Moore Trophy. Featured in Arabella Lennox-Boyd's Private Gardens of London. TEAS. *Adm £1 Chd 50p (Share to Royal Marsden®). Suns May 12, July 14 (2.30-6)*

Highgate Village, N6 % The Grove is between Highgate West Hill and Hampstead Lane Stations: Archway or Highgate (Northern Line, Barnet trains). Bus: 210, 271, 211 to Highgate Village. TEAS in aid of local Scouts, per cent to NGS, at 5 The Grove. *Adm £2.50 for 3 gardens £1 each garden Chd/OAP £1 for 3 gardens or 50p each garden. Sun June 16 (2-5)*

    4 The Grove ❀ (Cob Stenham Esq) 2-tiered with formal upper garden; view across Heath; orchard in lower garden

    5 The Grove (Mr & Mrs A J Hines) Newly-designed garden on 2 levels

    7 The Grove see separate entry

Highwood Ash, NW7 ❀ (Mr & Mrs R Gluckstein) Highwood Hill, Mill Hill. From London via A41 (Watford Way) to Mill Hill Circus; turn R up Lawrence St; at top bear L up Highwood Hill; house at top on R. Stations Totteridge and Whetstone or Edgware (Northern Line). Stanmore (Jubilee Line) Arnos Grove (Piccadilly Line). Bus from all these 251 (Sat only). House not within walking distance of stations. 3¼-acre incl rose garden, shrub and herbaceous borders, rhododendrons, azaleas, lake with waterfall, a mixture of formal and informal. TEAS. *Adm £1 Chd 50p (Share to The North London Hospice®). Sat, Sun May 18, 19 (2-6)*

5 Hillcrest Avenue, NW11 %❀ (Mrs R M Rees) Hillcrest Ave is off Bridge Lane. By bus to Temple Fortune, Buses 82, 102, 260. Nearest Tube Golders Green or Finchley Central. Walk down Bridge Lane. Small labour saving colourful garden with many interesting features; rockery, fish pond, conservatory, tree fern. Secluded patio, auriculum theatre, acid bed. TEAS. *Adm £1 Chd 50p (Share to ADS®). Sun June 23 (2-6) Private visits welcome, please* **Tel 0181 455 0419**

1 Hocroft Avenue, NW2 &%❀ (Dr & Mrs Derek Bunn) 113 bus (stop at Cricklewood Lane). Easy parking. Prizewinning garden with yr-round interest, especially in the spring. Front garden shown on BBC Gardeners' World, in their Front Garden series. Black and white bed featured in The Independent and The Evening Standard. Mixed borders in the back garden with a wide variety of plants against a background of trees. Subject of an article by Tony Venison in Country Life focusing on plant sales in the NGS. *Private visits welcome, please* **Tel 0171 435 1196**

The Holme &% (Lessees of The Crown Estate Commissioners) Positioned in Inner Circle, Regents Park opp Open Air Theatre. Nearest tube stations Regents Park and Baker St. 4-acre garden filled with interesting and unusual plants, with magnificent view over Regents Park Lake to the Nash terraces. Originally designed by J C Loudon, the Regency layout has been used to guide recent improvements. Sweeping lakeside lawns intersected by islands of herbaceous beds. Extensive rock garden recently rebuilt with waterfall, stream and pool. Formal flower garden with unusual annual and half hardy plants, sunken lawn, fountain pool and arbour. Teas available in Park Cafe adjacent. *Adm £2 Chd £1. For opening dates see local press or* **Tel NGS 01483 211535**

125 Honor Oak Park, SE23 ⚘❀ (Mrs Heather West) BR station: Honor Oak Park turn R. Off South Circular (A205) via Honor Oak Rd. Small 75' × 45' multifarious froth on two levels: the lower shady with small beds, the upper sunny with grass, verandah and pots. Strawberry TEAS in aid of BHHI. *Adm £1 Chd 50p. Suns June 23, 30 (2-6)*

¶**The Horticultural Therapy Demonstration Garden**, SW11 ᕕ❀ East Carriage Drive, Battersea Park, opp Tennis Courts. ⅓-acre; fully accessible garden with heated greenhouse, wildlife meadow and pond; vegetable and herb gardens, raised beds and containers, herbaceous beds, pergola and raised pond. Horticultural Therapy staff on hand for advice and information on accessible gardening tools, techniques and therapeutic gardening. TEAS. *Adm £1 Chd free (Share to Horticultural Therapy®). Sun July 14 (10.30-6)*

Islington Gardens, N1 ⚘❀ Station: Highbury and Islington. Bus: 4, 19, 30, 43, 104, 279 to Highbury Corner or Islington Town Hall, 30 to New Crown public house stops outside 60 St Paul's Rd. A1 runs through Canonbury Sq. *Combined adm £4 or £1.25 each garden Chd £1.50 or 50p each garden. Sun June 16 (2-6)*
  37 Alwyne Road ᕕ⚘❀ (Mr & Mrs J Lambert) Bordering the New River. Views over the river and the park would make you think you are in the country; an enclosed formal garden reminds you that you are in town. Old-fashioned roses if it hasn't been too hot, lilies if it hasn't been too cold. TEAS. *(Share to Friends of the New River Walk®)*
  8 College Cross, N1 ⚘ (Anne Weyman & Chris Bulford) Nearest Station Highbury and Islington. Buses to Highbury Corner or Islington Town Hall. Walled town garden, 70' × 20', many unusual shrubs and herbaceous plants, incl perennial geraniums; walls covered with climbers. List of plants in the garden available. TEA. *(Share to National Children's Bureau®)*
  ¶**13 College Cross** ⚘ (Diana & Stephen Yakeley) A small town garden behind a Georgian terrace house, measuring 5.2m × 16.8m enclosed by evergreen climbers with bay, box and fig trees. Paved areas with plants chosen for form and texture in shades of green. Large pots of white flowers incl lilies and Daturas, provide the only colour. *Sun June 16 (2-6)*
  60 St Paul's Road ⚘❀ (John & Pat Wardroper) This typical back-of-terrace town garden has been planted chiefly for shade, and to create a quiet, green enclosed atmosphere just off a busy street; designed on 3 levels with paved patios, border of flowering shrubs

¶**64 Kings Road** ⚘❀ (Jill & Ged Guinness) Richmond. 15 mins walk from Richmond Stn (District, N London & BR) or Buses 33, 337 to Belvedere PH and walk up Kings Rd. Nearly ½ an acre of slightly unkempt grass, vegetable, fruit and flower gardens. Mature trees from the original 1881 lay-out and numerous more recently planted trees and shrubs. Not much bedding out. TEAS. *Adm £1 Chd 50p. Sun May 12 (2.30-6)*

Lambeth Community Care Centre, SE11 ᕕ⚘❀ Monkton Street. Tube or buses to Elephant and Castle, cut behind Leisure Centre to Brook Drive. Turn into Sullivan Rd at Bakery, passage to Monkton St. (or drive) to Kenning-

ton Rd buses 3, 109 159. At The Ship turn into Bishop's Terrace, 1st R to Monkton St. ⅔-acre garden. Mixed shrubs, trees, small rose garden, herbs, interesting walkways and mixed borders. Prize winner in London Hospital Gardens Competition. TEAS. *Adm £1 OAP/Chd 50p (Share to St. Thomas's Trustees for the garden®). Sat, Sun June 8, 9 (2-5)*

Lambeth Palace, SE1 ᕕ⚘ (The Archbishop of Canterbury & Mrs Carey) Waterloo main line and underground, Westminster, Lambeth and Vauxhall tubes all about 10 mins walk. 3, 10, 44, 76, 77, 159, 170, 507 buses to Lambeth Palace Rd (not at gatehouse) 2nd largest private garden in London. Entry to garden on Lambeth Palace Rd (not at gatehouse) 2nd largest private garden in London. Land in hand of Archbishops of Canterbury since end C12. Work on garden carried out over last 100 years but significant renewal has taken place during last 6 years. *Adm £2 OAP/Chd 10-16 £1 (Share to Lambeth Palace Garden©). Sat March 9 (2-5)*

12 Lansdowne Rd, W11 ᕕ (The Lady Amabel Lindsay) Holland Park. Turn N off Holland Park Ave nr Holland Park Station; or W off Ladbroke Grove ½-way along. Bus: 12, 88, GL 711, 715. Bus stop & station: Holland Park, 4 mins. Medium-sized fairly wild garden; border, climbing roses, shrubs; mulberry tree 200 yrs old. *Adm £2 Chd £1. Wed May 15 (2-6)*

10 Lawn Road, NW3 ᕕ⚘ (Mrs P Findlay) Tube to Belsize Park or go up Haverstock Hill. Turn R at Haverstock Arms then L. House 200yds on R, with blue door. ¹⁄₁₀-acre approx; uniquely curvaceous design of intersecting circles, set in rectangular format. Organically cultured garden, very heavily stocked; many unusual and native species plants. *Adm £1 Chd 50p. Sun June 9 (2.30-6)*

15 Lawrence Street, SW3 ⚘ (John Casson Esq) Between King's Rd and the river down Old Church St S from King's Rd to the river, turn L round the statue of Sir Thomas More then L (behind garden) into Lawrence St. Garden at top of street on L. Nearest tubes: Sloane Square and South Kensington. Prize winning small Chelsea cottage type garden, old-fashioned flowers, clematis, roses and some unusual plants. Plants to cover each season. House built c1790, not open except for access to garden. *Adm £1 Chd 50p (Share to Chelsea Physic Garden®). Sun July 7 (2-6)*

20 Lessingham Avenue, SW17 ⚘ (George Hards) Tooting Bec underground (Northern Line). Buses 155, 219. Tranquil green and white small town garden 20' × 40' with water feature. Closely planted to provide yr-round variety, interesting plants incl trachelospermum jasminoides, catalpa bungei, auralia elata variegata, romneya coulteri. TEAS. *Adm 50p (Share to Imperial Cancer Research Fund®). Sun June 30 (2-6)*

Leyborne Park Gardens ⚘❀ Two minute walk from Kew Gardens station. Take exit signposted Kew Gardens. On leaving station forecourt bear R past shops. Leyborne Park is 1st rd on R. Bus 391, R68 to Kew Gdns station. Bus 65 to Kew Gdns, Victoria Gate. Access by car is from Sandycombe Rd. TEAS. *Combined adm £1.50 Chd free (Share to Arthritis and Rheumatism Council for Research®). Sun June 16 (2-5.30)*

36 Leyborne Park (David & Frances Hopwood) 120ft long mature, family garden; architect designed for minimum upkeep with maximum foliage effects; patio; imaginative children's play area; huge eucalyptus. TEAS
38 Leyborne Park ❀ (Mr & Mrs A Sandall) 120ft long organic family garden; lawn with mixed borders; containers; long established vine; alliums, lavenders, eryngiums, scented pelargoniums, bamboos; plants for the dry garden
40 Leyborne Park (Debbie Pointon-Taylor) 120ft long garden; heather and conifer garden; lawn and mixed borders; mature shrubs; patio with containers

1 Lister Road, E11 ✗ (Myles Challis Esq) Leytonstone underground station (central line). 5 mins to High Rd Leytonstone. Hills garage marks corner of Lister Rd which is directly off High Rd. Garden designer's unexpected, densely planted sub-tropical garden containing a mixture of tender plants such as daturas, gingers, cannas, tree ferns, bananas and hardy exotics including gunneras, bamboos, cordylines, phormiums and large leaved perennials in a space unbelievably only 40' × 20'. *Adm £1 Chd 50p. Sun Aug 11 (11-5)*

21a The Little Boltons, SW10 ❀ (Mrs D Capron) Between Fulham and Old Brompton Rd off Tregunter Rd. Nearest tube Earls Court, buses 30, 14, 74. 70ft prize winning herbaceous plant collection. Portrayed in the book 'Private Gardens of London' by Arabella Lennox-Boyd and House and Garden Magazine. *Adm £1 Chd 25p. Sun June 30 (2-6)*

Little Lodge ⬥✗❀ (Mr & Mrs P Hickman) Watts Rd, Thames Ditton (Station 5 mins). A3 from London; after Hook underpass turn left to Esher; at Scilly Isles turn R towards Kingston; after 2nd railway bridge turn L to Thames Ditton village; house opp library after Giggs Hill Green. A cottage style informal garden within 15m of central London. Many British native plants. Garden has an atmosphere of tranquillity, featuring plants with subtle colours and fragrance; small brick-pathed vegetable plot. TEAS. *Adm £1.50 Chd free (Share to Cancer Research®). Sun June 16 (11.30-6). Special evening opening Wed June 19 (6.30-9) £2.50 incl wine and light refreshments. Private visits welcome, please* Tel 0181 339 0931

22 Loudoun Road, NW8 ✗ (Ruth Barclay) 3 to 4 min walk to St. John's Wood tube station. Lies between Abbey Road and Finchley Rd serviced by buses, minutes from bus stop. A strong emphasis on design, water, arbour garden within a garden. Back Italianate courtyard, romantic and mysterious. Interesting water features, incl grotto with water cascading down mussel shells surrounded by ferns and tree ferns. Prizewinner for 4 consecutive years. Featured in 'Town Gardens'. TEAS. *Adm £1 Chd 25p. Sun May 26 (2-6)*

4 Macaulay Road, SW4 ⬥✗ (Mrs Diana Ross) Clapham Common Tube. Buses 88, 77, 77A, 137, 137A, 37, 45. Prize-winning garden whose owner appeared on the TV programme 'An Englishwoman's Garden' in 1993. The garden 80' × 50' was revamped last yr and now combines its original formal outline with roses, clematis and herbaceous perennials jockeying for space between exotic fo-

liage and architectural plants. Mini-grotto surrounded by a growing collection of ferns. *Adm £1.50 OAPs £1. Sun June 9 (2-6)*

Malvern Terrace, N1 ⬥❀ Barnsbury. Approach from S via Pentonville Rd into Penton St, Barnsbury Rd; from N via Thornhill Rd opp Albion public House. Tube: Highbury & Islington. Bus: 19, 30 to Upper St Town Hall. Unique London terrace of 1830s houses built on site of Thos Oldfield's dairy and cricket field. Cottage-style gardens in cobbled cul-de-sac; music. Victorian plant stall. Home-made TEAS. Music. *Combined adm £1.50 Chd free (Share to International Spinal Research Trust®). Sun May 12 (2-5.30)*
  1 Malvern Terrace (Mr & Mrs Martin Leman)
  2 Malvern Terrace (Mr & Mrs K McDowall)
  3 Malvern Terrace (Mr & Mrs A Robertson)
  4 Malvern Terrace
  5 Malvern Terrace
  6 Malvern Terrace (Dr B A Lynch)
  7 Malvern Terrace (Mr & Mrs Mark Vanhegan)
  8 Malvern Terrace (Mr & Mrs R Le Fanu)
  10 Malvern Terrace (Dr & Mrs P Sherwood)

13 Mercers Road, N19 ✗❀ (Dr & Mrs N Millward) off Holloway Rd (A1) N of Odeon Cinema. 30' × 15' front garden featuring cool whites, greys and greens. 30' × 20' rear garden on two levels. Profusion of pastel shades from April to Sept. Many small-flowered clematis, pink schizophragma, rosa soulieana and other interesting climbers and perennials. Featured on Channel 4 Garden Club, May 1994. Teas at **13 Trecastle Way**. *Adm £1 Chd 50p. Sun June 23 (2-6). Private visits welcome for small groups and individuals, please* Tel 0171 281 2674

2 Millfield Place, N6 ✗ Garden is off Highgate West Hill, E side of Hampstead Heath. Buses 210, 271 to Highgate Village or C2, C12, 214 to Parliament Hill Fields terminus. Nearest train stations Kentish Town, Tufnell Park and North London BR line to Gospel Oak. C11 bus runs locally. 1½-acre spring and woodland garden with camellias and rhododendrons. Long mixed herbaceous border with some formal bedding schemes; small orchard. TEAS. *Adm £1.50 Chd 50p. Suns May 12, July 21 (2-6)*

29 Mostyn Road, SW19 ✗❀ (Chris & Sue Spencer) Merton Park is 1m N of Wimbledon. From London cross Wimbledon Common, through Wimbledon Village, down Wimbledon Hill into The Broadway. Follow one-way system after Wimbledon Station following it round before turning L into Hartfield Rd. Turn R at the end of Hartfield Rd. Mostyn Rd is 3rd on L. Greystones is 200 metres on R. ⅓-acre small garden laid out by Gertrude Jekyll in 1913. The garden has been restored by the present owners, using Jekyll's original plant lists. Featured in Traditional Homes, Period House and Its Garden and BBC Gardeners' World. TEAS. *Adm £2 Chd 50p (Share to St Mary's The Virgin®). Sun June 30 (10-2)*

Museum of Garden History &✿ (The Tradescant Trust) St Mary-at-Lambeth, Lambeth Palace Road, SE1. Bus: 507 Red Arrow from Victoria or Waterloo, alight Lambeth Palace. 7,450 sq ft. replica of C17 garden planted in churchyard with flowers known and grown by John Tradescant. Tombs of the Tradescants and Admiral Bligh of the 'Bounty' in the garden. Opened by HM the Queen Mother in 1983. Museum being established in restored church of St Mary-at-Lambeth saved from demolition by The Trust. The new garden at The Ark, 220 Lambeth Road, also open. TEAS. *Adm £1 OAPs/Chd 25p (Share to Museum of Garden History®).* ▲*For NGS Sun June 2 (10.30-5)*

Myddelton House Gardens &✄✿ (Lee Valley Park) Bulls Cross, Enfield. Junction 25 (A10) off M25 S towards Enfield. 1st set of lights turn R into Bullsmoor Lane, L at end along Bulls Cross, garden signed on R. The 4 acres of garden were created by Edward A Bowles. The gardens feature a diverse and unusual plant collection incl a large selection of naturalised bulbs, as well as the national collection of award winning bearded irises. The grounds have a large pond with terrace, two conservatories and interesting historical artefacts. TEAS and plants for sale on NGS days and selected Suns. *Adm £1.25 Concessions 65p. Open Mon-Fri (10-3.30)(except Bank Hols) (2-5) selected Suns. For NGS Suns Feb 25, May 26, July 28; Feb 23 1997 (2-5). No concessions on NGS days & Suns.* **Tel 01992 713838**

17A Navarino Road, E8 ✄✿ (John Tordoff Esq) situated between Dalston and Hackney and connects Graham Rd with Richmond Rd. Buses 38, 22A, 22B, 277, 30. A formal Italian garden of clipped box and yew. Rambler roses make a spectacular display over arches and a pergola. The Japanese garden begun 3yrs ago features a large informal pond, tea house, ornamental bridge, and miniature Mount Fuji. Plantings of azaleas, acers and bamboo. *Adm £1 Chd 50p. Suns June 16, Aug 18 (12-6). Private visits welcome, please* **Tel 0171 254 5622**

15 Norcott Road, N16 ✄✿ (Amanda & John Welch) Buses 73, 149, 76, 67, 243 (see bus map and A to Z) Clapton or Stoke Newington Stations (Rectory Rd closed Suns). Largish (for Hackney) walled back garden. Pond, herbs, herbaceous plants especially irises, geraniums and campanulas. TEAS. *Adm £1 Chd 50p (Share to St Joseph's Hospice®). Suns June 2, July 14 (2-6)*

North Ruislip Gardens ✄ Ruislip, Middlesex. *Combined adm £2 Chd free. Sun June 9 (1-5)*
  235 Eastcote Road ✿ (T & J Hall) From Ruislip High Street take the B466 (Eastcote Road) nearest tube Ruislip Manor. Parking off Eastcote Rd in Evelyn Ave please. Medium sized suburban garden. 115ft × 80ft. Contains a wide variety of herbaceous perennials and shrubs, shady patio area and ponds. Homemade TEAS. *Adm £1 Chd free. Also open Sun July 21 (1-5)*
  82 Evelyn Avenue (Mr & Mrs K Morgan) Refer to A-Z. Nearest Underground Station – Ruislip Manor. Turn R out of Station. Continue up and over the hill; cross the Eastcote Rd and turn 1st R into Evelyn Ave. Suburban garden 40ft × 170ft. Curving borders and island beds planted with shrubs and herbaceous plants to give yr-round interests. Lawns and mature trees

86 Evelyn Avenue (Isabel & Frank Thornton) Medsized working garden approx 180' × 40'. Pond, productive vegetable plot, soft fruit, shrubs and herbaceous plants to give continuing interest. Mature fruit trees

2 Northbourne Road, SW4 ✿ (Mr & Mrs Edward A Holmes) Clapham Common tube. Buses 137, 137A, 37. W facing, walled garden 36' × 56' with good architectural planting and rose pergola. Soft landscaping by Judith Sharpe in Feb 1991. Featured in Sainsbury's Magazine. *Adm £1 OAPs/Chd 50p (Share to the Foundation for the Study of Infant Deaths®). Sun June 2 (2-6)*

Orchard Cottage See Kent

Ormeley Lodge ✄ (Lady Annabel Goldsmith) Ham Gate Avenue, Richmond. From Richmond Park, exit at Ham Gate into Ham Gate Avenue. 1st house on R. From Richmond A307, 1½m past New Inn on R, first turning on L. House is last on L. Bus: 65. Large walled garden in delightful rural setting on Ham Common. Newly designed formal garden, wide herbaceous borders, box hedges. Walk through to newly planted orchard with wild flowers. Vegetable garden. Secluded swimming pool area, trellised tennis court with roses and climbers. TEA. *Adm £1 Chd 50p. Sun June 23 (3-6)*

Osterley Park House & (The National Trust) Jersey Rd, Isleworth. Access is via Thornbury Rd on N side of A4 (Great West Rd) between Gillette Corner and Osterley Tube Station. Nearest station Osterley (Piccadilly Line). Car Park £1.50. Osterley is one of the last great houses with an intact estate in Greater London. The Pleasure Grounds are being restored. The NGS fund is contributing a substantial part of the cost of replanting the early C19 garden which stood in front of Robert Adams' elegant semi-circular garden house. TEAS. *Adm free. For NGS Sun May 19 (11-4)*

Flat 1, 1F Oval Road, NW1 ✄ (Sheila Jackson) Tube station Camden Town. Buses: any bus to Camden Town, C2 and 274 stop very near. Parking difficult near centre on Sunday. A small side garden approaches an illustrator's very small hidden back garden approx 24ft × 20ft which abuts the Euston railway line. A great variety of plants, mainly in pots, are banked to create interesting shapes, making use of a variety of levels. This garden is the subject of the book 'Blooming Small, A City Dwellers Garden'. *Adm £1 Chd 50p. Sun June 2 (2-5) Fri, Sat June 7, 8 (6-9)*

78 Palace Road, SW2 ✄✿ (Mr & Mrs D S Senior) BR station Streatham Hill 15min walk (NB Tulse Hill BR closed Sundays). Buses 2, 68, 196 to Tulse Hill station. By car S Circular Rd, just W of Tulse Hill one-way system. Located corner Palace Rd and Northstead Rd. 90' × 60' garden planted mainly for foliage effect and yr-round interest. Shrubs, bamboos, grasses, some interesting small trees. Part planted with Mediterranean plants to suit hot dry conditions, areas left wild to encourage wildlife, pond. *Adm £1 Chd free. Sun June 16 (2-6)*

10A The Pavement, SE27 ❀ (Brendan Byrne) Chapel Rd. Located off Ladas Rd down alleyway behind All Seasons Fish Bar. Buses 68 to Knights Hill alight at S London College. No. 2 to Norwood bus garage. BR W Norwood. Come out Knights Hill, turn L. Chapel Rd is 10 mins walk on L after passing bus garage. Smallest garden in London (entry restricted to 5 people at any one time). A hidden oasis behind houses and shops. Country type of garden, mostly in containers. Shrubs, herbaceous, bedding and rare plants. Featured in 'The Observer'. *Adm £1 Acc chd free with adult (Share to Horses & Ponies Protection Assoc®). Sun July 14 (10-12, 2-6)*

¶174 Peckham Rye, SE22 & (Mr & Mrs Ian Bland) Peckham Rye Common is about 1m NE of Dulwich Village, in S London. The house overlooks Peckham Rye Common from the Dulwich side. On either side of the house are 2 side rds both called The Gardens which can be used for parking. The rear garden is reached by a side alley and is about the size of a tennis court. It was designed by Judith Sharp to provide yr interest using mainly shrubs with varying foliage. It is an easy care, child friendly garden; at it's best in early June when the pink and blue flowers predominate. TEAS. *Adm £1 Chd free. Sun June 9 (2.30-5.30)*

43 Penerley Rd, SE6 &❀❀ (Mr & Mrs E Thorp) BR stations Catford, Catford Bridge (15 mins walk). Buses 36, 36B, 47, 54, 75, 124, 160, 172, 180, 181, 185, 202, 208, 284, 306, (5 mins walk). Off A21 just S of S Circular Rd. Plant lover's shady garden 33' × 100', full of interesting and unusual plants. Formal lawns, informal planting, paved areas with ferns, hostas and other foliage plants in pots. TEAS in aid of St Laurence Church. *Adm £1 Acc chd free. Suns May 12, June 16, Sept 8, (2-5.30)*

¶13 Queen Elizabeth Walk, N16 &❀ (Lucy Sommers) From Manor House tube go S down Green Lanes, then take 2nd L off Lordship Park. 100' × 25' plantsman's garden backing onto a woody wilderness. Many interesting and unusual shrubs, climbers, perennials set in a series of flowing borders around pergola, arch, pond and sculpture, in both sunny and woodland areas. Created by owner 4 yrs ago to provide interest and distraction through all seasons. TEA. *Adm £1 OAP/Chd 50p. Suns June 9, July 21 (2-6)*

3 Radnor Gardens ❀❀ (Ms Jill Payne) Twickenham. A-Z 2k 103. Train: Twickenham, Turn L 10 min walk. Train/tube: Richmond then bus 90, R70 to Heath Rd or 33, R68 to King St. From Heath Rd turn into Radnor Rd by Tamplins then R into Radnor Gardens. A narrow, green and secluded garden, 12' × 54' of a small terraced house; crammed with a wide range of plants. Tiny ponds and water features, small conservatory. *Adm 50p Chd 20p. Suns May 19, July 7, 14 (2-6)*

9 Ranelagh Avenue, SW6 ❀ (Mrs P Tham) Nearest tube Putney Bridge. Approx 60' × 40'. A semi-formal two level garden featuring shade tolerant plants, incl many hostas and trees; arbutus, judas, magnolia, crab apple. Small patio with container grown plants. *Adm £1.20 Chd 50p. Sun July 14 (2-6)*

Regents College, NW1 ❀ Regents Park. Regents College is located at the junction of York Bridge and the Inner Circle opp Queen Mary's Rose Garden in Regents Park. Baker Street tube is 5 mins walk. Buses: 1, 2, 2B, 13, 18, 27, 30, 74, 159. Enter gate or the Garden Gate which is reached via the footbridge at Clarence Gate. Within the 10-acre grounds of Regent's College is the Botany garden – a secret garden of charm. Layout and features have been sympathetically adapted and developed to create garden areas of pleasing atmosphere and form. Rock, water, a pergola and arbour, sun and shade offers homes to a large range of plants, incl unusual boxwood and herbaceous. Themes and colour schemes embellish the overall design and each year new projects are undertaken. TEA. *Adm £1.50 Concessions/Chd 50p. Sun May 26 (12-5). Private visits welcome, please* Tel 0171 487 7494

¶48 Rommany Rd, SE27 ❀❀ (Miss Belinda I Barnes & Mr Ronald Stuart-Moonlight). BR Gipsy Hill Stn (trains from Victoria). Buses 3, 322. Easiest access to Rommany Rd via Gipsy Rd. A luscious small 30' × 20' walled town garden created in 1995 by present owners. Ferns and hostas lead towards the York stone patio with small kitchen garden and herbaceous border. A vine and rose covered pergola forms the entrance to the rear secret garden with fountain and trachelospernum arch. For benefit of max 15 persons at any one time. *Adm 80p Chd 50p (Share to RNLI®). Suns June 30, July 28 (1-6)*

¶Roots & Shoots, SE11 &❀❀ (Roots & Shoots Training Scheme) Vauxhall Centre, Walnut Tree Walk. Tube: Lambeth North; Buses 159, 109, 3. Just off Kennington Rd, 5 mins from War Museum. Derelict site used by Civil Defence during the war, transformed by 'Roots & Shoots' Training Scheme (for young people with disabilities) into a garden. Mixed borders, plant nursery, ½ acre wildlife garden, superb walnut tree, acacia dealbata and other unusual shrubs. TEAS. *Adm £1 Chd 50p (Share to Roots & Shoots). Sat, Sun May 11, 12 (11-4)*

19 St Gabriel's Road, NW2 & (Mrs Penelope Mortimer) St Gabriel's Rd is a short walk from Willesden Green Tube (Jubilee Line). When Penelope Mortimer moved here in 1991 she brought two van-loads of plants from her Cotswold garden. With the help of a splendid balsam poplar, a great deal of muck and hard work, what was 150ft of exhausted grass and rubbish is now a miniature country garden brimming with roses and rare herbaceous plants. 'A sanctuary!' *Adm £1.50 Chd under 14 free. Sats June 29, Sept 14 (2-6). Private visits welcome, please* Tel 0181 452 8551

7 St George's Rd ❀❀ (Mr & Mrs Richard Raworth) St Margaret's, Twickenham. Off A316 between Twickenham Bridge and St Margarets roundabout. ½-acre maturing town garden backing onto private parkland. Garden divided into 'rooms'. Unusual shrubs, clematis and old English roses. Large conservatory with rare plants and climbers. Parterre garden. Sink garden, pergola, paved garden. Small gravel garden. Mist propagated specimens and unusual plants for sale. Featured in Penelope Hobhouse's 'Garden Style' and the The Conservatory Gardener by Anne Swithenbank. TEAS. *Adm £1 Chd 50p. Suns June 2, 16 (2-6) or private visits welcome, please* Tel 0181 892 3713

St Mary's Convent & Nursing Home, W4 ⚄❀ (Sister Jennifer Anne) Chiswick. Exit W from London on A4 to Hogarth roundabout. Take A316 signposted Richmond. St Mary's is 500yds down on L. Parking in Corney Rd, 1st turning L after Convent. 2½-acre walled garden with fine specimen trees; herbaceous borders and shrub borders being planted for yr-round interest, incl spring flowering shrubs and bulbs. Centenary Year 1896-1996. TEAS. *Adm £1 Chd free. Sun April 21 (2-5)*

St Michael's Convent, Ham ❀❀ (Community of The Sisters of The Church) 56 Ham Common. From Richmond or Kingston, A307, turn onto the common at traffic lights nr the New Inn, 100 yds on the R adjacent to Martingales Close. 4-acre walled organic garden. Bible garden and circle garden of meditation. Extensive herbaceous borders, two orchards, wild life areas, working kitchen garden, vinehouse and ancient mulberry tree. Wheelchairs with difficulty. TEAS. *Collection Box. Sat June 29 (11-3). Private visits welcome, please* **Tel 0181 940 8711**

57 St Quintin Avenue, W10 ❀❀ (H Groffman Esq) 1m from Ladbroke Grove/White City Underground. From Ladbroke Grove station, bus; 7 to North Pole Road, 30ft × 40ft walled garden; wide selection of plant material. Patio; small pond; hanging baskets; special features. Regular prizewinner in garden competitions. Featured on TV and in horticultural press. TEAS. *Adm £1.50 Chd 80p. Suns July 28, Aug 4 (2-7). Private visits welcome for parties of 10 and over, please* **Tel 0181 969 8292**

¶5 St Regis Close, N10 ❀❀ (Susan Bennett & Earl Hyde) Muswell Hill. 2nd turning on L in Alexandra Park Rd, coming from Colney Hatch Lane Tube: Bounds Green then Buses 102, 299 to Curzon Rd or East Finchley then Bus 102. Maureen Lipman's favourite garden chosen for an exhibition at Museum of Garden History, features architectural constructions, ponds, waterfalls and container planting; lawns and well-stocked borders. Collection of mirrors & ceramics made by owner in garden studio. Oriental enclosure conceals plant nursery. Collection of antique chimney pots. Ceramics and chimney pots for sale % to NGS. TEAS. *Adm £1.50 Chd 50p. Suns June 30, July 28 (2-8)*

¶Savoy Hotel Laundry, SW4 ❀ 17-19 Union Rd, Clapham. Tube to Clapham North Northern line. Buses 88, 345, 355 to Union Grove. Turn of the century garden with waterway and stocked pond. The fig tree, wisteria, albertine rose and many other plants are original to the layout, rose bed featuring the Savoy rose added 1992. TEA. *Adm £1 Chd free. Sat, Suns March 30, 31, May 12, June 30 (11-2)*

14 Sebright Road ⚄❀❀ (Rhian & Julian Bishop) High Barnet. 120' × 20' town garden, with traditional herbaceous borders, fruit trees and little wildlife pond. Many old-fashioned roses, honeysuckles, unusual foxgloves and geraniums. TEA. *Adm £1 Chd 25p (Share to Edgware Hospital Special Care Baby Unit®). Sun June 23 (2-6). Please ring* **0181 440 2042** *before visiting; owners may be moving house. Private visits welcome*

12a Selwood Place, SW7 ⚄ (Mrs Anthony Crossley) South Kensington, entrance opp 92 Onslow Gardens. South Kensington tube 8 mins walk, no. 14 bus down Fulham Rd (Elm Place request stop). Long green and white border; pink border in L-shaped walled garden; collection of roses, peonies, camellias, iris, lilies, poppies, vegetables; terraced herb garden. Suitable for wheelchairs only if dry. *Adm 70p Chd 35p. Wed June 19 (2.30-6)*

South London Botanical Institute, SE24 ❀❀ 323 Norwood Rd. From South Circular Rd (A205) at Tulse Hill, turn N into Norwood Rd; Institute is 100yds on R. Small botanic garden, formally laid out; many rare and interesting species; over 200 labelled plants. TEA. *Adm £1.50 Chd 75p (Share to South London Botanical Institute®). Suns May 19, June 16 (2-5). Private visits welcome, please* **Tel 0181 674 5787**

Southwood Lodge, N6 ❀❀ (Mr & Mrs C Whittington) 33 Kingsley Place. Off Southwood Lane. Buses 210, 271. Tube Highgate. A romantic, hidden garden laid out last century on a steeply sloping site, now densely planted with a wide variety of shrubs, bulbs, roses and perennials. Pond, waterfall, frogs. Many unusual plants are grown and propagated for sale. Featured in Gardens Illustrated Sept '94. *Adm £1 Chd 50p (Share to North London Hospice®). Suns May 5, June 9 (2-6). Special evening opening, Thurs June 20 (6.30-8.30) £2.50 incl wine. Private visits welcome, please* **Tel 0181 348 2785**

103 Thurleigh Road, SW12 ⚄❀❀ (Charles MacKinnon) Clapham S Tube Station (Northern Line) is 5 mins walk. Thurleigh Rd runs between Clapham Common (Wside) and Wandsworth Common (Bollingbroke Grove). A 100' x 120' walled garden surrounded by limes. Very deep herbaceous beds enable some large plants to flourish eg crambe, mallow. Careful planting to minimise upkeep and to balance my dreams of Sissinghurst with my children's footballs. TEAS. *Adm £1.50 Chd 50p. Suns June 9, 23 (1-6). Special evening opening, Wed June 19 (6.30-9) £2.50 incl wine and light refreshments*

13 Trecastle Way, N7 ❀❀ (Mrs Vera Quick) Carleton Rd. Camden Rd buses 29, 253 to Dalmeny Ave. 1st R from Dalmeny Ave into Trecastle Way (nr Holloway Prison). A very pretty garden. Small in size approx 60' × 30'. Full of colour, lots of interesting plants, ornamental pond and waterfall. Bedding plants grown from seeds and cuttings. TEAS. *Adm 80p Chd free. Sun June 23 (2-6)*

Trinity Hospice ⚄❀❀ 30 Clapham Common North Side, SW4. Tube: Clapham Common. Bus: 37, 137, 45 stop outside. 2-acre park-like garden restored by Lanning Roper's friends as a memorial to him and designed by John Medhurst. Ricky's sculpture a feature. TEAS. *Adm £1 Chd free. Sats, Suns April 27, 28; June 8, 9; July 20, 21; Sept 7, 8 (2-5)*

Trumpeters' House (Miss Sarah Franklyn) and **Trumpeters' Lodge** ⚄❀❀ (Mrs Pamela Franklyn) Old Palace Yard, Richmond. Off Richmond Green on S side. Car parking on the green and in car parks. Approx 3 acres, lawns, established old trees. Many old roses; shrubs; ponds; knot garden; mixed borders; aviary for doves. Featured in House & Garden, Country Life and in NGS Calendar 1995 (July). NCCPG collection of old-fashioned pinks (Dianthus). *Adm £2.50 OAP's £1.50 Chd 50p. Suns June 2, 23 (2-6)*

131 Upland Road &&& (Ms G Payne & Ms P Harvey) East Dulwich. Nearest BR Peckham Rye. Buses 78, 12, 63. 78, 12 to Barry Rd. Get off 1st stop opp Peckham Rye Common. Upland Rd 50yds on L. 63 to Peckham Rye Common. Get off Forest Hill Rd. Cross over to Piermont Green leading to Upland Rd. Small garden full of surprises. Unusual, semi-oriental-style stone rear garden with pond and waterfall. Informal planted areas. 20' × 40' designed for effect and low maintenance. Front and side areas incl shade loving plants, bamboos, camellias, magnolias and viticellas. TEAS. *Adm 75p Chd 25p. Sun May 19 (2-5.30)*

15 Upper Grotto Road ❀ (Jeane Rankin) Twickenham. Stations Strawberry Hill or Twickenham. Buses R68, 33 to Pope's Grotto; 90B, 267, 281, 290 to Heath Rd/Radnor Rd, 2nd R into Upper Grotto Rd. Small sunken suntrap courtyard garden designed and constructed with advancing age and arthritis in mind; raised borders with small shrubs, herbaceous perennials, self sown annuals; wall shrubs, clematis and other climbers; plants in pots and tiny fountain over pebbles. TEA. *Adm 75p. Suns July 7, 14 (2-6). Private visits welcome, please,* **Tel 0181 891 4454**

7 Upper Phillimore Gardens, W8 &❀ (Mr & Mrs B Ritchie) From Kensington High St take either Phillimore Gdns or Camden Hill Rd; entrance Duchess of Bedford Walk. 100' × 35' garden; rockery, sunken garden; Italian wall fountain, ground cover planting, pergola. TEA. *Adm £1 Chd 50p. Sun April 21 (2.30-6)*

66 Wallingford Avenue (off Oxford Gdns), W10 ✿ (Mrs R Andrups) Nearest underground station: Latimer Rd and Ladbroke Grove. Nearest bus stop Oxford Gdns (7) or Ladbroke Grove (7, 52, 70, 295, 302). Small garden 20' × 40'. Raised beds, mixed borders, ponds, conservatory. Yr-round garden. 7 times winner Brighter Kensington & Chelsea Gardens Competition. Refreshments 50p. *Adm £1 Chd 50p. Mons May 27, Aug 26 (2-6)*

The Water Gardens ✿ Warren Road, Kingston (Residents' Association). From Kingston take the A308 (Kingston Hill) towards London about ½m on R turn R into Warren Road. Japanese landscaped garden originally part of the Coombe Wood Nursery, approx 9 acres with water cascade features. *Adm £2 OAP £1 Chd 50p. Suns May 5, Oct 13 (2-5)*

3 Wellgarth Road, NW11 ✿❀ (Mr & Mrs A M Gear) Hampstead Garden Suburb. Turning off the North End Rd. Golders Green tube 6 mins walk. Buses, 268, 210. A walk all round the house, swathe of grass with long borders of bushes, trees and climbers. Close planting, herbaceous beds, roses, heathers, lavenders: herbs, mints, some uncommon plants. Paving, pots, and old oak tree; small pond with bubbling water. Winner of Hampstead Gardens Competition and All London Championship. Home-made TEAS. *Adm £1.50. Sun June 23 (2-6)*

10 Wildwood Rd, NW11 & (Dr J W McLean) Hampstead. Wildwood Rd is between Hampstead Golf Course and N end of Hampstead Heath. From North End Rd turn by Manor House Hospital into Hampstead Way, then fork R. Garden planned and maintained by owner; one of fi-

nest herbaceous borders in North London, pond, HT roses; owner-grown prize winning delphiniums and seedlings. TEA. *Adm £1.50 Chd free. Sun June 30 (2-7)*

Wimbledon Gardens, SW19 &✿ Train: BR or underground. TEAS Somerset Rd and 86 Copse Hill. *Combined adm £2 or £1 per garden Chd 50p. Sun May 19 (2-6)*

¶**4 Coach House Lane** (Dr & Mrs Davidson Parker) Cul-de-sac opp 21 Somerset Road. Take 93 bus from Wimbledon Hill or alternatively walk from Southfields Underground (turn R along Wimbledon Park Rd, R up Bathgate Rd, and L at Somerset Rd), 10 mins. Secluded ½-acre garden on 2 levels partly walled with York stone. Many mature trees and shrubs, sunken rose garden; C18 sundial; 2 attractive patios

86 Copse Hill &✿❀ (Mrs John Fox) Sunny Cottage garden with a good mix of bulbs, herbaceous and shrubs. TEAS

21 Somerset Road (Mr & Mrs John Perring) By train BR or underground, turn R take Bus 93 at bottom of Wimbledon Hill ask for Calonne Rd bus stop then walk on and take next R into Somerset Rd, garden a short way on L. Or walk 1½m up hill through village along Parkside to Somerset Rd on R. Partly walled garden in ⅓-acre with 2 fine specimen cedars, shrubs herbaceous, groundcover, climbing plants and small herb area around a lawn with lots of pine needles in it. TEAS

¶**35 Wincanton Rd**, SW18 ❀ (Helen Faulls) Off Wimbledon Park Rd, Southfields Tube. Bus 39. Sunny garden 17' × 45' located in a conservation area. Created by densely planting a wide variety of shrubs and herbaceous plants, incl many from the southern hemisphere. Colour, form and flowers yr-round. Terrace enclosed by mixed planting and fences clothed with shrubs and climbers to form a luxuriant setting for outdoor living. *Adm £1 Chd 50p (Share to International Spinal Research Trust). Sun June 23 (2-6)*

47 Winn Road, SE12 &❀ (Mr & Mrs G Smith) Lee. 8m SE central London. 15mins walk from either BR Lee station (Sidcup Line to Dartford) or Grove Park (Orpington Line) from Charing Cross. By car, ½m from A20 Sidcup bypass or A205 S Circular. ⅓-acre mature plantsman's garden maintained by owners. Mixed borders, alpine beds, fruit and vegetables, 3 greenhouses featuring colourful displays of pelargoniums, fuchsias, begonias, cacti and succulents and other interesting plants. TEAS. *Adm £1 Chd free (Share to The Fifth Trust©). Suns April 28, June 23, Aug 18 (2-5)*

27 Wood Vale, N10 ❀ (Mr & Mrs A W Dallman) Muswell Hill 1m. A1 to Woodman public house; signed Muswell Hill; Muswell Hill Rd sharp R Wood Lane leading to Wood Vale; Highgate tube station. ¾-acre garden with herbaceous borders; ponds; orchard and kitchen garden. Unusual layout full of surprises. Numerous shrubs, roses, trees and conifers; greenhouses. Visitors may also wander in neighbouring gardens, all of which are of high standard. TEAS. *Adm £1.50 Chd 50p under 5yrs free (Share to British Legion and Meeting Point For St Georges Church®). Sat, Sun July 20, 21 (2-6)*

66 Woodbourne Avenue ⚘ (Bryan d'Alberg & Keith Simmonds) Streatham. Cars enter from Garrads Rd by Tooting Bec Common. Easy parking. Garden designer's garden constantly evolving. Busy cottage style front garden 40′ × 60′ containing roses, irises and herbaceous plants. Rear garden approx 40′ × 80′ created over the last 6 yrs. Features shrubs, trees, gazebo and pool, creating a tranquil oasis in an urban setting. TEAS. *Adm £1 Chd 50p (Share to Crusaid®). Sun June 30 (1-6.30)*

7 Woodstock Road, W4 ⚘ (Mr & Mrs L A Darke) Buses E3, 94, 27. Underground to Turnham Green 5 mins. Unusual garden created by present owners over 45 yrs behind Norman Shaw house in Bedford Park, the earliest garden suburb. Original rockery and wide selection of fine flowering trees, shrubs, herbaceous plants, roses, bulbs and recently planted ferns. Featured in 'London Pride', the 1990 exhibition of the history of the capital's gardens in the Museum of London. *Adm £1.25 Chd free. Sun April 21 (2-5)*

23 Woodville Road, W5 ⚘❀ (Jill & Taki Argyropoulos) Ealing Broadway Station (Central and District Lines). Bus 65 from Kingston and Richmond. Garden within a few mins walk of the station. Mediterranean style part-paved front garden with lots of tubs and pots, planted for yr round colour. Secluded, walled garden at rear 100′ × 40′ well stocked with flowering shrubs, climbers and many herbaceous plants. Small fish pond with waterfall and bog garden, vegetable and herb area. TEAS. *Adm £1 Chd 25p. Sun June 16 (2-6)*

Norfolk

Hon County Organisers:	Mrs Neil Foster, Lexham Hall, King's Lynn PE32 2QJ Tel 01328 701 341 Mrs David McCosh, Baconsthorpe Old Rectory, Holt NR25 6LU Tel 01263 577611
Assistant County Organisers:	Mrs David Mcleod, Park House, Old Hunstanton, King's Lynn PE36 6JS The Hon Mrs Julian Darling, Intwood Hall, Norwich NR4 6TG
Hon Treasurer:	Denzil Newton Esq OBE, Briar House, Gt Dunham, King's Lynn PE32 2LX

DATES OF OPENING

March 31 Sunday
Wretham Lodge, East Wretham
April 7 Sunday
Desert World, Santon Downham
Lake House, Brundall
April 8 Monday
Lake House, Brundall
April 14 Sunday
Gayton Hall, nr King's Lynn
The Old House, Ranworth
April 21 Sunday
Bradenham Hall, East Dereham
April 28 Sunday
The Birches, Wreningham
Bradenham Hall, East Dereham
Minns Cottage, Potter Heigham
May 5 Sunday
Lake House, Brundall
May 6 Monday
Lake House, Brundall
May 12 Sunday
Alby Crafts Gardens, Erpingham ‡
How Hill Farm, Ludham
86 Hungate Street, Aylsham ‡
Ryston Hall, Downham Market
Wretham Lodge, East Wretham

May 17 Friday
Hoveton Hall Gardens, nr Wroxham
May 19 Sunday
Desert World, Santon Downham
The Mowle, Ludham
Rippon Hall, Hevingham, nr Norwich
Sheringham Park, Upper Sheringham
May 26 Sunday
Aylsham Gardens
Letheringsett Gardens
Lexham Hall, nr Swaffham
Selborne House, Harleston
Stow Hall, Stow Bardolph
May 27 Monday
Dell Farm, Aylsham
Selborne House, Harleston
May 29 Wednesday
The Old Vicarage, East Ruston
June 2 Sunday
Sheringham Park, Upper Sheringham
June 9 Sunday
Besthorpe Hall, Attleborough
The Dutch House, Ludham

The Garden in an Orchard, Bergh Apton
Gillingham Hall, nr Beccles
The Old Rectory, South Acre
Southgate House, South Creake
June 16 Sunday
Bayfield Hall, nr Holt
Conifer Hill, Starston
Cubitt Cottage, Sloley
Hoveton House, nr Wroxham
Mannington Hall, Aylsham
June 22 Saturday
Yewlands, Kings Lynn
June 23 Sunday
Baconsthorpe Old Rectory, Holt
72 Branthill Cottages, Wells-next-the-Sea
Felbrigg Hall, nr Cromer
Lexham Hall, nr Swaffham
Raveningham Gardens
Southgate Barn, South Creake
Stow Hall, Stow Bardolph
Wretham Lodge, East Wretham
Yewlands, Kings Lynn
June 29 Saturday
Rainthorpe Hall, Tasburgh
June 30 Sunday
Cubitt Cottage, Sloley

Elsing Hall, nr Dereham
Hedenham & Ditchingham
   Gardens
Intwood Hall, Norwich ‡
Minns Cottage, Potter Heigham
The Plantation Garden, Norwich ‡
Rainthorpe Hall, Tasburgh
Wicken House, Castle Acre
July 7 Sunday
Town Close House School,
   Norwich
July 14 Sunday
Easton Lodge, Easton
Hoveton House, nr Wroxham
The Lodge, Old Lakenham,
   Norwich
July 21 Sunday
Burlingham Gardens
Felbrigg Hall, nr Cromer
Oxburgh Hall Gardens, Oxburgh

Raveningham Gardens
July 26 Friday
Blickling Hall, Aylsham
July 28 Sunday
The Garden in an Orchard, Bergh
   Apton
Hoveton Hall Gardens, nr
   Wroxham
August 10 Saturday
Blickling Hall, Aylsham
August 11 Sunday
Oxburgh Hall Gardens, Oxburgh
August 18 Sunday
Minns Cottage, Potter Heigham
The Plantation Garden, Norwich
August 28 Wednesday
The Old Vicarage, East Ruston
September 12 Thursday
Holkham Hall, Wells

Regular openings
For details see garden description

Bradenham Hall, East Dereham
Hoveton Hall Gardens, nr Wroxham
Magpies, Green Lane, Mundford
Norfolk Lavender Ltd, Heacham
The Old Vicarage, East Ruston
Sandringham Grounds

By appointment only
For telephone numbers and other details see garden descriptions. Private visits welcomed

Lanehead, Garboldisham

DESCRIPTIONS OF GARDENS

Alby Crafts Gardens ৬৪ (Mr & Mrs John Alston) Erpingham. On A140 4m N Aylsham, parking by Alby Crafts car park. 4-acre garden. Primroses, spring bulbs, irises, hellebores, old-fashioned roses, mixed borders, 4 ponds (1 with wild flower and conservation area). Plantsman's garden. TEAS. *Adm £1.50 Chd free. Sun May 12 (10-5). Parties welcome, please* **Tel 01263 761226**

Aylsham Gardens *Combined adm £2.50 Chd free*
   5 Cromer Road ৬ (Dr & Mrs James) Aylsham. 100yds N of Aylsham Parish Church down old Cromer Rd on LH-side. Approx 1 acre of semi-wild garden nr town centre with large willow trees and grass. Mixed borders and shrubs. Small natural pond, hostas and primulas. Vegetables. *Adm £1 Chd free. Sun May 26 (2-5.30)*
   10 St Michael's Close ৪৪ (M I Davies Esq) Aylsham NW on B1354 towards Blickling Hall; 500yds from market place, turn R, Rawlinsons Lane, then R again. Front gravelled area with mixed shrub and herbaceous border; small rockery. Back garden with large variety of shrubs, herbaceous plants, bulbs, small lawn, roses, azaleas. Plant, pond. Aviary, guinea pigs. TEAS. *Adm £1 Chd free. Sun May 26 (11-6). Private visits welcome, please* **Tel 01263 732174**
   West Lodge ৬ (Mr & Mrs Jonathan Hirst) Aylsham. ¼m NW of market square on N side of B1354 (entrance in Rawlinsons Lane) Large 9-acre garden with lawns, mature trees, rose garden, herbaceous borders, ornamental pond and walled kitchen garden; Georgian House (not open) and outbuildings incl a well-stocked toolshed (open) and greenhouses. TEAS in aid of Aylsham Church. *Adm £1.50 Chd free. Sun May 26 (2-5.30)*

¶**Baconsthorpe Old Rectory** ৬৪৪ (Mr & Mrs David McCosh) Holt. Follow sign to Baconsthorpe from Holt bypass for 3m. Rectory is beside church at far end of village. Overgrown 3-acre garden undergoing excavation and restoration. Extensive box hedges dividing kitchen garden and newly planted herbaceous borders. 30ft conservatory. Thatched summer house, rosebeds and mulberry trees; lawns and large trees; decorative outbuildings. TEAS. *Adm £1.50 Chd free (Share to St Mary's PCC®). Sun June 23 (2-6)*

Bayfield Hall (Mr & Mrs R H Combe) 1m N of Holt, off A148. Formal but simple pleasure gardens with medieval church ruin. Old-fashioned roses, herbaceous and shrub borders; magnificent view over lake and park. Wildflower centre adjacent to garden. Church Fete stalls and entertainment in aid of St Martins Church, Glandford. TEAS. *Adm £1.50 Chd 50p. Sun June 16 (2-5)*

Besthorpe Hall ৬৪৪ (John Alston Esq) 1m E of Attleborough. On Attleborough-Bunwell Rd; adjacent to Besthorpe Church. Garden with shrubs, trees and herbaceous borders within Tudor enclosures; walled kitchen garden; tilting ground. Coach parties by appt. TEAS. *Adm £2 Chd free (Share to Besthorpe Church®). Sun June 9 (2-5). Also private visits welcome, please* **Tel 01953 452138**

The Birches ৬৪৪ (Mr & Mrs J McCarthy) Top Row. Wreningham. 8m S of Norwich on B1113 Norwich-New Buckenham Rd. Take 1st turning L ¼m after Bird in Hand Restaurant. 1¼- acre garden landscaped with lawns, herbaceous, shrub and rose beds. Rockery, pond and alpine scree garden, orchard with naturalized bulbs. Vegetable garden, greenhouses and conservatory. TEAS. *Adm £1.50 Chd free. Sun April 28 (2-6)*

Blickling Hall ৬৪৪ (The National Trust) 1¼ miles NW of Aylsham on N side of B1354. 15m N of Norwich (A140). Large garden, orangery, crescent lake, azaleas, rhododendrons, herbaceous borders. Historic Jacobean house. Wheelchairs available. Cream TEAS and lunches. *Adm £3.20 Chd £1.60. Fri July 26, Sat Aug 10 (11-5)*

¶**Bradenham Hall** &⚘❀ (Lt Col & Mrs R C Allhusen) Bradenham, Thetford. Off A47 6m E Swaffham, 3m W of East Dereham. Turn S signed Wendling, Scarning, Longham. Turn R 1m signed Bradenham. Follow NGS signs. A garden for all seasons with massed daffodil planting, in variety and labelled. Arboretum composed of over 1000 species and varieties all labelled. Rose garden, herbaceous borders and mixed plantings, wall shrubs, roses and fruit and vegetable garden and glasshouses opening to public for first time. This garden has been described as one of the best in Norfolk and is probably the county's best kept secret. TEAS. *Adm £3 Chd under 12 £1.50. Open 2nd and 4th Sun of every month from April 28 to Sept 8 (2-5.30). For NGS Suns April 21, 28 (11-5)*

72 Branthill Cottages ⚘ (Timothy Leese Esq.) Wells-next-the-Sea. 2m from Wells. Off Fakenham-Wells rd. At Xrds unmarked by signpost, turn L, opp yellow sign to Branthill Farm ¼m down lane, cottage on LH-side. NGS posters and signposts on open day. Around a farm cottage, a ¼ acre of rather impractical garden, planted over the last 10 yrs. Not uncommon flowers, old roses and shrubs, closely planted to make garden appear larger, and to cut down on weeding. TEAS. *Adm £1 Chd free (Share to Wells Cottage Hospital®). Sun June 23 (2-6). Private visits welcome, please* **Tel 01328 711273**

¶**Burlingham Gardens** &⚘❀ (Easton College) Easton, Norwich, 10mE of Norwich off A47 at Burlingham. Horticultural Education Gardens founded in 1926, with a range of continually varying features. Fine lawns and herbaceous borders with specimen trees and mature shrubs. Winter gardens with demonstration hedges. Glasshouses with cut flowers and pot plants throughout the year. TEAS. *Adm £1.50 Chd free. Sun July 21 (1.30-5.30)*

Conifer Hill &❀ (Mr & Mrs Richard Lombe Taylor) Starston, Harleston. 18m S of Norwich. A140 to Pulham Xrds. Turn L to B1134. 1m NW of Harleston, off B1134. Take Redenhall Rd out of Starston. Conifer Hill on L ½m out of village. Steep bend and white gates. 4-acre Victorian garden. Lawns, shrubs, roses, herbaceous and kitchen garden. ½-acre pinetum, in steep escarpment of old quarry. TEAS. *Adm £1.50 Chd free. Sun June 16 (2-6)*

Cubitt Cottage &⚘❀ (Mrs Janie Foulkes) Sloley. 11m N of Norwich just off B1150 Coltishall to North Walsham Rd. 2nd R after Three Horseshoes public house at Scottow. Into village, then Low Street, R at next signpost. 1-acre garden with lawns, herbaceous and shrub border, over 100 varieties of old roses, clematis and unusual plants; wildflower meadow; wild life pond and bog garden; vegetable garden and greenhouses. Cream TEAS. *Adm £2 Chd free. Suns June 16, 30 (2-6). Also private visits welcome, please* **Tel 01692 538295**

Dell Farm &⚘❀ (Mrs M J Monk) Aylsham. Approx ¼m W of centre of Aylsham. Turn L off Blickling Rd on to Heydon Rd (signposted Oulton). 400yds on to copper beech arching rd. Turn R through gate onto gravelled yard. 4-acre garden; magnificent mature trees and shrubs. Various rose collections, rhododendrons, azaleas, heathers. Spring bulbs, primroses etc in old orchard and wild flower garden. TEAS. *Adm £1.50 Chd 50p. Mon May 27 (2-6). Also private visits welcome especially for spring bulbs, please* **Tel 01263 732277**

¶**Desert World** ⚘❀ (Mr & Mrs Barry Gayton) Santon Downham. On B1107. Thetford 4m, Brandon 2m. 1¼ acres landscaped plantsman's garden, specialising in alpines, herbaceous and spring bulbs, incl sempreviviums. Glasshouses containing 12,500 cacti and succulents. Featured on radio and TV. TEAS. *Adm £1.50 Chd free. Suns April 7, May 19 (1-6). Private, group visits and gardening lectures by appt. Please,* **Tel 01842 765361**

The Dutch House &⚘ (Mrs Peter Seymour) Ludham. B1062 Wroxham to Ludham 7m. Turn R by Ludham village church into Staithe Rd. Gardens ¼m from village. Long, narrow garden designed and planted by the painter Edward Seago, leading through marsh to Womack Water. Approx 2½ acres. Newly replanted herbaceous borders and alterations in hand. TEAS. *Adm £1.50 Chd free. Sun June 9 (2-5.30)*

Easton Lodge ❀ (J M Rampton Esq) Easton, 6m W Norwich. Cross the new Southern Norwich Bypass at the Easton Roundabout and take the Ringland Rd. Large garden in magnificent setting above river surrounded by fine trees; walks amongst interesting shrubs, roses, plants; herbaceous border; walled kitchen garden. Late Georgian house with Jacobean centre portion (not open). TEAS. *Adm £1.50 Chd free. Sun July 14 (2.30-5.30)*

Ellingham Hall nr Bungay. See Suffolk for details

Elsing Hall ❀ (Mrs D Cargill) Dereham. 2m E of Dereham off A47; sign to Elsing. Medieval house surrounded by moat. Over 200 varieties of old-fashioned roses; wild flower lawn, walled kitchen garden with roses, fruit trees & clematis. Many water plants by moat and fish stew. Rare and interesting trees in arboretum; newly planted formal garden with clipped box, lavender, sage, santolina and thyme. Suitable wheelchairs in places. TEAS. *Adm £2 Chd free (Share to Elsing Church restoration fund®). Sun June 30 (2-6). Private parties welcome, please* **Tel 01362 637224**

Felbrigg Hall &⚘ (The National Trust) Roughton, 2½m SW of Cromer, S of A148; main entrance from B1436; signed from Felbrigg village. Large pleasure gardens; mainly lawns and shrubs; orangery with camellias; large walled garden restored and restocked as fruit, vegetable and flower garden; vine house; dovecote; dahlias; superb colchicum; wooded parks. 2 Electric wheelchairs available. Lunches, pre booking essential. TEAS. *Adm £2 Chd £1 Family ticket £4. For NGS Suns June 23, July 21 (11-5)*

The Garden in an Orchard &❀ (Mr & Mrs R W Boardman) Bergh Apton, Norwich. 6m SE of Norwich off A146 at Hellington Corner signed to Bergh Apton. Down Mill Rd 300 yds. 3½-acre garden set in an old orchard. Many rare and unusual plants set out in an informal pattern of wandering paths. ½-acre of wild flower meadows, many bamboos, specie roses, 9 species of eucalyptus. In all a plantsman's garden. TEAS. *Adm £1.50 Chd free. Suns June 9, July 28 (11-6)*

Gayton Hall &❀ (Mr & Mrs Julian Marsham) 6m E of King's Lynn off B1145; signs in Gayton village. 20 acres; wild woodland, water garden. Bulbs, TEAS. *Adm £2 Chd free (Share to ADAPT East Anglia®). Sun April 14 (2-5). Private visits welcome, please* **Tel 01553 636259**

Gillingham Hall &❀ (Mr & Mrs Robin Bramley) Beccles. 16m SE of Norwich, 1½m from Beccles off A146. 14-acre garden with lake, lawns, borders, rose garden, specimen plane trees, wild flower areas, bulbs; Mansion house (not open) c1600. TEAS. *Adm £1.50 Chd 50p (Share to Church Restoration Funds®). Sun June 9 (2-5). Parties welcome, please Tel 01502 713294*

¶Hedenham & Ditchingham Gardens ✿ 1m Bungay off the B1332 towards Norwich. TEA. *Adm £1 Chd free. Sun June 30 (2-5)*
13 Drapers Lane ❀ (Mr & Mrs Borrett) Ditchingham. ⅓-acre containing many interesting, unusual plants incl 80 plus varieties of hardy geraniums, climbers and shrubs. Herbaceous perennials a speciality. Owner maintained. *Also opening for Suffolk May 6*
¶Old Rectory & (Lady Matheson) Hedenham. 2 acres incl walled garden with herbaceous borders, climbers, trees and shrubs. Owner maintained

Holkham Hall & (The Earl of Leicester) Wells-next-the-Sea. 2m W of Wells off A149. Arboretum with many rare specimens of trees and shrubs; shell house. TEAS. *Adm 50p Chd 20p.* ▲For NGS Thurs Sept 12 (1.30-4.40)

Hoveton Hall Gardens &✿❀ (Mr & Mrs Andrew Buxton) nr Wroxham. 8m N of Norwich; 1m N of Wroxham Bridge on A1151 Stalham Rd. Approx 10-acre gardens and grounds featuring principally daffodils, azaleas, rhododendrons and hydrangeas in a woodland setting and a large, mature, walled herbaceous garden. Water plants, a lakeside walk and walled kitchen garden provide additional interest. Early C19 house (not open). TEAS. *Adm £2.50 Chd £1. Gardens open, every Wed, Fri, Sun and Bank Hols, Easter Sun to Sept 15 incl (11.30-5.30). For NGS Fri May 17, Sun July 28 (Share to Multiple Sclerosis Society Research®) (11.30-5.30)*

Hoveton House &✿❀ (Sir John & Lady Blofeld) 9m N Norwich, ½m Wroxham on B1062, Horning-Ludham Rd. Old-fashioned walled garden; magnificent herbaceous and other borders full of unusual plants and bulbs; rock garden. Established rhododendron grove. Kitchen garden. Park; lawns, walks with magnificent view. William & Mary House (not open.) Plants for sale June only. TEAS. *Adm £2 Chd free (Share to St John's Church®). Suns June 16, July 14 (2-5.30)*

How Hill Farm (P D S Boardman Esq) 2m W of Ludham on A1062; then follow signs to How Hill; Farm Garden – S of How Hill. Very pretty garden started in 1968 in water garden setting with three ponds; recent 3-acre broad (dug as conservation project) with variety of water lilies and view over the R Ant; fine old mill. Winding paths through rare conifers; unusual and rare rhododendrons with massed azaleas; other ornamental trees and shrubs; a few herbaceous plants and lilies; collection of English holly, ilex aquifolium (over 50 varieties). Collection of bamboos. Partly suitable for wheelchairs. TEA. *Adm £2 Chd free (Share to How Hill Trust©). Sun May 12 (2-5)*

86 Hungate Street ✿❀ (Mrs Sue Ellis) Aylsham. From Norwich towards Cromer on A140. Turn L at roundabout S of Aylsham towards Stonegate, turn R into Hungate St. Proceed along for ¾m to row of white cottages on L. A small town garden 95' × 45' laid out in a semi-formal style, consisting of sunken lawns, raised beds and pergolas. A plantswoman's garden densely planted with small specimen trees/shrubs. Rhododendrons, roses, primulas, ornamental pond. Raised vegetable area with propagation frame, greenhouse, enclosed by beech and laurel hedge. *Adm £1.50 Chd free. Sun May 12 (12-5)*

Intwood Hall &❀ (The Hon Julian & Mrs Darling) 3½m SW Norwich. Via A11 to Cringleford, fork L (avoid dual carriageway), over Cringleford bridge, L turn, over Xrds, level crossing, bypass for ½m. On R by thatched lodge. Tudor walled water garden and walled Victorian rose garden; herbaceous borders; 2 woodland walks, 1 to Saxon Church; park with lovely trees; walled kitchen garden with greenhousing. TEAS. *Adm £2 Chd free. Sun June 30 (2-5.30)*

Lake House ❀ (Mr & Mrs Garry Muter) Brundall. Approx 5m E of Norwich on A47; take Brundall turn at Roundabout. Turn R into Postwick Lane at T-junction. An acre of water gardens set among magnificent trees in a steep cleft in the river escarpment. Informal flower beds with interesting plants; a naturalist's paradise; unsuitable for young children or the infirm. Wellingtons advisable. 'Unusual plants for sale.' TEAS. *Adm £2 Chd free (Share to Water Aid®). Easter Sun & Mon April 7, 8; Sun, Mon May 5, 6 (11-5). Private parties welcome, please Tel 01603 712933*

Lanehead & (Mrs N A Laurie) Garboldisham, 8m W of Diss off A1066 at village Xrds take the A1111 for ½m to 1st R. Medium-sized garden created by owner; featured in a television programme, visited by many horticultural groups; well designed natural walks with shrubs and specimen trees; colour co-ordinated borders for all-year interest; water and bog garden; roses and woodland. Coffee, TEAS. *Adm £1.50 Chd free (Share to Garboldisham Church Fabric Fund®). Private visits welcome by appt April to Sept, please Tel 01953 81380*

Letheringsett Gardens & 1m W of Holt on A148. Car park King's Head, Letheringsett for disabled near church. TEAS in aid of Letheringsett Church. *Combined adm £2 Chd free. Sun May 26 (2-5.30)*
The Glebe &❀ (The Hon Beryl Cozens-Hardy) Medium-sized riverside garden, with island, wild flowers, water garden, shrub borders, clematis
Letheringsett Hall (Mrs English) Home for the Elderly; medium-sized garden and river
Letheringsett Estate Garden (Mr & Mrs Robert Carter) Large garden; wooded walks, fountain, lake, water plants, wild flowers. Hydraulic rams 1852 and 1905

Lexham Hall &✿❀ (Mr & Mrs Neil Foster) 2m W of Litcham off B1145. Fine 17th/18th century Hall (not open). parkland with lake and river walks. Formal garden with terraces, yew hedges, roses and mixed borders. Traditional kitchen garden with crinkle-crankle wall. 3-acre woodland garden with azaleas, rhododendrons, spring bulbs and rare trees. TEAS. *Adm £2 Chd free (Share to St Andrews Church, E. Lexham® May, All Saints Church, Litcham® June). Suns May 26, June 23 (2-6). Also groups (min 20) by appt May 1 to July 31 (weekdays only), please Tel 01328 701288*

The Lodge ✿❀ (Mr & Mrs P J E Smith) Sandy Lane, Old Lakenham. SE of Norwich just off ring rd (Barrett Rd). Turn out of city at Mansfield Lane traffic lights. 200yds on L opp St John's Church (also open). 1½-acres of contoured garden in beautiful setting leading down to R Yare. Herbaceous and shrub borders, enclosed croquet lawn, 1920's sunken garden, muscovy and other ducks. TEAS. *Adm £1.50 Chd free (Share to St John's Church®). Sun July 14 (2-6)*

Magpies ♿✿❀ (Mr & Mrs Dennis Cooper) Green Lane Mundford. From main Mundford roundabout take A1065 to Swaffham. After ¼m turn L down Green Lane. Divided into 'rooms' giving a cottage garden effect, a 1-acre garden filled with island beds, intensively planted with unusual perennials, ornamental grasses and cottage garden plants. Ponds and planted gravel areas. A wilder margin and tree belt encourages an abundance of birds throughout the year. Wide variety of unusual plants available from adjoining nursery. *Adm £1 Chd free. Open every day in June (12-6). Private visits welcome, please* **Tel 01842 878496**

Mannington Hall ♿✿❀ (The Lord & Lady Walpole) 2m N of Saxthorpe; 18m NW of Norwich via B1149 towards Holt. At Saxthorpe (B1149 & B1354) turn NE signed Mannington. 20 acres feature roses, shrubs, lake and trees. Heritage rose, scented and walled gardens. Extensive countryside walks and trails. C15 moated manor house (not open). Saxon church with C19 follies. Coffee, lunches and TEAS in aid of Village Hall, Itteringham. *Adm £3 OAPs/students £2.50 Chd free. Sun June 16 (12-5)*

Minns Cottage ♿✿❀ (Mr & Mrs Derek Brown) Chapel Rd, Potter Heigham. From Norwich take A1151 then A149 to Potter Heigham Xrds. Turn L into Station Rd on to T junction, turn L into School Rd, turning into Green Lane. At telephone box turn R into Chapel Rd. Approx 1¼-acres winding lawns leading through pergolas to rose garden with old English roses and other small gardens with mixed borders, recently planted woodland area with rhododendrons and bulbs. A garden to walk round peacefully at all seasons. TEAS. *Adm £1.50 Chd free. Suns April 28 (2-5), June 30, Aug 18 (2-6)*

The Mowle ✿❀ (Mrs N N Green) Ludham. B1062 Wroxham to Ludham 7m. Turn R by Ludham village church into Staithe Rd. Gardens ¼m from village. Approx 2½ acres running down to marshes. Interesting shrub borders, unusual trees etc incl tulip trees and a golden catalpa. TEAS. *Adm £1.50 Chd free. Sun May 19 (2-6)*

Norfolk Lavender Ltd ♿❀ Caley Mill, Heacham. On A149 13m N of Kings Lynn. National collection of lavenders set in 2 acres (lavender harvest July-Aug); herb garden with many varieties of native herbs; rose garden. TEA. *Adm free. Collecting box. Daily to Christmas (10-5). Closed for three weeks Christmas holiday.* **Tel 01485 570384**

Oak Tree House ✿❀ (W R S Giles Esq) 6 Cotman Rd, Thorpe. E of Norwich off A47 Thorpe Rd. ¼m from Norwich Thorpe Station. From Yarmouth direction follow one way system towards City Centre, turn R at traffic lights opposite Min. of Fisheries & Agric. Approx 300yds on, turn L opposite Barclays Bank. Botanical illustrators interesting plantsmans garden, of approx ½-acre on a hillside. Containing a mixture of hardy and tender plants giving a strong subtropical Mediterranean influence, containing tree ferns, bamboos, palms, bananas, cannas, agaves and many more. Also traditional herbaceous borders and a woodland garden with fernery. This garden has appeared in various TV programmes, magazines and books. TEAS. *Adm £1.60, Chd 30p. Suns July 28, Aug 11, Sept 1 (1.30-5.30)*

The Old House, Ranworth (Mr Francis & The Hon Mrs Cator) 9m NE of Norwich off B1140. Turn L in S Walsham to Ranworth on inner broad below church. Attractive linked and walled gardens alongside beautiful, peaceful Ranworth inner broad. Bulbs, shrubs, potager, mown rides through recently established arboretum where dogs may be walked on leads, pond with many species of ducks and geese. ½m of woodland walk adjacent to Norfolk Naturalist Trust Conservation Centre and Nature Trail (entrance extra). Historic church nearby. TEA. *Adm £1.50 Chd free. Sun April 14 (2-5)*

The Old Rectory ♿❀ (Mrs Clive Hardcastle) Southacre. 3m NW of Swaffham off A1065 opp Southacre Church. 3-acre garden with splendid views of Castle Acre Priory. Mixed borders, shrubs, small vineyard, herb garden, pool and old-fashioned rose garden. Interesting Saxon church. TEAS in aid of Southacre Church Restoration Fund. *Adm £2 Chd free. Sun June 9 (2-5.30). Private visits welcome by appt only May, June and July, please* **Tel 01760 755469**

The Old Vicarage ♿✿❀ (Alan Gray and Graham Robeson) East Ruston. Off A149 3m N of Stalham on Stalham to Walcott Rd (ignore all 3 signposts to East Ruston). At Xrds turn R 200 yds just N of East Ruston Church. 12-acre exotic coastal garden and grounds incl impressive herbaceous borders, autumn border, tropical border incl bananas and palms, sunken garden, walled garden, Mediterranean garden and wild flower meadows and walks. TEAS. *Adm £3 Chd £1. Open every Sun and Wed from May 1 to Oct 30 incl. For NGS Wed May 29, Wed Aug 28 (2-5)*

Oxburgh Hall Garden ♿✿ (The National Trust) 7m SW of Swaffham, at Oxburgh on Stoke Ferry rd. Hall and moat surrounded by lawns, fine trees, colourful borders; charming parterre garden of French design. Lunches. Cream TEAS. *Adm £2 Chd 50p. For NGS Suns July 21, Aug 11 (12-5)*

The Plantation Garden ♿✿❀ (Plantation Garden Preservation Trust) 4 Earlham Rd, Norwich. Entrance between Crofters and Beeches Hotels, nr St John's R C Cathedral. 3-acre Victorian town garden created 1856-96 in former medieval chalk quarry. Still undergoing restoration by volunteers, remarkable architectural features include 60ft Italianate terrace and unique 30ft Gothic fountain. Surrounded by mature trees. 10 min walk city centre, beautifully tranquil atmosphere. *Adm £1.50 Chd free (Share to Plantation Garden Preservation Trust©). Suns mid April to mid Oct (2-5). For NGS TEAS Suns June 30, Aug 18 (2-5). Private visits welcome, please* **Tel 01603 621868**

Rainthorpe Hall ර්ෂ (Mr & Mrs Alastair Wilson) Tasburgh. Approx 8m S of Norwich, just off the A140 - turn by garage in Newton Flotman. On 1m to red brick pillars and gates on L. Elizabethan/Victorian/Country House (not open) prettily set in interesting variety of gardens, incl knot hedge (said to be as old as the house) and hazel coppice (said to be older). Fine trees and collection of bamboos. [Croquet and bowls available, but *not* to high standard]. TEAS. *Adm £2.50 Chd free. Sat, Sun June 29, 30 (2-6). Private visits welcome, please* Tel 01508 470618

Raveningham Gardens ර්ෂ 14m SE of Norwich, 4m from Beccles off B1136.

> **Raveningham Hall** ර්ෂ (Sir Nicholas Bacon) Large garden specialising in rare shrubs, herbaceous plants, especially euphorbia, agapanthus and shrub roses. Victorian conservatory and walled vegetable garden, newly planted Arboretum. *Adm £2 Chd free. Nursery open 9-5 every day except weekends in November, December, January, February. Garden open every Sunday, Bank Hols and Weds March 17 to September 15 (2-5) Weds (1-4). For NGS TEAS Suns June 23, July 21 (2-5)*

> **Cossey Corner Farm** (Mr & Mrs M Myhill) From Norwich, ¼m before Hall. ¼-acre herbaceous and large variety of bedding plants. Colourful and delightful garden. *Combined adm with* **Orchards** *£1 Chd free. Sun June 23 (2-5)*

> **Orchards** (Priscilla Lady Bacon) From Norwich, ¼m before Hall. New garden planted over last 10 yrs. Very unusual shrubs and plants. Plantsman's garden. *Combined adm with* **Cossey Corner Farm** *£1 Chd free. Sun June 23 (2-5). Private visits welcome, please* Tel 01508 548 322/206

Rippon Hall ර්ෂ (Miss Diana Birkbeck) Hevingham, 8m N of Norwich. From A140 Norwich-Aylsham rd, turn R (E) at Xrds just N of Hevingham Church. Rhododendrons and azalea borders. Large herd of rare breed of British White Cattle. TEAS. *Adm £1.50 Chd 25p. Sun May 19 (2-5.30)*

Ryston Hall ර්๘ (Mr & Mrs Piers Pratt) Downham Market. 1m S of Downham Market off A10. 6-acre garden with azaleas and rhododendrons; rock garden and rare trees; walled kitchen garden and woodland walk. TEAS. *Adm £1.50 Chd under 14 50p (Share to Ryston Church).* ▲ *For NGS Sun May 12 (1-5) with guided tour to Ketts Oak*

Sandringham Grounds ර්๘ By gracious permission of H.M. The Queen, the House, Museum and Grounds at Sandringham will be open. 60 acres of informal gardens, woodland and lakes, with rare plants and trees. Donations are given from the Estate to various charities. For further information see p 13. TEAS. *Adm House and Grounds £4 OAPs £3 Chd £2; Grounds only £3 OAPs £2.50 Chd £1.50. April 4 to Oct 6 daily. House closed July 23 to Aug 7 incl & Grounds closed July 28 to Aug 6 incl. (Hours House 11-4.45; Grounds 10.30-5)*

Selborne House ර්๘ (Mr & Mrs Walland) Approx 5m off A140 Norwich to Ipswich Rd. Turn off to Harleston and follow one way signs or 8m from Scole A143. ¾-acre town garden, off Market Place opp. Magpie Hotel. Old Wellingtonia Spruces in front garden; rock garden and pond; clematis a speciality; mixed borders; plantsman's garden. TEAS. *Adm £1.50 Chd free. Sun May 26, Mon May 27 (2-5)*

Sheringham Park ර්ෂ (The National Trust) 2m SW of Sheringham. Access for cars off A148 Cromer to Holt Road, 5m W of Cromer, 6m E of Holt (signs in Sheringham Town). 50-acres of species rhododendron, azalea and magnolia. Also numerous specimen trees incl handkerchief tree. Viewing towers, waymarked walks, sea and parkland views. Special walk way and WCs for disabled. Teas at Felbrigg Hall nearby. *Adm £2.40 per car. For NGS Suns May 19, June 2 (dawn to dusk).* Tel 01263 823778

Southgate Barn ෂ (Mrs Philip Anley) South Creake. 5m N of Fakenham off B1355 to Burnham Market. 100yds past turning to R signed Waterden turn L down lane. Entrance 100yds on L. Small garden of approx 2 acres made 10 yrs ago around a converted barn. Shrubs and trees in front. At back large terrace, roses, pergola, herbaceous border. Cream TEAS. *Adm £1.50 Chd free (Share to Rumanian Relief for Children in Orphanages®). Sun June 23 (2-6)*

Southgate House ර්๘ෂ (Mr & Mrs Harry Schulman) South Creake. 5m NW of Fakenham. Follow B1355 towards Burnham Market. Just after sign to Waterden on R, turn L at signs. Entrance approx 200yds. A challenging garden of approx 1½ acres developed from 3 paddocks 8 yrs ago. Many interesting trees and unusual shrubs, plants and bulbs. A must for anyone discouraged by wind and lack of shelter. Cream TEAS. *Adm £1.50 Chd free (Share to St Mary's Church, S Creake®). Sun June 9 (2-5.30)*

Stow Hall ර්ෂ (Lady Rose Hare) Stow Bardolph. 2m N of Downham Market on A10, village of Stow Bardolph signposted to the E of the A10. Approx 20 acres of garden and grounds with many mature trees, high walls, climbing plants and shrub roses. Walled kitchen garden contains very old varieties of apple and pear trees one of which - Golden Noble Apple is mentioned in The English Apple by Rosanne Sanders as having been raised at Stow in 1820. Young apple trees with East Anglian interest are being planted. Newly landscaped gardens on site of old Hall. TEAS. *Adm £1.50 Chd free (Share to Holy Trinity Church, Stow Bardolph®). Suns May 26 June 23 (2-6). Private parties welcome, please* Tel 01366 383194

¶**Town Close House School** ර On A140 (Ipswich Rd) between Norwich outer ring rd and St Stephen's roundabout; entrance opp City College. Approx 4 acres of gardens of C18 Town Close House (now prep school). Part laid out to shrubs, flower and heather beds, part woodland with paths. Ponds, large lawn. TEAS. *Adm £1.50 Chd free. Sun July 7 (1-5)*

Wicken House ර්๘ෂ (Lord & Lady Keith) Castle Acre, 5m N of Swaffham off A1065; W at Newton to Castle Acre; then 2m N off the rd to Massingham. Large walled garden planted in sections with many roses and unusual herbaceous plants; gravel paths and greenhouses; swimming pool garden; spring and wild gardens. Fine views. Approx 6 acres. Rare plants for sale. Home-made cream TEAS. *Adm £2 Chd free (Share to the Friends of Castle Acre Church®). Sun June 30 (2-6)*

Wretham Lodge ₲♨❀ (Mrs Anne Hoellering) East Wretham. A11 E from Thetford; L up A1075; L by village sign; R at Xrds then bear L. In spring masses of specie tulips, hellebores, fritillaries, daffodils and narcissi; bluebell walk. In June hundreds of old roses. Walled garden, with fruit and interesting vegetable plots. Mixed borders and fine old trees. TEAS. *Adm £2 (£1 March) Chd free (Share to St Johns Ambulance in May, and Wretham Church in June®). Suns March 31 (11.30-5.30) May 12, June 23 (2.30-5.30). Also private visits and coach parties welcome, please write or Tel 01953 498366*

¶**Yewlands** ₲♨❀ (Mr & Mrs Eric Dent) 258 Wootton Rd, Kings Lynn. E side of Kings Lynn. Approx 1m N of Gaywood Clock, opp Mobil Garage. ¼-acre town garden developed over the past 15 yrs, packed with roses, perennials, alpines, ferns, hostas and over 250 flowering shrubs. Attractive pond complex with waterfalls and fountain. Garden featured recently in 'Amateur Gardening' and on ITV's 'Garden Club'. Radio Norfolk gardeners will attend on Sun. Raffle and cake stall. TEAS. *Adm £1.50 Chd free (Share to RNIB®). Sat, Sun June 22, 23 (2-6)*

Northamptonshire

Hon County Organiser: Mrs John Boughey, Butts Close, Farthinghoe, Brackley NN13 5NY
Tel 01295 710411

Asst Hon County Organisers: Mrs John Bussens, Glebe Cottage, Titchmarsh, Kettering NN14 3DB
Tel 01832 732510
Mrs R H N Dashwood, Farthinghoe Lodge, Nr Brackley, Northants NN13 5NX
Mrs R Blake, Lodge Lawn, Fotheringhay, Peterborough PE8 5HZ

Hon County Treasurer: R H N Dashwood Esq, Farthinghoe Lodge, nr Brackley, Northants NN13 5NX
Tel 01295 710377

DATES OF OPENING

March 24 Sunday
The Old Rectory, Sudborough
April 7 Sunday
Evenley Wood Garden, Brackley
April 8 Monday
Evenley Wood Garden, Brackley
Titchmarsh Gardens, nr Thrapston
April 10 Wednesday
Great Addington Manor,
nr Kettering ‡
Irthlingborough, 49 Finedon Road ‡
April 14 Sunday
Charlton, nr Banbury
Great Addington Manor,
nr Kettering
The Haddonstone Show Garden,
nr Northampton
Newnham Hall, Daventry
April 21 Sunday
Maidwell Hall, Northampton
April 28 Sunday
The Walnuts, Kings Cliffe
May 1 Wednesday
The Walnuts, Kings Cliffe
May 5 Sunday
The Haddonstone Show Garden,
nr Northampton
May 6 Monday
The Haddonstone Show Garden,
nr Northampton

May 12 Sunday
Bulwick Rectory, Bulwick
Finedon Gardens,
nr Wellingborough
Holdenby House, Northampton
Steane Park, Brackley
May 19 Sunday
Deene Park, nr Corby
Falcutt House, Brackley
Guilsborough & Hollowell Gardens
May 26 Sunday
Lois Weedon House, Weedon
Lois, nr Towcester
Newnham Gardens, nr Daventry
The Old Barn, Weedon Lois,
nr Towcester
Sholebroke Lodge, Towcester
May 27 Monday
Titchmarsh Gardens, nr Thrapston
May 29 Wednesday
Newnham Gardens, nr Daventry
June 2 Sunday
Litchborough Gardens, Towcester
The Old Rectory, Sudborough
Preston Capes Gardens
June 8 Saturday
Canons Ashby House, Daventry
June 9 Sunday
Benefield House, Lower
Benefield, nr Oundle
Coton Manor, Guilsborough
Evenley Gardens, Brackley

Falcutt House, Brackley
Slapton Gardens, nr Towcester
Stoke Park, Stoke Bruerne,
Towcester
Turweston Mill, Brackley ‡
Versions Farm, nr Brackley ‡
June 10 Monday
Evenley Gardens, Brackley
June 12 Wednesday
Badby Gardens, Badby,
nr Daventry
June 16 Sunday
Badby Gardens, Badby, nr
Daventry
Irthlingborough, 49 Finedon
Road
Maidwell Gardens
June 19 Wednesday
Maidwell Gardens
June 22 Saturday
Flore Gardens, nr Northampton
June 23 Sunday
Flore Gardens, nr Northampton
Geddington Gardens, nr Kettering
The Menagerie, Horton,
nr Northampton
June 26 Wednesday
Bradden House, nr Towcester
June 30 Sunday
Aynho Gardens, nr Banbury
Chacombe Gardens, nr Banbury
Cottesbrooke Hall, nr Creaton ‡

Easton Neston, Towcester
Gamekeepers Cottage,
nr Creaton ‡
Harpole Gardens, Northampton
Weedon Lois Gardens,
nr Towcester
Wilby Gardens, nr Wellingborough
July 7 Sunday
West Haddon Gardens,
nr Northampton
July 14 Sunday
Cranford Gardens, nr Kettering
1 The Green, Kingsthorpe Village
Ravensthorpe Gardens
July 17 Wednesday
1 The Green, Kingsthorpe Village
Ravensthorpe Gardens
July 21 Sunday
Castle Ashby House,
nr Northampton

August 4 Sunday
Bulwick Gardens, nr Corby
Cottesbrooke Hall, nr Creaton
Gamekeepers Cottage, nr Creaton
August 25 Sunday
The Old Rectory, Sudborough
September 5 Thursday
Coton Manor, Guilsborough
September 8 Sunday
Canons Ashby House, Daventry
September 22 Sunday
Hill Grounds, Evenley, Brackley
October 6 Sunday
Bulwick Rectory, Bulwick
October 13 Sunday
Newnham Hall, Daventry

Regular openings
For details see garden description

Coton Manor, Guilsborough
Cottesbrooke Hall, nr Creaton

By appointment only
*For telephone numbers and other
details see garden descriptions.
Private visits welcomed*

156 Balfour Road, Northampton
The Spring House, Nr Banbury

DESCRIPTIONS OF GARDENS

Aynho Gardens & 6m SE of Banbury on B4100. Teas in Village Hall. *Combined adm £2 Chd free (Share to Aynho Village Hall®). Sun June 30 (2.30-6)*
¶**Aynhoe Park** ⚥ (Country Houses Association) 14-acres of parkland surround the house (not open to visitors). Sweeping lawns, contrast with woodland left in its natural state to provide a rich habitat for wildlife and plants, incl small leafed ivy. Occasional, seasonal flower beds, herbaceous borders and graceful groupings of trees, incl those forming the lime walk which was the original main driveway to the house
Friars Well (Mr & Mrs T R Sermon) 3 acre garden on top of hill with magnificent view; divided into sections with mixed hedges and stone walls; pleached limes and hornbeams, unusual shrubs and roses
¶**1 Charlton Road** (Mr & Mrs C J Brownhall) Medium-sized garden with some mature trees, herbaceous borders and shrubs, small rockery and fish pond
¶**1 The Glebe** (Mr & Mrs G Paxton) Small garden, largely replanted in 1995 with shrubs and herbaceous borders. Also patio with tubs and containers
¶**Hansel House** (Mrs S Belcher) Cottage garden with roses, mixed borders and small pond
Catton House ⚥ (Mr & Mrs C H Harmer) Well established small walled garden with mature trees, various shrubs and specialising in roses and clematis - sunken walled rose garden
Puente Sierra ⚥ (Mr & Mrs R Sawbridge) 1 Cartwright Gardens. ½-acre walled garden with interesting mature evergreens, shrubberies and deciduous trees, bulbs, lilies, palms and hibiscus. Also a fruit and vegetable area
16 Roundtown (Mrs E A Bazin) Old-fashioned cottage garden with inner walled section, herbaceous borders, roses, shrubs and fruit trees

Badby Gardens ⚥❀ 3m S of Daventry on E side of A361. TEAS at Church Hill. *Combined adm £1.50 (Share to St Mary's Church®). Wed June 12, Sun June 16 (2-6)*

Church Hill ⚥ (Dr & Mrs C M Cripps) Close to Badby Woods and Fawsley Park (suitable for walks and picnics). Medium-sized country garden on an irregular sloping site, parts of which have been recently redesigned. Yew hedges, mixed borders thickly planted in colour groups. Some interesting plants, shady border, greenhouse and conservatory
¶**The Old House** & (Dr & Mrs C Rose) A medium-sized open garden overlooking Badby Woods. Mostly stone raised beds recently designed and planted with a good variety of traditional herbaceous plants, featuring many David Austin roses as a speciality

¶**156 Balfour Road, Northampton** ⚥❀ (Mrs R Thornton) 1m N of town centre between A508 and A43. A plantsman's garden with an emphasis on foliage and colour co-ordination. Steeply sloping, this ⅕-acre suburban garden is terraced to provide separate areas of interest and has been featured on TV's Garden Club. *Adm £1. Private visits welcome by appt only February to end of October, please* Tel 01604 714145

Benefield House &⚥ ❀ (Mr & Mrs John Nicholson) Lower Benefield. 3m W Oundle off A427. Oundle-Corby Rd. 2½-acre garden. Shrubbery and large herbaceous border with interesting plants. Old walled kitchen garden containing vegetables and flowers. TEA. *Adm £1.50 Chd free (Share to St Mary's Church®). Sun June 9 (2-6)*

Bradden House ❀ (Keith Barwell Esq) Bradden. 5m W of Towcester. 25 acres of garden with ornamental woodland and lake, the walled garden of Edwardian origin the rest has been laid out by present owners since 1991. Good mixed borders with colour themes, long rose pergola and rose garden planted with new English roses around an ornamental pool, vegetable, herb and fruit gardens. Walk through newly planted park and flower meadow with ponds. TEAS. *Adm £1.80 Chd 50p (Share to Home Farm Trust®). Wed June 26 (2-6). Private visits welcome March to Sept, please* Tel 01327 860902

Bulwick Gardens 7m NE of Corby, 10m SW of Stamford, ½m off A43. TEAS. *Combined adm £2 Chd free (Share to Multiple Sclerosis®). Sun Aug 4 (2-5.30)*

Bulwick Hall & (Mr & Mrs G T G Conant) In Bulwick Village turn in Red Lodge Rd, enter park over cattle grid. Formal terraced 8-acre walled garden leading to river and island. 50 metre double herbaceous borders. 100 metre holly walk ending at attractive C18 wrought iron gates. C19 orangery and colonnade; large newly planned kitchen garden; fine mature trees; peacocks. TEAS

¶**Hollyberry Barn** &❀ (Colin McAlpine) A newly planted cottage garden in an old cowyard; herbaceous plants, shrubs, old-fashioned roses and climbers; raised vegetable beds; greenhouse; cold frames; gravelled area with alpine plants and pots

The Shambles ✄ (Mr & Mrs M R Glithero) Approx ⅓-acre garden, mixed herbaceous borders, vegetable garden with fruit and an original village well; variety of flowering plants in pots and tubs

Bulwick Rectory &✄❀ (Revd & Mrs Mervyn Wilson) Bulwick. 8m NE of Corby; 13m NE of Kettering; next to Bulwick Church. 1½-acre old rectory garden largely remade and replanted since 1978 as a number of gardens with vistas and surprises. Dovecote; folly; stonewalls. Shrubs, old roses, mixed borders with wide variety of plants. Fruit trees 35 varieties of apple, 15 of pear and 12 of plum in various forms of training and quince medlar and vegetables cultivated on organic principles. TEAS and plants May only. *Adm £1 Chd 50p (Share to St Nicholas Church®). Suns May 12, Oct 6 (2-5). Private visits welcome, please* **Tel 01780 450 249**

Canons Ashby House &✄ (The National Trust) nr Daventry. Formal gardens enclosed by walls being developed. Gate piers from 1710; fine topiary; axial arrangement of paths and terraces; wild flowers, old varieties of fruit trees, newly planted gardens. Home of the Dryden family since C16, Manor House 1550 with contemporary wall paintings and Jacobean plastering. TEAS. *Adm £3.40 Chd £1.70 (includes house). Reduced party rate. For NGS Sat June 8, Sun Sept 8 (12-5.30)*

Castle Ashby House &❀ (The Marquis of Northampton) 6m E of Northampton. 1½m N of A428 Northampton-Bedford; turn off between Denton and Yardley Hastings. Parkland incl avenue planted at suggestion of William III in 1695; lakes etc by Capability Brown; Italian gardens with orangery; extensive lawns and trees. Nature trail. Elizabethan house (not open). TEA. *Adm £2.50 Chd & OAPs £1. For NGS Sun July 21 (11-5)*

Chacombe Gardens 4m NE of Banbury. On A361 from Banbury centre turn R signed to Chacombe. TEAS **Pear Tree House**. *Combined adm £1.50 Chd free (Share to St Peter & St Paul Church®). Sun June 30 (2-6)*

Cartmel ✄ (Mr & Mrs John Willis) Small informal elevated garden with herbaceous plants, spring bulbs, roses, shrubs and small trees; pond and rockery with wide variety of plants. Greenhouse with tender plants for summer planting. Surrounded on three sides by hedges and old stone walls

Pear Tree House (Capt & Mrs Peter Northey) A 1-acre garden leading up to church with spring bulbs, mature trees and shrubs surrounding an extended C17 cottage

Poplars Farm ❀ (Mr & Mrs Geoff Jones) 4 acres; mixed borders; streamside borders with ferns, species; primulas and bog plants; kitchen garden; dry garden with alpines; wild areas with some growing willow for fuel, spring and summer meadow areas being developed, greenhouse with cacti and carnivorous plants. Thatched 1654 farmhouse (not open)

17 Silver St (Dr & Mrs Stephen Large) 2 acres; paddocks with shetland pony; wild stream-side; mixed borders; rose garden planted with clematis; new tree plantings; small court

Charlton & 7m SE of Banbury, 5m W of Brackley. From A41 turn off N at Aynho; or from A422 turn off S at Farthinghoe. Home-made TEAS **The Cottage**. *Combined adm £1.50 Chd 75p (Share to Friends of Charlton Primary School©). Sun April 14 (2-6)*

The Cottage (Lady Juliet Townsend) Flowering shrubs, spring bulbs, roses, lawns, woodland walk, stream and lakes. House in village street

Holly House (The Hon Nicholas Berry) Walled garden with beautiful views. C18 house (not open)

Coton Manor &❀ (Mr & Mrs Ian Pasley-Tyler) 10m N of Northampton. 11m SE of Rugby nr Ravensthorpe Reservoir. From A428 & A50 follow Tourist signs. C17 stone manor house with old yew and holly hedges, extensive herbaceous borders, rose garden, water garden, herb garden, woodland garden, famous bluebell wood (early May) and exotic wildflower collection. Home-made Lunches and TEAS. *Adm £2.70 OAPs £2.20 Chd £1. Open daily Weds to Suns & Bank Hols April to end Sept. For NGS Sun June 9, Thurs Sept 5 (12-6). Private parties welcome, please* **Tel 01604 740219**

Cottesbrooke Hall &✄❀ (Captain & Mrs J Macdonald-Buchanan) 10m N of Northampton, nr Creaton on A50 and Brixworth on A508. (A14 link rd A1/M1). Car park free. Notable gardens of great variety incl fine old cedars and specimen trees, herbaceous borders, water and wild gardens. TEAS. *Adm house & gardens £4 Gardens only £2.50 Chd half price. House and Gardens open Thursdays and Bank Hol Mons (2-5.30) from Easter Mon to Sept, plus each Sun in Sept. Garden only open on Wed and Fri afternoons from Easter to Sept. For NGS Combined adm with* **Gamekeepers Cottage** *£2 Chd £1. House £2 extra (Share to All Saints Church®). Suns June 30, Aug 4 (2-6).* **Tel 01604 505808**

Cranford Gardens 4½m E of Kettering. A14 Kettering-Thrapston. TEAS, Station House, Oakrise. Car parking available. *Combined adm £1.50 Chd 50p (Share to Cranford Churches Restoration Fund®). Sun July 14 (2-6)*

16 Duck End (Miss Margaret Thompson) Very small cottage garden overlooking the church. Borders of perennials and shrubs

Oakrise & (Mr & Mrs G T Oakes) 5 The Green. ½-acre with variety of shrubs, perennials, dwarf conifers; Japanese water garden with Koi Carp and water plants; lovely view

Station House &❀ (Mr & Mrs A Bates) Garden created from the original railway station. Old platform now a walled patio with fish pond and rockery. Many varieties of trees, new planting of shrubs, herbaceous perennials. Natural wildlife pond
Also 3 small cottage gardens – "Over the garden wall"
¶4 The Green
¶6 The Green
¶8 The Green

Deene Park &❀ (Edmund Brudenell Esq) 5m N of Corby on A43 Stamford-Kettering Rd. Large garden; long mixed borders, old-fashioned roses, rare mature trees, shrubs, natural garden, large lake and waterside walks. Parterre designed by David Hicks echoing the C16 decoration on the porch stonework. Interesting Church and Brudenell Chapel with fine tombs and brasses. TEAS. *Adm £2 Chd 50p. Sun May 19 (2-5)*

Easton Neston & (The Lord & Lady Hesketh) Towcester. Entrance on Northampton Rd (old A43). Hawkesmoor's only Private house. Large formal garden; ornamental water, topiary; walled garden; woodland walk with C14 church (not open) in grounds. TEA. *Adm £2 Chd 50p. Sun June 30 (2-6)*

Evenley Gardens From Brackley 1m S on A43. Teas at Evenley Hall. *Combined adm £1.80 Chd 50p. Sun, Mon June 9, 10 (2-6)*
15 Church Lane (Mr & Mrs K O'Regan) ⅓-acre garden with pond, mixed borders and vegetables. Terrace and herb garden on S side of house
Five Gables ❀❀ (Mr & Mrs M Bosher) SE facing of 1½ acres, sloping to pond, and designed in compartments. New area being taken in this year
Hill Grounds &❀ (Mr & Mrs C F Cropley) 2-acres S facing sheltered garden re-developed since 1982; mature trees, 200yds of yew hedge; terrace; old roses, winter garden; wide range of unusual plants. TEAS. *Adm £1 Chd 50p. Sun Sept 22 (2-6)*
The Manor House (Mr & Mrs H Bentley) Established garden on ½-acre sloping site; topiary and an ambience in harmony with fine Elizabethan Manor House (not open)

Evenley Wood Garden (R T Whiteley) Brackley. A43 ¾m S turn L to Evenley straight through village towards Mixbury 1st turning L. A woodland garden spread over a 60-acre mature wood. Acid and alkaline soil. Magnolias, rhododendrons, azaleas, malus, quercus, acers, euonymus collection and many other species. A large collection of bulbous plants. TEAS. *Adm £2 Chd £1. Suns, Mons May 5, 6; 26, 27 (2-7). For NGS Sun, Mon April 7, 8 (2-6). Private visits welcome, please* Tel 01280 703329

Falcutt House &❀❀ (Paul & Charlotte Sandilands) Falcutt, Helmdon. 4m N of Brackley, 2m to the W of A43, ½m SE of Helmdon Church. 3-acre garden in secluded rural setting; fine hedges incl yew topiary; mixed borders; lilacs, ancient mulberry tree; garden in process of being restored; young tree plantation. Small nursery with unusual plants. TEAS. *Adm £1.50 Chd free. Suns May 19, June 9 (1.30-5). Private visits welcome by prior appt, please* Tel 01280 850204

Finedon Gardens ❀ Wellingborough. 2m NE of Wellingborough on the A510, 6m SE Kettering on the A6. Teas in aid of Finedon Church, at Finedon Antique Centre. *Combined adm £1.50 Chd free. Sun May 12 (2-6)*
4 Harrowden Lane & (Mr & Mrs D J West) ½-acre garden on a steep slope, created since 1982 from waste land; lawns, rose and flower beds; ornamental fish pond with cascade fountain, aviary and greenhouses
23 Regent Street ❀ (Mr & Mrs G Perkins) ½-acre garden with raised lawn, mature trees, fruit trees. 2 large ponds with koi carp, golden orfe and terrapins; inc filter system. Aviaries, ducks and numerous pets. Free-flying budgerigars
Thingdon Cottage (Mrs M A Leach) 4½ acres of garden, originally Finedon Hall grounds. Lawns, ancient trees, shrubs, spring flowers, brook, hillside pasture with unique view of Finedon Hall and Church

Flore Gardens 7m W of Northampton, 5m E of Daventry on A45. Flower Festival at All Saints Church and U.R Chapel incl light lunches, Teas, plants, etc. *Combined adm £2 Chd free (Share to Flower Festival®). Sat, Sun June 22, 23 (11-6)*
Beech Hill ❀ (Dr & Mrs R B White) 1 acre facing S over the Nene Valley. Lawns, herbaceous and shrub borders with mature trees. There is a vegetable garden, an orchard, alpine house, cool greenhouse. Hanging baskets and tubs
The Croft (John & Dorothy Boast) ⅓-acre garden of C17 cottage with mature trees, shrubs, lawns and interesting perennials
The Grange ❀ (Mr & Mrs C R Buswell) Mature 2½-acre garden with lawns, trees, herbaceous beds, shrubs and pond. Partly suitable for wheelchairs
The Manor House ❀ (Richard & Wendy Amos) 1-acre garden with established lawns and herbaceous border surrounded by mature trees. Formal pond and walled kitchen garden. Partly suitable for wheelchairs
The Old Manor ❀ (Mr & Mrs Keith Boyd) Medium-sized garden of early C18 house comprising lawn, herbaceous border, rose garden, vegetables, fruit and paddock with pond and shrubs
9 Thornton Close ❀ (Mr & Mrs Dinsdale) Informal flowering shrub garden, incl rhododendrons. Variety of conifers and beginnings of a cranesbill collection

Gamekeepers Cottage Garden &❀❀ (Mr & Mrs D Daw) Cottesbrooke. 10m W of Northampton, nr Creaton on A50; nr Brixworth on A508. Cottage garden featuring unusual herbaceous plants, flowers for drying, fruit, vegetables. *For NGS only Combined adm £2 Chd £1 with* **Cottesbrooke Hall.** *Suns June 30, Aug 4 (2-6)*

Geddington Gardens 3m N of Kettering on the A43 Northampton-Stamford Rd. Attractive village with C13 Eleanor Cross. TEAS at **The Long Barn.** *Combined adm £2 Chd free (Share to The Samuel Lee Charity®). Sun June 23 (2-6)*
¶**11 Grafton Road** ❀❀ (Mr & Mrs D Whitworth) and ¶**15 Grafton Road** ❀ (Mrs M Spence) Adjoining gardens, ½-acre approx; mixed borders, shrubs, fruit and vegetable garden

Grange Farmhouse &% (Mr & Mrs D Slater) 1m from village on Grange Rd. ⅓-acre informal country garden. Lawns, mixed borders, climbing roses, reclaimed orchard

The Long Barn &% (Mr & Mrs A Gordon) 2-acre garden with fine mature trees, shrubs, herbaceous borders and lawns sweeping down to the river

Priory Cottage % (Mr & Mrs G Johns) Medium-sized, informal garden on 3 levels. Large variety of plants and shrubs.

¶**49 Queen Street** &% (Mr & Mrs D Steele) 1½-acres with attractive entrance, pergolas, paddock, stable yard, vegetable garden

Willow View &% (Mr & Mrs R Sallabanks) ⅕-acre garden newly developed; lawns, flower beds, vegetables, herb garden and patio. Access to **Wisteria Cottage** garden

Wisteria Cottage &% (Mr & Mrs Charles Lockwood) 1½-acre cottage garden with adjoining paddock under development, bordered by the Ise Brook. Access from **Willow View**

Great Addington Manor (Mr & Mrs G E Groome) Great Addington. 7m SE of Kettering, 4m W Thrapston, A510 exit off A14 signed Finedon and Wellingborough. Turn 2nd L to the Addingtons. 4½-acre manor gardens with lawns, mature trees, mulberry, yew hedges, pond and spinney. Spring daffodils. A garden being rejuvenated. Teas in Village Hall. *Adm £1.50 Chd over 5yrs 50p (Share to Great Addington Church Maintenance Fund®). Wed, Sun April 10, 14 (2-6). Private visits welcome during April only, please* Tel 01536 330204

1 The Green Kingsthorpe Village %® (Mrs D Nightingale). 2m N of Northampton Town Centre. Turn off A508 into Mill Lane at Cock Hotel, taking 2nd turn R. ⅓-acre well-established garden on steep slope, partly terraced. Planned for yr-round interest with a variety of shrubs, herbaceous and climbing plants; to be explored with many surprises. TEAS. *Adm £1.20 Chd 50p. Sun July 14 (12-5) Wed July 17 (2-6)*

Guilsborough and Hollowell Gardens 10m NW of Northampton between A50 - A428. 10m E of Rugby. Cream TEAS at **Dripwell House** by Guilsborough WI. Teas at Hollowell Village Hall. *Combined adm £1.50 Chd free. Sun May 19 (2-6). Private visits welcome for parties of 12 and over*

Dripwell House %® Guilsborough (Mr & Mrs J W Langfield, Dr C Moss, Mr & Mrs P G Moss) 2½-acre mature garden; many fine trees and shrubs on partly terraced slope. Rock garden, herbaceous border, herb garden. Some unusual shrubs and many rhododendrons and azaleas in woodland garden. Cream TEAS in garden. Tel 01604 740140

Gower House ® (Peter & Ann Moss) Small garden evolving since 1991 on part of Dripwell vegetable garden. A plantsman's garden with herbaceous alpine, climbing plants and shrubs. Tel 01604 740755

Rosemount, Hollowell &%® (Mr & Mrs J Leatherland) In centre of village, up hill behind bus shelter towards Church, entrance 100yds on R. ½-acre plantsman's garden reconstructed in 1982, unusual plants and shrubs, alpine garden, fish pond, small collections of clematis, conifers, camellias, daphne and abutilons.

Partly suitable for wheelchairs. Car parking and teas at village hall behind Church, Tel 01604 740354

The Haddonstone Show Garden, East Haddon Manor &%® (Mr & Mrs R Barrow) 10m N of Northampton, 12m S of Rugby, from A428. Walled garden on different levels, old shrub roses, ground cover plants, conifers, clematis and climbers; swimming pool surrounded by Haddonstone Colonnade, over 30 planted pots and containers: Special Spring opening April 14 (2-5) TEAS. Refreshments. Many specialist plant stands. Exhibition of flower paintings. *Adm £2 Chd free. Garden Festival Weekend Sun, Mon May 5, 6, (10-5). Adm £2 Chd free (Share to NSPCC)*

Harpole Gardens 4m W Northampton on A45 towards Weedon. Turn R at The Turnpike Hotel into Harpole. TEAS and stalls at The Close. The Gardens below are varied and unique, incl an old fashioned country garden, cactus and succulents, water gardens and unusual plants. *Combined adm £1.50 Chd free. Sun June 30 (2-6)*

The Close &%® (Mr & Mrs Orton Jones) 68 High Street

Darnley % (Mr & Mrs Peter Rixon) 47b High St

72 Larkhall Lane % (Mr & Mrs R G Murton)

¶**33 High St** (Mr S Orton Jones)

19 Manor Close % (Mr & Mrs E Kemshed)

Holdenby House ® (Mr & Mrs James Lowther) 7m NW of Northampton. Signposted from A50 and A428. Impressive remains of terrace gardens of Holdenby Palace, where Charles I was imprisoned; Elizabethan garden; fragrant and silver borders. Rare breeds farm animals; museum, falconry centre, armourer, C17 Homestead. TEAS. *Adm £2.75 (groups of 25 or more £2.25) OAP £2.25 Chd £1.75.* ▲*For NGS Sun May 12 (2-6)*

Irthlingborough &%® (Mr & Mrs D Ingall) 49 Finedon Rd. 5m E of Wellingborough, off the A6. A garden of approx 1 acre full of interest and unusual plants, incl spring bulbs, herbaceous border, shrubs, pools, gravel bed and rock garden, wild and scented areas. Also fruit and vegetables. TEAS in aid of Barnardos. *Adm £1 Chd free. For NGS Wed April 10, Sun June 16 (2-6). Private visits welcome between Easter and end of July, please* Tel 01933 650343

Litchborough Gardens % Nr Towcester, Litchborough village is mid-way between Northampton and Banbury. Teas in WI Hall. *Combined adm £2 Chd free (Share to Litchborough Baptist Church®). Sun June 2 (2-6.30)*

Bruyere Court, Farthingstone Rd & (Mr & Mrs R Martin) 4 acres of landscaped garden featuring lawns; 2 ornamental lakes with rock streams and fountain; shrub borders; rhododendron and azalea borders; herbaceous border; old-fashioned rose hedge; ornamental trees and conifers

Good Reste ® (Mr & Mrs J B Guy) Banbury Rd. An unusual late Victorian/Edwardian acre, with lawns, sunken stone gardens and grotto linked by York stone paths to shaded walks under old trees and shrubs incl venerable magnolia; thatched gazebo. Kitchen garden and orchard. Original layout intact with general renewal and replanting underway

The Hall & (Mr & Mrs A R Heygate) Large garden with open views of parkland; laid to lawns and borders with clipped hedges around the house; the extensive woodland garden has large numbers of specimen trees and shrubs; walks wind through this area and round the lakes

The Old Rectory (Mr & Mrs T R Sykes) Partly walled garden approx 1 acre with fishpond, mixed herbaceous and shrub borders, established heather bank surrounds newly planted raised beds. Small kitchen garden area. The garden is still being developed with new features each year

Orchard House ❀ (Mr & Mrs B Smith) Banbury Rd, Landscape architects country garden designed for low maintenance; orchard, pools, conservatory and working pump. *Private visits welcome by parties of less than 5, please* Tel 01327 830144

¶**The House on the Green** (Mr & Mrs K E Ellis) 1 Ivens Lane. ¼-acre cottage garden which includes well, summerhouse, water feature, rockery, variety of trees, shrubs, roses and bulbs; unusual garden foliage, flowering plants, herbs, soft fruit and apple, pear and plum trees

Stone End & (Mr & Mrs F Smith) Chapel Close. A recently developed garden of 2 acres with central rockery incorporating waterfall and pool planted with alpines; many flowering shrubs and views of surrounding country

Lois Weedon House ❀ (Sir John & Lady Greenaway) Weedon Lois. 7m from Towcester on the edge of Weedon Lois village. Pass through village going E towards Wappenham; as you leave village Lois Weedon House entrance on R, further on is 2nd entrance which has a lodge. Large garden with terraces and fine views; lawns; pergola; water garden; mature yew hedges; pond. TEAS. *Combined adm with* **The Old Barn** *£1.50 Chd free (Share to Lois Weedon PCC®). Sun May 26 (2-6)*

Maidwell Gardens ✕ 8m N of Northampton on A508, 6m S of Market Harborough. TEAS. *Adm £2 Chd free. Sun June 16 (2-6), Wed June 19 (10-6)*

    The Old Bake House (Ken & Angela Palmer) Small walled garden with herbaceous borders, shrubs, old fruit trees and a large gravel courtyard under redevelopment. Many plants are grown for preserving or drying for arrangements

    The Old Barn &❀ (Mr & Mrs John Groocock) ¾-acre garden developed around an old stone barn. Mixed herbaceous and shrub borders. Newly-planted area surrounding gazebo with clematis and roses.

    School Farmhouse & (Mr & Mrs D J Carter-Johnson) ¾-acre walled cottage garden brimful of traditional mid-summer flowering perennials

    Wisteria Cottage ✕❀ (Mr & Mrs P J Montgomery) A plantsman's cottage garden of approx ½ acre, developed over the last 7yrs. A series of rooms in themed colours, sunken garden, water feature, knot garden, herbaceous borders. *Private visits welcome, April 28 to Sept 29, for 2 and over, please* Tel 01604 686308

Maidwell Hall &❀ (Mr & Mrs P R Whitton, Maidwell Hall School) A508 N from Northampton, 6m S of Market Harborough, entrance via cattle grid on S fringe of Maid-

well village. 45 acres of lawns, playing fields, woodland. Colourful display of spring bulbs, magnolias and early flowering shrubs; mature rose garden; lake and arboretum. TEA. *Adm £2 Chd free (Share to St Mary's Church, Maidwell®). Sun April 21 (2-6). Private visits welcome April to July, Sept to Oct, please* Tel 01604 686234

The Menagerie &✕❀ (The Executors of the late G Jackson-Stops) On B526, 6m S of Northampton, 1m beyond Horton, turn L at lay-by, across field. These newly developed gardens are set around an C18 folly. Most recently completed is the Wetland Garden, planted with native material from the Horton park. The Vernal garden, now in its 4th year, uses spring bulbs, hellebores and early perennials under a canopy of spring flowering trees and shrubs. TEAS. *Adm £2.50 Chd £1. Thurs (10-4). House, garden and shell grotto open to parties by written appt. For NGS Sun June 23 (2-6)*

¶**Newnham Gardens** & 1m E of Daventry on B4037. Cream Teas in Village Hall. *Combined adm £2 Chd free. Sun May 26 (2-6) Wed May 29 (2-5)*

    ¶**The Cross** ✕❀ (M Dawkins) Manor Lane. A cottage garden incl wall plants, perennials, a few unusual plants and pond

    Newnham Grounds (Mr & Mrs Roy Hodges) 2-acres nature garden planted in late 20's on 3 levels with lovely view. Interesting shapes and paths, lime avenue, rose garden, early spring rockery

    ¶**Newnham Fields** ❀ (Mr & Mrs E R Mobbs) Church St. Plant enthusiast's small garden next to church, island beds, climbers, conifers, alpines. Rockery, 1 small pond

¶**Newnham Hall** &✕❀ (Mr & Mrs David Barrie) Newnham on B4037 1½m S of Daventry. 4-acre garden and parkland. Beautiful views, topiary walk, walled garden. Woodland walk around informal pond. Massed bulbs, autumn colour. TEAS. *Adm £2 Chd free. Suns April 14, Oct 13 (2-6)*

The Old Barn ✕❀ (Mr & Mrs John Gregory) Weedon Lois. Small ⅓-acre plantsman's garden designed by the owners to compliment converted C18 barn; with interesting selection of herbaceous perennials, climbing plants, shrub roses and gravel gardens. An interesting patchwork garden and unusual plants for sale. *Combined adm with* **Lois Weedon House** *£1.50 Chd free. Sun May 26 (2-6), and combined adm with* **Weedon Lois Gardens** *£1.50 Chd free Sun June 30 (2-6). Private visits welcome June to July, please* Tel 01327 860577

The Old Rectory, Sudborough &% (Mr & Mrs Huntington) Corby exit off A14. Village just off A6116 between Thrapston & Brigstock. Classic English country garden containing many rare and unusual plants which fill this 3-acre plantsman's garden surrounding a fine Georgian Rectory (not open). Features incl colour themed mixed and herbaceous borders; formal rose garden; shrubberies and pond; woodland walk; intricate potager designed by Rosemary Verey and developed by the owners with Rupert Golby. Many well planted containers; in March a comprehensive display of helleborus x orientalis (Lenten Rose) can be seen massed with spring bulbs. Featured in House & Garden, June 93. TEA (depending on weather) March 24, TEAS June 2, Aug 25. *Adm £2 (March) £2.50 (June and Aug) Chd free (Share to All Saints Church, Sudborough®). Suns April 7, May 12, 26, June 16, 23 (2-6). For NGS Suns March 24, June 2, Aug 25 (2-6). Private visits welcome, please* **Tel 01832 733247**

Preston Capes Gardens % Approx 7m S of Daventry, 3m N of Canon's Ashby. Homemade TEAS at **Old West Farm**. TEAS and plants in aid of St Peter's & St Paul's Church. *Combined adm £2 Chd 50p. Sun June 2 (2-6)*

    Archway Cottage (Mr & Mrs King) Approx ½-acre garden, with outstanding views over Northants countryside. Lawns with specimen shrubs, herbaceous borders and ornamental fish pond. Sloping plot converted to nature garden, with natural pond, marginal plants and berry-bearing trees and shrubs

    City Cottage &% (Mr & Mrs Gavin Cowen) A mature garden in the middle of an attractive village, with a walled herbaceous border, rose beds, flowering shrubs, wisteria and a newly planted sunken garden with unusual shrubs

    Old West Farm &% (Mr & Mrs Gerard Hoare) Little Preston. Between Charwelton (A361) and Maidford. 2-acre garden re-designed since 1980. Woodland area underplanted with shrubs and bulbs. Roses and borders designed for yr-round interest

Ravensthorpe Gardens Halfway between Rugby and Northampton. Signposted Ravensthorpe 1½m from the A428. TEAS in aid of Eric Hickman Memorial Fund at Ravensthorpe Nursery. *Combined adm £1.50 Chd free. Sun July 14 (2-6)*

    32 The High St (Mr & Mrs J Patrick) Moderate size garden planted over the last 8yrs. Mostly perennials but some shrubs and roses; also greenhouse and vegetables

    Lingles Farm & (Mr & Mrs A Mold) Large garden with mixed island beds

    Ravensthorpe Nursery &% (Mr & Mrs Richard Wiseman) Approx 1-acre new show garden being developed to display plants; wide range of shrubs, trees and hardy perennials, incl shrub rose and mixed borders with fine views; also private ¼-acre owners' plantsman's garden. *Also open Wed July 17 (6.30-9).* **Tel 01604 770548**

Sholebroke Lodge &% (A B X Fenwick Esq) Whittlebury, 3m S of Towcester. Turn off A413 Towcester end of Whittlebury village. 5-acre informal garden. Many interesting plants and walks through flowering shrubs. Pond planting and wall plants. Garden shop in old barn. Homemade TEAS. *Adm £2 Chd 50p. Sun May 26 (1-6)*

Slapton Gardens %% Slapton, a tiny village 4m W of Towcester ¼m N of the Towcester to Wappenham Rd. Superb small 13/14th century church, public footpath round village passing the Old Mill and stream. TEAS at Slapton Lodge. Car park by church. *Combined adm £1.50 Chd free. Sun June 9 (2-6)*

    Fellyard (Mr & Mrs R Owen) Mature 1½-acre garden with orchard, herbaceous and walled garden areas. Stream walk, new ha-ha and rose plantings. Some unusual specimen trees and shrubs. Large vegetable garden

    The Old Royal Oak (Mrs D Mumford) A garden for the gardener and plantsman, approx ⅓-acre, started from bare site 1989. Imaginative use of layout to take in different levels and difficult soil conditions. Trees, flowering shrubs, herbaceous, large cottage borders and scree bed

    Slapton Lodge (Mr & Mrs Webster) In beautiful grounds and parkland

The Spring House % (Mr & Mrs C Shepley-Cuthbert) Mill Lane, Chipping Warden on A361 between Banbury and Daventry. Garden originally laid out by Miss Kitty Lloyd Jones in the thirties and now mature. Approx 3 acres app through a 16' tapestry hedge. April-May spring flowers, bulbs and blossom. June-Sept bog and water garden at its most colourful. Other times unconventional borders, shrub roses and specimen trees with many new plantings. Ploughmans lunches and Teas available for groups & clubs by arrangement. *Private visits welcome April to Oct, please* **Tel 01295 660261**

¶Steane Park % (Sir Michael & Lady Connell) Brackley. On the N side of the A422 6m E of Banbury 3m W of Brackley. Beautiful trees in 80 acres of parkland, old water ways and fish pond, 1620 church in the garden. The garden has been remade over last 5 yrs, designed in sympathy with the old, stone house and church. TEAS. *Adm £1.20 Chd 50p. Sun May 12 (10-6)*

Stoke Park & (A S Chancellor Esq) Stoke Bruerne, Towcester. Stoke Bruerne village lies 1m off A508 between Northampton and Stony Stratford. Stoke Park is down a private road ¾m, 1st turning L, ¼m beyond village. Approx 3-acres. Terraced lawn with ornamental basin, orchard, herb garden, shrub and other borders, as setting to two C17 pavillions and colonnade. TEA. *Adm £1 Chd 50p.* ▲*Sun June 9 (2-6)*

Titchmarsh Gardens 2m N of Thrapston, 6m S of Oundle on A605, Titchmarsh signposted as turning to E. TEAS. *Combined adm £2 Chd free (Share to St Marys Church, Titchmarsh©). Mons April 8, May 27 (2-6)*

    Glebe Cottage &% (Mr & Mrs J Bussens) ⅓ acre; NE aspect; informal herbaceous and shrub borders and beds. Clematis in a variety of situations

    16 Polopit % (Mr & Mrs C Millard) ½ acre. Developed since 1984; rockeries, ornamental and herbaceous borders; fruit decorative shrubs

    Swallows &% (Mr & Mrs W Melvin) ⅓-acre informal garden with rockery, fish and lily ponds, mixed beds leading to vegetable area. Panoramic view of open countryside

Titchmarsh House ⅋✗ (Mr & Mrs Ewan Harper) 4 acres extended and laid out since 1972; cherries, magnolias, herbaceous irises; shrub roses, clematis, range of wall shrubs, walled borders

Turweston Mill ✗ (Mr & Mrs Harry Leventis) A43 from Oxford, in Brackley turn R at traffic lights. A422 towards Buckingham, 1m turn L signposted Turweston. 5 acres, mill stream, water garden, lawns. *Combined adm with* **Versions Farm** *£1.50 Chd free. Sun June 9 (2-6)*

Versions Farm ⅋✗❀ (Mrs E T Smyth-Osbourne) Brackley 2m N of Brackley on the Turweston Rd. 3-acres plantsman's garden; old stone walls; terraces; old-fashioned rose garden; iris border; shrubs and trees some unusual; pond. Conservatory. Cream TEAS. *Combined adm £1.50 Chd free with* **Turweston Mill** *(Share to Whitfield Church®). Sun June 9 (2-6). Parties welcome by appt May to July, please* **Tel 01280 702412**

The Walnuts, King's Cliffe (Mr & Mrs Martin Lawrence). 7m NE of Oundle, 7m SW of Stamford, 4m W of Wansford from A1 and A47; last house on L leaving King's Cliffe on rd to Apethorpe. 2½-acre country garden with lawns, mature trees and hedges, mixed herbaceous and shrub borders, sunken rose garden. Mown pathway through meadow to pond, R Willowbrook and woodland walk. TEAS in aid of All Saints Church. *Adm £1.50 Chd free. Sun April 28, Wed May 1 (2-5). Private visits welcome, please* **Tel 01780 470312**

Weedon Lois Gardens Nr Towcester. 8m W of Towcester. TEAS. *Combined adm £1.50 Chd free. Sun June 30 (2-6)*
    Elizabeth House ✗❀ (Mr & Mrs A Cartwright) A C17 vicarage garden of 1½ acres. Herbaceous beds, a walled vegetable garden and wild wooded area
    The Old Barn ✗❀ (Mr & Mrs John Gregory) See under **The Old Barn**

West Haddon Gardens As seen on BBC TV in 1992. The village is on the A428 between Rugby and Northampton and lies 4m E of M1 exit 18. Teas in village hall. *Com-*

bined adm £2 Chd free (Share to West Haddon Parish Church and West Haddon Baptist Church©). Sun July 7 (2-6)
    Beech Trees ✗ (Gerald & Daphne Kennaird) Small partially walled garden with views over rolling Northamptonshire countryside. Terrace, lawns, mixed borders and small pond
    Hardays House ⅋ (Guy Ballantyne) 1½ acres, lawns and shrubbery on sloping ground with S-facing views, pond, vegetable garden, flower beds
    Lime House ✗ (Leslie and David Roberts) ½-acre of walled garden with rockeries, herbaceous borders, walk-through shrubbery, rose beds; croquet lawn. Summerhouse and patio with greenhouse
    The Mews ✗ (Rob and Jane Dadley) ½-acre of secluded walled garden including lawns, secret garden, herbaceous border, formal and informal ponds, statuary and pergolas
    The Shambles ✗ (Jan & Frank Penrose) Large country garden on several levels with mixed beds and borders, pond with ducks and small cottage garden
    Well Cottage ✗ (Sandra and Roger Woodcock) Very small walled garden on various levels displaying many containers, pond and a variety of plants
    ¶6 West End ✗ (Jill & Graham Lord) Large informal gardens with greenhouses, pond and many baskets and containers

Wilby Gardens. 3m SW of Wellingborough on the A4500 to Northampton signposted Wilby. TEAS at The Old Chapel. *Combined adm £1.50 Chd free. Sun June 30 (2-6)*
    ¶The Farm ⅋✗ (Mr & Mrs R H Thompson) ½-acre old-walled farm garden to its original pattern. Herbs, vegetable garden, fruit trees, roses and clematis
    7 Mears Ashby Road ✗ (Mr & Mrs K H Coleman) Small garden containing shrubs and herbaceous borders. Variety of plants in containers, plenty of colour
    Wilby Cottage ❀ (Mrs B K Gale) Well established cottage garden, surrounded by walls and hedge, shrubs, herbaceous border, rockery and tubs, a plantsman's garden

---

Open by appointment Please do not be put off by this notation. The owner may consider his garden too small to accommodate the numbers associated with a normal opening or, more often, there may be a lack of car parking space. It is often more rewarding than a normal opening as the owner will usually give a guided tour of the garden. The minimum size of party is either stated in the garden description or can be found out when making the appointment; usually 2. If the garden has normal open days, the entrance fee is as stated in the garden description.

Northumberland & Tyne and Wear

Hon County Organiser: Mrs G Baker Cresswell, Preston Tower, Chathill, Northumberland NE67 5DH
Tel 01665 589210

Assistant Hon County Organiser: Mrs T Sale, Ilderton Glebe, Ilderton, Alnwick, Northumberland NE66 4YD
Tel 01668 217293

DATES OF OPENING

April 10 Wednesday
Bide-a-Wee Cottage,
Netherwitton, Morpeth
April 14 Sunday
Ashfield, Hebron
April 21 Sunday
66 Darras Road, Ponteland
Preston Tower, Chathill
May 12 Sunday
Wallington, Morpeth
May 19 Sunday
66 Darras Road, Ponteland
Lilburn Tower, Alnwick
May 26 Sunday
Belsay Hall, Castle & Gardens
May 29 Wednesday
Bide-a-Wee Cottage,
Netherwitton, Morpeth
June 2 Sunday
Ashfield, Hebron
Chillingham Castle, Chillingham
June 8 Saturday
Chipchase Castle, Wark-on-Tyne
June 16 Sunday
Chesters, Humshaugh
Hexham Herbs, Chesters Walled
Garden, nr Hexham

June 20 Thursday
Herterton House, Morpeth
June 22 Saturday
Kirkley Hall Gardens, Ponteland
June 23 Sunday
66 Darras Road, Ponteland
Kirkley Hall Gardens, Ponteland
June 30 Sunday
Berryburn, Ancroft
Kirkwhelpington Village Gardens
Mindrum, Cornhill on Tweed
July 3 Wednesday
Bridge House, Fox Covert Lane,
Ponteland
July 7 Sunday
Hartford Bridge House, nr Bedlington
Northumbria Nurseries, Walled
Gardens, Ford,
Berwick-upon-Tweed
Ravenside, East Heddon,
Heddon-on-the-Wall
July 10 Wednesday
Bridge House, Fox Covert Lane,
Ponteland
July 14 Sunday
49 Coronation Terrace, Ashington
July 17 Wednesday
Bridge House, Fox Covert Lane,
Ponteland

July 18 Thursday
Herterton House, Morpeth
July 24 Wednesday
Bide-a-Wee Cottage,
Netherwitton, Morpeth
Bridge House, Fox Covert Lane,
Ponteland
July 28 Sunday
49 Coronation Terrace, Ashington
Cragside, Rothbury
Kiwi Cottage, Scremerston
August 8 Thursday
Herterton House, Morpeth
August 18 Sunday
66 Darras Road, Ponteland
September 8 Sunday
Belsay Hall, Castle & Gardens

By appointment only
For telephone numbers and other details see garden descriptions. Private visits welcomed

Loughbrow House, Hexham

DESCRIPTIONS OF GARDENS

Ashfield ✿❀ (B & R McWilliam) Hebron. S side of Hebron 3m N of Morpeth. Hebron is ½m E of the A1. Turn 1st R, N of the Morpeth by-pass and A697 (Wooler) junction. The garden extends to 5 acres and is in course of development. The area close to the house has many bulbs, a collection of alpines, herbaceous and mixed borders. A woodland garden is being developed and collections of sorbus, acer and betula are planned. TEAS. *Adm £1 Chd free. Suns April 14, June 2 (1.30-5). Private visits welcome, please Tel 01670 515616*

Belsay Hall, Castle & Gardens &❀ (English Heritage) Ponteland. Belsay village lies 14m NW of Newcastle-upon-Tyne, on the A696 [OS map 88. Ref NZ 082785]. 30 acres newly restored C19 garden incl formal terraces; large heather garden; rhododendrons, rare trees & shrubs. Quarry garden covering several acres. Belsay Hall & Castle within the grounds. TEAS and refreshments. *Adm (incl Hall and Castle) £3 Concessions £2.30 Chd £1.50. Suns May 26, Sept 8 (10-6). Private parties welcome, please Tel 01661 881636*

Berryburn ✿❀ (Mr & Mrs W J Rogers-Coltman) Ancroft. 5m S of Berwick. Take Ancroft Mill Rd off A1 for 1m; drive entrance 2nd turn on R beside council bridge. 4 acres created from wilderness since 1981. Mixed borders; shrubs; shrub roses; woodland walk alongside burn with progressive tree planting. Partially suited for wheelchairs. TEA. *Adm £1.50 Chd free. Sun June 30 (2-5). Private visits welcome, please Tel 01289 387332*

Bide-a-Wee Cottage ✿❀ (M Robson) Stanton. 7m NNW of Morpeth. Turn L off A192 out of Morpeth at Fairmoor. Stanton is 6m along this road. Both a formal and informal garden developed out of a small stone quarry as well as some surrounding higher land. Natural rock is featured as are water and marsh areas. Garden contains mixed planting with a large number of perennial species. *Adm £1.75. Weds April 10, (1.30-4), May 29, July 24 (2-5)*

Bridge House &&✿ (Dr & Mrs J C White) Fox Covert Lane, Ponteland. 8m NW of Newcastle. Just off A696, last L turn before leaving Ponteland village (travelling W). ¼m down Fox Covert Lane. 1¼-acre garden. Incl riverside planting, vegetable garden, herbs, mixed borders and summer meadow. Winner of 'Northumbria in Bloom' 1993 – Best Garden open to the public. TEAS. Adm £1.50 Chd free. Weds July 3, 10, 17, 24 (2-5). Private visits welcome, please **Tel 01661 823780**

Chesters &✿ (Mr & Mrs G J K Benson) Humshaugh. 5m N of Hexham. ½m W of Chollerford on B6318. Curved terraced border in front of C18 house with 1891 wings designed by Norman Shaw. Herbaceous borders, rock garden, lawns overlooking ha-ha and parkland with fine views over the North Tyne. TEA. *Combined adm with* **Hexham Herbs, Chesters Walled Garden** *£1.50 Chd under 10 free. Sun June 16 (1-5)*

Chillingham Castle ✿✿ (Sir Humphry Wakefield) Chillingham. N from Alnwick, S from Berwick-upon-Tweed. Parkland landscaped with avenues and lodges by Sir Geoffrey de Wyattville fresh from his Royal triumph at Windsor in 1828. Lake and woodland walks with fine specimen trees. Moats removed and gardens brought up to castle 1752. Italian and French topiary garden with largest herbaceous border in N England restored with urns and fountains. TEAS. *Adm £3.50 OAPs £2.50 Chd free.* ▲*For NGS Sun June 2 (12-5).* **Tel 01668 215359**

Chipchase Castle &✿✿ (Mrs P J Torday) Wark-on-Tyne. Situated on the E banks of the North Tyne, 10m N of Hexham, between Barrasford and Wark. It can be approached via A68, taking the exit to Hexham-Barrasford N of Corbridge or via A69 turning onto the A6079, then take minor rd to Barrasford. Approx 3 acres; incl a walled vegetable garden and orchard, woodland garden, pond and formal borders. The gardens are approached through a second walled garden which is dedicated to the sale of specialist herbaceous plants. *House open Adm £2. June only (2-5). Thurs, Fri, Sat, Sun April 1 to July 31 incl Bank Hol Mons (10-5). For NGS Adm £1.50 Chd 50p. Sat June 8 (10-5)*

49 Coronation Terrace ✿✿ (Sean & Eileen Murray) Ashington. From Ashington Town Centre, down North Seaton Rd across mini roundabout, L at North Seaton Hotel. Created since 1989 from scratch. Approx 100' × 20', colour-themed cottage garden with perennials, shrubs and climbers. Small lawn onto curving brick path which leads to small raised pool and arbour. Conservatory. TEAS. *Adm £1 Chd 50p (Shore to St Oswalds Hospice Gosforth®). Suns July 14, 28 (2-5)*

Cragside ✿✿ (The National Trust) Rothbury, 13m SW of Alnwick (B6341); 15m NW of Morpeth (B6344). Formal garden in the 'High Victorian' style created by the 1st Lord Armstrong with special features incl fully restored orchard house, carpet bedding, dahlia walk and fernery. 3½ acres of rock garden surrounding the House and a pinetum and valley garden beside the Debdon Burn. Extensive grounds of over 1000 acres famous for rhododendrons and beautiful lakes. House designed by Richard Norman Shaw, containing original furniture and paintings. The 1st house in the world to be lit by electricity gener-

ated by water power. Restaurant. Shop. Grounds, Power Circuit and Armstrong Energy Centre. TEAS. *Adm House, Garden & Grounds £5.60; Garden & Grounds £3.60 Chd £1.80. Family ticket House, Garden & Grounds (2 adults & 2 chd) £14.* ▲*For NGS Sun July 28 (10.30-6.30). Large parties by appt, please* **Tel 01669 620333**

66 Darras Road &✿ (Mr & Mrs D J Goodchild) Ponteland. SW of A696 at Ponteland. Turn L after crossing the R Pont. Travelling W, signposted Darras Hall. 1m on R. Medium-sized garden, owner designed and maintained, with herbaceous and shrub borders incl some unusual varieties. Conifers, kitchen garden, water garden and greenhouses. Bulbs in spring. TEA. *Adm £1.50 Chd free. Suns April 21, May 19, June 23, Aug 18 (2-6)*

Hartford Bridge House ✿✿ (Dr & Mrs F J B Taylor) Bedlington. On A1068/A192 where it crosses R Blyth, opposite Plessey Woods Country Park. 2m S of Bedlington. Parking as directed on the day. 1¼-acre garden sloping down to river with a large variety of trees and shrubs and woodland walk; old-fashioned roses; herbaceous beds, rock garden and pond. TEAS. *Adm £1.50 Chd free. Sun July 7 (2-5)*

Herterton House ✿✿ (Frank Lawley Esq) Hartington. Cambo, Morpeth. 2m N of Cambo on the B6342 signposted to Hartington. (23m NW of Newcastle-on-Tyne). 1 acre of formal garden in stone walls around a C16 farmhouse. Incl a small topiary garden, physic garden, flower garden and a nursery garden. Planted since 1976. *Adm £1.60 Chd free.* ▲*For NGS Thurs June 20, July 18, Aug 8 (1.30-5.30)*

Hexham Herbs, Chesters Walled Garden &✿✿ Chollerford. 6m N of Hexham, just off the B6318. ½m W of Chollerford roundabout, past the entrance to Chesters Roman Fort, take L turning signposted Fourstones and immediately L through stone gateposts. 2-acre walled garden containing a very extensive collection of herbs. Raised thyme bank, home to the National Thyme Collection, Roman garden; National Collection of Marjoram. Elizabethan-style knot garden, gold and silver garden and collection of dye plants. Herbaceous borders contain many unusual plants and old-fashioned roses. Woodland walk with wildflowers and pond. Hexham Herbs won a large gold medal at National Garden Festival, Gateshead 1990 and featured on BBC2's 'Gardener's World' and Channel 4's 'Over the Garden Wall'. Shop sells herbal gifts, honey and dried flowers. TEA. *Combined adm with* **Chesters** *£1.50 Chd under 10 free. Sun June 16 (1-5)*

Kirkley Hall Gardens &✿✿ (Dr R McParlin) Ponteland. 2½m NW of Ponteland on C151 to Morpeth. Turn L at main college entrance. Car park. These beautiful gardens and Victorian walled garden form a showcase for the gardening enthusiast. Walled garden with climbers, wall-trained fruit trees, borders and unusual and colourful herbaceous plants all grouped and labelled. Grounds contain shaped island beds following the contours of the land each composed for variety of profile and continuity of colour. TEA. *Adm £1.50 OAPs 70p family £3 Chd under 8 free. Sat, Sun June 22, 23 (10-4). Private visits welcome, please* **Tel 01661 860808**

Kirkwhelpington Village Gardens ✕❀ On A696 approx 10m N of Belsay. Turn R into village. A number of small gardens in an attractive village. Each garden entirely different with something of interest for everyone. Teas in village hall. *Combined adm £1.50 Chd 50p tickets at village hall (Share to village hall fund®). Sun June 30 (2-5)*

> **Cliff House** (Mr & Mrs I Elliot)
> **3 The Green** (Mrs K Buchanan)
> **The School House** (Mr & Mrs F Young)
> **Sike View** (Prof & Mrs D Kinniment)
> **Welburn** (Prof D Wise)
> **West House** (Mr & Mrs C Sott)
> **Whitridge House** (Mr & Dr C Keating)

Kiwi Cottage ✕❀ (Mrs D Smail) Scremerston. Kiwi Cottage is in the village of Scremerston, about 2½m due S of Berwick-upon-Tweed. It is the 1st house on the R hand side of the village, off the A1 rd coming from the S and the last house on the L hand side of the village when travelling S from Berwick-upon-Tweed. Entrance through gateway next to War Memorial. Please drive in and do not park on the rd. 3-acre garden with lawns, annuals, herbaceous plants, providing colour and interest throughout the year. Shrubs, orchard and large vegetable garden. *Adm £1.50 Chd 50p. Sun July 28 (2.30-5)*

Lilburn Tower ✕ (Mr & Mrs D Davidson) Alnwick. 3m S of Wooler on A697. 10 acres of walled and formal gardens incl conservatory and large glass house. About 30 acres of woodland with walks and pond garden. Also ruins of Pele Tower and C15 Chapel. Rhododendrons and azaleas. TEAS. *Adm £1.25 Chd 25p under 5 free. Sun May 19 (2-6)*

Loughbrow House ও✕❀ (Mrs K A Clark) Hexham. Take B6306 from Hexham fork R, lodge gates in intersection of 2nd fork, ½m up drive. 5 acres; woodland garden; herbaceous borders, roses, wide lawns; kitchen garden. *Adm £1.50 Chd 50p. Private visits welcome, please Tel 01434 603351*

Mindrum ❀ (Hon P J Fairfax) Cornhill on Tweed. On B6352, 4m from Yetholm, 5m from Cornhill on Tweed. Old-fashioned roses; rock and water garden; shrub borders. Wonderful views along Bowmont Valley. Approx 2 acres. TEAS. *Adm £1.50 Chd 50p. Sun June 30 (2-6). Private visits welcome, please Tel 01890 850246*

Northumbria Nurseries, Walled Gardens ও❀ (Northumbria Nurseries) Ford. Follow the flower signs on the brown Ford Etal Heritage signs to Ford village, 10m N of Wooler, off A697. 1¾-acre walled garden incl display beds and growing areas. Teas available in village. *Open all year Mon to Fri (8-6, or dusk), March to Oct Sat, Sun (10-6, or dusk). Donations for NGS Sun July 7 (10-6)*

Preston Tower ও✕❀ (Maj & Mrs T Baker Cresswell) Chathill. 7m N of Alnwick, take the turn signed to Preston and Chathill. Preston Tower is at the top of a hill, in 1¼m. Mostly shrubs and woodland; daffodils and azaleas. C14 Pele Tower with great views from the top. TEAS. *Adm £1.50 Chd 50p (Share to local church®). Sun April 21 (2-5). Parties by appt, please Tel 016655 89210*

¶**Ravenside** ✕❀ (Mrs J Barber) East Heddon. 9m from Newcastle on the A69 take the Heddon on the Wall B6528 turn off, at end of slip rd turn R under bridge then L to East Heddon. 3rd house on R. ⅓-acre plantswoman's garden filled with shrubs, shrub roses, herbaceous borders, alpine, many in troughs and pond with bog area. TEAS. *Adm £1.50 Chd free. Sun July 7 (2-5)*

Wallington ও❀ (The National Trust) Cambo. From N 12m W of Morpeth (B6343); from S via A696 from Newcastle, 6m W of Belsay, B6342 to Cambo. Walled, terraced garden with fine shrubs and species roses; conservatory with magnificent fuchsias; 100 acres woodland and lakes. House dates from 1688 but altered and interior greatly changed c.1740; exceptional rococo plasterwork by Francini brothers; fine porcelain, furniture, pictures, needlework, dolls' houses, museum, display of coaches. Restaurant. Shop. *Adm to Walled garden, garden and grounds £2.30 Chd £1.15. Last admission (5). For NGS Sun May 12 (10-7)*

SYMBOLS USED IN THIS BOOK (See also Page 15)

‡   Following a garden name in the Dates of Opening list indicates that those gardens sharing the same symbol are nearby and open on the same day.

‡‡   Indicates a second series of nearby gardens open on the same day.

¶   Opening for the first time.

❀   Plants/produce for sale if available.

ও   Gardens with at least the main features accessible by wheelchair.

✕   No dogs except guide dogs but otherwise dogs are usually admitted, provided they are kept on a lead. Dogs are not admitted to houses.

●   Gardens marked thus do not necessarily give all their takings to the National Gardens Scheme. Instead they give a guaranteed contribution.

▲   Where this sign appears alongside dates in the descriptive entry for a garden it denotes that this garden is also open regularly to the public on days other than those for the NGS.

Nottinghamshire

Hon County Organisers: Mr & Mrs A R Hill, The White House, Nicker Hill, Keyworth, Nottinghamshire NG12 5EA Tel 0115 9372049

Assistant Hon County Organisers: Mr & Mrs J Nicholson, 38 Green Lane, Lambley, Nottingham NG4 4QE Tel 0115 9312998

Hon County Treasurer: Mr J Gray, 43 Cliffway, Radcliffe-on-Trent, Nottinghamshire NG12 1AQ Tel 0115 9334272

DATES OF OPENING

March 31 Sunday
Skreton Cottage, Screveton
April 3 Wednesday
The Willows, Radcliffe-on-Trent
April 7 Sunday
Hodsock Priory, Blyth
St Helen's Croft, Halam
April 8 Monday
Gateford Hill Nursing Home, nr Worksop
Holme Pierrepont Hall, Nottingham
The Old Rectory, Kirkby in Ashfield
April 11 Thursday
Springwell House, Brinkley
April 14 Sunday
Felley Priory, Underwood
37 Loughborough Road, Ruddington
April 17 Wednesday
Mill Hill House, East Stoke
April 21 Sunday
Morton Hall, Retford
April 24 Wednesday
38 Green Lane, Lambley
May 5 Sunday
The Chaff Barn, Post Office, Redmile
Colley Hill Cottage, Gringley on the Hill
Greenways, Bathley
Mill Hill House, East Stoke
Morton Hall, Retford
14 Temple Drive, Nuthall
May 6 Monday
Holme Pierrepont Hall, Nottingham
May 8 Wednesday
Hazel Cottage, Treswell, nr Retford
May 9 Thursday
7 Barratt Lane, Attenborough
May 11 Saturday
7 Barratt Lane, Attenborough
May 12 Sunday
7 Barratt Lane, Attenborough
St Helen's Croft, Halam ‡
Springwell House, Brinkley ‡
May 13 Monday
7 Barratt Lane, Attenborough

May 15 Wednesday
Rose Cottage, 82 Main Road, Underwood
May 18 Saturday
Epperstone Gardens
May 19 Sunday
17 Bridle Road, Burton Joyce ‡
Epperstone Gardens ‡
61 Lambley Lane, Burton Joyce ‡
144 Lambley Lane, Burton Joyce ‡
May 22 Wednesday
38 Green Lane, Lambley
May 26 Sunday
Bracken House, Caythorpe
Gateford Hall, nr Worksop ‡
Morton Hall, Retford ‡
Papplewick Gardens, Papplewick
May 27 Monday
Mill Hill House, East Stoke
The White House, Keyworth
June 2 Sunday
Cream Cottage, Misterton
Park Farm, Normanton
Springwell House, Brinkley
June 6 Thursday
7 Barratt Lane, Attenborough
June 8 Saturday
7 Barratt Lane, Attenborough
June 9 Sunday
7 Barratt Lane, Attenborough
Holmes Villa, Walkeringham
Rose Cottage, 82 Main Road, Underwood
Southwell, Bishops Manor
June 10 Monday
7 Barratt Lane, Attenborough
June 12 Wednesday
Mill Hill House, East Stoke
June 16 Sunday
The Chaff Barn, Post Office, Redmile
Gardeners Cottage, Papplewick
37 Loughborough Road, Ruddington
The Manor House, Gonalston
Wednesday 19 June
Gardeners Cottage, Papplewick
June 23 Sunday
Cream Cottage, Misterton
Field House Nursing Home, Radcliffe-on-Trent

Flintham Hall, Flintham, nr Newark
St Helen's Croft, Halam
June 25 Tuesday
St Helen's Croft, Halam
June 26 Wednesday
Hazel Cottage, Treswell, nr Retford
June 30 Sunday
12 Dunster Road, West Bridgford
Felley Priory, Underwood
Skreton Cottage, Screveton
July 7 Sunday
Holme Pierrepont Hall, Nottingham
Rose Cottage, 82 Main Road, Underwood
Sutton Bonington Hall, Sutton Bonington ‡
Thrumpton Hall, Nottingham ‡
July 14 Sunday
Brackenhurst College, Southwell
Mill Hill House, East Stoke
14 Temple Drive, Nuthall
July 21 Sunday
The White House, Keyworth
August 6 Tuesday
Hodsock Priory, Blyth
August 7 Wednesday
Hodsock Priory, Blyth
Mill Hill House, East Stoke
August 8 Thursday
Hodsock Priory, Blyth
August 11 Sunday
Rose Cottage, 82 Main Road, Underwood
August 15 Thursday
Springwell House, Brinkley
September 8 Sunday
Rose Cottage, 82 Main Road, Underwood
September 11 Wednesday
Mill Hill House, East Stoke
September 15 Sunday
St Helen's Croft, Halam
September 18 Wednesday
Springwell House, Brinkley
October 6 Sunday
Springwell House, Brinkley
October 13 Sunday
Morton Hall, Retford

**October 16 Wednesday to
October 22 Tuesday incl**
St Helen's Croft, Halam

Regular openings
For details see garden description

Felley Priory, Underwood
Hodsock Priory, Blyth
Holme Pierrepont Hall, Nottingham

The National Gardens Scheme is
a charity which traces its origins
back to 1927. Since then it has
raised a total of over £14 million
for charitable purposes.

DESCRIPTIONS OF GARDENS

7 Barratt Lane ৬❀ (Mrs D Lucking & Mr & Mrs S J
Hodkinson) Attenborough. Beeston, 6m SW of Nottingham. Off A6005 nr Attenborough Station. ¾-acre established plantsman's garden featured in 'Garden Answers'
1992 & 1993. Mature trees, unusual flowering shrubs,
bulbs, hostas and bearded irises. *Adm £1 Chd 40p (Share
to Nottinghamshire Wildlife Trust®). Thurs May 9, June 6
(3-8) Sat, Sun May 11, 12, June 8, 9 (11-6) Mons May 13,
June 10 (3-8)*

Bracken House ৬✄ (Mr & Mrs A Wheelhouse) Caythorpe. Approx 9m NE Nottingham. A612 to Lowdham at
Magna Carta Inn. Follow signs Caythorpe, immed over
level-Xing turn L Caythorpe Rd. Through village 1½m
past Black Horse Inn, Brackenhill on L. Park at bottom on
main rd. Last house up Brackenhill. Approx ¼-acre garden. Re-designed 1991. Colourful densely planted mixed
borders and rockeries with shrubs and bulbs, small pond.
Picturesque views over open countryside and Trent valley. TEAS in aid of St Aidans Church, Caythorpe. *Adm
£1.20 Chd free. Sun May 26 (2-5.30)*

Brackenhurst College ৬❀ (The Secretary) Southwell.
Brackenhurst 1m S of Southwell on A612. Ornamental
shrubs, lawns, rose, sunken, and walled gardens, glasshouses, views. Organic vegetable plot. Wheelchair users
please notify in advance. Careers information. TEAS. *Adm
£1.50 Chd 50p. Sun July 14 (2-6)*

17 Bridle Road ৬❀ (Mr & Mrs C P Bates) Burton Joyce.
In Burton Joyce turn N off A612, Nottingham to Southwell Rd, into Lambley Lane, Bridle Rd ½m on R, an impassable looking rd. 1-acre mixed borders, woodland
slopes, stream and water garden with naturalised ferns,
primulas, hostas and moisture loving plants. Terrace and
orchard with spring and summer bulbs in grass. *Adm £1
Chd free (Share to St Helens Church, Burton Joyce®). Sun
May 19 (2-6). Private visits welcome at weekends, please*
Tel 0115 9313725

The Chaff Barn ✄ (Mr & Mrs D Maddock) Redmile. 1m
N of Belvoir Castle. From A52 turn S by Haven Hotel
signed Belvoir Castle and Redmile. Post Office Lane is
past Peacock and Windmill Inns on LH-side. Park in main
st. ⅓-acre created from stackyard since 1987. Features
native plants encouraged to self seed with birds and wildlife in mind. Pond, herbs, old roses, herbaceous, spring
bulbs, trees and shrubs. Enclosed garden with terrace,
green courtyard and conservatories. TEAS. *Adm £1 Chd
25p. Suns May 5, June 16 (1.30-5.30)*

Colley Hill Cottage ✄❀ (Mrs Sue Tallents) Gringley on
the Hill. 6m E of Bawtry. 5m W of Gainsborough on A631.
A densely planted, small cottage garden, created by the
owner with flower arranging and nature in mind; raised
beds; small pond and herbaceous area; some unusual
plants and shrubs. Also alpines, spring bulbs and ferns.
TEAS in aid of Gringley Church. *Adm £1 Chd 50p. Sun
May 5 (2-6)*

Cream Cottage ✄❀ (Susan & Philip Cross) Misterton.
Approx 7m NW Gainsborough. Follow the A161 to Goole,
continue through Misterton, Cream Cottage on R, approx
⅓m after church. Walled cottage garden. Cottage dates
from early C18. Re-designed and planted 1992 by present owners. Contains many traditional and some unusual
cottage garden plants in mixed borders incl selection of
hardy geraniums and species clematis. Herb bed, evergreen border, wildlife pond and formal fish pond. TEAS.
Adm £1 Chd free. Suns June 2, 23 (1-6)

12 Dunster Road ✄❀ (Mr & Mrs M Jones) West Bridgford. Approx 2m S of Nottingham. From Trent Bridge follow A606 Melton Rd. Approx 1m turn L into Burleigh Rd,
400yds turn 4th R into Dunster Rd. 90' × 30' garden developed since 1989. Mixed borders with varied trees,
shrubs and perennials especially penstemons, pinks, rhododendrons, alpines and climbers. Small woodland bed,
patio and summerhouse. Ornamental pond, bog area and
numerous containers. *Adm £1 Chd 25p (Share to Alzheimer's Disease Society®). Sun June 30 (2-5)*

Epperstone Gardens 8m NE Nottingham off A6097 between Lowdham and Oxton. TEAS at White Gates. *Combined adm £1.50 Chd free (Share to Epperstone Village
Hall Fund©). Sat, Sun May 18, 19 (2-6)*
    The Old Rectory ❀ (Mr & Mrs Cedric Coates) Enter
from churchyard. Approx 2 acres mature garden in
superb setting incl lawns, borders, spring bulbs, mature yews forming 'The Dark Walk'. Lovely sculptured
large box hedge
    White Gates ৬ (Mrs V Pilsworth) 2 acres rhododendrons, azaleas, heathers, shrubbery, herbs and orchard. Parking in field opp White Gates

Felley Priory ৬❀ (The Hon Mrs Chaworth Musters)
Underwood. 8m SW Mansfield, leave M1 junction 27,
take A608, entrance is ½m W of M1. Old-fashioned garden round Elizabethan house. Orchard of daffodils, herbaceous borders, pond. Topiary, rose garden, featured in
Good Garden Guide and Gardeners Year Book; unusual
plants for sale. Refreshments. *Adm £1.50 Chd free. Weds
Feb 14, 28, March 13, 27, April 10, 24, May 8, 22, June
12, 26, July 10, 24, Aug 14, 28, Sept 11, 25, Oct 9, 23 (9-
4). For NGS Suns April 14, June 30 (11-4). Private visits
welcome for parties of 15 min, please* **Tel 01773 810230**

Field House Nursing Home ᕴᕗᕤ (Mr & Mrs R C Pring) 11 Main Road, Radcliffe-on-Trent. 6m E Nottingham. Follow A52 and turn N into Radcliffe-on-Trent. Opp Co-op supermarket, turn into Radcliffe Health Centre car park. 1-acre garden with many specimen conifers and rare shrubs. Large conservatory, colourful bedding schemes; thatched cottage reconstructed from old materials in 1987 within grounds; and set in a typical cottage garden. Cream TEAS. *Adm £1 Chd 25p (Share to Residents' Comfort Fund©). Sun June 23 (2-6). Private visits welcome, please* **Tel 0115 9335811**

Flintham Hall ᕤ (Myles Thoroton Hildyard Esq) 6m SW of Newark on A46. Large garden, herbaceous border, shrub roses, wilderness, fine trees, park, lake, in Vale of Belvoir, woodland walk. Important Lucombe oaks, Regency pheasantry, unique conservatory. Mansion (not open), church adjacent. Leaflet free. TEAS in courtyard. *Adm £1.50 Chd 50p (Share to St Augustines Church, Flintham®). Sun June 23 (2-5.30)*

Gardeners Cottage ᕴᕗᕤ (Mr & Mrs J Hildyard) Papplewick; nr Papplewick Hall. 6m N of Nottingham off A60. Interesting old-fashioned garden of 1½ acres with 150yd long border, shrub and rhododendrons; shrub rose garden. Large rockery and water feature; scree beds. TEAS (June 16) TEA (June 19). *Adm £1.50 Chd 25p. Sun, Wed June 16, 19 (2-6)*

The Gardens of Plungar See Leicestershire & Rutland

Gateford Hall ᕗᕤ (Roland Machin Esq) Worksop. 1m NW of Worksop on the A57. Surrounded by a moat, is of mediaeval foundation with C16 and C17 additions. Garden is quite new and being created on 3 sides of the house, using a dry section of the moat as a ha ha. TEAS. *Adm £1.20 Chd 50p. Sun May 26 (2-5.30)*

Gateford Hill Nursing Home ᕴᕤ 1m N of Worksop on the A57. Nursing home is well signed from main rd. Impressive house built 1860. Large walled garden. Spectacular display of daffodils with many varieties. A fine collection of mature, native and evergreen trees. Cream TEAS and plants incl specialist alpines in aid of Princess Royal Trust for Carers. *Adm £1.20 Chd 50p. Mon April 8 (1-5). Private parties by appt only, please* **Tel 01909 475402**

38 Green Lane ᕗᕤ (Mr & Mrs J E Nicholson) Lambley. 6m N of Nottingham. Take B684 Woodborough Rd turn R to Lambley. Main St turn L into Church St, R into Green Lane. Buses hourly from Nottingham. Barton No 7a. Small cottage garden densely planted, spring bulbs, herbaceous beds, varied climbers. Separate formal vegetable garden. Beautiful views across open countryside. Morning coffee and TEA pm. *Adm £1 Chd free. Weds April 24, May 22 (11-5). Private group visits welcome, please* **Tel 0115 9312998**

Greenways ᕴᕗᕤ (Mr & Mrs D Smith) Bathley. 1m A1. B6325 North Newark. 1½-acre. Mixed trees and shrubs, orchard and vegetables. Profuse cherry and fruit blossom.

Tennis court. Formal beds with masses of spring bulbs and flowers. Rose garden, golden laburnum pergola. Plenty of seating and quiet spots. Garden treasure hunt. TEAS. *Adm £1.50 Chd free (Share to Arthritis Care, Newark®). Sun May 5 (2-6)*

Hazel Cottage ᕴᕗᕤ (Jean & Mike Rush) Treswell. Treswell is approx 6m E of Retford; 4½m NW of A57 at Dunham-on-Trent. Parking in village st. A packed plantpersons garden now extended to almost 1 acre. Containing many unusual trees, shrubs and herbaceous plants, spring bulbs, old roses. Many interesting features incl newly developed gravel garden linked by bridge over beck. Paintings by the garden owners for sale in small gallery. Featured in Yorks TV Great Little Gardens. TEAS. *Adm £1 Chd free. Weds May 8, June 26 (1-5.30) Private visits and parties welcome, please* **Tel 01777 248089**

Hodsock Priory ᕴᕗᕤ (Sir Andrew & Lady Buchanan) Blyth. Off B6045, Blyth-Worksop rd approx 2m from A1. 5 acres bounded by dry moat. Grade 1 listed gatehouse. Victorian mansion (not open). Mature cornus, indian bean, tulip tree, swamp cypress; small lake; snowdrops and spring bulbs; mixed borders; roses, lilies. Beech and holly hedges; featured in 'Country Life', and other magazines. TEAS. *Adm £2 Wheelchairs/Acc chd under 16 free. Daily Feb Mon to Fri (12-4) Sat, Sun (10-4). April to end August Tues, Weds, Thurs (2-5). Also 2nd Sun April, May, June (2-5). For NGS Easter Sun April 7, Tues, Wed, Thurs Aug 6, 7, 8 (2-5)*

Holme Pierrepont Hall ᕴᕤ (Mr & Mrs Robin Brackenbury). Follow the signs from the A52 Nottingham-Grantham rd to the National Water Sports centre and continue for 1½m. The courtyard garden enclosed on 3 sides by the house with the church on the 4th side is a formal, listed garden laid out in 1875 with lawns, flower beds and elaborate box parterre probably influenced by Nesfield. In this 'Secret Garden' repeat flowering shrub roses, herbs and herbaceous plants have replaced Victorian hybrid tea roses and annuals, showing how contemporary planting fits into an earlier authentic framework. There is a second garden to the E of the house, clipped yews and shrubs with a long June border of old-fashioned roses. The parkland is grazed by Jacob sheep with Easter lambs. TEAS. *Adm £1.50 Chd 50p. Every Sun June; Thurs, Suns July; Tues, Thurs, Fris, Sun Aug. For NGS Mons April 8, May 6, Sun July 7 (2-6). Private visits welcome for groups, please* **Tel 0115 933 2371**

By Appointment Gardens. These owners do not have a fixed opening day usually because they do not like crowds or have insufficient parking space. Owner will often give guided tour.

Regular Openers. Too many days to include in diary. Usually there is a wide range of plants giving year-round interest. See end of county section for the name and garden description for times etc.

Holmes Villa &.&& (Sheila & Peter Clark) Holmes Lane, Walkeringham; NE Retford and within 4m Gainsborough. Take A620 from Retford or A631 from Bawtry/Gainsborough and A161 to Walkeringham then towards Misterton. Turn at sign R. Trent and follow signs for last mile. Interesting plantsman's and flower arranger's garden created and maintained by owners incl collections of ivies, alliums and many unusual herbaceous plants; new wild life pond and rhododendron bank. TEAS in aid of The Red Cross. Specialist plant and craft stalls. *Adm £1.20 Chd free. Sun June 9 (1.30-5.30). Also private visits welcome, please* Tel 01427 890233

61 Lambley Lane && (Mr & Mrs R B Powell) In Burton Joyce turn N off A612 Nottingham to Southwell Rd. Approx ⅔-acre of spring flowering plants; shrubs; azaleas; bulbs and trees; mixed borders. *Adm £1 Chd free (Share to Burton Joyce Parish Church, St Helens®). Sun May 19 (2-6)*

144 Lambley Lane && (Mr & Mrs B P Collyer) Burton Joyce. In Burton Joyce turn N off A612 Nottingham to Southwell Rd, up Lambley Lane to top. Parking in field close by. Sloping ½-acre garden with mature trees, spring flowering shrubs, conifers, rockeries, troughs, containers. TEA. *Adm £1 Chd free (Share to St Helens Church Centre®). Sun May 19 (2-6)*

37 Loughborough Road && (Mr & Mrs B H C Theobald) Ruddington. 4m S of Nottingham via A60 Loughborough Rd, cross A52 Ring Rd at Nottingham Knight. Take 1st L 400yds beyond roundabout and immed L again up Old Loughborough Rd. 1-acre plantsman's garden with many unusual varieties of bulbs, perennials, roses, shrubs, climbers and trees in borders, island beds, shady walk and walled patio. Colour yr-round. *Adm £1.50 Chd free. Suns April 14, June 16 (2-5) Private visits welcome by appt, please* Tel 0115 984 1152

¶The Manor House &.& (Mr & Mrs John Langford) Gonalston. ⅛m on the N-side of A612 between Lowdham and Southwell. Walled C17 farmhouse in centre of the village. ¾-acre garden made from farmyard over past 25yrs by present owners. Pergolas, terraces, obelisks, Irish yews, box hedges, ponds used to give formality and to divide garden into separate areas. Enthusiasm for herbaceous plants, climbers, shrubs and their propagation. TEAS and plants in aid of Amnesty International (British Section). *Adm £1.20 Chd 50p. Sun June 16 (2-6)*

Mill Hill House &.& (Mr & Mrs R J Gregory) Elston Lane, East Stoke. 5m S of Newark on A46 turn to Elston. Garden ½m on R. Entrance through nursery car park. ½-acre country garden close to the site of the Battle of East Stoke (1487). A series of small gardens closely planted with many unusual hardy/half hardy plants provide yr-round interest and a tranquil atmosphere. Teas in Newark. *Adm £1.20 Chd free. Weds April 17, June 12, Aug 7, Sept 11, Suns May 5, July 14, Mon May 27 (10-6). Private visits welcome, please* Tel 01636 525460

Morton Hall &.& (Lady Mason) Retford, 4m W of Retford. Entrance on Link Rd from A620 to S bound A1. Medium-sized woodland garden, flowering shrubs, rhododendrons, azaleas, specimen trees; pinetum in park, cedars and cypresses. Bulbs, autumn colour. Picnics. Partly suitable for wheelchairs. TEAS in aid of Ranby Church. *Adm £2.50 per car or £1.50 per person whichever is the least. Suns April 21, May 5, 26, Oct 13 (2-6). Also groups by appt, please* Tel 01777 701142

The Old Rectory && (Mr & Mrs M F Brown) Kirkby in Ashfield. Adjacent to St Wilfrids Church on B6018, 1½m W of Kirkby town centre. Ample parking. 2½-acre garden restored and developed. Mature trees, much to see; opening this year at different season for the multitude of spring flowers. TEA. *Adm £1.50 Chd free. Mon April 8 (2-5)*

Papplewick Gardens & North end of Papplewick Village on B683, 7m N of Nottingham off the A60. Parking at Hall only. *Combined adm £2 Chd free (Share to St James Church, Papplewick®). Sun May 26 (2-6)*

    Altham Lodge (C G Hill Esq) Lovely garden of rhododendrons; azaleas and spring flowers

    Papplewick Hall (Dr & Mrs R B Godwin-Austen) Woodland garden of approx 8 acres underplanted with rhododendrons; spring bulbs and hostas

Park Farm & (Mr & Mrs John E Rose) Normanton, Bottesford. Park Farm is half way between Bottesford and Long Bennington on A1 side of Normanton village and sited on the old Normanton Airfield. 2½-acre garden, developed since 1987 comprising formal and mixed borders; natural and formal ponds; scree gardens and small woodland area. Mature trees moved to flat open field prior to the creation of this garden. Large scented, colour co-ordinated herb garden, now 2yrs old. *Adm £1.50 Chd free. Sun June 2 (2-6)*

Rose Cottage && (Mr & Mrs Allan Lowe) 82 Main Rd, Underwood. 1½m from junction 27 M1. Take B608 to Heanor. Join B600; after about 200-300yds turn R into Main Rd by large sign for 'the Hole in the Wall' Inn. Flower arranger's cottage garden with ponds; shrubs; small secret garden. Rear garden of approx 1,000 sq yds with surprise features, partly developed from a field very recently; goat and other animals. Bed of show spray chrysanthemums; greenhouses. TEAS. *Adm £1.20 Chd free. Wed May 15, Suns June 9, July 7, Aug 11, Sept 8 (2-6)*

St Helen's Croft &.&& (Mrs E Ninnis) Halam. A614 Nottingham-Doncaster, turn off at White Post roundabout to Southwell and Halam. ½m beyond Halam Village, towards Edingley. 3m W of the lovely Southwell Minster. 9 acres in all. A tranquil plantsman's country garden beside an English meadow; cowslips, wild fritillaries and violets grow; primroses abound in copses planted with trees for superb autumn colour and berries. Mown roadway within meadow for disabled sticker cars. Teas in Southwell. *Adm £1.20 Chd free. For NGS Suns April 7, May 12, June 23, Sept 15, Wed Oct 16 to Tues Oct 22 incl (2-5), Tues June 25 (5-8). Private visits welcome, please* Tel 01636 813219

Skreton Cottage &❀ (Mr & Mrs J S Taylor) Screveton, 8m SW of Newark, 12m E of Nottingham. From A46 Fosse Rd turn E to Car Colston; L at green and on for 1m. 1¾-acre mature garden, created during the last 30yrs to be a 'garden for all seasons' with separate areas of different character. Fine display of spring bulbs followed by old and English roses and a wide variety of trees, shrubs and herbaceous plants; spacious lawns, pool, orchard, kitchen garden, greenhouses and many interesting design features. Set in delightful unspoilt village. TEAS and plants in aid of St Wilfrid's Church, Screveton. *Adm £1.50 Chd free. Suns March 31, June 30 (2-6)*

Southwell, Bishops Manor & (The Rt Rev the Lord Bishop of Southwell & Mrs Harris) End of Bishops Drive on S side of Minster. The house is built into a part of the old medieval Palace of the Archbishops of York. The ruins form a delightful enclosed garden, lawns, 4 seasons tree garden, orchard and vegetable garden. Rockery, attractive borders in an unusual setting. TEAS (Share to Mirasol Charitable Trust). *Adm £1.50 Chd free. Sun June 9 (2-5)*

Springwell House ⚸ (Mrs Celia Steven) Brinkley. In Southwell turn off A612 by The White Lion towards Fiskerton. Springwell House ¾m on RH-side. Approx 2 acres, many unusual trees and shrubs; perennials in informal beds. Lovely country setting. Part of garden incl pond and waterfall redeveloped by disabled students from Portland Training College. Collection of daffodils featuring local names supplied by world famous specialist. Autumn foliage colour; selection of plants; climbers and trees available from adjoining nursery. *Adm £1 Chd free. Thurs April 11, Aug 15, Suns May 12, June 2, Oct 6, Wed Sept 18 (2-5). Private visits welcome, please* **Tel 01636 814501**

Sutton Bonington Hall &❀ (Anne, Lady Elton) 5m NW of Loughborough, take A6 to Kegworth, turn R (E) onto A6006. 1st L (N) for Sutton Bonington into Main St. Conservatory, formal white garden, variegated leaf borders. Queen Anne house (not open). Plant stall consisting shrubby, herbaceous and some alpine plants. Picnics. TEA. *Adm £1.50 Chd 50p (Share to St Michael's & St Ann's Church, Sutton Bonington®). Sun July 7 (12-5.30). Also open for Leicestershire*

14 Temple Drive &⚸❀ (Mr & Mrs T Leafe) Nuthall. 4m N W of Nottingham. From M1 leave at junction 26 and take A610 towards Nottingham. Circle 1st roundabout in

A6002 lane and leave on minor rd marked 'Cedarlands and Horsendale'. From Nottingham take A610, turning off at the Broxtowe Inn, Cinderhill. Parking restricted, use Nottingham rd. ⅓-acre garden with herbaceous borders; informal island beds, ornamental trees and shrubs; troughs; old-fashioned roses; clematis. Mostly labelled. Colour all seasons of year. Fruit and vegetable garden. TEAS and cake stall. *Adm £1.20 Chd 50p (Share to Cats Protection League®). Suns May 5, July 14 (2-5.30). Also private visits by appt, please* **Tel 0115 9271118**

Thrumpton Hall &❀ (The Hon Mrs Rosemary Seymour) 8m SW of Nottingham. W of A453; 3m from M1 at Exit 24. Large lawns; massive yew hedges; rare shrubs; C17 larches, cedars, planted to commemorate historic events since George III. Lake. Early Jacobean house shown. NO DOGS in house. TEA. *Adm to Garden £1 Chd 50p; House £2 extra Chd £1 (Share to The Tradescant Trust, London®). Sun July 7 (2.30-6)*

The White House ⚸❀ (Mr & Mrs A R Hill) Nicker Hill, Keyworth. Approx 8m SE Nottingham. From A606 at Stanton-on-the-Wolds, by Shell Garage, turn into Browns Lane. Follow Keyworth signs into Stanton Lane, and continue into Nicker Hill. Great diversity of very unusual plants (many available on stall) of interest to the plantsman, grown in informal mixed beds in ¾-acre garden, esp. euphorbia, primula, penstemon, grasses, geranium, tender perennials. Designed and developed by owners since 87 incl brick pergola with climbers, extensive water and bog garden, newly developing raised area. Many interesting plants in pots. Featured on video 2. *Adm £1.20 Chd free. Bank Hol Mon May 27, Sun July 21 (2-5). Also private visits welcome, March (esp primulas, hellebores) to Sept (esp asters) incl, please* **Tel 0115 9372049**

The Willows ⚸❀ (Mr & Mrs R A Grout) 5 Rockley Ave, Radcliffe-on-Trent. 6m E of Nottingham; Radcliffe-on-Trent is N of A52; from High St PO turn into Shelford Rd; over railway bridge, 300yds opp green seat turn L into Cliff Way, then 2nd R. Restricted parking. Designed 1982 62yds × 12yds garden; a quart in a pint plot; featured 'Gardeners World' and 'Great Little Gardens'. Many rare and unusual plants; collections of hostas, hellebores, pulmonarias, paeonies, clematis, snowdrops. Colour planned island beds throughout the year. Coaches strictly by appt **Tel 0115 9333621.** TEAS. *Adm £1 Chd free (Share to NCCPG®). Wed April 3 (2-5.30)*

Oxfordshire

Hon County Organisers:	Col & Mrs J C M Baker, Hartford Greys, Sandy Lane, Boars Hill Oxford, OX1 5HN Tel 01865 739360
Hon County Treasurer:	Col J C M Baker

Assistant Hon County Organisers:

Vale of the White Horse & SW Oxon (Abingdon, Bampton, Faringdon & Wantage areas) — Mrs D J Faulkner, Haugh House, Longworth, Abingdon, Oxon OX13 5DX Tel 01865 820286

N Oxon (Banbury, Charlbury and Chipping Norton areas) — Mr & Mrs B A Murphy, Hundley Cottage, Hundley Way, Charlbury OX7 3QU Tel 01608 810549

S Oxon (Didcot, Goring, Henley and Wallingford areas) — Mr & Mrs R J Baldwin, Northfield Cottage, High Street, Long Wittenham, Oxon OX14 4QJ Tel 01865 407258

E Oxon (Headington, Iffley, Bicester, Steeple Aston & Thame areas) — Mr & Mrs J Lankester, Park Wall, Otmoor Lane, Beckley, Oxford OX3 9TB Tel 01865 351312

W Oxon (Witney, Burford & Woodstock areas), Central Oxford & Colleges — Mrs M Curtis, Bradwell, Blackditch, Stanton Harcourt, Witney OX8 1SB Tel 01865 881957

DATES OF OPENING

March 10 Sunday
Greystone Cottage, Kingwood Common, nr Henley

March 24 Sunday
Ashbrook House, Blewbury
Magdalen College, Oxford ‡
St Hilda's College, Oxford ‡
Wadham College, Oxford

March 31 Sunday
Bampton & Weald Gardens
Buckland, nr Faringdon
The Mill House, Sutton Courtenay
Taynton House, nr Burford

April 7 Sunday
Clifton Hampden Manor
Faringdon House, Faringdon
Shotover House, nr Wheatley
Wilcote House, nr Finstock

April 8 Monday
Broadwell Gardens, nr Lechlade ‡
Brook Cottage, Alkerton, nr Banbury
Epwell Mill, nr Banbury
Kencot Gardens, nr Lechlade ‡

April 13 Saturday
Blenheim Palace, Woodstock

April 14 Sunday
Blenheim Palace, Woodstock
Broughton Poggs & Filkins Gardens
Haseley Court, nr SE Oxford
The Old Rectory, Coleshill
Swyncombe House, nr Nettlebed
Tadmarton Gardens
Upper Wolvercote Gardens

April 21 Sunday
Kingston Bagpuize House
Kingstone Lisle Park, Wantage
Lime Close, Drayton
The Mill House, Stadhampton
Stanton Harcourt Manor

April 28 Sunday
Charlbury Gardens
40 Osler Road, Headington, Oxford
St Hugh's College, Oxford
Town Farm Cottage, Kingston Blount
Wick Hall, Radley, nr Abingdon

May 5 Sunday
Adderbury Gardens
Barton Abbey, Steeple Barton
Westwell Manor, nr Burford

May 6 Monday
Brook Cottage, Alkerton, nr Banbury
Garsington Manor, S Oxford

May 12 Sunday
Checkendon Court, nr Reading ‡
Greystone Cottage, Kingwood Common, nr Henley ‡
The Manor House, Sutton Courtenay

May 17 Friday
Hearns House, Gallows Tree Common

May 18 Saturday
Greys Court, nr Henley
Hearns House, Gallows Tree Common

May 19 Sunday
The Clock House, Coleshill
Epwell Mill, nr Banbury
Foxcombe End, Boars Hill
Headington Gardens, Oxford
Hearns House, Gallows Tree Common
Home Close, Garsington
Wardington Gardens
Wood Croft, Boars Hill

May 26 Sunday
Adwell House, Tetsworth
Dundon House, Minster Lovell
Field House, Murcott

Hornton Gardens
Nettlebed Gardens
Nutford Lodge, nr Faringdon
Seven Bells Cottage, Southend, Garsington
Wolfson College, Oxford

May 27 Monday
Brook Cottage, Alkerton, nr Banbury
Lower Chilworth Farm, Milton Common
Nutford Lodge, nr Faringdon
Sparsholt Manor, nr Wantage
Swerford Park, nr Chipping Norton
Wroxton Gardens

May 28 Tuesday
Nutford Lodge, nr Faringdon

May 29 Wednesday
Nutford Lodge, nr Faringdon

May 30 Thursday
Nutford Lodge, nr Faringdon

May 31 Friday
Nutford Lodge, nr Faringdon

June 1 Saturday
Nutford Lodge, nr Faringdon

June 2 Sunday
Balscote Gardens, nr Banbury
Nutford Lodge, nr Faringdon
South Newington Gardens, nr Banbury
University Arboretum, Nuneham Courtenay

June 9 Sunday
Bloxham Gardens, nr Banbury
Friars Court, Clanfield, nr Bampton
Haseley Court, SE Oxford
Hill Farm, Elsfield, nr Oxford
Lime Close, Drayton
Stansfield, Stanford-in-the-Vale
Stanton Harcourt Manor
Steeple & Middle Aston Gardens
Stratton Audley Gardens

Town Farm Cottage, Kingston
Blount
Waterperry Gardens, nr Wheatley
June 15 Saturday
Hill Court, Tackley
June 16 Sunday
The Clock House, Coleshill
Green College, Oxford
Hill Court, Tackley
The Mill House, Sutton Courtenay
Pettifers, Lower Wardington
Sibford Gower Gardens
Swalcliffe Lea House
June 19 Wednesday
Sibford Gower Gardens, Oxford
June 22 Saturday
Hook Norton Gardens
June 23 Sunday
Broughton Castle, nr Banbury
Exeter & New Colleges, Oxford
Gattendon Lodge,
Goring-on-Thames
Hook Norton Gardens
Iffley Gardens, S Oxford
Langford Gardens
Lower Chilworth Farm, Milton
Common
Manor Farm, Old Minster Lovell
The Manor House, Wheatley
New College, Oxford
Querns, Goring Heath
Salford Gardens, nr Chipping
Norton
Souldern Gardens
White's Farm House, Letcombe
Bassett
Yelford Gardens
June 30 Sunday
Adwell House, Tetsworth
Broadwell House, nr Lechlade ‡
Field House, Murcott ‡‡
Green Place, Rotherfield Greys
Holywell Manor, Oxford
Kencot Gardens, nr Lechlade ‡
Kiddington Hall, nr Woodstock
Sibford Ferris Gardens
Swinbrook House, nr Burford
Upper Green, Horton cum
Studley ‡‡
July 7 Sunday
Heron's Reach, Whitchurch, nr
Pangbourne

Hornton Gardens
Shotover House, nr Wheatley
July 14 Sunday
Brightwell-cum-Sotwell Gardens,
Wallingford
Chastleton Gardens, nr
Moreton-in-Marsh
Headington Gardens, Oxford
Seven Bells Cottage, Southend,
Garsington
Stonewalls, Hempton, nr
Deddington
July 21 Sunday
Adwell House, Tetsworth
Benson Gardens
Chivel Farm, Heythrop, nr
Chipping Norton ‡
Haughton House, Churchill ‡
Queen's & Wadham Colleges,
Oxford
Rewley House, Oxford
Temple Close, Sibford Gower,
Oxford
White's Farm House, Letcombe
Bassett
July 28 Sunday
Ashbrook House, Blewbury
The Old Rectory, Brightwell
Baldwin
Rewley House, Oxford
August 4 Sunday
Home Farm, Balscote
Broughton Castle, nr Banbury
East Oxford Gardens
Stansfield, Stanford-in-the-Vale
Wroxton Gardens
August 11 Sunday
Christ Church Corpus Christi &
Trinity Colleges
Friars Court, Clanfield,
nr Bampton
Headington Gardens, Oxford
Waterperry Gardens,
nr Wheatley
August 25 Sunday
Salford Gardens, nr Chipping
Norton
August 26 Monday
Broadwell House, nr Lechlade ‡
Brook Cottage, Alkerton, nr
Banbury
Kencot Gardens, nr Lechlade ‡

September 1 Sunday
Charlbury Gardens
Templeton College, Kennington,
Oxford
September 8 Sunday
The Clock House, Coleshill
Rofford Manor, Little Milton
September 15 Sunday
Epwell Mill, nr Banbury
The Old Rectory, Coleshill
Pettifers, Lower Wardington
September 22 Sunday
Kingston Bagpuize House
Tadmarton Gardens
September 29 Sunday
The Clock House, Coleshill
The Mill House, Sutton Courtenay
October 6 Sunday
Garsington Manor, S Oxford
Hook Norton Manor, nr Banbury
Wilcote House, nr Finstock

Regular openings
For details see garden description

Brook Cottage, Alkerton, nr Banbury
The Clock House, Coleshill
Kingston Bagpuize House
4 Northfield Cottages, Water Eaton
Old Church House, Wantage
Salford Gardens, nr Chipping Norton
Stansfield, Stanford-in-the-Vale
Stanton Harcourt Manor
Waterperry Gardens, nr Wheatley

By appointment
*For telephone numbers and other
details see garden descriptions.
Private visits welcomed*

23 Beech Croft Road, Summertown,
Oxford
Clematis Corner, Shillingford
14 Lavender Place, Carterton
Mount Skippet, Ramsden
Shucklets, Ramsden
Towersey Manor, nr Thame
Yeomans, Tadmarton

DESCRIPTIONS OF GARDENS

Adderbury Gardens On A4260, 3m S of Banbury. A large village with many quaint lanes and a beautiful church. TEAS. *Combined adm £2 Chd free. Sun May 5 (2-6)*
West of A423
Berry Hill House ♿✿❀ (Mr & Mrs J P Pollard) Berry Hill Rd, off A4260 signed Milton, Bloxham, W Adder-

bury. 2-acre garden reclaimed since 1982. Mature trees; lawns; shrubbery; mixed herbaceous and shrub borders. Kitchen garden
Briarwood (Mr & Mrs W Johnson) Berry Hill Road. ¼-acre cottage style garden with interesting collection of shrubs and herbaceous plants. No dogs
Crosshill House ♿ (Mr & Mrs Gurth Hoyer Millar) Manor Rd. 4-acre classic Victorian walled gardens around stone Georgian House

Adwell House & (Mr & Mrs W R A Birch-Reynardson) Nr Tetsworth, 4m SW of Thame. From London leave M40 at exit 6, turn L in Lewknor. From Oxford A40, turn R after Tetsworth. Roses, formal and water gardens, ornamental lakes, fine trees, lawns; new tree and shrub planting. Commemorative garden with monument. Recently designed potager. TEAS not July 21. Plant sale (subject to availability as all plants propogated by owner). *Adm £2 Chd free (Share to Adwell Church PCC© and National Asthma Campaign®). Suns May 26, June 30; July 21 (2.30-5.30)*

Arboretum See Oxford University Gardens under University Arboretum

Ashbrook House ❀ (Mr & Mrs S A Barrett) Blewbury. 4m SE of Didcot on A417; 3½-acre chalk garden with small lake, stream, spring bulbs. Teas Lantern Cafe March, Ashbrook House July. *Adm £1 Chd free. Suns March 24, July 28 (2- 6)*

Balscote Gardens ❀ Pretty hill village ½m off A422 5m W of Banbury. TEAS (May only) at a nearby garden in aid of Church (C14 St Mary Magdalene). *Combined adm £2 Chd free. Sun June 2 (2-6)*
> **Home Farm** & (Mr & Mrs G C Royle) C17 house and barn with attractive views from ½-acre closely planted elevated garden designed for year-round interest with unusual plants, contrasting foliage, flowering shrubs, bulbs, heathers, alpines, herbaceous, roses, lilies, young trees. Featured in Mon Jardin et Ma Maison Feb 1995. Teas. *Also open Sun Aug 4 with* **Wroxton Gardens**. *Combined adm £2. Private visits also welcome by appt April 1 to Oct 31 Adm £1.50, please* **Tel 01295 738194**
> **Homeland** (Dr & Mrs J S Rivers) ¾-acre, developed since 1982 with shrubs, roses, perennials and rock garden, includes field adjacent to church, planted with trees
> **Manor Cottage** (Mrs P M Jesson) This is both a ⅓-acre garden crafted from a steep slope using local stone and treated timbers and a ⅔-acre woodland scheme. Variety of decorative trees and shrubs. 250 broad-leaved indigenous trees

Bampton & Weald Gardens On A4095 Witney-Faringdon rd. TEAS at **Weald Manor**. *Combined adm £1.50 Chd free (Share to Dr Clark Memorial Fund®). Sun March 31 (2-5.30)*
> **Bampton Manor** &❀ (Earl & Countess of Donoughmore) Interesting wild spring garden with beautiful views of church. Masses of varied spring flowers. *(Share to Dr Clark Memorial Fund®)*
> **Weald Manor** & (Maj & Mrs R A Colvile) Medium-sized old garden; woodland area with many spring bulbs; topiary and shrub borders; fine trees; small lake *(Share to Bampton Church Spire Fund®)*

Barton Abbey &❀ (Mrs R Fleming) On B4030; 1m Middle Barton; ½m from junction of A4260 and B4030. 4 acres lawns; 3 acres of lake; fine trees; kitchen garden and glasshouses. Plants and home produce stall. TEAS. *Adm £1.50 Chd free. Sun May 5 (2-5.30)*

23 Beech Croft Road ✿ (Mrs A Dexter) Summertown, Oxford. A 23yd by 7yd, south-facing, plant lover's paved garden of a terraced house has been made secluded by planting evergreen shrubs, roses and clematis all round the brick walls; the 2 herbaceous, 2 alpine, 2 shady beds all contain many unusual plants, shrubs, ferns; troughs filled with small alpines. NO push-chairs. *Adm £3 Private visits welcome April to Sept 30* Tel 01865 56020

Bellevue ✿❀ (Mr & Mrs E W Turner) Bell St, Hornton. 6m NW of Banbury. Between A422 and B4100. Approx 1½-acre hillside garden of many aspects. Bordered walks; a 'surprise' garden leading to water falling to pools, flower beds and the finest views of Hornton Village. Added attraction miniature windmill ⅓ scale of original at Hornton. TEAS in aid of Hornton School May 26; Hornton Cubs and Brownies July 9. *Adm £1 Chd free. Suns May 26, July 7 (2-6)*

Benson Gardens Off High St. Benson off A4074 Oxford-Henley, 2m from Wallingford. Parking in High St. TEAS at **Mill Lane House** in aid of Benson Voluteer Help-Line. *Combined adm £1.50. Sun July 21 (2-6)*
> **Hethersett** ❀ (Dr Anne Millar) ½-acre garden on natural chalk stream; climbing plants and bog area; colour co-ordination and plant-form a feature of mixed beds. *Private visits welcome for parties of 15 or under, please* **Tel 01491 838116**
> **Mill Lane House** ✿ (Marion & Geoff Heywood) ¼-acre garden with alpine rockeries and banks sloping to stream, pond, small island and spring. Dried flower crafts display

Blenheim Palace ✿ (His Grace the Duke of Marlborough) Woodstock, 8m N of Oxford. Bus: 44 Oxford-Chipping Norton-Stratford, alight Woodstock. Original grounds and garden plan by Henry Wise. Park landscaped and lake created by 'Capability' Brown in late C18. Maze; butterfly house; cafeteria; adventure play area; *Adm charge not available on going to press.* ▲For NGS Sat, Sun April 13, 14 (10.30- 4.45)

Bloxham Gardens ✿❀ A large village near Banbury on A361 to Chipping Norton. Has a fine church with a 198ft spire. TEAS in village by WI. *Combined adm £1.50 Chd free. Sun June 9 (2-6)*
> **25 The Avenue** (Miss E Bell-Walker) A small informal garden with emphasis on small shrubs; sub shrubs and herbaceous plants
> **71 Courtington Lane** (Mr P Sheasby) About ⅓ acre with herbaceous borders, shrubs, rockeries and small peat beds; there is a small pond and a series of alpine troughs; the greenhouse contains cacti and a large succulent collection especially Lithops, Haworthia and Echeveria; a wide range of herbaceous species are grown
> **Frog Lane Cottage** (Mr & Mrs R Owen) An artists and a plantsmans garden. Steeply terraced on many levels, extending to the brook. Mixture of shrubs and herbaceous plants, incl camomile lawn, wonderful views across valley (approx ½ acre)
> **Rose Cottage** (Mr & Mrs David Willmott) Small cottage garden on elevated site incl alpines, herbaceous bed and climbing roses

Brightwell-cum-Sotwell Gardens Off A4130 between Didcot (4m) and Wallingford (2m) Ancient village with many timber-framed cottages. Parking in village centre. Teas at Sotwell House. *Combined adm £2 Chd free. Sun July 14 (2-6)*

> **Lucksall Cottage** *⚘* (Miss P Grierson) Informal ⅓-acre garden. Mixed borders, old roses and unusual plants
>
> **The Priory** ⅊*⚘* (Mr & Mrs C Scroggs) Walled garden, C16 farmhouse. 2000 plantings in shrubbery; herbaceous border and rose bed. Brick paved vegetable garden
>
> **Sotwell House** ⅊*⚘* (Mr & Mrs D Dobbin) 3-acre moated informal garden with roses, shrubs and annuals
>
> **Sotwell Manor** ⅊ (Mrs D Twentyman) ⅓-acre informal garden with 'Hidcote' features. Incl trees, ponds and potager
>
> ¶**Spring Cottage** *⚘* (Mr & Mrs M C Dix) Small pretty cottage garden featuring shrubs, roses, clematis and perennials
>
> ¶**Sunnyside** ⅊ *⚘* (Mr D Batten) 1-acre garden featuring annuals, mixed border and 2 fishponds

Broadwell Gardens 5m NE Lechlade, E of A361 to Burford. Delightful Cotswold village with interesting church. TEAS. *Combined adm with Kencot Gardens £2 Chd free. Mons April 8, Aug 26. Adm Broadwell House £1.50 Chd free. Sun June 30 (2-6)*

> **Broadwell House** ⅊⚘ (Brigadier & Mrs C F Cox) Mature 2-acre garden planted for colour throughout the year. Many interesting trees and shrubs including wellingtonia, ginkgo, acers, aralias, salix, clematis. Topiary, rare plants, many golden, silver and variegated; unusual grasses, penstemons and osteospermums, also many hardy geraniums. Featured in 'Over the Hills from Broadway'. Listed house and old barn. Gardening clubs welcome. *Adm £1.50. Mons April 8, Aug 26; Sun June 30 (2-6). Private visits welcome, please* Tel 01367 860230
>
> **Broadwell Old Manor** *⚘* (Mr & Mrs M Chinnery) 1-acre garden with listed house. Shrub borders, courtyard and topiary garden. Pleached lime hedge, old mulberry tree, young tulip and sorbus trees. *April 8 only*

Brook Cottage ⚘ (Mr & Mrs D Hodges) Alkerton, 6m W of Banbury. From A422, Banbury-Stratford, turn W at sign to Alkerton, L opp Alkerton War Memorial, into Well Lane, R at fork. 4-acre hillside garden, formed since 1964, surrounding C17 house. Wide variety of trees, shrubs and plants of all kinds in areas of differing character; water garden; alpine scree; one-colour borders; over 200 shrub and climbing roses; many clematis. Interesting throughout season. DIY Tea & Coffee. Refreshments for groups by arrangement. *Adm £2 OAPs £1.50 Chd free. Mon to Fri April 1 to Oct 31 incl Bank Hols (9-6). Evenings, weekends and all group visits by appt Tel 01295 670303 or 670590*

Broughton Castle ⅊⚘ (Lord Saye & Sele) 2½m W of Banbury on Shipston-on-Stour rd (B4035). 1-acre shrub, herbaceous borders, walled garden, roses, climbers seen against background of C13-C16 castle surrounded by moat in open parkland. House also open, extra charge. TEAS. *Adm Garden only £2 Chd £1. ▲For NGS Suns June 23, Aug 4 (2-5)*

Broughton Poggs & Filkins Gardens ⅊ Enchanting limestone villages between Burford and Lechlade, just E of A361. A number of gardens varying in size from traditional cottage garden to over 2 acres, growing wide variety of plants. TEAS. *Combined adm £2 Chd free. Tickets from The Court House, Broughton Hall or Little Peacocks (Share to Broughton & Filkins Church Funds®). Sun April 14 (2-5.30)*

Broughton Poggs:
> **Broughton Hall** (Mr & Mrs C B S Dobson)
> **Corner Cottage** (Mr & Mrs E Stephenson)
> **The Court House** ⚘ (Richard Burls Esq)
> **The Garden Cottage** (Mr & Mrs R Chennells)
> **Rose Cottage** (Mr & Mrs R Groves)

Filkins:
> **Fox House** (Lady Cripps)
> **Little Peacocks** (Colvin & Moggridge, Landscape Consultants)
> **St Peter's House** (John Cambridge Esq)

Buckland ⚘ (Mrs Richard Wellesley) Signposted to Buckland off A420, lane between two churches. Beautiful lakeside walk; fine trees; daffodils; shrubs. Norman church adjoins garden. TEAS. *Adm £1 Chd free (Share to Buckland Church Restoration Fund®). Sun March 31 (2-7). Private visits welcome Tues and Thurs, please Tel 01367 870203*

Charlbury Gardens ⚘ Large historic village on B4022 Witney-Enstone. TEAS. *Combined adm £1.50 Chd 50p (Share to Wytham Hall Sick Bay for Medical Care of Homeless®). Suns April 28, Sept 1 (2-6)*

> **Gothic House** *⚘* (Mr & Mrs Andrew Lawson) Near Bell Hotel. ⅓-acre walled garden, planted for sculpture display and colour association. False perspective, pleached lime walk with bulbs, trellis, alpine pyramid, terrace pots and new gravel plantings
>
> **The Priory** ⅊ (Dr D El Kabir and others) Adjacent church. Formal terraced topiary gardens with Italianate features, incl foliage colour schemes, parterres, specimen trees and shrubs, water features and over 3 acres of recently planted arboretum

Chastleton Gardens 3m SE of Moreton-in-Marsh and W of Chipping Norton off A44. TEAS in aid of Chastleton Church. *Combined adm £2 Chd free. Sun July 14 (2-6)*

> **Chastleton Glebe** ⅊⚘ (Prue Leith) 1m from village on lane to Moreton-in-Marsh. 5 acres; old trees; terraces (one all red); small lake, island; Chinese-style bridge, pagoda; formal vegetable garden; views; rose tunnel
>
> **Kitebrook End Farm** ⅊ (Mr & Mrs W G Bamford) Directions as for Chastleton Glebe. ½-acre garden designed to be labour-saving; walls; paving and shaped borders around a lawn. Massed shrubs and perrenials, southerly aspect beyond raised ha-ha wall

Checkendon Court ⅊*⚘* (Sir Nigel Broackes) Checkendon, NW of Reading. 2m NE of Woodcote off A4074 nr Checkendon church. 15 acres, attractively laid out with yew hedges, herbaceous borders, roses, kitchen garden. New rhododendrons and azalea planting and new laburnum pergola walk now complete. TEAS at **Greystone Cottage**. *Adm £2 Chd free. Sun May 12 (2-5)*

Chivel Farm &✿❀ (Mr & Mrs J D Sword) Heythrop, 4m E of Chipping Norton, off A44 or A361. High and open to extensive view, medium-sized garden designed for continuous interest. Colour schemed borders with many unusual shrubs, roses, herbaceous plants; small formal white garden, conservatory. TEAS in aid of St Nicholas Church, Heythrop. *Adm £1.50 Chd free. Sun July 21 (2-6)*

Christ Church See Oxford University Gardens

Clematis Corner &✿ (Mike & Dorothy Brown) 15 Plough Close. At Shillingford roundabout (10m S of Oxford on A4074), take A329 towards Warborough and Thame. Clematis Corner is 200yds from roundabout, 1st on L inside Plough Close, just round sharp L bend. ¼ acre garden. Specialising in clematis (over 200 varieties) grown in a variety of ways. Enthusiastic amateurs. TEA in aid of ICRF. *Adm £1 Chd 50p. Private visits welcome May 1 to Sept 30, please* **Tel 01865 858721**

Clifton Hampden Manor &✿ (Mr C Gibbs) 4m E of Abingdon on A415. 4-acre romantic C19 garden above R. Thames with statuary and far-reaching views; long pergola, new lime tunnel, herbaceous borders, bulbs, wild riverside walks, much new planting in progress. TEAS in aid of St Michael's and All Angels Church. *Adm £2 Chd free. Sun April 7 (2.30-5.30). Parties welcome, please* **Tel 01830 7720**

Clock House &✿ (Denny Wickham & Peter Fox) Coleshill, 3½m SW of Faringdon on B4019. Garden at top of village. Planted around site of Coleshill House, which was burnt down in the 50's, the main floor plan has been laid out and is being planted as a memorial to this famous house. Walled garden in old laundry drying ground; with big greenhouse, unusual plants with emphasis on foliage, vegetables and herbs; good views across Vale of the White Horse and parkland. Toilets not suitable disabled. TEAS. *Adm £1.50 Chd free. Open every Thurs May to Sept (2-5). Suns May 19, June 16, Sept 8, 29 (2-6). Private visits welcome, please* **Tel 01793 762476**

Corpus Christi College See Oxford University Gardens

Dundon House &✿❀ (Mr & Mrs W Pack) In Minster Lovell, charming Cotswold village on R Windrush. Off B4047 Witney- Burford Rd opp White Hart, signed to Minster Lovell Hall, 1st drive on R, parking in field to L. Disabled parking at house. Mainly C16 house, (not open), owned in C18 by the Dundons, a notorious family of highwaymen; moved in 1930s to old quarry. Beautiful views across Windrush valley. 4-acre terraced garden. Yew hedges and stone walls enclose flower, shrub rose and wild gardens. Planted pool and new woodland gardens. TEAS by WI. *Adm £1.50 OAPs £1 Chd free. Sun May 26 (2-6). Parties welcome by appt, please* **Tel 01993 775092**

East Oxford Gardens &✿ Off Cowley Rd, Oxford 1m E from the Plain. Parking at **Restore**. TEAS at **Restore** and **St John's Home**. *Combined adm £1.50 OAPs £1 Chd free (Share to Restore and St John's Home®). Sun Aug 4 (2-5)*
  Restore, Manzil Way N off Cowley Rd leading to E Oxford Health Centre. A town garden and plant nursery run as a mental health rehabilitation project. Sample beds of shrubs, perennials, herbs, alpines and annuals.

Large range of plants for sale, also hand-made crafts and cards
  St John's Home, St Mary's Rd, off Leopold St S of Cowley Rd. 3-acre grounds of All Saints Convent and St John's Home for the Elderly. Mature trees, lawns, secluded prayer garden and vegetable garden. Comper chapel open

Epwell Mill &✿ (Mr R A Withers) Epwell, 7m W of Banbury, between Shutford and Epwell. Medium-sized garden, interestingly landscaped in open country, based on former water-mill; terraced pools; bulbs; azaleas. TEAS. *Adm £1 Chd free (Share to Epwell Church®). Suns April 8, May 19, Sept 15 (2-6). Please apply in writing for groups outside opening dates*

Exeter College See Oxford University Gardens

Faringdon House &✿ (Dr S Zinovieff) Faringdon. Large garden; spring bulbs; autumn borders; orangery; park; lakeside walk; fine trees; Norman church adjoining. Parking in town. Entrance via main drive, next to Church. TEAS in aid of All Saints Church. *Adm £1 Chd free. Sun April 7 (2-5)*

¶Field House &✿ (Roy & Nora Cartwright) Murcott, nr Islip. 5m NE of Oxford. From B4027 at Islip take turning E to Charlton-on-Otmoor, then turn R to Fencott and Murcott. 3½-acre garden created entirely by present owners from 3 flat paddocks linking early Victorian stone house to outer dyke on N boundary of Otmoor. Lawns lead through trees and shrubs, to a small lake with lily ponds, fish pools, water gardens, summer houses, a wild garden and many other features. Teas in Village Hall in aid of Village Hall. *Adm £2 Chd free. Suns May 26, June 30 (2-6)*

Foxcombe End &✿ (Mr & Mrs R Stevens) Foxcombe Lane, Boars Hill, 3 m S of Oxford. From roundabout at junction of ring rd with A34 follow signs to Wootton and Boars Hill. Foxcombe Lane is 1st on L after entering Boars Hill. Parking in garden reserved for infirm **only**. 7 acres oak woodland, 4 acres natural garden. Garden trail, donkey, wild orchids, azaleas, rhododendrons, magnolias and extensive yew hedges. TEAS in aid of Sobell House Hospice. *Adm £1 Chd free. Sun May 19 (2-6)*

Friars Court &✿ (Mr & Mrs J H Willmer) Clanfield. A4095 Faringdon to Witney, S of Clanfield [OS 285009]. C16 part moated farmhouse. New/mature gardens and woodland walks. Working displays on alternative energy. Cream TEAS. *Adm £1.50 Chd under 12 free. Suns June 9, Aug 11 (2-6)*

Garsington Manor ✿ (Mr & Mrs L V Ingrams) SE of Oxford N of B480. House C17 of architectural interest (not open). Monastic fish ponds, water garden, dovecot c.1700; flower parterre and Italian garden laid out by Philip and Lady Ottoline Morrell; fine trees and yew hedges. Free car park. TEAS. *Adm £2 Chd free. Mon May 6, Sun Oct 6 (2-6)*

Regular Openers. See end of county section.

¶Gattendon Lodge ♿✂❀ (Mr & Mrs A N Campbell-Harris) Goring-on-Thames, 5m S of Wallingford. Approx ½m along Gatehampton Rd after passing Goring-on-Thames station. 1½ acres with herbaceous and mixed borders. Features incl shrubbery, potager, specimen trees and many varieties of roses and fuschias. *Adm £2 Chd free (Share to Riding for the Disabled®). Sun June 23 (2-6)*

Green College See Oxford University Gardens

Green Place ♿✂❀ (Mr & Mrs R P Tatman) Rotherfield Greys. 3m W of Henley-on-Thames next to Greys War Memorial. Extensive views towards the E from secluded 1-acre garden containing a pergola walk, herbaceous borders, rose beds and many varieties of fuchsia. Teas by WI in nearby village hall. *Adm £1 Chd free. Sun June 30 (2-6)*

Greys Court ✂❀ (Lady Brunner; The National Trust) Rotherfield Greys, 3m W of Henley-on-Thames on rd to Peppard. 8 acres amongst which are the ruined walls and buildings of original fortified manor. Rose, cherry, wisteria and white gardens; lawns; kitchen garden; ice house; Archbishop's maze. Jacobean house open with C18 alterations on site of original C13 house fortified by Lord Grey in C14. Donkey wheel and tower. Large sale of unusual plants. TEAS. *Adm garden £3 Chd £1.50 House £1 extra, Chd 50p extra. ▲For NGS Sat May 18 (2-5.30)*

Greystone Cottage ♿✂❀ (Mr & Mrs W Roxburgh) Colmore Lane, Kingwood Common. Between B481 Nettlebed-Reading rd and Sonning Common-Stoke Row rd. 2-acre garden in woodland setting. Many unusual shrubs and plants, including varied colletion of hostas, geraniums, grasses, fritillary and wild flower meadow, ferns and old fashioned roses. Woodland walk with azaleas, narcissus, hellebores, bilberries and cistus. 80-year-old arched pear tree walk, wildlife ponds, sink gardens, small Mediterranean garden, small pinetum. Planted for year round interest. Featured in 'Practical Gardening', 'Good Gardeners Guide' and Gardeners Year Book. Small nursery. TEAS in aid of Oxfam (March) Peppard C of E School (May). *Adm £2 Chd free. Suns March 10, May 12 (2-6). Private visits welcome March 1 to Sept 1 by appt, please* **Tel 01491 628559**

Haseley Court ♿✂❀ (Mr & Mrs D Heyward) From London M40 exit 7, L to A329, 1st L to Great Haseley then to Little Haseley. From Oxford A40, L on A418 to Aylesbury, 1st R onto A329 and over M40. Topiary chess set in box and yew. Hornbeam and laburnum tunnels, walled garden with box hedges. Collection of old roses. Potager, woodland with many spring flowers. Ornamental canal. TEAS in aid of Great Haseley Hall. *Adm £2 Chd free. Suns April 14, June 9 (2-6)*

Haughton House ♿❀ (Mr & Mrs A D Loehnis) Churchill. 3m SW of Chipping Norton on B4450. From Burford, W for Churchill via A361. Medium-sized garden. Terrace with fine views, borders, formal white garden, meadow. All season interest. Also fine kneelers in nearby church. TEAS in aid of village church. *Adm £1 Chd free. Sun July 21 (2-6)*

Headington Gardens ✂❀ East Oxford, off London Road, ¾m W of ring road. TEAS in garden April 28, parish hall, Dunstan Rd other dates. Plants stall May 19, July 14 only. *Adm £1. Sun April 28,* **40 Osler Rd** *only. Combined adm £2 Chd free. Suns May 19, July 14, Aug 11 (2-6)*

2 Fortnam Close (Mr & Mrs D Holt) Off Headley Way. Winner best back garden, Oxford in Bloom 1991 and 1993. Featured on TV. ¼-acre garden on 3 levels, trees, shrubs including heathers, azaleas and a large wisteria. Roses, bearded iris and other herbaceous plants in a planned layout which includes a pond and pergola. There are watercolour paintings and pressed flower arrangements to view if you wish. *May 19, July 14, Aug 11*

40 Osler Road (Mr & Mrs N Coote) ⅔-acre 'secret garden' on the edge of Old Headington. Semi-formal design; tender shrubs and plants in pots supporting Mediterranean atmosphere of house. Luxuriant spring display. Plants for dry soil, many chosen for foliage effect, some rare or unusual, many late flowering. Featured on 'Gardeners World' and in many publications. *April 28, May 19, July 14, Aug 11. Private visits for groups welcome, please* **Tel 01865 67680 (after dark)**

Pumpkin Cottage ♿ (Mr & Mrs M Davis) 6 St Andrew's Lane, Old Headington, off St Andrew's Rd, nr to Church. Small garden, 20m × 16m, enclosed within stone walls situated at rear of Grade II listed cottage. Small pool and rockery; mixed planting; paved areas with some container grown plants. Small cobble paved front garden. Wheelchair access possible by arrangement. *May 19, July 14, Aug 11*

1 Stoke Place ♿ (Mrs Sarah McCabe) The garden takes its shape from a network of old stone walls which happen to have survived in the area. A scattering of trees blending with stone work provides a framework for a linked series of paths and flower beds which gives an atmosphere of seclusion. A number of small pools and many contrasting shrubs and plants provide variety and do not diminish the sense of privacy of the whole garden. The area is just short of an acre. *Open May 19 only (Share to Toxoplasmosis Trust®)*

Hearns House ♿❀ (Mr & Mrs J Pumfrey) Gallows Tree Common, 5m N of Reading, 5m W of Henley. From A4074 turn E at The Fox, Cane End. Limited car parking in the garden so additional Friday and Saturday openings. Architects house in 2-acre garden in woodland setting. Designed for maintenance by two people with full time careers. Featured in Amateur Gardening. Emphasis on design, good foliage and single colour areas with paved courtyard and shady walks. New small garden. Unusual plants for sale. TEAS or coffee in aid of Water Aid. *Adm £2 Chd free. Fri, Sat, Sun May 17, 18, 19, (10-12; 2-5)*

Heron's Reach ♿❀ (Mr & Mrs B Vorhaus) Eastfield Lane, Whitchurch-on-Thames. From Pangbourne take tollbridge rd over Thames to Whitchurch; at The Greyhound turn R into Eastfield Lane. 1 acre in beautiful Thames-side setting with views to the Chiltern hills; woodland garden with pond, stream, shrubs, and herbaceous borders. TEAS. *Adm £1.50 Chd free. Sun July 7 (2-6). Private visits also welcome in July, please* **Tel 01734 843140**

Hill Court ♿🌢❀ (Mr & Mrs Andrew Peake) Tackley. 9m N of Oxford. Turn off A4260 at Sturdy's Castle. Walled garden of 2 acres with clipped yew cones at the top of the terrace as a design feature by Russell Page in the 1960s. Terraces incl silver, pink and blue plantings, white garden, herbaceous borders, shrubberies, orangery. Many rare and unusual plants. Entry incl History Trail (not suitable for wheelchairs) with illustrated leaflet giving notes on unique geometric fishponds (1620), C17 stables and pigeon house, C18 lakes, icehouse etc (stroll of at least 1hr). TEAS. Pied Pipers recorder group (Sun only) *Adm £1.50 Chd free (Share to Sir Michael Sobell House and Tackley Church Bell Appeal®). Sat, Sun June 15, 16 (2-6)*

Hill Farm ✿❀ (Mr & Mrs J Garson) Elsfield. 5m N of Oxford. A40 flyover signed Marston and Elsfield. Mixed borders, shrubs, trees; good view of Oxford. TEAS. *Adm £1.50 Chd free. Sun June 9 (2-6)*

Holywell Manor See Oxford University Gardens

Home Close ✿❀ (Dr P Giangrande and Miss M Waud) Southend, Garsington. SE of Oxford, N of B480. 2-acre garden, being redeveloped, surrounding C17 listed bailiff's house and granary. Mixed borders; walled garden with water feature; herb garden; pergola; kitchen garden; orchard; woodland areas. TEA. *Adm £1 Chd free. Sun May 19 (2-6). Private visits welcome April to Sept 30, please* **Tel 01865 361394**

Home Farm, Balscote See Balscote Gardens

¶**Hook Norton Gardens** ✿❀ Between Banbury and Chipping Norton signposted on A361. TEAS at Talbot House in aid of Katherine House. *Combined adm £1.50 Chd 50p. Sat, Sun June 22, 23 (2-6)*

¶**Homefield House** (Val & Andy Bourne) ½-acre garden incl gravel garden, woodland area, cottage garden and flower beds. A plant collector's garden, still being completed, on a dry, free-draining site. *Also open Thurs May to July (2-6) and by appt, please* **Tel 01608 730187**

¶**Talbot House** (Mr & Mrs Hummer) ½-acre garden on 2 levels, with emphasis on cottage garden flowers and roses. Entirely new garden with borders being developed

Hook Norton Manor ❀ (Mr & Mrs N Holmes) SW of Banbury. From A361, 1m from Chipping Norton turn N and follow signs. 2½-acres terraced lawns leading down to streams; trees, shrubs and bog garden. TEAS in aid of St Peter's Church. *Adm £1 Chd free. Sun Oct 6 (2-5.30)*

Iffley Gardens ✿❀ S Oxford. Secluded old village within Oxford's ring road, off A4158 from Magdalen Bridge to Littlemore roundabout. Renowned Norman church, featured on cover of Pevsner's Oxon guide. Short footpath from Mill Lane leads to scenic Iffley Lock and Sandford-Oxford towpath. TEAS from 3-5 at thatched village hall, Church Way. Plant stall in aid of the White House Nursery. *Combined adm £2 OAPs £1.50 Chd free. Sun June 23 (2-6)*

8 Abberbury Road ♿ (F S Tordoff Esq) Off Church Way. ½-acre plantsman's garden developed since 1971. Mature trees, shrubs, coloured and variegated foliage, many old and modern shrub roses and climbers. *Private visits welcome, please* **Tel 01865 778644**

24 Abberbury Road ♿ (Mr & Mrs E Townsend-Coles) ½-acre family garden with fruit, flowers and vegetables

65 Church Way ❀ (Mrs J Woodfill) Small cottage garden planted with shrubs, perennials and herbs, many of them grown for their historical associations. *Private visits welcome, please* **Tel 01865 770537**

71 Church Way (Mrs M L Harrison) A small, low maintenance professionally designed, front garden with mixed shrubs and herbaceous plantings. *Private visits welcome, please* **Tel 01865 718224**

122 Church Way (Sir John & Lady Elliott) Small secluded cottage style garden with trees, shrubs, roses and herbaceous plants behind listed house with view of church tower

The Mill House (Mrs P A Lawrence) 30 Mill Lane. A terraced garden dropping westwards to the river at the old mill-race

Rosedale ❀ (Mrs T Bennett) Mill Lane, off Church Way. ½-acre garden on different levels, hidden behind walls. A mixture of trees, shrubs, roses and herbaceous plants with a large rockery and tiny woodland garden. *Private visits welcome, please* **Tel 01865 714151**

Kencot Gardens 5m NE of Lechlade, E of A361 to Burford. A most charming Cotswold village with interesting church. TEAS. *Combined adm with* **Broadwell Gardens** *£2 Chd free. Mons April 8, Aug 26. £1.50 Chd free. Also* **Kencot House** *and* **Manor Farm** *open Sun June 30 with* **Broadwell House.** *Combined adm £2 Chd free*

De Rougemont ♿ (Mr & Mrs D Portergill) ½-acre garden with very varied planting: over 350 named plants; beds for perennials, conifers, fuchsias, herbs and roses; spring bulbs; vegetables and fruit trees; soft fruit cage; greenhouse with vine; well

The Gardens (Lt-Col & Mrs J Barstow) ¼-acre cottage garden featuring spring bulbs, iris, roses, herbaceous, rock plants, old apple trees and a well

Ivy Nook (Mr & Mrs W Gasson) Cottage garden; rockeries, lawns, mixed borders. *Mon April 8, Mon Aug 26*

Kencot Cottage ❀ (Mrs M Foster) Very small garden with spring bulbs and bedding, also bonsai trees

Kencot House ❀ (Mr & Mrs A Patrick) 2-acre garden with lawns, trees, borders; quantities of daffodils and other spring bulbs; roses and over 50 different clematis; notable ginkgo tree. Interesting carved C13 archway. *Also open Sun June 30. Adm £1.50*

Manor Farm (Mr & Mrs J R Fyson) 2-acre garden with lawns and herbaceous borders; naturalised spring bulbs; incl long-established fritillaries; clipped yew, pleached lime walk, pergola with rambling and gallica roses. Mature orchards. C17 listed farmhouse. *Mon April 8, Sun June 30 only*

Kiddington Hall ✿❀ (Hon Maurice & Mrs Robson) 4m NW of Woodstock. From A44 Oxford-Stratford, R at Xrds in Kiddington and down hill; entrance on L. Partly suitable for wheelchairs. Large grounds with lake, parkland designed by Capability Brown; terraced rose garden and orangery beside house designed by Sir Charles Barry; C12 church, C16 dovecote and large walled kitchen garden. TEAS in aid of St Nicholas Church, Kiddington. *Adm £1.50 Chd free. Sun June 30 (2-6)*

Kingston Bagpuize House &※❀ (Mr & Mrs Francis Grant) Kingston Bagpuize, A415, 5½m W of Abingdon. Surrounded by mature parkland the gardens, incl shrub border and woodland garden, contain many interesting and unusual trees, shrubs, perennials and bulbs. Guided tours of Charles II manor house not suitable for wheelchairs. *Adm garden only £1, under 5's free. House and garden £3 OAP's £2.50 Chd £2 (under 5's not admitted to the house). Open Bank Hol weekends Sat, Sun, Mon and also April 17, 20, 21; June 12, 15, 16; July 17, 20, 21; Aug 7, 10, 11 and Sept 4, 7, 8, 18, 21, 22 (2.30-5.30) last adm 5pm. For NGS Suns April 21 and Sept 22. Groups welcome by written appt Feb to Nov, please Tel 01865 820259*

Kingstone Lisle Park (Mr & Mrs J L S Lonsdale) nr Wantage. 5m W of Wantage along B4507. 12 acres of gardens incl a shrubbery, pleeched limes, an avenue leading up to an ornamental pond and a replica of Queen Mary's rose garden in Regents Park. 3 acres of lakes. TEAS. House and garden open Mons May 6, 27. *Adm £6. For NGS garden only Adm £2.50 Chd free (Share to St John the Baptist Church, Kingstone Lisle®). Sun April 21 (2-5)*

Langford Gardens &※❀ E of A361 Burford-Lechlade; W of A409 Burford-Faringdon. Mixture of cottage and formal gardens in old limestone village which makes a feature of roses. Saxon church decorated with flowers. Large free car park. TEAS in aid of St Matthew's Church. *Combined adm £2.50 Chd free. Sun June 23 (2-6)*
   Bakery Cottage (Miss R Amies)
   The Barn (Mr & Mrs D E Range)
   Bridgewater House (Mrs P M C Scott)
   ¶**Cotswold Bungalow** (Mr & Mrs J Dudley)
   Lime Tree Cottage (Dr & Mrs M G Schulz)
   Lockey House (Mrs M A Kemp & Mr & Mrs N Gardner)
   ¶**Lower Farm** (Mr & Mrs T Brown)
   The Old School & Barn (Sir Hardy Amies)
   Rectory Farm (Mr & Mrs R J Kirby)
   Rosefern Cottage (Mr & Mrs J Lowden)
   Stonecroft (Mr & Mrs D Romanek)
   Threeways (Mrs R G Wilson)
   Wellbank (Mr & Mrs J Hudson-Davies)
   Wellbank House (Mr & Mrs P G Booth)

14 Lavender Place ※❀ (Mrs Angela Chambers) Carterton. 4m SE of Burford on B4020. After entering Carterton from Burford, turn R at lights into Upavon Way (towards Alvescot & Faringdon). Lavender Place fourth L. Plant enthusiast's tiny 35' square garden behind small modern house. Clematis and other climbers provide secluded setting for densely packed collection of unusual and exotic perennials. Small pond, shaded area, raised beds. Colour and interest all year. *Adm 80p Chd free. Private visits welcome by appt June 1 to Aug 31, please Tel 01993 843216*

Lime Close &❀ (Miss de Laubarede) 35 Henleys Lane, Drayton. 2m S of Abingdon. 3-acre mature garden with very rare and unusual trees, shrubs, perennials and bulbs. Raised beds, rock garden and troughs with alpines, Creation of new borders, pond, and much new planting in progress. Ornamental kitchen garden with pergola. Herb garden designed by Rosemary Verey. Listed C16 house (not open). Unusual plants for sale from Green Farm Plants. TEAS. *Adm £2 Chd free (Share to Alzheimers Disease Soc®) Suns April 21, June 9 (2-6)*

Lower Chilworth Farm &※ (Mr & Mrs Michael Hedges) Milton Common is on A329 Thame to Wallingford Rd by junction 7 and 8 off M40 and signposted off A418 Thame to Oxford Rd. The farm is ½m NW of village on old A40 (line of poplar trees down drive). 1-acre informal garden in a lovely setting, incl walled, sunken and courtyard gardens, scree, herbaceous and shrub borders; water feature. Nature trail incl a 2-acre lake and old railway track. Dogs welcome on trail only. TEAS. *Adm £1 Chd free. Mon May 27, Sun June 23 (2-6)*

Magdalen College See Oxford University Gardens

Manor Farm &❀ (Sir Peter & Lady Parker), Old Minster Lovell. Off B4047 Witney-Burford rd; turn R at sign to Old Minster Lovell and Leafield; in ¼m cross Windrush bridge, turn R at Old Swan; no parking in village, follow signs to large free car park. Adjoining churchyard and ruins of Minster (open); C14 dovecote. Owner is author of book about her garden: 'Purest of Pleasures'. TEAS by WI. *Adm £2 Chd free. Sun June 23 (2-5). Parties welcome by appt*

The Manor House, Sutton Courtenay &※❀ (The Hon David Astor) 4m S of Abingdon. Out of Abingdon on the A415. Turn off to Culham − Sutton Courtenay. From A34 going N come into Milton Village take last rd on R to Sutton Courtenay. 10 acres of garden approx 100 acres of land. ½m R Thames Bank. TEAS. *Adm £1.50 Chd 50p. Sun May 12 (2-6)*

The Manor House, Wheatley ※❀ (Mr & Mrs T G Hassall) 26 High St, Wheatley. Off A40 E of Oxford. 1½-acre garden of Elizabethan manor house; formal box walk. Herb garden, cottage garden with rose arches and a shrubbery with old roses. A romantic oasis in this busy village. TEAS in aid of Wheatley Windmill Restoration Society. *Adm £1 Chd free. Sun June 23 (2-6)*

The Mill House, Stadhampton & (Mr & Mrs F A Peet) A329/B480, 8m SE of Oxford. 1-acre family garden with old mill and stream. Mill not working but machinery largely intact and wheel turning with pumped water. Parking on green; parking for disabled only at house. TEAS in aid of Stadhampton Church Restoration Fund. *Adm £1 Chd free. Sun April 21 (2-5.30)*

The Mill House, Sutton Courtenay &※❀ (Mrs J Stevens) S of Abingdon. Approx 8½ acres; R Thames runs through garden which is on several islands with mill pond and old paper mill. TEAS. *Adm £3 Chd £1; under 4's free. Suns March 31, June 16, Sept 29 (2-6). Parties of 10 and over welcome, please Tel 01235 848219*

Mount Skippet &※❀ (Dr & Mrs M A T Rogers) Ramsden, 4m N of Witney. At Xrds turn E towards Finstock; after 30yds, turn R (sign-post Mount Skippet). After 400yds turn L (No Through Way sign) for 75yds. 2 acres; 2 rock gardens; alpine house; stone troughs; shrubs; herbaceous; primulas; conservatory; many rare plants. Fine views. Cotswold stone house largely C17. Teas for groups by prior arrangement. *Adm £1 Chd free. Private visits welcome April 1 to Sept 30, please Tel 01993 868253*

Nettlebed Gardens On A4130, some 5m NW of Henley-on-Thames. Take B481 towards Reading and after 200yds turn R into Sue Ryder Home where there is ample parking. Teas and Plant sales in aid of Sue Ryder Home. *Combined adm £2 Chd free. Sun May 26 (2-5.30)*
   Sue Ryder Home ㅗ⚘❀ (The Sue Ryder Foundation) 26-acre garden surrounding large Edwardian house (not open). Fine rhododendrons and rare trees. Large lawns, pond and Italian terrace. The dell and secret garden are in the course of replanting
   ¶**Red Lion House** ㅗ⚘ (Mr & Mrs G Freeman)
   ¶**The Small House** ⚘ (Mrs A Gordon) Two cottage gardens with unusual plants

New College See Oxford University Gardens

4 Northfield Cottages ㅗ❀ (Miss S E Bedwell) Water Eaton, nr Kidlington. From Sainsbury Roundabout S of Kidlington on A4260 take exit for A34 N. Take 1st R Water Eaton lane opp Kings Arms. Then 1st L following signs for Northfield Farm. A cottage garden of approx ¼-acre designed over last 7yrs. Mainly herbaceous, unusual plants, fruit, vegetables and greenhouse. *Adm £1. Every Tues, Fri, Sat, March 16 to Sept 14 (2-5). Private visits welcome all year, please* **Tel 01865 378910**

Nutford Lodge ㅗ❀ (Mr & Mrs K Elmore) In Longcot Village next to The King & Queen public house. S of A420 between Faringdon and Shrivenham. 1½-acre sculpture garden with accent on fragrance, for the blind. Ponds, rockeries, colour schemed borders, potager, views to White Horse; indoor gallery. *Adm 75p Chd free (Share to Headway in Oxford®). Sun May 26 to Sun June 2 incl (2-6). Also private visits welcome, please* **Tel 01793 782258**

¶**Old Church House** ㅗ (Dr & Mrs Dick Squires) Wantage. At the crossway of A417 and A338. Situated next to Parish Church nr the Wantage market square. An unusual town garden running down to the Letcombe brook. Much interest with different levels, follies, water, mature trees and many special plants. Tickets and teas at Vale & Downland Museum close by in Church St. *Adm £1 Chd free (Share to Vale & Downland Trust®) Tues to Fris. Private visits also welcome, please* **Tel 01235 762785**

The Old Rectory, Brightwell Baldwin ㅗ❀ (Mr & Mrs Donald Chilvers) 2m W of Watlington via Cuxham (B480) or 1½m E of Benson on B4009 and then signposted to Brightwell Baldwin. On R side E of Church 100 yds. 1½-acre garden and parkland surrounding beautiful Georgian rectory. Open views to S over ha-ha. Formal garden layout with herb, rose and herbaceous beds, terracing and walls. Designed by owners and planted 1990, yet mature; rare breed sheep. Teas and plant sales in aid of local church (C14). *Adm £2 Chd free. Sun July 28 (2.30-6)*

The Old Rectory, Coleshill ㅗ (Mr & Mrs Martin) 3m W of Faringdon. Coleshill (a Nat Trust village) is on B4019, midway between Faringdon and Highworth. Medium-sized garden; lawns and informal shrub beds; wide variety shrubs, incl old-fashioned roses; 40-yr-old standard wisteria. Distant views of Berkshire and Wiltshire Downs. House dates from late C14. *TEAS. Adm £1 Chd free. Suns April 14 (2-6), Sept 15 (2-5)*

The Old Rectory, Farnborough nr Wantage. See Berkshire

Oxford See also 23 Beech Croft Road, East Oxford, Headington, Iffley

Oxford University Gardens
   Christ Church ⚘ **Masters' Garden** Entrance on Christ Church Meadow (through War Memorial garden on St Aldates'). Created in 1926, has herbaceous borders and a new border with some unusual shrubs. A walk through the newly designed and replanted Pocock Garden, past Pocock's plane, an oriental plane planted in 1636, leads to the Cathedral Garden. *Adm £1 Chd free Combined adm £2.50 with* **Corpus Christi** *and* **Trinity College** *gardens. Sun Aug 11 (2-5)*
   Corpus Christi ㅗ⚘ Entrance from Merton St or Christ Church **Fellows' garden**. Several small gardens and courtyards overlooking Christchurch meadows. Fellow's private garden not normally open to the public. TEAS in aid of 'Breakthrough Breast Cancer'. *Adm £1. Combined adm £2.50 with* **Christ Church** *and* **Trinity College** *gardens. Sun Aug 11 (2-5)*
   Exeter College, Rector's Lodgings The Turl, between High & Broad Sts, Oxford. Small enclosed garden, herbaceous and shrubs, especially clematis. Fellows' Garden and Chapel also open. *Combined adm with* **New College** *£1.50 Chd free. Sun June 23 (2-5)*
   Green College ㅗ⚘ Woodstock Rd, next to Radcliffe Infirmary. 3 acres; lawns, herbaceous borders, medicinal garden with notes on traditional usage of plants. Radcliffe Observatory (Tower of the Winds) open for views of Oxford and TEAS. *Adm £1 Chd free (incl Observatory). Sun June 16 (2-6)*
   Holywell Manor ⚘ (Balliol College) Central Oxford at corner of Manor Rd and St Cross Rd on L of St Cross Church opp law library. College garden of about 1 acre, not normally open to the public. Imaginatively laid out 50 yrs ago around horse chestnut to give formal and informal areas. Mature ginkgo avenue, spinney with spring flowers and bulbs. *Adm £1 Chd free. Sun June 30 (10-4). Private visits welcome, please* **Tel 01865 271501**
   Magdalen College and Fellows' Garden (and **President's Garden** not normally open to the public) ㅗ⚘ High Street Oxford. Entrance in High St. 60 acres including deer park, college lawns, numerous trees 150-200 yrs old, notable herbaceous and shrub plantings; Magdalen Meadows is surrounded by Addison's Walk, a tree lined circuit by the R Cherwell developed since the late C18. An ancient herd of 60 deer is located in the grounds. TEAS. *Adm £1.50 Chd £1. Sun March 24 (1-5). Private visits welcome by arrangement with Home Bursar* **Tel 01865 276050**
   New College ⚘ **Warden's Garden** Entered from New College Lane, off Catte St. Secret walled garden, replanted 1988 with interesting mix of herbaceous and shrubs. *Adm £1 Chd free. Combined adm with* **Exeter College** *£1.50. Sun June 23 (2-5). Private visits welcome for parties of 4 and over, please* **Tel 01865 249002**

Queen's College, Provost's, Fellows' and Nuns' Gardens ⚲ High Street. ½ acre with splendid herbaceous borders, rose garden, high old stone walls; large ilex tree. Magnificent statues set in wall of Hawksmoor's library (viewed from Provost's garden). Teas 43 St Giles (in their garden if fine). *Combined adm with* **Wadham College** *£1.50. Sun July 21 (2-5)*

Rewley House ♿⚲ (Oxford University Dept for Continuing Education) Wellington Sq., St John Street. Roof Garden, 60ft × 26ft, and courtyard gardens, planted by townscaper, Jeanne Bliss, with variegated shrubs, climbers, trailing plants in mobile boxes on wheels. Maintained by the University Parks under the direction of Walter Sawyer. TEA. *Adm £1 Chd free. Suns July 21, 28 (2-5). Private visits welcome, please* **Tel 01865 270375**

St Hilda's College ♿ Approx 15 mins walk E from city centre. Cross Magdalen Bridge and turn R at roundabout into Cowley Place. College Lodge at end on R. Or park in public car park at St Clements. Approx 5 acres laid to lawns and flower beds with flood plain meadow containing interesting wild flowers. TEA. *Adm £1 Chd under 12 free. Sun March 24 (2-5)*

St Hugh's College ♿⚲ At intersection of St Margaret's Rd and Banbury Rd, N of city centre. 10 acres comprising main garden, Principal's and Fellows' gardens largely developed from grounds of 3 early C19 houses with some original features remaining. Fine trees, many shrubs, herbaceous plants; dell garden developed from Victorian fernery; large terrace. TEAS. *Adm £1 Chd free. Sun April 28 (2-5.30)*

Templeton College ♿❀ Kennington. Signposted off Oxford S Ring Rd, in triangle before it joins A34. Landscaped for ease of maintenance by the late Alan Mitchell, author of Collins 'Field Guide to the Trees of Britain & Northern Europe', the College's 37 acres have been planted with more than 20,000 trees during the past 25yrs and are ringed with footpaths. Alan's mastery of shape, colour and form in trees and shrubs is noticeable in this low maintenance layout. Informal, pond and cottage garden plantings, many designed by Stephanie Carter to harmonise with the uncompromisingly modern main buildings and the more traditional graduate residences at Egrove Farmhouse. Formal herb garden designed by Paul Edwards. Exceptional plant stall in aid of British Heart Foundation. TEAS. *Adm £1.50 Acc chd free. Sun Sept 1 (2-5.30)*

Trinity College ♿⚲❀ **President's Garden**. Entrance in Broad St. Surrounded by high old stone walls, recently redesigned, has mixed borders of herbaceous and shrubs, and statuary. Historic main college gardens with specimen trees incl 200-yr-old forked catalpa and splendid ailanthus, fine long herbaceous border and handsome garden quad originally designed by Wren. **Fellows' Garden** Small walled terrace, herbaceous borders; water feature formed by Jacobean stone heraldic beasts. TEAS in aid of local charities. *Adm £1 Chd free. Combined adm £2.50 with* **Christ Church** *and* **Corpus Christi College** *gardens. Sun Aug 11 (2-5)*

University Arboretum ⚲❀ 6m S of Oxford on A4074 (formerly A423), 400yds S of Nuneham Courtenay. 55 acres incl informal rhododendron walks, camellia, bamboo and acer collections, natural woodland and oak woodland, meadow with pond and associated aqu-

atics and marginals; fine collection of mature conifers; many 150 yrs old. Staff available to answer queries. Large sale of unusual plants. Plant stall in aid of Oxford University Botanic Garden. *Adm £1 Chd free. Sun June 2 (2-5)*

Wadham College ♿⚲ **Fellows' Private Garden & Warden's Garden** Parks Rd. 5 acres, best known for trees and herbaceous borders. In the Fellows' main garden, fine ginkgo and Magnolia acuminata, etc; in the Back Quadrangle very large Tilia tomentosa 'Petiolaris'; in Mallam Court white scented garden est 1994; in the Warden's garden an ancient tulip tree; in the Fellows' private garden Civil War embankment with period fruit tree cultivars, recently established shrubbery with unusual trees and ground cover amongst older plantings. Teas 43 St Giles (July 21 only). *Adm £1 Chd free. Sun March 24. Combined adm with* **Queen's College** *£1.50. Sun July 21 (2-5)*

Wolfson College ♿❀ End of Linton Rd, off Banbury Rd, between city centre and Summertown shops. 9 acres by R Cherwell; garden developed in recent years with comprehensive plant collection tolerant of alkaline soils, grown in interesting and varied habitats both formal and informal, around a framework of fine mature trees; award winning building designed by Powell & Moya; President's garden. TEAS. *Adm £1 Chd free. Sun May 26 (2-6)*

Pettifers See Wardington Gardens

Queen's College See Oxford University Gardens

Querns ♿⚲❀ (Mr M & the Hon Mrs Whitfeld) Goring Heath. 3m NE of Pangbourne. Take B4526 from A4074 Reading-Oxford Rd. After ½m follow signs. 2-acre garden: shrub and herbaceous borders, rose garden, shrub rose garden, courtyard and formal pond. Listed house dating from early C16 with large thatched C17 barn. TEAS. *Adm £1.25 Chd free. Sun June 23 (2-6)*

Rewley House See Oxford University Gardens

Rofford Manor ♿⚲❀ (Mr & Mrs J L Mogford) Little Milton. 10m SE of Oxford. 1m from Little Milton on Chalgrove Rd. Signposted Rofford only. 2 acres of gardens, within old walls laid out since 1985. Vegetable, herb, rose and swimming pool gardens. Box garden with raised pool. Yew hedges and pleached limes. Twin herbaceous borders planted Autumn 1989 flanking lawn leading to recently constructed ha-ha. TEAS. *Adm £2 Chd free. Sun Sept 8 (2-6). Private visits welcome following written application*

St Hilda's College and **St Hugh's College** See Oxford University Gardens

Salford Gardens ⚲ 2m W of Chipping Norton. Off A44 Oxford-Worcester. TEAS. *Combined adm £1.50 Chd free. Suns June 23, Aug 25 (2-6). Also open 2nd Tuesday of month April to July (2-5)*

⠀⠀**Old Rectory** ♿❀ (Mr & Mrs N M Chambers) 1½-acre garden mainly enclosed by walls. A garden of year round interest with unusual plants in mixed borders, many old roses, orchard and traditional vegetable garden

Willow Tree Cottage ✿ (Mr & Mrs J Shapley) Small walled twin gardens; one created by owners since 1979 with shrub and herbaceous borders, many clematis; other created 1985 from old farmyard with heathers and large alpine garden. Featured in 'Successful Gardening'

Seven Bells Cottage ఈ✿✿ (Dr & Mrs M Pusey) Southend Garsington. SE of Oxford, N of B480. An intriguing 1-acre garden developed since 1986, with wide-ranging views of the countryside. Herbaceous border, island beds, vegetables, dell, wildlife areas, ponds and bog garden. Garden sculptures. Small C16 thatched farmhouse. TEAS in aid of Women's Aid/Sacred Heart Church. *Adm £1. Suns May 26, July 14 (2-6). Private visits welcome, please* **Tel 01865 361488**

Shotover House ఈ✿ (Lt-Col Sir John Miller) Wheatley, 6m E of Oxford on A40. Bus: Oxford-Thame or Oxford-High Wycombe-London; alight Islip turn. Large unaltered landscape garden with ornamental temples, lawns and specimen trees. Also small collection of rare cattle, sheep and birds. TEAS (in arcade with view of lake). *Adm £1.50 Chd free. Suns April 7, July 7 (2-6)*

Shucklets ✿✿ (Dr & Mrs G Garton) High Street Ramsden. 3m N of Witney off B4022, near centre of village. Plantsman's garden of 2 acres, with a variety of different areas: rock garden, raised beds, troughs; foliage plants, shrubs, old-fashioned roses; ornamental vegetable garden, small vineyard. Teas for large parties by WI in village hall. *Adm £1.50 Chd free. Private visits welcome April 1 to Sept 30, please* **Tel 01993 868659**

Sibford Ferris Gardens ✿ Near the Warwickshire border, S of B4035 (Banbury 6½m, Shipston-on-Stour 7½m). TEAS in aid of Sibford Primary School PTA. *Combined adm £1.50 Chd free. Sun June 30 (2-6)*

> **Back Acre** ✿ (Mr & Mrs F A Lamb) Almost an acre, much of which is wild woodland and rough grass with wild flowers; rockery and pond, constructed about 100 years ago and restored over the last few years
>
> **Home Close** (Mr & Mrs P A Randall) Cotswold stone house fronting formal 1¼-acre garden designed by Baillie-Scott in 1911, under restoration. Courtyard with ornamental fountain and Roman-style stone recesses. Terraced garden, large variety of shrubs including rare species
>
> **Maria's House** ఈ (Mr & Mrs B R Mills) ¼-acre old cottage garden, surrounded and subdivided by low stone walling. Features incl box hedge porch, small pond, rockeries and herbaceous borders
>
> **Sibford School** ✿ (The Manor Walled Gardens) 1½ acres of walled gardens, completely reconstructed and replanted since 1984. Designed with central pergola covered pathways, with many varieties of climbing roses and clematis. The garden is subdivided to provide vegetable plots, soft fruit, greenhouses and herb garden. The gardens are used for the teaching of horticulture and are maintained by students at the school

Sibford Gower Gardens Near the Warwickshire border, S of B4035 (Banbury 7m, Shipston-on-Stour 7m) Superlative views and numerous intriguing tucked away lanes

are features of this village. TEAS in aid of Sibford Primary School

Sun, Wed June 16, 19 *(2-6) Combined adm £2 Chd free*

> **Handywater Farm** ✿✿ (Mr & Mrs W B Colquhoun) ½m N of Sibford Gower on rd to Epwell; 1½ acre family garden in process of creation since 1980. Lovely setting in open rolling countryside. Westerly sloping lawns, stream and ponds, shrub and herbaceous beds
>
> **Meadow Cottage** ఈ✿✿ (Mr & Mrs Roger Powell) 6 The Colony. At S end of village. A 1.3-acre garden started from a field in 1988. Large 'shrubaceous' borders; over 1300 different plants; many unusual. Conifers; shrub roses and alpines in raised beds; budding arboretum and series of waterfalls leading to stream. Views

Sun July 21 *(2-6) Combined adm £2 Chd free*

> **Carters Yard** (Mr & Mrs W J S Clutterbuck) Next to Wykeham Arms. ⅓-acre very private cottage garden. Various beds and rockeries in soft colours
>
> **The Manor House** ఈ (Mr & Mrs Roger Garner) Opp Wykeham Arms. Completely reconstructed May 1989, the gardens (under 1 acre) are already well established and complement the romantic atmosphere of this recently renovated rambling thatched manor house
>
> **Meadow Cottage** (as described for earlier dates)
>
> **Temple Close** ఈ✿ (Mrs Vera Jones) E of Wykeham Arms. 1¼ acres with rockery, various beds of shrubs, roses, perennials and herbs; paved stream-side walk running through extensive water garden between two ponds with fountains; pets paddock; good view

Souldern Gardens Between Banbury (8m) and Bicester (7m) off B4100. 4 gardens in picturesque 'Best Kept' prizewinning village. TEAS. *Combined adm £2 Chd free (Share to Souldern Trust®). Sun June 23 (2-6)*

> **The Barn** ✿ (Mr J Talbot) Sheltered garden with pond; wide mixed borders
>
> **Great House Close** ఈ✿ (Mrs C E Thornton) Long, varied garden and orchard framed by old farm buildings
>
> **The Old Forge** (Mr & Mrs D Duthie) Resourceful, densely planted cottage garden with stone walling
>
> **Souldern Manor** ఈ✿ (Mr & Dr C Sanders) 25 acres of C17 house with much fresh development. Linked ponds, rock garden, waterfall, fountains, temple, pavilions and view of Cherwell valley are enhanced by many newly planted mature trees. Children's play area

South Newington Gardens A small village 1½m from Bloxham, nr Banbury on A361 to Chipping Norton. It has a fine church, with superb mediaeval wall paintings. TEA at the village hall with stalls. 3 gardens within easy walking distance. *Combined adm £1.50 Chd free. Sun June 2 (2-6)*

> **Applegarth** ✿ (Mrs Jenny Butcher) ¾- acre cottage garden with a rose walk featuring old-fashioned roses and lavenders; herbaceous borders and mixed borders with some unusual shrubs and young trees; small water garden and pond
>
> **The Barn** ఈ✿ (Mrs Rosemary Clark) Green Lane. 1 acre of lawns and mixed borders with outdoor chess game, croquet lawn, trompe l'oeuil, vine walk and vegetable patch
>
> **The Little Forge** ఈ (Mr M B Pritchard) Small garden with shrubs; trees and vegetable patch

Sparsholt Manor (Sir Adrian & Lady Judith Swire) Off B4507 Ashbury Rd 3½m W of Wantage. Spring garden, lakes and wilderness. Teas in village hall. *Adm £1 Chd free (Share to St John Ambulance, Wantage Division®). Mon May 27 (2- 6)*

Stansfield ✿✿ (Mr & Mrs D Keeble) 49 High St, Stanford-in-the-Vale. 3½m SE of Faringdon. Turn off A417 opp Vale Garage into High St 300yds. Park in street. Plantsman's 1¼-acre garden on alkaline soil. Wide range of plants, many uncommon. Scree bed, sinks and troughs, damp garden, herbaceous borders, ornamental grasses. Copse underplanted with hellebores and shade loving plants. Aromatic plants. Unusual trees and shrubs. Yr-round interest. Wide range of plants for sale. Listed in Good Gardens Guide. Featured in TV's Secret Garden 95. TEAS. *Adm £1 Chd free. Every Tues April 2 to Sept 24 (10-4) Suns June 9, Aug 4 (2-6). Private visits also welcome, please* **Tel 01367 710340**

Stanton Harcourt Manor ও (Mr Crispin & The Hon Mrs Gascoigne) W of Oxford on B4449. Picturesque stone manor house with unique C15 Great Kitchen, Chapel and Pope's Tower. Formal gardens leading to woodland area with remains of moat and medieval stew ponds. TEAS. *Adm House and garden £4 Chd/OAP's £2. Garden only £2.50 Chd/OAP's £1.50. Thurs April 18, May 2, 16, June 6, 20, July 4, 18, Aug 1, 15, Sept 5, 19, Suns April 7, 21, May 5, 19, 26, June 9, 23, July 7, 21, Aug 4, 18, 25, Sept 8, 22, Bank hol Mons April 8, May 6, 27, Aug 26. For NGS Suns April 21, June 9 (2-6)*

Steeple & Middle Aston Gardens. Beautiful stone villages midway between Oxford & Banbury, ½m off A4260. Villages bordering Cherwell valley; interesting church and winding lanes with a variety of charming stone houses and cottages. Map available at all gardens. TEAS at Canterbury House in aid of local scout group. *Combined adm £2 Chd free. Sun June 9 (1-6)*

   Home Farm House ✿✿ (Mr & Mrs T J G Parsons) ¾m N of Steeple Aston, opp Middle Aston House. 1-acre informal garden surrounding C17 farmhouse, fine view. Mixed planting, incl unusual perennials, shrubs and roses. Interesting small nursery. *Private visits welcome May to Oct, please* **Tel 018693 40666**

   Middle Aston House ও✿ (Pera Group) ¾m N of Steeple Aston. 20 acres of grounds landscaped in C18 by William Kent, incl 2 lakes, granary and icehouse

   Canterbury House ও✿ (Mr & Mrs M G Norris) Former rectory in 2-acre garden with mature trees and interseted by walls. The garden is continually being redeveloped for ease of maintenance, interest and attraction of wildlife. *(Share to Specialcare Baby Unit, John Radcliffe)*

   The Longbyre (Mr & Mrs V Billings) Hornton stone house in ¼ acre. Garden constructed out of old orchard. Water feature, mixed perennials, shrubs, tubs on different levels

   Kralingen (Mr & Mrs Roderick Nicholson) 2-acre informal garden designed for low maintenance without any professional help. Great variety of interesting trees and shrubs. Water garden and wild flower area

   Willow Cottage ✿ (Mr & Mrs M Vivian) The Dickredge, opp White Lion. Hornton stone cottage with ½-acre garden. Old-fashioned shrub roses, many unusual plants in garden and conservatory. Fish pond with Koi

Rowans ও✿ (Mr & Mrs M J Clist) The Dickredge, opp White Lion. An acre of orchard and mixed garden, incl shrubs, herbaceous borders, alpines, vegetables and small streamside area

Stonewalls ও✿ (Mr & Mrs B Shafighian) Hempton. 1½m W of Deddington on B4031. A plantsman's garden of 1½ acres divided into many interesting areas, incl shrubbery, herbaceous border, conifer and heather bed, nearly 200 clematis and climbers. Sunken pool. TEAS in aid of St John's Church, Hempton. *Adm £1 Chd free. Sun July 14 (2-6)*

Stratton Audley Gardens ও✿ 3m NE of Bicester, off A421 to Buckingham. Village dates from Roman times. Church is largely mediaeval with spectacular late C17 tomb. TEAS at Red Lion Inn. *Combined adm £1.50 Chd free (Share to Helen House Hospice®). Sun June 9 (2-6)*

   1 Church Cottages (Mr & Mrs L Sweetman) About ½-acre. A proper country cottage garden with rockery pools and stonework, vegetables, seasonal bedding, orchids

   Mallories (Mr P Boyd) Mainly walled garden of ¾ acre behind row of C17 cottages converted to house. Sunny and shady herbaceous borders, bearded irises, old roses and other shrubs, wall plants and climbers, small conservatory

Swalcliffe Lea House ✿✿ (Jeffrey & Christine Demmar) Swalcliffe Lea. Situated between Tadmarton and Shutford. The garden has been developed during the last 8 yrs. It covers 7 acres with lawns, flower beds, water, herb garden, pergola, vegetables, orchard and 'nature reserve'. There is a wide range of young trees, shrubs and plants. *Adm £1.50 Chd free. Sun June 16 (2-6)*

Swerford Park (Mr & Mrs J W Law) 4m NE of Chipping Norton, just off A361 to Banbury, ½m W of Swerford Church. In extensive parkland setting with lakeside walks, garden of Georgian house overlooks spectacular wooded valley with series of lakes linked by waterfalls. Approach along front drive where signed; parking at rear only, may not be very close. TEAS. *Adm £1.50 Chd free (Share to Swan Lifeline, Windsor®). Mon May 27 (2-6)*

Swinbrook House ও✿ (Mr & Mrs J D Mackinnon) 1½m N of Swinbrook on Shipton-under-Wychwood Rd. Large garden; herbaceous border; shrubs; shrub roses; large kitchen garden; fine views. Picnics allowed. TEA. *Adm £1 Chd free. Sun June 30 (2-6)*

Swyncombe House ও✿ (Mr & Mrs W J Christie-Miller) Follow main rd from Cookley Green towards Ewelme. Turn L at Rectory corner. Parkland with mature trees, flowers and spring bulbs. TEAS and plants in aid of St Botolph Church. *Adm £1 Chd free. Sun April 14 (2-7)*

Tadmarton Gardens 5m SW of Banbury on B4035. Refreshments (2-5) at village hall in aid of St Nicholas Church, Tadmarton. *Combined adm £1.50 Chd free. Suns April 14, Sept 22 (2-6)*

   The Arches ও✿ (Mr & Mrs J Bolland) ⅓-acre garden hidden at back of 30's house, lovingly designed for disabled occupant. Stone paths, open air 'rooms', summer houses. A garden for sitting in

Buxton House ♿✿ (Mr & Mrs J Steele) Small garden created in last 10yrs incl a waterfall and two fountains
Tadmarton Manor ♿✿ (Mr & Mrs R K Asser) Old established 2½-acre garden; beautiful views of unspoilt countryside; field of daffodils; fine trees, great variety of perennial plants and shrubs; hardy cyclamen, tunnel arbour; C15 barn and C18 dovecote

Taynton House ♿✿✿ (Mr & Mrs David Mackenzie) Taynton, off A424 Burford to Stow-on-the-Wold. Medium-sized garden behind listed stone house in delightful Cotswold village with interesting church. Stream and copse with thousands of daffodils and spring flowers. TEAS. *Adm £1 Chd free (Share to St John's Church, Taynton®). Sun March 31 (2-6)*

Templeton College See Oxford University Gardens

Towersey Manor ♿✿ (Mr & Mrs U D Barnett) Towersey, 1½m SE of Thame, 300 yds down Manor Rd from Xrds in middle of village. Main garden of 2 acres lies behind house. Designed and planted within last 20 yrs by present owners. Formal hornbeam hedges frame smaller informal areas incorporating many shrubs, trees and old-fashioned and modern shrub roses. *Adm £1.50 Chd free. Private visits welcome on weekdays May to July, please* **Tel 01844 212077**

Town Farm Cottage ♿✿✿ (Mr & Mrs J Clark) Kingston Blount. 4m S of Thame. 4m NE of Watlington. 1½m NE of junction 6, M40 on B4009. 1-acre colourful garden developed over 7 yrs by present plantaholic owners. Herbaceous borders, rockeries, scree beds and shrubs, rare English native black poplar trees by small lake. Many unusual plants. TEAS. *Adm £1 Chd under 14 free. Suns April 28, June 9 (2-6). Private visits also welcome, please* **Tel 01844 352152**

Trinity College see Oxford University Gardens

¶**Upper Green** ♿✿ (Peter & Susan Burge) Horton cum Studley. 6m NE of Oxford off B4027. Follow road through village past Studley Priory Hotel. Turn L at T-junction. Garden is 200yds on R. Informal ½-acre, plant-lover's garden on clay. Developed over 10yrs in an old orchard. Incl gravel planting, small wild-life pond, wet bed, climbers, shrub and climbing roses, many herbaceous plants and herbs. Combine with visit to **Field House, Murcott**, less than 2m away. *Adm £1.50 Chd free (Share to Skin Disease Research Fund®). Sun June 30 (2-5.30)*

¶**Upper Wolvercote Gardens** N Oxford. Secluded old village within Oxford's ring rd. From Oxford take 'First Turn' L off Woodstock Rd; park at Plough Inn or beside village green. TEAS at Plough. Walk up Church Lane (unmetalled) from Green. Cluster of old houses by church, with hillside gardens overlooking Port Meadow and Wytham woods. *Combined adm £1 Chd free. Sun April 14 (2-5)*

¶**The Close** ♿✿✿ (Dr & Mrs H G Reading) ¾-acre terraced front garden with spectacular views framed by trees. Orchard with daffodils at rear
¶**Old Church House** ♿✿ (Mr & Mrs E M Loft-Simson) C17 vine-covered cottage with small walled 'hortus conclusus', with fountain

¶**Church Farm House** ♿✿ (Mr & Mrs S Franks) C17 house with ½-acre garden. Fruit trees and roses bordered by low box hedges; Cotswold stone walls, lawn with daffodils, marble statue among lime trees

University Arboretum See Oxford University Gardens

Wadham College See Oxford University Gardens

Wardington Gardens 5m NE of Banbury. TEAS. *Combined adm £2.50 Chd free. Sun May 19 (2-5.30)*
Pettifers ♿✿✿ (Mr J & the Hon Mrs Price) Lower Wardington C17 village house. 1-acre plantsman's garden frames an exceptional view of sheep pastures and wooded hills. A lot of new planting, with some areas reaching maturity. Unusual plants for sale. TEAS. *Adm £1.50 Chd free. Also open Suns June 16, Sept 15 (2-6)*
Wardington Manor ♿ (The Lord & Lady Wardington) 5-acre garden with topiary, rock garden, flowering shrub walk to pond. Carolean manor house 1665 (2-5.30). *Private visits by parties also welcome adm £2, please* **Tel 01295 750202**

Waterperry Gardens ♿✿ 2½m from Wheatley M40 Junction 8. 50m from London, 62m from Birmingham, 9m E of Oxford. Gardens well signed locally with Tourist Board 'rose' symbol. 20-acres; ornamental gardens, nurseries, parkland; many interesting plants; shrub, herbaceous and alpine nurseries; glasshouses and comprehensive fruit section. High quality plant centre, garden shop (**Tel 01844 339226**). TEA SHOP, Art and Craft Gallery. Saxon church with famous glasses and brasses in grounds. *Adm Gardens & Nurseries £2.30 OAPs £1.80 Chd £1 under 10 free.* **OPEN DAILY** *except Christmas and New Year hols and July 18 to 21. Coach parties by appt only* **Tel 01844 339254**. *For NGS (Share to NCCPG®). Suns June 9, Aug 11 (10-6)*

Weald Manor See Bampton & Weald Gardens

Westwell Manor ✿✿ (Mr & Mrs T H Gibson). 2m SW of Burford, from A40 Burford-Cheltenham, turn L after ½m on narrow rd signposted Westwell. Unspoilt hamlet with delightful church. 6 acres surrounding old Cotswold manor house, knot and water gardens, potager, shrub roses, herbaceous borders, topiary, moonlight garden. *Adm £2 Chd 50p (Share to St Mary's Church Westwell®). Sun May 5 (2-6.30)*

White's Farm House ♿✿ (Dr & Mrs M Shone) Letcombe Bassett 3m SW of Wantage. Take B4507 signed Ashbury, then through Letcombe Regis. 2½ acres; mixed borders; wild garden with 30 yrs growth of chalk-tolerant trees, shrubs, unusual herbaceous plants, summer bulbs. Gravel scree bed, plants in pots and tubs, pond, playground and monster adventure walk. New wood and willow features. TEAS in C18 barn. *Adm £1.50 Chd free. Suns June 23, July 21 (2-6)*

By Appointment Gardens. These owners do not have a fixed opening day usually because they do not like crowds or have insufficient parking space. Owner will often give guided tour.

Wick Hall & Nurseries ▲✿❀ (Mr & Mrs P Drysdale) Between Abingdon & Radley on Audlett Drive. Parking for disabled at house, some off-street parking. Approx 10 acres lawns and wild garden; topiary; ericaceous bed; pond garden; rockeries; walled garden enclosing knot garden. Young arboretum. Early C18 house (not open), barn and greenhouses garden restored and developed since 1982. TEAS. *Adm £1.50 Chd free. Sun April 28 (2-5)*

Wilcote House ▲❀ (The Hon C E & Mrs Cecil) Finstock. Between Finstock & North Leigh. East of B4022 Witney-Charlbury Road. Approx 7 acres set in parkland surrounding an early C17-C19 Cotswold stone house. Shrub and herbaceous borders, old-fashioned rose garden and 40yd laburnum walk (planted 1984). Old orchard being replanted as an arboretum. Spring bulbs, flowering trees, sheep and lovely views. TEAS. *Adm £1.50 Chd free (Share to Homelife DGAA & British Legion®). For NGS Suns April 7, Oct 6 (2-5.30). Private visits also welcome on weekdays, please contact Mr Pollard on* **Tel 01993 868 606**

Wolfson College see Oxford University Gardens

Wood Croft ✿❀ (St Cross College) Foxcombe Lane, Boars Hill, S of Oxford. From ring rd follow signs to Wootton and Boars Hill. From junction at top Hinksey Hill, house first on L. 1½ acres designed and planted by the late Prof G E Blackman FRS. Rhododendrons, camellias, azaleas, many varieties primula in woodland and surrounding natural pond; fine trees. TEA. *Adm £1 Chd free (Share to Royal Marsden Hospital Development Appeal®). Sun May 19 (2-6)*

Wroxton Gardens ▲❀ 3m NW of Banbury off A422. Grounds of Wroxton Abbey open free. Teas at village fete May. TEAS in aid of Wroxton Church Bell Fund, **Laurels Farm** Aug. *Combined adm £1.30 Chd free. Mon May 27. Also open with* **Home Farm, Balscote** *Sun Aug 4 (1-6)*

    6 The Firs Stratford Rd (Mr & Mrs D J Allen) Approx ⅓-acre family garden with island beds, shrubs, herbaceous perennials and alpines incl large collection of cranesbill geraniums

    Laurels Farm (Mr & Mrs R Fox) ½-acre with island beds, shrubs, old roses and herbaceous perennials. *(Share to Katherine House Hospice)*

¶**Yelford Gardens** ▲✿❀ From Witney 2m from A40 take A415. 1m S towards Standlake or Abingdon just past Cokethorpe School at Hardwick X-rd turn R. Single track rd with passing places. TEAS. *Adm £3 Chd free (Share to St Nicholas & St Swithuns, Yelford®). Sun June 23 (2-6)*

    ¶**Broad Leas House** (Mr & Mrs Rogers) 1-acre plantsman's garden started 16 years ago. Herbaceous borders, shrubberies, lawns, spindle apple trees, vegetable garden with soft fruit area and small formal rose garden

    ¶**College Farm** (Mr & Mrs P M Strainge) 1-acre garden surrounding a farm house. Colourful shrubberies and mixed borders. Lawns, orchard and vegetable garden

    ¶**Yelford Manor** (R Rosewell Esq) 3-acre garden surrounding C15 timber framed manor house (not open). Knot gardens, clipped yews, shrubs, borders, moat garden and lawns

Yeomans ❀ (Mrs M E Pedder) Tadmarton 5m SW of Banbury on B4035. Small garden on 4 levels, featured in 'Easy Plants for Difficult Places' by Geoffrey Smith; C16 thatched cottage. Colourful from spring to autumn; wide variety annuals, perennials, shrubs; many climbers inc roses, clematis; shrub roses with hips. *Adm £1 Chd free (Share to Katherine House Hospice Trust®). Private visits welcome for 2 and over, by appt, please. April to Sept* **Tel 01295 780285**

Scotland's Gardens Scheme. The National Gardens Scheme has a similar but quite separate counterpart in Scotland. Called Scotland's Gardens Scheme, it raises money for the Queen's Nursing Institute (Scotland), the Gardens Fund of the National Trust for Scotland and over 160 registered charities nominated by garden owners. The Handbook is available (£3.25 incl p&p) from Scotland's Gardens Scheme, 31 Castle Terrace, Edinburgh EH1 2EL. Telephone 0131-229-1870, Fax 0131-229-0443

Powys

See separate Welsh section beginning on page 310

Rutland

See Leicestershire

Shropshire

Hon County Organisers:	Mrs J H M Stafford, The Old Rectory, Fitz, Shrewsbury SY4 3AS Tel 01743 850555 Mr & Mrs James Goodall, Rectory Cottage, Chetton, Bridgnorth, Shropshire WV16 6UF Mrs K Cooke, Harnage Farm, Cound, Shropshire SY5 6EJ
Hon County Treasurer:	Mrs P Trevor-Jones, Preen Manor, Church Preen, nr Church Stretton SY6 7LQ

DATES OF OPENING

February 25 Sunday
Erway Farm House, Dudleston Heath

March 26 Tuesday
Radnor Cottage, Clun

March 31 Sunday
Erway Farm House, Dudleston Heath
Swallow Hayes, Albrighton

April 6 Saturday
Erway Farm House, Dudleston Heath

April 7 Sunday
Erway Farm House, Dudleston Heath

April 8 Monday
Erway Farm House, Dudleston Heath

April 14 Sunday
Badger Farmhouse, Badger, nr Shifnal

April 16 Tuesday
Radnor Cottage, Clun

April 21 Sunday
Morville Hall Gardens, nr Bridgnorth

April 28 Sunday
Erway Farm House, Dudleston Heath
Field House, Clee St Margaret, nr Ludlow

May 5 Sunday
Adcote School, nr Shrewsbury
Swallow Hayes, Albrighton

May 6 Monday
Millichope Park, Munslow

May 8 Wednesday
Cricklewood Cottage, Minsterley

May 9 Thursday
Cricklewood Cottage, Minsterley

May 12 Sunday
Astley Abbotts House, Bridgnorth
Gatacre Park, Six Ashes
Limeburners, Ironbridge

May 13 Monday
Mawley Hall, nr Cleobury Mortimer

May 14 Tuesday
Radnor Cottage, Clun

May 19 Sunday
Adcote School, nr Shrewsbury

Brownhill House, Ruyton XI Towns
Gatacre Park, Six Ashes
Hatton Grange, Shifnal
Ridgway Wood, Edgton
Willey Park, Broseley

May 26 Sunday
Bitterley Court, Ludlow
Erway Farm House, Dudleston Heath
Longnor Hall, nr Dorrington
Ridgway Wood, Edgton
Walcot Hall, Lydbury North

May 27 Monday
Dudmaston, nr Bridgnorth
Longnor Hall, nr Dorrington
Oteley, Ellesmere
Ridgway Wood, Edgton
Walcot Hall, Lydbury North

May 30 Thursday
Preen Manor, nr Church Stretton

June 1 Saturday
Brownhill House, Ruyton XI Towns

June 2 Sunday
Adcote School, nr Shrewsbury
Brownhill House, Ruyton XI Towns
Lower Hall, Worfield
Swallow Hayes, Albrighton

June 4 Tuesday
Radnor Cottage, Clun

June 7 Friday
Wollerton Old Hall, Market Drayton

June 9 Sunday
The Old Rectory, Fitz
The Old Vicarage, Cardington
The Patch, Acton Pigot

June 11 Tuesday
Weston Park, Shifnal

June 12 Wednesday
Cricklewood Cottage, Minsterley

June 13 Thursday
Cricklewood Cottage, Minsterley

June 14 Friday
Wollerton Old Hall, Market Drayton

June 15 Saturday
Hartshill Gardens, Oakengates
Peplow Hall, Hodnet

June 16 Sunday
Adcote School, nr Shrewsbury

Gate Cottage, nr Ellesmere
Hartshill Gardens, Oakengates
Morville Hall Gardens, nr Bridgnorth
The Old Vicarage, Cardington
The Patch, Acton Pigot
Peplow Hall, Hodnet

June 17 Monday
Mawley Hall, nr Cleobury Mortimer

June 20 Thursday
Preen Manor, nr Church Stretton

June 21 Friday
Wollerton Old Hall, Market Drayton

June 22 Saturday
Moortown, nr Wellington
Whittington Village Gardens, nr Oswestry

June 23 Sunday
Acton Round, Bridgnorth
Brownhill House, Ruyton XI Towns
David Austin Roses, nr Wolverhampton
Harnage Farm, Cound, Shrewsbury ‡
Lower Hall, Worfield
The Mill Cottage, Cound, Shrewsbury ‡
Moortown, nr Wellington
The Old Vicarage, Cardington
Whittington Village Gardens, nr Oswestry

June 25 Tuesday
Radnor Cottage, Clun

June 28 Friday
Wollerton Old Hall, Market Drayton

June 29 Saturday
Glazeley Old Rectory, nr Bridgnorth
Nordybank Nurseries, nr Ludlow
Ruthall Manor, Ditton Priors

June 30 Sunday
Benthall Hall, Broseley
Bitterley Court, Ludlow
Erway Farm House, Dudleston Heath
Field House, Clee St Margaret, nr Ludlow ‡
Glazeley Old Rectory, nr Bridgnorth

Millichope Park, Munslow
Nordybank Nurseries, nr Ludlow ‡
July 4 Thursday
Preen Manor, nr Church Stretton
July 5 Friday
Wollerton Old Hall, Market
Drayton
July 6 Saturday
Nordybank Nurseries, nr Ludlow
July 7 Sunday
Herbert Lewis Garden, Merton
Nurseries, Bicton
Nordybank Nurseries, nr Ludlow
The Old Vicarage, Cardington
July 9 Tuesday
Weston Park, Shifnal
July 10 Wednesday
Burford House Gardens,
nr Tenbury Wells
Cricklewood Cottage, Minsterley
July 11 Thursday
Cricklewood Cottage, Minsterley
July 12 Friday
Wollerton Old Hall, Market
Drayton
July 13 Saturday
Nordybank Nurseries, nr Ludlow
July 14 Sunday
Nordybank Nurseries, nr Ludlow
July 15 Monday
Mawley Hall, nr Cleobury
Mortimer
July 18 Thursday
Preen Manor, nr Church Stretton
July 19 Friday
Wollerton Old Hall, Market
Drayton
July 21 Sunday
Astley Abbotts House, Bridgnorth
Church Bank, Westbury
July 23 Tuesday
Radnor Cottage, Clun
July 26 Friday
Wollerton Old Hall, Market
Drayton
July 27 Saturday
Brownhill House, Ruyton XI
Towns
July 28 Sunday
Brownhill House, Ruyton XI
Towns

Erway Farm House, Dudleston
Heath
Herbert Lewis Garden, Merton
Nurseries, Bicton
Morville Hall Gardens,
nr Bridgnorth
August 1 Thursday
Preen Manor, nr Church
Stretton
August 2 Friday
Wollerton Old Hall, Market
Drayton
August 3 Saturday
Hodnet Hall Gardens,
nr Market Drayton
August 5 Monday
Hawkstone Hall,
Shrewsbury
August 6 Tuesday
Hawkstone Hall, Shrewsbury
August 9 Friday
Wollerton Old Hall, Market
Drayton
August 10 Saturday
Hodnet Hall Gardens, nr Market
Drayton
August 11 Sunday
Oakly Park, Bromfield
August 14 Wednesday
Burford House Gardens,
nr Tenbury Wells
Cricklewood Cottage,
Minsterley
August 15 Thursday
Cricklewood Cottage, Minsterley
August 16 Friday
Wollerton Old Hall, Market
Drayton
August 18 Sunday
Herbert Lewis Garden, Merton
Nurseries, Bicton
August 23 Friday
Wollerton Old Hall, Market
Drayton
August 25 Sunday
Church Bank, Westbury
Erway Farm House, Dudleston
Heath
Stottesdon Village Gardens
August 26 Monday
Stottesdon Village Gardens

August 28 Wednesday
Herbert Lewis Garden, Merton
Nurseries, Bicton
August 30 Friday
Wollerton Old Hall, Market
Drayton
September 1 Sunday
Herbert Lewis Garden, Merton
Nurseries, Bicton
September 8 Sunday
Brownhill House, Ruyton XI
Towns
September 11 Wednesday
Cricklewood Cottage, Minsterley
September 12 Thursday
Cricklewood Cottage, Minsterley
September 22 Sunday
Herbert Lewis Garden, Merton
Nurseries, Bicton
September 29 Sunday
Erway Farm House, Dudleston
Heath
October 6 Sunday
Preen Manor, nr Church Stretton

Regular openings
For details see garden description

Field House, Clee St Margaret,
nr Ludlow
Hawkstone Hall, Shrewsbury
Hodnet Hall Gardens, nr Market
Drayton
Nordybank Nurseries, nr Ludlow
Weston Park, Shifnal
Wollerton Old Hall, Market Drayton

By appointment only
*For telephone numbers and other
details see garden descriptions.
Private visits welcomed*

Ashford Manor, nr Ludlow
Farley House, Much Wenlock
Haye House, nr Bridgnorth

DESCRIPTIONS OF GARDENS

Acton Round ♿✿❀ (Mr & Mrs Hew Kennedy) 6m W of
Bridgnorth. A458 Morville-Shrewsbury, 2m after Morville
turn L (W). 1½-acre garden with yew hedges; rose, herbaceous and newly planted borders; various follies; attractive church and beautiful early Georgian house (not
open). TEAS. *Adm £1.50 Chd £1 (Share to Acton Round
Church®). Sun June 23 (2-6.30). Garden also open by
appt* Tel 01746 714203

Adcote School ✿ (Adcote School Educational Trust Ltd)
Little Ness, 8m NW of Shrewsbury via A5 to Montford
Bridge, turn off NE follow signs to Little Ness. 20-acres;
fine trees incl beeches, tulip trees, oaks (American and
Evergreen); atlas cedars, Wellingtonia etc; rhododen-
drons, azaleas; small lake; landscaped garden. House
(part shown) designed by Norman Shaw RA; Grade 1 listed
building; William Morris windows; De Morgan tiles. TEAS.
*Adm £1.20 Acc chd free. Suns May 5, 19, June 2, 16 (2-5).
Other times strictly by appt only* Tel 01939 260202

Ashford Manor ふ (Kit Hall Esq) Ashford Carbonel, 2¾m S of Ludlow. E of A49 Ludlow-Leominster. Garden of 2 acres, herbaceous foliage and shrubs grown in the hope of maintaining interest through the entire year, hence very few flowers. Worked entirely by owner. Picnic area – Dogs welcomed. Reasonably level ground. *Adm 50p. Private visits welcome all year, please* Tel 01584 872100

Astley Abbotts House ❀ (Mrs H E Hodgson) 2m NW of Bridgnorth. B4373 from Bridgnorth turn R at Cross Lane Head. 10 acres, 5 acres PYO lavender, bee village; herbs; wild woodland garden; fine trees; lawns; rhododendrons. Only partly suitable for wheelchairs. TEAS. *Adm £1.50 Chd free (Share to Wolverhampton Eye Infirmary®). Suns May 12 (2-6), July 21 (11-6)*

Badger Farmhouse ふ❀ (Mr & Mrs N J D Foster) Badger. From A464 Shifnal to Wolverhampton Rd turn S to Burnhill Green. In Burnhill Green turn W to Beckbury. At T junction in Beckbury turn S, ¾m on R. 3-acre garden. Over 200 varieties of daffodils and narcissi in a mature setting. Mainly in three orchards, one of apple one pear and plum and one of cherry. Also fine trees, shrubs and roses. TEAS. *Adm £1.50 Chd free (Share to Neighbourhood Initiative Foundation®). Sun April 14 (2-6). Private visits welcome, please* Tel 01746 783222

Benthall Hall ふ❀ (Mr & Mrs James Benthall; The National Trust) 1m NW of Broseley, 4m NE of Much Wenlock (B4375); turning up lane marked with brown sign. Garden 3 acres; shrub roses; rockery banks; lawns; former kitchen garden; wild garden. Interesting plants and fine trees. C16 house also open. *Adm £2 Chd £1 (House & Garden £3 Chd £1). Sun June 30 (1.30-5.30)*

Bitterley Court ふ❀ (Mr & Mrs J V T Wheeler) Ludlow. Next to Bitterley Church. Follow A4117 E from Ludlow and turn off to Bitterley after about 2m. 5m from Ludlow altogether. A 6-acre garden featuring specimen and rare trees, shrubs, woodland walks, ornamental kitchen garden and herbaceous borders. TEAS in aid of British Heart Foundation and Leukaemia Research. *Adm £1.50 Chd free. Suns May 26, June 30 (2-6)*

Brownhill House ❀❀ (Roger & Yoland Brown) Ruyton XI Towns. 10m NW of Shrewsbury on B4397. Park at Bridge Inn. Unusual and distinctive hillside garden bordering River Perry. Great variety of features and style including laburnum walk; formal terraces; extensive shrub planting; woodland paths; glasshouses; fruit and large kitchen garden. New developments every year. 200 varieties of plants for sale, proceeds to NGS. TEAS. *Adm £1.50 Chd free. Sun May 19; Sat, Sun June 1, 2; Sun June 23, Sat, Sun July 27, 28, Sun Sept 8 (1.30-5.30). By appt please* Tel/Fax 01939 260626

Burford House Gardens ふ❀❀ (Treasures of Tenbury) 1m W of Tenbury Wells. 400yds S of A456. Bus: CM Ludlow-Tenbury Wells. 4-acre garden designed in 1954 by the late owner John Treasure in beautiful surroundings on R Teme. Flowering shrubs, herbaceous plants, extensive lawns. National Clematis Collection (held on behalf of NCCPG). Nursery specializing in clematis, herbaceous, many unusual shrubs and climbers. Fine church adjacent containing Cornwall monuments. Gift shop. DOGS on lead, nursery only. TEAS; light lunches. *Adm £2.50 Chd £1. Weds July 10, Aug 14 (10-5)*

Church Bank ❀❀ (Mr & Mrs B P Kavanagh) Rowley 12m SW of Shrewsbury on B4386 Montgomery Rd continuing through Westbury. After ⅓m turn R for Rowley. After 3½m turn L at Xrds for Brockton. Church Bank is on L after 120yds. A plant enthusiast's, S facing garden set in a beautiful and little known part of the county, begun 8 years ago and continuing to develop and change. *Adm £1.50 Chd free. Suns July 21, Aug 25 (2-6); also private visits welcome May to Sept, please* Tel 01743 891661

Cricklewood Cottage ❀❀ (Paul & Debbie Costello) Plox Green. On A488 1m SW of Minsterley. Park on grass verge opposite. Pretty ⅓-acre cottage garden, bordered by trout stream with waterfalls and natural bog garden; colour-schemed borders of shrubs and perennials, all packed with plants, particularly shrub roses, day lilies and hardy geraniums. Featured in Your Garden magazine. TEAS. *Adm £1 Chd free (Share to League of Friends of Shrewsbury Hospitals®). Weds, Thurs, May 8, 9, June 12, 13, July 10, 11, Aug 14, 15, Sept 11, 12 (1.30-5.30). Private visits also welcome, please* Tel 01743 791229

David Austin Roses ふ❀ (Mr & Mrs David Austin) Bowling Green Lane, Albrighton, 8m NW of Wolverhampton. 4m from Shifnal (A464) left into Bowling Green Lane; or junc 3, M54 to Albrighton, right at sign 'Roses & Shrubs', Bowling Green Lane 2nd R. Breeders of the famous English roses. Nursery and gardens; 900 varieties old roses, shrub, species and climbing roses; rose fields; herbaceous display garden, semi-wild. Private garden, trees and water garden with many plants. Sculpture by Pat Austin. TEAS. *Adm £1.50 Chd free. Sun June 23 (2-6)*

Dudmaston ふ❀❀ (The National Trust; Sir George & Lady Labouchere) 4m SE of Bridgnorth on A442. Bus stop at gates ½m. 8 acres with fine trees, shrubs; lovely views over Dudmaston Pool and surrounding country. Dingle walk. TEAS. *Adm £2.50 Chd £1. Mon May 27 (2-6)*

Erway Farm House ❀❀ (Mr & Mrs A A Palmer) 3m N of Ellesmere, 2m S of Overton on Dee. Signposted from B5068 Ellesmere-St Martins Rd and B5069 Overton-Oswestry rd. 1-acre Plantswoman's garden packed with rare and interesting plants. Hellebores in profusion, many varieties of snowdrop. Later, hardy geranium and other shade loving plants. Sunny gravel garden, and new wild garden in the making. Permanent display of garden sculpture. Unusual plants from garden for sale. *Adm £1.50 Chd free. Sat, Sun, Mon April 6, 7, 8 (2-6), also last Sun in every month Feb to Sept (2-6) (February 1-5). Coach parties by appt, please* Tel 01691 75479

Farley House ❀ (Mr & Mrs R W Collingwood) From A458 at Much Wenlock turn N on to A4169 signed Ironbridge; house 1m on L. 1-acre garden made since 1980 by owners; alpines, herbaceous island beds, shrubs and trees. Gardening clubs and WI welcome. *Adm £1 Chd free. Open by appt April to Oct, please* Tel 01952 727017

Field House &⌀❀ (Dr & Mrs John Bell) Clee St Margaret. 8m NE of Ludlow. Turning to Stoke St Milborough and Clee St Margaret. 5m from Ludlow, 10m from Bridgnorth along B4364. Through Stoke St Milborough to Clee St Margaret. Ignore R turn to Clee Village. Carry on to Field House on L. Parking. 1-acre garden created since 1982 for yr-round interest. Mixed borders; rose walk; pool garden; herbaceous borders; organic vegetable garden; spring bulbs and autumn colours. TEAS. *Adm £1.50 Chd 50p. Garden and nursery open Sat, Sun, Bank Hol Mons March 31 to Oct 15 (12-5). For NGS Suns April 28, June 30 (12-5). Private visits welcome, please* **Tel 01584 823242**

Gatacre Park &❀ (Lady Thompson) Six Ashes, 6m SE of Bridgnorth on A458. Stourbridge-Bridgnorth Rd. 8 acres. Originally a Victorian garden partly redeveloped over the last 56 years by present owner. Flowering shrubs, fine trees, incl 100ft tulip tree and manna ash; topiary walk; large woodland garden with pieris, azaleas, rhododendrons inc many interesting species now fully grown. Lovely views over Park. TEAS. *Adm £2 Chd free (Share to Tuck Hill Church, Six Ashes®). Suns May 12, 19 (2-6)*

Gate Cottage ⌀❀ (G W Nicholson & Kevin Gunnell) nr Ellesmere 10m N of Shrewsbury on A528. At village of Cockshutt take rd signposted English Frankton. Garden is 1m on R. Parking in adjacent field. A developing garden at present about 2 acres. Informal mixed plantings of trees, shrubs, herbaceous of interest to flower arrangers and plantsmen. Pool and rock garden; informal pools. Large collection of hostas; old orchard with roses. TEA. *Adm £1.50 Chd 50p. Sun June 16 (1-5). Parties by appt at other times, please* **Tel 01939 270606**

Glazeley Old Rectory &⌀❀ (Mr & Mrs R Arbuthnott) 3m S of Bridgnorth on B4363 Bridgnorth-Cleobury Mortimer Rd. 2-acre garden in beautiful natural setting. Herbaceous borders, bulbs, alpines, old-fashioned roses, shrubs and trees. Paved, heather and bog gardens. TEAS. *Adm £1.50 Chd 50p. Sat, Sun June 29, 30 (2-6). Private visits welcome, please* **Tel 01746 789443**

Harnage Farm &⌀ (Mr & Mrs Ken Cooke) Cound. 8m SE of Shrewsbury on A458. Turn to Cound 1m S of Cross Houses. Harnage Farm 1m, bearing L past church. ½-acre farmhouse garden; well stocked with unusual herbaceous plants, shrubs and climbers and a collection of old roses. Extensive views over beautiful Severn Valley. TEAS. *Combined adm with* **The Mill Cottage** *£2 Chd 50p (Share to Ward 21, Nurses Fund, Shrewsbury Hospital©). Sun June 23 (2-6)*

Hartshill Gardens &⌀❀ Oakengates E of Shrewsbury. Once within the Telford/Wrekin district. Follow local signs to Oakengates. TEAS. *Combined adm £1 Chd free. Sat, Sun June 15, 16 (2-5.30)*

> **Longmede** (Mr & Mrs D J Steele) 13 Hartshill Road. Approx ½-acre ornamental garden with specimen trees, shrubs and raised alpine beds. Yr-round interest. *Private visits welcome (April-Oct), please* **Tel 01952 612710**
>
> **Northcote** (Mr & Mrs R A Woolley) 15 Hartshill Road. ¼-acre garden with vegetables, flowers and shrubs. *Private visits welcome (April-Oct), please* **Tel 01952 613644**

Hatton Grange &❀ (Mrs Peter Afia) Shifnal. Lodge gate entrance on A464, 2m S of Shifnal. 1m up drive. Large dingle with pools, rhododendrons, azaleas, fine old trees; shrubbery; rose-garden; lily pond garden. TEAS. *Adm £1.50 Chd 50p (Share to BACUP®). Sun May 19 (2-7). Parties by appt, please* **Tel 01952 460415**

Hawkstone Hall (Redemptorist Study Centre) 13m NE of Shrewsbury. 6m SW of Market Drayton on A442. Entrance from Marchamley. Large formally laid out garden. Features incl ornamental flower beds; herbaceous border; rockery; pools and magnificent trees. Georgian mansion (open) with courtyard garden and winter garden. TEAS. *Adm garden only £1.50 Chd £1. Open Aug 5 to 31. For NGS Mon, Tues Aug 5, 6 (2-5)*

Haye House &⌀❀ (Mrs Paradise) Eardington. 2m S of Bridgnorth, sign Highley B4555. 1m through village Eardington. 1-acre garden especially planted by the owner, for her work as a National & International flower demonstrator. Grade 2 listed house (not open). TEAS. *Adm £1.50 Chd free. Private visits welcome, April to Oct (10-6), please* **Tel 01746 764884**

Herbert Lewis Garden, Merton Nurseries &❀ (Herbert Lewis & Family) Bicton. 3m NW of Shrewsbury on B4380 (old A5) towards Oswestry. The Herbert Lewis is attached to Merton Nurseries. The acre of garden is a plantsman's collection of widely available and unusual plants. A garden for all seasons containing over 200 varieties of conifers and heathers for autumn and winter interest. The outstanding feature is the vast collection of herbaceous perennials growing in borders and island beds. A woodland garden contains rhododendrons and azaleas also a selection of moisture and shade loving plants incl magnificent specimens of gunnera manicata. Guided tours if required; coach parties. TEA. *Adm £1.50 Chd free (Share to Shropshire Mid Wales Hospice®). Wed Aug 28, Suns July 7, 28; Aug 18; Sept 1, 22 (11-6). Private evening visits welcome, please* **Tel 01743 850773**

Hodnet Hall Gardens &❀ (Mr & the Hon Mrs A Heber-Percy) 5½m SW of Market Drayton; 12m NE Shrewsbury; at junc of A53 and A442. 60-acre landscaped garden with series of lakes and pools; magnificent forest trees, great variety of flowers, shrubs providing colour throughout season; featured on TV and Radio. Unique collection of big-game trophies in C17 tearooms. Gift shop and kitchen garden. TEAS; parties to pre-book. Free car-coach park. *Adm £2.80 OAP £2.30 Chd £1. April to end of Sept (Tues to Sat 2-5; Suns & Bank Hols 12-5.30). Reduced rates for organised parties of 25 or over* **Tel 01630 685 202.** *For NGS Sats Aug 3, 10 (2-5)*

Limeburners &⌀ (Mr & Mrs J E Derry) Lincoln Hill. On outskirts of Ironbridge, Telford. From Traffic Island in Ironbridge take Church Hill and proceed up hill for ½m, garden on L 300yds below The Beeches Hospital. Prize-winning garden formerly site of a rubbish tip developed by owners as a Nature garden to attract wildlife. Many unusual shrubs giving year round interest. Featured on TV Channel 4, Garden Club. TEAS in aid of Arthritis & Rheumatism Council for Research. *Adm £1.50 Chd free. Sun May 12 (2-6). Private visits also welcome April to Sept, please* **Tel 01952 433715**

Lingen Nursery, Lingen Village See Hereford and Worcester

Longnor Hall ᕃᕱ❀ (Mr & Mrs A V Nicholson) Longnor. Take A49 road S of Shrewsbury to Longnor. Entry to Longnor Hall garden through grounds of Longnor Church. 70-acre garden and parkland. Interesting varieties of trees; herbaceous borders, yew and beech hedges; walled kitchen garden; stable yard and C17 house (not open); sheep and deer; Cound Brook; views of The Lawley and Caer Caradoc hills. Adjacent C13 Longnor Church. TEAS. *Adm £1.50 Chd 50p (Share to St. Mary's Church, Longnor®). Sun, Mon May 26, 27 (2-6)*

Lower Hall ᕃ❀ (Mr & Mrs C F Dumbell) Worfield, E of Bridgnorth. ½m N of A454 in village centre. 4 acres on R Worfe. Garden developed by present owners over past 31 yrs. Courtyard with fountain, walled garden with old-fashioned roses, clematis and iris. Water garden with pool, primula island and rock garden. Woodland garden incl rare magnolias and paper bark trees. Plant sales to local charity. WI TEAS. *Adm £2 Chd free. Suns June 2, 23 (2-6). Private visits welcome. Coach and evening parties by appt, local catering can be arranged.* Tel 01746 716607

Mawley Hall ᕃ❀ (Mr & Mrs R A Galliers-Pratt) 2m NE of Cleobury Mortimer. On A4117 Bewdley-Ludlow Rd. Bus: X92, alight at gate. A natural garden in beautiful country with magnificent views; designed for wandering amongst roses, herbs, flowering shrubs; fine old trees. TEAS. *Adm £1.50 OAPs £1 Chd under 15, 50p. Mons May 13, June 17, July 15 (2-6)*

The Mill Cottage ᕃᕱ❀ (Mrs A J Wisden & Miss J M Hawkes) Cound. 8m SE of Shrewsbury on A458. Turn to Cound 1m S of Cross Houses. Mill Cottage 300yds on L. ¼-acre cottage garden. Many unusual & lovely herbaceous & alpine plants. Good & varied collection of hostas and ferns. *Combined adm with Harnage Farm £2 Chd 50p (Share to Ward 21, Nurses Fund, Shrewsbury Hospital©). Sun June 23 (2-6)*

Millichope Park (Mr & Mrs L Bury) Munslow, 8m NE of Craven Arms. From Ludlow (11m) turn L off B4368, ¾m out of Munslow. 13-acre garden with lakes; woodland walks; fine specimen trees, wild flowers; herbaceous borders. TEAS. *Adm £2 Chd 50p. Mon May 6 (2-6), Sun June 30 (12-6). Private visits welcome, please* Tel 0158 841234

Moortown ᕃᕱ❀ (David Bromley Esq) 5m N of Wellington. Take B5062 signed Moortown 1m between High Ercall and Crudgington. Approx 1-acre plantsman's garden. Here may be found the old-fashioned, the unusual and even the oddities of plant life, in mixed borders of 'controlled' confusion. *Adm £2 Chd 50p. Sat, Sun June 22, 23 (2-5.30)*

Morville Hall Gardens ᕃ❀ nr Bridgnorth. 3m NW of Bridgnorth on A458 at junction with B4368. TEA, Hall, Dower House, Gatehouse Gardens Sun June 16. *Combined adm £2 Chd 50p. Dower House, Gate House only Suns April 21, July 28 £1.50 Chd 50p (Share to Morville Church®) (2-6)*

The Dower House (Dr K Swift) 1½-acre formal garden begun 1989; incl ornamental kitchen garden and knot garden

The Gate House (Mr & Mrs A Rowe) Mature 0.4-acre garden with cottage, formal and woodland sections together with small vineyard

Morville Hall (Mr & Mrs John Norbury & The National Trust) Recently restored 2-acre garden with newly planted parterre and vineyard; C12 Church, Elizabethan House (not open) in fine setting

Nordybank Nurseries ❀ (P Bolton) Clee St Margaret. 7½m NE of Ludlow. Turning to Stoke St Milborough and Clee St Margaret 5m from Ludlow, 10m from Bridgnorth along B4364, through Stoke St Milborough on the Lane to Clee St Margaret. 1-acre cottage garden on sloping site. Informal plantings of trees, shrubs and unusual herbaceous, incl herbs and wildflowers. Also 'Rose Garden' with over 60 varieties of old roses and 'Field Garden' with 700 varieties of herbaceous plants. TEAS. *Adm £1.50 Chd free. Nursery open Mons, Weds & Suns from Easter to Oct. For NGS Sats, Suns June 29, 30, July 6, 7, 13, 14 (11-6)*

¶Oakly Park ᕃ❀ (Plymouth Estates) Bromfield. [OS 488 763] 2m NW of Ludlow on A49. Take A4113 Leintwardine Turn and immed L signed thereafter. 2-acre walled kitchen garden in traditional use. Parkland and ornamental gardens, specimen native and exotic trees in extensive woodland. TEAS. *Adm £2 Chd 50p (Share to Action Research®). Sun Aug 11 (2-6)*

The Old Rectory ᕱ❀ (Mrs J H M Stafford) Fitz; A5 NW of Shrewsbury; turn off at Montford Bridge, follow signs; from B5067 turn off at Leaton, follow signs. 1¼-acre botanist's garden; shrub roses, vegetables; water garden. TEAS. *Adm £1.50 Chd 20p. Sun June 9 (12-6)*

The Old Vicarage ᕃ (W B Hutchinson Esq) Cardington, 2m N of B4371 Church Stretton/Much Wenlock rd, signed, or turn off A49 Shrewsbury-Ludlow rd at Leebotwood, 2½-acre scenic garden; trees, shrubs, roses, primulas, alpines, water and bog garden. Lunch and tea; picnics allowed; on site parking. *Adm £1.20 Chd free. Suns June 9, 16, 23; July 7 (12-5.30). Private visits welcome, June, July, please* Tel 01694 771354

Oteley ❀ (Mr & Mrs R K Mainwaring) Ellesmere 1m. Entrance out of Ellesmere past Mere, opp Convent nr to A528/495 junc. 10 acres running down to Mere, incl walled kitchen garden; architectural features many interesting trees, rhododendrons and azaleas, views across Mere to Ellesmere Church. Wheelchairs only if dry. TEAS in aid of NSPCC. *Adm £1.50 Chd 50p. Mon May 27 (2-6). Private visits also welcome, please* Tel 01691 622514

The Patch ᕃᕱ❀ (Mrs J G Owen) Acton Pigot. 8m SE of Shrewsbury between A49 and A458. Take Cressage Rd from Acton Burnell. Turn L after ½m, signpost Acton Pigot. This is not a garden in the strict sense but an unconventional developing patch for the plant connoisseur in excess of ½ acre. June early herbaceous, shrubs and trees. Plants in aid of St. Anthony's Cheshire Home. *Adm £1.50 Chd free. Suns June 9, 16 (2-6). Private visits for groups over 5 welcome, please* Tel 01743 718846

Penwardine Cottage See Hereford and Worcester

Peplow Hall &♣ (The Hon & Mrs R V Wynn) 3m S of Hodnet via A442; turn off E. 10-acre garden with lawns, azaleas, rhododendrons, etc; roses, herbaceous borders; walled kitchen garden; 7-acre lake. TEAS. *Adm £2.50 Chd 50p. Sat, Sun June 15, 16 (2-5.30)*

Preen Manor ♣♣ (Mr & Mrs P Trevor-Jones) Church Preen, nr Church Stretton; 5m SW of Much Wenlock. On B4371 3m R for Church Preen and Hughley; 1½m turn L for Church Preen; over Xrds, 1¼m drive on R. Not suitable for wheelchairs. 6-acre garden on site of Cluniac monastery and Norman Shaw mansion. Kitchen; chess; water and wild gardens. 1995 Roy Lancaster award. Fine trees in park; woodland walks. Featured in NGS video 1. Replanning still in progress. TEAS (except Oct 6 TEA). *Adm £2 Chd 50p. Thurs May 30, June 20, July 4, 18, Aug 1 (2-6); Sun Oct 6 (2-5). Private visits of min 15 and coach parties by appt June & July only* **Tel 01694 771207**

Radnor Cottage ♣♣ (Pam and David Pittwood) Clun. 8m W of Craven Arms, 1m E of Clun on B4368 midway between Clunton and Clun. 2 acres S-facing slope, overlooking Clun Valley. Recently developed for all-year-round interest. Daffodils; cottage garden borders; dry stone wall and terracing with herbs and alpines; stream and bog garden with willow collection; native trees, orchard, wild flower meadow. TEAS. *Adm £1 Chd 50p (Share to Clun Methodist Church®). Tues March 26, April 16, May 14, June 4, 25, July 23 (2-6). Private visits welcome, please* **Tel 01588 640451**

Ridgway Wood ♣♣ (Mr & Mrs A S Rankine) Edgton 4m NW of Craven Arms. Turn W off A49 on to A489, 2½m, then left towards Edgton ¾m, drive on right. Informal 2-acre garden set in 20 acres woodland created and maintained for all year round colour. Extensive heather beds; azaleas, shrubs, trees; woodland walks. TEAS. *Adm £1.50 Chd 50p (Share to Shropshire and Mid Wales Hospice®). Suns May 19, 26; Mon May 27 (11-6)*

Ruthall Manor &♣ (Mr & Mrs G T Clarke) Ditton Priors, Bridgnorth. Weston rd from village church 2nd L, garden ¾m. 1-acre garden with pool and specimen trees. Designed for easy maintenance with lots of ground-covering and unusual plants. Old Shires Tea Room in village open (10-5) except Weds. *Adm £1.50 Chd free. Sat June 29 (2.30-6). Parties welcome April to Sept, please* **Tel 01746 712 216/608**

Stottesdon Village Gardens &♣♣ (Stottesdon Garden Committee). 7m from Bridgnorth on B4363 turn R 3m. From Kidderminster 11m on A4117 turn R 4m. A village community in unspoilt countryside. A variety of gardens, new and old; cottage flowers; unusual plants; vegetables; bedding displays. TEAS in aid of St Mary's Church. *Combined adm £1.50 Chd 50p. Sun, Mon Aug 25, 26 (2-6)*

Swallow Hayes &♣ (Mrs P Edwards) Rectory Rd, Albrighton WV7, 7m NW of Wolverhampton. M54 exit 3 Rectory Rd 1m towards Wolverhampton off A41 just past Roses and Shrubs Garden Centre. 2-acres; planted since 1968 with emphasis on all-the-year interest and ease of maintenance; National collection of Hamamellis and Russell Lupins. Nearly 3000 different plants, most labelled. TEAS. *Adm £1.50 Chd 10p (Share to Compton Hospice®). Suns March 31, May 5, June 2 (2-6); also by appt for parties, please* **Tel 01902 372624**

Walcot Hall &♣ (The Hon Mrs E C Parish) Bishops Castle 3m. B4385 Craven Arms to Bishops Castle, turn L by Powis Arms, in Lydbury N. Arboretum planted by Lord Clive of India's son, now undergoing restoration. Cascades of rhododendrons, azaleas amongst specimen trees and pools. Fine views of Sir William Chambers Clock Towers, with lake and hills beyond. TEAS. *Adm £1.50 Chd 15 and under free. Sun, Mon May 26, 27 (2-6). Also by appt for parties, please* **Tel 01588 680232**

Weston Park & (The Weston Park Foundation) Shifnal. 7m E of Telford on the A5 in the village of Weston-under-Lizard. Easy access junction 12 M6 and junction 3 M54. Free car/coach park. 28 acres Capability Brown landscaped gardens and arboretum, incl fine collection of nothofagus, rhododendrons and azaleas. Formal gardens of SW terrace recently restored to original C18 design, together with colourful adjacent Broderie Garden. Wide variety of trees, shrubs and flowers provides colour throughout the season. C17 house open (adm £1.50). TEAS and light meals available in The Old Stables restaurant. *Adm £3.50, OAP's £2.50, Chd £2, reduced rates for parties of 20 or more. Open Easter to September (enquiries for dates and times,* **Tel 01952 850207***). For NGS Tues June 11, July 9 (11-5)*

Whittington Village Gardens &♣ Daisy Lane Whittington. 2½m NE of Oswestry. Turn off B5009 150yds NW of church into Top St then into Daisy Lane. Car parking at Whittington Castle and Top St. A group of adjacent country gardens with mature trees, fruit and vegetables. Ornamental shrubs and a collection of unusual and traditional herbaceous perennials for all aspects. A range of water features and patio areas. TEAS at *The Bramleys*; Top St. *Adm £2 Chd free. Sat, Sun June 22, 23 (1-5.30)*

Willey Park ♣♣ (The Lord & Lady Forester) Broseley 5m NW of Bridgnorth. Turn W off B4373. Much Wenlock 4m. 6-acre formal garden set in extensive parkland. Fine views. 10-acre woodland rhododendron/azalea walk. Magnificent mature trees. Recently planted herbaceous borders. Spectacular azalea bed near house. TEAS. *Adm £2 Chd/OAP £1 (Share to Willey & District Village Hall®). Sun May 19 (2-6)*

Wollerton Old Hall &♣♣ (John & Lesley Jenkins) Wollerton, nr Market Drayton on A53 between Hodnet and A53/A41 junction. From S turn R after 'Wollerton' sign. From N & E turn L after 'Wollerton' sign. Both rds lead to a brick pound. Garden ahead on L. Award-winning 3-acre garden created around C16 house (not open). Featured in Homes & Gardens, House & Garden, NGS Video 1. A combination of formal design and intensive cultivation of perennials. A painter's garden using planting combinations with an emphasis on colour and form. Light lunches, TEAS. *Adm £2 Chd 50p. Every Fri & Sun June 2 to Aug 30 (12-5). For NGS, Fris. Parties by appt at other times, please* **Tel 01630 685769**

Somerset

Hon County Organiser:	Mrs Lyn Spencer-Mills, Hooper's Holding, Hinton St George, Somerset TA17 8SE Tel 01460 76389
Assistant Hon County Organisers:	
Somerset Leaflet:	Mrs M R Cooper, 21 Lower St, Merriott, Somerset TA16 5NL Tel 01460 76105
	Miss P Davies-Gilbert, Coombe Quarry, West Monkton, Taunton
Publicity Officer:	Mrs Alison Kelly, The Mount, Wincanton, Tel 01963 32487
	Mrs B Hudspith, Rookwood, West St, Hinton St George, Somerset TA17 8SA Tel 01460 73450
Hon County Treasurer:	John A Spurrier Esq, Tudor Cottage, 19 Comeytrowe Lane, Taunton, Somerset TA1 5PA Tel 01823 333827

DATES OF OPENING

March 31 Sunday
Elworthy Cottage, Elworthy
Peart Hall, Spaxton
Smocombe House, Enmore
April 4 Thursday
Clapton Court, Crewkerne
April 5 Friday
Beryl, Wells
Clapton Court, Crewkerne
April 7 Sunday
Broadview, Crewkerne ‡
Fairfield, Stogursey
Wayford Manor, Crewkerne ‡
April 8 Monday
Broadview, Crewkerne
Stowleys, Bossington Lane, Porlock
April 13 September
Greencombe, Porlock
April 14 Sunday
Hangeridge Farm, Wellington
Poundisford Park, Taunton
April 21 Sunday
Barrington Court, Ilminster
The Time-Trail of Roses, Wells
April 28 Sunday
Broadview, Crewkerne ‡
Hadspen Garden, nr Castle Cary
Wayford Manor, Crewkerne ‡
May 5 Sunday
Broadview, Crewkerne
Higher Luxton Farm, Churchinford
The Old Mill House, Spaxton
Pear Tree Cottage, Stapley
May 6 Monday
Broadview, Crewkerne ‡
Clapton Court, Crewkerne ‡
Forge House, Oake
Higher Luxton Farm, Churchinford
Pear Tree Cottage, Stapley
May 11 Saturday
The Mount, Wincanton
May 12 Sunday
Court House, East Quantoxhead
Hangeridge Farm, Wellington
7 Little Keyford Lane, Frome

Milton Lodge, Wells
The Mount, Wincanton
Smocombe House, Enmore
Wayford Manor, Crewkerne
West Bradley House, Glastonbury
May 15 Wednesday
Elworthy Cottage, Elworthy
May 18 Saturday
Hinton St George Gardens, Crewkerne
Kingsdon, Somerton
May 19 Sunday
Cannington College Gardens
Elworthy Cottage, Elworthy
Hinton St George Gardens, Crewkerne
Kingsdon, Somerton
May 22 Wednesday
Withey Lane Farmhouse, Barton St David
May 26 Sunday
Broadview, Crewkerne ‡
Chinnock House, Middle Chinnock ‡
Greencombe, Porlock
The Mill House, Castle Cary
Milton Lodge, Wells
Wayford Manor, Crewkerne ‡
Westhay, Kingston St Mary
May 27 Monday
Broadview, Crewkerne ‡
Chinnock House, Middle Chinnock ‡
Forge House, Oake
The Mill House, Castle Cary
June 1 Saturday
Kingsdon, Somerton
June 2 Sunday
Harptree Court, East Harptree
Kingsdon, Somerton
Kites Croft, Westbury-sub-Mendip
Landacre Farm, Withypool
The Mill, Cannington
The Time-Trail of Roses, Wells
June 5 Wednesday
Kites Croft, Westbury-sub-Mendip
June 8 Saturday
Pear Tree Cottage, Stapley

Stone Allerton Gardens, nr Wedmore
June 9 Sunday
Broadview, Crewkerne ‡
Hangeridge Farm, Wellington
7 Little Keyford Lane, Frome
Lower Severalls, Crewkerne ‡
Milton Lodge, Wells
The Mount, Chelston, Wellington
Pear Tree Cottage, Stapley
Stone Allerton Gardens, nr Wedmore
June 15 Saturday
Pendower House, Taunton
Wellesley Park Gardens, Wellington
June 16 Sunday
Darkey Pang Too Gang, Oakhill
Dodington Hall, Nether Stowey
Gaulden Manor, Tolland
Hatch Court, Hatch Beauchamp
Montacute Gardens, nr Yeovil
The Mount, Chelston, Wellington ‡
Pendower House, Taunton ‡
Stogumber Gardens, Taunton ‡
The Time-Trail of Roses, Wells
Wellesley Park Gardens, Wellington ‡
June 19 Wednesday
Elworthy Cottage, Elworthy
Wellesley Park Gardens, Wellington
Withey Lane Farmhouse, Barton St David
June 22 Saturday
Greencombe, Porlock
The Mount, Wincanton
Park Wall House, Bruton
June 23 Sunday
Broadview, Crewkerne
Fernhill, nr Wellington
7 Little Keyford Lane, Frome
Milverton Gardens, Taunton
The Mount, Wincanton
Park Wall House, Bruton
Stapleton Manor, Martock

Wambrook Gardens, nr Chard

June 26 Wednesday
Elworthy Cottage, Elworthy

June 29 Saturday
190 Goldcroft, Yeovil
Kingsdon, Somerton
Pendower House, Taunton
Stowleys, Bossington Lane,
Porlock

June 30 Sunday
Benchmark, Wells
Butleigh House, Butleigh
Cothay Manor, Greenham
190 Goldcroft, Yeovil
Kingsdon, Somerton
Leaside, Bruton
Montacute House, Montacute
Pendower House, Taunton
Rimpton Gardens, nr Yeovil

July 3 Wednesday
Benchmark, Wells

July 6 Saturday
Holywell House, Yeovil

July 7 Sunday
Broadview, Crewkerne
Holywell House, Yeovil
Landacre Farm, Withypool
7 Little Keyford Lane, Frome
Milton Lodge, Wells

July 10 Wednesday
Elworthy Cottage, Elworthy

July 14 Sunday
Barrington Court, Ilminster
Fernhill, nr Wellington
Hangeridge Farm, Wellington
The Old Rectory, Limington
Sutton Hosey Manor, Long Sutton

July 17 Wednesday
Fernhill, nr Wellington
Tintinhull House, nr Yeovil

July 21 Sunday
Brent Knoll Gardens, Highbridge
Broadview, Crewkerne
Greencombe, Porlock
7 Little Keyford Lane, Frome
Stapleton Manor, Martock

July 28 Sunday
Barford Park, nr Bridgewater
Birdwood, Wells ‡
Walnut Farm, Yarley, nr Wells ‡

August 1 Thursday
Dunster Castle, nr Minehead

Saturday 3 August
The Mill, Cannington

Sunday 4 August
Broadview, Crewkerne
Coombe House, Bove Town,
  Glastonbury
Cothay Manor, Greenham
Landacre Farm, Withypool
The Mill, Cannington

August 11 Sunday
Lower Severalls, Crewkerne

August 18 Sunday
Poundisford Park, Taunton

August 25 Sunday
Broadview, Crewkerne
Fernhill, nr Wellington

August 26 Monday
Beryl, Wells
Broadview, Crewkerne

August 28 Wednesday
Fernhill, nr Wellington

September 1 Sunday
Kites Croft, Westbury-sub-Mendip

September 4 Wednesday
Kites Croft, Westbury-sub-Mendip

September 15 Sunday
Broadview, Crewkerne
Elworthy Cottage, Elworthy

Harptree Court, East Harptree
The Time-Trail of Roses, Wells

September 29 Sunday
7 Little Keyford Lane, Frome

October 6 Sunday
Glencot House, Wookey Hole

October 19 Saturday
Greencombe, Porlock
Pendower House, Taunton

October 20 Sunday
Pendower House, Taunton

Regular openings
For details see garden description

Clapton Court, Crewkerne
Cothay Manor, Greenham
Elworthy Cottage, Elworthy
Greencombe, Porlock
Hadspen Garden, nr Castle Cary
Hatch Court, Hatch Beauchamp
Lower Severalls, Crewkerne
Milton Lodge, Wells
Poundisford Park, Taunton
The Time-Trail of Roses, Wells

By appointment only
*For telephone numbers and other
details see garden descriptions.
Private visits welcomed*

Littlecourt, West Bagborough
The Mill, Henley Lane, Wookey
Watermeadows, Clapton
Wootton House, Butleigh Wootton

DESCRIPTIONS OF GARDENS

Barford Park ⟨ (Mr & Mrs M Stancomb) Spaxton. 4½m
W of Bridgwater, midway between Enmore and Spaxton.
10 acres including woodland walk. Formal garden, wild
garden and water garden, surrounding a Queen Anne
house with park and ha ha. TEAS. *Adm £1.50 Chd free.
Sun July 28 (2-5.30)*

Barrington Court ⟨⟨⟨ (The National Trust) Ilminster.
NE of Ilminster. Well known garden constructed in 1920
by Col Arthur Lyle from derelict farmland (the C19 cattle
stalls still exist). Gertrude Jekyll approved of the design
and layout; paved paths with walled iris, white and lily
gardens, large kitchen garden. Licensed restaurant, plant
sales and garden shop. Lunches and TEAS. *Adm £3.10
Chd £1.50. Suns April 21, July 14 (11-5.30)*

Benchmark ⟨⟨ (Mr & Mrs Terence Whitman) 99
Portway, Wells. On A371 Cheddar Rd out of Wells, ½m
from city centre on L. ¾-acre mature garden with mixed
borders and potager, interesting perennials incl more

than 100 varieties of penstemon. TEAS in aid of Cancer
Relief. *Adm £1. Sun June 30, Wed July 3 (2-5). Private
visits welcome, please* **Tel 01749 677155**

Beryl ⟨⟨ (Mr & Mrs E Nowell) 1m N of Wells off B3139
to Bath. Left at Hawkers Lane. Victorian park created in
1842. Walled vegetable garden broken into quadrangles
with box hedging and double flower picking borders.
More recent planting of trees and shrubs and creation of
walks and vistas. Morning coffee and TEAS. *Adm £1
OAP/Chd 50p. Fri, Mon April 5, Aug 26 (11-5.30).* **Tel
01749 678738**

Birdwood ⟨⟨ (Mr & Mrs R A Crane) 1½m NE Wells on
B3139. Last house in Wells on edge of Mendip Hills nr
double bend sign. House has long stone garden wall
close to rd. Traditional Victorian garden with stone walls,
lawns, herbaceous border, organic vegetable garden,
small wood and wild area with conservation in mind.
Special features incl many stone walls and terraces at
different levels and interesting trees. *Adm £1 Chd free.
Sun July 28 (2-5)*

Brent Knoll Gardens ❀ off A38 2m N of Highbridge and M5 exit 22. A mixture of 3 colourful country gardens. TEAS at Copse Hall in aid of Parish Hall. *Combined adm £2.50 Chd free. Sun July 21 (2-6)*

Copse Hall ❀ (Mrs N Hill & Mrs S Boss) Terraced gardens, crinkle crankle kitchen garden wall, kiwi fruit. Shrubs, trees and Beechwood. *Private visits welcome, please* Tel 01278 760856 *evenings*

¶**Pen Orchard** ❀ (Major & Mrs J Harper) A busy people's garden, recently planted

Pippins ❀ (Mrs S Allen) Collection of medicinal plants used in therapy

Broadview ❀ (Mr & Mrs R Swann) East Street, Crewkerne. Take the A30 Yeovil Rd out of Crewkerne approx 200 yds on the left hand side. Please enter drive by turning R from the E Yeovil side. 1-acre terraced garden on elevated site with panoramic views. Interesting plants and shrubs, many for sale. *Adm £1 Chd free. Suns, Mons April 7, 8, 28, May 5, 6, 26, 27, June 9, 23, July 7, 21, August 4, 25, 26, Sept 15 (11-5). Also private visits welcome, please* Tel 01460 73424

Butleigh House ❀ (Sir Dawson & Lady Bates) Butleigh. 4m SE of Glastonbury and N of B3153 at Kingweston. Turn down High St in centre of village. About 3 acres of well laid out garden. Large herbaceous borders with chosen colours; fine trees; high semi-circular yew hedge; many roses and other good plants. TEAS in aid of St Leonard's Church, Butleigh. *Adm £1.50 Acc chd free. Sun June 30 (2-6). Private visits welcome June, July, please* Tel 01458 850383

Cannington College Gardens ❀ Cannington, 3m NW of Bridgwater. On A39 Bridgwater-Minehead Rd. Old College: Benedictine Priory 1138; fine Elizabethan W front; 7 old sandstone walled gardens protect wide range of plants, incl many less hardy subjects, ceanothus, Fremontias, Wistarias etc; 10 very large greenhouses contain exceptionally wide range of ornamental plants. New College (built 1970); magnificent views to Quantocks; tree and shrub collections; ground cover plantings; lawn grass collection and trials; horticultural science garden; one of the largest collections of ornamental plants in SW England including 8 national plant collections. TEA. *Adm for both College grounds £1.50 Chd (& organised parties of OAPs) 75p. Special rates for party bookings. For NGS Sun May 19 (2-5)*

Chinnock House ❀ (Guy & Charmian Smith) Middle Chinnock. Off A30 between Crewkerne and Yeovil. 1½-acre walled gardens, silver, white and herbaceous; recently redesigned. TEAS in aid of West Chinnock Primary School. *Adm £1.50 Chd free. Sun, Mon May 26, 27 (2-6). Private visits welcome for parties of 2 or over, please* Tel 01935 881229

Clapton Court ❀ (Mr & Mrs P Giffin) 3m S of Crewkerne on B3165 to Lyme Regis in Clapton village. 10 acres of beautiful gardens, under new ownership. Woodland garden with streams, the largest Ash tree in Gt Britain. Many rare and interesting plants. Terraced formal gardens with ornamental lily pond, white border, yellow border, mixed herbaceous and rose garden, rockery and fine collection of narcissus and other bulbs. *Adm £3 Chd free. Tues,*

Weds, Thurs April to Sept incl (2-5). For NGS Thur, Fri April 4, 5, Mon May 6 (2-5) Coach parties by appt, please Tel Mike & Penny Cox 01460 73220

Coombe House ❀ (Colin Wells-Brown & Alan Gloak) Glastonbury. Bove Town top of Glastonbury High St, park in town, follow signs. Approx 1½ acres. A young garden for an old house on an ancient site. Walled formal and romantic shrub and herbaceous garden with delightful views and some unusual plants. Vegetable garden, 2 orchards, nut walk, water features, newly planted pergola and grass garden. TEAS. *Adm £2 Chd 50p (Share to Aled Richards Trust®). Sun Aug 4 (2-6)*

¶**Cothay Manor** ❀ (Mr & Mrs A H B Robb) Greenham. 5m SW of Wellington. From A38 at Beambridge Hotel turn R signposted Thorne St Margaret. Go straight for 1½m turn R signposted Cothay. 1½m keep L, entrance on L. Over the last 3yrs this plantsman's garden of 7 acres has been reconstructed and replanted within the original framework. Set with a backdrop of a medieval house (not open). Imaginatively planted courtyard, garden rooms, 200yd yew walk. An oxbow bog garden. 5 acres have been newly planted with specimen trees. The R Tone runs through the gardens. Cream TEAS. *Adm £2 Chd free. Every Thurs and 1st Sun May to Sept. For NGS Suns June 30, Aug 4 (2-6)*

Court House ❀ (Sir Walter & Lady Luttrell) East Quantoxhead 12m W of Bridgwater off A39; house at end of village past duck pond. Lovely 5-acre garden; trees, shrubs, roses and herbaceous. Woodland garden started 1992. Views to sea and Quantocks. Partly suitable for wheelchairs. Teas in Village Hall. *Adm £2 Chd free. Sun May 12 (2-5.30)*

¶**Darkey Pang Too Gang** ❀ (Graham & Chrissy Price) Oakhill. 3m N of Shepton Mallet off A367 in Oakhill High St opp converted chapel. ¾-acre. Creatively designed and landscaped by owner since 1981. Crammed with trees, shrubs, herbaceous and climbers, with a lushness of greens and leaf combinations. Winding path link wild and cultivated areas with grotto, pergola, wildlife pond and bog garden. TEAS. *Adm £1.50 Chd free (Share to Mendip Relate®). Sun June 16 (2-6). Private visits welcome Weds only June 17 to July 31, please* Tel 01749 840795

Dodington Hall ❀ (Grania & Paul Quinn) A39 Bridgwater-Minehead. 2m W of Nether Stowey turn at signpost opp Castle of Comfort. 1½m turn R. Entrance through churchyard. Reclaimed 1½-acre terrace garden; clematis, shrub roses, bulbs; Tudor house (part open). TEAS in aid of Meningitis Research. *Adm £2 Chd free (Share to The Parachute Regimental Assoc®). Sun June 16 (2.30-5.30). Private visits welcome, please* Tel 01278 741400

Dunster Castle ❀ (The National Trust) On A396 3m SE of Minehead. Terraces of sub-tropical plants, shrubs and camellias surrounding the fortified house of the Luttrells for 600 yrs; fine views. Self-drive battery operated car available. Teas in village. *Adm Garden Only £2.70 Chd £1.30. Family ticket £6.50. For NGS Thurs Aug 1 (10-6)*

Elworthy Cottage ⚘❀ (Mike & Jenny Spiller) Elworthy, 12m NW of Taunton. Leave Taunton on A358 signed Minehead. In 5m turn L onto B3224 signed Monksilver. After 6m turn R into Elworthy village. 1-acre garden, cottage-style plantings, island beds. Many unusual herbaceous plants. Large collection of hardy geraniums (over 200 varieties); pulmonarias, campanulas, penstemons, grasses and plants for foliage effect. Wide selection of plants from the garden for sale. *Adm £1 Chd free (Share to Cancer and Leukaemia in Childhood Trust®). Nursery open Tues and Thurs afternoons mid March to mid Oct. Garden open Suns, Weds, March 31, May 15, 19, June 19, 26, July 10, Sept 15 (1-5.30). Parties welcome, please* Tel 01984 656427

Fairfield ♿⚘ (Lady Gass) Stogursey, 11m NW of Bridgwater 7m E of Williton. From A39 Bridgwater-Minehead turn N; garden 1½m W of Stogursey. Woodland garden with bulbs and shrubs; paved maze. Views of Quantocks. Dogs in park and field only. TEA. *Adm £1.50 Chd free (Share to Stogursey Church®). Easter Sun April 7 (2-5.30)*

Fernhill ⚘❀ (Peter & Audrey Bowler) White Ball, Wellington. W on A38 from Wellington. Past Beam Bridge Hotel on L. Look for garden signs on L just before dual carriageway. Mature garden with specimen trees in approx 2 acres. Many shrub, herbaceous and mixed borders, all interestingly different, one with walkway from rose garden. Extensive alpine water and bog gardens with ponds and waterfalls on various levels leading to terraced arbour. Ha-ha with views to Wellington Monument. TEAS. *Adm £1.50 Chd free. Suns, Weds June 23, July 14, 17, Aug 25, 28 (2-6). Private visits welcome* Tel 01823 672423

Forge House ♿⚘❀ (Peter & Eloise McGregor) Oake. On A38 midway between Taunton & Wellington. Take signpost for Oake. 1st house on R entering village. ¾-acre informal country garden with emphasis on colour borders. Bee and butterfly plants and fragrance. Unmanaged wildlife area and pond. TEAS if fine. *Adm £1 Chd 50p. Mons May 6, 27 (2-5.30). Disabled & parties welcome following written application by appt weekends May to June, please* Tel 01823 461 500 after 7

Gaulden Manor ♿⚘❀ (Mr & Mrs J Le G Starkie) Tolland. Nr Lydeard St Lawrence. 9m NW Taunton off A358. Medium-sized garden made by owners. Herb; bog; scent and butterfly gardens. Bog plants, primulas and scented geraniums. Partly suitable for wheelchairs. Cream TEAS. *Adm house & garden £3.50, garden only £1.75, Chd £1.75. Sun June 16 (2-5.30)*

Glencot House ⚘❀ (Mrs Jenny Attia) Wookey Hole. ½m SW of Wells. From Wells follow the signs to Wookey Hole. Through the village, past the Wookey Hole Caves and take 1st turning L into Titlands Lane. Proceed for approx ½m and the entrance to Glencot Cricket field is on LH-side. Drive across field and park to L of bridge. 18 acres of parkland of which approx 4 acres are formal gardens with frontage to R Axe. Herbaceous borders, rose walk and terraced walk with a water feature. TEAS. *Adm £1.50 Chd 50p. Sun Oct 6 (2-5)*

¶190 Goldcroft ♿⚘❀ (Mr & Mrs E Crate) Yeovil. Take A359 from roundabout by Yeovil College, then 1st R. ¼-acre. Colour-themed shrub and herbaceous borders and island beds, rose garden, raised pond, vegetable garden designed for visual handicap. TEAS in aid of Castle School, Stoke Sub Hamdon. *Adm £1.50 Chd 50p. Sat, Sun June 29, 30 (2-5)*

Greencombe ♿⚘❀ (Miss Joan Loraine, Greencombe Garden Trust) ½m W of Porlock, left off road to Porlock Weir. 50 year old garden on edge of ancient woodland, overlooking Porlock Bay. Choice rhododendrons, azaleas, camellias, maples, roses, hydrangeas, ferns, small woodland plants and clematis. National collection of Polystichum, the 'thumbs up' fern, and of Erythronium, Vaccinium and Gaultheria. Completely organic, with compost heaps on show. Featured in NGS video 1. *Adm £3 Chd under 16 50p. Sats, Suns, Mons, Tues, April, May, June, July, Oct and early Nov (2-6); private visits welcome by appt, please* Tel 01643 862363. *For NGS Sats, Suns, April 13, May 26, June 22, July 21, Oct 19 (2-6)*

Hadspen Garden ♿⚘❀ (N & S Pope) 2m SE of Castle Cary on A371 to Wincanton. 5-acre Edwardian garden featuring a 2-acre curved walled garden with extensive colourist borders of shrub roses and choice herbaceous plants; woodland of fine specimen trees. National Rodgersia Collection. Lunches, TEAS Thurs, Fri, Sat, TEAS only Sun & Bank Hol Mon. *Adm £2.50 Chd 50p (Share to C.R.M.F.®). Garden and Nursery open Thurs, Fri, Sat, Sun & Bank Hol Mon (9-6); private visits welcome, March 1 to October 1, please* Tel 01749 813707 *(after 6pm). For NGS Sun April 28 (9-6)*

Hangeridge Farm ♿⚘❀ (Mr & Mrs E E & J M Chave) Wrangway. Wellington, 1m off A38 bypass signposted Wrangway. 1st L towards Wellington Monument over motorway bridge 1st R. 1-acre garden, herbaceous borders, flowering shrubs and heathers, raised rockeries, spring bulbs. Lovely setting under Blackdown Hills. Wide selection of plants available from garden. Accommodation available. TEAS. *Adm £1.50 Chd free. Suns April 14, May 12, June 9, July 14 (2-7)*

Harptree Court ♿❀ (Mr & Mrs Richard Hill) East Harptree. 8m N of Wells via A39 Bristol Rd to Chewton Mendip, then B3114 to East Harptree, gates on L. From Bath via A368 Weston-super-Mare Rd to West Harptree. Large garden; fine old trees in lovely setting, woodland walks, handsome stone bridge, subterranean passage, Doric temple, lily pond and paved garden. TEAS. *Adm £1.50 Chd free. Suns June 2, Sept 15 (2-6)*

Hatch Court ♿⚘❀ (Dr & Mrs Robin Odgers) Hatch Beauchamp. 5m SE of Taunton (M5 junction 25) off A358 to Ilminster. Turn L in village at Hatch Inn. 5-acre garden with 30 acres of parkland and deer park surrounding a perfect 1750 Palladian mansion. Extensive, recent and continuing restoration redesign and replanting. Magnificent walled kitchen garden, fine display of roses, shrubs, clematis and many young trees. Glorious views and a lovely setting. TEAS. *Garden only Mon to Thurs April 15 to Sept 30 (10-5). House Thurs June 13 to Sept 12 (2-5). For NGS Adm £2 Chd 12-16 £1. Sun June 16 (2.30-5.30)*

Higher Luxton Farm ⚘ (Mr & Mrs Peter Hopcraft) 1½m out of Churchingford on Honiton Rd. Over county boundary into Devon past thatched farmhouse on R; next turning on L before Xrds. 9m S of Taunton, 9m N of Honiton. Approx 1 acre with species trees and bulbs; walls with clematis; ponds with primula; lovely views. Pony stud. Partially suitable for wheelchairs. TEAS in aid of Churchstanton Church. *Adm £1 Chd free. Sun, Mon May 5, 6 (2-6)*

Hinton St George Gardens 2m NW of Crewkerne. N of A30 Crewkerne-Chard; S of A303 Ilminster Town Rd, at roundabout signed Lopen & Merriott, then R to one of Somerset's prettiest villages. TEAS & dog park provided at Hooper's Holding. *Combined adm £2.50 Chd free. Sat, Sun May 18, 19 (2-6)*
  Fig Tree Cottage ♿⚘ (Mr & Mrs Whitworth) Old walled cottage garden and courtyard of stables made from kitchen garden of neighbouring rectory, over the past 16 years by owners inspired by Margery Fish. Ground cover, shrubs, old-fashioned roses. Three giant fig trees, all perennials. *Private visits welcome, please* Tel 01460 73548
  ¶**The Firs** ⚘ (Mr & Mrs B Cable) ½-acre informal garden mixture of shrubs, herbaceous borders and climbing plants
  ¶**Greenbank** (Danielle & Roger Paul) 46′ × 50′ informal family garden, pond, shrubs, herbaceous border, hamstone bothy
  Hooper's Holding ♿⚘ (Ken & Lyn Spencer-Mills) High St. ⅓-acre garden, in a formal design; lily pool; dwarf conifers, rare herbaceous and shrubby plants; NCCPG National Collection of Hedychiums; fancy poultry. TEAS in aid of Cats Protection League. (Hedychiums flowering Sept and Oct). *Private visits welcome, please* Tel 01460 76389
  Rookwood ♿ (Ian & Betty Hudspith). ¼-acre, modern garden, herbaceous borders, pond, greenhouse, vegetable garden and fruit cage. Accommodation available Tel 01460 73450
  Springfield House ♿⚘ (Capt & Mrs T Hardy) 1½-acres; semi-wild wooded dell, mature trees framing view to Mendips, shrubs, herbaceous plants, bulbs

Holywell House ⚘⚘ (Mr & Mrs Ronald D N Somerville) East Coker, Yeovil. Take the A30 Yeovil to Crewkerne for 2m. Pass the Yeovil Court Hotel then 1st L to North Coker & Hardington. Pass Foresters Arms on the L. Holywell House is next drive on R. 3-acre garden in the making; in beautiful setting with 2 streams, lge pond and lovely mature trees; variety of micro-climates used to create a range of planting with extended flowering season. Pond is fed by a spring and surrounded by bamboos. Stream and banks a special feature. Fine collection of ferns and many plants of special interest. TEAS. *Adm £1.50 Chd free. Sat, Sun July 6, 7 (2-6)*

Iford Manor See Wiltshire

Kingsdon ♿⚘⚘ (Mr & Mrs Charles Marrow) 2m SE of Somerton off B3151 Ilchester Rd. From Ilchester roundabout on A303 follow NT signs to Lytes Cary; left opp gates ½m to Kingsdon. 2-acre plantsman's garden and nursery garden. Over 500 varieties of unusual plants for sale. Teas in Village Hall. *Adm £2 Chd free. Sats, Suns May 18, 19; June 1, 2, 29, 30 (2-7). Private visits welcome, please* Tel 01935840 232

Kites Croft ⚘⚘ (Dr & Mrs W I Stanton) Westbury-sub-Mendip 5m NW of Wells. At Westbury Cross on A371 turn uphill, right to square and left up Free Hill to Kites Croft 2-acre garden with fine views to Glastonbury Tor. Winding paths lead from the terrace to different levels; lawn, ponds, rockery, herbaceous borders, shrubs and wood. As featured on TV. *Adm £1.50 Chd free. Sun June 2, Wed June 5, Sun Sept 1, Wed Sept 4 (2-5). Private visits welcome, please* Tel 01749 870328.

Landacre Farm ⚘⚘ (Mr & Mrs Peter Hudson) Withypool, nr Minehead. On the B3223 Exford/S. Molton Rd 3m W of Exford not in Withypool village. 9m NW of Dulverton ¼m above Landacre Bridge. ½-acre terraced garden 1000ft up on Exmoor. Developed from a field over past 19yrs by present owners; rockery, stream and bog garden, octagonal pergola, rhodedendrons and shrub roses. Exposed position with fantastic views of Barle Valley and open moorland; specializing in climbers and hardy perennials. TEAS. *Adm £1 Chd free. Suns June 2, July 7, Aug 4 (2-5.30). Private visits welcome, please* Tel 0164 383 1223

Leaside ♿⚘ (Mr & Mrs M Hedderwick) Bruton. 1m SE of Bruton on B3081 (signposted Wincanton) turn E to Stourton 1st cottage on R. 1-acre field transformed into a nature garden with nearly 1000 fragrant shrubs and trees. Informal pond and old-fashioned roses. Informative fun quiz. Worth seeing in each season. TEAS. *Adm £1 Chd free (Share to Bristol Area Kidney Patients Association®). Sun June 30 (11-6.30). Private visits welcome, please* Tel 01749 813759

7 Little Keyford Lane ⚘⚘ (Duncan Skene) Frome. B3092 to Frome outskirts. 1st major L. Follow signs. ½-acre family garden recently designed and planted from scratch. Herbaceous emphasis. Good collections of iris (June), hemerocallis/lavender (July), michaelmas daisies (Sept), native plants, bog, poultry and play area. *Adm £1 (Share to Horticultural Therapy®). Suns May 12 (11-5) June 9, 23, July 7, 21, (1-5) Sept 29 (11-4) Private visits welcome Fri April to July, please* Tel 01373 472879

Littlecourt ♿⚘ (Jane Kimber & John Clothier) West Bagborough. 7m N of Taunton signed from A358. 6-acre garden in fine setting with woodland and water; spectacular new borders, interesting and extensive planting; wonderful views. *Adm £2. Private visits very welcome any time, please* Tel 01823 432281

Lower Severalls ♿⚘⚘ (Howard & Audrey Pring) 1½m NE of Crewkerne. Turning for Merriott off A30; or Haselbury from A356. 2½-acre plantsman's garden beside early Ham stone farmhouse. Herbaceous borders incl collection of salvias and herbaceous geraniums. Herb gardens. Shrub borders. Nursery (open daily March 1 to Oct 31 10-5, Suns 2- 5. Closed all day Thurs.) Sells herbs, unusual herbaceous plants and half-hardy conservatory plants. TEAS on Suns June 9, Aug 11. *Adm £1.50 Chd free. Coaches by appointment. Garden open daily April 1 to Sept 30 (2-5). For NGS Suns June 9, Aug 11 (2-6).* Tel 01460 73234

The Mill &⚘❀ (Peter & Sally Gregson) Wookey. 2m W of Wells off A371. Turn L into Henley Lane, driveway 100 yds on L. 2½ acres beside R Axe. Traditional and unusual cottage plants informally planted in formal beds with roses, pergola, lawns and 'hot red border'. Ornamental kitchen garden adjoining Nursery. Wide selection of plants from garden for sale. *Adm £1 Chd free. Private visits welcome, please* **Tel 01749 676966**

The Mill ⚘❀ (Mr & Mrs J E Hudson) 21 Mill Lane, Cannington. 4m W of Bridgwater on A39. Turn opposite Rose & Crown. ¼-acre cottage type plantsman's garden with waterfall and pond, over 70 clematis and National Caltha Collection. Featured in NGS video 1. TEA in aid of Cannington W.I. *Adm £1.50 Chd free (Share to NCCPG®). Sats June 1, Aug 3 (2-6), Suns June 2, Aug 4 (11-5). Private visits welcome by appt, please* **Tel 01278 652304**

The Mill House &⚘❀ (Mr & Mrs P J Davies) Castle Cary. Do not go into Castle Cary Town Centre, but follow signs to Torbay Rd Industrial Estate (W). Entrances to Trading Estate on L proceed E along Torbay Rd about 200yds. Garden on the R. Approx 1-acre terraced sloping garden, with stream and waterfalls. Emphasis on Natural look. Many interesting plants mingled with native flora. Bog garden; and vegetable plot. TEAS and plants in aid of Oncology Centre BRI Bristol and Butler Ward Cosham Hospital, Bristol. *Adm £1.50 Chd free. Sun, Mon May 26, 27 (2-6)*

Milton Lodge ⚘❀ (D C Tudway Quilter Esq) ½m N of Wells. From A39 Bristol-Wells, turn N up Old Bristol Rd; car park first gate on L. Mature Grade II listed terraced garden with outstanding views of Wells Cathedral and Vale of Avalon. Mixed borders; roses; fine trees. Separate 7-acre arboretum. TEAS in aid of Children's Society. Suns & Bank Hol Mons April to Sept. *Adm £2 Chd under 14 free. Open daily (2-6) ex Sats, Good Friday to end Oct; parties by arrangement. For NGS Suns May 12, 26, June 9, July 7 (2-6). Private visits welcome, please* **Tel 01749 672168**

Milverton Gardens 9m W of Taunton on the new B3227 (old A361) L at roundabout to Milverton. *Combined adm £2 Chd free. Sun June 23 (2-6)*
¶**Barn Elms** &⚘ L at Globe Inn, down Rosebank Rd, R at Houndsmoor Lane. 1-acre wild garden and ponds. Small formal garden; many interesting plants; imaginative design
Cobbleside &⚘❀ (Mr & Mrs C Pine) ¾-acre walled garden incl herb garden and potagere. Completely redesigned, with photographs illustrating the old layout. *Private visits welcome May to Sept, please* **Tel 01823 400404**
3 The College &⚘ (Mr Eric Thresher) Small interesting garden, featuring fireplaces amongst shrubs and borders; interesting water features. *Private visits welcome, please* **Tel 01823 400956**
Garden Cottage &⚘❀ (Mr & Mrs R Masters) Interesting plantsman's garden with many unusual plants for sale. Something of interest most of the year. TEAS in aid of Milverton Surgery Fund. *Private visits welcome April to Sept, please* **Tel 01823 400601**
Old Halls ⚘ (Mr M Priscott) A Victorian walled garden developed as market garden; vegetables, fruit and flowers

Montacute Gardens 4m from Yeovil follow A3088, take slip road to Montacute, turn L at T-junction into village. TEAS. *Combined adm £2 Chd free. Sun June 16 (2-5.30)*
Abbey Farm &⚘❀ (Mr & Mrs G Jenkins) Turn R between Church and Kings Arms (no through Rd). 2½-acre of mainly walled gardens on sloping site provide setting for mediaeval Priory gatehouse. Roses; herbaceous borders. Clematis, white garden. Parking available. TEAS in aid of St Catherine's Church Fund. *Private visits welcome, please* **Tel 01935 823572**
Park House &⚘❀ (Mr & Mrs Ian McNab) Turn L (signposted Tintinhull) after red brick council houses and immediately R. Approx 2-acres, spacious lawns; shrubs; walled garden with herbaceous borders and vegetable garden; clematis and white garden. The literary Powys family lived here during their father's lifetime. Cream TEAS in aid of St Catherines Church Fund

Montacute House &⚘❀ (The National Trust) Montacute. NT signs off A3088 4m W of Yeovil and A303. Magnificent Tudor House with contemporary garden layout. Fine stonework provides setting for informally planted mixed borders and old roses; range of garden features illustrates its long history. Lunch and TEAS. *Adm Garden only £2.80 Chd £1.20. For NGS Sun June 30 (11.30-5.30)*

The Mount, Chelston ⚘❀ (Jim & Gilly Tilden) Chelston. Off M5 1m NW of junction 26. At A38 Chelston roundabout take Wellington rd. After 200yds turn R to Chelston. 1st house on R. Enclosed garden with herbaceous borders and shrubs; trees, old roses, more shrubs and pond outside. 1 acre altogether. TEAS in aid of Wellington Stroke Club. *Adm £1 Chd free. Suns June 9, 16 (2-6)*

The Mount, Wincanton ⚘❀ (Alison & Peter Kelly) Follow one-way system round lower half of town, bear L at signposted Castle Cary, on up hill, house on L. 1¼-acre. Plantswoman's garden with hidden suprises. Speciality an alpine lawn and garden, half terraced shrub borders, gravel bed, rock garden and pond. TEAS Suns in aid of CRMF. *Adm £1.50 Chd free. Sats, Suns May 11, 12, June 22, 23 (2-5.30). Private visits welcome at weekends April to end June, please* **Tel 01963 32487** *after sundown*

Oare Manor Cottage See Devon

The Old Mill House, Spaxton ⚘❀ (Mr & Nrs W Bryant) Take A39 and Spaxton Rd. W from Bridgewater. In village take Splatt Lane opp school for car park. 2-acre peaceful plantsman's garden beside weir and trout stream. Plant stall in aid of St Mary's Church, Bridgwater. Teas in village hall in aid of Spaxton Church General Fund. *Adm £1 Chd free Sun May 5 (2-5.30)*

¶**The Old Rectory** &⚘ (David Mendel & Keith Anderson) Limington. From A303 or A37 turn off at Ilchester. Follow signpost to Limington. House in centre of village next to church. Approx 1-acre. Recently replanted garden surrounding Georgian Rectory. Mixed borders containing some unusual plants, shrub roses, small knot and ornamental kitchen gardens are set within existing old walls, fruit trees and box hedges. TEA in aid of St Mary's Church. *Adm £1.50 Chd free. Sun July 14 (11-6) Private visits welcome, please* **Tel 01935 840035**

Park Wall House & (Capt & Mrs J J Howard) Bruton. ¼m SE of Bruton. Take B3081 out of Bruton towards Wincanton. 300yds after railway bridge on R. 1 acre multi-interest garden. Wide variety of mature trees, shrubs and roses. Herbaceous borders, pond, wild garden and pergola walk. Spectacular views. TEAS. *Adm £1.50 Chd 75p. Sat, Sun June 22, 23 (2-6)*

Pear Tree Cottage &֎ (Mr & Mrs Colvin Parry) Stapley. 9m S of Taunton nr Churchingford. Charming cottage garden leading to 2½-acre newly made park; well planted with interesting trees and shrubs leading to old leat and mill pond. Cream TEAS. *Adm £1 Chd 50p. Sat, Sun, Mon May 4, 5, 6, Sat, Sun, June 8, 9 (2-6)*

Peart Hall (Mr & Mrs J Lawrence-Mills) Spaxton. Bridgwater 6m. Taunton 9m. In village High St. take Splatt Lane opp school, then L to church and garden. Extensive gardens include rockeries sloping to trout stream, riverside walk with weirs, waterfalls; Victorian herb garden; daffodils; many rare trees. TEAS in aid of SCOPE. *Adm £1.50 Chd free. Sun March 31 (2-5)*

Pendower House &֎֎ (Mrs O M Maggs) Hillcommon. 5m W of Taunton off B3227 (old A361) turn R at Oake Xrds. 1st on R, parking on L verge. 1-acre landscaped garden created since 1980 on fairly level site. Shrub and herbaceous borders, collection of ceanothus. Fine display of roses, incl old-fashioned. Lge variety of young specimen and mature trees incl acers. Good autumn colour. Cream TEAS in aid of International Tree Foundation. *Adm £1.50 Chd free. Sats, Suns June 15, 16, 29, 30 (2-5.30) Oct 19, 20 (2-4)*

¶**Poundisford Park** & (Charles Woodruff Esq) Taunton. Signposted on B3170 between Taunton and Corfe. Old garden with interesting plants around a grade 1 mansion. Walled gardens, C17 gazebo, woodland walks, parkland, fine avenue of limes leading towards Blackdown Hills. TEAS. *Adm £1.50 Chd 50p (Share to RAF Benevolent Fund®). Mon to Fri Aug only. For NGS Suns April 14, Aug 18 (2-5)*

¶**Rimpton Gardens** &֎ Rimpton. 3m from Sherborne turn off B3148 at White Post Inn down hill to Rimpton. TEAS. *Combined adm £2 Chd free. Sun June 30 (2-6)*
  Ash House (Mr & Mrs Malcolm Shennan) 1st house on L after ½m. Garden planted in 1988/89. 1½ acres, mixed borders, small pond, collection of ornamental garden trees. Many rare and interesting plants. *Private visits welcome May to Sept, please* Tel 01935 851179
  Red House (Mr & Mrs Colin Lloyd) 1st on R after ½m. Cottage style with mixed borders and vegetable garden. Exceptional spinney areas comprised of native trees and shrubs which provide ideal habitat for wildlife

Smocombe House ֎֎ (Mr & Mrs Dermot Wellesley Wesley) Enmore. 4m W of Bridgwater take Enmore Rd, 3rd L after Tynte Arms. 5-acres S facing in Quantock Hills. Lovely woodland garden; views down to stream and pool; waterside stocked with interesting plants for spring display; arboretum designed by Roy Lancaster; charming old kitchen garden. TEAS in aid of Enmore Parish Church. *Adm £1.50 Chd free. Suns March 31, May 12 (2-6)*

Stapleton Manor &֎ (Mr & Mrs G E L Sant) 1m N of Martock on B3165 Long Sutton Rd. 2½-acres of roses, shrubs; herbaceous and mixed borders; pool/bog garden; dahlia walk; grass area with small trees and shrubs; fine mature trees. Scheduled Georgian Hamstone house (not open). *Adm £1.50 Chd free. Suns June 23, July 21 (12-6)*

Stogumber Gardens ֎֎ A358 NW from Taunton for 11m. Sign to Stogumber W near Crowcombe. Seven delightful gardens of interest to plantsmen in lovely village at edge of Quantocks. TEAS. *Combined adm £2.50 Chd free. Sun June 16 (2-6)*
  Brook Cottage &֎ (Mrs M Field) Good plants incl lilies in a lovely setting; small pond for added interest
  Butts Cottage (Mr & Mrs J A Morrison) Cottage garden with old roses, old-fashioned perennials, alpines, pond, small vine house and vegetable garden
  Cridlands Steep (Mrs A M Leitch) Large and interesting garden with young collection of trees
  Manor House (Mr & Mrs R W Lawrence) Large garden with borders and beds planted to give yr-round interest and colour
  Manor Linney (Dr F R Wallace) A medium-sized walled garden full of colour and interest
  Manor Mill (Mr G Dyke) A colourful garden on a slope bounded by a stream
  Wynes ֎ (Mr & Mrs L Simms) Large garden with orchard; shrubs; ponds; perennials; alpines and vegetable garden

Stone Allerton Gardens 11m NW of Wells, 2m from A38, signposted from Lower Weare. TEAS. *Combined adm £1.50 Chd free. Sat, Sun June 8, 9 (2-6)*
  Berries Brook (Mr & Mrs D J Searle) ½-acre cottage garden, roses, shrubs and pond
  Fallowdene ֎ (Prof & Mrs G H Arthur) ½-acre of walled garden. Rose and honeysuckle pergola, mixed shrub and herbaceous borders, lawns, kitchen garden. Splendid views over levels to Quantocks
  Greenfield House ֎ (Mr & Mrs D K Bull) ½-acre walled garden, colourful mixed planting, further ½-acre to explore
  Manor Farm &֎֎ (Mr & Mrs P Coate) 1-acre of mixed herbaceous and shrub beds, foliage bed, wall borders, water garden. Old orchard and many climbing plants, a painter's garden. *Private groups welcome, please* Tel 01934 713015

Stowleys ֎ (Rev R L Hancock) Bossington Lane, Porlock. NE of Porlock off A39. 6m W of Minehead. Medium-size garden, approx 2 acres with magnificent views across Porlock Bay and Bristol Channel. Daffodils, roses, unusual tender plants incl leptospermum, drimys and embothrium. Parking in paddock next door to garden. TEAS. *Adm £1 Chd free. Mon April 8, Sat June 29 (Plants June only) (2-6)*

Sutton Hosey Manor &֎֎ (Roger Bramble Esq) On A372 just E of Long Sutton. 2-acres; ornamental kitchen garden, lily pond, pleached limes leading to amelanchier walk past duck pond; rose and juniper walk from Italian terrace; Judas tree avenue; new ptelea walk. TEA. *Adm £2 Chd over 3 yrs 50p. Sun July 14 (2.30-6)*

¶The Time-Trail of Roses ✗ (Mrs Susan Lee) Wells. No on-site parking. Use free car park in Tucker St and walk to entrance at top of Westfield Rd. Magnificent collection of 1200 different roses, planted in ½-acre garden in date order of their introduction to show their beauty, diversity and evolution; plus collection of 240 miniatures. Also many spring bulbs, lilies and herbs. TEA Suns April 21 to Oct 27, Thurs, Fris, Sats June and July. For NGS Suns April 21, Sept 15. Adm £2 June, July, £1 other times Chd free. Suns June 2, 16 (2-6) parties by appt Tel 01749 674677

Tintinhull House ✗ (The National Trust) NW of Yeovil. Tintinhull Village, Yeovil. Signs on A303, W of Ilchester. Famous 2-acre garden in compartments, developed 1900-1960, influenced by Gertrude Jekyll and Hidcote; many good and uncommon plants. C17 & C18 house (not open). TEAS in aid of St Margaret's Church. Adm £3.50 Chd £1.60 (Party rate £2.60 Chd £1.20). For NGS Wed July 17 (12-6)

Walnut Farm ✗❀ (Angela & John Marsh) Yarley. 3m W of Wells. On B3139 turn L at Yarley Cross. Island site 200yds up Yarley Hill. ⅔-acre plantsman's garden developed over 5 yrs. Many unusual and traditional plants. Informal and mixed planting. 2 ponds and bog garden. Yr-round interest. Splendid views of Mendips. Conservatory. Small conservation area in adjoining field. TEA and plants in aid of The Coeliac Society. Adm £1.50 Chd 50p. Sun July 28 (2-6). Private visits welcome for parties of 2 and over, please Tel 01749 676942

Wambrook Gardens 2m SW Chard. Turn off A30 Honiton rd 1m W of Chard at top of hill. 4 gardens in beautiful wooded countryside; romantic views. Flower festival in church. TEAS and plants in aid of Wambrook Church Fabric Fund. Combined adm £2 or 50p each garden. Sun June 23 (2-6)

   Cotley ⬤❀ (Mr & Mrs T V D Eames) Wooded country garden with a pond, mature trees, shrubs, mixed borders and walled vegetable garden
   Dennetts Farm ✗❀ (Mr & Mrs F J Stubbings) Working cottage garden with many herbs and vegetables grown for sale. Emphasis on ease of working and use of salvaged materials
   Wambrook House ✗❀ (Mrs Stephanie Wheeler) 2-acre organically run garden surrounding Regency rectory (not open). Mature trees, mixed borders, walled vegetable garden
   Yew Tree Cottage ✗❀ (Mr & Mrs Ronald White) ⅓-acre planted to attract butterflies. Soft colours in mixed borders plus a small enclosed scented garden with tiny ponds for wildlife and a well tended organic vegetable plot

Watermeadows (Mr & Mrs R Gawen) 2½m S of Crewkerne on B3165 Lyme Regis Rd. A sophisticated cottage garden made from a field over 16yrs. There is something of everything including one hundred and twenty of the old-fashioned roses. Car park. Adm £1 Chd free. Private visits welcome May 1 to Aug 31, please Tel 01460 74421

Wayford Manor ❀ (Mr & Mrs Robin L Goffe) SW of Crewkerne. Turning on B3165 at Clapton; or on A30 Chard-Crewkerne. 3 acres, noted for magnolias and acers. Bulbs; flowering trees, shrubs; rhododendrons. Garden redesigned by Harold Peto in 1902. Fine Elizabethan manor house (not open). TEAS. Adm £2 Chd 50p. Suns April 7, 28, May 12, 26 (2-6); also private parties welcome, but please Tel 01460 73253

Wellesley Park Gardens ⬤✗ Wellington. ½m from centre of Wellington on S side, or can be found by turning down Hoyles Rd off the Wellington Relief Rd and taking 3rd rd L. 4 gardens situated just below the brow of the hill. TEAS. Combined adm £2. Sat, Sun, Wed June 15, 16, 19 (2-6)

   ¶Grayston, 18 Wellesley Park (Judy & David Parry) A small structured garden surrounding a 1930's house. Formal paving and planting leading to an enclosed rear garden with a variety of shady and open planted areas, together with a garden studio showing original paintings and prints on a horticultural theme. This garden is in its second year of construction
   Greenlands, 46 Wellesley Park ❀ (Jack & Pat Kenney) A ½-acre 1930's town garden in process of refurbishment, planted in cottage garden style with herbaceous plants and shrubs, all organically grown. Small wildlife pond. TEA and plants
   Miraflores, 49 Wellesley Park (Dr & Mrs R W Phillips) ½-acre town garden with more than 60 specimens of old roses, lawn with pond, herbaceous border, vegetable garden and small orchard
   48 Wellesley Park (John & Julie Morton) Approx ⅕-acre small town garden. Front low maintenance with trees. Rear designed for pleasing views from house and to give breadth to garden. Central rockery and pond. Trees, shrubs and herbaceous plants augmented by pots and baskets. Screened fruit and vegetable area

West Bradley House ⬤❀ (Mr & Mrs E Clifton-Brown) Glastonbury. 2½m due E of Glastonbury. Turn S off A361 (Shepton Mallet/Glastonbury Rd) at W Pennard. C17 octagonal stone house in 3-acre open garden next to church. 3 old carp ponds at different levels, with waterfall between 2. Range of unusual perennial and waterside plants. 70 acres of apple orchards around house, hopefully in full blossom when garden open. Visitors welcome to walk (or even drive) through orchards. Parking available. TEAS in aid of W Bradley Church. Adm garden & orchards £1.50 Chd 50p (Share to National Listening Library®). Sun May 12 (2-6)

Westhay ⬤✗❀ (Mr & Mrs T F Thompson) Kingston St Mary Taunton. 1st house on the R up the hill after the White Swan Inn, Kingston St Mary. Landscaped walled garden, bog garden, small lake; wood walk; spring daffodil lawn; streams and informal shrubberies. Plant sale. Suitable for wheelchairs in parts. Cream TEAS. Adm £1.50 Chd free. Sun May 26 (2-6). Private visits April 1 to Sept 30 by prior arrangement, please Tel 0182345 1226

Regular Openers. See end of county section.

Withey Lane Farmhouse ఉ ఉ ఉ (Sqn Ldr & Mrs H C Tomblin) Barton St David. 4m E of Somerton, turn off B3153 in Keinton Manderville. Turn R in Barton at Barton Inn. 200yds turn L at Manor House. 300yds turn R into small lane; farmhouse 300yds on right. ½-acre plantsman's garden with many unusual and interesting plants; herbaceous beds with shrubs; raised alpine beds; old roses; climbing plants; 1½- acre old cider orchard. *Adm £1 Chd 50p. Weds May 22, June 19 (2-5.30). Private visits welcome April to Sept, please* **Tel 01458 850875**

Wootton House ఉ ఉ (The Hon Mrs John Acland-Hood) Butleigh Wootton, 3m S of Glastonbury. Herbaceous borders; rose garden; shrubs, trees, spring and autumn bulbs; rock garden; woodland garden. C17 house (not open). *Adm £2 Chd under 5 free. Private visits welcome, please* **Tel 01643 831586**

1996 Special Events. For information on special National Gardens Scheme events in 1996 see Pages 18-19.

Staffordshire & part of West Midlands

Hon County Organisers: Mr & Mrs D K Hewitt, Arbour Cottage, Napley, Market Drayton, Shropshire TF9 4AJ Tel 01630 672852

DATES OF OPENING

10 April Wednesday
The Old Doctors House, Loggerheads
19 April Friday
Arbour Cottage, Napley, Market Drayton
26 April Friday
Arbour Cottage, Napley, Market Drayton
3 May Friday
Arbour Cottage, Napley, Market Drayton
5 May Sunday
Edgewood House, nr Kinver
6 May Monday
Park Farm, Park Lane, High Offley
8 May Wednesday
The Old Doctors House, Loggerheads
10 May Friday
Arbour Cottage, Napley, Market Drayton
12 May Sunday
Hales Hall, nr Market Drayton
Little Onn Hall, Church Eaton, nr Stafford
17 May Friday
Arbour Cottage, Napley, Market Drayton
19 May Sunday
Heath House, nr Eccleshall
Moor Croft, Pattingham
Wightwick Manor, Compton
24 May Friday
Arbour Cottage, Napley, Market Drayton

26 May Sunday
The Wombourne Wodehouse, Wolverhampton
29 May Wednesday
The Old Doctors House, Loggerheads
31 May Friday
Arbour Cottage, Napley, Market Drayton
1 June Saturday
Stonehill, Hollington
2 June Sunday
Eastfield House, Kings Bromley
The Garth, Milford, Stafford
The Hollies Farm, Pattingham
9 June Sunday
12 Darges Lane, Great Wyrley
Little Onn Hall, Church Eaton, nr Stafford
Park Farm, Park Lane, High Offley
15 June Saturday
Lower House, Sugnall Parva, Eccleshall
16 June Sunday
Lower House, Sugnall Parva, Eccleshall
21 June Friday
Arbour Cottage, Napley, Market Drayton
23 June Sunday
Flashbrook Lodge, Flashbrook
Grafton Cottage, Barton-under-Needwood
Moseley Old Hall, Fordhouses, Wolverhampton
26 June Wednesday
The Old Doctors House, Loggerheads

30 June Sunday
Flashbrook Lodge, Flashbrook
The Garth, Milford, Stafford ‡
Grafton Cottage, Barton-under-Needwood
38 Park Avenue, Stafford ‡
7 July Sunday
Bleak House, Bagnall
The Covert, nr Market Drayton
12 Darges Lane, Great Wyrley
Kings Bromley Gardens ‡
Woodside House, Barton-under-Needwood ‡
13 July Saturday
Brookside, Abbots Bromley
14 July Sunday
Brookside, Abbots Bromley ‡
Eccleshall Castle Gardens
Heath House, nr Eccleshall
Strawberry Fields, Hill Ridware ‡
17 July Wednesday
The Old Doctors House, Loggerheads
Strawberry Fields, Hill Ridware
21 July Sunday
25 Clifford Street, Glascote, Tamworth
Strawberry Fields, Hill Ridware
28 July Sunday
Biddulph Grange Garden, Biddulph
25 Clifford Street, Glascote, Tamworth
4 August Sunday
25 Clifford Street, Glascote, Tamworth
Grafton Cottage, Barton-under-Needwood

The Willows, Trysull
7 August Wednesday
The Old Doctors House,
Loggerheads
10 August Saturday
Brookside, Abbots Bromley
11 August Sunday
Brookside, Abbots Bromley

Grafton Cottage,
Barton-under-Needwood
29 September Sunday
Biddulph Grange Garden, Biddulph
13 October Sunday
Wightwick Manor, Compton

Regular openings
For details see garden description

Manor Cottage, Chapel Chorlton,
Newcastle

DESCRIPTIONS OF GARDENS

Arbour Cottage &*&* (Mr & Mrs D K Hewitt) Napley. 4m N of Market Drayton. Take A53 then B5415 signed Woore, turn L 1¾m at telephone box. Cottage garden 2 acres of alpine gardens, grasses, shrub roses and many paeonias, bamboos etc. Colour all yr from shrubs and trees of many species. Featured in NGS Video III. TEAS. *Adm £2 Chd free. Fris April 19 to May 31 and June 21 (2-5.30). Private visits welcome, please* Tel 01630 672852

Biddulph Grange Garden *&* (The National Trust) Biddulph. 3½m SE of Congleton, 7m N of Stoke-on-Trent on A527. An exciting and rare survival of a high Victorian garden extensively restored since 1988. Conceived by James Bateman, the 15 acres are divided into a number of smaller gardens designed to house specimens from his extensive plant collection. An Egyptian Court; Chinese Pagoda, Willow Pattern Bridge; Pinetum and Arboretum together with many other settings all combine to make the garden a miniature tour of the world. TEAS. *Adm £4 Chd £2 Family £10. March 30 to Oct 30, Wed to Fri (12-6), Sat to Sun (11-6). For NGS Suns July 28, Sept 29 (11-6)* Tel 01782 517999

Bleak House *&* (Mr & Mrs J H Beynon) Bagnall. A5009 to Milton Xrds turn for Bagnall. 2m up hill past golf course to corner opp Highlands Hospital. 1-acre plantswoman's garden on 3 levels with roses, herbaceous borders. Terraces leading to informal garden incl stone quarry with pool and waterfall. TEAS. *Adm £1.50 Chd free. Sun July 7 (2-6). Parties welcome, please* Tel 01782 534713

¶**Brookside** *&* (Mr & Mrs L Harvey) Abbots Bromley. Approach village from Uttoxeter or Rugeley via B5013; from Burton via B5017. Turn opp the Bagot Arms Inn situated in the main street. ⅓-acre garden comprising shrubs, herbaceous and bedding plants. Rose, herb and water gardens. TEAS. *Adm £1.50 Chd free. Sats, Suns July 13, 14; Aug 10, 11 (2-6)*

¶**25 Clifford Street** &*&* (Mr & Mrs J Sippitts) Glascote. From new A5 bypass, take B5440 signed Glascote to B5000 approx ½m. Follow sign for town centre at roundabout for 300yds. Clifford St 1st R opp Glascote WMC. ¼-acre garden of mixed borders, shrubs and trees; small wildlife pond, ornamental pond with bridge; emphasis on creating a colourful summer garden featured in 'Garden News' 1995. TEAS. *Adm £1 Chd 25p. Suns July 21, 28; Aug 4 (2-6)*

The Covert &*&* (Mr & Mrs Leslie Standeven) Burntwood Loggerheads. On Staffs/Shrops borders. Turn off A53 Newcastle-Market Drayton Rd onto Burntwood at Loggerheads Xrds. Approx ¾-acre of plantsperson's garden featuring many rare and unusual plants. Mediterranean beds, yucca bank, scree beds, pool, bog garden; alpine/tuffa beds and recently added alpine house. Partially suitable for wheelchairs. TEAS. *Adm £2 Chd 50p. Sun July 7 (2-5.30). Private visits welcome, please* Tel 01630 672677

12 Darges Lane *&* (Ann and Ken Hackett) Great Wyrley. From A5 take A34 towards Walsall. Darges Lane is 1st turning on R (over brow of hill). House on R on corner of Cherrington Drive. ¼-acre well stocked plantsman's and flower arranger's garden. Foliage plants a special feature. Mixed borders incl trees, shrubs and rare plants giving yr-round interest. Features constantly changing. As featured in Channel 4 Garden Club Aug 95. TEAS. *Adm £1.50 Chd 50p. Suns June 9, July 7 (2-6). Also private visits welcome, please* Tel 01922 415064

Eastfield House & (Mr & Mrs A Rogers) Kings Bromley. Kings Bromley lies 5m N of Lichfield on A515 Lichfield to Ashbourne rd and 3m W of the A38 on the A513 Tamworth to Rugeley rd. Eastfield House is ½m E of the village centre on the A513. 2-acre garden surrounding a Victorian House, shrubs, lawns herbaceous plants, pond and bog garden. TEA. *Adm £1.50 Chd 50p. Sun June 2 (2-5.30)*

Eccleshall Castle Gardens & (Mr & Mrs Mark Carter) ½m N of Eccleshall on A519; 6m from M6, junction 14 (Stafford); 10m from junction 15 (Stoke-on-Trent). 20 acres incl wooded garden with moat lawns around William and Mary mansion house; herbaceous, rose garden, wide variety of trees and shrubs; also recently renovated C14 tower. Home-made cream TEAS. Free car/coach parking. *Adm £2 Chd 50p.* ▲*For NGS Sun July 14 (1.30-5.30)*

Edgewood House * (Mr & Mrs G E Fletcher) Stourton. 4m W of Stourbridge 11m E of Bridgnorth. Take A458 from Stew Poney Junction on A449 (Wolverhampton/Kidderminster) towards Bridgnorth. 1st lane on R (Greenforge Lane). ¾m along lane on L. 12 acres of woodland with winding paths through bluebells and assorted trees from cultivated natural garden with small pools. Rhododendrons and azaleas. TEAS. *Adm £1.50 Chd 50p. Sun May 5 (2-6)*

¶**Flashbrook Lodge** *&* (Mrs Minnie A Mansell) Flashbrook. On A41 4m N of Newport, take rd signed Knighton. A garden newly established over last 3 yrs from green field site of approx 1 acre. Features large pool, rockery, waterfall, pergola, gazebo, arbour, trees, shrubs, old-fashioned shrub roses and herbaceous perennials with all yr interest. TEAS. *Adm £1.50 Chd 50p (Share to St Michael and All Angels Church, Adbaston®). Suns June 23, 30 (2-6)*

The Garth ❀ (Mr & Mrs David Wright) 2 Broc Hill Way, Milford, 4½m SE of Stafford. A513 Stafford-Rugeley Rd; at Barley Mow turn R (S) to Brocton; L after 1m. ½-acre; shrubs, rhododendrons, azaleas, mixed herbaceous borders, naturalized bulbs; plants of interest to flower arrangers. Rock hewn caves. Fine landscape setting. Coach parties by appt. TEAS. *Adm £1 Chd 50p. Suns June 2, 30 (2-6). Private parties welcome, please* Tel **01785 661182**

Grafton Cottage ⚘❀ (Margaret & Peter Hargreaves) Bar Lane, Barton-under-Needwood. 5m NE of Lichfield. Take B5016 between Barton-under-Needwood and Yoxall. Bar Lane is ½m W of Top Bell public house. ¾m along lane. A plant lover's cottage garden. ¼-acre. Designed and maintained by owners. Trellises covered with many old roses and clematis; wide range of unusual perennials with all-summer interest, stream and vegetables. Some of the unusual plants for sale. TEAS. *Adm £1.50 Chd free (Share to Arthritis Rheumatism Council for Research®). Suns June 23, 30, Aug 4, 11 (1.30-5.30)*

Hales Hall ⚘❀ (Mr & Mrs R Hall) Hales. Signposted to Hales due S from A53 between Market Drayton and Loggerheads. C18 house (not open) in beautiful setting. 15 acres of mixed garden particularly rhododendrons, azaleas, woodland and wild garden. Partially suitable for wheelchairs by prior arrangement. Bring picnic lunches to have in park beforehand. TEAS. *Adm £2 Chd 50p. Sun May 12 (2-5.30)*

Heath House ⚘❀ (Dr & Mrs D W Eyre-Walker) Nr Eccleshall. 3m W of Eccleshall. Take B5026 towards Woore. At Sugnall turn L, after 1½m turn R immediately by stone garden wall. After 1m straight across Xrds. 1½-acre garden. Borders, bog garden, woodland garden and alpine bed. Many unusual plants. Car parking limited and difficult if wet. TEAS. *Adm £2 Chd free (Share to Parish Church®). Suns May 19, July 14 (2-6). Also private visits welcome, please* Tel **01785 280318**

The Hollies Farm ⚘❀ (Mr & Mrs J Shanks) Pattingham. From Wolverhampton A454 W, follow signs to Pattingham. Cross traffic lights at Perton, 1½m R for Hollies Lane. From Pattingham take Wolverhampton Rd 1m turn L to Hollies Lane. 2-acre plantsman's landscaped garden with interesting trees and shrubs. TEAS in aid of NSPCC. *Adm £1.50 Chd free. Sun June 2 (2-6)*

¶**Kings Bromley Gardens** ⚘ A515. 5m N of Lichfield. Car park and Teas at Village Hall on Alrewas Rd (A513). *Adm £1.50 Chd free. Sun July 7 (2-6)*
  ¶**37 Leofric Close** (Mr & Mrs B Harber) Prize-winning small ornamental garden; mixed borders; small water feature; new scree and rock bed for 1996. *Private visits welcome by parties not exceeding 12, May to Sept, please* Tel **01543 472762**
  ¶**21 Manor Road** (Mr & Mrs D O'Dea) Perennials, shrubs, mixed borders, many newly planted beds planned for 1996
  ¶**Forge House** (Mr & Mrs A Reid) Adjacent to War Memorial. Cottage garden, roses, mixed borders, annuals, continually being developed by owners

Little Onn Hall ⚙ (Mr & Mrs I H Kidson) Church Eaton, 6m SW of Stafford. A449 Wolverhampton-Stafford; at Gailey roundabout turn W on to A5 for 1¼m; turn R to Stretton; 200yds turn L for Church Eaton; or Bradford Arms - Wheaton Aston and Marston 1¼m. 6-acre garden; herbaceous lined drive; abundance of rhododendrons; formal paved rose garden with pavilions at front; large lawns with lily pond around house; old moat garden with fish tanks and small ruin; fine trees; walkways. Paddock open for picnics. TEAS. *Adm £2 Chd 50p. Suns May 12, June 9 (2-6)*

Lower House ⚙❀ (Mr & Mrs J M Treanor) Sugnall Parva, Eccleshall. 2m W of Eccleshall. On B5026 Loggerheads Rd turn R at sharp double bend. House ½m on L. Large cottage garden with all yr colour and interest, mixed borders, shrubs, pond and rockery in rural setting. TEAS. *Adm £2 Chd free. Sat, Sun June 15, 16 (1-6). Also private visits welcome, please* Tel **01785 851 378**

Manor Cottage ⚙❀ (Mrs Joyce Heywood) Chapel Chorlton. 6m S of Newcastle-U-Lyme. On A51 Nantwich to Stone Rd turn behind Cock Inn at Stableford; white house on village green. The garden is full of interesting and unusual plants especially fern, euphorbias, grasses and geraniums. TEAS. *Adm £1.50 Chd 50p. Every Mon May 6 to Aug 26 (2-5). Also private visits welcome, please* Tel **01782 680206**

Moor Croft ⚙ (Mr & Mrs Peter Hollingsworth) Pattingham. Take the A454 signed to Bridgnorth. Follow signs to Pattingham. Cross traffic lights at Perton, 1m turn L Gt Moor Rd. Coming from Pattingham follow main rd to Wolverhampton for 1½m. Turn R at top of small rise for Great Moor. An interesting landscaped garden of mixed beds and trees leading to an old water meadow with stream. Fine old willows and alders together with more recent plantings. *Adm £1.50 Chd free. Sun May 19 (2-6)*

Moseley Old Hall ⚙⚘❀ (The National Trust) Fordhouses, 4m N of Wolverhampton, between A460 & A449 south of M54 motorway; follow signs. Small modern reconstruction of C17 garden with formal box parterre; mainly includes plants grown in England before 1700; old roses, herbaceous plants, small herb garden, arbour. Late Elizabethan house. TEAS. *Adm House & Garden £3.30 Chd £1.65; Garden £1.60 Chd 80p. For NGS Sun June 23 (1.30-5.30)*

¶**The Old Doctors House** ⚙⚘❀ (Mr & Mrs David Ainsworth) The Burntwood, Loggerheads. On Staffs/Shrops border. Turn off A53 Newcastle to Market Drayton rd onto Kestrel Drive/The Burntwood nr Loggerheads Xrds, adjacent hotel. A garden of approx ¾ acre created within the framework of mature trees and shrubs; mixed borders and woodland plantings give interest over many months. Pool, waterfall and kitchen garden. TEA. *Adm £1.50 Chd 50p (Share to Ashley and Loggerheads Day Centre/Luncheon Club©). Weds April 10; May 8, 29; June 26; July 17; August 7 (2-5.30)*

The National Gardens Scheme is a charity which traces its origins back to 1927. Since then it has raised a total of over £14 million for charitable purposes.

38 Park Avenue ⌀❀ (Mr & Mrs Eric Aspin) Rising Brook. Leave M6 at junction 13, A449 towards Stafford, approx 2m, past Royal Oak on R, past Westway on L, next turn L. From Stafford take A449 over railway bridge, 4th turn on R. 600 plant varieties in small town garden from oak trees to cyclamen. Shady stream, secluded white garden. Comprehensive collection of old roses and clematis. Some interesting design features. TEA. *Adm £1.50 Chd free. Sun June 30 (2-6). Private visits welcome, please* **Tel 01785 212762**

Park Farm ⌀⌀❀ (Mr & Mrs Peter Celecia) High Offley. 4m W of Eccleshall. Take A519 towards Newport. At Woodseaves sign turn R into Back Lane, at T-junction turn R Park Lane 1m on R. A developing informal country cottage garden of 1 acre. Interesting trees, shrubs, mixed borders; pool and vegetable garden. TEA. *Adm £1.50 Chd free (Share to Multiple Sclerosis®). Mons May 6; June 9 (2-6). Parking available off High Offley Rd (see signs). Private visits by telephone arrangement only.* **Tel 01785 284248** *evenings*

¶**Stonehill** ⌀⌀❀ (David & Caroline Raymont) Great Gate. 4m NW Uttoxeter. A50 to Uttoxeter. R onto B5030 to JCB Rocester, L to Hollington and Croxden Abbey (signposted). 3rd R to abbey and Great Gate. L for Stonehill. 5 acres of developing quarry gardens. Light woodland with rhododendrons and azaleas, spring bulbs and bog gardens. Good spring colour. Parking for disabled only. TEAS in aid of St Giles Church. *Adm £1.50 Chd 50p. Sat June 1 (2-6)*

¶**Strawberry Fields** ⌀ (Mr & Mrs T Adams) Hill Ridware. 5m N of Lichfield. B5014 Lichfield/Abbots Bromley. At Hill Ridware turn into Church Lane by Royal Oak Inn, then 1st R. A surprise round every corner of this delightful ⅓-acre award winning garden. Water trail leading through herbaceous beds, pergolas, arbours, Japanese garden; interesting shrubs and trees; unusual climbers.

Pleasing country views. TEAS. *Adm £1.50 Chd free. Suns July 14, 21; Wed July 17 (11-5). Private visits welcome, please* **Tel 01543 490516**

Wightwick Manor ⌀ (The National Trust) Compton, 3m W of Wolverhampton A454, Wolverhampton-Bridgnorth, just to N of rd, up Wightwick Bank, beside Mermaid Inn. Partly suitable for wheelchairs. 17-acre, Victorian-style garden laid out by Thomas Mawson; yew hedges; topiary; terraces; 2 pools; rhododendrons; azaleas. House closed. TEAS. *Adm £2 Chd £1. For NGS Suns May 19, Oct 13 (2-6)*

The Willows ⌀⌀❀ (Mr & Mrs Nigel Hanson) Trysull. 7m SW of Wolverhampton. From A449 at Himley B4176 towards Bridgnorth, 2¼m turn R to Trysull. ¾m on L. 2-acre garden created and maintained by owners since 1981. Natural pool, hostas, rhododendrons, salvias, old-fashioned roses, colour theme borders with a wide range of interesting and unusual plants. Teas in village hall in aid of Trysull Church. *Adm £1.50 Chd free. Sun Aug 4 (2-6)*

The Wombourne Wodehouse ⌀⌀❀ (Mr & Mrs J Phillips) 4m S of Wolverhampton just off A449 on A463 to Sedgley. 18-acre garden laid out in 1750. Mainly rhododendrons, herbaceous and iris border, woodland walk, water garden. TEAS. *Adm £2 Chd free. Sun May 26 (2-5.30); also private visits welcome in May, June, July, please* **Tel 01902 892202**

¶**Woodside House** ⌀❀ (Mr & Mrs R C Webster) Barton-under-Needwood. Take B5016 out of Barton-under-Needwood. Turn R at Top Bell public house, 300yds turn R into signed gravel drive. 1-acre plantsman's garden fully landscaped incl Japanese garden with stream and waterfalls; rose walk; cottage garden; large koi pond with rockery; plant lovers walks. TEAS. *Adm £1.50 Chd free (Share to RNIB (Midland Region)®). Sun July 7 (1.30-6). Private visits welcome Sats only by appt June 22 to Aug 3 (1.30-6), please* **Tel 01283 716046**

Scotland's Gardens Scheme. The National Gardens Scheme has a similar but quite separate counterpart in Scotland. Called Scotland's Gardens Scheme, it raises money for the Queen's Nursing Institute (Scotland), the Gardens Fund of the National Trust for Scotland and over 160 registered charities nominated by garden owners. The Handbook is available (£3.25 incl p&p) from Scotland's Gardens Scheme, 31 Castle Terrace, Edinburgh EH1 2EL. Telephone 0131-229-1870, Fax 0131-229-0443

Open by appointment Please do not be put off by this notation. The owner may consider his garden too small to accommodate the numbers associated with a normal opening or, more often, there may be a lack of car parking space. It is often more rewarding than a normal opening as the owner will usually give a guided tour of the garden. The minimum size of party is either stated in the garden description or can be found out when making the appointment; usually 2. If the garden has normal open days, the entrance fee is as stated in the garden description.

Suffolk

Hon County Organisers:

(East) Mrs Robert Stone, Washbrook Grange, Washbrook, Nr Ipswich IP8 3HQ
Tel 01473 730244

(West) Lady Mowbray, Hill House, Glemsford, Nr Sudbury CO 10 7PP
Tel 01787 281930

Asst Hon County Organiser: (East) Mrs T W Ingram, Orchard House, Chattisham Lane, Hintlesham, Suffolk
IP8 3NW Tel 01473 652 282

Mrs R I Johnson, The Old Farmhouse, Flixton Road, Bungay NR35 1PD

(West) Mrs M Pampanini, The Old Rectory, Hawstead, Bury St Edmunds IP29 5NT
Tel 01284 386 613

Mrs A Kelsey, The Priory, Church Road, Little-waldingfield, Suffolk CO10 OSW
Tel 01787 2477335

Hon County Treasurer: (West) Sir John Mowbray

DATES OF OPENING

March 31 Sunday
Great Thurlow Hall, Haverhill
April 7 Sunday
Barham Hall, Barham
April 8 Monday
East Bergholt Place, East Bergholt
April 14 Sunday
Giffords Hall, Wickhambrook
April 21 Sunday
Garden House Farm, Drinkstone
April 28 Sunday
The Abbey, Eye
Blakenham Woodland Garden,
Little Blakenham
East Bergholt Place, East Bergholt
Somerleyton Hall, Lowestoft
Tollemache Hall, Offton
May 1 Wednesday
Blakenham Woodland Garden,
Little Blakenham
May 5 Sunday
13 Drapers Lane, Ditchingham
May 6 Monday
Bucklesham Hall, Bucklesham
13 Drapers Lane, Ditchingham
Letheringham Watermill, Easton
May 18 Saturday
The Old Hall, Barsham
May 19 Sunday
The Abbey, Eye
Battlies House, Rougham
The Old Hall, Barsham
The Priory, Stoke by Nayland
May 26 Sunday
Magnolia House, Yoxford
The Rookery, Eyke
Rosedale, Bures, nr Sudbury
Washbrook Grange, nr Ipswich
Woottens, Wenhaston
May 27 Monday
Bucklesham Hall, Bucklesham ‡
Washbrook Grange, nr Ipswich ‡
June 2 Sunday
Hillside, Freston

Little Thurlow Hall, Haverhill
June 9 Sunday
Giffords Hall, Wickhambrook
Hengrave Hall, Hengrave
Rosemary, East Bergholt
Thrift Cottage, Cowlinge,
nr Newmarket ‡
Thrift Farm, Cowlinge, nr Newmarket ‡
June 16 Sunday
The Abbey, Eye
Clipt Bushes, Cockfield ‡
Felsham House, Bury St Edmunds
Garden House, Moulton,
nr Newmarket
Moat Cottage, Great Green,
Cockfield ‡
The Spong, Groton
Western House, Cavendish
Woottens, Wenhaston
Wyken Hall, Stanton
June 19 Wednesday
Felsham House, Bury St Edmunds
June 23 Sunday
Gable House, Redisham
Long Melford Gardens
The Old Rectory, Wetherden
Rosedale, Bures, nr Sudbury
Upland Hall, Bungay
Western House, Cavendish
June 30 Sunday
Boxted Hall, Bury St Edmunds ‡
The Dhoon, Barton Mills
The Hill House, Glemsford ‡
North Cove Hall, Beccles
Reydon Grove House, Reydon
St Stephens Cottage,
Spexhall
Western House, Cavendish
July 7 Sunday
Highfields Farm, Bures
Redisham Hall, Beccles
Western House, Cavendish
July 13 Saturday
The Old Hall, Barsham
July 14 Sunday
Holbecks, Hadleigh

The Old Hall, Barsham
Woottens, Wenhaston
July 17 Wednesday
Highfields Farm, Bures
July 21 Sunday
Highfields Farm, Bures
Rosedale, Bures, nr Sudbury
July 28 Sunday
Porters Lodge, Cavenham
Riverside House, Clare
August 4 Sunday
The Beeches, Walsham-le-Willows
August 11 Sunday
Akenfield, 1 Park Lane, Charsfield
August 12 Monday
Akenfield, 1 Park Lane, Charsfield
August 13 Tuesday
Akenfield, 1 Park Lane, Charsfield
August 14 Wednesday
Akenfield, 1 Park Lane, Charsfield
August 15 Thursday
Akenfield, 1 Park Lane, Charsfield
August 16 Friday
Akenfield, 1 Park Lane, Charsfield
August 17 Friday
Akenfield, 1 Park Lane, Charsfield
August 18 Sunday
Washbrook Grange, nr Ipswich
August 25 Sunday
Rosedale, Bures, nr Sudbury
St Stephens Cottage, Spexhall ‡
Woottens, Wenhaston ‡
August 26 Monday
Letheringham Water Mill, Easton
September 1 Sunday
Ellingham Hall, nr Bungay
September 8 Sunday
Ickworth House, Park & Gardens,
Horringer
September 14 Saturday
The Old Hall, Barsham
September 15 Sunday
The Old Hall, Barsham

Regular openings
For details see garden description

Akenfield, 1 Park Lane, Charsfield
Blakenhall Woodland Gardens
Euston Hall, nr Thetford
Somerleyton Hall, Lowestoft

By appointment only
For telephone numbers and other details see garden descriptions.
Private visits welcomed

4 Church Street, Hadleigh
Grundisburgh Hall, Woodbridge
Rumah Kita, Bedfield
Thumbit, Walsham-le-Willows

> The National Gardens Scheme is a charity which traces its origins back to 1927. Since then it has raised a total of over £14 million for charitable purposes.

DESCRIPTIONS OF GARDENS

The Abbey *※❀* (Mrs K Campbell) Eye. 6m S of Diss, Norfolk. Leaving Eye on B1117 passing Eye Church on L cross River Dove and The Abbey is immediately on the L with ample parking. Marked remains of Benedictine Priory on some maps. The garden is approx 3 acres and surrounds a red brick and flint timber framed house incorporating a Benedictine Abbey founded in the 11th century. The remains of the church such as are above ground make for interesting gardening with walls and courtyards. Raised beds and sink gardens and 2 large glasshouses. Unusual plants, many double primroses and auriculas, iris and roses and a large herbaceous collection. Miniature geraniums and succulents are in the glasshouses. Ample parking. TEAS in aid of Eye Church. *Adm £1.50 OAP & Chd 75p. Suns April 28, May 19, June 16 (2-5.30). Parties welcome by appt May to July, please* **Tel 01379 870263**

Akenfield, 1 Park Lane *※❀* (Mrs E E Cole) Charsfield, 6m N of Woodbridge. On B1078, 3m W of Wickham Market. ½-acre council house garden; vegetables, flowers for drying, 2 greenhouses; small fishponds with water wheel; many pot plants etc. In village of Charsfield (known to many readers and viewers as Akenfield). *Adm £1 OAPs 75p Chd free. Daily from Easter to Sept 30. For NGS Sun Aug 11 daily to Sun Aug 17 (10.30-7). Parties welcome by appt, please* **Tel 01473 737402**

Barham Hall *&※❀* (Mr & Mrs Richard Burrows) Barham. Ipswich to A45 going W. 4m sign Great Blakenham to roundabout beneath motorway. Leave by 3rd turning to Claydon. Through Claydon, after decontrolled signs turn R up Church Lane to Barham Green. ½m up Church Lane. Barham church on L.h.s Barham Hall behind long brick wall. 7 acres of undulating gardens mainly recreated during the last 5yrs. 3 herbaceous borders, a lake surrounded by azaleas and bog plants, a woodland shrub garden full of spring flowers; a very considerable collection of victorian roses set in well kept lawns with mature trees; a water garden and many other interesting features. St Mary's and St Peter's Church open with famous Henry Moore sculpture. TEA. *Adm £2 OAPs £1 Chd 25p (Share to St Mary's & St Peters Church Barham®). Sun April 7 (2-5)*

Battlies House *&※* (Mr & Mrs John Barrell) Bury St Edmunds. Turn N off A14 at GT Barton and Rougham industrial estate turning, 3m E of Bury St Edmunds. In ½m turn R by lodge. 8-acre garden, lawns; shrubberies, woodland walk with a variety of old trees; rhododendrons; elms and conifers. TEAS. *Adm £1.50 Chd free (Share to St Nicholas' Hospice®). Sun May 19 (2-5.30)*

The Beeches *&* (Dr & Mrs A J Russell) Walsham-le-Willows. 10m NE of Bury St Edmunds; signed Walsham-le-Willows off A143. At Xrds in village pass Church on L, after 50yds turn L along Grove Rd. Pink house behind Church. 3 acres; lawns, herbaceous border, mature and newly-planted trees. Potager, thatched summer house with ornamental pond, gazebo and wild garden by stream. TEAS. *Adm £1.50 Chd under 14 free (Share to St Mary's Church, Walsham-le-Willows®). Sun Aug 4 (2-6)*

Blakenham Woodland Garden *※* Little Blakenham. 4m NW of Ipswich. Follow signs from 'The Beeches' at Lt Blakenham, 1m off the old A1100, now called B1113. 5-acre bluebell wood densely planted with fine collection of trees and shrubs; camellias, magnolias, cornus, azaleas, rhododendrons, roses, hydrangeas. *Adm £1 Chd £1. Open daily (1-5) except Sats, March 1 to June 30. For NGS Suns April 28, Wed May 1 (1-5). Parties welcome by appt, please* **Tel 0171 411 2201**

¶Boxted Hall *&* (Mrs Weller-Poley) Bury St Edmunds. Boxted Hall is approached by a drive off the B1066 Bury St Edmunds-Long Melford back rd ½m S of Boxted Village. Moated House (not open) with 4 acres of grounds, extensive lawns, trees and roses in outstanding setting. Strawberry TEAS. *Adm £1.50 Chd 50p. Sun June 30 (2-6)*

Bucklesham Hall *※* (Mr & Mrs D R Brightwell) Bucklesham. 6m SE of Ipswich, 1m E of village opp to Bucklesham School. 7 acres created by previous owners in 1973 and maintained by present owners since 1994. Unusual plants, shrubs and trees. Shrub/rose garden, water and woodland gardens. Partly suitable for wheelchairs. TEAS in aid of St Mary's Church, Bucklesham. *Adm £2 Chd £1. Mons May 6, 27 (2-6). Private visits welcome by parties of 4 or more, please* **Tel 01473 659263**

4 Church Street *※* (Lewis Hart) Hadleigh. Approx 6m W of Ipswich on the A1071. 25yds from St Mary's Church. ⅓-acre old walled garden. Wide range of lesser known plants. Many clematis, penstemon, iris, euphorbia, alpines; crocosmias, kniphofias, trees and shrubs incl sorbus, skimmia, indigofera, daphnes. Collection of plants in sinks and tubs. *Donation box. Private visits welcome, please* **Tel 01473 822418**

> **1996 Special Events.** For information on special National Gardens Scheme events in 1996 see Pages 18-19.

Clipt Bushes & (Mr & Mrs H W A Ruffell) Cockfield. Just off the A1141 8m S of Bury St Edmunds and 3m N of Lavenham. Ample parking. Farmhouse gardens, approx 2 acres designed for easy maintenance. Shrubberies, specimen trees and old roses. TEAS. *Combined adm with* **Moat Cottage** *£2.50 OAP £1 Chd free. Sun June 16 (2-6)*

¶**The Dhoon** &⚘❀ (Mr & Mrs H H Morriss) 19 The Street, Barton Mills. Opp the PO in the Old Street in Barton Mills, take signs off the A11 to Barton Mills. New garden of 6 yrs going down to the R Lark. Herbaceous borders, pergola, conservatory and raised vegetable beds. Sir Alexander Fleming's former country house. TEAS. *Adm £1.50 Chd free (Share to Newmarket Day Centre©). Sun June 30 (2-5.30)*

13 Drapers Lane ⚘❀ (Mr & Mrs Borrett) Ditchingham. 1¼m Bungay off the B1332 towards Norwich. ⅓-acre containing many interesting, unusual plants including 80 plus varieties of hardy geraniums, climbers and shrubs. Herbaceous perennials a speciality. Owner maintained. TEAS. *Adm £1 Chd free. Sun, Mon May 5, 6 (12-4) also open on Sun June 30 under Hedenham and Ditchingham Gardens, Norfolk*

¶**East Bergholt Place Garden** &⚘❀ (Mr & Mrs Rupert Eley) East Bergholt. On the B1070 towards Manning Tree, 2m E of A12. 15-acre garden originally laid out at the beginning of the century by the present owner's great Grandfather. Full of many fine trees and shrubs some of which are rarely seen in East Anglia. Particularly beautiful in spring when the rhododendrons, magnolias and camellias are in full flower. TEAS. *Adm £1.50 Chd free. Mon, Sun April 8, 28 (2-6)*

Ellingham Hall &⚘❀ (Col & Mrs H M L Smith) On A143 between Beccles 3m and Bungay 2m. Georgian house set in parkland. The 2-acre garden, designed by Sue Gill (see Great Campston, Gwent) is planted in deep borders with a wide and unusual variety of plants and trees. The recently planted 'Terracotta Garden' has a Mediterranean atmosphere. The walled garden includes fan trained fruit trees and a nuttery. Exhibition of sculptures by Rosemary Cook. TEAS. *Adm £1.50 Chd under 12 free. Sun Sept 1 (2-6)*

●**Euston Hall** ⚘ (The Duke & Duchess of Grafton) on the A1088 12m N of Bury St Edmunds. 3m S of Thetford. Terraced lawns; herbaceous borders, rose garden, C17 pleasure grounds, lake and watermill. C18 house open; famous collection of paintings. C17 church; temple by William Kent. Craft shop. Wheelchair access to gardens, tea-room and shop only. TEAS in Old Kitchen. *Adm house & garden £2.50 OAPs £2, Chd 50p Parties of 12 or more £2 per head (Share to NGS®). Thurs June 6 to Sept 26; Suns June 30 & Sept 1 (2.30-5)*

Felsham House &❀ (The Hon Mrs Erskine) Felsham 7m SE of Bury St Edmunds off A134, 8m W of Stowmarket via Rattlesden. 5 acres incl meadow with wild flowers, established trees, shrubs, roses; herb garden. TEAS. *Adm £1.50 Chd 50p. Sun, Wed June 16, 19 (2-6)*

Gable House &⚘❀ (Mr & Mrs John Foster) Redisham. 3½m S of Beccles. Mid-way between Beccles and Halesworth on Ringsfield-Ilketshall St Lawrence Rd. Garden of 1 acre, mixed borders, alpines, fruit and vegetables.

Home-made TEAS. *Adm £1.50 (Share to St Peters Church Redisham, Beccles, Suffolk®). Sun June 23 (2-5.30). Private visits welcome Suns from May to Sept* Tel 01502 575298

¶**Garden House** &⚘❀ (Mr & Mrs John Maskelyne) Brookside. Moulton is 3m due E of Newmarket on B1085. The garden is close to the Pack Horse Bridge and faces the village green. Interesting ¾-acre plantsman's garden, roses, small woodland area, alpines and mixed borders. Small water feature, pergola: large number of clematis. Committee member of British Clematis Society; maintained by owners. TEAS. *Adm £1.50 Chd free. Sun June 16 (2-6)*

Garden House Farm &⚘❀ (Mr & Mrs Seiffer) Drinkstone. A45 now A14. Turn off at Woolpit, go through village and follow signs to Drinkstone and then Drinkstone Green, past Cherry Tree Inn and then 1st L, Rattlesden Rd. After ¾m turn L down lane and drive to end. 3m from Woolpit. Formerly the gardens of Barcock's Nursery. The woodland garden is particularly delightful in Spring with many camellias, magnolias and Spring flowers. This is a plantsman's garden with many rare and unusual plants, trees and shrubs. 11 acres incl pond and lake. New owners are currently creating new areas of interest. TEAS and plant stall in aid of NACC. *Adm £2 Chd free. Sun April 21 (2-5.30). Private visits welcome, please* Tel 01449 736434

¶**Giffords Hall** & (Mr & Mrs David Rowland) Wickhambrook. 10m SW of Bury St Edmunds, 10m NE of Haverhill. ¾m from Plumber's Arms, Wickhambrook in direction of Bury St Edmunds on A143. Garden ¾m up lane signposted Giffords Hall. C15 moated Suffolk Hall (not open). Gardens with herbaceous borders and rose beds. TEAS. *Adm £1.50 Chd free. Suns April 14, June 9 (2-5.30)*

Great Thurlow Hall & (Mr & Mrs George Vestey) Haverhill. N of Haverhill. Great Thurlow village on B1061 from Newmarket; 3½m N of junction with A143 Haverhill-Bury St Edmunds rd. 20 acres. Walled kitchen garden, herbaceous borders, shrubs, roses, spacious lawns, river walk, trout lake. Daffodils and blossom. TEA. *Adm £2 Chd free. Sun March 31 (2-5)*

Grundisburgh Hall &⚘ (Lady Cranworth) 3m W of Woodbridge on B1079, ¼m S of Grundisburgh on Grundisburgh to Ipswich Rd. Approx 5 acres walled garden with yew hedges; wisteria walk and mixed borders. Old rose garden; lawns and ponds. *Adm £2.50 Chd free (Share to St Marys Grundisburgh, St Botolphs Culpho®). Private visits welcome May 20 to July 20, please* Tel 01473 735 485

Hengrave Hall &⚘❀ Hengrave. 3½m NW Bury St Edmunds on A1101. Tudor mansion (tours available). Lake and woodland path. 5-acre formal garden with spacious lawns. Mixed borders with some unusual plants. Kitchen garden. TEAS in aid of Hengrave Bursary Fund. *Adm £2 OAPs £1 Chd free. Sun June 9 (2-6)*

Highfields Farm &❀ (Mr & Mrs John Ineson) Bures. 6m SE of Sudbury. From Bures Church take Nayland Rd. In 2m turn L signposted Assington. Take 1st R Tarmac Drive. From other directions take Assington-Wormingford rd. Approx 1½-acre plantsman's garden started in 1984 with mixed borders, shrubs, chamomile lawn and herbaceous. Various features incl lily pond, wildlife pond and folly. No WCs. TEAS. *Adm £1.50 Chd under 16 free. Suns July 7, 21, Wed July 17 (2-6)*

¶**The Hill House** &❀ (Sir John and Lady Mowbray) Glemsford. 100yds N of village of Glemsford on the back rd to Hawkedon and Boxted. Lately renovated garden of 1 acre with interesting mixed borders and conservatory. Strawberry teas at Boxted Hall. *Adm £1.50 Chd free. Sun June 30 (2-6)*

Hillside ❀❀ (Mr & Mrs J M Paul) Freston. 3m S of Ipswich on the S bank of the R Orwell on the B1456 to Shotley just before the Freston Boot public house on the R. Approx 3 acres of gently sloping garden on well-drained light land. A wide variety of trees, shrubs and herbaceous plants, incl some more tender species due to the proximity to the R Orwell and lack of hard frosts. Vegetable garden, greenhouses and newly developed swimming pool garden. TEAS. *Adm £1.50 Chd free. Sun June 2 (2.30-5.30)*

Holbecks ❀ (Sir Joshua & Lady Rowley) Hadleigh. From Hadleigh High St turn into Duke St signed to Lower Layham; immediately over bridge go right up concrete rd to top of hill. 3 acres; early C19 landscape terraced and walled gardens, flowerbeds, roses and ornamental shrubs. TEAS. *Adm £1.50 Chd free (Share to Suffolk Historic Churches Trust®). Sun July 14 (2-5.30)*

Ickworth House, Park & Gardens &❀ (The National Trust) Horringer. 3m SW of Bury St. Edmunds on W side of A143 [155:TL8161] 70 acres of garden. South gardens restored to stylized Italian landscape to reflect extraordinary design of the house. Fine orangery, agapanthus, geraniums and fatsias. North gardens informal wild flower lawns with wooded walk; the Buxus collection, great variety of evergreens and Victorian stumpery. New planting of cedars. The Albana Wood, a C18 feature, initially laid out by Capability Brown, incorporates a fine circular walk. Restaurant TEAS. *Adm £4.75 (house, park and garden) Chd £2. £1.75 (park and garden) Chd 50p. Sun Sept 8 (10-5.30). Private visits of 15 and over welcome, please* **Tel 01284 735270**

Letheringham Watermill &❀❀ (Mr & Mrs Rod Allen) nr Easton. 7m N of Woodbridge. Letheringham turn off B1078, 1m W of Wickham Market. 5 acres of garden with the rare lathraea clandestina and river walks. Aviary. Watermill has picture gallery and restored waterwheel. Unusual plants for sale. Home-made TEAS. *Adm £1.50 OAP's £1 Chd free (Share to St Elizabeth Hospice©). Open every Sun April, May, July, Aug (2-6). For NGS Mons May 6, Aug 26 (2-6)*

Little Thurlow Hall &❀ (Mr & Mrs E Vestey) Thurlow. On B1061 between Newmarket and Haverhill, in the middle of village. A re-made garden started in 1987; herbaceous and lily borders; sunken garden; rose garden, ancient canals; orchard, formal box edged herb and kitchen gardens, greenhouses and conservatory, shrubberies, many unusual plants; woodland and lakeside walks woodland stream garden under construction. Approx 20 acres in all. Paddocks with horses. TEA. *Adm £1.50 Chd 50p. Sun June 2 (2-6)*

Long Melford Gardens TEAS at Sun House. Long Melford is 3½m N of Sudbury on A134. *Combined adm £4 or £1.50 per garden Chd free (Share to Long Melford Community Trust©). Sun June 23 (2-6)*

   Conduit House & (Sir Harold and Lady Atcherley) The Green. 50yds S of Black Lion off A1096 to Clare; on the Green. Approx 1 acre of a pretty and well planted partly walled garden, interesting old-fashioned roses mixed borders

   Ely House & (Miss Jean M Clark) Church Walk. Interesting small walled garden; mixed borders home of a potter making fountains and garden sculptures. Adjacent orchard

   Sun House &❀ (Mr & Mrs John Thompson) Centre of village opp Cock and Bell Inn. Two attractive adjacent walled gardens with roses, shrubs and herbaceous borders. Interesting collection of clematis. Water and architectural features, with paved courtyards. Runner-up in Daily Mail National Garden Competition 1995

Magnolia House ❀ (Mr Mark Rumary) On A1120 in centre of Yoxford. Small, completely walled village garden. Mixed borders with flowering trees, shrubs, climbers, bulbs, hardy and tender plants. Featured in UK and foreign gardening books and magazines. TEA. *Adm £1.50 Chd free. Sun May 26 (2.30-6)*

Moat Cottage ❀ (Stephen & Lesley Ingerson) Great Green. Cockfield. Take A134 S from Bury St Edmunds. After Sicklesmere village turn sharp L for Cockfield Green and R at 1st Xrds. Follow winding rd through Bradfield St Clare. At Great Green fork L Moat Cottage is opp garage at far end. 1 acre of enchanting cottage garden created over the last 9yrs and forever changing. The garden is divided into smaller areas incl white, herb and rose gardens, herbaceous borders, with a kitchen garden that provides the owners with all year round vegetables. Teas at Clipt Bushes (½m). *Combined adm with* **Clipt Bushes** *£2.50 OAPs £1 Chd free. Sun June 16 (2-6)*

North Cove Hall &❀ (Mr & Mrs B Blower) Beccles. Just off A146 3½m E of Beccles on Lowestoft Rd. Take sign to North Cove. 5 acres of garden; large pond; new water feature; mature and interesting young trees. Walled kitchen garden; shrub roses; herbaceous borders; woodland walks. Home-made TEAS. *Adm £1.50 Chd free. Sun June 30 (2-5.30)*

¶**The Old Hall** &❀ (Mr & Mrs Maurice Elliott) Barsham. Off B1062 1½m W of Beccles. Recently restored C16 Hall, Civic Trust Award 1994. Young garden, many unusual trees, shrubs and climbers. 70 clematis, herb garden (over 300 different grown); greenhouse. Small nursery. TEAS. *Adm £1.50 OAP £1 Chd free. Sats, Suns May 18, 19, July 13, 14, (2-6) Sept 14, 15 (2-5). Private visits welcome, please* **Tel 01502 717475**

¶**The Old Rectory** (Mr & Mrs James Bowden) Wetherden. Between Stowmarket and Bury St Edmunds off A14 just outside village on rd to Bacton. 3-acre garden created in the last decade with many old-fashioned roses, white garden surrounded by yew hedges, ancient beech trees and orchard with unusual fruit varieties. TEAS. *Adm £1.50. Sun June 23 (2-6)*

Porters Lodge ♿ (Mr Craig Wyncoll) Cavenham. 5m W of Bury St Edmunds; 1m SW of Cavenham on the rd to Kentford. 2 acres of woodland walks surrounding an acre of semi-formal ponds, mixed borders and lawns laid out during the last 7 yrs. TEAS. *Adm £1.50 Chd free. Sun July 28 (2-6)*

The Priory ♿❀ (Mr & Mrs H F A Engleheart) Stoke-by-Nayland (1m); 8m N of Colchester, entrance on B1068 rd to Sudbury. Interesting 9-acre garden with fine views over Constable countryside, with lawns sloping down to small lakes & water garden; fine trees, rhododendrons & azaleas; walled garden; mixed borders & ornamental greenhouse. Wide variety of plants; peafowl. TEAS. *Adm £2 Chd free. Sun May 19 (2-6)*

Redisham Hall ♿✂ (Mr Palgrave Brown) SW of Beccles. From A145 1½m S of Beccles, turn W on to Ringsfield-Bungay Rd. Beccles, Halesworth or Bungay, all within 6m. 5 acres; parkland and woods 400 acres. Georgian house C18 (not shown). Safari rides. TEAS (3.30-5 only). *Adm £2 Chd free (Share to East Suffolk Macmillan Nurses®). Sun July 7 (2-6)*

Reydon Grove House ♿❀ (Cmdr & Mrs J Swinley) Reydon. Situated ½m N of Reydon Church. Turnings off the Wangford-Southwold rd. 1½-acre mature garden. Large herbaceous borders, many interesting and unusual shrubs, plants, old-fashioned roses. Large vegetable garden. TEAS. *Adm £1.50 Chd free (Share to Suffolk Historic Churches Trust®). Sun June 30 (2-6) Private visits welcome June to Sept, please* **Tel 01502 723655**

¶**Riverside House** ✂ (Mr & Mrs A C W Bone) Clare. On the A1092 leading out of Clare, towards Haverhill. A peaceful walled garden of 1 acre, bordering the R Stour, with lawns, trees, mixed herbaceous beds and shrubs. Spot the stone pig! Teas at Kate's Kitchen in Clare opp Town Hall. *Adm £1.50 Chd free. Sun July 28 (2-5.30)*

The Rookery ♿✂❀ (Captain & Mrs Sheepshanks) Eyke. 5m E of Woodbridge turn N off B1084 Woodbridge-Orford Rd when sign says Rendlesham. 10-acre garden; planted as an arboretum with many rare specimen trees and shrubs; landscaped on differing levels, providing views and vistas; the visitor's curiosity is constantly aroused by what is round the next corner; ponds, bog garden, shrubbery, alpines, garden stream, bulbs, herbaceous borders and a 1-acre vineyard. Wine tastings and farm shop. Home-made TEAS. *Adm £2 Chd 50p. Sun May 26 (2-5.30). Private visits welcome for parties of 10 and over, please* **Tel 01394 460271**

Rosedale ✂❀ (Mr & Mrs Colin Lorking) 40 Colchester Rd, Bures. 9m NW of Colchester on B1508. As you enter the village of Bures, garden is on the L or 5m SE of Sudbury on B1508, follow signs through village towards Colchester, garden is on the R as you leave village. Approx ⅓-acre, plantsman's garden; many unusual plants, herbaceous borders, pond, woodland area, rose beds. TEA. *Adm £1.50 Acc chd free. Suns May 26, June 23, July 21, Aug 25 (12-6). Private visits welcome, please* **Tel 01787 227619**

Rosemary ♿✂❀ (Mrs N E M Finch) Rectory Hill. Turn off the A12 at East Bergholt and follow rd round to church. Rosemary is 100yds down from the church on L. Mature 1-acre garden adapted over 20yrs from an old orchard loosely divided into several smaller gardens; mixed borders; herb garden; over 80 old roses, unusual plants. TEAS. *Adm £1.50 Chd free. Sun June 9 (2-6) and private visits welcome May & June, please* **Tel 01206 298241**

Rumah Kita ♿ (Mr & Mrs I R Dickings) Bedfield is situated 2½m NW of the A1120 on secondary rd turning between Earl Soham and Saxted Green. 1½-acre garden designed and planted by owners; mixed borders of many unusual plants. Parterre, scree, peat and raised alpine beds. *Adm £2 Chd free. Private visits welcome, individual or parties, please* **Tel 01728 628401**

St Stephens Cottage ✂❀ (Mrs W Gibbs) Spexhall. 2m from Halesworth off A144 Halesworth to Bungay Rd take signposted lane to Spexhall Church. 1-acre cottage garden with island beds surrounding mature trees, natural pond, unusual plants. New 3 acres which incl formal scented garden, rosary and newly planted arboretum. Large conservatory featured on TV and national journals. *Adm £1.50 Chd free. Suns June 30, Aug 25 (2-5.30)*

Somerleyton Hall ♿✂ (The Lord & Lady Somerleyton) 5m NW of Lowestoft. Off B1074. Large garden; famous maze, beautiful trees and borders. House C16 150 yrs old lavishly remodelled in 1840's. Grinling Gibbons' carving, library, tapestries. Mentioned in Domesday Book. Miniature railway. Light lunches & TEAS. *Adm £3.95 OAP £3.50 Chd £1.75. House open 2-5 Gardens 12.30-5.30: Sun April 28 Easter Sun to end Sept, Thurs, Suns, Bank Hol Mons; in addition Tues, Weds, July and Aug; miniature railway will be running on most days. For NGS Sun April 28. Group private visits welcome by prior arrangement (Min 20)*

The Spong ❀ (Joseph Barrett Esq & John Kirby Esq) Groton, Boxford. 5m W of Hadleigh on A1071. Leave Boxford via Swan Street, bear R at Fox and Hounds follow main road past Groton Church, take next R. The Spong is the pink house at the bottom of the hill. Approached over stream; planned as a series of small gardens due to irregular shape; ever changing with mixed herbaceous/shrubs; ponds; pergola. TEAS. *Adm £1 Chd 50p. Sun June 16 (2-6)*

¶**Thrift Cottage** ✂❀ (Mrs Ray Curtis) Cowlinge. 7m SE of Newmarket, centrally between Cowlinge, Kirtling and Gt Bradley. On the Gt Bradley rd from Kirtling. A delightful cottage garden extending to approx ⅓-acre full of interest around every corner. Teas at Thrift Farm. *Combined adm £1.50 Chd free with* **Thrift Farm**. *Sun June 9 (2-6)*

Thrift Farm &✿ (Mrs J Oddy) Cowlinge. 7m SE of Newmarket, centrally between Cowlinge, Kirtling and Gt Bradley. On the Gt Bradley rd from Kirtling. Picturesque thatched house set in a cottage style garden extending to approx 1½ acres. Forever changing island beds filled with herbaceous plants amongst shrubs and ornamental trees in great variety. It is a garden which encourages you to walk round but many will just sit and enjoy the vistas. TEAS. *Combined adm £1.50 Chd 50p with* **Thrift Cottage** *Sun June 9 (2-6). Private visits welcome, please* **Tel 01440 783274**

Thumbit & (Mrs Ann James) Walsham-le-Willows. 10m NE of Bury St Edmunds. Leave A143 at Walsham-le-Willows sign and continue to Xrds by church at centre of village. Take Badwell Rd to outskirts of village (½m). House is part of thatched C16 one-time inn. Shared driveway - (please do not drive in). Small informal garden with strong emphasis on design and plant association for subtlety of form and colour. Pergola, pool, topiary. 500 choice herbaceous plants and shrubs, roses and climbers. Featured in Weekend Telegraph and Practical Gardening. TEAS, lunches by arrangement. *Adm £1.50 OAP £1 Chd free. Private visits welcome June to Oct, please* **Tel 01359 259 414**

Tollemache Hall &✗ (Mr & Mrs M Tollemache) Offton, nr Ipswich. S of the B1078 opp the Ringshall turning. 4 acres of recently renovated garden in a lovely rural setting. Shrubs, rose and knot gardens. A large walled garden with interesting herbaceous borders. Also woodland walk planted with many conifer species. Suffolk punches. TEAS. *Adm £1.50 Chd free. Sun April 28 (2-6)*

¶**Upland Hall** ✗✿ (Sir Lawrence & Lady Magnus) Bungay. 1m S of Bungay on the Flixton Rd B1062. 2 completely different gardens in all 4 acres with lovely views over the Waveney Valley, one being an extensive Victorian shrubbery with many varied plants and shrubs, the other an outstanding walled rose garden. There is also a special vegetable potager. TEAS. *Adm £1.50 Chd 50p. Sun June 23 (2-6)*

Washbrook Grange ✗✿ (Mr & Mrs Robert Stone) From Ipswich take A1071 to Hadleigh. L at 1st roundabout and then 1st R to Chattisham. ½m on L. 5 acres with small lake, ornamental vegetable garden, maple walk, herbaceous borders, roses, iris, shrubs and trees both old and new; woodland walk and river garden. TEAS. *Adm £1.50 Chd 75p. Suns May 26, Aug 18, Mon May 27 (2-6)*

¶**Western House** (Mr & Mrs Marshall) Cavendish. On the A1092 between Clare and Long Melford in village of Cavendish. Signposted 'Full of Beans B & B', garden to the rear. 1-acre garden divided into three sections. It has shrubs and herbaceous plants, a small herb garden and it aims to be a cottage type garden, a little wild and natural. *Adm £1.50 Chd free. Suns June 16, 23, 30, July 7 (2-6)*

Woottens &✗✿ (M Loftus) Blackheath Rd. Woottens is situated between A12 and B1123 follow signposts to Wenhaston. Woottens is a small romantic garden with attached plantsman nursery, in all about 1-acre; scented leafed pelargoniums, violas, cranesbills, lilies, salvias, penstemons primulas, etc. Featured in Gardens Illustrated and RHS Journal. *Adm £1 OAPs 50p Chd 20p. Suns May 26, June 16, July 14, Aug 25 (10-5)*

Wyken Hall &✿ (Sir Kenneth and Lady Carlisle) Stanton, 9m NE from Bury St Edmunds along A143. Follow signs to Wyken vineyards on A143 between Ixworth and Stanton. 4-acre garden much developed recently; with knot and herb gardens; old-fashioned rose garden; wild garden; nuttery, gazebo and maze, herbaceous borders and old orchard. Woodland walk, vineyard. TEAS. *Adm £2 OAPs £1.50 Chd free. Sun June 16 (10-6)*

Surrey

Hon County Organiser:	Lady Heald, Chilworth Manor, Guildford GU4 8NL Tel 01483 561414
Assistant Hon County Organisers:	Mrs J Foulsham, Vale End, Albury, Guildford GU5 9BE Tel 01483 202296
	Miss C Collins, Knightsmead, Rickman Hill Rd, Chipstead, Surrey CR5 3LB Tel 01737 551694
	Mrs P Karslake, Oakfield Cottage, Guildford Road, Cranleigh GU6 8PF Tel 01483 273010
	Mrs D E Norman, Spring Cottage, Mannings Hill, Cranleigh GU6 8QN Tel 01483 272620
	Mrs J Pearcy, Far End, Pilgrims Way, Guildford GU4 8AD Tel 01483 563093
Hon County Treasurer:	Mr Ray Young, Paddock View, 144 Dorking Road, Chilworth, Guildford GU4 8RJ Tel 01483 569597

DATES OF OPENING

March 31 Sunday
  Albury Park, Albury
  Whinfold, Hascombe
April 7 Sunday
  Lodkin, Hascombe

April 9 to 14 Tuesday to Sunday
  Vann, Hambledon
April 13 to 17 Saturday to Wednesday
  Chilworth Manor,
  Guildford

April 14 Sunday
  Vann, Hambledon
  Wintershall Manor,
  Bramley
April 17 Wednesday
  The Coppice, Reigate ‡
  Knightsmead, Chipstead ‡

April 20 Saturday
Woodside, Send
April 21 Sunday
Coverwood Lakes and Gardens,
  Ewhurst
Munstead Wood, nr Godalming
Street House, Thursley
Woodside, Send
April 24 Wednesday
The Coppice, Reigate
41 Shelvers Way, Tadworth
April 28 Sunday
Coverwood Lakes and Gardens,
  Ewhurst
22 Knoll Road, Dorking
May 1 Wednesday
22 Knoll Road, Dorking
May 4 Saturday
The Old Croft, South Holmwood
May 5 Sunday
Compton Lodge, Moor Park,
  Farnham
Coverwood Lakes and Gardens,
  Ewhurst
Feathercombe, nr Hambledon
High Meadow, Churt
The Old Croft, South Holmwood
Westbourn, Virginia Water
May 6 Monday
Feathercombe, nr Hambledon
High Meadow, Churt
Walton Poor, Ranmore Common
May 7 to 12 Tuesday to Sunday
Vann, Hambledon
May 11 Saturday
Greathed Manor, Dormansland
Pyrford Court, nr Woking
**May 11 to 15 Saturday to
Wednesday**
Chilworth Manor, Guildford
May 12 Sunday
Coverwood Lakes and Gardens,
  Ewhurst
Highlands, Givons Grove,
  Leatherhead
Polesden Lacey, Bookham
Pyrford Court, nr Woking
87 Upland Road, Sutton
Vann, Hambledon
Westland Farm, Ewhurst
Whinfold, Hascombe ‡
Winkworth Arboretum,
  Hascombe ‡
Wintershall Manor, Bramley
May 15 Wednesday
Unicorns, Farnham
May 16 Thursday
Halnacker Hill,
  nr Godalming
May 19 Sunday
Brook Lodge Farm Cottage,
  Blackbrook
Compton Lodge, Moor Park,
  Farnham

Copt Hill Shaw, Kingswood,
  Tadworth
Coverwood Lakes and Gardens,
  Ewhurst
Montfleury, Virginia Water
Olivers, Church Road, Hascombe
Postford House, Chilworth ‡
Snowdenham House, Bramley ‡
Stonywood, Haslemere
Street House, Thursley
Windlesham Park, nr Bagshot
May 22 Wednesday
Brook Lodge Farm Cottage,
  Blackbrook
May 25 Saturday
Crosswater Farm, Churt
Merrist Wood, Worplesdon
May 26 Sunday
Claremont Landscape Garden,
  Esher
Coverwood Lakes and Gardens,
  Ewhurst
Crosswater Farm, Churt
Feathercombe, nr Hambledon
Merrist Wood, Worplesdon
Munstead Wood, nr Godalming
Postford House, Chilworth
May 27 Monday
Crosswater Farm, Churt
Feathercombe,
  nr Hambledon ‡
Merrist Wood, Worplesdon
Vann, Hambledon ‡
**May 28 to June 2 Tuesday to
Sunday**
Vann, Hambledon
May 29 Wednesday
Coverwood Lakes and Gardens,
  Ewhurst
June 2 Sunday
Alderbrook, Cranleigh
The Copse Lodge, Burgh Heath
Dovecote, Cobham
Ridings, 56 Cross Road, Tadworth
Vann, Hambledon
Walton Poor, Ranmore Common
Wintershall Manor, Bramley
June 5 Wednesday
Walton Poor, Ranmore Common
**June 8 to 12 Saturday to
Wednesday**
Chilworth Manor, Guildford
June 9 Sunday
Hatchlands Park, East Clandon
High Hazard, Blackheath
Lodkin, Hascombe
Ridings, 56 Cross Road, Tadworth
June 12 Wednesday
Sutton Place, Guildford
June 15 Saturday
Brookwell, Bramley
June 16 Sunday
Brook Lodge Farm Cottage,
  Blackbrook

Brookwell, Bramley
Four Aces, Pirbright
Halnacker Hill, nr Godalming
Hampton, Seale, Farnham
47 Harvest Road, Englefield Green
Haslehurst, Haslemere ‡
Merrist Wood, Worplesdon
Street House, Thursley
6 Upper Rose Hill, Dorking
Yew Tree Cottage, Haslemere ‡
June 17 Monday
Four Aces, Pirbright
June 22 Saturday
Knightsmead, Chipstead
South Park Farm, South Godstone
Thanescroft, Shamley Green
June 23 Sunday
Brockhurst, Chiddingfold
Four Aces, Pirbright
High Meadow, Churt
Knightsmead, Chipstead
Moleshill House, Cobham
South Park Farm, South Godstone
Thanescroft, Shamley Green
Vale End, Albury
June 24 Monday
High Meadow, Churt
South Park Farm, South Godstone
June 26 Wednesdaay
Brook Lodge Farm Cottage,
  Blackbrook
41 Shelvers Way, Tadworth
June 30 Sunday
Addlestone Gardens
Chinthurst Lodge, Wonersh
Marlin, West End, Woking
White House, nr Guildford
**July 1 to July 7 Monday to
Sunday**
Vann, Hambledon
July 3 Wednesday
Brockhurst, Chiddingfold
Moleshill House, Cobham
67 Shepherds Lane, Stoughton,
  Guildford
July 6 Saturday
Little Mynthurst Farm, Norwood
  Hill
The Old Croft, South Holmwood
Tanyard Farmhouse, Horley
July 7 Sunday
47 Harvest Road, Englefield Green
Little Mynthurst Farm, Norwood
  Hill
The Old Croft, South Holmwood
Tanyard Farmhouse, Horley
Vann, Hambledon
**July 13 to 17 Saturday to
Wednesday**
Chilworth Manor, Guildford
July 14 Sunday
41 Shelvers Way, Tadworth
July 17 Wednesday
41 Shelvers Way, Tadworth

July 21 Sunday
Brook Lodge Farm Cottage,
  Blackbrook
The Copse Lodge, Burgh Heath
July 27 Saturday
Street House, Thursley
Stuart Cottage, East Clandon
July 28 Sunday
Stuart Cottage, East Clandon
Vale End, Albury
July 31 Wednesday
The Coppice, Reigate
August 1 Thursday
Park House, Chiddingfold
August 3 Saturday
South Cheam Gardens
August 4 Sunday
Odstock, Bletchingley
Park House, Chiddingfold
South Cheam Gardens
August 10 to 14 Saturday to Wednesday
Chilworth Manor, Guildford
August 18 Sunday
Brook Lodge Farm Cottage,
  Blackbrook
August 21 Wednesday
Brook Lodge Farm Cottage,
  Blackbrook
August 25 Sunday
Haslehurst, Haslemere
High Meadow, Churt

August 26 Monday
High Meadow, Churt
September 1 Sunday
Munstead Wood, nr Godalming
September 4 Wednesday
Knightsmead, Chipstead
September 18 Wednesday
Brook Lodge Farm Cottage,
  Blackbrook
September 22 Sunday
Claremont Landscape Garden,
  Esher
October 6 Sunday
Albury Park, Albury
Painshill, Cobham
Walton Poor, Ranmore Common
White House, nr Guildford
October 13 Sunday
Pyrford Court, nr Woking
Winkworth Arboretum, Hascombe
October 20 Sunday
Coverwood Lakes and Gardens,
  Ewhurst
November 3 Sunday
Lodkin, Hascombe

1997
January 1 Wednesday
Claremont Landscape Garden,
  Esher
February 2 Sunday
Wintershall Manor, Bramley

March 2 Sunday
Wintershall Manor, Bramley

Regular openings
For details see garden description

Crosswater Farm, Churt
25 Little Woodcote Estate,
  Wallington
Painshill, Cobham
Ramster, Chiddingfold
Titsey Place Gardens

By appointment only
For telephone numbers and other details see garden descriptions. Private visits welcomed

Chauffeur's Flat, Tandridge
2 Court Avenue, Old Coulsdon
The Homestead, Old Lodge Lane,
  Kenley
Hookwood Farm House, West
  Horsley
Lansdowne House, West Ewell, nr
  Epsom
Pinewood House, Woking

DESCRIPTIONS OF GARDENS

Addlestone Gardens ⚘❀ Situated within ½m of each other, 5m NE of Woking off B3121. From M25 junction 11 take A320 signposted Woking then L into B3121 or A317 signposted Weybridge and R into B3121 and follow yellow signs. Maps available at each garden. TEAS in aid of St Paul's Church Roof Fund. *Combined adm £2 Chd free. Sun June 30 (11-5)*

Charton (Daphne & John Clarke-Williams) Ongar Hill. ⅓-acre upward sloping mature garden, with trees, shrubs, climbing plants, hardy perennials and sink gardens, pond and vegetable garden. Extensive use of home-made compost

106 Liberty Lane (Mrs Ann Masters) 100' × 30' suburban garden belonging to self confessed 'plantaholic' imaginatively laid out containing an interesting mix of shrubs, grasses, hardy perennials, climbers and hardy geraniums, a pond and some unusual plants. Very interested in propagation

St Keverne (Lynne & Julian Clarke-Willams) ⅓-acre garden created by owners over last 5 yrs. Inspired use of companion planting. Hardy perennials - specialising in geraniums and alliums; many trees, shrubs and roses. Gravel and pots a feature

Albury Park Garden ⚘⚘ (Trustees of Albury Estate) Albury 5m SE of Guildford. From A25 take A248 towards Albury for ¼m, then L up New Rd, entrance to Albury Park immediately on L. 14-acre pleasure grounds laid out in 1670's by John Evelyn for Henry Howard, later 6th Duke of Norfolk, ¼m terraces, fine collection of trees, lake and river. The gardens of Albury Park Mansion also open (by kind permission of Country Houses Association Ltd). TEAS. *Adm £1.50 Chd 50p. Suns March 31, Oct 6 (2-5)*

¶Alderbrook (Mr & Mrs P Van den Bergh) Smithwood Common. Cranleigh. A281 from Guildford turn L 1m out of Bramley. Turn R at roundabout then immediately L. Drive on L just beyond far end of Smithwood Common. Approx 8 acres of woodland walks with azaleas and rhododendrons. Terraces with magnificent views to S Downs. Re-opening after 24 yrs. TEA. *Adm £1.50 Chd free. Sun June 2 (2-6)*

Brockhurst ⚘❀ (Prof & Mrs C F Phelps) Chiddingfold. On the Green at Chiddingfold A283. Entrance through small gate RH-side of Manor House. Parking around Village Green. A series of surprising gardens, tucked behind the village green, beginning with an old walled cottage border and expanding successively into 2½ acres of lawns, shrubs, walkways, flower beds and watergarden. Within the garden created over the last 10 yrs by the present owners are many species and foliage plants, incl lilies and clematis; fruit and vegetable garden. TEAS. *Adm £1.50 Chd free. Sun June 23, Wed July 3 (2-6). Private visits welcome for parties of 10 and over April, May, June, July, Aug, please* Tel 01428 683092

Brook Lodge Farm Cottage ㅖ✿❀ (Mrs Basil Kingham) Blackbrook, 3m S of Dorking. Take L-hand turning for Blackbrook off A24, 1m S of Dorking 500yds past Plough Inn. 3½-acre 50-yr-old plantsman's garden made by present owner. Entrance provides vista of spacious lawns, curving borders of shrubs, flowering trees and shrub roses; hosts of unusual plants frame main house. Fine collection of conifers cradles summer-house. Swimming pool, hidden by Hoathly stone wall leads to waterfall and rockery with woodland walk beyond. On leaving garden, pass herbaceous borders, roses, herb and kitchen gardens, greenhouses and 2 cottage gardens full of interest. Light lunches Weds in May and June, TEAS every Sun and Weds in Aug, Sept. *Adm £1.50 Chd free (Share to St Catherine's Hospice, Crawley®). Weds May 22, June 26 (11-3), Aug 21, Sept 18 (2-5). Suns May 19, June 16, July 21, Aug 18 (2-5)*

Brookwell ㅖ✿❀ (Mr & Mrs P R Styles) 1½m S of Bramley on A281; turn R into private road-bridleway in Birtley Green. 2-acre garden with lake and woodland. Mixed borders, sunken garden, and knot garden planted with scented flowers and herbs. Collection of old roses, fruit tunnel and vegetable garden; greenhouses and conservatory. TEA. *Adm £1 Chd 25p (Share to St Andrews Church, Grafham Conservation Fund®). Sat, Sun June 15, 16 (2-6) also private visits welcome June, July, please Tel 01483 893423 (evenings)*

Chauffeur's Flat ✿ (Mr & Mrs Richins) Tandridge. Tandridge Lane lies 1m W of Oxted off the A25. Drive adjacent to church ½m from A25. Pass Lodge to your R. Fork R. Continue through to Courtyard. Surprise yourself with this 1 acre eclectic, romantic, artists' garden with superb views. Only for the surefooted. *Adm £1 Chd 25p. Private visits welcome Mons to Suns May 20 to 26, June 17 to 23 (10-5), please Tel 01883 715937 between 7-9.30am or 7-9.30pm*

Chilworth Manor ㅖ✿ (Lady Heald) 3½m SE of Guildford. From A248, in centre of Chilworth village, turn up Blacksmith Lane. House C17 with C18 wing on site of C11 monastery recorded in Domesday Book; stewponds in garden date from monastic period. Garden laid out in C17; C18 walled garden added by Sarah, Duchess of Marlborough; spring flowers; flowering shrubs; newly designed herbaceous border. Flower decorations in house (Sats, Suns): April Daisy Tuffen Flower Club, May Ashtead Flower Arrangement Group, June Chobham Floral Club, July Michael Kemp, August Dorking Flower Arrangement Group, The Reigate Flower Club. Free car park in attractive surroundings open from 12.30 for picnicking. TEAS (Sat, Sun, only). *Adm to garden £1.50 Chd free. Adm to house £1 Sat & Sun only (Share to Marie Curie Foundation Guildford Branch®); Open Sats to Weds April 13 to 17, May 11 to 15, June 8 to 12, July 13 to 17, Aug 10 to 14 (2-6); also private visits welcome, please Tel 01483 561414*

Chinthurst Lodge ㅖ✿❀ (Mr & Mrs M R Goodridge) Wonersh. 4m S Guildford, A281 Guildford-Horsham. At Shalford turn E onto B2128 towards Wonersh. Just after Wonersh rd sign, before village, garden on R. 1-acre yr-round garden, herbaceous borders, white garden, large variety specimen trees and shrubs; kitchen garden; fruit

cage; two wells; ornamental pond and conservatory. TEAS. *Adm £1.50 Chd free (Share to Guildford Branch Arthritis & Rheumatism Council®). Sun June 30 (2-6)*

Claremont Landscape Garden ㅖ✿ (The National Trust) 1m SE of Esher; on E side of A307 (No access from A3 by-pass). Station: Esher. Bus GL 415, alight at entrance gates. One of the earliest surviving English landscape gardens; begun by Vanbrugh and Bridgeman before 1720; extended and naturalized by Kent; lake; island with pavilion; grotto and turf amphitheatre; viewpoints and avenues. TEAS 11-5.30. *Adm £3 Chd £1.50.* ▲*For NGS Suns May 26, Sept 22 (10-7). 1997 Wed Jan 1 (1-4) no teas*

Compton Lodge ✿❀ (Mr & Mrs K J Kent) Farnham. 2m E of Farnham along A31 Hogs Back (new rd) follow signs Runfold. Turn S down Crooksbury Rd at Barfield School signposted Milford & Elstead. 1m on R Compton Way, Compton Lodge 2nd house on R. 1¼-acre S-facing sloping mixed garden. Mature rhododendrons, heather bed, azaleas. TEAS. *Adm £1.50 Chd 50p. Suns May 5, 19 (11-5)*

Cooksbridge, Fernhurst (See Sussex)

The Coppice ❀ (Mr & Mrs Bob Bushby) Reigate. M25 to junction 8. A217 (direction Reigate) down Reigate Hill, immediately before level Xing turn R into Somers Rd cont as Manor Rd. At very end turn R into Coppice Lane.. Please park carefully. 'The Coppice' approx 200yds on L. Partly suitable wheelchairs. 6½ acres redeveloped in last 8yrs. Mixed borders with interesting and unusual plants giving yr-round interest. Pergola, 2 large ornamental ponds. Thousands of fritillarias and spring bulbs, April. Cream TEAS. *Adm £1.50 Chd 50p (Share to Winged Fellowship®). Weds April 17, 24; July 31 (2-5)*

¶**The Copse Lodge** ㅖ✿❀ (Marian & Eddie Wallbank) Burgh Heath. 6m S of Sutton on A217 dual carriageway. Heathside Hotel car park 200yds on L from traffic lights at junction A217 with Reigate Rd. Please park in overflow car park at rear of hotel (our thanks to Heathside Hotel). Garden 100yds on L from hotel. ½-acre architectural garden with unusual planting featuring yuccas, palms and grasses; large tender specimens in pots; Japanese garden with bamboos, acers and Tea House; ornamental pond with waterfalls, rock garden, conservatory with specimen palms. Designed, built and maintained by owners. TEAS. *Adm £1.50 Chd free. Suns June 2, July 21 (10-5)*

Copt Hill Shaw ㅖ✿❀ (Mr & Mrs M Barlow) Alcocks Lane, Kingswood. 6m S of Sutton off the A217. 1st turn on L after Burgh Heath traffic lights, Waterhouse Lane, signposted Kingswood Station and Coulsdon. Alcocks Lane 1st on L. Parking in Furze Hill, courtesy of Legal and General. A formal garden of 1½ acres laid out in 1906. Fine yew hedges and topiary with azaleas, mature trees and rhododendrons and pergola of old roses and clematis, spring bulbs, geraniums, alliums, small collection of unusual plants. Fruit and vegetable garden. TEAS. *Adm £1.50 Chd free (Share to National Asthma Campaign®). Sun May 19 (2-5.30)*

2 Court Avenue &⚘ (Dr K Heber) Old Coulsdon. Approach from London-Brighton Rd. A23 from S or M23/25, turn R B276 Old Coulsdon; from N after leaving Purley turn L B2030 Old Coulsdon. Follow rd to top of hill, immediately past parade of shops. Garden opp Tudor Rose public house (food available). Flat compact garden approx ⅓-acre filled with herbaceous plants and shrubs in cottage garden layout; small ponds; good selection of unusual plants. Gives ideas for small gardens and use of foliage. *Adm £1 Chd 50p. Private visits welcome, please* **Tel 017375 54721**

Coverwood Lakes and Gardens &⚘⚘ (Mr & Mrs C G Metson) Peaslake Rd, Ewhurst. 7m SW of Dorking. From A25 follow signs for Peaslake; garden ½m beyond Peaslake. Landscaped water, bog garden and cottage gardens in lovely setting between Holmbury Hill and Pitch Hill; rhododendrons, azaleas, primulas, fine trees. 3½-acre Arboretum planted March 1990. Featured in NGS video 1. Marked trail through working farm to see herd of pedigree Poll Hereford cattle and flock of sheep. (Mr & Mrs Nigel Metson). Home-made TEAS. *Adm £2 Chd £1 car park and Chd under 5 free (Share to NGS®). Suns April 21, 28, May 5, 12, 19, 26; Wed May 29 (2-6); Sun Oct 20 hot soup and sandwiches (11-4.30). Also private visits welcome, please* **Tel 01306 731103/1**

Crosswater Farm &⚘⚘ (Mr & Mrs E G Millais) Churt. Farnham and Haslemere 6m, from A287 turn E into Jumps Road ½m N of Churt village centre. After ¼m turn acute L into Crosswater Lane and follow signs for Millais Nurseries. 6-acre woodland garden surrounded by NT heathland. Plantsman's collection of rhododendrons and azaleas including many rare species collected in the Himalayas, and hybrids raised by the owners. Ponds, stream and companion plantings. Plants for sale from specialist Rhododendron nursery. TEAS in aid of Frensham Church Restoration on NGS days only. *Adm £1.50 Chd free. Daily May 1 to June 2. For NGS Sat, Sun, Mon May 25, 26, 27 (10-5) + 25% other receipts. Private parties welcome, please* **Tel 01252 792698**

Dovecote ⚘⚘ (Mr & Mrs R Stanley) Cobham. Off A307 Esher to Cobham rd near A3 bridge. Turn R from Cobham, L from Esher into Fairmile Lane. Then 4th L into Green Lane. ⅓-acre plot surrounding extended bothy. Secluded plant lovers yr-round garden with natural boundaries of mature trees, shrubs and hedges developed by present owners to incl many hardy plants on light sandy soil. TEA. *Adm £1.50 Chd free. Sun June 2 (10.30-5.30)*

The Elms Kingston-on-Thames (see London)

Feathercombe ⚘ (Wieler & Campbell families) Hambledon, S of Godalming. 2m from Milford Station off Hambledon Rd, between Hydestile Xrds and Merry Harriers. 12-acre garden of mature rhododendrons, azaleas, shrubs and topiary. Fine views of Blackdown, Hindhead and Hogs Back. House by Ernest Newton. Garden designed and made from 1910 by Surrey author and journalist Eric Parker and his wife Ruth (neé Messel) of Nymans. Now maintained by his grandchildren. *Adm £1.50 Chd 10p (Share to Order of St John, Surrey®). Suns, Mons May 5, 6; 26, 27 (2-6)*

Four Aces ⚘⚘ (Mr & Mrs R V St John Wright) 5m NW of Guildford on A322 Bagshot Road. Just before Brookwood arch, directly opp West Hill Golf Club, turn L into Cemetery Pales. After ⁹⁄₁₀m turn sharp L after village sign into Chapel Lane. Four Aces is 5th house on R. Overflow parking in village green car park, 250yds. Approx ⅔-acre 9yr-old garden with 2 ponds, terraces with pergolas, loggias and pots; mixed borders with shrubs, perennials and old roses planted in informal cottage garden style. TEAS. *Adm £1 Chd 50p. Suns June 16, 23 (12-6) Mon June 17 (11-3) Private visits welcome May to July, please* **Tel 01483 476226**

Greathed Manor ⚘⚘ (Country Houses Association) Lingfield. 2½m SE of Lingfield, follow the B2028, Lingfield/Edenbridge rd to the Plough Inn, Dormansland and take the private rd, Ford Manor Rd opp and follow the signs for about 1m to Greathed Manor (not open) and Gardens. Parkland with sunken garden. Stepped terraces and flower beds surround an oval pool set in decorative paving which is enclosed by a balustraded sandstone wall attributed to Harold Peto early this century. 4 acres of attractive garden set in parkland with rhododendrons, azaleas, specimen trees, and many other spring flowers. TEAS. *Adm £2.50 Chd free (Share to Country Houses Association®). Sat May 11 (2-5)*

Hall Grange, Croydon (see London)

¶**Halnacker Hill** ⚘⚘ (Mr & Mrs C N Daubeny) Bowlhead Green. From A3 southbound turn L signposted Bowlhead Green (opp Thursley exit); at Xrds turn R and go 0.7m. From A286 turn off just S of Brook into Park Lane; after 2m turn R signposted Bowlhead Green. 1-acre terraced cottage garden designed as series of small informal labour-saving plantsman's gardens maintained by the owners. Large variety of trees, shrubs, perennials, old roses and climbers and many tender and less common plants. 5 acres of woodland with walks and fine views. TEAS and plants in aid of GUTS. *Adm £1 Chd free. Thurs May 16, Sun June 16 (11.30-5)*

Hampton &⚘ (Mr & Mrs Richard Thornton) Hampton. Situated S of A31 Hogs Back mid-way between Farnham and Guildford, approach from Seale, Puttenham or Elstead following rd to Cutt Mill ponds. Parkland and lakes unaltered from Humphrey Repton's original design of early C19; extensive lawns; summer flowering herbaceous borders; traditional walled garden. TEAS. *Adm £1 Chd free. Sun June 16 (2-6)*

¶**47 Harvest Road** ⚘ (Mr Tony Faulkner) Englefield Green. Directly opp Royal Holloway College on A30. Nearest BR station is Egham. Car parking facilities are a short walk away in Victoria Street. Small cottage garden, shrubs, mixed borders and ornamental trees; gazebo and small pond. TEAS. *Adm £1 Chd free. Suns June 16, July 7 (2-6)*

> **Regular Openers.** Too many days to include in diary. Usually there is a wide range of plants giving year-round interest. See end of county section for the name and garden description for times etc.

Haslehurst ✿❀ (Mrs W H Whitbread) Bunch Lane, Haslemere. Turn off High St into Church Lane, leave church on L, carry on to T-junction, turn R, Hazelhurst, 2nd on L. 2½ acres; lawns, superb trees, rhododendrons, azaleas; various shrubs; paved rose garden, double herbaceous border; woodland rockery & waterfall. C15 Barn. See **Yew Tree Cottage**. *June TEA Adm £1 Chd 50p. Aug TEAS. Adm £1.50 Chd 50p (Share to Queen Mary's Clothing Guild®). Suns June 16, Aug 25 (2.15-6). Private visits welcome, please* **Tel 01428 643471**

Hatchlands Park ♿✿ (The National Trust) Situated near East Clandon, off A246. If using A3 from London direction, follow signposts to Ripley to join A247 and proceed via West Clandon to A246. If coming from Guildford take A25 and then A246 towards Leatherhead at West Clandon. The garden and park were designed by Repton in 1800 and there are 3 newly restored walks in the park. On the S side of the house is a small parterre designed by Gertrude Jekyll in 1913. This has been restored to Jekyll's original design with May/June flowering. The house is open to the public on this day. TEAS. *Adm £1.50 Chd 75p gardens only.* ▲*For NGS Sun June 9 (12 noon-5.30)*

High Hazard ♿❀ (Mr & Mrs P C Venning) Blackheath, Guildford. 4½m SE of Guildford from A281 Guildford to Horsham at Shalford turn E on B2128 towards Wonersh, at entry to Wonersh, turn L into Blackheath Lane, straight on at Xrds in village. Access to garden is 300yds on R. Park in Heath car park a further 150yds up lane. (No access to front of house which faces the cricket ground in use). ½-acre garden designed and laid out by the present owners. Herbaceous and mixed borders containing interesting and some unusual herbaceous perennial plants, a large number of which are for sale on the premises. TEAS. *Adm £1.50 Chd free (Share to St Joseph's Centre for Addiction, Holy Cross Hospital, Haslemere®). Sun June 9 (2-6)*

High Meadow ✿❀ (Mr & Mrs J Humphries) Tilford Rd, Churt. From Hindhead A3 Xrds take A287 signposted Farnham. After ½m take R fork signposted Tilford. 1.9m to Avalon PYO farm. Park here, short walk to garden. Disabled visitors park on grass verge in drive. Approx 1 acre maintained by owners. Large collection of rare and unusual plants attractively planted to provide all-year interest; large collection of old and modern shrub roses and David Austin English Roses; pergola walk, sunken garden with pond, colour co-ordinated borders, alpines in troughs; featured in Daily Mail and Woman's Weekly. TEAS. *Adm £1.50 Chd free (Share to G.U.T.S. at Royal Surrey County Hospital). Suns, Mons May 5, 6; June 23, 24; Aug 25, 26 (2-6). Groups welcome, please* **Tel 01428 606129**

Highlands ✿❀ (Mr & Mrs R B McDaniel) Givons Grove, Leatherhead. From Leatherhead By-pass (A24) at roundabout by Texaco garage 1m S of Leatherhead turn into Givons Grove and proceed up hill (The Downs) for ¾m, ignoring side turnings. Highlands is on the R. Chalk garden of 1 acre on a steep slope. Large rock garden, alpine house and sinks; mixed borders; orchard; pond; fruit and vegetable garden. Fine views over Mole Valley. TEAS in aid of Cystic Fibrosis. *Adm £1.25 Chd free. Sun May 12 (2-6)*

The Homestead ♿✿❀ (Mr & Mrs P Wallace) Kenley. 3rd dwelling down Old Lodge Lane from Wattendon Arms at junction on Old Lodge Lane (SE off A23 Brighton Road at Reedham Station) and Hayes Lane. (SSW from A22 Godstone Road at Kenley Station). Designed, developed and maintained by present (amateur) owners. ½-acre prize-winning suburban garden close to Kenley Airfield (Battle of Britain fame). Lawns with water feature, colourful beds and borders, well stocked with shrubs and flowers, vegetable garden and greenhouses; patio with outstanding display of hanging baskets, tubs, troughs etc. TEAS. *Adm £1.50 Chd free. Private visits welcome July, please* **Tel 0181 660 9816**

Hookwood Farmhouse ♿✿❀ (Eric & Sarah Mason) West Horsley. Off A246 Guildford-Leatherhead Rd. Turn R from Guildford, L from Leatherhead into Shere Rd. 1½m up, turn R into Fullers Farm Rd. 1½ acres on S facing slope of N Downs. Garden made over past 20 yrs by present owners. Wide range of plants from trees to alpines. Large collection of hardy geraniums. Walled garden in old farmyard. *Adm £1.50 Chd free. Individuals and parties welcome May to July, please* **Tel 01483 284760**

Knightsmead ✿❀ (Mrs Jones & Miss Collins) Rickman Hill Rd, Chipstead. From A23 in Coulsdon turn W onto B2032. Through traffic lights, L fork into Portnalls Rd. Top of hill at Xrds, turn R into Holymead Rd. R into Lissoms Rd. R into Bouverie Rd. ½-acre plantsman's garden, designed and maintained by owners. Wide variety of shrubs and perennials for yr-round interest; hellebores, spring bulbs and woodland plants; pond; scented roses; raised alpine and peat beds, clematis, hostas, hardy geraniums etc. April and Sept coffee, lunches, teas. June small craft exhibition. TEAS. Refreshments in aid of Surrey Wildlife Trust. *Adm £1.30 Chd 50p. Weds April 17, Sept 4 (10-4) Sat, Sun June 22, 23 (2-5.30). Private visits welcome, please* **Tel 01737 551694**

22 Knoll Road ✿❀ (David & Anne Drummond) Dorking. S part of Dorking. From one way system after May's Garage turn L up the Horsham rd (A2003 which runs to N Holmwood roundabout A24). Knoll Road is the 4th turning R just beyond The Bush Inn. ⅓-acre town garden with many interesting and unusual plants labelled and with notes available. Mixed borders, raised beds, sinks, mini-meadow and peat bed, fern alley and some fruit and vegetables, a surprising front garden; conservatory. (Mostly suitable for wheelchairs if driven to front door). TEAS. *Adm £1 Chd free. Sun April 28, Wed May 1 (10.30-5.30). Private visits welcome, please* **Tel 01306 883280**

Lansdowne House ✿ (Mr & Mrs J Lucas) West Ewell. Between Chessington and Ewell on the B2200 opposite Hook Rd Arena. Parking and entrance in Lansdowne Rd. Lansdowne House is on corner of Chessington Rd and Lansdowne Rd; small garden (0.18 acre) developed over past 10yrs by garden designer, lecturer, broadcaster and author John Lucas. Planted mainly with shrubs and small trees, the garden is divided into rooms of various styles and atmospheres. A garden of texture with interesting focal points, for the 'green' garden lover. *Adm £1 Chd 50p. Private visits welcome during June, please* **Tel 0181 393 9946**

Little Lodge, Thames Ditton (see London)

Little Mynthurst Farm ఈ๕❀ (Mr & Mrs G Chilton) Norwood Hill. Between Leigh (2m) and Charlwood (3m); from Reigate take A217 to Horley; after 2m turn R just after river bridge at Sidlowbridge; 1st R signed Leigh; then L at T junction. 12-acre garden; walled, old-fashioned roses, herbaceous borders and shrubs around old farm house (not open), rose beds and lake setting; Tudor courtyard and orchard; bird and butterfly garden; rose walk. Kitchen garden with greenhouses and secret garden. TEAS. *Adm £2 Chd free. Sat, Sun July 6, 7; (12-5). Coach parties welcome on NGS days only by prior arrangement please contact Head Gardener Mark Dobell* Tel **01293 862639 or 863318**

25 Little Woodcote Estate ఈ๕❀ (Mr & Mrs Brian Hiley) Wallington. Garden is on Telegraph Track, a private rd off Woodmansterne Lane. Access is only off Woodmansterne Lane by either Oaks Track or Telegraph Track. Woodmansterne Lane links A2022 to A237. An exciting 1-acre plantsman's garden full of many rare unusual, tender and interesting plants; several large mixed borders; annual border; extensive display of tender plants in containers around yard area during summer months. Interesting collection of farm and garden bygones. Suitable in parts for wheelchairs. *Adm £1.20 Chd free (Share to Motor Neurone Disease Association®). Every Wed to Sat April 20 to Sept 29 (9-5). Private visits welcome for parties, please* Tel **0181 647 9679**

Lodkin ❀ (Mr & Mrs W N Bolt) Lodkin Hill, Hascombe, 3m S of Godalming. Just off B2130 Godalming-Cranleigh, on outskirts of Hascombe; take narrow lane off signposted Thorncombe Street. About 5½ acres incl woodland, stream and prolific daffodils and cherries. 4 old Victorian greenhouses have been completely rebuilt and are in full use to produce fruit, flowers and vegetables. Chrysanthemums in November. Much of the old cast staging etc has been retained. In parts suitable for wheel chairs. TEAS. *Adm £1.50 Chd 20p. Suns April 7, June 9 (2-6), Nov 3 (greenhouses). Adm 50p that day Chd free (2-4). Private parties welcome, please* Tel **01486 32323**

¶**Marlin** ఈ๕❀ (Mrs W Prestwich) Lucas Green Rd, West End. From junction 3 M3 take A322 towards Guildford/Woking. Past Gordon Boys School on L and Wheatsheaf inn on R. Turn R at next roundabout, then immed 1st L. Garden in front of herb nursery. A traditional herb garden 110′ × 90′ with formal and informal areas of aromatic, decorative and medicinal herbs incl old-fashioned weeping standard roses, a wild ditch and spiral box. A wide variety of herb plants in a delightful open setting. Herb plants for sale. TEAS. *Adm £1 Chd 50p. Sun June 30 (2-6)*

Merrist Wood College ఈ๕❀ Worplesdon 4m NW of Guildford. 40 acres of amenity areas, landscape demonstration gardens, 16 acres nursery stock, house a listed building (Norman Shaw 1877). Only reception hall open. One of the largest colleges of agriculture and horticulture in the UK with students from many countries. Information available for courses in Nursery, Landscape, Agriculture, Arboriculture, Countryside, Equestrian and Golf Studies. TEA. *Donation.* Rare plants for sale. Percentage

of Plant Shop takings to NGS. *For NGS Sat, Sun, Mon, May 25, 26, 27, June 16 (10-6) with Surrey Horticultural Federation Summer Flower Show June 16 only. Parties welcome please,* Tel **01483 232424**

Moleshill House ఈ๕❀ (Mr & Mrs M Snell) Cobham. House is on A307 Esher to Cobham Rd next to free car park by A3 bridge. Flower arranger's romantic garden. Topiary and garlanded cisterns around house; circular lawn surrounded by informal borders; gravel bed; dovecote; silver and white garden; paving and pots. TEAS. *Adm £1.50 Chd free. Sun June 23 (2-6). Wed July 3 (6.30-9) Adm £2.50 incl wine and light refreshment*

Montfleury ๕❀ (Cdr & Mrs Innes Hamilton) Christchurch Rd, Virginia Water. From A30 at Virginia Water, opp Wheatsheaf Restaurant, turn down B389. Over roundabout. Last house on R before village. Former National Award Winners' new small garden. Interesting plant sales. Also wide choice of professional nursery stock for immediate effect. Unlimited parking. TEA. *Adm £1 Chd 10p. Sun May 19 (2-6)*

29 Mostyn Road, Merton Park (see London)

Munstead Wood ఈ๕❀ (Sir Robert & Lady Clark) nr Godalming. Take B2130 Brighton Rd out of Godalming towards Horsham. After 1m church on R, Heath Lane just thereafter on L. 400yds on R is entrance to Munstead Wood. Parking on L of Heath Lane. 10 acres of rhododendrons, azaleas, woods and shrub and flower beds. Home until 1931 of Gertrude Jekyll; parts of garden recently extensively refurbished. The architect for the house (not open) was Edwin Lutyens. TEAS. *Adm £2 OAPs £1 Chd 50p (Share to Meath Trust®). Suns April 21, May 26, Sept 1 (2-6)*

Odstock ఈ๕❀ (Mr & Mrs J F H Trott) Bletchingley. Between Godstone 2m and Redhill 3m on A25, at top of village nr Red Lion pub. Parking in village, no parking in Castle Square. ⅔ of an acre maintained by owners and continually being developed for all-yr interest. Covered walk created by training old apple trees plus other climbers. Interesting variety of plants and shrubs with imaginative complementary and contrasting groupings of form and colour. Japanese features; dahlias. No dig, low maintenance vegetable garden. TEAS. *Adm £1.50 Chd free (Share to St Mary's Church, Bletchingley®). Sun Aug 4 (1-5.30). (Disabled welcome – please telephone first* Tel **01883 743100***)*

The Old Croft ๕❀ (David and Virginia Lardner-Burke) South Holmwood. 3m S of Dorking. From Dorking take A24 S for 3m. Turn L at sign to Leigh-Brockham into Mill Road. ¾m on L, 2 free car parks in NT Holmwood Common. Follow directional signs for 400yds along woodland walk. 5-acre parkland garden with lake, stream, ponds, woodland, wild and formal areas, herb garden, wide variety of specimen trees and shrubs; recent new developments. Garden redeveloped by Virginia Lardner-Burke. TEAS. *Adm £1.50 Chd free (Share to St Catherine's Hospice, Crawley®). Sats, Suns May 4, 5; July 6, 7 (2-6)*

Olivers ❀ (Mr & Mrs Charles Watson) Church Road, Hascombe. On B2130, Godalming to Cranleigh Road (Godalming 3m). Park by White Horse in Hascombe village. Olivers is 50yds up Church Rd, between public house and pond. 2½-acre informal country garden; wide variety, herbaceous borders, interesting trees, shrubs and perennials, some new development areas. See what can be done on 1 day a week! Beautiful village location by historic church. TEAS. *Adm £1.20 Chd 25p (Share to Church Fabric Fund®). Sun May 19 (2-6)*

Painshill ᶜᵃ⚮ (Painshill Park Trust) 1m W Cobham on A245. Entrance on R, 200yds E of A3/A245 roundabout. Painshill is one of Europe's finest C18 landscape gardens, contemporary with Stourhead & Stowe. Created by the Hon Charles Hamilton between 1738-1773. Ornamental pleasure grounds dominated by 14-acre lake fed from river by immense waterwheel; grotto, ruined Abbey, Temple, Chinese Bridge, castellated Tower, Mausoleum. Turkish tent and newly planted vineyard. In 1981 the Painshill Park Trust was formed and following meticulous restoration the beautiful gardens are now emerging from the wilderness. Suitable for wheelchairs with exceptions. TEAS. *Adm £3.50, disabled, students and OAPs £3 Chd 5-16 £1 Acc chd under 5 free (Share to Painshill Park Trust®). Suns only April 7 to Oct 13 (11-6). Private groups of 10 and over on other days, please* **Tel 01932 868113.** *For NGS Sun Oct 6 (11-5)*

Park House ᶜᵃ⚮❀ (The Viscount & Viscountess Leathers) Chiddingfold. ½m from top of village green (signposted Dunsfold) in E direction on the Pickhurst Rd. Park House is on the R. Parking by kind permission of Mr & Mrs Stamp. Disabled drive up to the house. A S facing interesting garden of mixed borders featuring many unusual trees and shrubs; agapanthus. Places to sit and relax. 6 acres in all incl woodland and wildlife area. TEAS (Sun Aug 4). *Adm £2 Chd 25p (Share to South West Surrey Mobile Physiotherapy Service®). Thurs, Sun Aug 1, 4 (2.30-5.30). Private visits and parties welcome, please* **Tel 01428 683222**

Pinewood House ᶜᵃ⚮ (Mr & Mrs J Van Zwanenberg) Heath House Rd, Worplesdon Hill. 3m Woking, 5m Guildford off A322 opp Brookwood Cemetery Wall. 4 acres. Walled garden and arboretum; water garden; bulbs in April. Interesting new house finished in Dec '86 with indoor plants. *Adm house & gardens £2. Private visits welcome for parties of 2-30 April to Oct, please* **Tel 01483 473241**

Polesden Lacey ᶜᵃ⚮❀ (The National Trust) Bookham, nr Dorking. 1½m S of Great Bookham off A246 Leatherhead-Guildford rd. 60 acres formal gardens; extensive grounds, walled rose garden, winter garden, lavender garden, iris garden, lawns; good views on landscape walks. House originally a Regency villa dating early 1820's, remodelled after 1906 by the Hon Mrs Ronald Greville, well-known Edwardian hostess; fine paintings, furniture, porcelain and silver, also many photographs from Mrs Greville's albums on display. King George VI and Queen Elizabeth (now the Queen Mother) spent part of their honeymoon here. For wheelchair details **Tel 01372 458203.** Gift shop. Lunch and TEAS in licensed restaurant in grounds (11-6). *Adm garden and grounds £3, Chd £1.50; house £3 extra, Chd £1.75. ▲For NGS garden only Sun May 12 (11-6)*

Postford House ❀ (Mrs R Litler-Jones) Chilworth. 4m SE Guildford Route A248 Bus LC 425 Guildford-Dorking alight nr entrance. 25 acres woodland; bog garden; stream; rose garden; vegetable garden; rhododendrons, azaleas and shrubs; swimming pool open. Home-made TEAS. *Adm £1.50 Chd free. Suns May 19, 26 (2-6). Private visits welcome, please* **Tel 01483 202657**

Pyrford Court ᶜᵃ⚮ (Mr & Mrs C Laikin) Pyrford Common Rd, 2m E of Woking. B367 junction with Upshott Lane; M25 exit 10 onto A3 towards Guildford off into Ripley signed Pyrford. 20 acres; wild gardens; extensive lawns; azaleas, rhododendrons, wisterias, autumn colour. As well as many fine established species of wisteria, there are several new plantings which together comprise the probationary National Wisteria Collection. TEAS. *Adm £2.50, Chd 80p (Share to NCCPG®). Sat, Suns May 11, 12 (2-6), Oct 13 (12-4). Private visits and parties welcome, please* **Tel 01483 765880**

●**Ramster** ᶜᵃ⚮ (Mr & Mrs Paul Gunn) Chiddingfold. On A283, 1½m S of Chiddingfold; large iron gates on R. Mature 20-acre woodland garden of exceptional interest with lakes, ponds and woodland walks. Laid out by Gauntlett Nurseries of Chiddingfold in early 1900s. Fine rhododendrons, azaleas, camellias, magnolias, trees and shrubs. Picnic area. TEAS daily in May. *Adm £2 Chd under 16 free (Share to NGS®). Daily from April 20 to July 21 (11-5.30). Parties welcome, please* **Tel 01428 644422**

Ridings ᶜᵃ⚮❀ (Mr & Mrs K Dutton) Tadworth. On A217 at large roundabout 6m S of Sutton and 3m N of junction 8 on M25 take B2220 sign posted Tadworth. Take 2nd R into Tadorne Rd; L into Cross Rd. House on corner of Epsom Lane S. ¾-acre informal garden containing interesting trees, shrubs and herbaceous plants with emphasis on colour, texture and foliage; vegetable plot. *Adm £1.50 Chd free. Suns June 2, 9 (2-5.30). Private visits welcome (May to July), please* **Tel 01737 813962**

41 Shelvers Way ⚮❀ (Mr & Mrs K G Lewis) Tadworth. 6m S of Sutton off the A217. 1st turning on R after Burgh Heath traffic lights heading S. 400 yds down Shelvers Way on L. ⅓-acre plantsman's garden. Attractive cobbled area leading to a wide variety of herbaceous and other plants. Many spring bulbs followed by azaleas and old roses. Designed and developed by owners. Coffee and TEAS. *Adm £1.50 Chd free. Weds April 24, June 26, July 17, Sun July 14 (10.30-5)*

¶**67 Shepherds Lane** ⚮❀ (Mr & Mrs C Graham) Stoughton, Guildford. From Guildford, 1m from A3 on A322 Worplesdon Rd. Turn L at traffic lights at Emmanuel Church, Stoughton into Shepherds Lane. Garden is on L on brow of hill. From Aldershot, A323 to Guildford town boundary. 1st exit at 1st roundabout, past The Cricketers inn into Rydes Hill Rd. Shepherds Lane is 2nd R. No 67 is 100yds on R. ¼-acre suburban garden with mixed borders, lawn, specimen small trees, pond, alpine bed, fruit garden with dwarf trees; Guildford in Bloom award winners. Plants in aid of Abbeyfield (Guildford) Society. TEA. *Adm £1 Chd 50p. Wed July 3 (10.30-5). Private visits welcome, please* **Tel 01483 566445**

Snowdenham House &❀ (The Hon Lady Hamilton) Snowdenham Lane, Bramley. S of Guildford A281 from Guildford, R at Bramley mini-roundabout. House is ½m on L. Georgian house, outbuildings and water mill (not open). 9 acres of water, woodland, formal and walled gardens. Wide range of rhododendrons, azaleas and specimen trees and shrubs in woodland garden bordering stream. TEAS in aid of Bramley Church. *Adm £2 Chd free. Sun May 19 (11.30-5)*

¶South Cheam Gardens ⚘❀ Situated approx 1m S of Cheam village. *Combined adm £2 Chd 50p. Sat, Sun Aug 3, 4 (11-5)*
¶87 Sandy Lane (Mr & Mrs B West) ⅓-acre garden featuring sub-tropical plants, incl palm trees, a tree fern, bananas, algaves, bamboos and acers. Large collection of cannas; rockery with small water feature. Fruit trees, dahlia borders and vegetable garden and much more. TEAS in aid of St Raphael's Hospice
¶89 Sandy Lane (Mr & Mrs Jeff Jones) ⅓-acre with a lower, middle and upper garden. Lower garden features conifers, bedding plants and pots; the middle garden has a pond, rockery, dahlia and sweet pea beds and herbaceous border. The upper garden is devoted to all vegetables with 30 feet of greenhouse space. Plants in aid of Shere & Peaslake Cubs & Venture Scouts

South Park Farm & (Mrs P J Stewart-Smith) South Godstone. Take A22 London to East Grinstead rd and 1m S of railway bridge at South Godstone turn R into Carlton Rd just before Walker's Garden Centre; follow signs for 1m. Medium-sized garden; wide variety of roses; herbaceous border; fine trees and landscape; small lake. C17 (listed) farm house (not open). Peacocks. Home-made TEAS till 6 in large C17 barn. *Adm £2 Chd free. Sat, Sun, Mon June 22, 23, 24 (2-6). Also private visits welcome, please* Tel 01342 892141

Spur Point, nr Fernhurst (See Sussex)

Stonywood ⚘❀ (Mr & Mrs Noble) Chase Lane, Haslemere. From centre of town take B2131 E towards Petworth. Take 2nd turning R for Blackdown. At junction of 5 lanes go straight on towards Tennyson's Lane. At next junction (150yds) go straight on. House on L, ⅓m down lane. Parking space very limited in narrow lane. ⅓-acre steeply sloping garden. Many rhododendrons, azaleas, shrubs, spring bulbs; pleasant views across Chase Valley and NT woods. TEAS. *Adm £1 Chd 50p (Share to Foundation for the study of Infant Deaths®). Sun May 19 (2-5). Private visits welcome for parties of 10 and over following written application*

Street House &❀ (Mr & Mrs B M Francis) Thursley. From London take A3. 8m past Guildford turn R at sign Thursley/Churt/Frensham, 50yds past Three Horseshoes inn, bear L at fork signed The Street and No through road. Garden ahead. from Portsmouth/Petersfield turn L from A3 into Thursley village. Parking on recreation ground 100yds past house. Please park carefully in wet weather. Street House (not open), a listed Regency building and childhood home of Sir Edwin Lutyens where he first met Gertrude Jekyll. Garden of 1¼ acres divided into three separate and individual gardens. Beautiful views towards Devils Punch Bowl. Ancient wall; special features include magnificent specimen cornus kousa; Japanese snowball tree; rare old roses; special rhododendrons and camellias; rubus tridel and many surprises. Special feature Astrological Garden now completed. Home-made TEAS. *Adm £1.50 Chd 50p (Share to Thursley Cricket Club©). Suns April 21, May 19, June 16, Sat July 27 (2-6)*

Stuart Cottage &❀ (Mr & Mrs J M Leader) East Clandon. This C16 hamlet, public house and C12 church is well worth a visit. Situated 4m E of Guildford on the A246 or from A3 via Ripley turning L in centre of Ripley, Rose Lane, then 2nd R. East Clandon is 4m. ½-acre partly walled garden with rose walk, well-stocked herbaceous beds, water features, paved areas with planting. Planted antique chimney pots reflect the charm of this C16 cottage. TEAS. *Adm £1.50 Chd free (Share to Cherry Trees, respite care for handicapped children®). Sat, Sun July 27, 28 (2-6)*

¶Sutton Place &⚘ (Sutton Place Foundation) Guildford. From A320 (Guildford-Woking) turn into Clay Lane. At X-rds take Blanchards Lane towards Sutton Green. Lodge gates approx ¼m on R. Gardens extend to about 60 acres, around the Tudor Manor House. The area comprises of a series of individual gardens each with its own theme and interest. There is a woodland garden which runs down to the R Wey. Many of the gardens were designed by Sir Geoffrey Jellicoe and the more recently established gardens were designed by Patrick Bowe. TEAS. *Adm £5 Chd £1.50. Wed June 12 (10-4) Suitable for wheelchairs in parts. NO COACH PARTIES ON JUNE 12. Private visits welcome by prior appt. for parties of 12-40 please* Tel 01483 504455

¶Tanyard Farmhouse &❀ (Mr & Mrs E Epson) Langshott Lane, Horley. At edge of Horley on A23. Travelling from Redhill turn L into Ladbroke Rd at Chequers Hotel roundabout. Continue ½m, garden on L. Park in Lake Lane. ⅓-acre 2-yr-old garden designed by owners on a flat site, with heavy clay, around a C15/17 wealden farmhouse. Formal layout, with informal planting, incl small white garden with pond, scented rose garden with lavender and clematis, rustic trellises and arches. Mixed borders with shrubs and perennials, some unusual. Terrace with pots and baskets containing herbs, perennials and annuals. TEAS. *Adm £1.50 Chd free. Sat, Sun July 6, 7 (2-6)*

Thanescroft &⚘❀ (Mr & Mrs Peter Talbot-Willcox) Shamley Green. 5m S of Guildford, A281 Guildford-Horsham rd, at Shalford turn E onto B2128 to Wonersh and Shamley Green. At Shamley Green Village sign turn R to Lord's Hill, ¾m on L. 4-acres mixed formal and informal garden, incl vegetables; lawns; roses; herbaceous; shrubs and specialist trees. Interesting icehouse. Cream TEAS. *Adm £1.50 Chd 25p. Sat, Sun June 22, 23 (2-6)*

●Titsey Place and Gardens &% (The Trustees of the Titsey Foundation) Oxted. 2m N of Oxted. On A25 between Oxted and Westerham, turn L into Limpsfield Village. On bend at end of village, turn L (straight on) into Bluehouse Lane and follow signs to Titsey Place and Gardens. 18 acres of landscaped gardens and lakes surrounded by parkland together with a rare opportunity to see a recently restored Victorian walled garden. *Adm £4 House and Garden, £2 Gardens only. Weds and Suns May 29 to Sept 29 (1-5)*

Unicorns % (Mr & Mrs Eric Roberts) Long Hill, The Sands, Farnham. Approx 4½m E of Farnham take A31 towards Guildford. 1st slip rd to Runfold turn R, then L into Crooksbury Rd through 's' bend then L turn to The Sands through village past Barley Mow public house on R. Park tactfully in Littleworth Rd. Long Hill 1st turning on R. Partly woodland garden on a sloping site, rhododendrons, azaleas, ferns, plants for ground cover and many other interesting and unusual plants and shrubs. Teas at Manor Farm, Seale. *Adm £1 Chd free. Wed May 15 (2-5). Private visits welcome from mid April to end of August please* **Tel 01252 782778** *after 6pm. Due to terrain 2 to 15 adults only*

87 Upland Road &%❀ (Mr & Mrs David Nunn) 50yds S Carshalton Beeches station into Waverley Way, at shops into Downside Rd, then 1st on L. 0.4-acre secluded suburban plantsman's garden overlaying chalk. Shrubs; herbaceous; orchard; fruit and vegetable garden. Developed and maintained by owners. Exhibition of botanical watercolour paintings. TEAS. *Adm £1.50 Chd free. Sun May 12 (2-6)*

6 Upper Rose Hill %❀ (Peter & Julia Williams) Dorking. From roundabout at A24/A25 junction follow signs to town centre and Horsham. ½m S of town centre turn L after Pizza Piazza and 2nd R at top of hill. Parking available in rd and in large car park behind Sainsbury's (5 min walk). ½-acre informal suburban terraced garden on dry sand. Wide range of foliage and form; fruit and vegetables; some unusual plants; good autumn colour. TEAS in aid of Mole Valley Crossroads for Carers. *Adm £1.50 Chd free. Sun June 16 (2-6) Private visits welcome, please* **Tel 01306 881315**

Vale End ❀ (Mr & Mrs John Foulsham) Albury, 4½m SE of Guildford. From Albury take A248 W for ¼m. 1-acre walled garden on many levels in beautiful setting; featured in Homes and Gardens 1994; views from terrace across sloping lawns to mill pond and woodland; wide variety herbaceous plants and old roses; attractive courtyard. Ornamental fruit and vegetable garden. Featured in NGS video 2. Morning coffee and home-made TEAS in aid of Albury Parish Church Fabric Fund. *Adm £1.50 Chd free. Suns June 23, July 28 (10-5)*

Vann %❀ (Mr & Mrs M B Caroe) Hambledon, 6m S of Godalming. A283 to Wormley. Turn L at Hambledon Xrds signed 'Vann Lane'. Follow yellow 'Vann' signs for 2m. House on left. GPO box on gate. An English Heritage Registered garden of 4½ acres surrounding Tudor/William & Mary house with later additions and alterations incorporating old farm buildings by W D Caröe 1907-1909. Formal yew walk, ¼-acre pond, Gertrude Jekyll water garden

1911, pergola, old cottage garden. Spring bulbs, woodland, azaleas, roses. New vegetable garden borders. Featured in Country Life and Gardeners World 1995. Maintained by family with 2 days assistance per week. Part of garden suitable for wheelchairs. Guided tours, morning coffee, lunches, home-made teas in house from Easter-July by prior arrangement. TEAS (Mon May 27 only). *Adm £2.50 Chd 50p (Share to Hambledon Village Hall®). Tues-Sun April 9-14, May 7-12 (10-6); Mon May 27 (2-7); Tues-Sun May 28-June 2 (10-6); Mon-Sun July 1 to 7 (10-6). Private visits welcome, please* **Tel 01428 683413**

Walton Poor &❀ (Mr & Mrs Nicholas Calvert) 4m W of Ranmore. From N and W off A246 on outskirts of East Horsley take Greendene 1st fork L Crocknorth Rd. From E take A2003 to Ranmore Rd from Dorking to E Horsley. Approx 3 acres; tranquil, rather secret garden; paths winding between areas of ornamental shrubs; landscaped sunken garden; pond; herb garden. Autumn colour. Extensive range of foliage, scented plants and herbs for sale; garden next to miles of forest paths leading to North Downs with fine views over Tillingbourne valley. TEAS (May and June) (from 3pm). *Adm £1.50 Chd 50p (Share to Leukaemia Research®). Mon May 6, Sun, Wed June 2, 5, Sun Oct 6 (11-5) Herb garden open daily Wed to Sun Easter to Sept 30. Private visits of 10 and over welcome to the main garden, please* **Tel 01483 282273**

Westbourn % (Mr & Mrs John Camden) Virginia Water. From Egham 3m S on A30. Turn L into Christchurch Rd opp the Wheatsheaf Hotel. After 200yds turn R into Pinewood Rd; Westbourn is 50yds on the R. 4 acres landscaped woodland on 2 levels extensively planted with unusual trees and shrubs. Rhododendrons and azaleas predominate with over 80 different species and as many hybrids. Other notable collections well represented include acer, prunus, sorbus, hydrangea, ferns, ornamental cherries and hosta. The R Bourne, a narrow winding rivulet, forms the southern boundary of the garden. TEA. *Adm £1 Chd free. Sun May 5 (2-6)*

Westland Farm &%❀ (Mrs E J Burnet) Ewhurst. 11m SE of Guildford. Join Ockley Rd (B2127) at Bull's Head N of village. Go E for ¾m. See sign on RH-side. 2½ acres plus 14 acres bluebell woodland; rhododendrons, azaleas, other acid-loving plants, lake with woodland walk, spring bulbs. Interesting use of horticultural plastic for low maintenance and growth promotion. Australian TEAS and pavlova icecream; dried flower arrangements. *Adm £1.50 Chd free (Share to Guildford Scouts 2nd Troop©). Sun May 12 (1.30-5.30). Parties by prior arrangement, please* **Tel 01483 277270**

Whinfold &%❀ (Mr & Mrs A Gash) Hascombe. 3½m SE of Godalming. Turn off B2130 at top of Winkworth Hill between Godalming and Hascombe. Woodland garden about 15 acres originally planned by Gertrude Jekyll in 1897. The garden is maintained by the owners with weekend help and includes a pond, herb garden, specimen trees, magnolias, rhododendrons, azaleas and camellias with spring bulbs followed by masses of bluebells. TEA. *Adm £1.50 Chd free (Share to Hydon Hill Cheshire Home®). Suns March 31, May 12 (2-5)*

White House ♿❀ (Lt Cdr & Mrs Michael Lethbridge) Stringers Common, Guildford. On A320 Guildford to Woking Rd 2m N of Guildford centre just beyond junction with Jacob's Well Rd. 3 acres, shrubs and herbaceous borders in setting of stone walls, roses, old orchard and pond. Quiet garden beside busy rd. Aims to maintain natural surroundings and habitat for birds, insects and wild flowers and to avoid unnecessary chemicals. A 'controlled' wild look. TEA. *Adm £1 Chd free (Share to Jacobs Well Ecological Society®). Suns June 30 (2-6), Oct 6 (2-5.30)*

Windlesham Park ♿✗ (Mr & Mrs Peter Dimmock) Woodlands Lane. 2m E of Bagshot. S of Sunningdale, NW of Chobham; from Windlesham Church S to T-junction, turn L into Thorndown Lane becoming Woodlands Lane over M3; entrance 100yds on R, white pillars. 9-acre parkland setting with many and varied well established azaleas and rhododendrons. Fine cedars and mature trees; wet areas. TEAS. *Adm £1 Chd 25p (Share to St John the Baptist Church®). Sun May 19 (2-6)*

Winkworth Arboretum (The National Trust) Hascombe, Godalming. Entrances with car parks; Upper 3m SE of Godalming on E side of B2130; Lower 2¼m S of Bramley on Bramley-Hascombe rd, turn R off A281 from Guildford by Bramley Grange Hotel, up Snowdenham Lane. Coaches (by written arrangement) should use Upper car park on B2130. Station: Godalming 3m. 95 acres of hillside planted with rare trees and shrubs; 2 lakes; many wild birds; view over N Downs. Tours on both days with Eric Barrs, Head of Arboretum. 10.30; tours only available by written application £2. Limited suitability for wheelchairs. Disabled visitors use lower car park. Disabled WC. TEAS 11-5.30. *Adm £2.50 Chd 5-17 £1.25 Family ticket £6.25.* ▲*Suns May 12, Oct 13 (dawn-dusk)*

Wintershall Manor ✗ (Mr & Mrs Peter Hutley) 3m S of Bramley village on A281 turn R, then next R. Wintershall drive next on L. Bus: AV 33 Guildford-Horsham; alight Palmers Cross, 1m. 2-acre garden and 200 acres of park and woodland; snowdrop walk, acres of bluebell walks in spring; banks of wild daffodils; rhododendrons; specimen trees; several acres of lakes and flight ponds; Domesday yew tree. St Francis Chapel by Chapel Lake. Path commences The Stations of the Cross by contemporary young sculptors leading up the hill to Hollybarn and The Chapel of St Mary, Queen of Peace, with superb views. Partially suitable for wheelchairs. TEA from 3.30 pm. *Adm £2 OAPs £1.50 Chd 4-14 50p (Share to Wintershall Charitable Trust®). Suns April 14, May 12. June 2 (1-5) Stations of the Cross and Rosary Way only. 1997 Suns Feb 2, March 2 (2-4). Private parties welcome, please* **Tel 01483 892167**

Woodside ✗❀ (Mr & Mrs J A Colmer) Send Barns Lane, Send, nr Ripley, 4m NE of Guildford; on A247 (Woking/Dorking Rd) 200yds west (Send side) at junction with B2215. If travelling via M25 leave at junction 10. ⅓-acre garden; main feature rock garden and alpine house; many shrubs incl rhododendrons, ericaceous species etc; herbaceous planting; specialist collection of alpines. *Adm £1 Chd free. Sat, Sun April 20, 21 (2-6). Private visits welcome in May, please* **Tel 01483 223073**

Yew Tree Cottage ✗❀ (Mr & Mrs E E Bowyer) Bunch Lane, Haslemere. Turn off High St into Church Lane, leave church on L, carry on to T junction, turn L, 1st house on L. 2-acre garden created by owners since 1976 on hillside. Large variety of trees and shrubs, water garden, kitchen garden, Jacob and Shetland sheep, rare breed poultry, Shetland pony in paddock beyond garden. Partially suitable wheelchairs. See **Haslehurst.** Tea at Haslehurst. *Adm £1 Chd 50p (Share to Haslemere Educational Museum®). Sun June 16 (2-6). Coach parties by prior arrangement. Private visits welcome, please* **Tel 01428 644130**

SYMBOLS USED IN THIS BOOK (See also Page 15)

‡   Following a garden name in the Dates of Opening list indicates that those gardens sharing the same symbol are nearby and open on the same day.

‡‡   Indicates a second series of nearby gardens open on the same day.

¶   Opening for the first time.

❀   Plants/produce for sale if available.

♿   Gardens with at least the main features accessible by wheelchair.

✗   No dogs except guide dogs but otherwise dogs are usually admitted, provided they are kept on a lead. Dogs are not admitted to houses.

●   Gardens marked thus do not necessarily give all their takings to the National Gardens Scheme. Instead they give a guaranteed contribution.

▲   Where this sign appears alongside dates in the descriptive entry for a garden it denotes that this garden is also open regularly to the public on days other than those for the NGS.

Sussex

Hon County Organisers:

(East & Mid-Sussex)	Mrs Janet Goldsmith, Sunnymead, Tapsells Lane, Wadhurst TN5 6RS Tel 01892 783264
(West Sussex)	Mrs Mark Dunn, Wildham, Stoughton, Chichester PO18 9JG. Tel 01243 535202

Assistant Hon County Organisers:

(East & Mid-Sussex)	Mrs J Charlesworth, Snape Cottage, Snape Lane, Wadhurst
(West Sussex)	Mrs Nigel Azis, Coke's Barn, West Burton, Pulborough RH20 1HD Tel 01798 831636
(West Sussex)	Mrs Jane Burton, Church Farmhouse, Lavant, nr Chichester
(West Sussex)	Mrs Jean Jackman, Five Oaks Cottage, West Burton, Pulborough
(West Sussex)	Mrs Jennifer Woodall, Nyewood House, Petersfield, Hants GU31 5JL

Hon County Treasurers:

(East & Mid-Sussex)	D C Goldsmith Esq, Sunnymead, Tapsells Lane, Wadhurst TN5 6RS
(West Sussex)	W M Caldwell Esq, The Grange, Fittleworth, Pulborough

DATES OF OPENING

March 17 Sunday
Champs Hill, Coldwaltham,
nr Pulborough
March 18 Monday
Denmans, Fontwell, nr Arundel
March 23 Saturday
The Manor of Dean, Tillington,
Petworth ‡
Petworth House Pleasure
Ground ‡
March 24 Sunday
Champs Hill, Coldwaltham,
nr Pulborough
Hurst Mill, Petersfield
The Manor of Dean, Tillington,
Petworth
Orchards, Rowfant
March 25 Monday
The Manor of Dean, Tillington,
Petworth
March 27 Wednesday
Orchards, Rowfant
March 31 Sunday
Berri Court, Yapton
April 1 Monday
Berri Court, Yapton
Northwood Farmhouse,
Pulborough
April 2 Tuesday
Northwood Farmhouse,
Pulborough
April 6 Saturday
High Beeches Gardens,
Handcross
April 7 Sunday
Bignor Park, nr Pulborough
Chidmere House, Chidham
April 8 Monday
Bignor Park, nr Pulborough
Chidmere House, Chidham
Highdown Gardens, Goring-by-Sea
Orchards, Rowfant

Penns in the Rocks, Groombridge
Stonehurst, Ardingly
April 9 Tuesday
Little Thakeham, Storrington
April 10 Wednesday
Little Thakeham, Storrington
April 13 Saturday
The Manor of Dean, Tillington,
Petworth
April 14 Sunday
Bates Green Farm, Arlington
The Manor of Dean, Tillington,
Petworth
April 15 Monday
The Manor of Dean, Tillington,
Petworth
April 17 Wednesday
Orchards, Rowfant
April 21 Sunday
Cooke's House, West Burton
Ghyll Farm, Sweethaws,
Crowborough
Hurst Mill, Petersfield ‡
Malt House, Chithurst,
nr Rogate ‡
New Grove, Petworth
Newtimber Place, Newtimber
Offham House, Offham
Stonehurst, Ardingly
April 22 Monday
Cooke's House, West Burton
April 23 Tuesday
Cooke's House, West Burton
April 24 Wednesday
West Dean Gardens, nr Chichester
April 25 Thursday
Duckyls, Sharpthorne
April 27 Saturday
Cedar Tree Cottage, Washington
King Edward VII Hospital,
nr Midhurst
April 28 Sunday
Cooke's House, West Burton
Malt House, Chithurst, nr Rogate

Wadhurst Park, Wadhurst
April 29 Monday
Cooke's House, West Burton
April 30 Tuesday
Cooke's House, West Burton ‡
Duckyls, Sharpthorne
Houghton Farm, nr Arundel ‡
Michelham Priory, Upper Dicker,
Hailsham
May 1 Wednesday
Cedar Tree Cottage, Washington
May 5 Sunday
Cedar Tree Cottage, Washington
Gaywood Farm, Pulborough
Malt House, Chithurst, nr Rogate
Standen, East Grinstead
Warren House, Crowborough
May 6 Monday
Highdown Gardens,
Goring-by-Sea
Ghyll Farm, Sweethaws,
Crowborough
Malt House, Chithurst,
nr Rogate
Orchards, Rowfant
Stonehurst, Ardingly
May 8 Wednesday
Middle Coombe, East Grinstead
Nyewood House, Nyewood,
nr Rogate
May 9 Thursday
Duckyls, Sharpthorne
May 11 Saturday
Champs Hill, Coldwaltham,
nr Pulborough
Selehurst, Lower Beeding,
nr Horsham
May 12 Sunday
Berri Court, Yapton
Champs Hill, Coldwaltham,
nr Pulborough
Chidmere House, Chidham
Cobblers, Crowborough ‡
Hammerwood House, Iping ‡‡

Malt House, Chithurst,
nr Rogate ‡‡
Merriments Gardens, Hurst Green
Tinkers Bridge Cottage, Ticehurst
Warren House, Crowborough ‡
May 13 Monday
Berri Court, Yapton
Chidmere House, Chidham
May 14 Tuesday
Duckyls, Sharpthorne
May 15 Wednesday
Sheffield Park Garden, nr Uckfield
May 16 Thursday
Duckyls, Sharpthorne
May 18 Saturday
Champs Hill, Coldwaltham,
nr Pulborough ‡
Fittleworth Gardens,
nr Pulborough ‡
The Manor of Dean, Tillington,
Petworth
May 19 Sunday
Champs Hill, Coldwaltham,
nr Pulborough ‡
Coke's Barn, West Burton ‡
Fittleworth Gardens,
nr Pulborough ‡
Fitzhall, Iping, nr Midhurst ‡‡
Greenacres, Crowborough ‡‡‡‡
Ghyll Farm, Sweethaws,
Crowborough ‡‡‡‡
Hammerwood House, Iping ‡‡
6 Holbrook Park, nr Horsham
Legsheath Farm, nr Forest Row
Malt House, Chithurst,
nr Rogate ‡‡
The Manor of Dean, Tillington,
Petworth
Morris Down, Piltdown,
nr Maresfield
Mountfield Court,
nr Robertsbridge
New Grove, Petworth ‡
North Springs, Fittleworth ‡
Sennicotts, nr Chichester ‡‡‡
Trotton Old Rectory, nr Rogate ‡‡
Trotton Place, nr Rogate ‡‡
Woodstock, West Broyle,
Chichester ‡‡‡
May 20 Monday
Coke's Barn, West Burton ‡
The Manor of Dean, Tillington,
Petworth ‡
Morris Down, Piltdown,
nr Maresfield
Mountfield Court,
nr Robertsbridge
New Grove, Petworth ‡
Sennicotts, nr Chichester
May 21 Tuesday
Coke's Barn, West Burton
Duckyls, Sharpthorne
May 22 Wednesday
Houghton Farm, nr Arundel

May 23 Thursday
Duckyls, Sharpthorne ‡
6 Holbrook Park, nr Horsham
The Priest House, West Hoathly,
nr East Grinstead ‡
May 25 Saturday
Lane End, Midhurst
May 26 Sunday
Baker's Farm, Shipley, nr Horsham
Cookscroft, Earnley
Gaywood Farm, Pulborough
Lane End, Midhurst ‡
Malt House, Chithurst,
nr Rogate ‡
Moorlands, nr Crowborough
May 27 Monday
Cobblers, Crowborough ‡‡
Cookscroft, Earnley
Gaywood Farm, Pulborough
Highdown Gardens, Goring-by-Sea
Lane End, Midhurst ‡
Malt House, Chithurst,
nr Rogate ‡
Orchards, Rowfant
Round Hill Cottage, East Dean
Warren House, Crowborough ‡‡
May 28 Tuesday
Duckyls, Sharpthorne
Gaywood Farm, Pulborough
Round Hill Cottage, East Dean
May 30 Thursday
Duckyls, Sharpthorne ‡
The Priest House, West Hoathly,
nr East Grinstead ‡
June 1 Saturday
Lane End, Midhurst
June 2 Sunday
Frith Hill, Northchapel
The Garden in Mind, Stansted
Park
Greenacres, Crowborough
Hailsham Grange, Hailsham
Lane End, Midhurst
Neptune House, Cutmill, Bosham
North Springs, Fittleworth
Nymans, Handcross
Offham House, Offham
Pembury, Clayton, nr Brighton
June 3 Monday
Lane End, Midhurst
June 5 Wednesday
Parham House & Gardens,
nr Pulborough
June 6 Thursday
Parham House & Gardens,
nr Pulborough
June 8 Saturday
Coombland, Coneyhurst,
Billingshurst
The Garden in Mind, Stansted
Park
King John's Lodge, Etchingham ‡
Lilac Cottage, Duncton ‡‡
Little Hutchings, Etchingham ‡

Somerset Lodge, North St,
Petworth ‡‡
June 9 Sunday
Cobblers, Crowborough ‡
The Garden in Mind, Stansted
Park
Greenacres, Crowborough ‡
King John's Lodge,
Etchingham ‡‡
Kingston Gardens, nr Lewes
Lilac Cottage, Duncton ‡‡‡
Little Hutchings, Etchingham ‡‡
Merriments Gardens, Hurst Green
Moorlands, nr Crowborough ‡
Nyewood House, Nyewood,
nr Rogate
Somerset Lodge, North St,
Petworth ‡‡‡
Warren House, Crowborough ‡
The White House, Burpham,
nr Arundel
June 10 Monday
Little Thakeham, Storrington
June 11 Tuesday
Coombland, Coneyhurst,
Billingshurst
Little Thakeham, Storrington
June 12 Wednesday
Ashburnham Place, Battle
Gaywood Farm, Pulborough ‡
Lilac Cottage, Duncton ‡
Nyewood House, Nyewood,
nr Rogate
Somerset Lodge, North St,
Petworth ‡
June 13 Thursday
Ashburnham Place, Battle
Town Place, Freshfield,
nr Sheffield Park
June 14 Friday
Ashburnham Place, Battle
June 15 Saturday
Chantry Green House, Steyning
Coombland, Coneyhurst,
Billingshurst
Frith Hill, Northchapel ‡
Frith Lodge, Northchapel ‡
King Edward VII Hospital,
nr Midhurst
Somerset Lodge, North St,
Petworth ‡
Winchelsea Gardens, Winchelsea
June 16 Sunday
Ashburnham Place, Battle
Chantry Green House,
Steyning
Clinton Lodge, Fletching ‡
Ebbsworth, Nutbourne,
nr Pulborough ‡‡
Knabbs Farmhouse, Fletching ‡
Mount Harry Gardens, Offham
New Barn, Egdean ‡‡‡
Orchards, Rowfant
Priesthawes Farm, Polegate

Somerset Lodge, North St,
  Petworth ‡‡‡
Upper House, West Burton ‡‡
Warren House, Crowborough
June 17 Monday
Clinton Lodge, Fletching ‡
Ebbsworth, Nutbourne,
  nr Pulborough ‡‡
Knabbs Farmhouse, Fletching ‡
New Barn, Egdean
Northwood Farmhouse,
  Pulborough ‡‡
Priesthawes Farm, Polegate
Upper House, West Burton ‡‡
June 18 Tuesday
New Barn, Egdean
Northwood Farmhouse,
  Pulborough ‡
Upper House, West Burton ‡
June 19 Wednesday
Houghton Farm, nr Arundel ‡
Somerset Lodge, North St,
  Petworth
Upper House, West Burton ‡
June 20 Thursday
Frith Hill, Northchapel ‡
Frith Lodge, Northchapel ‡
June 21 Friday
Dallington Cottage Gardens
Down Place, South Harting ‡
Uppark, South Harting ‡
June 22 Saturday
Buckhurst Park, Withyham
Coombland, Coneyhurst,
  Billingshurst
Dallington Cottage Gardens
Down Place, South Harting ‡
The Manor of Dean, Tillington,
  Petworth
Telegraph House, North Marden,
  nr Chichester ‡
June 23 Sunday
Ambrose Place Back Gardens,
  Worthing ‡
Baker's Farm, Shipley,
  nr Horsham ‡‡
Belsize Road Gardens, Worthing ‡
Berri Court, Yapton
Chidmere House, Chidham
Cobblers, Crowborough
Down Place, South Harting ‡‡‡
6 Holbrook Park, nr Horsham ‡‡
Ketches, Newick
The Manor of Dean, Tillington,
  Petworth
Moat Mill Farm, Mayfield
The Old Vicarage, Firle
Rustington Convalescent Home,
  Rustington ‡
Sherburne House, Eartham
Telegraph House, North Marden,
  nr Chichester ‡‡‡
Town Place, Freshfield,
  nr Sheffield Park

Trotton Old Rectory, nr
  Rogate ‡‡‡
Trotton Place, nr Rogate ‡‡‡
The White House, Burpham,
  nr Arundell
June 24 Monday
Berri Court, Yapton
Chidmere House, Chidham
Clinton Lodge, Fletching
The Manor of Dean, Tillington,
  Petworth
June 25 Tuesday
The White House, Burpham,
  nr Arundel
June 26 Wednesday
Bateman's, Burwash
Clinton Lodge, Fletching
The Old Rectory, Newtimber
June 27 Thursday
Frith Hill, Northchapel
6 Holbrook Park, r Horsham
The Old Rectory, Newtimber
Town Place, Freshfield,
  nr Sheffield Park
June 28 Friday
Casters Brook, Cocking, nr
  Midhurst ‡
Hurst Mill, Petersfield ‡
June 29 Saturday
Bankton Cottage, Crawley Down
Casters Brook, Cocking,
  nr Midhurst ‡
South Harting Gardens,
  Petersfield ‡
June 30 Sunday
Bankton Cottage, Crawley Down
Brighton Gardens, Wayland
  Avenue
Casters Brook, Cocking,
  nr Midhurst ‡
Home Farm House, Buckham Hill ‡‡
Mayfield Cottage Gardens,
  Mayfield
Pheasants Hatch, Newick ‡‡
South Harting Gardens,
  Petersfield ‡
Udimore Gardens, nr Rye
Wilderness Farm, Hadlow Down
July 1 Monday
Casters Brook, Cocking,
  nr Midhurst
Clinton Lodge, Fletching
Home Farm House, Buckham
  Hill ‡
Pheasants Hatch, Newick ‡
July 7 Sunday
Cobblers, Crowborough
Hailsham Grange, Hailsham
North Springs, Fittleworth
Town Place, Freshfield,
  nr Sheffield Park
July 13 Saturday
Bumble Cottage, W Chiltington ‡
Crown House, Eridge

The Manor of Dean, Tillington,
  Petworth
Palmer's Lodge, West Chiltington
  Village ‡
Telegraph House, North Marden,
  nr Chichester
July 14 Sunday
Bates Green Farm, Arlington
Bumble Cottage,W Chiltington ‡
Crown House, Eridge
Fitzhall, Iping, nr Midhurst ‡‡
The Manor of Dean, Tillington,
  Petworth
Nyewood House, Nyewood,
  nr Rogate ‡‡
Nymans, Handcross
Palmer's Lodge, West Chiltington
  Village ‡
Telegraph House, North Marden,
  nr Chichester ‡‡
Wadhurst Gardens, Wadhurst
Warren House, Crowborough
July 15 Monday
The Manor of Dean, Tillington,
  Petworth
Wadhurst Gardens, Wadhurst
July 17 Wednesday
Merriments Gardens, Hurst Green
Middle Coombe, East Grinstead
Nyewood House, Nyewood,
  nr Rogate
July 19 Friday
Pashley Manor, Ticehurst
Wakehurst Place, Ardingly
July 20 Saturday
Bumble Cottage, W Chiltington ‡
Cooksbridge, Fernhurst
Palmer's Lodge, West Chiltington
  Village ‡
July 21 Sunday
Ansty Gardens, nr Haywards Heath
Bumble Cottage, W Chiltington ‡
Cobblers, Crowborough ‡‡
Cooksbridge, Fernhurst
Kingston Gardens, nr Lewes
Moorlands, nr Crowborough ‡‡
Palmer's Lodge, West Chiltington
  Village ‡
July 24 Wednesday
Orchards, Rowfant
July 28 Sunday
Belsize Road Gardens, Worthing
Brickwall, Frewen, Northiam
August 3 Saturday
Neptune House, Cutmill, Bosham
August 4 Sunday
Cobblers, Crowborough
Wilderness Farm, Hadlow Down
August 9 Friday
St Mary's House, Bramber
August 10 Saturday
Champs Hill, Coldwaltham,
  nr Pulborough
St Mary's House, Bramber

August 11 Sunday
Champs Hill, Coldwaltham,
nr Pulborough
Merriments Gardens, Hurst Green
August 16 Friday
Latchetts, Dane Hill, nr Haywards
Heath
August 17 Saturday
Champs Hill, Coldwaltham,
nr Pulborough
Latchetts, Dane Hill, nr Haywards
Heath
The Manor of Dean, Tillington,
Petworth
August 18 Sunday
Champs Hill, Coldwaltham,
nr Pulborough
Cobblers, Crowborough
The Manor of Dean, Tillington,
Petworth
August 19 Monday
The Manor of Dean, Tillington,
Petworth
August 21 Wednesday
Merriments Gardens, Hurst Green
August 25 Sunday
Chidmere House, Chidham
Newtimber Place, Newtimber
August 26 Monday
Chidmere House, Chidham
Cobblers, Crowborough
Orchards, Rowfant
Penns in the Rocks, Groombridge
September 1 Sunday
Bates Green Farm, Arlington
Wilderness Farm, Hadlow Down
September 3 Tuesday
Michelham Priory, Upper Dicker,
Hailsham
September 4 Wednesday
Round Oak, Wadhurst
West Dean Gardens, nr Chichester
September 5 Thursday
Round Oak, Wadhurst

September 7 Saturday
High Beeches Gardens, Handcross
September 8 Sunday
Fitzhall, Iping, nr Midhurst
Merriments Gardens, Hurst Green
September 14 Saturday
The Manor of Dean, Tillington,
Petworth
September 15 Sunday
The Manor of Dean, Tillington,
Petworth
Standen, East Grinstead
September 16 Monday
The Manor of Dean, Tillington,
Petworth
Septmber 18 Wednesday
Houghton Farm, nr Arundel
September 25 Wednesday
Orchards, Rowfant
September 29 Sunday
The Garden in Mind, Stansted
Park
Orchards, Rowfant
September 30 Monday
The Garden in Mind, Stansted
Park
October 5 Saturday
The Manor of Dean, Tillington,
Petworth
October 6 Sunday
Bates Green Farm, Arlington
The Manor of Dean, Tillington,
Petworth
Warren House, Crowborough
October 7 Monday
The Manor of Dean, Tillington,
Petworth
October 9 Wednesday
Orchards, Rowfant
October 12 Saturday
Great Allfields, Petworth
October 16 Wednesday
Sheffield Park Garden,
nr Uckfield

October 20 Sunday
Coates Manor, Fittleworth
October 21 Monday
Coates Manor, Fittleworth
Denmans, Fontwell, nr Arundel
October 27 Sunday
Berri Court, Yapton
October 28 Monday
Berri Court, Yapton

Regular openings
For details see garden description

Borde Hill Garden, nr Haywards
Heath
Great Dixter, Northiam
High Beeches Gardens, Handcross
Merriments Gardens, Hurst Green
Moorlands, nr Crowborough
Parham House & Gardens,
nr Pulborough
Pashley Manor, Ticehurst
St Mary's House, Bramber
Wilderness Farm, Hadlow Down
West Dean Gardens, nr Chichester

By appointment only
*For telephone numbers and other
details see garden descriptions.
Private visits welcomed*

Birch Walk, Fittleworth
Combehurst, Frant
Cowbeech Farm, Rushlake Green
Little Dene, Chelwood Gate
The Old Chalk Pit, Hove
64 Old Shoreham Road, Hove
Rosemary Cottage, Rotherfield
Spur Point, nr Fernhurst
46 Westup Farm Cottages, Balcombe
Whitehouse Cottage, Staplefield
Yew Tree Cottage, Crawley Down

DESCRIPTIONS OF GARDENS

Ambrose Place Back Gardens, Richmond Rd &#
Worthing. Take Broadwater Rd into town centre, turn R at
traffic lights into Richmond Rd opp Library; small town
gardens with entrances on left; parking in rds. TEAS.
*Combined adm £1.25 Chd 25p (Shore to Christ Church
and St Paul's Worthing®). Sun June 23 (11-1, 2-5)*

 No 1 (Mrs M M Rosenberg) Walled garden; shrubs,
pond, climbing plants
 No 3 (Mr & Mrs M Smyth) Paved garden with climbing
plants, lawn and pond
 No 4 (Mr & Mrs T J Worley) Paved garden with raised
herbaceous borders, lawn and flowering summer
plants
 No 5 (Mr & Mrs P Owen) Paved with borders
 No 6 (Mrs Leslie Roberts) Attractive garden with conservatory

 No 7 (Mr & Mrs M Frost) Patio garden, with conservatory
 No 8 (Mr & Mrs P McMonagle) Summer flowering
plants and lawn
 No 10 (Mrs C F Demuth) Paved garden with roses and
interesting trees
 No 11 (Mrs M Stewart) Roses, summerhouse, flowering plants
 No 12 (Mr & Mrs P Bennett) Original paved small garden with trees
 No 14 (Mr & Mrs A H P Humphrey) Roses, flowering
plants, greenhouse and bonsai collection
 Ambrose Villa (Mr & Mrs Frank Leocadi) Italian style
small town garden

¶**Ansty Gardens** &# On A272. 3m W of Haywards
Heath. 1m E of A23. Start in car park signposted in Ansty
village. Coffee, Ploughmans, TEAS at Whydown Cottage.
Combined adm £2 Chd free. Sun July 21 (11-6)

¶**Apple Tree Cottage** (Mr & Mrs Longfield) Cottage garden, herbaceous borders, mature trees
¶**Greenacre** (Mr & Mrs Owen) 2½-acre mixed garden
¶**Brenfield** (Mr & Mrs Mace) Major private collection of cacti and succulents
¶**Netherby** (Mr & Mrs Gilbert) Cottage garden
¶**Whydown Cottage** (Mr & Mrs Gibson) 1-acre woodland garden

Ashburnham Place &&& (Ashburnham Christian Trust) Battle. 5m W of Battle on A271 (formerly B2204). 220 acres of beautifully landscaped gardens with glorious views over 3 lakes designed by George Dance and Capability Brown. Extensive 4-acre walled garden being restored incl newly planted scented garden and kitchen gardens. Peaceful woodland walks. Features from several centuries. Cream TEAS in C18 orangery. *Adm £2 Chd 50p. Wed, Thurs, Fri, Sun June 12, 13, 14, 16 (2-5.30)*

Baker's Farm & (Mr & Mrs Mark Burrell) Shipley, 5m S of Horsham. Take A24 then A272 W, 2nd turn to Dragon's Green, L at George and Dragon then 300yds on L. Large Wealden garden; lake; laburnum tunnel; shrubs, trees, rose walks of old-fashioned roses; scented knot garden and bog gardens. TEAS. *Adm £1.50 Chd 30p (Share to St Mary the Virgin, Shipley®). Suns May 26, June 23 (2-6). Parties by appt, please Tel 01403 741215*

Bankton Cottage & & (Mr & Mrs Robin Lloyd) Crawley Down. 4m W of East Grinstead. 2½m E of M23 (J.10). On B2028 1m N of Turners Hill Xrds. 3½-acre partially walled cottage garden, herbaceous borders, shrub and climbing roses, small lake and pond with bog gardens. Enormous number of terracotta pots planted up, many seconds for sale. TEAS in aid of Cheshire Homes. *Adm £1.50 Chd free. Sat, Sun June 29, 30 (2-6) Parties welcome by appt May to July, please Tel 01342 718907 or 714793*

Bateman's && (The National Trust) Burwash ½m S (A265). From rd leading S from W end of village. Home of Rudyard Kipling from 1902-1936. Garden laid out before he lived in house and planted yew hedges, rose garden, laid paths and made pond. Bridge to mill which grinds local wheat into flour. LUNCHES & TEAS. *Adm £4 Groups 15 or more £3 Chd £2. ▲For NGS Wed June 26 (11-5.30). Parties welcome by appt on open days, please Tel 01435 882302*

Bates Green &&& (Mr & Mrs J R McCutchan) Arlington. 2½m SW of A22 at Hailsham and 2m S Michelham Priory, Upper Dicker. Approach Arlington passing the 'Old Oak Inn' on R continue for 350yds then turn R along a small lane. [TQ5507.] Plantsman's tranquil garden of over 1 acre gives year-round interest; rockery; water; mixed borders with colour themes, and shaded foliage garden. B & B accommodation. TEAS. *Adm £2 Chd free. Suns April 14, July 14, Sept 1, Oct 6 (2.30-5). Private visits welcome, please Tel 01323 482039*

Belsize Road Gardens && Worthing. 10m E of Bognor, 10m W of Brighton. Take Broadwater Rd into town centre. Turn R at traffic lights into Richmond Rd, continue straight for approx 1m. After Heene Rd Xrds/traffic lights take 2nd turning R. Medium-sized part-walled town gardens. TEAS. *Combined adm £1 Chd 50p. Suns June 23, July 28 (1-5)*
     No 10 (Mr Robin Spare) Combined ornamental and vegetable garden, incl conservatory with vine and small greenhouse
     No 12 (Mr P & Mrs C L Pearce) Large variety of perennials, shrubs, climbers, some unusual. Interesting features incl many pots and hanging baskets

Berri Court && (Mr & Mrs J C Turner) Yapton, 5m SW of Arundel. In centre of village between PO & Black Dog public house. A2024 Littlehampton-Chichester rd passes. Intensely planted 3-acre garden of wide interest; trees, flowering shrubs, heathers, eucalyptus, daffodils, shrub roses, hydrangeas and lily ponds. *Adm £1.50 Chd free. Suns, Mons March 31, April 1, May 12, 13; June 23, 24 (2-5); Oct 27, 28 (12-5). Private visits welcome for 4 and more, please Tel 01243 551663*

Bignor Park (The Viscount & Viscountess Mersey) Pulborough, 5m from Petworth on West Burton rd. Nearest village Sutton (Sussex). 11 acres of trees, shrubs, flowers and magnificent views of the South Downs, from Chanctonbury Ring to Bignor Hill. Music in the temple. TEAS. *Adm £2 Chd free. Sun, Mon April 7, 8 (2-5)*

¶**Birch Walk** (Mr & Mrs Martin Paterson) Fittleworth. On B2138, Lower St. Approx 3m from Petworth and Pulborough, 500yds down from junction with A283. Garden concealed from rd. Parking beside the common at top of rd, or by church. The garden is approx 2 acres, partly shaded by many varieties of trees incl tulip, sorbus and magnolia and is devoted to species and hybrid rhododendrons and azaleas, over a carpet of bluebells in season. TEA. *Adm £1 Chd 20p. May 6 to 17 incl except Suns. By appt, please Tel 01798 865355*

● **Borde Hill Garden** && 1½m N of Haywards Heath on Balcombe Rd. Informal garden of great botanical interest and beauty; rare and champion trees and shrubs; extensive views; woodland and lakeside walks, rhododendrons, azaleas, camellias, magnolias, at its best in the spring. Picnic area. Tea rooms, bar and restaurant. *Adm £2 Chd £1. Daily from March 16 to Sept 29 (10-6)*

¶**Brighton Gardens** && 2 gardens in Wayland Ave, off Dyke Road Ave with adequate parking. Teas and plants at 91, 95 Wayland Ave in aid of Coppercliff Hospice. *Combined adm £1.50 Chd 50p. Sun June 30 (2-6)*
     ¶**89 Wayland Avenue** (Brenda & Ron Humphrey) Small, attractive garden. Cottage style planting of trees, shrubs and herbaceous borders, ponds, bog garden, some unusual plants and a variety of planted containers
     ¶**93 Wayland Avenue** (Sylvia & Brian Jackson) Creatively designed small garden, with mixed borders and raised beds, with emphasis on dense, informal planting, incl some unusual plants, shrubs, grasses and many clematis, tender perennials and climbers. Focal points are provided by rose arch and water features with cascades and pools in rockery and bog garden areas. The whole garden is designed to encourage wildlife

Buckhurst Park ❀❀ (Earl & Countess De La Warr) Withyham. On B2110 between Hartfield and Groombridge. Drive adjacent to Dorset Arms public house. Historic garden undergoing complete restoration. Repton park, large lake with woodland walk and ornamental waterfall and rocks created by James Pulham. Terraces, lily pond and pergolas designed by Lutyens and originally planted by Jekyll. Shetland pony stud. TEAS. *Adm £2 Chd £1 (Share to Withyham Recreation Association©). Sat June 22 (2-5.30). Private visits welcome, please* **Tel 01892 770790 or 770220**

Bumble Cottage ❀ (Mr & Mrs D Salisbury-Jones) West Chiltington. 2m E of Pulborough, 2m N of Storrington. From Pulborough turn off A283 E of Pulborough into W Chiltington Rd then R into Monkmead Lane (signed Roundabout Hotel) follow yellow signs. From Storrington take B2139 W into Greenhurst Lane, R at T Junction 100yds fork L into Monkmead Lane then 2nd entrance after Hotel. Charming 'all seasons' garden of 1 acre created from a sandy slope. Wide variety of interesting trees, shrubs and plants combined with ponds all set off by very fine lawn. *Adm £1.50 Chd 25p. Sats, Suns July 13, 14; 20, 21 (2-6)*

Cabbages & Kings see Wilderness Farm

Casters Brook ❀❀ (Mr & Mrs John Whitehorn) Cocking; 3m S of Midhurst at Cocking PO on A286 take sharp turn E; garden is 100yds to right. Interesting 2-acre chalk garden full of surprises; slopes to old mill pond; good collection of old roses; fine downland setting. TEAS. *Adm £1.50 Chd free (Share to Cocking Church®) Fri June 28 (5-7.30) Sat, Sun June 29, 30 (2-6) Mon July 1 (5-7.30) Private visits welcome, please* **Tel 01730 813537**

Cedar Tree Cottage ❀❀ (Mr & Mrs G Goatcher) Rock Rd, Washington. Turn W off A24 ¼m N. of Washington Roundabout. Park in 'Old Nursery' Car Park. Mixed borders with many unusual shrubs and perennials, leading into newly developing 5 acre arboretum with many rare subjects and also some fine mature trees and shrubs dating from early C20. Fine views of S Downs. Picnics welcome. TEAS in aid of Sussex Wildlife Trust *Adm £1.50 Chd free. Sat April 27, Wed May 1, Sun May 5 (2-5.30)*

Champs Hill ❀❀❀ (Mr & Mrs David Bowerman) Coldwaltham, S of Pulborough. From Pulborough on A29, in Coldwaltham turn R to Fittleworth Rd; garden 300yds on R. From Petworth turn off B2138 just S of Fittleworth to Coldwaltham, garden approx ½m on L. 27 acres of formal garden and woodland walks around old sand pit. Conifers and acid-loving plants, many specie heathers labelled. Superb views across Arun valley. Special features. March - Winter heathers and spring flowers. May - rhododendrons, azaleas, wild flowers. August - heathers and other specialities. Tea (March only), TEAS. *Adm £2 Chd free. Suns March 17, 24, Sat, Suns May, 11, 12, 18, 19, Aug 10, 11, 17, 18 (1-6). Private visits welcome for parties of 10 and over, please* **Tel 01798 831868**

Chantry Green House ❀❀ (Mr R S Forrow & Mrs J B McNeil) Steyning. 5m N of Worthing, 10m NW of Brighton off A283. Turn into Church St from High St opp White Horse Inn. Garden 150yds down on LH-side. Parking on Fletchers Croft car park, entrance opp church. An interesting 1-acre garden, recently redesigned by Jack Grant White. Features incl a wall fountain, herbaceous borders and extensive shrub borders with a predominance of colourful evergreens providing interest throughout the year. There is also a small arboretum and rock and water garden. TEAS and plants in aid of NSPCC. *Adm £1.50 Chd 50p. Sat, Sun June 15, 16 (2-5)*

Chidmere House ❀ (Thomas Baxendale Esq) Chidham, 6m W of Chichester. A259 1m Bus: SD276/200 Chichester-Emsworth. Interesting garden; subject of article in 'Country Life'; yew and hornbeam hedges; bulbs, and flowering shrubs bounded by large mere, now a private nature reserve. C16 house (not open). *Adm £1.50 Chd free under 12. Suns, Mons April 7, 8; May 12, 13 (2-6) June 23, 24, Aug 25, 26 (2-7). Parties welcome, please* **Tel 01243 572287 or 573096**

Clinton Lodge ❀❀ (Mr & Mrs H Collum) Fletching, 4m NW of Uckfield; from A272 turn N at Piltdown for Fletching, 1½m. 6-acre formal and romantic garden overlooking parkland with old roses, double herbaceous borders, yew hedges, pleached lime walks, copy of C17 scented herb garden, medieval-style potager, vine and rose allée, wild flower garden. Carolean and Georgian house (not open). TEAS. *Adm £2.50 Chd £1 (Share to Fletching Church Fabric Fund®). Sun June 16; Mons June 17, 24, July 1 Wed June 26 (2-6). Parties over 20 welcome, please* **Tel 01825 722952**

Coates Manor ❀❀ (Mrs G H Thorp) nr Fittleworth. ½m S of Fittleworth; turn off B2138 at signpost marked 'Coates'. 1 acre, mainly shrubs and foliage of special interest. Small walled garden with tender and scented plants. Often featured in UK and foreign gardening magazines. Elizabethan house (not open) scheduled of historic interest. Garden organised by Church of England Children's Society Committee. *Adm £1.50 Chd free. Sun, Mon, Oct 20, 21 (11-5). Private visits welcome, please* **Tel 01798 865356**

Cobblers ❀❀❀ (Mr & Mrs Martin Furniss) Mount Pleasant, Jarvis Brook, Crowborough. A26, at Crowborough Cross take B2100 towards Crowborough Station. At 2nd Xrds turn into Tollwood Rd for ¼m. 2-acre sloping site designed by present owners since 1968 to display outstanding range of herbaceous and shrub species and water garden, giving all season colour. Subject of numerous articles. *Adm £3.50 Chd £1 (incl home-made TEAS). Suns May 12, June 9, 23, July 7, 21, Aug 4, 18; Mons May 27, Aug 26 (2.30-5.30). Groups welcome by appt, please* **Tel 01892 655969**

Cokes Barn ❀❀ (Mr & Mrs Nigel Azis) West Burton. 5m SW of Pulborough-Petworth. At foot of Bury Hill turn W off A29 to West Burton for 1m then follow signs. Just under 1-acre garden around converted barn (1670 not open) which divides into 2 natural spaces: the yard a sheltered enclosure with gravelled areas, mixed shrubs and roses and other traditional cottage perennials. Walls covered in decorative ivies, vines, roses and clematii. 2nd part of garden subdivided by hedges. Planting follows gentle contours; at far end 2 small pools surrounded by damp loving plants. Conservatory on S side of barn. *Adm £1.50 Chd 50p. Sun May 19 (2-5); Mon, Tues May 20, 21 (11-5). Private visits for parties of 4 and over Adm £2, please* **Tel 01798 831636**

Combehurst &❀ (Mrs E E Roberts) 3m S of Tunbridge Wells off A267, 400yds S of B2099. 2½-acre beautifully laid out garden; shrubs, trees, plants. TEAS. *Adm £2 Chd free. Private visits and small coach parties welcome by appt, April to Sept please* **Tel 01892 750367**

Cooke's House &❀ (Miss J B Courtauld) West Burton, 5m SW of Pulborough. Turn off A29 at White Horse, Bury, ¾m. Old garden with views of the Downs, Elizabethan house (not open); varied interest, spring flowers, topiary, herbaceous borders, herbs. Free car park. Tea. *Adm £1.50 Chd free under 14. Suns, Mons, Tues April 21, 22, 23, 28, 29, 30 (2-6). Private visits welcome, please* **Tel 01798 831353**

Cooksbridge ❀❀ (Mr & Mrs N Tonkin) Fernhurst. On A286 between Haslemere and Midhurst, ¾m S of Fernhurst Xrds. 6 acres, and adjoining bluebell wood beside the R Lodd. Pictured in GRBS 1993 Gardens calendar this is a plantsman's garden for all seasons. Features incl the herbaceous border, vine and ornamental plant houses, lily pond and lake with waterfowl. TEAS. *Adm £1.50 Chd 50p 5 and under free (Share to Sussex Wildlife Trust®). Sat, Sun July 20, 21 (2-6). Private visits and groups welcome by appt, please* **Tel 01428 652212**

¶**Cookscroft** &❀ (Mr & Mrs John Williams) Earnley. 6m S of Chichester. At end of Birdham Straight take L fork to E Wittering. 1m on, before sharp bend turn L into Bookers Lane. 2nd house on L. 5-acre garden started from fields 7yrs ago. Many trees grown from provenance seeds or liners. Collections of eucalyptus, birch, snake bark maples and unusual shrubs. 3 ponds with waterfalls and a Japanese garden. An interesting and developing garden, incl a woodland area. TEAS in aid of St Wilfrids Hospice. *Adm £1.50 Chd free. Sun, Mon May 26, 27 (2-6). Private visits welcome by appt, please* **Tel 01243 513671**

Coombland ❀❀ (Mr & Mrs Neville Lee) Coneyhurst. In Billingshurst turn off A29 onto A272 to Haywards Heath; approx 2m, in Coneyhurst, turn S for further ¾m. Large garden of 5 acres developed since 1981 with the help and advice of Graham Stuart Thomas. Undulating site on heavy clay. Old shrub-rose beds, rose species and ramblers scrambling up ageing fruit trees; extensive planting of hardy geraniums; herbaceous border with interesting planting. Oak woodland; orchard dell with hybrid rhododendrons; hostas; primulas and meconopsis. Nightingale wood with water area under development, water wheel recently added leading to 1-acre arboretum. National collection of hardy geraniums held here. TEAS. *Adm £1.50 Chd 50p. Sats June 8, 15, 22 (10-5) Tues June 11 (2-5). Nursery open Mon to Fri (2-4). Parties welcome, please* **Tel 01403 741549**

Cowbeech Farm ❀ (Mrs M Huiskamp) Cowbeech. 4m NE of Hailsham. A271 to Amberstone, turn off N for Cowbeech. 5-acre garden with knot herb garden and water feature. Bog garden with many unusual plants, Japanese garden with bridge, moongate and waterfall - carp and koi carp. Beautiful colours in spring and autumn. Light lunches and farmhouse TEAS. *Adm £2.50 Chd £1.25. Private visits welcome by appt for minimum of 10 May to Oct, please* **Tel 01323 832134**

Crown House &❀❀ (Maj L Cave) Eridge, 3m SW of Tunbridge Wells. A26 Tunbridge Wells-Crowborough rd; in Eridge take Rotherfield turn S, then take 1st R, house 1st on L. 1½ acres with pools; alpine garden; herbaceous border; herb garden; aviary. Full size croquet lawn. Prize winner in Sunday Express garden of the year competition. Plant and produce stalls. TEAS. *Adm £1.50 Chd under 14 free (Share to Multiple Sclerosis®). Sat, Sun July 13, 14 (2-6). Private visits welcome May to Aug, please* **Tel 01892 864389** *or* **864605**

¶**Dallington Cottage Gardens** 6m NW of Battle. 5m E of Heathfield. Turn S off B2096 for ¼m nr school. Cream TEAS. *Combined adm £2.50 Chd under 12 free. Fri, Sat June 21, 22 (11-6)*
    Brookfield (Mr & Mrs John Britten) Approx ⅔-acre, lawns, varied shrubs and clematis collection
    Staces (Mr & Mrs J Steel) Approx ⅔-acre, terraced hillside garden with extensive downland views, old roses, rockery with waterfall

Denmans &❀❀ (Mrs J H Robinson, Mr John Brookes) Denmans Lane, Fontwell. Chichester and Arundel 5m. Turn S on A27 at Denmans Lane, W of Fontwell Racecourse. Renowned gardens extravagantly planted for overall, all-year interest in form, colour and texture; areas of glass for tender species. Plant Centre, Garden Café. *Adm £2.50 OAPs £2.25 Chd £1.50. Groups over 15 persons £1.95.* ▲*Mons March 18, Oct 21 (9-5)*

Down Place ❀❀ (Mr & Mrs D M Thistleton-Smith) 1m E of South Harting. B2124 to Chichester, turn L down unmarked lane below top of hill. This large hillside, chalk garden is surrounded by woodlands, with fine views of surrounding countryside. The garden sweeps down through terraced herbaceous, shrub and rose borders to a natural meadow containing many wild flowers incl several species of orchid. Woodland walks and interesting kitchen and cottage gardens. TEAS. *Adm £1.50 Chd 50p (Share to Harting Parish Church®). Fri, Sat, Sun June 21, 22, 23 (2-6)*

Duckyls ❀ (Lady Taylor) Sharpthorne. 4m SW of E Grinstead. 6m E of Crawley. At Turners Hill take B2028 S 1m fork left to W Hoathly, turn L signed Gravetye Manor. Interesting old 12-acre woodland garden. Partly suitable for wheelchairs. TEAS. *Adm £3 Chd £1 (Share to Elizabeth Fitzroy Homes®). Thurs April 25, May 9, 16, 23, 30; Tues April 30, May 14, 21, 28 (2-5). Parties weclome by appt, please* **Fax/Tel 01342 811038**

Ebbsworth ❀ (Mrs F Lambert) Nutbourne nr Pulborough. Take A283 E from junction with A29 (Swan Corner) 2m with 2 L forks signposted Nutbourne. Pass Rising Sun and follow signs to garden. Charming, well-planted, owner maintained cottage garden, surrounding old cottage. Roses and lilies, together with herbaceous borders. Man-made stream and ponds planted with water plants. Flower arranging demonstration by Brinsbury College students. TEAS. *Adm £1.50 Chd free. Sun, Mon June 16, 17 (2-5)*

Fittleworth Gardens &❀❀ Fittleworth A283 midway Petworth-Pulborough; in Fittleworth turn onto B2138 then turn W at Swan. Car parking available. TEAS and plants in aid of NSPCC and St Mary's Church, Fittleworth. *Combined adm £1.50 Chd free. Sat, Sun May 18, 19 (2-6)*

The Grange & (Mr & Mrs W M Caldwell) 3-acre garden; spring flowering shrubs, specimen trees, herbaceous borders; pond and stream; small walled garden redesigned and replanted 1995. Old roses, clematis and herbaceous
The Hermitage (Mr & Mrs P F Dutton) Charming informal garden; azaleas, rhododendrons sloping to the R Rother with riverside walk and lovely views to the S Downs
Lowerstreet House (L J Holloway Esq) Small garden with shrubs, bulbs, herbaceous

Fitzhall *&* (Mr & Mrs G F Bridger) Iping, 3m W of Midhurst. 1m off A272, signposted Harting Elsted. 9 acres; herb garden; herbaceous and shrub borders; vegetable garden. Farm adjoining. House (not open) originally built 1550. Garden and teas all year round. *Adm £2 Chd £1. For NGS Suns May 19, July 14, Sept 8 (2-6). Private visits welcome please* **Tel 01730 813634**

Frewen College (Brickwall) &* (Frewen Charitable Trust) Northiam. 8m NW of Rye on B2088. Tudor home of Frewen family since 1660. Featured in the filming of 'Cold Comfort Farm'. Gardens and walls built and laid out by Jane Frewen c1680; chess and lavender gardens; arboretum. *Adm £2 Chd £1 under 10 free. Sun July 28 (2-5). Parties welcome of 30 to 50, please* **Tel 01797 223329**

Frith Hill *&&* (Mr & Mrs Peter Warne) Northchapel 7m N of Petworth on A283 turn E in centre of Northchapel into Pipers Lane (by Deep Well Inn) after ¾m turn L into bridleway immed past Peacocks Farm. 1-acre garden, comprising walled gardens with herbaceous border; shrubbery; pond; old-fashioned rose garden and arbour. Herb garden leading to white garden with gazebo. Outstanding views of Sussex Weald. TEAS. *Adm £1.50 Chd free (Share to 1st Northchapel Scouts®). Thurs, Sat, Sun June 2, 20 (2-6) 15, 27 (5-8)*

Frith Lodge (Mr & Mrs Geoffrey Cridland) Northchapel. 7m N of Petworth on A283 turn E in centre of Northchapel into Pipers Lane (by Deep Well Inn) after ¾m turn L into bridleway immediately past Peacocks Farm. 1-acre cottage style garden created around pair of Victorian game-keepers cottages. Undulating ground with roses, informal planting with paved and hedged areas; outstanding views of Sussex Weald. *Adm £1.50 Chd 50p. Sat, Thurs June 15 (5-8) 20 (2-6). Parties welcome, please* **Tel 01428 707241**

The Garden in Mind *&* (Mr & Mrs Ivan Hicks - Stansted Park Foundation) Stansted Park, Rowlands Castle. Follow brown signs. Stansted is 3m NE of Havant, 7m W of Chichester. A surreal symbolic ½-acre walled garden. Began in 1991 as a concept for BBC2 Dream Garden series. Extravagant planting combined with sculpture, assemblage, found objects, mirrors and chance encounters. Wide range of plants; sequioa to sempervivum, marigolds to melianthus, grasses, foliage plants, topiary and tree sculpture. Featured in numerous publications and TV — come with an open mind. *Adm £2.01 Chd donation. Sun June 2 (10-6), Sun, Mon Sept 29, 30 (2-5)*

Gaywood Farm &*&* (Mrs Anthony Charles) nr Pulborough. 3m S of Billingshurst turn L off A29 into Gay

Street Lane. After railway bridge at 2nd junction fork L and at T junction turn L signed 'no through rd'. 2-acre garden, surrounding ancient farm house, built between C14 and C18. Fine weeping Ash, black Mulberry, Irish yews and extravagantly planted borders with interesting plant assoc. Large pond surrounded by good planting. TEAS. Wine (Jun only). *Adm £1.50 Chd free. Sat, Suns, Mon May 5, 26, 27, 28 (2-5) Wed June 12 (5-7.30). Private visits groups only welcome, please* **Tel 01798 812223**

Ghyll Farm Sweethaws Lane *&* (Mr & Mrs I Ball) Crowborough. 1m S of Crowborough centre on A26. L into Sheep Plain Lane immed R Sweethaws Lane ½m. 'The Permissive Garden' planted by the late Lady Pearce. 1-acre, azaleas, camellias, woodland bluebell walk; spectacular views. TEAS. *Adm £1.50 Chd 50p. Suns April 21, May 19; Mon May 6 (2-5.30). Private visits welcome April to end July please* **Tel 01892 655505**

Great Allfields *&&* (Lord & Lady Birkett) Balls Cross. 3m N of Petworth. Take A283 out of Petworth, turn 2nd R signed Balls Cross, Kirdford. At Balls Cross take L turn after Stag Inn to Ebernoe, Northchapel (Pipers Lane) 250yds entrance on R. 1 acre of garden, 2 acres of woodland, plus old walls and barns covered with many interesting climbers; autumn colour. TEAS and light lunches. *Adm £1.50 Chd 50p (Share to Fairbridge®). Sat Oct 12 (10-6). Private visits welcome, please* **Tel 01403 820226** *Also fine evenings in June*

● **Great Dixter** *&&* (Christopher Lloyd) Northiam, ½m N of Northiam, off A28 8m NW of Rye. Buses infrequent 340, 342, 348. Hastings & District. Alight Northiam P Office 500yds. Topiary; wide variety of plants. Historical house open (2-5). *Adm house & garden £3.80 Chd 50p OAPs & NT members (Fris only) £3.30; garden only £2.80 Chd 25p. April 1 to Oct 15 daily except Mons but open on Bank Hols (2-5). Gardens open at 11 on May 25, 26, 27; also Suns in July, Aug; Mon Aug 26*

Greenacres *&&* (Mr & Mrs John Hindley) Crowborough. From A26 at Crowborough Cross take B2100 S. At 1st Xrd R into Montagis Way, then 2nd L into Luxford Rd for ⅓m. 2-acre sloping woodland garden maintained wholly by present owners. Developed over the years with interesting water features fed by natural springs: ponds, bog area, naturalised area, raised island beds. Many trees, shrubs and foliage plants. A tranquil garden with views over countryside. TEA. *Adm £1.50 Chd free. Suns May 19, June 2, 9 (2-6)*

Hailsham Grange &*&* (John Macdonald Esq) Hailsham. Turn off Hailsham High St into Vicarage Rd, park in public car park. Formal garden designed and planted since 1988 in grounds of former C17 Vicarage (not open). A series of garden areas representing a modern interpretation of C18 formality; Gothic summerhouse; pleached hedges; herbaceous borders, romantic planting in separate garden compartments. Featured in Country Living and Grass Roots. Teas in adjacent church in aid of The Children's Society. *Adm £1.50. Suns June 2, July 7 (2-5.30). Private visits welcome, please* **Tel 01323 844248**

Hammerwood House & (The Hon Mrs J Lakin) Iping, 1m N of A272 Midhurst to Petersfield Rd. Approx 3m W of Midhurst. Well signposted. Large informal garden; fine trees, rhododendrons, azaleas, acers, cornus, magnolias; wild garden (¼m away), bluebells, stream. TEAS. *Adm £2 Chd free (Share to King Edward VII Hospital, Midhurst®). Suns May 12, 19 (1.30-5.30)*

● **High Beeches Gardens** ⚹ (High Beeches Gardens Conservation Trust) Situated on B2110 1m E of A23 at Handcross. 20-acres of enchanting landscaped woodland and water gardens; spring daffodils; bluebell and azalea walks; many rare and beautiful plants; wild flower meadows, glorious autumn colours. Picnic area. Car park. *Daily April, May, June, Sept, Oct (1- 5) closed on Weds. Adm £3 Acc chd free (Share to St Mary's Church, Slaugham®). For NGS Sats April 6, Sept 7 (1-5). Also by appt for organised groups at any time, please Tel 01444 400589*

Highdown, Goring-by-Sea &⚹ (Worthing Borough Council) Littlehampton Rd (A259), 3m W of Worthing. Station: Goring-by-Sea, 1m. Famous garden created by Sir F Stern situated in chalk pit and downland area containing a wide collection of plants. Spring bulbs, paeonies, shrubs and trees. Many plants were raised from seed brought from China by great collectors like Wilson, Farrer and Kingdon-Ward. TEAS. *Collecting box. ▲Mons April 8, May 6, 27 (10-8). Parties by appt, please Tel 01903 239999 ext 2544*

6 Holbrook Park &⚹❀ (Mr & Mrs John Pollard) Northlands Road, nr Horsham. 3m N of Horsham. ⅓m N side of A264 Horsham northern bypass. From Horsham drive on to A24 Dorking direction. At roundabout where dual carriage ends on A24 turn R signposted Gatwick. Follow dual carriageway, take 2nd on L marked Northlands Rd. Please park carefully on RH-side of lane. 2½-acre garden on sloping site. Informal areas created in a park-like setting to provide colour and interest throughout the year. Some fine trees, azaleas, rhododendrons, golden shrub border and herbaceous borders; small pond; conservatory. Partially suitable for wheelchairs. TEAS. *Adm £1.50 Chd free. Suns, Thurs May 19, 23, June 23, 27 (2-6). Private visits welcome Thurs pm, April, May, June, please Tel 01403 252491*

Home Farm House ❀ (Mrs P Cooper) Buckham Hill. Uckfield-Isfield back rd. Small attractive cottage garden; interesting shrubs. *Adm £1.25 Chd free. Sun, Mon June 30, July 1 (2-5.30). Private visits also welcome Jan to March to see 20ft mimosa, please Tel 01825 763960. Also open Pheasants Hatch*

Houghton Farm ⚹❀ (Mr & Mrs Michael Lock) Arundel. Turn E off A29 at top of Bury Hill onto B2139 or W from Storrington onto B2139 to Houghton. 1-acre garden with wide variety of shrubs and plants, interesting corners and beautiful views. Tea Houghton Bridge Tea Gardens. *Adm £1 Chd free. Tues April 30, Weds May 22, June 19, Sept 18 (2-5)*

Hurst Mill ⚹ Hurst. 2m SE of Petersfield on B2146 midway between Petersfield and S Harting. 8-acre garden on many levels in lovely position overlooking 4-acre lake in wooded valley with wildfowl. Waterfall and Japanese water garden beside historic mill. Bog garden; large rock garden with orientally inspired plantings; acers, camellias, rhododendrons, azaleas, magnolias, hydrangeas and ferns; shrubs and climbing roses; forest and ornamental trees. TEAS. Wine (June only). *Adm £2.50 Chd free. Suns March 24 (2-5) April 21 (2-6); Fri June 28 (5-7.30)*

Ketches &⚹❀ (David Manwaring Robertson Esq) Newick, 5m W of Uckfield on A272. Take Barcombe Rd S out of Newick, house is on right opp turning to Newick Church. 3 acres; lovely old-fashioned roses; specimen trees; shrub and herbaceous borders. TEAS. *Adm £1.50 Chd free. Sun June 23 (2-6). Parties welcome by appt, mid May to mid July, please Tel 01825 722679*

King Edward VII Hospital & Midhurst. 3m NW of Midhurst. Hospital built early this century, stands in grounds of 152 acres elevated position of great natural beauty; extensive views across Downs. Gardens by Gertrude Jekyll. Aspect over gardens and pine woods little changed. TEAS. *Collecting box. Sats April 27, June 15 (10-4)*

King John's Lodge &⚹❀ (Mr & Mrs R A Cunningham) Etchingham. Burwash to Etchingham on the A265 turn L before Etchingham Church into Church Lane which leads into Sheepstreet Lane after ½m. L after 1m. 3-acre romantic garden surrounding a listed house. Formal garden with water features, wild garden, rose walk, large herbacous borders, old shrub roses and secret garden. B & B accommodation. Garden Statuary for sale. TEAS. *Adm £2 Chd free. Sat, Sun June 8, 9 (11-6). Also private visits welcome, please Tel 01580 819232*

Kingston Gardens ❀ 2½m SW of Lewes. Turn off A27 signposted Kingston at roundabout; at 30 mph sign turn R. Home-made TEAS **Nightingales**. *Combined adm (payable at Nightingales only) £2 Chd free. Suns June 9, July 21 (2-6)*
 Nightingales (Geoff & Jean Hudson) The Avenue. Informal sloping ½-acre garden for all-year interest; wide range of plants incl shrub roses, hardy geraniums, perennials, ground cover. Mediterranean plants, conservatory. Childrens play area. Short steep rough walk or drive, parking limited, to:-
 The White House (John & Sheila Maynard Smith) The Ridge. ½-acre garden on a chalk ridge. Shrubs, herbaceous border, alpines; greenhouse with unusual plants

Knabbs Farmhouse &❀ (Mrs W G Graham) 4m NW of Uckfield; from A272 turn N at Piltdown for Fletching, [TQ430/240] 1½m. Garden at N- end of village and farm. ½-acre informal garden; mixed beds and borders; shrubs, roses, perennials, foliage plants. Good views over ha-ha. TEAS at **Clinton Lodge**. *Adm £1 Chd 20p. Sun, Mon June 16, 17 (2-6). Private visits welcome, please Tel 01825 722198*

By Appointment Gardens. These owners do not have a fixed opening day usually because they do not like crowds or have insufficient parking space. Owner will often give guided tour.

Lane End ✗ (Mrs C J Epril) Sheep Lane, Midhurst. In North St turn L at Knock-hundred Row, L into Sheep lane, L to garden. Park at church or in lane. 2 acres incl wild garden; alpine rockery with pools; rhododendrons, azaleas, heath border. Below ramparts of original castle with fine views over water meadows to ruins of Cowdray House. Tea Midhurst. *Adm £1 Chd free. Sats, Suns, Mons May 25, 26, 27, June 1, 2, 3 (11-6)*

¶**Latchetts** ✗✿ (Mr & Mrs Laurence Hardy) Dane Hill. 5m NE Haywards Heath. SW off A275 into Freshfield Lane. 1m on R. Parking in field. 3-4 acre well maintained country garden still being developed bordering fields and woods. Overlooking lake. Lawns, shrubs, mixed borders, terraces with interesting brick and stone paving, water features, vegetable garden. TEAS. *Adm £2 Chd 50p. Fri, Sat Aug 16, 17 (2-5.30)*

Legsheath Farm &✿ (Mr & Mrs Michael Neal) Legsheath Lane. 2m W of Forest Row, 1m S of Weirwood Reservoir. Panoramic views over reservoir. Exciting 10-acre garden with woodland walks, water gardens and formal borders. Of particular interest, clumps of wild orchids, a fine davidia, acers, eucryphia and rhododendrons. TEAS. *Adm £2 Chd free. Sun May 19 (2-6)*

Lilac Cottage ✗ (Mrs G A Hawkins) Willet Close, Duncton. 3m S of Petworth on the W side of A285 opp entrance to Burton Park. Park in Close. ¼-acre village garden on several levels with shrubs, small trees and approx 90 varieties of shrub and climbing roses and herb garden. TEAS. *Adm 75p. Sat, Sun, Wed June 8, 9, 12 (2-6). Private visits welcome, please Tel 01798 343006*

Little Dene &✗✿ (Prof & Mrs D Anderson) Chelwood Gate. 8m S of East Grinstead. Take A275 off A22 at Wych Cross, then 1st L and 2nd R. Plantsman's garden yr-round interest. Many unusual shrubs and climbers, over 80 clematis, raised alpine bed. *Adm £1.50. Open mid-April to mid-Sept (not Fri). Private visits and parties welcome, please Tel 01825 740657*

Little Hutchings &✗✿ (Mr & Mrs P Hayes) Fontridge Lane, Etchingham. [TQ 708248.] Take A265 to Etchingham from A21 at Hurst Green. 1st turning L after level crossing. R after ½m. Colourful 1½-acre old-fashioned cottage garden laid out over 20 years. At least 300 different roses, over 100 metres of tightly packed herbaceous borders full of many different perennials. Large collection of clematis. Shrubberies containing specimen trees and shrubs. Kitchen garden. TEAS. *Adm £2 Chd free. Sat, Sun June 8, 9 (11-5)*

Little Thakeham ✗✿ (Mr & Mrs T Ratcliff) Storrington. Take A24 S to Worthing and at roundabout 2m S of Ashington return N up A24 for 200yds. Turn L into Rock Rd for 1m. At staggered Xrds turn R into Merrywood Lane and garden is 300yds on R. From Storrington take B2139 to Thakeham. After 1m turn R into Merrywood Lane and garden is 400yds on L. 4- acre garden with paved walks, rose pergola, flowering shrubs, specimen trees, herbaceous borders and carpets of daffodils in spring. The garden laid out to the basic design of Sir Edward Lutyens in 1902 is entering its final year of restoration. All surrounding one of the finest examples of a Sir Edward Lutyens

manor house now a luxurious country house hotel. No toilet fac. House closed to public. Partially suitable for wheelchairs. TEAS. *Adm £2 Chd £1. Tues, Wed April 9, 10; Mon, Tue June 10, 11 (2-5)*

Malt House ✿ (Mr & Mrs Graham Ferguson) Chithurst, Rogate. From A272, 3½m W of Midhurst turn N signposted Chithurst then 1½m; or at Liphook turn off A3 onto old A3 for 2m before turning L to Milland, then follow signs to Chithurst for 1½m. 5 acres; flowering shrubs incl exceptional rhododendrons and azaleas, leading to 50 acres of lovely woodland walks. TEA. *Adm £2 Chd 50p (Share to King Edward VII Hospital Midhurst). Suns April 21, 28; May 5, 12, 19, 26; Mons May 6, 27 (2-6); also private visits welcome for parties or plant sales, please Tel 01730 821433*

The Manor of Dean ✗✿ (Miss S M Mitford) Tillington, 2m W of Petworth. Turn off A272 N at NGS sign. Flowers, shrubs, specimen trees, bulbs in all seasons. A miniature pony, 2 pigmy goats, Vietnamese pigs, tame lambs. House (not open) 1400-1613. TEA 50p. *Adm £1 Chd over 5 50p. Sats, Suns, Mons March 23, 24, 25; April 13, 14, 15; May 18, 19, 20; June 22, 23, 24; July 13, 14, 15; Aug 17, 18, 19; Sept 14, 15, 16; Oct 5, 6, 7 (2-6). Private visits welcome*

Mayfield Cottage Gardens ✗ 8m S of Tunbridge Wells on A267. In Fletching St E off A267 by Marchants Garage signposted Witherenden. *Combined adm £2 Chd 20p. Sun June 30 (2-5.30)*

   Courtney Cottage (Mr & Mrs D Clark) ⅕-acre steeply sloping garden

   Hopton (E Stuart Ogg Esq) ½-acre, Delphinium specialist

   The Oast ✿ (Mr & Mrs R G F Henderson) Charming ½-acre sloping garden, fine views

   Knowle Way (J Freeman Esq) West St. S of High St by Barclays Bank. ¼-acre shrubs and trees

   ¶**The Vicarage St Dunstans Church** (Fr Grant Holmes) High St. ¼-acre terraced. TEAS in aid of Organ Fund

Merriments Gardens &✿ (Mark & Mandy Buchele) Hawkhurst Rd, Hurst Green. Situated between Hawkhurst and Hurst Green. 2m SW Hawkhurst. Young 4-acre garden with richly planted mixed borders in country setting. Ponds, stream and rare plants give beautiful display all season. TEA. *Adm £1.50 Chd free. Open daily April 5 to Oct 6. For NGS Suns May 12; June 9; Aug 11; Sept 8; Weds July 17, Aug 21 (10-5). Parties welcome by appt, please Tel 01580 860666*

¶**Michelham Priory** &✗✿ (Sussex Past) Upper Dicker. 2m W Hailsham, 8m NW Eastbourne. Signposted from A22 and A27. Cradled in beautiful Cuckmere Valley, guarded by the Sussex Downs, the gardens have been carefully designed to complement the historic priory buildings and to allow visitors to relax and enjoy their informal splendour. The 7-acre island site is enclosed by a C14 moat nearly 1m long. The gardens incl an orchard, kitchen garden, water and physic gardens (copying a mediaeval priory garden with medicinal and culinary herbs) and new in 1996 the cloister garden. All-yr colour and interest. TEAS. Garden only *Adm £2 Chd £1 (Share to Sussex Archaeological Society®). Tues April 30, Sept 3 (11-5)*

Middle Coombe &✿❀ (Andrew & Ann Kennedy) From E Grinstead 1½m SW on B2110. Turn L into Coombe Hill Rd. ¼m on L. 4½-acre garden and woodland walk with small lake. Garden designed in Victorian rooms using Agriframes. Formal and informal planting to give all year colour. TEAS. *Adm £2 Chd free. Weds May 8, July 17 (2-5). Parties welcome by appt, please write to Middle Coombe, Coombe Hill Rd, E Grinstead, W Sussex RH19 4LZ*

Moat Mill Farm & (Mr & Mrs C Marshall) Newick Lane, Mayfield. 1m S on Mayfield-Broadoak Rd. 8 acres, formal rose garden, herbaceous border and wild gardens. Nature Trail for Children. Picnic area (12.30-2). TEAS and ice creams. *Adm £1.50 Chd 50p. Sun June 23 (2-5.30)*

Moorlands ❀ (Dr & Mrs Steven Smith) Friar's Gate, 2m N of Crowborough. St Johns Rd to Friar's Gate. Or turn L off B2188 at Friar's Gate. 3 acres set in lush valley adjoining Ashdown Forest; water garden with ponds and streams; primulas, rhododendrons, azaleas, many unusual trees and shrubs. New river walk. TEAS. *Adm £2 OAPs £1.50 Chd free. Every Wed April to Oct 1 (11-5). Suns May 26, June 9, July 21 (2-6). Private visits welcome, please* Tel 01892 652474

¶**Morris Down** ❀ (Mr & Mrs Hugh Dibley) Down St, Piltdown. 8m E Haywards Heath, 3m N Uckfield turn N off A272 for 1m. Parking in field. Established 2-acre garden with outstanding panoramic views, mature and ornamental trees, azalea and rhododendron walk, colourful mixed borders and feature pond. TEAS. *Adm £1.50 Chd free. Sun, Mon May 19, 20 (2-6)*

¶**Mount Harry House & Mount Harry Lodge** & (2 adjoining gardens). 2m NW of Lewes on S of Ditchling Rd B2116, ½m W of A275 (sign Mount Harry Trees at entrance to drive). Coach parking. 7 acres and 1-acre terraced gardens on chalk, herbaceous and shubbery borders, specimen trees, laburnum walks, new walled garden, dell garden, conservatory, ornamental tree nursery in beautiful downland setting. TEA. *Combined adm £2.50 Chd free (Share to St Peter's Church, Hamsey®). Sun June 16 (2-6)*

Mountfield Court &✿ (T Egerton Esq) 2m S of Robertsbridge. On A21 London-Hastings; ½m from Johns Cross. 2-3-acre wild garden; flowering shrubs, rhododendrons, azaleas and camellias; fine trees. Homemade TEAS. *Adm £2 Chd free (Share to All Saints Church Mountfield®). Sun, Mon May 19, 20 (2-6)*

Neptune House ✿❀ (The Hon & Mrs Robin Borwick) Cutmill. From Chichester take A259 to Bosham roundabout, after ½m move into reservation in rd and turn R into Newells Lane. 150yds turn L and park (ample space). From W take A259 through Emsworth. Turn L after Bosham Inn at Chidham into Newells Lane. Garden extended by 3½ acres incl a lake. The R Cut runs through the garden feeding 3 ponds. Planting is being increased, particularly around the lake which is home to various waterfowl. **Pondfield** is adjacent. Live classical music. TEAS with strawberries and cream. *Combined adm with Pondfield £1.50 Chd 50p. Sun June 2 (2-6), Sat Aug 3 (5.30-7.30). Private visits and coach tours welcome April 4 to Sept 30, please* Tel 01243 576900

New Barn &✿ (Mr & Mrs A Tuck) Egdean. 1m S of Petworth turn L off A285, at 2nd Xrds turn R into lane or 1m W of Fittleworth take L fork to Midhurst off A283. 200yds turn L. 2 acres, owner maintained garden round converted C18 barn in farmland setting. Large natural pond and stream, water irises, roses, shrubs and herbaceous; lawns and woodland area. Autumn colour. *Adm £1.50 Chd 20p. Sun, Mon, Tues June 16, 17, 18 (12-5.30) Private visits and small parties welcome Sept 22 to mid-Oct, please* Tel 01798 865502

New Grove &✿ (Mr & Mrs Robert de Pass) Petworth. 1m S of Petworth turn L off A285 and take next L. Follow signs. From the N at Xrds in Petworth straight across into Middle Street then L into High Street follow signs. A mature garden of about 3 acres. Mainly composed of shrubs with all year interest incl a small parterre; magnolias, camellias, azaleas, cornuses, roses etc. lovely views to the South Downs. TEAS in aid of King Edward VII Hospital, Midhurst. *Adm £1.50 Chd free. Suns, Mon April 21, May 19, 20 (2-6)*

Newtimber Place &❀ (Andrew Clay Esq) Newtimber. 7m N of Brighton off A281 between Poynings and Pyecombe. Beautiful C17 moated house. Walled garden, roses, mixed borders and water plants. TEAS in aid of Newtimber Church. *Adm £1.50 Chd 50p. Suns April 21, Aug 25 (2-6)*

North Springs ✿❀ (Mr & Mrs Michael Waring) Fittleworth. Approach either from A272 outside Wisborough Green or A283 at Fittleworth and follow signs. Steep hillside garden with walls, terraces, water gardens and pools, mixed borders containing wide variety of trees, shrubs, herbaceous plants, roses and clematis. *Adm £2 Chd £1. Suns May 19, June 2, July 7 (2-6). Private visits welcome May to Sept please,* Tel 01798 865731

Northwood Farmhouse &✿ (Mrs P Hill) Pulborough. 1m N of Pulborough on A29. Turn NW into Blackgate Lane and follow lane for 2m then follow the signs. Cottage Garden with bulbs, roses, pasture with wild flowers and pond all on Wealded clay surrounding Sussex farmhouse dating from 1420. TEA. *Adm £1. Mon, Tues April 1, 2; June 17, 19 (2-5)*

Nyewood House &❀ (Mr & Mrs Timothy Woodall) Nyewood. From A272 at Rogate take rd signposted Nyewood, S for approx 1¼m. At 40 mph sign on outskirts of Nyewood, turn L signposted Trotton. Garden approx 500yds on R. 3-acre S facing garden recently renovated, with colour planted herbaceous borders, newly planted knot garden, pleaching, rose walk, water feature, and new potager. TEAS. *Adm £1.50 Chd free. Weds May 8, June 12, July 17; Suns June 9, July 14 (2-5.30)*

Nymans &✿❀ (The National Trust) Handcross. On B2114 at Handcross signposted off M23/A23 London-Brighton rd, SE of Handcross. Bus: 137 from Crawley & Haywards Heath [TQ265294]. Glorious herbaceous borders, June borders, old-fashioned rose garden, rare trees and shrubs. New Tea Rooms and shop. *Adm £4.20 Chd £2.10.* ▲*For NGS Suns June 2, July 14 (11-7)*

Offham House &❀ (Mr & Mrs H N A Goodman; Mrs H S Taylor) Offham, 2m N of Lewes on A275. Cooksbridge station ½m. Fountains; flowering trees; double herbaceous border; long paeony bed. Queen Anne house (not open) 1676 with well-knapped flint facade. Featured in George Plumptre's Guide to 200 Gardens in Britain. Home-made TEAS. *Adm £2 Chd over 14 25p (Share to St Peters, Hamsey, Old Church Repairs®). Suns April 21, June 2 (2-6)*

The Old Chalk Pit ❀❀ (Mr & Mrs Hugo Martin) 27 Old Shoreham Road, Hove, E Sussex BN3 6NR. A270. Unexpected, romantic garden redesigned to form 5 differing areas, with white garden, ponds, wildlife and shady places to sit. *Adm £1 Chd 50p. Private visits by written request very welcome*

The Old Rectory, Newtimber &❀ (Lambert & Rosalyn Coles) 7m N of Brighton off A281 between Poynings and Pyecombe. 2 acres with views of South Downs and Newtimber Church. Pond garden, fine tulip tree, perennial borders; combined kitchen and flower garden. TEAS. *Adm £1.50 Chd 50p. Wed, Thurs June 26, 27 (2-6). Parties welcome by appt, please Tel 01273 857288*

64 Old Shoreham Road &❀ (Brian & Muriel Bailey) Hove. A270. Mainly walled garden 12.6metres by 33.6metres on flint and chalk. Alpine bed, arches, bog garden, conservatory, fruit bushes and trees, herb parterre, 2 ponds with fountain and waterfall, pergola, rose arbour, trellises, vegetables. Over 750 different varieties of plants - all named. 100 pots, many containing acid loving plants. *Adm £1 Chd 50p. Private visits by appt welcome evenings and weekends (2-6), please Tel 01273 889247*

The Old Vicarage (Arabella & Charlie Bridge) Firle. 5m SE Lewes on A27 towards Eastbourne. Sign to Firle. 3½-acre garden with downland views. Walled garden with mixed vegetable and flower borders. TEAS. *Adm £1.30 Chd 20p. Sun June 23 (2-5)*

Orchards ❀❀ (Penelope S Hellyer) Rowfant. Wallage Lane off B2028. 8½m N of Haywards Heath, 4½m W of East Grinstead. Garden created by Arthur and Gay Hellyer after 2nd World War. 6 acres mature trees, herbaceous borders, orchard, bluebell wood, heather/conifer garden, rhododendrons and camellias. Yr-round interest. Restoration, redesign and replanting by their daughter. TEA. *Adm £2 Acc chd free. Suns March 24, June 16, Sept 29, Mons April 8, May 6, 27, Aug 26 (11-4) Weds March 27, April 17, July 24, Sept 25, Oct 9 (2-4)*

Palmer's Lodge ❀ (R Hodgson Esq) West Chiltington Village. At Xroads in centre of West Chiltington Village opp Queens Head. 2m E of Pulborough 3m N Storrington. A charming plantsman's ½-acre garden with herbaceous and shrub borders. TEAS in aid of Motor Neurone (14, 21 July only) *Adm £1.50 Chd free. Sats, Suns July 13, 14, 20, 21 (2-6). Private visits welcome following written application (July only)*

Parham House and Gardens & (gdns) ❀ (Hse) ❀ 4m SE of Pulborough on A283 Pulborough-Storrington Rd. Beautiful Elizabethan House with fine collection of portraits, furniture, rare needlework. 4 acres of walled garden; 7 acres pleasure grounds with lake. 'Veronica's Maze' a brick and turf maze designed with the young visitor in mind. Picnic area. Light refreshments. *Open Easter Sun to first Sun in Oct; Weds, Thurs, Suns & Bank Hols. Adm House & garden (1995 rates) £4.25 OAPs £3.75 Chd £2.50. Garden £3 Chd £1.50. For NGS. Wed, Thurs June 5, 6. (Garden & picnic area (1-6), House (2-6) last adm 5)*

Pashley Manor &❀❀ (J Sellick Esq) Ticehurst. 10m S of Tunbridge Wells. 1½m SE Ticehurst on B2099. Pashley Manor is a grade 1 Tudor timber-framed ironmaster's house. Standing in a well timbered park with magnificent views across to Brightling Beacon. The 8 acres of formal garden, dating from the C18, were created in true English romantic style and are planted with many ancient trees and fine shrubs, new plantings over the past decade give additional interest and subtle colouring throughout the year. Waterfalls, ponds and a moat which encircled the original house built 1262. *Adm £3 OAPs £2.50 Chd £1 6 to 14 years, under 6 free. Tues, Wed, Thurs, Sat and Bank Hols April 6 to Sept 28. For NGS Fri July 19 (11-5). TEAS in aid of CRMF. Tel 01580 200692*

Pembury &❀ (Nick & Jane Baker) Clayton. 6m N of Brighton. On B2112, 100yds from A273. Parking on village green; disabled only at garden. Owner maintained 2-acre garden on heavy clay, with fine views of South Downs. Jack and Jill windmills (Jill open pm). Saxon Church with restored wall paintings and children's play area nearby. Light refreshments in village hall in aid of Clayton Church Fund. *Adm £1.50 Chd free. Sun June 2 (11-6)*

Penns in the Rocks &❀ (Lord & Lady Gibson) Groombridge. 7m SW of Tunbridge Wells on Groombridge-Crowborough Rd just S of Plumeyfeather corner. Bus: MD 291 Tunbridge Wells-East Grinstead, alight Plumeyfeather corner, ¾m. Large wild garden with rocks; lake; C18 temple; old walled garden. House (not open) part C18. Dogs under control in park only (no shade in car park). TEAS. *Adm £2 – Up to two chd 50p each, further chd free. Bank Hol Mons April 8, Aug 26 (2.30-5.30). Parties welcome, please Tel 01892 864244*

Petworth House &❀ (The National Trust) Petworth. In centre of Petworth A272/A283. Car park on A283 Northchapel Rd. 30-acre woodland garden of Elizabethan origin and redesigned by 'Capability Brown' in 1751. Millions of daffodils and early wild flowers in March, plus new wild walks through 10,000 trees and shrubs planted since Great Storm. Park also open. 1 guided walk (Adm £2) with NT head gardener and staff at 2pm (about 1½hr) starting from car park kiosk. (House closed). *Adm £1.50 Chd free. Sat March 23 (1-4.30)*

Pheasants Hatch &❀ (Mrs G E Thubron) Piltdown. 3m NW of Uckfield on A272. 2 acres, rose gardens with ponds and fountains; beautiful herbaceous borders; foliage; wild garden; peacocks. TEAS. *Adm £1 Chd free. Sun, Mon June 30, July 1 (2-6.30). Parties welcome June to July, please Tel 01825 722960. Also open Home Farm, Buckham Hill*

Pondfield ♿❀ (Dr & Mrs Peter Sainsbury) Cutmill. E from Chichester, take A259 to Fishbourne and Bosham: over roundabout at Bosham and after ½m move into reservation in rd and turn R into Newells Lane, 150yds turn L and park. From W take A259 to Emsworth. Turn L after the Bosham Inn at Chidham, into Newells Lane. Approx 2 acres laid out by owners with specific emphasis on specimen trees. This garden is very informal with interesting vistas. Neptune House is reached over small bridge. TEAS. *Combined adm with* **Neptune House** *£1.50 Chd 50p. Sun June 2 (2-6)*

¶The Priest House ❀ (Sussex Past) West Hoathly. 4m SW of East Grinstead, 6m E Crawley. At Turners Hill take B2028 S, 1m fork L to West Hoathly, 2m S turn R into North Lane. C15 timber-framed house with small cottage garden. Features large selection of herbs in formal garden plus mixed herbaceous borders with long established yew topiary, box hedges and espalier fruit trees. *Adm £1 Chd free. Thurs May 23, 30 (11-5.30). Also open* **Duckyls**

Priesthawes ♿❀❀ (Mr & Mrs Andrew Wadman) Polegate. On B2104 2½m. S Hailsham 4m N Eastbourne. 1m N of Stone Cross. C15 listed house of historical interest (not open) surrounded by 2½ acres. Walls used to full advantage with large clematis collection, climbers, old roses, herbaceous borders and pergola. Mainly replanted in the last 10 yrs. Lovely views over farmland. Cream TEAS. *Adm £2 Chd free (Share to St Wilfreds Hospice®). Sun, Mon June 16, 17 (2-6). Private visits also welcome mid-May to July, please* **Tel 01323 763228**

¶Rosemary Cottage ❀ (Mr & Mrs D R Coe) Bletchinglye Lane, nr Rotherfield. From Mark Cross on the A267, 9m S of Tunbridge Wells, turn W on the B2100 towards Crowborough, after 1m turn L into Bletchinglye Lane signed as no through rd. 150yds on R. ⅓-acre informal garden with mixed borders, herbs, ponds and paved pathways. The garden is managed following organic principles and incl planting for beneficial insects and wildlife. Interesting vegetable garden based on 4' beds with extensive compost area. TEAS. *Adm £1 Chd 50p. Open by appt May to Sept, please* **Tel 01892 852584**

¶Roundhill Cottage ❀ (Mr Jeremy Adams) East Dean. Take A286 Chichester-Midhurst. At Singleton follow signs to Charlton/East Dean. In East Dean turn R at Hurdlemakers Inn and Roundhill is approx 100yds on R. 1-acre country garden of surprises set in tranquil fold of the South Downs, designed in 1980 by Judith Adams whose inspiration came from French impressionists. *Adm £1.50 Chd free. Mon, Tues May 27, 28 (2-6)*

¶Round Oak ♿❀❀ (Mr & Mrs B J Mitchell) Wadhurst. 6m SE Tunbridge Wells. At Lamberhurst take B2100 off A21. ⅓m after Wadhurst sign turn R at phone box, L into Gloucester Rd, turn R, 200yds on R. 1-acre garden in the early yrs of restoration. Designed to provide all season interest. Wide variety of shrubs, roses and perennials with interesting features incl a secret garden, rockeries and pond. TEAS. *Adm £1 Chd free. Wed, Thurs Sept 4, 5 (10.30-4.30)*

Rustington Convalescent Home ♿❀ (Worshipful Company of Carpenters). On seafront 1m E of Littlehampton and ½m S of Rustington on B2140. A Grade 11 listed convalescent home built and endowed by Sir Henry Har-

ben, founder of the Prudential Assurance Company in 1897. 6 acres with grass frontage to the seafront, with a variety of herbaceous borders and roses largely within the shelter of hedges from the sea winds. Extensive vegetable gardens beautifully maintained which serve the Home. TEAS. *Adm £1 Chd 50p. Sun June 23 (2-6)*

St Marys House ♿❀ (Mr Peter Thorogood) Bramber. 10m NW of Brighton in Bramber Village off A283 or 1m E of Steyning. Medium-sized formal gardens with amusing topiary, large example of living-fossil Gingko tree and Magnolia Grandiflora; pools and fountains, ancient ivy-clad 'Monk's Walk', all surrounding listed Grade I C15 timber-framed medieval house, once a monastic inn. TEAS. *(House open but not in aid of NGS) Easter to Sept 30, Suns and Thurs (2-6). For NGS garden only Adm £1 Chd 50p. Fri, Sat Aug 9, 10 (2-5.30)*

Selehurst ❀❀ (Mr & Mrs M Prideaux) Lower Beeding, 4½m S of Horsham on A281 opp Leonardslee. Large woodland garden recently extended with a chain of five ponds and a romantic bridge. Newly rediscovered Victorian waterfall restored. Fine collection of camellia, azaleas, rhododendrons; walled garden, 60' laburnum tunnel underplanted with cream and silver, fine views. TEAS. *Adm £1.50 Chd free (Share to St. John's Church, Coolhurst®). Sat May 11 (1-5)*

Sennicotts ♿❀ (John Rank Esq) Chichester. From Chichester take B2178 signed to Funtington for 2m. Entrance on R. Long drive ample parking near house. From Fishborne turn N marked Roman Palace then straight on until T junction. Entrance opp. 6-acre mature garden with intriguing spaces, lawns, rhododendrons and azaleas. Large walled kitchen and cutting garden, greenhouses and orchard. TEAS. *Adm £1.50 Chd free (Share to Garden History Society®). Sun, Mon May 19, 20 (2-6)*

Sheffield Park Garden ♿❀ (The National Trust) Midway between E Grinstead and Lewes, 5m NW of Uckfield; E of A275. The garden, with 5 lakes, was laid out by Capability Brown in C18, greatly modified early in the C20. Many rare trees, shrubs and fine waterlilies; the garden is beautiful at all times of year. Teas Oak Hall (not NT). *Adm £4 Chd £2.* ▲*For NGS Weds May 15, Oct 16 (11- 6) last adm 5*

Sherburne House ♿❀❀ (Mr & Mrs Angus Hewat) Eartham, 6m NE of Chichester, approach from A27 Chichester-Arundel Rd or A285 Chichester-Petworth Rd, nr centre of village, 200yds S of church. Chalk garden of about 2 acres facing SW. Shrub and climbing roses; lime-tolerant shrubs; herbaceous, grey-leaved and foliage plants, pots; water feature; small herb garden, kitchen garden potager and conservatory. TEAS. *Adm £1.50 Chd 50p. Sun June 23 (2-6)*

Somerset Lodge (Mr & Mrs R Harris) North St, Petworth. On A283 and A272 100 yds N of church. Parking in town car park. Charming ½-acre town garden with ponds and walled kitchen garden, small collections of old and English roses and wildflower garden. Cleverly landscaped on slope with beautiful views. TEAS. *Adm £1 Chd 25p (Share to the Petworth Cottage Trust®). Sat, Sun June 8, 9, 15, 16, (12-6), Weds June 12, 19 (2-6). Parties by appointment, please* **Tel 01798 343842**

¶**South Harting Gardens** 4m SE of Petersfield from B2146 take turning signed Nyewood-Rogate. Cream TEAS at Pyramids. *Combined adm £1.50 Chd 50p. Sat, Sun June 29, 30 (2-6)*

¶¶**Ivy House** &% (Mr & Mrs David Summerhayes) At S end of village opp Harting Church on B2136. 1½-acre terraced village garden, sloping down to brook with orchard and paddock beyond, Specimen trees, shrubs and roses. Views to Harting Down

¶**The Old House** (Captain & Mrs Duncan Knight) The Street. Small village walled garden. Herbaceous borders, roses and delphiniums

Pyramids &%❀ (Mrs S J Morgan) 200yds on R up North Lane. ½-acre with mainly chalk loving plants; old-fashioned roses, rose arbour; pool; uniquely shaped old apple trees. Interesting modern house (designed 1965 by Stout & Lichfield) linked to garden by paved areas. Fine views

Spur Point %❀ (Mr & Mrs T D Bishop) Marley Heights, Kingsley Green. Plantsman's garden created by owners since 1970. 3 acres of S facing terraces containing rhododendrons, azaleas, roses, mixed borders and scree beds. Not suitable for children. *Adm £2. Private visits welcome May to June by individuals, and parties of no more than 20, please* **Tel 01428 643050**

Standen % (The National Trust) 1½m from East Grinstead. Signed from B2110 and A22 at Felbridge. Hillside garden of 10½-acres with beautiful views over the Medway Valley. Partly suitable for wheelchairs. TEAS. *Adm £3 Chd £1.50.* ▲*Suns May 5, Sept 15 (12.30-6 Last adm 5pm)*

Stonehurst ❀ (Mr D R Strauss) Ardingly. 1m N of Ardingly. Entrance 800yds N of S of England showground, on B2028. 30-acre garden set in secluded woodland valley. Many interesting and unusual landscape features; chain of man made lakes and waterfalls; natural sandstone rock outcrops and a fine collection of trees and shrubs. TEAS. *Adm £2.50 Chd £1 (Share to Homelife®). Mons April 8, May 6, Sun April 21 (11-5)*

Telegraph House ❀ (Mr & Mrs David Gault) North Marden, 9m NW of Chichester. Entrance on B2141. From Petersfield to South Marden for 2m. From Chichester via A286 for 4m N of Lavant turn W on to B2141. 1-acre enclosed chalk garden 700 ft asl; chalk-tolerant shrubs, shrub roses, herbaceous plants; 1m avenue of copper beeches; walks through 150-acre yew wood; lovely views. TEAS. *Adm £1.50 Chd 75p. Sats, Suns June 22, 23; July 13, 14 (2-6). Also private visits welcome May to Aug (2-5), please* **Tel 01730 825206**

Tinkers Bridge Cottage ❀ (Mr & Mrs Michael Landsberg) Ticehurst. From B2099 1m W Ticehurst; turn N to Three Leg Cross for 1m; R after Bull Inn. House at bottom of hill. 12 acres attractively landscaped; stream garden nr the house leading to herbaceous borders, newly planted trees and shrubs, pond, wild flower meadow and woodland with bluebell walk. *Adm £1.50 to incl TEA Chd 25p. Sun May 12 (2.30-5.30)*

¶**Town Place** &%❀ (Mr & Mrs A C O McGrath) Freshfield. 3m E Haywards Heath. From A275 turn W at Shef-field Green into Ketches Lane for Lindfield. 1¾m on L. 3 acres with sunken rose garden, 150' herbaceous border, walled herb and shrub rose gardens, shrubbery, ancient hollow oak, orchard and spring-cabbage patch. C17 Sussex farmhouse (not open). TEAS. *Adm £2 Chd free (Share to St Peter & St James Home & Hospice®). Thurs June 13, 27, Suns June 23, July 7 (2-6) Groups welcome by appt, please* **Tel 01825 790221**

Trotton Old Rectory %❀ (Captain & Mrs John Pilley) nr Petersfield 3m W of Midhurst on A272. This typical English garden with its rose beds designed by Hazel Le Rougetel, framed in box and yew, has 2 levels with beautiful and interesting trees and shrubs running down to a lake and the R Rother. Plants for sale in the adjoining vegetable garden. *Adm £1.50 Chd 50p. Suns May 19, June 23 (2-6)*

Trotton Place &% (Mr & Mrs N J F Cartwright) 3½m W of Midhurst on A272. Entrance next to church. Garden of over 4 acres surrounding C18 house (not open). Walled fruit and vegetable garden; C17 dovecote with small knot garden. Fine trees; mature borders with shrub roses; lake and woodland walk. TEAS in aid of Trotton Church PCC. *Adm £1.50 Chd free. Suns May 19, June 23 (2-5.30)*

Udimore Gardens %❀ 4m from Broad Oak Xrds, 2½m from Rye on B2089. 3 contrasting gardens with views of the beautiful unspoilt Tillingbourne Valley. TEAS and swimming at White Fox Lodge. *Adm £2 Chd free. Sun June 30 (2-6)*

   The Hammonds (Prince & Princess Romanov) Georgian walled rose garden, large Victorian walled kitchen garden

   Wick Farm (Mr & Mrs R Mair) Long established terraced farm garden with old-fashioned roses, herbaceous borders, 200-yr-old weeping ash tree

   White Fox Lodge (Mrs J Horniblow) Garden designed by Sylvia Crowe, large shrub planting and old-fashioned roses

Uppark &% (The National Trust) 5m SE of Petersfield on B2146, 1½m S of S Harting. Fine late C17 house situated high on the South Downs with magnificent views towards the Solent. Garden replanned and replanted since major fire in 1989. Woodland walk. Shop. TEAS. *Garden only open. Collection for NGS Adm £2.50 Chd £1.25. Fri June 21 (2-5)*

Upper House % (Mr & Mrs C M Humber) West Burton. 5m SW of Pulborough, R off A29 at Bury-West Burton Xrds; garden is ½m from Roman Villa at Bignor. Large garden, formal yew lawn, interesting roses, walled garden incl herbs and raised beds, water garden; many unusual plants, shrubs, large Victorian greenhouse. TEAS. *Adm £1.50 Chd free. Sun, Mon, Tues, Wed June 16, 17, 18, 19 (10-6). Private visits welcome, please* **Tel 01798 831604**

The National Gardens Scheme is a charity which traces its origins back to 1927. Since then it has raised a total of over £14 million for charitable purposes.

Wadhurst Gardens *&❀* 6m SE of Tunbridge Wells. 3 gardens all created by present owners. *Combined adm £2.50 Chd free. Sun, Mon July 14, 15 (2-5.30)*
   Sunnymead (Mr & Mrs D Goldsmith) On B2099 ¾m SE Wadhurst Station at junction of Tapsells Lane. 1¼-acre landscaped garden imaginatively designed for the sporting family, small kitchen garden
   The Robins (Mr & Mrs D G Leney) Mayfield Lane. ⅓m on L on B2100 going SW to Mark Cross from junction with B2099. ¾-acre garden created in 1991 with many unusual shrubs and beautifully planted pond
   Westerleigh (Mr & Mrs M R Toynbee) Mayfield Lane. ⅔m on R on B2100 going SW to Mark Cross from junction with B2099. 5-acre garden opening again after re-creation of enlarged herbaceous and shrub border and gravel gardens. Kitchen garden. Beautiful views. TEAS

Wadhurst Park *&❀* (Dr & Mrs H Rausing) Wadhurst. 6m SE of Tunbridge Wells. Turn R along Mayfield Lane off B2099 at NW end of Wadhurst. L by Best Beech public house, L at Riseden Rd. 800-acres park with 7 different species of deer. Re-created garden on C19 site; restored C19 conservatories. Trailer rides into park. TEAS. *Adm £2 Chd 50p. Sun April 28 (2-5.30)*

Wakehurst Place *&&* (National Trust & Royal Botanic Gardens, Kew) Ardingly, 5m N of Haywards Heath on B2028. National botanic garden noted for one of the finest collections of rare trees and flowering shrubs amidst exceptional natural beauty. Walled gardens, heath garden, Pinetum, scenic walks through steep wooded valley with lakes, attractive water courses and large bog garden. Guided tours 11.30 & 2.30 most weekends, also pre-booked tours. The ranger **Tel 01444 892701**. Restaurant. *Adm £4 OAPs/Students/Chd £2 under 5's free.* ▲*For NGS Fri July 19 (10-7)*

Warren House *&❀* (Mr & Mrs M J Hands) Warren Rd, Crowborough. From Crowborough Cross take A26 towards Uckfield. 4th turning on R. 1m down Warren Rd. Beware speed ramps. 9-acre garden with views over Ashdown Forest. Series of gardens old and new, displaying a wealth of azaleas, rhododendrons, impressive trees and shrubs. Sweeping lawns framed by delightful walls and terraces, woodlands, ponds and ducks. Planted and maintained solely by owner. TEA. *Adm £2 Chd free. Suns May 5, 12; June 9, 16; July 14; Oct 6; Mon May 27 (2-5). Groups welcome by appt, please* **Tel 01892 663502**

West Dean Gardens *&&❀* (Edward James Foundation) On A286, 5m N of Chichester. Historic garden of 35 acres in tranquil downland setting. Noted for its 300' long Harold Peto pergola, mixed and herbaceous borders, rustic summerhouses, water garden and specimen trees. Newly restored 2½-acre walled garden contains fruit collection, 13 Victorian glasshouses, apple store, large working kitchen garden and a tool and mower collection. Circuit walk (2¼m) climbs through parkland to 45-acre St Roches Arboretum with its varied collection of trees and shrubs. TEAS. *Adm £3 OAP £2.50 Chd £1.50. Prebooked parties over 20, £2.50, March 2 to Nov 3 (11-5). For NGS Weds April 24, Sept 4 (11-5)*

46 Westup Farm Cottages *&❀* (Chris & Pat Cornwell) Balcombe. Midway Cuckfield and Crawley. 1¼m Balcombe Station off B2036. Telephone for further directions. Well stocked cottage garden, designed to provide yr-round interest in idyllic setting. *Adm £1 Chd free. Private visits incl parties welcome all yr, please* **Tel 01444 811891**

Whitehouse Cottage (Barry Gray Esq) Staplefield Lane, Staplefield 5m NW of Haywards Heath. Garden is ⅓m. E of A23; and 2m S of Handcross. In Staplefield at Xrds by cricket pavilion take turning marked Staplefield Lane for 1m. Large garden with mixed shrubs, old roses; woodland path beside stream linked by ponds; interesting paved and planted areas around house. TEAS. *Adm £1.50 Chd 50p. Private visits welcome, please* **Tel 01444 461229**

The White House *&* (Elizabeth Woodhouse) Burpham. Turn off A27 Arundel-Worthing Rd ½ S of Arundel. Proceed through Wepham to Burpham for 2m. Charming garden planned and planted by practicing garden designer artist. Great attention to plant forms and colour associations. New wild garden with pond and poisonous plants, not suitable for children. TEAS. Wine (Tues only). *Adm £1 (Share to Arundel Cathedral Organ Fund®). Suns June 9, 23 (2.30-6), Tues June 25 (5.30-7.30). Private visits welcome, please write for appt*

Wilderness Farm *&❀* (Andrew & Ryl Nowell of Cabbages & Kings) Hadlow Down. ½m S of A272 from village. A charming terraced garden, converted from a derelict farmyard, forms the centrepiece of a garden designed by owner/designer Ryl Nowell. Richly planted with herbaceous plants and grasses. Shrubberies at the edge of the garden merge imperceptibly with the spectacular Wealden landscape. In adjoining buildings, an exhibition explains design ideas; demonstrates the use of materials and plants, and displays English hand-crafted furniture, pots and sculpture. TEAS. *Adm £2 Chd £1. Open Fri, Sat, Sun April to Sept (10-5). For NGS Suns June 30, Aug 4, Sept 1 (2-6) Private visits by appt welcome, please* **Tel 01825 830552**

Winchelsea Gardens *&* S of Rye. TEAS at Five Chimneys. *Combined adm £2 Chd 75p. Sat June 15 (2-6)*
   The Armoury (Mr & Mrs T Jasper) ½-acre old walled garden being re-developed
   Cleveland House (Mr & Mrs S Jempson) 1½-acre semi-formal walled garden, many varied plants, ornamental trees, water feature, beautiful views, swimming in heated pool
   Firebrand (Mr & Mrs R Comotto) Well hidden from street, visitors will be surprised to find this newly planted garden, roses, wooded glade around lawn
   Five Chimneys (Mr & Mrs Dominic Leahy) Formal town garden
   Nesbit (Mr & Mrs G Botterell) Formal enclosed ¼-acre garden, many and varied plants
   Old Castle House (Mr & Mrs R Packard) Walled garden with roses, varied trees and shrubs
   The Old Rectory (June & Denis Hyson) ½-acre of open lawn garden with views overlooking the Brede Valley

No 1 Trojans Plat (Mr & Mrs Norman Turner) C13 Grade 11 listed archway providing access to small garden of great variety

Woodstock ⚘ (Group Captain A R Gordon-Cumming) West Broyle. From roundabout N of Chichester take B2178 (Funtingdon) rd NW for 1⅓m. Turn L into Pine Grove and after 100yds R into West Way. Woodstock is at far end. ⅔-acre mainly woodland garden specialising in ground cover plants, camellias, asiatic primulas and hostas. TEAS at The Spinney in aid of Save the Children Fund. *Adm £1.50 Chd free. Sun May 19 (1.30-5.30). Private visits welcome mid March to mid July, please* **Tel 01243 776413**

Yew Tree Cottage (Mrs K Hudson) Crawley Down. 4m W of East Grinstead. 2½m E of M23 (J10). On B2028 N of Turners Hill. ¼-acre garden planted for yr round interest and easy management. Featured in RHS 1989 and book 'Cottage Garden'. *Adm £1 Chd free. Parties welcome May to July, please* **Tel 01342 714633**

Warwickshire & West Midlands

Hon County Organiser:	Mrs D L Burbidge, Cedar House, Wasperton, Warwick CV35 8EB
Assistant Hon County Organiser:	Mrs C R King-Farlow, 8 Vicarage Road, Edgbaston, Birmingham B15 3EF
	Mrs Michael Perry, Sherbourne Manor, Sherbourne, Warwick CV35 8AP
Hon County Treasurer:	Michael Pitts, Hickecroft, Mill Lane, Rowington, Warwickshire CV35 7DQ

DATES OF OPENING

March 3 Sunday
Birmingham Botanical Gardens & Glasshouses
March 24 Sunday
Elm Close, Welford-on-Avon
March 31 Sunday
Elm Close, Welford-on-Avon
April 7 Sunday
Alveston Gardens
April 13 Saturday
Castle Bromwich Hall Gardens Trust, Castle Bromwich
April 14 Sunday
Greenlands, Wellesbourne
Ilmington Gardens
Ivy Lodge, Radway
April 21 Sunday
The Mill Garden, Warwick
Moseley Gardens
April 28 Sunday
The Hiller Garden & Dunnington Heath Farm
Ryton Organic Gardens, nr Coventry
May 5 Sunday
55 Elizabeth Road, Moseley, Birmingham
Greenlands, Wellesbourne
Idlicote Gardens, Shipston-on-Stour
May 8 Wednesday
55 Elizabeth Road, Moseley, Birmingham

89 Harts Green Road, Harborne
May 12 Sunday
Brook Farm, Abbots Salford
The Mill Garden, Warwick
May 13 Monday
Arbury Hall, Nuneaton
May 15 Wednesday
Brook Farm, Abbots Salford
May 19 Sunday
Ilmington Manor, Ilmington
Pear Tree Cottage, Ilmington
Wroxall Abbey School, nr Warwick
May 26 Sunday
52 Tenbury Road, Kings Heath, Birmingham
Warwickshire Constabulary Headquarters
May 27 Monday
Balsall Common Gardens, Balsall Common
Cedar House, Wasperton, nr Warwick
June 2 Sunday
Bodymoor Green Farm, Kingsbury
Loxley Hall, nr Stratford-on-Avon
Maxstoke Castle, nr Coleshill
Packington Hall, Meriden
June 4 Tuesday
Baddesley Clinton
Packwood House, nt Hockley Heath
June 8 Saturday
Hunningham Village Gardens

June 9 Sunday
Brook Farm, Abbots Salford
Hunningham Village Gardens
June 12 Wednesday
Brook Farm, Abbots Salford
The Folly Lodge, Halford
89 Harts Green Road, Harborne
June 16 Sunday
Dorsington Gardens
55 Elizabeth Road, Moseley, Birmingham
Holywell Gardens, nr Claverdon
The Mill Garden, Warwick
Shrewley Pools Farm, Haseley
Whichford & Ascott Gardens
June 22 Saturday
17 Gerrard Street, Warwick
Hickecroft, Rowington
June 23 Sunday
Alscot Park, nr Stratford-on-Avon
The Bevingtons, Ilmington
Compton Scorpion Farm, nr Ilmington
The Folly Lodge, Halford
17 Gerrard Street, Warwick
Hickecroft, Rowington
Ilmington Manor, Shipston-on-Stour
The Lord Leycester Hospital, Warwick
Paxford, Leamington Road, Princethorpe
Sherbourne Manor, nr Warwick
50 Wellington Road, Edgbaston

June 29 Saturday
Coughton Court, Alcester
52 Tenbury Road, Kings Heath,
Birmingham
June 30 Sunday
Alveston Gardens
Bodymoor Green Farm, Kingsbury
Honington Village Gardens
Orchard Cottage, Hurley
Pereira Road Gardens
Roseberry Cottage, Fillongley
120 Russell Road, Hall Green
8 Vicarage Road, Edgbaston
July 3 Wednesday
The Folly Lodge, Halford
52 Tenbury Road, Kings Heath,
Birmingham
July 7 Sunday
Alscot Park, nr Stratford-on-Avon
Avon Dassett Gardens
The Hiller Garden & Dunnington
Heath Farm
Ilmington Manor,
Shipston-on-Stour
Upton House, nr Banbury
July 8 Monday
Arbury Hall, Nuneaton
July 10 Wednesday
Charlecote Park, Warwick
89 Harts Green Road, Harborne
July 14 Sunday
Brook Farm, Abbots Salford
Martineau Centre Gardens,
Edgbaston

Moseley Gardens
Orchard Cottage, Hurley
Warmington Village Gardens
July 17 Wednesday
Brook Farm, Abbots Salford
The Folly Lodge, Halford
July 21 Sunday
The Mill Garden, Warwick
26 Sunnybank Road,
Wylde Green
July 28 Sunday
55 Elizabeth Road, Moseley,
Birmingham
Greenlands, Wellesbourne
Paxford, Leamington Road,
Princethorpe
August 4 Sunday
Alne View, Pathlow, nr
Stratford-on-Avon
August 11 Sunday
4 Arnold Villas, Rugby
2 Paddox House, Hillmorton
August 18 Sunday
The Hiller Garden & Dunnington
Heath Farm
The Mill Garden, Warwick
August 25 Sunday
Greenlands, Wellesbourne
September 8 Sunday
Wheelwright House, Long
Compton
September 15 Sunday
The Mill Garden, Warwick
Tysoe Manor, Warwick

September 28 Saturday
Castle Bromwich Hall Gardens
Trust, Castle Bromwich
September 29 Sunday
Birmingham Botanical Gardens &
Glasshouses
Ryton Organic Gardens,
nr Coventry
October 13 Sunday
The Hiller Garden & Dunnington
Heath Farm
The Mill Garden, Warwick

Regular openings
For details see garden description

Birmingham Botanical Gardens &
Greenhouses, Edgbaston
The Mill Garden, Warwick
Ryton Organic Gardens, nr Coventry

By appointment only
*For telephone numbers and other
details see garden descriptions.
Private visits welcomed*

11 Hillwood Common Road, Four
Oaks
Sherbourne Park, nr Warwick
Woodpeckers, Bidford-on-Avon

DESCRIPTIONS OF GARDENS

¶**Alne View** &♣❀ (Mrs E Butterworth) Pathlow 5m from Henley-in-Arden; 3m N of Stratford on the A3400. Approx ⅓-acre. Shrubs, perennials, 2 small ponds and rockery. Aviary, collection of fuchsia, greenhouses. TEAS. *Adm £1.50 Chd free (Share to Wilmcote CE J & I School©). Sun Aug 4 (2-5)*

Alscot Park &❀ (Mrs James West) 2½m S of Stratford-on-Avon A3400. Fairly large garden; extensive lawns, shrub roses, new lavender parterre planted in 1995. fine trees, orangery, with C18 Gothic house (not open), river, deer park, lakes. TEAS in aid of Warwickshire Assoc of Boys Clubs. *Adm £1.50 Chd free. Suns June 23, July 7 (2-6)*

Alveston Gardens &♣❀ 2m NE of Stratford-upon-Avon. Turn left at War Memorial off B4086 Stratford-Wellesbourne rd; Alveston ¼m. TEAS at The Malt House in aid of Alveston WI. *Combined adm £1.50. Sun June 30 (2-6)*
  The Bower House (Mr & Mrs P S Hart) 1 acre, owner-designed, unusual trees, water garden and rockeries. Pergolas, alpine sinks, choice shrubs. *Also open Sun April 7 (2-5) with* **Parham Lodge** *(no teas). Combined adm £1*

Court Leys (Mr & Mrs E Barnard) 1 acre; shrubs, trees and herbaceous borders, circular raised brick planters, conservatory
Long Acre (Dr & Mrs N A Woodward) Owner designed, 1 acre; interesting trees, shrubs and roses; rockery, barbecue area, pergola, terraces and ponds
Parham Lodge (Mr & Mrs K C Edwards) 1 acre organic garden; designed by owners. Choice trees, shrubs; plants, bulbs; island beds, heathers, large pond, patios, tubs, rose garden

¶**Arbury Hall** ❀ (Rt Hon The Viscount Daventry) Nuneaton, 3m SW of Nuneaton off the B4102 (Junction 3 M6/A444). Free Car Park. Delightful 10 acre garden with a sense of peace. Bulbs at start of season, followed by rhododendrons, azalea and wisteria, then roses in June and autumn colours from trees and shrubs. Formal rose garden. Lakes with wildfowl. Bluebell woods. Pollarded limes and arboretum in old walled garden. *Adm to Hall & Gardens £3.50 Chd £2. Gardens only £2 Chd £1. Easter Sun to last Sun in Sept. Hall, Suns and Bank Hol Mons. Gardens, Suns, Mons. For NGS Mons May 13, July 8 (2-6)*

Regular Openers. See end of county section.

¶4 Arnold Villas ✂ (Mr P Pratt) Rugby. From Paddox House, Dunsmore Avenue continue along A428 towards Rugby for approx 1¼m. After roundabout take 1st L into Horton Crescent. Cross A428 and follow signs to Church Walk. Arnold Villas on R. Secluded small town garden specialising in exotic, tender trees, shrubs and unusual plants, incl palms, agave and varied climbers. *Combined adm with* **2 Paddox House** *£2 Chd free. Sun Aug 11 (2-5.30)*

Avon Dassett Gardens ♿❀ 7m N of Banbury off B4100 (use Exit 12 of M40). Car parking in the village and in car park at top of hill. TEAS at **Old Mill Cottage**. *Combined adm £2 Chd free (Share to Myton Hamlet Hospice®). Sun July 7 (2-6). Coaches welcome, please* **Tel 01295 690643**

Hill Top Farm (Mrs N & Mr D Hicks) 1-acre garden. Dramatic display of bedding plants, perennials and roses. Extensive kitchen garden. Greenhouses

Old Mill Cottage (Mr & Mrs M Lewis) Conservation garden of ½ acre with shrubs, perennial borders and rockeries. Collection alpines and herbs. Two ponds and kitchen garden. Newly planted tropical garden

Old Pumphouse Cottage (Mr & Mrs W Wormell) Cottage garden with mixed borders featuring varieties of pinks and shrub roses and clematis. Kitchen garden and greenhouse

The Old Rectory (Mrs L Hope-Frost) 2-acre garden surrounding listed building mentioned in Doomsday Book (not open). Large variety of fine trees and shrubs. Small wood

The Coach House (Mr & Mrs G Rice) 2-acre former Victorian kitchen garden. Woodland area. Extensive new planting

Baddesley Clinton ♿✂ (The National Trust) ¾m W off A4141 Warwick-Birmingham rd near Chadwick End. 7½m NW of Warwick. Mediaeval moated manor house little changed since 1633; walled garden and herbaceous borders; natural areas; lakeside walk. Lunches and TEAS. *Adm Grounds only £2.25 Chd £1.10. Shop and restaurant open from noon. ▲For NGS Tues June 4 (2-5.30) with* **Packwood House**

Balsall Common Gardens ♿✂❀ Balsall Common. 5m S of M42/M6 intersection, 6m W of Coventry, 10m N of Warwick, junction of A452 and B4101. From traffic lights of this intersection go W along B4101 towards Knowle for ¾m. Map available for each garden. TEAS at **White Cottage and Silver Trees Farm**. *Combined adm £2 Chd 50p (Share to CRMF®). Mon May 27 (1.30-6). Private visits welcome May & June, please* **Tel 01676 533143**

The Bungalow (Mr & Mrs G Johnson) Table Oak Lane, Fen End. 2 acres mixed borders, pond and lawn. New areas developing

¶Firs Farm (Mr & Mrs C Ellis) Windmill Lane. ½-acre garden, courtyard with tubs, walled garden, formal garden with rose bed and mixed borders

Meriglen (Mr & Mrs J Webb) Windmill Lane, Balsall Common. ¾-acre mixed borders, small woodland

¶The Pines (Mr & Mrs C Davis) Hodgetts Lane. 1½-acre formal garden. Avenue of flowering trees, series of small gardens, vegetable, herb garden and rose walk

Silver Trees Farm (Mr & Mrs B Hitchens) Balsall Street. 1½ acres, mixed borders, orchard, bog area, woodland garden. Large formal pond

140 Station Road (Mr & Mrs J Matts) Balsall Common. Small village garden with range of perennials, shrubs and climbing plants

White Cottage Farm (Mr & Mrs J Edwards) Holly Lane. 1½ acres cottage garden, mixed borders, pond, sunken garden

32 Wootton Green Lane (Dr & Mrs Leeming) Balsall Common. Lawns, water features, greenhouses

¶The Bevingtons ✂ (Mr & Mrs N Tustain) Ilmington. 8m S of Stratford-on-Avon, 4m NW of Shipston-on-Stour. Cottage garden with many old favourites, old roses, shrubs, herb garden. TEA at **Ilmington Manor**. *Adm £1 Chd free. Sun June 23 (2-6). Also open Sun April 14 with* **Ilmington Gardens**

Birmingham Botanical Gardens & Glasshouses ♿✂❀ 2m SW of Birmingham City Centre, signposted from Hagley Rd (A456). 15 acres; Tropical House with large lily pond and many economic plants. Palm House; Orangery; Cactus House. Outside bedding displays; rhododendrons and azaleas; rose garden; rock garden; 200 trees. Theme, herb, historic and cottage gardens. Fun area for children. Plant centre. Bands play every Sun afternoon. TEAS in the Pavilion. *Adm £3.50 Chd, Students & OAPs £1.90 (Share to Birmingham Botanical & Hort Soc Ltd®). Open daily. For NGS Suns March 3, Sept 29 (10-6)*

Bodymoor Green Farm ✂❀ (Mr & Mrs P J Maiden) ¾m S of Kingsbury on B4098 to Coventry. Easy approach from junction 9, M42; take A4097 signposted Kingsbury, Nether Whitacre. Traditional C18 farmhouse with courtyard and outbuildings. 1-acre country garden with old roses and herbaceous borders. Formal secret garden with pergola and white roses, silver scheme; ornamental pools, orchard with collection of spring bulbs; large kitchen garden, many interesting features incl treillage; ducks, hens, geese, sheep and lambs. TEAS. *Adm £1.50 Chd free. Suns June 2, 30 (2-6)*

Brook Farm ♿❀ (Mr & Mrs R B Hughes) Abbots Salford, Salford Priors 5m N of Evesham on B439. 1½-acre plantsman's garden. Many unusual plants and shrubs. Large mixed borders, island beds, pool, bog scree and peat gardens. *Adm £1 Chd free. Suns, Weds May 12, 15, June 9, 12, July 14, 17 (12-5). Also private visits welcome all year, please* **Tel 01386 871122**

Castle Bromwich Hall Garden Trust Chester Rd. ♿❀ 4m E of Birmingham. 1m from junction 5 of the M6 (exit Northbound). An example of the Formal English Garden of the C18. The ongoing restoration, started 10 yrs ago now provides visitors, academics and horticulturalists opportunity of seeing a unique collection of historic plants, shrubs, medicinal and culinary herbs and a fascinating vegetable collection. Guided tours Weds, Sats & Suns. Shop. Refreshments available; meals by arrangement. TEAS. *Adm £2 OAPs £1.50 Chd 50p. ▲For NGS Sats April 13, Sept 28 (2-6)*

Cedar House &% (Mr & Mrs D L Burbidge) Wasperton. 4m S of Warwick on A429, turn R between Barford and Wellesbourne, Cedar House at end of village. 3-acre mixed garden; shrubs, herbaceous borders, ornamental trees, woodland walk. TEAS. *Adm £2 Chd free (Share to St John's Church, Wasperton®). Mon May 27 (2-6)*

Charlecote Park &% (The National Trust) Warwick. 1m W of Wellesbourne signed off A 429. 6m S of Warwick, 5m E of Stratford upon Avon. Landscaped gardens featuring clipped yews and terraces with urns, contain a C19 orangery; a rustic thatched summer house by the cedar lawn; a River Parterre and a Wilderness garden under development. A 1m walk follows a route round the park along the banks of the R Avon, giving fine vistas to two churches. TEAS in Orangery. *Adm £2 (incl NT members & Chd). ▲For NGS Wed July 10 (2-6)*

Compton Scorpion Farm % (Mrs T M Karlsen) nr Ilmington. As for Ilmington Manor then fork L at village hall; after 1½m L down steep narrow lane, house on L. Garden designed and created by owners in 1989 from meadow hillside, aiming at Jekyll single colour schemes. *Adm £1.25 Chd free. Sun June 23 (2-6)*

¶Coughton Court &%❀ (Mrs C Throckmorton) Alcester. On A435 2m N of Alcester. 12 acres of new garden designed by Christina Birch with a courtyard containing an Elizabethan knot garden; beyond are lime walks and a yew rotunda with views of parkland; a walled garden, and by the lake a new rose labyrinth. There are a series of 'rooms' culminating in an herbaceous garden; a walk planted with willows and native shrubs and trees beside the River Arrow; a bog garden and a formal orchard. TEAS. *Adm £2.95 Chd £1.50 (Share to Coughton Catholic Church Restoration Appeal®). Sat June 29 (11-5.30)*

Dorsington Gardens &❀ 6m SW of Stratford-on-Avon. On B439 from Stratford turn L to Welford-on-Avon, then R to Dorsington. TEAS. *Combined adm £2.50 Chd free (Share to St Peter's Church, Dorsington®). Sun June 16 (2-5.30)*

Aberfoyle (Mr & Mrs B Clarke) Well established cottage garden, fine trees and shrubs

Knowle Thatch (Mr & Mrs P Turner) Large garden, mature trees, shrubs and herbaceous borders

Milfield (Mr & Mrs P Carey) Typical cottage garden with pond and access to

Whitegates (Mrs A Turner) Shrubs, mature trees and shrub roses

The Moat House (Mr & Mrs I Kolodotschko) 6-acre moated garden incl walled vegetable garden, conservatory with mediterranean plants

New House Farm (Mr & Mrs G Wood-Hill) Walled garden, climbing roses, herbaceous borders

The Old Manor (Mr F Dennis) 3 acres with fairy walk, herb garden, Japanese dry garden, willow walk, and rare arboretum, Oz Maze and Udde Well. TEAS

The Old Rectory (Mr & Mrs N Phillips) 2-acre Victorian garden with mature trees incl old espalier fruit trees, box hedges, herbaceous borders, many old roses, large pool, small wood

Windrush (Mrs M Mills) Country garden with shrubs, cottage plants and roses

Elizabeth Road Gardens %❀ Moseley. 4m S of Birmingham City centre, halfway between Kings Heath Centre & Edgbaston Cricket Ground. Off Moor Green Lane. TEAS at No 63 in aid of Cats-in-Care. *Combined adm £1.20 Chd 50p. Suns May 5, June 16, July 28, Weds May 8 (2-6)*

No 55 (Rob & Diane Cole) Plantsman's garden 100' × 30' on 3 levels, with scree area and mixed borders of alpines, rhododendrons, primulas and perennials, many unusual. Alpine House, and tubs

¶No 63 (Barbara & Derek Colley) Informal garden, 115' × 120' with mature trees, lawns and island beds containing shrubs, herbaceous borders and rockery plants

Elm Close &%❀ (Mr & Mrs E W Dyer) Binton Rd, Welford-on-Avon. From Stratford-on-Avon, take A4390 towards Evesham; turn L after approx 5m (signed Welford and Long Marston). Elm Close is between Welford Garage and The Bell Inn. ⅔-acre plantsman's garden designed and maintained by owners and stocked for yr-round effect. Bulbs, alpines, clematis and hellebores a particular speciality. Listed in The Good Gardens Guide. TEAS in aid of Red Cross. *Adm £1.50 Chd free. Suns March 24, 31 (2-6). Parties other days by appointment, please Tel 01789 490803*

Fenny Drayton Gardens, nr Nuneaton see Leicestershire

The Folly Lodge %❀ (Mrs Susan Solomon) Halford. On A429 (Fosse Way) 9m NE Moreton in Marsh. 9m SE Stratford on Avon. In Halford take turning opp PO to Idlicote. House is 300yds down on R. ⅓-acre designed, constructed and maintained by owners since 1983. Colour themed borders, roses, shrubs and small pond; wide variety of plants many unusual. TEAS. *Adm £1.50 (Share to Stratford & District Samaritans®). Sun June 23 (2-6), Weds June 12, July 3, 17 (2-5). Private visits welcome weekdays May to July, please Tel 01789 740183*

17 Gerrard Street (Mr T K Meredith) Warwick. 100yds from castle main gate. Car park at St Nicholas. Small town garden with interesting plants. *Adm 40p Chd free. Sat, Sun June 22, 23 (11-1 & 2-6). Private visits welcome, please Tel 01926 496305*

Greenlands &❀ (Mr Eric T Bartlett) Wellesbourne. Leave Statford-upon-Avon due E on the B4086. Garden on Xrds at Loxley/Charlecote by airfield. An acre of mature trees; shrubs; shrub roses and herbaceous borders. TEAS. *Adm £1 Chd free (Share to Intermediate Technology®). Suns April 14, May 5, July 28, Aug 25 (11-5). Parties welcome, please Tel 01789 840327*

¶89 Harts Green Road %❀ (Mrs Barbara Richardson) Harborne. 3m Birmingham City Centre [A-Z A2 p88] off Fellows Lane/War Lane. ½-acre split level informal garden with troughs, scree, rockery and mixed borders of unusual plants, shrubs and climbers. Pond and vegetable garden. Adjoining orchard contains small nursery offering wide range of plants, many propagated from garden. *Adm £1 Chd 50p (Share to NCCPG®). Open every Wed in May, June, July and Sept. Mon to Fri, May to July. For NGS Weds May 8, June 12, July 10 (2-5.30). Private visits and groups welcome. Please Tel 0121 427 5200*

Hickecroft &% (Mr J M Pitts) Rowington. 6m NW of Warwick, 15m SE of Birmingham on B4439 between Hockley Heath and Hatton. Turn into Finwood Rd (signed Lowsonford); at Rowington Xrds 1st L into Mill Lane. 2-acre garden reaching maturity following redesigning and replanting. Interesting plants, mixed borders. Home to part of the NCCPG Digitalis collection. TEA. *Adm £1.50 Chd 50p (Share to Myton Hospice®). Sat, Sun June 22, 23 (2-5.30)*

The Hiller Garden & Dunnington Heath Farm &%❀ (Mr & Mrs R Beach) Alcester. On A441 nr junction with B4088 (was A435), 3m S Alcester. 2-acre garden of all-yr interest displaying unusual herbaceous perennials, old-fashioned species roses, and English roses. *Adm by donation. Open all yr. For NGS Suns April 28, July 7, Aug 18, Oct 13 (10-4). Private gardens of Dunnington Heath Farm (adjacent) also open on NGS days. Adm £1 Chd free*

11 Hillwood Common Road % (Mr & Mrs C T Smith) Four Oaks, Sutton Coldfield. From A5127 at Mere Green traffic island take Hill Village Rd. 2nd R into Sherifoot Lane and follow L bend. Straight on into Hill Wood Common Rd. [AZ ref 27.4H]. ½-acre Japanese style garden with tea house; stone and water feature; Japanese courtyard. Low heeled shoes, please. *Adm £2. Private visits welcome, please Tel 0121 3081180*

Holywell Gardens &%❀ 5m E of Henley-in-Arden, nearest village Claverdon. Coffee and TEAS in aid of Myton Hospice. *Combined adm £1.50 Chd free. Sun June 16 (11-6)*
   Holywell Farm (Mr & Mrs Ian Harper) 2½-acre natural garden; lawn, trees, shrubs. Laid out in 1963 for easy maintenance, surrounding C16 half timbered house
   Manor Farm (Mr & Mrs Donald Hanson) Cottage type garden surrounding C16 farmhouse with natural duck pond, yew and box hedges, herb garden; white and grey border

Honington Village Gardens &% 1½m N of Shipston-on-Stour. Take A3400 towards Stratford then R signed Honington. TEAS **Honington Hall**. *Combined adm £2 Chd free (Share to All Saints Church, Honington®). Sun June 30 (2.15-5.30)*
   Holts Cottage (Mr M Harvey)
   Honington Glebe (Mr & Mrs John Orchard) Over 2 acres of informal garden interesting ornamental trees; shrubs and foliage. Parterre and raised lily pool recently laid out in old walled garden
   Honington Hall (Lady Wiggin) Extensive lawns; fine trees. Carolean house (not open); Parish Church adjoining house
   Honington Lodge (Lord & Lady Tombs)
   The Old Cottage (Mrs Wigington)
   ¶**The Old House** (Mr & Mrs R S Smith)
   Old Mullions (Mr & Mrs R Lawton)

Hunningham Village Gardens &%❀ Hunningham. From Leamington Spa B4453 to Rugby. Signposted Hunningham R after Weston-under-Wetherley. Or A425 to Southam at Fosseway (B4455) turn L. At Hunningham Hill turn L then follow signs to church (open). Teas at Vicarage in aid of St Margarets Church. *Adm £2 Chd free. Sat, Sun June 8, 9 (2-5)*

High Cross (Mr & Mrs T Chalk) Secluded garden with alpines
Moat Cottage (Mr & Mrs Murchek) New garden with interesting features and planting
The Olde School House (Mr & Mrs G Longstaff) 1 acre of borders, shrubs, pond and wilflife paddock area
Sandford Cottage (Mr & Mrs A Phillips) Village cottage garden

Other gardens may open

Idlicote Gardens &❀ 3m NE of Shipston-on-Stour. TEAS. *Combined adm £2 OAPs £1 Chd free (Share to Parish Church of St James the Great®). Sun May 5 (2-6)*
   Idlicote House (Mrs R P G Dill) About 4 acres. Fine views. Small Norman church in grounds. House C18 (not open) listed Grade II partly attributed to Sir John Soane
   Badgers Farm (Sir Derek & Lady Hornby)
   1 Bickerstaff Cottages (Mr & Mrs C Balchin)
   Bickerstaff Farm (Sir John & Lady Owen)
   Home Farm (Mr & Mrs G Menzies-Kitchen)
   Mews Cottage (Mr & Mrs D Colton)
   The Old Rectory (Lord & Lady Howe)
   Stone Cottage (Mr & Mrs M Batsford)
   Woodlands (Capt & Mrs P R Doyne)

Ilmington Gardens ❀ 8m S of Stratford-on-Avon, 4m NW of Shipston-on-Stour. Ilmington traditional Morris dancers. Teas in the Village Hall. Start anywhere, all gardens well signed and within walking distance. *Combined adm £3 Chd free. Sun April 14 (2-6)*
   Crab Mill (L Hodgkin)
   The Bevingtons (N Tustain) See individual entry
   Foxcote Hill (M Dingley)
   Foxcote Hill Cottage (A Terry)
   Frog Orchard (N Naish)
   The Manor (D Flower) (see next entry)
   Pear Tree Cottage (Dr & Mrs A F Hobson) See individual entry
   Puddocks (H Syme)

Ilmington Manor &❀ (Mr D & Lady Flower). 4m NW of Shipston-on-Stour, 8m S of Stratford-on-Avon. Daffodils in profusion (April). Hundreds of old and new roses, ornamental trees, shrub and herbaceous borders, rock garden, pond garden, topiary, fish pond with Koi. House (not open) built 1600. TEAS. *Adm £2 Chd free (Share to The Gardeners Royal Benevolent Society®). Suns May 19, June 23, July 7 (2-6). Also open Sun April 14 with* **Ilmington Gardens**. *Private visits welcome, please Tel 01608 682230*

Ivy Lodge & (Mrs M A Willis) Radway 7m NW of Banbury via A41 and B4086, turn R down Edgehill; 14m SE of Stratford via A422. L below Edgehill. 4-acres; spring bulbs and blossom; wildflower area; climbing roses; site Battle of Edgehill. TEAS. *Adm £1.50 OAP £1 Chd free. Sun April 14 (2-6). Also parties welcome May to July and throughout Oct (Autumn colours), please Tel 01295 670371 or 670580*

Lord Leycester Hospital ✂ High Street, Warwick. Town centre beside West Gate. Garden adjoins historic C14 Guildhall, Chapel, courtyard, Great Hall and Museum of the Queen's Own Hussars also open to public. 1-acre walled garden, partly under reconstruction, including Norman arch and ancient finial of Nilometer. TEAS. *Adm £1 Chd free. Sun June 23 (11-5) private visits welcome, please* **Tel 01926 491422**

Loxley Hall ♿ (Col A Gregory-Hood) 4m SE of Stratford-on-Avon. Turn N off A422 or W off A429 1½m SW of Wellesbourne. Modern sculpture, iris, shrubs, roses, trees. Small Japanese Garden. Old church adjacent can be visited. TEAS. *Adm £1.50 Chd 20p. Sun June 2 (2-7)*

Martineau Centre Gardens ♿✂❀ (City of Birmingham Education Dept) Priory Rd, Edgbaston. From Birmingham S via A38; R at Priory Rd (lights and box junction); entrance 100yds on R opp Priory Hospital. 2-acre demonstration gardens; hardy ornamentals, vegetables, small orchard; glasshouses; nature reserve/wild garden. TEAS. *Adm £1 Chd 50p. Sun July 14 (10-6)*

Maxstoke Castle ♿✂ (Mr & Mrs M C Fetherston-Dilke) nr Coleshill, E of Birmingham, 2½m E of Coleshill on B4114 take R turn down Castle Lane; Castle Dr 1¼m on R. 4 to 5 acres of garden and pleasure grounds with flowers, shrubs and trees in the immediate surroundings of the castle and inside courtyard; water-filled moat round castle. *Adm £2.50 OAP/Chd £1.50 under 6 free. Sun June 2 (2-5)*

The Mill Garden ♿✂❀ (Mr A B Measures) 55 Mill St, Warwick off A425 beside castle gate. 1 acre; series of informal, partially enclosed areas, on river next to castle. Superb setting; herb garden; raised beds; small trees, shrubs, cottage plants and some unusual plants. Use St Nicholas Car Park. Tea in Warwick. *Adm £1 Chd free (Share to Lord Leycester Hospital®). Open daily 9 till dusk. Open for NGS Suns April 21, May 12, June 16, July 21, Aug 18, Sept 15, Oct 13. Parties welcome, please* **Tel 01926 492877**

Moseley Gardens ✂❀ Approx 3m from Birmingham City Centre halfway between Kings Heath Centre & Moseley Village. TEA April 21. TEAS July 14. *Combined adm £1.50 Chd free. Suns April 21, July 14 (2-6)*

- **¶7 Ashfield Rd** (Mr & Mrs Bartlett) Small garden with secluded, cottage feel. Attractive pond with rockery, waterfall and shingle bank
- **No 14A Clarence Rd** (Ms C Fahy) Small suburban garden with a difference. *July 14 only*
- **No 16 Prospect Rd** ❀ (Mrs S M & Mr R J Londesborough) Small garden with wide range of plants. Large collection of containers. *Also private visits welcome all year, please* **Tel 0121 449 8457**
- **No 19 Prospect Rd** (Mr A White) Well planted spring suburban garden. *April 21 only*
- **No 20 Prospect Rd** (Martin Page & Annie Sofiano) Large town garden on 3 levels. *July 14 only*
- **No 30 Prospect Rd** (Mrs J Taylor) South-facing terraced garden incorporating rockery-covered air-raid shelter
- **No 33 School Rd** (Ms J Warr-Arnold) Mixed garden containing plants with interesting histories. *Sun July 14 only*
- **No 65 School Rd** (Mrs W Weston) Small shady garden with patio, pergola and pond. *Sun July 14 only*

¶Orchard Cottage ♿ (Mr & Mrs G Roberts) Hurley. M42, junction 9, take A4097 to Kingsbury. 2nd island, R to Coventry, 1st L to Hurley. Approx 1½m, R into Dexter Lane cottage at end of lane. C17 property in ⅔ acre. Cottage style garden with informal plantings of mixed beds and borders containing interesting plants, water feature, evolving meadow orchard. *Adm £1 Chd under 12 free. Suns June 30, July 14 (2-6)*

¶Packington Hall ♿✂ (Lord & Lady Guernsey) Meriden. On A45, towards Coventry, after Stonebridge Roundabout. Packington's pleasure grounds were laid out in 1750 by Capability Brown. The lawns run down to the 18 acre Hall Pool and are studded with clumps of azaleas and rhododendrons, together with specimen trees. The more formal area around the House has recently been replanted. TEAS. *Adm £2 Chd £1 (Share to Assoc for Brain Damaged Children, Coventry®). Sun June 2 (2-5.30)*

Packwood House ♿✂❀ (The National Trust) 11m SE of Birmingham. 2m E of Hockley Heath. Carolean yew garden representing the Sermon on the Mount. Tudor house with tapestries, needlework and furniture of the period. Teas at Baddesley Clinton (NT) Henley in Arden or Knowle. *Adm garden only £2.50 Chd £1.25. ▲For NGS June 4 (2-5.30). Open with* **Baddesley Clinton**

¶2 Paddox House ✂❀ (Anne Sutton) Hillmorton. From Rugby take A428 to Hillmorton signed Northampton M1. Approx 1½m from town centre turn R opposite Rover garage into Rainsbrook Avenue, which leads to Dunsmore Ave. Garden on R. From Motorway junction 18 follow signs to Rugby. A small town garden designed by the owner. Some unusual plants and shrubs. Paved area with pots and informal pool/bog garden. Herbaceous borders, climbers and ivy mound for wildlife - an organic garden. *Combined adm with* **4 Arnold Villas** *£2 Chd free. Sun Aug 11 (2-5.30)*

Paxford ♿✂❀ (Mr & Mrs A M Parsons) Princethorpe. 7m SE of Coventry, on B4453 Leamington Rd approx 200yds from junction with A423. A flower arranger's garden with heathers and fuchsias which has been designed and maintained by the owners as a series of rooms. Parking on road on one side only please. TEA. *Adm £1 (Share to Stretton-on-Dunsmore Parish Church®). Suns June 23, July 28 (2-6)*

Pear Tree Cottage ❀ (Dr & Mrs A F Hobson) Ilmington 8m S of Stratford-on-Avon, 4m NW of Shipston-on-Stour. Cottage garden with many interesting plants and bulbs. Designed and maintained by owners; rock garden and terrace. Partially suitable for wheelchairs. TEA at **Ilmington Manor**. *Adm 50p Chd 20p. Sun May 19 (2-6). Also open Sun April 14 (2-6) with* **Ilmington Gardens**

Pereira Road Gardens ✂❀ Birmingham A-Z 5c p.72 between Gillhurst Rd and Margaret Grove, ¼m from Hagley Rd or ½m Harborne High St. TEAS at **No. 84** in aid of St Peter's Church Restoration Fund. Harborne Nature Reserve and Bird Sanctuary can be visited. *Combined adm £1.50 Chd 30p. Sun June 30 (2-5)*

No. 45 (Wyn & Alfred White) Harborne. ⅕ acre on four levels. Spring bulbs, rhododendrons, roses, shrubs, herbaceous borders, ornamental and fruit trees in formal and informal areas. *(Share to Break Through Trust for the Deaf®)*

No. 50 ❀ (Prof M Peil) About ⅕ acre, with over 900 shrubs and perennials for all seasons; fruit and vegetables. Large bed of plants with African connections. (Plants sold in aid of Catholic Fund for Overseas Development.)

No. 84 & (Mrs R E Barnett) ⅕ acre with 30 degree sloping concreted bank, now extensive rockery, interesting shrubs, herbaceous borders

Roseberry Cottage &✿❀ (Mr & Mrs Richard G Bastow) Fillongley. 6m N of Coventry on B4098 Tamworth Road. Go under motorway bridge to top of hill, take Woodend Lane, sign on R. Turn L into Sandy Lane, opp triangle of beech trees. 1st house on R in Sandy Lane. Please use one way system due to restricted parking. Garden of 1¾ acres incl herbaceous border, rock garden, pool, peat and bog area, scree and small herb garden. Stone troughs, orchard with wild flowers, organically grown fruit and vegetables. Herbs for sale, thymes a speciality. TEA. *Adm £1 Chd 30p (Share to NCCPG®). Sun June 30 (2-5.30)*

120 Russell Road ✿❀ (Mr D Worthington) Hall Green. Turn off A34 E at Reg Vardy Motors, Hall Green, down York Rd then L into Russell Rd. Small suburban garden designed by owner; shrubs, herbaceous, climbers, old roses and fountain; tubs, hanging baskets and window boxes. TEAS. *Adm 75p Acc chd free (Share to Acorns Childrens Hospice and St Mary's Hospice®). Sun June 30 (2-5)*

Ryton Organic Gardens &✿❀ 5m SE of Coventry (off A45 to Wolston). 8-acre site demonstrating organic gardening methods as seen on Channel 4's 'All Muck and Magic' series: composting display, herb, rose and bee garden; shrub borders; vegetable plots and fruit; garden for the blind and partially sighted; conservation area with pond and wild flowers meadow. Shop; children's play area; award winning restaurant serving organically grown food. Guide dogs allowed. TEAS. *Adm £2.50 Concessions £1.75, Chd £1.25 Family £6.50. Open daily except Christmas period. For NGS Suns April 28, Sept 29 (10-5.30)*

Sheepy Magna Gardens, nr Atherstone see Leicestershire

Sherbourne Manor &✿❀ (Mr & Mrs M Perry) 2m S of Warwick just off A429 Barford Rd. Large garden contains herbaceous borders; stream; old fish pond and large variety of established trees and many new trees. TEAS in aid of All Saints Church, Sherbourne. *Adm £3 OAPs £1 Chd up to 12 free. Sun June 23 (2-5.30)*

Sherbourne Park & (The Hon Lady Smith-Ryland) 3m S of Warwick off A429; ½m N of Barford. Medium-sized garden; lawns, shrubs, borders, roses, lilies; lake; temple; church by Gilbert Scott 1863 adjacent to early Georgian House (not open) 1730. Featured in 'New Englishwoman's Garden' (R Verey) and 'English Gardens' (P Coats). Featured in 1991 & 1992 Gardeners Royal Benevolent Society Calendar. Lunches, teas or coffee for private tours by arrangement. Free car park. *Adm £3 OAPs and Chd (13-16) £2, under 12 free (Share to All Saints Church, Sherbourne®). Open for private tours and coaches by appt only, please* Tel 01926 624255 *or* 624506

Shrewley Pools Farm ✿ (Mrs C W Dodd) Haseley. 4m NW of Warwick through Hatton. At roundabout turn L along Five Ways Rd, after approx ¾m farm entrance on L opp Audholi poultry farm. ¾m off A4177 from Falcon Inn (Warwick). 1-acre garden, herbaceous borders, rhododendrons, roses, irises, peonies etc. Many interesting shrubs and trees, terrace and garden pool. Farm animals and C17 farmhouse and barn. TEAS. *Adm £1.50 Chd 30p (Share to AFASIC®). Sun June 16 (2-6). Private visits welcome for 4 and over, please* Tel 01926 484315

26 Sunnybank Road ✿❀ (Chris & Margaret Jones) Wylde Green. ¾m S of Sutton Coldfield. Turn off A5127 towards Wylde Green Station then; 2nd L. Medium-sized town garden on sandy soil, redesigned in mid-80's by present owners as a series of 'rooms'. Yr-long interest achieved by use of bulbs, shrubs and herbaceous plants. Featured on Garden Club Aug 93 (Channel 4), Secret Gardens (BBC) Spring 96, and 'Your Garden' magazine Dec 93. TEAS in aid of Save the Children Fund. *Adm £1 OAPs 50p Chd free. Sun July 21 (2-6)*

52 Tenbury Road &✿❀ (Mrs V Grace Darby) Kings Heath. 5m S of city centre off A435 (Alcester Rd). 4¾m from junction 3 off M40. ⅛ of an acre suburban garden in cottage garden style. Informal plantings of mixed beds and borders with interesting and unusual plants, shrubs, climbers. Small vegetable and fruit area, minimum use of chemical pest control. TEAS in aid of South Birmingham Talking Newspaper (for the Blind) May 26 and Muscular Dystrophy June 29 and July 3 (2-5). *Adm £1.50 Chd free. Suns May 26, June 29, Wed July 3 (2-5). Private visits welcome April to July, please* Tel 0121 444 6456

Tysoe Manor &✿❀ (Mr & Mrs W A C Wield) Tysoe. 5m NE of Shipston-on-Stour. Take the 4035 to Banbury. In Brailes turn L to Tysoe. The Manor is the 1st house on the L after reaching Upper Tysoe. 4-acre garden, large lawns with stone walls, herbaceous and flower borders; roses and mature ornamental and fruit trees. TEAS in aid of Tysoe Church. *Adm £1.50 Chd free. Sun Sept 15 (2-6)*

Upton House ✿❀ (The National Trust) 7m NW of Banbury on A422; 2m S of Edgehill. Terraced garden, rockeries, herbaceous borders, roses, water gardens, lawns. House contains a connoisseur's collection of porcelain, tapestries and paintings. Partially suitable for wheelchairs. Coaches by appt. TEAS. *Adm garden only £2.40 Chd £1.20.* ▲*For NGS Sun July 7 (2-6 last adm 5.30)*

8 Vicarage Rd &✿❀ (Charles & Tessa King-Farlow) Edgbaston, 1½m W of City Centre off A456 (Hagley Rd). ¾-acre retaining in part its Victorian layout but informally planted with mixed borders of interesting and unusual plants; shrub rose border; walled potager and conservatory. Featured in House and Garden Sept 1995. TEAS. *Adm £1 Chd free. Sun June 30 (2-6). Private visits very welcome, please* Tel 0121 455 0902

Warmington Village Gardens ➳✿❀ 5m NW of Banbury on B4100. Teas at **The Village Hall**. *Combined adm £1.50 Chd free (Share to Warmington PCC Restoration Fund®). Sun July 14 (2-6) Car park; coaches welcome, please* **Tel 01295 690 318**

Berka (Mr & Mrs B J Castle) Chapel Street
3 Court Close (Mr & Mrs C J Crocker)
The Glebe House (Mr & Mrs G Thornton) Village Road
Holly Cottage (Dr & Mrs T W Martin) The Green
Rotherwood (Miss M R Goodison) Soot Lane
Sunnyside (Yvonne Farley & Michael Borlenghi)
Underedge (Mr & Mrs J Dixon) 1 Church Hill
¶**Woodcote** (Mrs S Mellor) School Lane

Warwickshire Constabulary, Police HQ ❀ Leek Wootton. Mid-way between Warwick and Kenilworth, 1m N of the Gaveston Island, on the Kenilworth Rd, off the A46 Warwick to Coventry by-pass. From Warwick, turn L after Anchor Public House in centre of village, signposted Police Headquarters. Approx 6 acres of mixed garden, large and small shrubs, herbaceous borders, Chinese garden, walk around lakes. TEAS. *Adm £1.50 Chd free (Share to Victim Support®). Sun May 26 (12-4)*

50 Wellington Rd ➳✿❀ (Mrs Anne Lee) Edgbaston. Corner of Ampton Rd and Wellington Rd. 1-acre walled town garden. Terraces, paving, brick paths and architectural features. 100-yr-old rhododendrons and mature trees with woodland walk. Two long mixed borders, fountain, croquet lawn. TEAS. *Adm £1.50 Chd free. Sun June 23 (2-6). Private visits also welcome April to Oct, please* **Tel 0121 440 1744**

¶**Wheelwright House** ➳❀ (Richard & Suzanne Shacklock) Long Compton. 6m S of Shipston-on-Stour on A3400; at S end of Long Compton village take rd signed to Little Compton; Wheelwright House is 300yds on L. 1-acre garden surrounding C18 house. Stream with attractive bridges forms centrepiece. Bog garden, shade gardens, colourful mixed borders with wide variety of traditional and unusual plants. Formal lily pool with rose pergola. Mediterranean garden. TEAS in aid of Long Compton Church. *Adm £1.50 Chd free. Sun Sept 8 (2-6). Private visits welcome, please* **Tel 01608 684478**

Whichford & Ascott Gardens ✿❀ 6m SE of Shipston-on-Stour. Turn E off A3400 at Long Compton for Whichford. Cream TEAS. *Combined adm £2 Chd free (Share to Shakespeare Hospice Trust®). Sun June 16 (2-6)*

Brook Hollow (Mr & Mrs J A Round) Garden on a bank, stream and large variety of plants
Combe House (Mr & Mrs D C Seel) Hidden garden surrounding house; mature fine trees
¶**Hill House** (Mr & Mrs D M Child) Newly planted hillside garden
The Old House (Mr & Mrs T A Maher) Undulating garden. Natural ponds, trees and shrubs
Roman Row (Mr & Mrs S C Langdon) Beautiful well kept cottage garden
Stone Walls (Mrs J Scott-Cockburn) Walled garden; paved garden in foundations of old stable
The Whichford Pottery (Mr & Mrs J B M Keeling) Secret walled garden, unusual plants, large vegetable garden and rambling cottage garden. Adjoining pottery

Woodpeckers ➳✿❀ (Dr & Mrs A J Cox) The Bank, Marlcliff, nr Bidford-on-Avon 7m SW of Stratford-on-Avon. Off the B4085 between Bidford-on-Avon and Cleeve Prior. 2½-acre plantsman's country garden designed and maintained by owners; colour-schemed herbaceous and mixed borders, old roses, meadow garden, alpines in troughs and gravel, pool, knot garden, ornamental kitchen garden. Featured on BBC2 'Gardener's World' and in 'Practical Gardening'. *Adm £2. Private visits by Societies or individuals welcome at all seasons, please* **Tel 01789 773416**

Wroxall Abbey School ➳✿ (Mrs J M Gowen, Headmistress) Wroxall 6m NW of Warwick. Nr Fiveways junction on A4141. 27 acres; spring flowers, shrubs, rhododendrons, small enclosed flower garden. 'Nature trail' incl comments on plants, flowers, etc. Work in progress on surveying and re-instatement of historical pleasure grounds, by Warwickshire Garden Trust. TEAS. *Adm £1.50 Chd 50p (Share to St Leonard's Church, Wroxall®). Sun May 19 (2-5)*

Open by appointment Please do not be put off by this notation. The owner may consider his garden too small to accommodate the numbers associated with a normal opening or, more often, there may be a lack of car parking space. It is often more rewarding than a normal opening as the owner will usually give a guided tour of the garden. The minimum size of party is either stated in the garden description or can be found out when making the appointment; usually 2. If the garden has normal open days, the entrance fee is as stated in the garden description.

Wiltshire

Hon County Organiser:	Brigadier Arthur Gooch, Manor Farmhouse, Chitterne, Warminster BA12 OLG
Assistant Hon County Organisers:	Mrs David Armytage, Sharcott Manor, Pewsey
	Mrs Anthony Heywood, Monkton House, Monkton Deverell, Warminster
	Mrs Colin Shand, Ashton House, Worton, Devizes
(& PR)	Mrs John Nicolls, Barn Flat, Ark Farm, Old Wardour, Tisbury, Salisbury SP3 6RP
	Tel 01747 870162

DATES OF OPENING

February 18 Sunday
Lacock Abbey, nr Chippenham
February 25 Sunday
Lacock Abbey, nr Chippenham
March 3 Sunday
Lacock Abbey, nr Chippenham
March 31 Sunday
Corsham Court, nr Chippenham
April 3 Wednesday
Sharcott Manor, nr Pewsey
April 8 Monday
Conock Manor, nr Devizes
Long Hall Gardens & Nursery,
Stockton
April 14 Sunday
Broadleas, nr Devizes
Crudwell Court Hotel,
nr Malmesbury ‡
Easton Grey House,
nr Malmesbury ‡
Fonthill House, nr Tisbury
Kingfisher Mill, Great Durnford
Upper Chelworth Farm,
nr Cricklade
April 17 Wednesday
Down's Lodge,
nr Ogbourne-St-George
April 21 Sunday
Great Chalfield Manor,
nr Melksham
Sharcott Manor, nr Pewsey
April 27 Saturday
Stourton House, nr Mere
April 28 Sunday
Baynton House, Coulston
Iford Manor, nr Bradford-on-Avon
Luckington Manor, nr Malmesbury
Oare House, nr Pewsey
Spye Park, nr Chippenham
Stourton House, nr Mere
May 1 Wednesday
Sharcott Manor, nr Pewsey
May 5 Sunday
Hyde's House, Dinton,
nr Salisbury ‡
Inwoods, nr Bradford-on-Avon
Lackham Gardens, nr Chippenham
Little Durnford Manor,
nr Salisbury ‡
Ridleys Cheer, Mountain Bower

May 12 Sunday
Home Covert, Devizes
Luckington Court, nr Chippenham
Stourhead Garden, Stourton, Mere
Waterdale House, East Knoyle
May 19 Sunday
Fonthill House, nr Tisbury
May 22 Wednesday
Kingsmead Mill, Little Somerford
May 26 Sunday
Landford Lodge, nr Salisbury
The Old School House, Baverstock
May 29 Wednesday
Bryher, Bromham
June 2 Sunday
Baynton House, Coulston
Bowood Rhododendron Walks,
nr Chippenham
Kingsmead Mill, Little Somerford
June 5 Wednesday
Bryher, Bromham
Sharcott Manor, nr Pewsey
June 8 Saturday
Mompesson House, The Close,
Salisbury
June 9 Sunday
Corsham Court, nr Chippenham
Edington & Coulston Gardens
Foscote Gardens, Grittleton
13 Kingsdown Road, Stratton St
Margaret ‡
Mallards, Chirton, nr Devizes
Upper Chelworth Farm,
nr Cricklade ‡
June 12 Wednesday
Bryher, Bromham
June 15 Saturday
Barters Farm Nurseries,
Chapmanslade
June 16 Sunday
Avebury Manor, Avebury
Barters Farm Nurseries,
Chapmanslade
Chisenbury Priory, nr Upavon
Guyers House, Pickwick,
nr Corsham
The Old Rectory, Stockton
June 19 Wednesday
Bryher, Bromham
Down's Lodge,
nr Ogbourne-St-George
Kingsmead Mill, Little Somerford

June 23 Sunday
Bolehyde Manor, nr Chippenham
The Courts, nr Bradford-on-Avon
Goulters Mill Farm, Nettleton ‡
Hillbarn House, Great Bedwyn
Lower Burytown, nr Blunsdon
Manningford Bruce Gardens,
nr Pewsey
Ridleys Cheer, Mountain Bower
St Margarets House, Corsley
61 Whitegate, Castle Combe
nr Chippenham ‡
June 26 Wednesday
Ridleys Cheer, Mountain Bower
June 29 Saturday
Long Hall Gardens & Nursery,
Stockton
June 30 Sunday
Ark Farm, Old Wardour,
nr Tisbury
Chisenbury Priory, nr Upavon
Garden House, Sandridge Park,
nr Melksham
Job's Mill, Crockerton,
nr Warminster ‡
Little Durnford Manor,
nr Salisbury
Pound Hill House, West Kington
Sharcott Manor, nr Pewsey
Sutton Veny Gardens,
nr Warminster ‡
Thompson's Hill, Sherston
July 3 Wednesday
Sharcott Manor, nr Pewsey
July 7 Sunday
Baynton House, Coulston
Courtlands, nr Corsham
Ridleys Cheer, Mountain Bower
July 10 Wednesday
Kingsmead Mill, Little Somerford
July 13 Saturday
Great Somerford Gardens
July 14 Sunday
Crudwell Court Hotel,
nr Malmesbury ‡
The Grange, Winterbourne
Dauntsey
Great Somerford Gardens ‡
Lackham Gardens,
nr Chippenham
Luckington Manor,
nr Malmesbury ‡

Waterdale House, East Knoyle
Worton Gardens, Devizes
July 21 Sunday
Home Covert, Devizes
July 27 Saturday
Hazelbury Manor, nr Box
July 28 Sunday
Hazelbury Manor, nr Box
Mallards, Chirton, nr Devizes
Oare House, nr Pewsey
August 4 Sunday
Heale Gardens & Plant Centre,
Middle Woodford
Lower Farm House, Milton
Lilbourne ‡
The Old Bakery, Milton
Lilbourne ‡
August 7 Wednesday
Sharcott Manor, nr Pewsey
August 10 Saturday
Stourton House, nr Mere
August 11 Sunday
Broadleas, nr Devizes
Luckington Manor, nr Malmesbury
The Mead Nursery, Brokerswood
Stourton House, nr Mere
Upper Chelworth Farm,
nr Cricklade

August 25 Sunday
Hyde's House, Dinton,
nr Salisbury
September 1 Sunday
The Courts, nr Bradford-on-Avon
September 4 Wednesday
Sharcott Manor, nr Pewsey
September 15 Sunday
Avebury Manor, Avebury
September 22 Sunday
Hillbarn House, Great Bedwyn
October 2 Wednesday
Sharcott Manor, nr Pewsey
October 6 Sunday
Great Chalfield Manor,
nr Melksham
Lackham Gardens, nr Chippenham
1997
February 16 Sunday
Lacock Abbey, nr Chippenham
February 23 Sunday
Great Chalfield Manor,
nr Melksham
Lacock Abbey, nr Chippenham
March 2 Sunday
Lacock Abbey, nr Chippenham

Regular openings
For details see garden description

Barters Farm Nurseries,
Chapmanslade
Bowood House & Gardens,
nr Chippenham
Broadleas, nr Devizes
Easton Grey House, nr Malmesbury
Hazelbury Manor, nr Box
Heale Gardens & Plant Centre,
Middle Woodford
Iford Manor, nr Bradford-on-Avon
Lackham Gardens, nr Chippenham
Long Hall Gardens & Nursery,
Stockton, nr Warminster
The Mead Nursery, Brokerswood
Pound Hill House, West Kington
Stourton House, nr Mere
Upper Chelworth, nr Cricklade

By appointment only
*For telephone numbers and other
details see garden descriptions.
Private visits welcomed*

Lower House, Whiteparish
7 Norton Bavant, nr Warminster

DESCRIPTIONS OF GARDENS

Ark Farm ⚘❀ (Mr & Mrs Edmund Neville-Rolfe) Tisbury. 9m from Shaftesbury. 2½m from Tisbury. From Tisbury follow English Heritage signs to Old Wardour Castle. Private rd from Castle car park to Ark Farm. 1¼ acres incl water and woodland gardens, as featured in Country Life and the Daily Telegraph. TEAS. *Adm £2 Chd free (Share to The Mental Health Foundation®). Sun June 30 (2-6)*

Avebury Manor Garden ⚘❀ (The National Trust) Avebury on A4361 9m N of Devizes 2m from Beckhampton roundabout on A4. Use main car park and follow signs to Manor. 5-acre garden undergoing restoration to planting, hedges and walls. Ancient walled garden on site of former priory, divided by stone walls and topiary hedges, incl a rose garden, herbaceous border, new orchard, topiary garden, herb garden. Italian walk and half moon garden. Late mediaeval manor house under restoration (open). *Adm House and Garden £3.50 Chd £1.75; Garden only £2.20 Chd £1.40.* ▲Suns June 16, Sept 15 *(Garden 11-5) (House 2-5)*

Barters Farm Nurseries ♿⚘❀ (Mr & Mrs C L C Walker) Chapmanslade. On A3098, 3m E of Frome, 3m W of Westbury. 3m N of Warminster, turn off A36 towards Frome. Potters garden, featuring groundcover plants, trees and half hardy perennials. 14-acre wholesale nursery, incl 2 acres of stock beds, retail plant centre. Container gardening demonstration at 3.00pm. *Adm £1 Chd free. Open daily (9-5), Suns (10- 5). For NGS Sat June 15 (9-5), Sun June 16 (10-5)*

¶**Baynton House** ⚘❀ (Sir Raymond and Lady Burrell) Coulston. 4m E of Westbury on B3098 between Edington and Erlestoke. 4 acres with spring bulbs, rock garden, wild woodland and water garden. C17 Georgian house (not open). TEAS in aid of Coulston Church. *Adm £2 Chd free. Suns April 28, June 2, July 7 (2-6). Visits of parties over 5 welcome by appt, please* **Tel 01380 830273**

Bolehyde Manor ♿❀ (Earl and Countess Cairns) Allington. 1½m W of Chippenham on Bristol Rd (A420). Turn N at Allington Xrds. ½m on R. Parking in field. A series of gardens around C16 Manor House; enclosed by walls and topiary, densely planted with many interesting shrubs and climbers, mixed rose and herbaceous beds; inner courtyard with troughs full of tender plants; wild flower orchard, vegetable, fruit garden and greenhouse yard. TEAS. *Adm £1.50 Chd 50p (Share to Kingston St Michael Church©). Sun June 23 (2.30-6). Also private visits welcome, please* **Tel 01249 652105**

Bowood Rhododendron Walks ⚘❀ (The Earl of Shelburne) nr Chippenham. Entrance off A342 between Sandy Lane and Derry Hill villages. A breath-taking display of rhododendrons and azaleas from the minute detail of the individual flower to the grand sweep of colour formed by hundreds of shrubs, surrounded by a carpet of bluebells. *Open May & June. For NGS Adm £2.50 Sun June 2 (11-6).* **Tel 01249 812102**. *Also open* **Bowood House & Gardens** *Luncheon, TEAS. Garden centre. Adm £4.80 OAP £4.10 Chd £2.60. March 30 to Oct 27 (11-6)*

Broadleas ❀ (Lady Anne Cowdray) S of Devizes on A360. Bus: Devizes-Salisbury, alight Potterne Rd. Medium-sized garden; attractive dell planted with unusual trees, shrubs, azaleas and rhododendrons; many rare plants in secret and winter gardens. Home-made TEAS (on Suns). *Adm £2.50 Chd £1. April 2 to Oct 29 every Sun, Wed & Thurs. For NGS (Share to Animal Health Trust®). Suns April 14, Aug 11 (2-6)*

Bryher ⬥❀❀ (Mr & Mrs Richard Packham) Yard Lane Bromham. 4m N of Devizes on A342 to Chippenham turn R into Yard Lane at Xrds. A compact level garden, approx ⅔ acre created around a bungalow home. Borders planted mainly for foliage effect using a wide range of red, gold, silver and variegated plants, with many unusual varieties; short wildlife walk; display greenhouses with small nursery beds. *Adm £1 Chd free. Weds May 29; June 5, 12, 19 (11-5). Also private visits welcome, please Tel 01380 850455*

Chisenbury Priory ⬥❀❀ (Mr & Mrs John Manser) 6m SW of Pewsey, turn E from A345 at Enford then N to E Chisenbury, main gates 1m on R. Mediaeval Priory with Queen Anne face (not open) in middle of 5-acre garden on chalk; walled gardens; mature trees; shrubs; lawns; water; fine herbaceous borders; many unusual plants. TEAS. *Adm £2 Chd free. Suns June 16, 30 (2-6)*

Conock Manor ⬥❀❀ (Mr & Mrs Bonar Sykes) 5m SE of Devizes off A342. Mixed borders, flowering shrubs; extensive replanting incl new arboretum and woodland walk; collection of eucalyptus trees. C18 house in Bath stone (not shown). TEA. *Adm £1.50 Chd free under 16. Mon April 8 (2-6)*

Corsham Court ⬥❀ (James Methuen-Campbell Esq) 4m W of Chippenham. S of A4. Park and gardens laid out by Capability Brown and Repton. Large lawns with fine specimens of ornamental trees; rose garden; lily pond with Indian bean trees; spring bulbs; young arboretum; C18 bath house; Elizabethan mansion with alterations. TEAS. *Adm gardens £2 OAP £1.50 Chd £1.* ▲*For NGS Suns March 31, June 9 (2-6)*

Courtlands ⬥❀❀ (Mr Julius Silman) 4m S of Chippenham on Corsham-Lacock Road, 2m E of Corsham. 4-acre formal garden divided by splendid yew hedges into three connecting lawned gardens. Features include 2 gazebos; sunken lily pond with fountain, large fish pond with waterfall; walled kitchen garden; greenhouse with vines. Use of heated swimming pool available £1. TEAS. *Adm £1.50 Chd under 10 free. Sun July 7 (2-6)*

The Courts ⬥❀❀ (National Trust) Holt, 2m E of Bradford-on-Avon, S of B3107 to Melksham. In Holt follow National Trust signs, park at Village Hall. 3½-acres different formal gardens divided by yew hedges, raised terraces and shrubberies. Features incl conservatory, lily pond, herbaceous borders, pleached limes with interesting stone pillars, venetian gates and stone ornaments. 3½ acres wildflower and arboretum; many fine trees. NT C15 House (not shown) open every day except Sat April to Oct. Plant sales in Sept in aid of Bath Cancer Research Unit. Teas (on NGS days only) in church hall in aid of Church Hall Fund. *Adm £2.80 Chd £1.40.* ▲*For NGS Suns June 23, Sept 1 (2-5)*

Crudwell Court Hotel ⬥❀ (Nicholas Bristow Esq) Crudwell. On the A429 between Cirencester and Malmesbury. E of the rd, beside the church. 2½-acre garden surrounding C17 Rectory (now a hotel). Fine specimen 'rivers' beech, blue atlas cedar, magnolias, C12 dovecote surrounded by ancient yew hedges; Victorian sunken pond with wrought iron surround and lavender hedging. Rose garden and spring colour border outside conservatory. Herbaceous; shrub and herb borders; climbing roses; espaliered fruit trees and an Edwardian wooded walk; also spectrum and pastel coloured herbaceous border in rose garden. Swimming pool available in July; July opening with village strawberry fayre and craft fete. Coffee, lunch TEAS. *Adm £1 Chd 50p. Suns April 14, July 14 (11-5). Private visits welcome, please Tel 01666 577194*

¶**Downs Lodge** ❀❀ (Mrs D S Jones) nr Ogbourne St George. On A346 midway between Marlborough and Swindon, nr golf course. About 1½ acres, very close underlying chalk, reclaimed from overgrown farmland in 6 yrs. 'Before', 'during' and 'after' photos available. Very cold and late garden necessitating raised beds and imported soil to maximise high production of vegetables and special flowers. Far reaching views of Marlborough downland and plenty of seating. TEAS. *Adm £1 Chd under 12 free. Weds April 17, June 19 (2-6)*

Easton Grey House ⬥❀❀ (Mr & Mrs Sheldon Gordon) 3½m W of Malmesbury on B4040. Intensively cultivated 9-acre garden of beautiful C18 house. Also contains Easton Grey Church with its interesting Norman tower, font etc. Superb situation overlooking R Avon and surrounding countryside; lime-tolerant shrubs; tremendous display of spring bulbs, clematis, many roses; large walled garden containing traditional kitchen garden, large greenhouses, rose garden and borders. Home-made TEAS; produce, cake, and other stalls (in aid of Easton Grey Parish Church). *Adm £2 Chd free. Sun April 14 (2-6)*

Edington and Coulston Gardens 4m Westbury on B3098 halfway between Westbury and West Lavington. Follow signs and park outside The Monastery Garden for the Priory or in Church car park for The Grange, and walk through churchyard and along path, and for The Old Vicarage walk up hill to B3098. TEAS at The Monastery Garden. *Combined adm £3.50 Chd free (Share to Wiltshire Garden Trust®). Sun June 9 (2-6)*

    Bonshommes Cottage ❀ (Michael Jones Esq) Through Old Vicarage garden. ¼-acre garden with mixed herbaceous, roses, shrubs. There is renewed effort to reduce the dominant Japanese knotweed, long established in this part of the former Vicarage garden

    Edington Priory ⬥ (Mr & Mrs Rupert Cooper) 4-acre gardens with medieval well, walls and carp lake. Herbaceous borders, kitchen garden and extensive lawns with shrubs and roses

    Font House ❀ (Mr & Mrs R S Hicks) Coulston. 1½m E of Edington on B3098 take 1st L to Coulston, 1st house on L. 1-acre garden in rural surroundings which has been restored from a wilderness over past 30yrs and is still evolving; on 2 levels with courtyard, herbaceous borders, shrubs, herb and small specimen trees

    The Grange ⬥ (Col J S Douglas) Mature ¾-acre garden with interesting plants, shrubs and trees

The Monastery Garden & (Mr & Mrs Allenson-Bailey) 2½-acre garden with many varieties of spring bulbs; orchard and shrub roses; mediaeval walls of national importance

The Old Vicarage &✿❀ (J N d'Arcy Esq) A 2-acre garden on greensand situated on hillside with fine views; intensively planted with herbaceous borders; newly built wall borders, gravel garden; shrubs; a small arboretum with a growing range of trees; woodland plants; bulbs; lilies and recently introduced species from abroad. NCCPG National Collection of Evening primroses, over 20 species

Fonthill House ❀ (The Lord Margadale) 3m N of Tisbury. W of Salisbury via B3089 in Fonthill Bishop. Large woodland garden; daffodils, rhododendrons, azaleas, shrubs, bulbs; magnificent views; formal garden, limited for wheelchairs. TEAS. *Adm £1.50 Chd 30p (Share to Hindon Church Roof Appeal® May 19 only). Suns April 14, May 19 (2-6)*

Foscote Gardens ✿❀ Grittleton, 5m NW of Chippenham. A420 Chippenham-Bristol; after 2m turn R on B4039 to Yatton Keynell, fork R for Grittleton; in village for 2m, just over motorway turn R at Xrds; house on right. Homemade TEAS. *Combined adm £1.50 Chd 30p. Sun June 9 (2-6)*

Foscote Stables ✿❀ (Mr & Mrs Barry Ratcliffe) 2½-acres; many clematis; shrub roses; unusual shrubs, trees; small collection ornamental ducks
Foscote Stables Cottage ❀ (Mrs Beresford Worswick) This adjoining garden has been re-designed and replanted but still retains its cottage character. Unusual and some rare plants for sale

¶**Garden House** &✿❀ (J Reeve) Sandridge Park. 2m E of Melksham on A3102 (Calne) Rd. Walled garden, approx 1 acre with mixed borders, shrub roses and pond. *Adm £1 Chd free. Sun June 30 (2-6)*

Goulters Mill Farm &✿❀ (Mr & Mrs Michael Harvey) the Gibb, Burton. On B4039 5m W of Chippenham; 2m NW of Castle Combe, through the Gibb. Park at top of 300 metre drive and walk down to garden. Approx ¾-acre cottage garden; mixed perennials, eremurus, old-fashioned roses; water garden and woodland walk. Home-made cream TEAS and plant stall in aid of Russian Immigrants to Israel. *Adm £1 Chd 20p. Sun June 23 (2-6)*

The Grange &✿❀ (Mr & Mrs Rebdi) Winterbourne Dauntsey. Winterbourne Dauntsey is 4m NNE of Salisbury on the A338. Spacious 6-acre garden, still being developed, with R Bourne running through. Immaculate lawns, clipped box, borders. Laburnum, rose and clematis arched walk; lily pond; vegetable and herb garden. Wild natural area with peacocks. Restored C17 thatched barn (open). TEAS in aid of Winterbourne Glebe Hall. *Adm £1.50 Chd under 16 free. Sun July 14 (2-6)*

Great Chalfield Manor ✿❀ (The National Trust; Mr & Mrs Robert Floyd) 4m from Melksham. Take B3107 from Melksham then 1st R to Broughton Gifford signed Atworth, turn L for 1m to Manor. Park on grass outside. Garden and grounds of 7 acres laid out 1905-12 by Robert Fuller and his wife; given to NT in 1943, it re-

mains the home of his family. Garden paths, steps, dry walls relaid and rebuilt in 1985 and roses replanted; daffodils, spring flowers; topiary houses, borders, terraces, gazebo, orchard, autumn border. C15 moated manor (not open) and adjoining Church. Evensong Service 6pm Oct 6. TEAS. *Adm £2 Chd free (Share to All Saints Church®).* ▲*For NGS Suns April 21, Oct 6 (2-6) 1997 Feb 23 (2-4)*

Great Somerford Gardens &✿❀ 2m N of M4 between junctions 17 and 18; 2m S of B4042 MalmesburyWootton Bassett rd; 3m E of A429 Circencester-Chippenham rd. TEAS. *Combined adm £3, Chd under 12 free (Share to Wessex Children's Hospice®). Sat, Sun July 13, 14 (1.30-6)*

Old Church School (Cdr & Mrs Peter Neate) A ¾-acre garden created over the last 3 yrs from the school playing field. It is centred around a formal yew-hedged area containing a flourishing pool, parterre and shrubs, surrounded by herbaceous, hebe and rose beds, pergolas and arches, rockery and heathers as well as a good collection of trees and shrubs
The Old Maltings (Mr & Mrs Peter Prophet) The front garden has been recently designed with extensive and interesting herbaceous and shrub borders. Behind the house there is a walk down to and across the R Avon into a conservation area with plantations of young native trees and shrubs. TEAS
Somerford House (Mr & Mrs Derek Bayliss) The owners and their family over the past 14 yrs have designed and developed a 3-acre garden, which incorporates the original orchard and features roses, shrubs, old wisteria, perennials, rockery and pool, vegetables and soft fruit. A flower arranger's delight
White Lodge, Startley (Major & Mrs Jonathan Oliphant) A partially-walled garden, developed gradually over the last 20 yrs. Old-fashioned roses, clematis and herbaceous borders, incl unusual plants. Topiary and catalpa tree. TEAS

¶**Guyers House** &✿❀ (Mr & Mrs Guy Hungerford) Pickwick, Corsham. N of A4, just W of Corsham. A garden which has been recently restored and is being extended. 5 acres of herbaceous borders, new yew walks, lawns, pond, climbing and shrub roses; walled garden; kitchen garden. TEAS. *Adm £1.50 Chd free. Sun June 16 (2-5.30)*

Hazelbury Manor Gardens &✿❀ Wadswick, nr Box. 5m SW of Chippenham; 5m NE of Bath; 3m N of Bradford-on-Avon. From A4 at Box, take A365 to Melksham, L onto B3109; L again at Chapel Plaister; drive immed on R. 8 acres of Grade II landscaped formal gardens surrounding a charming C15 fortified manor house. An impressive yew topiary and clipped beeches surround the large lawn; herbaceous and mixed borders blaze in summer; laburnums and limes form splendid walkways. Other features include rose garden, stone ring ponds, an enchanting fountain and rockery. Beyond the house is a new plantation of specimen trees. *Adm Gardens only £2.80 OAP £2 Chd £1. For NGS Sat, Sun July 27, 28 (2-6). Private visits welcome, please* **Tel 01225 812952/812088**

General Information. For general information on the use of this book see Page 15.

Heale Gardens & Plant Centre ♿❀ (Guy Rasch Esq) Middle Woodford, 4m N of Salisbury on Woodford Valley Rd between A360 and A345. 8 acres beside R Avon; interesting and varied collection of plants, shrubs; and roses in formal setting of clipped hedges and mellow stonework surrounding C17 manorhouse where Charles II hid after the battle of Worcester. Water garden with magnolia and acer frames, an authentic Japanese Tea House and Nikki bridge. Well stocked plant centre. Gift shop. Open all year. TEAS in the house on NGS Sunday pm only. *Adm £2.50 Acc chd under 14 free (Share to Garden History Society®). For NGS* Sun Aug 4 (10-5). **Tel 01722 782504**

Hillbarn House ✄❀ (Mr & Mrs A J Buchanan) Great Bedwyn, SW of Hungerford. S of A4 Hungerford-Marlborough. Medium-sized garden on chalk with hornbeam tunnel, pleached limes, herb garden; some planting by Lanning Roper; a series of gardens within a garden. Swimming pool may be used (under 12) Topiary. TEA. *Adm £2 Chd 50p.* Suns June 23, Sept 22 (2-6). *Private visits of 10 and over welcome, please* **Tel 01672 870207**

Hodges Barn Shipton Moyne See Gloucestershire

Home Covert ♿❀ (Mr & Mrs John F Phillips) Roundway, Devizes. 1m N of Devizes on minor rd signed Roundway linking A361 to A342. 1m from each main road, house signed. An extensive garden developed since 1960 by present owners, with many unusual trees, shrubs, and hardy plants. Formal herbaceous borders, small garden of pastel colours and foliage and water gardens 80ft below with waterfall, streams and a small lake planted with bog primulas, various waterside plants and fern collection. Also many varieties hydrangeas and late-flowering clematis. Optional woodland walk, ¾m bluebells. Featured in NGS video 2. TEAS on May 12 in aid of Wilts Wildlife Trust, July 21 in aid of St James Church Repair Fund. *Adm £2 Chd free.* Suns May 12, July 21 (2-6). *Private parties welcome, please* **Tel 01380 723407**

Hyde's House ❀ (George Cruddas Esq) Dinton. 5m W of Wilton, off B3089, next to church. 2 acres of wild and formal garden in beautiful situation with series of hedged garden rooms and numerous shrub and herbaceous borders. Much interest in layout, old and new planting especially shrub roses. Large walled kitchen garden, herb garden and C13 dovecote (open). Charming C16/18 Grade 1 listed house (not open), with lovely courtyard; short walk to lake and park currently being restored by National Trust; TEAS in adjacent thatched 'old school room'. *Adm £1.75 Chd under 14 free (Share to St Mary's Church, Dinton®).* Suns May 5, Aug 25 (2-5). *Private visits of 20 and over welcome, please* **Tel 01722 716203**

Iford Manor (Mr & Mrs Hignett) Off A36 7 miles S of Bath — sign to Iford 1m or from Bradford-on-Avon/Trowbridge via Lower Westwood village (brown signs). Entrance and free parking at Iford Bridge. Very romantic Italian-style terraced garden, listed Grade 1, home of Harold Peto between 1898 and 1933. House not shown. TEAS May to Sept, Sats, Suns and Bank Hol Mons. *Adm £2.20 OAPs/Student/Chd 10+ £1.60. Open daily May to Sept (except Mons & Fris), April & Oct Suns only. For NGS* Sun April 28 (2-5). *Private visits welcome, please* **Tel 01225 863146**

Inwoods ♿✄❀ (Mr & Mrs D S Whitehead) Farleigh Wick, 3m NW of Bradford-on-Avon. From Bath via A363 towards Bradford-on-Avon; at Farleigh Wick, 100yds past Fox & Hounds, R into drive. 5 acres with lawns, borders, flowering shrubs, wild garden, bluebell wood. TEAS in aid of Home Farm Trust. *Adm £1.50 Chd 50p.* Sun May 5 (2-6)

Job's Mill ❀ (Virginia, Marchioness of Bath) Crockerton, 1½m S of Warminster. Bus: Salisbury-Bath, alight Warminster. Medium-sized garden; small terraced garden, through which R Wylye flows; swimming pool; kitchen garden. TEAS. *Adm £1.50 Chd 50p (Share to WWF®).* Sun June 30 (2-6)

Kingfisher Mill (The Hon Aylmer Tryon) Gt Durnford. 2m Amesbury. From A345 turn W at High Post. Or 1m from Bridge Inn at Upper Woodford. Park in Village Road. Down short avenue of poplars. 3 acres very watery garden on R Avon with primulas and wild garden to encourage butterflies and show beauty of wild flowers. Good daffodils from Lionel Richardson's nursery in Waterford. Spring bulbs and variety of magnolias. Garden begun 1962 from old water meadow by enthusiastic amateur. Tea at Black Horse in village. *Adm £2 Chd free (Share to Wiltshire Wildlife Trust®).* Sun April 14 (2-5.30)

¶13 Kingsdown Road ✄❀ (Mr & Mrs Kenneth Tomlin) Stratton St Margaret. Approach from S on A419. L at Kennedys Garden Centre (signposted Upper Stratton). ½m turn L at t-lights and park opp Kingsdown inn. Long and narrow garden on edge of town closely planted with shrubs and herbaceous plants. Vegetable garden. Unusual plants with some for sale. O-gauge model railway added attraction. Example of maximum use of space available. TEAS. *Adm 75p Chd free.* Sun June 9 (2-6)

¶Kingsmead Mill ♿ (Sir David Puttnam) Little Somerford. Leave M4 exit 16 by A3102 to Wootton Basset, then B4042 to Malmesbury through Brinkworth; L into lane signed Somerfords to Xrds. Turn L then R through village past church then R before railway bridge. Or leave M4 exit 17 by A420 to Sutton Benger. Turn L at Bell House Hotel and through Great Somerford. Turn L into lane after railway bridge. Please see Estate Manager on arrival. Mill stream, mill pond, 5 acres of graden incl islands, streams, lake and kitchen garden all on the R Avon plus a 6-acre arboretum, now in its 12th yr. TEA Sun June 2 only. *Adm £1.50 Chd 50p (Share to the Kingsmead Charity Trust®).* Sun June 2, Weds May 22, June 19, July 10 (3-6)

Lackham Gardens ఉ఑ (Lackham College Principal Peter Morris) Lacock, 2m S of Chippenham. Signposted N of Notton on A350. Few mins S of junction 17 on M4. Station: Chippenham. Bus: Chippenham-Trowbridge, alight drive entrance, 1m. Large gardens; walled garden with greenhouses, carnations, alstroemeria, pot plants, warm greenhouse plants, giant fruited Citron tree, propagating house, fuchsias, begonias; lawn paths separating plots well laid out, labelled with great variety of interesting shrubs, usual and unusual vegetables, herbaceous plants, fruit. Modern style Bradstone paved garden and gazebo. Pleasure gardens featuring a major historical collection of roses depicting the development of the modern rose; mixed borders, herbs, shrubs, lawns; woodland walks down to river; large bird viewing hide. New for summer 1996 an extension to the gardens with 17, 18, 19th century gardens, a maze, a pond and shrub collections. Raffle drawn shortly after demonstrations at 3.30pm; walled garden; (May 5) Mulching (July 14) Chip budding apple stocks (Oct 6) Containerised bulbs. Particulars of Lackham full and part-time courses available. Museum of Agricultural Equipment, RARE breeds. Adventure playground. Coffee shop; TEAS Bookable menu etc on request within coach party organiser pack (11-4). *Adm £3 Chd £1 (Share to Horticultural Therapy of Frome, Somerset®). Open daily April 1 to Oct 29. For NGS Suns May 5, July 14, Oct 6 (2-5)*

Lacock Abbey Gardens ఉ఑఑ (National Trust) Chippenham. A350 midway between Melksham-Chippenham. Follow National Trust signs. Use public car park just outside the Abbey. 9 acres of parkland surrounding the Abbey with a pond and exotic tree specimens. Display of early spring flowers with carpets of aconites; snowdrops; crocuses and daffodils. C13 Abbey with C18 gothic additions. (Mediaeval cloisters open on NGS days, house closed until April). Teas available in village. *Adm £1.50 Chd free.* ▲*Suns Feb 18, 25, Mar 3 (2-5). 1997 Suns Feb 16, 23, Mar 2 (2-5). Parties welcome on NGS days only, please* **Tel 01249 730227**

Landford Lodge ఉ఑ (Mr & Mrs Christopher Pilkington) 9m SE of Salisbury turn W off A36; garden ½m N of Landford. C18 House (not open) in lovely parkland overlooking lake; many fine trees. Special feature 3-acre wood with rhododendrons and azaleas. Herbaceous; ornamental terrace and swimming pool (open). Tree nursery. 500 varieties of trees planted in alphabetical order in walled garden. TEAS. *Adm £1.50 Chd 50p (Share to Salisbury Mencap Horticultural Trust®). Sun May 26 (2-5). Private parties of 10 and over welcome, please* **Tel 01794 390247**

Little Durnford Manor ఑ (Earl & Countess of Chichester) 3m N of Salisbury, just beyond Stratford-sub-Castle. Extensive lawns with cedars; walled gardens, fruit trees, large vegetable garden; small knot and herb gardens, terraces, borders, gravel garden, water garden, lake with islands, river walks. Cottage Garden also on view. Home-made TEAS. *Adm £1.50 Chd 50p (Share to Wessex Medical School Trust®). Suns May 5, June 30 (2-6)*

Long Hall Gardens and Nursery ఉ఑఑ (Mr & Mrs N H Yeatman-Biggs) Stockton 7m SE of Warminster; S of A36; W of A303 Wylye interchange. Follow signs to church in Stockton. 4-acre mainly formal garden featured recently in House and Garden; a series of gardens within a garden; clipped yews; flowering shrubs, fine old trees; masses of spring bulbs; fine hellebore walk. C13 Hall with later additions (not open). TEAS. *Adm £2 Chd free (Share to St John the Baptist's Church, Stockton). 1st Sat of the month from May 4 to August 3 (2-6). Private visits welcome, please* **Tel 01985 850424.** *For NGS Mon April 8; Sat June 29 (2-6).* Adjacent nursery specialising in chalk tolerant plants, all organically grown, many uncommon varieties and new introductions. *Wed to Sat, March 20 to Sept 28 (9.30-5.30)*

Lower Burytown ఉ఑఑ (Capt Francis Burne) Nr Blunsdon ¾m off B4019 (between Blunsdon and Highworth). 1¼m from A419; 8m from M4 exit 15. Approached by private drive. A 3-acre garden which has been entirely made in last 5 yrs. Herbaceous borders, shrubs and a water garden. TEAS. *Adm £1.50 Chd free (Share to St Leonards, Stanton Fitzwarren Parish Church®). Sun June 23 (2-6). Private parties of 10 and over welcome, please* **Tel 01793 706696**

Lower Farm House ఉ఑఑ (Mrs John Agate) Milton Lilbourne. E of Pewsey on B3087. Turn down village street by garage at Xrds. Garden down street on L. An enlarged and developing 5-acre garden designed by Tim Rees and planted over the last 7 yrs; facing S towards Salisbury Plain over 2 ponds. Winter garden; water garden; shrubs and herbaceous borders; young trees chosen for their bark; spring bulbs; gazebo; and conservatory. *Adm £1.50 Chd free (Share to Milton Lilbourne Parish Church®). Sun Aug 4 (2-6). Private visits welcome March to Sept, please* **Tel 01672 562911**

¶**Lower House** ఉ఑ (D J Wood Esq) Whiteparish. On A27 between Salisbury and Romsey (7m). Garden is N side of A27, Salisbury end of village, opp Newton Bungalows. Informal garden of 1 acre containing part of National Collection of Hellebores. *Adm £1 Chd free. Private visits welcome by appt Mon to Sat, Feb 19 to March 16 (10-12 and 2-4), please* **Tel 01974 884306**

Luckington Court ఉ఑ (The Hon Mrs Trevor Horn) Luckington village, 10m NW of Chippenham; 6m W of Malmesbury. Turn S off B4040 Malmesbury-Bristol. Bus: Bristol-Swindon, alight Luckington. Medium-sized garden, mainly formal, well-designed, amid exquisite group of ancient buildings; fine collection of ornamental cherries; other flowering shrubs. House much altered in Queen Anne times but ancient origins evident; Queen Anne hall and drawing-room shown. TEAS in aid of Luckington Parish Church. *Collecting box. Sun May 12 (2.30-6). Private visits welcome, please* **Tel 01666 840205**

Luckington Manor ఉ఑఑ (Mr & Mrs K Stanbridge) NW of Chippenham 7½m SW of Malmesbury on the B4040 Malmesbury-Bristol. 3½ acres, walled flower gardens; many more additions of unusual and special plants, shrubberies; arboretum, sunken rose garden, well garden, herbs and healing plants. Special Spring feature. Garden now organically run attracting more and more wildlife. C17 Manor House (not open). Home-made TEAS and plants in aid of Parish Church Roof Fund. *Adm £2 Senior Citizens £1 Chd free. Suns April 28, July 14, Aug 11 (2-6)*

Mallards &&☀ (Mr & Mrs T Papé) Chirton. 4½m SE of Devizes just N of A342. Go right through village and garden is on R. 1-acre informal garden beside the upper R Avon with mixed borders, new rose garden, woodland glade and bog garden. Also a woodland walk under development. TEAS in aid of Chirton & Marden Parish Churches. *Adm £1.50 Chd free. Suns June 9, July 28 (2-6)*

Manningford Bruce Gardens &☀ 2m SW of Pewsey on A345 on R after Manningford Bruce sign. From Upavon or Devizes 1m after Woodbridge Inn on L. Car park suitable for picnics. TEAS at Manor. *Combined adm £3 Chd free. Sun June 23 (2-5.30)*

    Manningford Bruce House (Maj & Mrs Robert Ferguson) 1½ acres; lawns, shrubbery and walled garden of C17/C18 Rectory (not open). Herbaceous borders with many unusual plants, shrubs and a folly. Small kitchen garden

    The Manor (Visconde & Viscondessa de Pereira Machado) 4-acre garden recently refurbished, incl large walled garden with herbaceous borders and great variety of shrubs and plants; tennis court; croquet lawn; conservatory and herb garden. Swimming pool and rustic arbour

The Mead Nursery &&☀ (Mr & Mrs S Lewis-Dale) Brokerswood. Equidistant Frome and Westbury E of Rudge. Follow signs for Woodland Park. Halfway between Rudge and Woodland Park. 1¼-acre nursery with over 1,000 varieties of herbaceous perennials, alpines and bulbs, many unusual. Display beds for colour and design ideas. Raised beds, sink garden, and bog bed. TEAS on NGS day only. *Adm £1.50 Chd £1 to incl teas. Nursery open Feb 1 to Oct 31 Wed to Sat (9-5), Sun (12-5). For NGS Sun Aug 11 (12-5)*

Mompesson House &&☀ (The National Trust) The Close. Enter Salisbury Cathedral Close via High St Gate and Mompesson House is on the R. The appeal of this comparatively small but attractive garden is the lovely setting in Salisbury Cathedral Close and with a well-known Queen Anne House. Planting as for an old English garden with raised rose and herbaceous beds around the lawn. Climbers on pergola and walls; shrubs and small lavender walk. TEAS. *Adm £1 Chd free.* ▲*Sat June 8 (11-5)*

7 Norton Bavant &&☀ (Mr & Mrs J M Royds) nr Warminster. 2m E of Warminster on A36 turn W to Sutton Veny on Cotley Hill roundabout at Heytesbury, then R to Norton Bavant. Turn R in village 1st house on R after tall conifer hedge. Alpine plant collector's garden with numerous varieties (many rare). Spring bulbs, alpine house, many troughs, borders, dwarf conifers and specialised collection of daphnes. Members of AGS especially welcome. TEA in aid of Norton Bavant Church. *Adm £2 Chd free. Private visits and parties welcome March to Oct, please Tel 01985 840491*

Oare House & (Henry Keswick Esq) 2m N of Pewsey on Marlborough Rd (A345). Fine house (not open) in large garden with fine trees, hedges, spring flowers, woodlands; extensive lawns and kitchen garden. TEA. *Adm £1 Chd 20p (Share to The Order of St John®). Suns April 28, July 28 (2-6)*

The Old Bakery &&☀ (Joyce, Lady Crossley) Milton Lilbourne E of Pewsey on B3087. Turn down village street by garage at Xrds. The Old Bakery is opp churchyard. Fairly intensive 1-acre garden. Mixed shrub and herbaceous plantings. 3 small glasshouses; small rock garden; some rare plants. Home-made TEAS. *Adm £1 Chd free. Sun Aug 4 (2-6). Private parties welcome, please Tel 01672 562716*

The Old Rectory &&☀ (Mr & Mrs David Harrison) Stockton. 7m SE of Warminster, S of A36 W of A303 Wylye interchange. The Old Rectory is just beyond the church. The 2-acre garden surrounds an attractive C18 house, with lawns and some fine old trees incl a cedar and a magnificent beech, in the front. To the S it splits into several smaller gardens; an entirely walled herb garden with a variety of herbs, leavened with climbers and some fine roses and vines; and the orchard, dominated by a stunning walnut tree, leads to 3 separate smaller walled gardens with a great variety of plants incl roses and peonies. Featured recently on TV. TEAS. *Adm £1.50 Chd free. Sun June 16 (2-6). Private visits welcome, please Tel 01985 850607*

Old School House &☀ (Mr & Mrs Malcolm Lyell) Baverstock. 1m E of Dinton turn N off B3089 for Baverstock. Garden adjoins church. A 1-acre garden created from a meadow since 1989. Ponds and rock garden. Many unusual trees and shrubs incl 13 varieties of magnolias incl a yellow one which will hopefully be in flower. *Adm £1.50 Chd free (Share to Baverstock Church®). Sun May 26 (2-6)*

Pound Hill House &&☀ (Mr & Mrs P Stockitt) West Kington. 8m NNW of Chippenham, 2m NE of Marshfield exit 18 on M4 take A420 Chippenham-Bristol road N signed West Kington. At village take No Through Road at Xrds. Around C15 Cotswold Stone House 2-acre garden in charming setting, continually developing and planted to provide interest throughout yr. Made up of small gardens, an old-fashioned rose garden with clipped box, small Victorian vegetable garden, pergola with wisteria, roses, clematis; grass walk with large shrub roses, newly planted double herbaceous borders backed by clipped yew hedges, shade and water garden. Courtyard garden with clipped yews and box, paved area with interesting plants, raised alpine beds. Wide selection of imaginatively planted pots and containers. Extensive retail plant area with plants drawn from adjacent nursery with 2000 varieties. TEAS in aid of West Kington Church. *Open Tues to Sun and Bank Hols Feb to Dec. Adm £1.75 OAPs £1.15. Sun June 30 (2-6). Private parties welcome, please Tel 01249 782781*

Ridleys Cheer &&☀ (Mr & Mrs A J Young) Mountain Bower, N Wraxall. 8m NW of Chippenham. At 'The Shoe' on A420 8m W of Chippenham turn N then take 2nd L and 1st R. 1½-acre informal garden containing interesting and unusual trees and shrubs; incl acers, liriodendrons, magnolias, salix and zelkova. Some 75 different shrub rose varieties incl hybrid musks, albas and species roses; planted progressively over past 20 yrs; also potager and 2 acres woodland planted 1989, now with more than 20 different oak species suitable for limestone soils. Cream TEAS in aid of N Wraxall Church and Dorothy House Foundation. *Adm £1.50 Chd under 14 free. Suns May 5, June 23, July 7; Wed June 26 (2-6). Private visits welcome, please Tel 01225 891204*

¶**St Margarets House** ✿✿ (Mr & Mrs L N Lacey) Corsley. Mid-way between Frome and Warminster. Leave A36 at junction with A3098. Take Frome Rd. At Chapmanslade (½m) turn L signpost Corsley. Also accessible from A361. This sheltered former Rectory garden has been completely re-established by the owners over the last 15 yrs. Over 2½ acres designed to incl mixed shrubs and herbaceous planting, rose garden, woodland walk and other areas of interest which carefully combine the older trees and shrubs with more recent planting. Significant collection of clematis. TEAS. *Adm £1.50 Chd 50p. Sun June 23 (2-6)*

Sharcott Manor ✿✿✿ (Capt & Mrs David Armytage) 1m SW of Pewsey via A345. 5-acre garden with water planted for yr-round interest. Many young trees, bulbs, climbers and densely planted mixed borders of shrubs, roses, perennials and unusual plants, some of which are for sale in the small garden nursery. TEAS in aid of IFAW and Wiltshire Air Ambulance appeal. *Adm £2 Chd free. First Weds in every month from April to Oct (11-5). Suns April 21, June 30 (2-6) all for NGS. Also private visits welcome, please* Tel 01672 563485

Spye Park ✿ (Mr & Mrs Simon Spicer) nr Chippenham. Take A342 Chippenham and Devizes rd, turn E at Sandy Lane opp 'The George' public house. Turn S after ½m at White Lodge. Follow signs to car park. Exit only through the village of Chittoe. 25-acre woodland walk through carpets of bluebells with paths cut through the wood. Some fine old trees mostly oak and beech, survivors of the 1989 hurricane, incl the remnants of 1000-yr-old King Oak with the 900-yr-old Queen still alive. TEAS. *Adm £1 Chd free (Share to Southmead Hospital Special Care Baby Unit©). Sun April 28 (11-5). Private parties welcome when bluebells are out, please* Tel 01249 730247

Stourhead Garden ✿✿ (The National Trust) Stourton, 3m NW of Mere on B3092. One of earliest and greatest landscape gardens in the world; creation of banker Henry Hoare in 1740s on his return from the Grand Tour, inspired by paintings of Claude and Poussin; planted with rare trees, rhododendrons and azaleas over last 240yrs. Open every day of year. Lunch, tea and supper Spread Eagle Inn at entrance. NT shop. Teas (Buffet service Village Hall). *Adm March to Oct £4.20 Chd £2.20 parties of 15 or over £3.60. Nov to Feb £3.20 Chd 1.50.* ▲*For NGS Sun May 12 (9-7)*

Stourton House ✿✿✿ (Mrs Anthony Bullivant) Stourton. 3m NW of Mere (A303) on rd to Stourhead. Park in NT car park. 4½-acres informal gardens; much to attract plantsmen and idea seekers. Interesting bulbs, plants and shrubs, through all seasons. Speciality daffodils and hydrangeas. Well known for 'Stourton Dried Flowers' whose production interest visitors (BBC Gardeners World '92). Coffee, lunch, TEAS in Stourton House Garden. *April 3 to November 28, Sun, Wed, Thurs and Bank Hol Mons. Adm £2 Chd 50p (Share to St Peters Church, Stourton®). Sats, Suns April 27, 28, Aug 10, 11 (11-6), all for NGS. Private visits welcome for parties of 12 and over, please Tel 01747 840417*

Sutton Veny Gardens ✿✿✿ 3m SE of Warminster. Turn W off A36 at Heytesbury Roundabout or E off A350 at Longbridge Deverill. TEAS. Plants at Little Newnham. *Combined adm £2.50 Chd free (Share to R.A.B.I.® and I.L.P.H.®). Sun June 30 (2-6)*

1 Greenhill (Mr & Mrs Peter Crane) A 1-acre garden facing SE on 2 levels interconnected by a natural slope with commanding views towards hills and downland through impressive pines. Mixed borders with shrubs and interesting plants, old roses and clematis. Lower level has mixed shrubs underplanted with massed spring bulbs. Area of vegetables and various fruit plots

Little Newnham (Mrs Caroline Ellert) Partly walled 1-acre garden overlooked by C17/18 house (not open), referred to in 'The Buildings of England' by Nikolaus Pevsner. The garden with open views to the downs, has been recently restored and recreated. Many old roses, herbaceous borders, kitchen garden and newly planted orchard. Lawn dominated by rare weeping beech. Plant sale. *Also open Suns July 7 to Aug 4 (2-6). Adm £1.50*

Thompson's Hill (Mr & Mrs J C Cooper) Sherston. 5m Malmesbury-Tetbury. In Sherston village turn L at Church down hill, bear R up Thompson's Hill. ½-acre fully planted, interestingly designed garden made since 1980. Pretty conservatory added to house 1992. Illustrated in 'House & Garden' Magazine, new issue 'The Englishwoman's Garden', 'The English Garden' by Peter Coates and the 'Good Gardens Guide'. *Adm £1.50 Chd 50p (Share to Cancer Research®). Sun June 30 (2-6.30). Private visits welcome, please* Tel 01666 840766

¶**Upper Chelworth Farm** ✿✿✿ (Mr & Mrs Hopkins) nr Cricklade. Take B4040 off A419, through Cricklade, L at 1st Xrds, 1st house on L. Approx ½-acre garden of mixed perennials, shrubs and water garden. Small nursery. TEAS on NGS Suns. *Adm £1 Chd free. 1st & 2nd Sat & Sun of each month April 6 to Oct 6. For NGS Suns April 14, June 9, Aug 11 (2-6)*

Waterdale House ✿ (Mr & Mrs Julian Seymour) Milton, East Knoyle. North of East Knoyle on A350 turn W signed Milton, garden signed from village. 4-acre mature woodland garden with rhododendrons, azaleas, camellias, maples, magnolias, ornamental water and bog garden; herbaceous borders and hydrangeas. Gravelled pot garden. TEAS if fine. *Adm £1.50 Chd free. Suns May 12, July 14 (2-5). Private visits welcome April to July, lunches for parties up to 20 if required, please* Tel 01747 830262

61 Whitegate ✿✿ (Mr & Mrs C J Pratt) Castle Combe. Chippenham 5m M4 exit 17 S B4039 Chippenham Burton. Large car park clearly signed at top of hill. Originally Norman, now mostly C15, one of England's prettiest villages. Small garden with yr-round planting. An example of care and initiative in achieving variety in a small garden. Teas at Goulters Mill Farm, The Gibb. *Adm £1 Chd free. Sun June 23 (2-6)*

Worton Gardens ✿✿ Devizes 3m. Devizes-Salisbury A360 turn W in Potterne or just N of West Lavington. From Seend turn S at Bell Inn, follow signs to Worton. TEAS at Ivy House. *Combined adm £2 Chd free. Sun July 14 (2-6)*

Ashton House ❀ (Mrs Colin Shand) ½-acre garden in 3 sections with herbaceous borders, many shrubs and birch grove; walled courtyard and raised vegetable garden; lovely views across Avon Vale

¶**Brookfield House** &.❀ (Mr & Mrs Graham Cannon) A new 1-acre garden owned since 1993, and being developed with small children in mind. Part-walled garden with mixed borders and separate fruit and vegetable garden

Ivy House (Lt Gen Sir Maurice and Lady Johnston) 2-acre series of gardens separated by yew hedges and walls; herbaceous borders; shrubs; pond garden with maples and many fine trees incl swamp cypress, holm and red oak, medlar and mulberry; interesting vegetable garden and large greenhouse

Oakley House ❀ (Mr & Mrs Michael Brierley) ½-acre village garden with herbaceous borders, roses, many shrubs; small pond and bog garden within a rockery; planted by owners since 1974

Worcestershire

See Hereford

Yorkshire & Cleveland

Hon County Organisers:
(N Yorks - Districts of Hambleton, Richmond, Ryedale, Scarborough & Cleveland)

Mrs William Baldwin, Riverside Farm, Sinnington, York YO6 6RY
Tel 01751 431764

(West & South Yorks & North Yorks Districts of Craven, Harrogate, Selby & York)

Mrs Roger Marshall, The Old Vicarage, Whixley, York YO5 8AR
Tel 01423 330474

(E Yorks)

Mrs Philip Bean, Saltmarshe Hall, Howden, Goole, Yorkshire DN14 7RX
Tel 01430 430199

DATES OF OPENING

March 3 Sunday
Fairview, Summerbridge
March 31 Sunday
Otterington Hall, Northallerton
April 7 Sunday
The Croft, North Cave
Netherwood House, Ilkley
April 14 Sunday
Bolton Percy Gardens, Tadcaster ‡
Harlsey Manor, East Harlsey
Victoria Cottage, Stainland
Windy Ridge, Bolton Percy ‡
April 21 Sunday
Parcevall Hall, nr Skipton
Wytherstone House, nr Helmsley
April 28 Sunday
Boston Spa Gardens, nr Wetherby
Ling Beeches, Scarcroft, nr Leeds
St Nicholas, Richmond
May 5 Sunday
Evergreens, 119 Main Road ‡
Il Giardino, Bilton ‡
54a Keldgate, Beverley

May 6 Monday
The Old Vicarage, Whixley
May 12 Sunday
Blackbird Cottage, Scampston
Hemble Hill Farm, Guisborough
Lanhydrock Cottage, Skerne
The Spaniels, Hensall, nr Selby
Victoria Cottage, Stainland
May 15 Wednesday
Beacon Hill House, nr Ilkley
May 19 Sunday
Fairview, Summerbridge ‡
Fieldhead, Boston Spa ‡‡
Hillbark, Bardsey ‡‡
Oxenber House, nr Settle
Stillingfleet Lodge, nr York
8 Welton Old Road, Welton
The White Cottage, Halsham, nr Hull
Woodlands Cottage, Summerbridge ‡
May 22 Wednesday
The Chimney Place, Bilton Grange
May 25 Saturday
The Chimney Place, Bilton Grange

Nawton Tower, Nawton
Old Sleningford, nr Ripon
May 26 Sunday
Castle Farm Nurseries, Barmby Moor
High Farm, Bilton ‡
Il Giardino, Bilton ‡
Lanhydrock Cottage, Skerne
Nawton Tower, Nawton
Old Sleningford, nr Ripon
Shandy Hall, Coxwold ‡‡
Woodcock, Thirsk ‡‡
May 27 Monday
Nawton Tower, Nawton
Old Sleningford, nr Ripon
June 1 Saturday
Pennyholme, Fadmoor ‡
Sleightholme Dale Lodge, Fadmoor ‡
York Gate, Adel, Leeds 16
June 2 Sunday
Castle Farm Nurseries, Barmby Moor
Creskeld Hall, Arthington ‡
Elvington Gardens, nr York

Glebe House, Thrybergh,
  Rotherham ‡‡
Pennyholme, Fadmoor ‡‡‡
Plants of Special Interest,
  Braithwell ‡‡
Shadwell Grange, Leeds ‡
Shandy Hall, Coxwold
Sleightholme Dale Lodge,
  Fadmoor ‡‡‡
Victoria Cottage, Stainland
York Gate, Adel, Leeds 16 ‡

June 8 Saturday
Burton Agnes Hall, Driffield
Pennyholme, Fadmoor

June 9 Sunday
Brookfield, Oxenhope
Burton Agnes Hall, Driffield
Derwent House, Osbaldwick ‡
Helmsley Gardens
Hunmanby Grange,
  nr Scarborough
Lanhydrock Cottage, Skerne
Littlethorpe Gardens, nr Ripon
Nunburnholme Gardens
Pennyholme, Fadmoor
55 Rawcliffe Drive, York ‡
Secret Garden, York ‡
Snilesworth, Northallerton

June 16 Sunday
Fieldhead, Boston Spa
Inglemere Lodge, Ilkley
The Old Vicarage, Whixley ‡
Oxenber House, nr Settle
Parcevall Hall, nr Skipton
Parkview, South Cave
Saltmarshe Hall, Saltmarshe
Sinnington Gardens, Pickering
Springfield House, Tockwith ‡
Victoria Cottage, Stainland ‡‡
The Willows, nr Brighouse ‡‡
Wytherstone House, nr Helmsley

June 19 Wednesday
The Chimney Place, Bilton Grange
Windsong, Osgodby

June 22 Saturday
The Chimney Place, Bilton Grange

June 23 Sunday
Blackbird Cottage, Scampston
Bossall Gardens, Bossall
Fieldhead, Boston Spa ‡
Goddards, York
Hillbark, Bardsey ‡
Kelberdale, Knaresborough
54a Keldgate, Beverley ‡‡
80 Lairgate, Beverley ‡‡
Lanhydrock Cottage, Skerne
Norton Conyers, Wath, nr Ripon
Park House, Moreby, nr York
Wincroft, Swanland
Windsong, Osgodby

June 26 Wednesday
Ness Hall, Nunnington

Wass Gardens, nr Coxwold

June 30 Sunday
Bankfield, Huddersfield
Bolton Percy Gardens, Tadcaster ‡
Boynton Hall
8 Dunstarn Lane, Adel
The Green, Lund ‡‡‡
High Farm, Bilton ‡‡‡‡
32 Hollybank Road, York
Holly Cottage, Wressle
Hovingham Hall, Hovingham
Il Giardino, Bilton ‡‡‡‡
Kelberdale, Knaresborough ‡‡
5 Lockington Road, Lund ‡‡‡
Lullaby, Hull ‡‡‡
Shandy Hall, Coxwold
Stillingfleet Lodge, nr York
Stockeld Park, Wetherby ‡‡
Windy Ridge, Bolton Percy ‡

July 3 Wednesday
Ness Hall, Nunnington
Shandy Hall, Coxwold
Three Gables, Markington

July 7 Sunday
Bishopscroft, Sheffield
Evergreens, 119 Main Road
Fernwood, Cropton
Grimston Gardens, Gilling East
Hunmanby Grange,
  nr Scarborough
Millgate House, Richmond
The Old Rectory, Mirfield
Plants of Special Interest,
  Braithwell
Victoria Cottage, Stainland
26 West End, Walkington
The White House, Husthwaite

July 10 Wednesday
Shandy Hall, Coxwold

July 11 Thursday
Grimston Gardens, Gilling East

July 13 Saturday
Sleightholme Dale Lodge,
  Fadmoor

July 14 Sunday
Beamsley Hall, nr Skipton
8 Dunstarn Lane, Adel ‡
30 Latchmere Road, Leeds 16 ‡
Low Askew, Cropton, Pickering ‡‡
Lullaby, Hull
Parcevall Hall, nr Skipton
Rudston House, Rudston,
  nr Driffield
Sedbury Hall, nr Richmond
Sleightholme Dale Lodge,
  Fadmoor ‡‡
5 Wharfe Close, Leeds 16 ‡
The White Cottage, Halsham,
  nr Hull
Wincroft, Swanland

July 17 Wednesday
The Chimney Place, Bilton Grange

July 20 Saturday
The Chimney Place, Bilton Grange

July 21 Sunday
30 Latchmere Road, Leeds
55 Rawcliffe Drive, York ‡
Secret Garden, York ‡

July 28 Sunday
30 Latchmere Road, Leeds 16
The Spaniels, Hensall, nr Selby

August 11 Sunday
Woodlands Cottage,
  Summerbridge

August 4 Sunday
30 Latchmere Road, Leeds 16

August 18 Sunday
32 Hollybank Road, York
Three Gables, Markington

September 8 Sunday
Hillbark, Bardsey

September 15 Sunday
Maspin House, Hillam, nr Selby
Plants of Special Interest,
  Braithwell
The White Cottage, Halsham,
  nr Hull

September 22 Sunday
The Dower House, Great
  Thirkleby

September 29 Sunday
Bolton Percy Gardens, Tadcaster

October 6 Sunday
Fairview, Summerbridge

Regular openings
For details see garden description

Burton Agnes Hall, Driffield
Castle Howard, nr York.
Constable Burton Hall, nr Leyburn
Gilling Castle, Gilling East
Harewood House, nr Leeds.
Land Farm, nr Hebden Bridge.
Newby Hall, Ripon.
Shandy Hall, Coxwold.
Stockeld Park, Wetherby.

By appointment only
*For telephone numbers and other
details see garden descriptions.
Private visits welcomed*

50 Hollins Lane, Hampsthwaite
Holly Cottage, Scholes
The Mews Cottage, Harrogate
Stonegate Cottage, nr Keighley
Tan Cottage, Cononley, nr Skipton
Les Palmiers, Barnsley
York House, Claxton

DESCRIPTIONS OF GARDENS

Bankfield &# (Norma & Mike Hardy) Edgerton. 1m N of Huddersfield. From Huddersfield ring rd follow A629 towards Halifax for ½m. Cross traffic lights at Blacker Rd, turn R after 100yds into Queens Rd. From M62, turn S at junction 24 towards Huddersfield on A629. After ¾m pass 30mph sign, turn L after 200yds into Queens Rd. ⅔-acre cottage style garden which has evolved over 11yrs from a neglected Victorian town garden. Large number of perennials incl many unusual and rare of interest to plant collectors. Rambling paths, informal beds, pond, gazebo, conifer arch, terraced beds around lawn. Huddersfield Examiner 'Best Kept Garden'. Featured in Amateur Gardening 1994. TEA. *Adm £1 Chd 50p. Sun June 30 (11-5). Private visits also by appt, please* Tel 01484 535830

Beacon Hill House &# (Mr & Mrs D H Boyle) Langbar. 4m NW of Ilkley. 1¼m SE of A59 at Bolton Bridge. Fairly large garden sheltered by woodland 900' up, on the southern slope of Beamsley Beacon. Several features of interest to garden historians survive from the original Victorian garden. Early flowering rhododendrons, large shrub roses, mixed borders, unusual hardy and half-hardy shrubs and climbers making use of south facing walls. TEAS. *Adm £1.50. Wed May 15 (2-6.30)*

Beamsley Hall &# (Marquess & Marchioness of Hartington) Beamsley. 5m E of Skipton. 6-acre traditional English garden with new plantings; including extensive herbaceous border and kitchen garden. Minor restrictions for wheelchairs. TEAS. Also at Bolton Abbey or at Devonshire Arms. *Adm £2 OAPs £1.50 Chd under 15 free. Sun July 14 (1-5)*

Betula & Bolton Percy Cemetery &&# (Roger Brook Esq) Tadcaster. 5m E of Tadcaster 10m SW of York. Follow Bolton Percy signs off A64. An acre of old village churchyard gardened by Roger Brook, in which garden plants are naturalised and grow wild. Featured in numerous TV programmes, national magazines and publications. The National Dicentra Collection will be on view in Roger Brook's garden and allotment. Light lunches and TEAS in aid of Church. *Combined adm with* **Windy Ridge** *£2 Chd free Sun April 14, June 30. Adm £1 Chd free. Sun Sept 29 (1-5)*

Bishopscroft &# (Bishop of Sheffield) Sheffield. 3m W of centre of Sheffield. Follow A57 (signposted Glossop) to Broomhill then along Fulwood Road to traffic lights past Ranmoor Church. Turn Right up Gladstone Rd and then L into Snaithing Lane. Bishopscroft on R at top of hill. 1¼-acres of well-established suburban woodland garden. Small lake and stream; the aim is to present something of the feeling of countryside in the nearby Rivelin Valley; a good variety of elders, brambles and hollies; herbaceous, shrub and rose borders. TEAS. *Adm £1 Chd free (Share to the Church Urban Fund©). Sun July 7 (2-6)*

Blackbird Cottage &# (Mrs Hazel Hoad) Scampston. 5m from Malton off A64 to Scarborough through Rillington turn L signposted Scampston only, follow signs. ⅓-acre plantswoman's garden made from scratch since 1986. A great wealth of interesting plants, with shrub, herbaceous border. Alpines are a speciality. Please visit throughout the day to ease pressure on a small but inspirational garden. Unusual plants for sale. Morning coffee and TEAS in aid of Scampston Village Hall & Church. *Adm £1 Chd free. Suns May 12, June 23 (10-5)*

Bossall Hall & (Brig I D & Lady Susan Watson) Bossall. From York proceed in NE direction on A64 (York to Malton and Scarborough) for 7m and turn R at signpost marked Claxton-Bossall. Straight across Xrds in Claxton to Bossall (2m) C12 Church will be open. 6-acre garden with moat surrounding C17 hall. Many old trees, lawns, orchard, walled kitchen garden, shrub and rose borders. *Adm £1.25 Chd free. Sun June 23 (2-5)*

Boston Spa Gardens A659 1m S of Wetherby. Church St immed opp Central Garage. TEA at Acorn Cottage. *Combined adm £2.50 incl coffee/tea Chd free (Share to Northern Horticultural Society®). Sun April 28 (11-4)*

    Acorn Cottage &# (Mr & Mrs C M Froggatt) Garden adjacent to **Four Oaks**. A small walled Alpine rock garden with the plant collection spanning 70 yrs - 2 generations. *Also by appt April to May, please* Tel 01937 842519

    Four Oaks &# (Richard Bothamley & Glenn Hamilton) A medium-sized established flower and foliage garden of particular interest to flower arrangers. Pergolas and a series of garden 'rooms' on differing levels create a sense of intimacy. A wide selection of the genera - acer. Terrace with pots and a pool with good waterside plantings

Boynton Hall &# (Mr & Mrs R Marriott) Bridlington. On B1253 2m W of Bridlington S from Boynton Xrds. Lawn and yew hedge around Elizabethan house and lovely old walled garden with shrubs and roses; also gate house and knot garden. House Tour and TEAS in aid of church. *Adm £2 Chd £1. Sun June 30 (1.30-5). Also private visits welcome by written appt*

Brookfield &# (Dr & Mrs R L Belsey) Oxenhope. 5m SW of Keighley, take A629 towards Halifax. Fork R onto A6033 towards Haworth. Follow signs to Oxenhope. Turn L at Xrds in village. 200yds after P O fork R, Jew Lane. A little over 1 acre, intimate garden, including large pond with island and mallards. Many varieties of candelabra primulas and florindaes, azaleas, rhododendrons. Unusual trees and shrubs; screes; greenhouse and conservatory. TEA 50p. *Adm £1.50 Chd free. Sun June 9 (2-6). Also by appt, please* Tel 01535 643070

●**Burton Agnes Hall** &# (Mr & Mrs N Cunliffe-Lister) nr Driffield. Burton Agnes is on A166 between Driffield & Bridlington. 8 acres of gardens incl lawns with clipped yew and fountains, woodland gardens and a walled garden containing a potager, herbaceous and mixed borders; maze with a thyme garden; jungle garden; campanula collection garden and coloured gardens containing giant games boards also collections of hardy geraniums, clematis, penstemons and many unusual perennials. 'Gardeners' Fair' Adm £2.30 Chd £1 Sat, Sun June 8, 9; specialist nurseries; gardening advice; dried flower & herb craft. TEAS. *Adm £1.80 Chd 80p. April 1 to Oct 31 (11-5)*

Castle Farm Nurseries &&& (Mr & Mrs K Wilson) Barmby Moor. Turn off A1079 Hull/York rd, ¾m from Barmby Moor at Hewson & Robinson's Garage, towards Thornton; ½m on R is sign for nursery. 1¼ acre garden created in 1978, which is constantly changing will be gradually extended to 2 acres. Incl trees, shrubs, mixed borders, scree and rock garden. Rhododendrons, water garden, heathers and conifers. Nursery open. Cream TEAS in aid of local Methodist Church. *Adm £1 Chd free. Suns May 26, June 2 (2-5.30)*

● **Castle Howard** ❀ (The Hon Simon Howard & Castle Howard Estate Ltd) York. 15m NE of York off the A64. 6m W of Malton. Partially suitable for wheelchairs. 300 acres of formal and woodland gardens laid out from the C18 to present day, including fountains, lakes, cascades and waterfalls. Ray Wood covers 50 acres and has a large and increasing collection of rhododendron species and hybrids amounting to 600 varieties. There is also a notable collection of acers, nothofagus, arbutus, styrax, magnolia and a number of conifers. There are walks covering spring, summer and autumn. Two formal rose gardens planted in the mid 1970's include a large assembly of old roses, china roses, bourbon roses, hybrid teas and floribunda. Refreshments are available in the House Restaurant, in the Lakeside Cafe and the Stables Cafe. During the summer months there are boat trips on the lake in an electric launch. There are gift shops in the House and Stable courtyard. Plant centre by the car park. TEAS. *Adm Grounds and Gardens £4.50 Chd £2.50. Every day March 1 to Nov 3 (10-4.30)*

The Chimney Place, 23 Parthian Road &❀ (Mrs Paddy Forsberg) Bilton Grange, E Hull. Take Holderness Rd, R into Marfleet Lane, R at roundabout into Staveley Rd, L into Griffin Rd, Parthian Rd 1st on R. A small secluded, hedge enclosed, 30 yr old garden, designed and maintained by owner, for the welfare of birds, fish, frogs and butterflies. 9 Victorian chimneys used as containers for alpines and rockery plants, many other containers. New features added, obelisk, wildlife, pool, stumpery, summerhouse. *Adm 85p Acc chd free. Weds, Sats May 22, 25, June 19, 22, July 17, 20 (1.30- 4.30). Private visits welcome, please* **Tel 01482 783804**

● **Constable Burton Hall Gardens** & (Charles Wyvill Esq) 3m E of Leyburn on A684, 6m W of A1. Large romantic garden, with terraced woodland walks; garden and nature trails. An array of naturalized daffodils set amidst ancient trees. Rock garden with choice plants. Fine John Carr house (not open) set in spledour of Wensleydale countryside. *Adm £2 OAPs £1.50 Chd 50p. March 25 to Oct 20 daily (9-5.30). Guided tours of gardens by appt, please* **Tel 01677 460225**

Creskeld Hall &&& (The Exors of Lady Stoddart-Scott) Arthington. 5m E of Otley on A659. Well established 3-4-acre large garden with woodland plantings; rhododendrons, azaleas, attractive water garden with canals, walled kitchen and flower garden. TEA. *Adm £1.50 Chd free. Sun June 2 (12-5)*

The Croft &&& (Mr & Mrs Peter Carver) North Cave. On B1230 (1½m from exit 38, M62). Entrance 100yds S War Memorial in village centre (towards South Cave). Stewardship by same family since Queen Victoria's reign

pervades this large garden of much pleasure and permanence. Yew hedging, Tapis-vert statue garden, established bulbs. Included in garden books; press articles and featured on BBC TV with Geoffrey Smith and ITV with Susan Hampshire. NGS video 2. Private car parking. TEAS in aid of St John Ambulance. *Adm £1.50 Acc chd free. For NGS Sun April 7 (2-5). Private visits welcome, please* **Tel 01430 422203**

Derwent House &&& (Dr & Mrs D G Lethem) Osbaldwick. On village green at Osbaldwick. 2m E of York city centre off A1079. Approx ¾ acre, a most attractive village garden extended in 1984 to provide a new walled garden with yew hedges and box parterres. Conservatories, terraces and herbaceous borders. TEAS. *Adm £1.50 Chd free. Sun June 9 (1.30-5)*

The Dower House &❀ (Mrs M J Coupe) Great Thirkleby. 4m from Thirsk on A19 on alternative route avoiding Sutton Bank. Smallholding run as a nature reserve bounded by a stream with ponds, wildflowers, birds, fish, donkeys. Rare trees with autumn colour, fruit and rose hips. TEA. *Adm £1 Chd free (Share to Ripon Choral Soc© and St Leonards Hospice®). Sun Sept 22 (2-5). Private visits (max 20) welcome, please* **Tel 01845 501375**

8 Dunstarn Lane & (Mr & Mrs R Wainwright) Adel. Leeds 16. From Leeds ring rd A6120 exit Adel, up Long Causeway. 4th junction R into Dunstarn Lane, entrance 1st R. 28 bus from Leeds centre stops near gate. Entire garden formerly known as The Heath. Featured on YTV and BBC TV. 2 acres of long herbaceous and rose borders incl 60 varieties of delphiniums. Large lawns for picnics. *Adm £1 Chd free. Suns June 30, July 14 (2-6)*

Elvington Gardens &&& 8m SE of York. From A1079, immed. after leaving York's outer ring road turn S onto B1228 for Elvington. Light lunches and Teas in Village Hall in aid of village hall. *Combined adm £2.50 Chd free. Sun June 2 (11-5)*

> **Brook House** (Mr & Mrs Christopher Bundy) Old established garden with fine trees; herb garden with rustic summer house; kitchen garden and new pond garden
> **Elvington Hall** (Mr & Mrs Pontefract) 3-4-acre garden; terrace overlooking lawns with fine trees and views; sanctuary with fish pond
> **Eversfield** (David & Helga Hopkinson) Modest sized garden with a wide variety of unusual perennials; grasses and ferns divided by curved lawns and gravel beds. Small nursery. **Tel 01904 608332**
> **Red House Farm** (Dr & Mrs Euan Macphail) Entirely new garden created from a field 11 years ago. Courtyard with interesting plantings and half-acre young wood

Evergreens &&& (Phil & Brenda Brock) Bilton. 5m E of Hull. Leave city by A165. Exit B1238. Bungalow ¼m on R nearly opposite the Asda Store. Over 1 acre developed since 1984. Features incl mosaics and sundials; tower; raised beds; rockeries and landscaped pond; Japanese garden; conifer, heather and mixed beds. Collection of dwarf conifers, many labelled. Photographs showing development of garden; small conifer/plant nursery open. Yorkshire recipe TEAS in aid of National Childrens' Homes. *Adm £1 Acc chd free. Suns May 5, July 7 (2-5). Private visits welcome May to Sept* **Tel 01482 811365**

Fairview ✿✿ (Michael D Myers) Smelthouses nr Summerbridge. From B6165 12m NW of Harrogate turn R in Wilsill Village to Smelthouses. Fairview is immed after the bridge on the R. A ⅛-acre small plantsman's garden on a steep slope, packed with unusual bulbs, alpines and woodland plants. 3 NCCPG National Collections; anemone nemorosa, hepatica and primula marginata; alpine house, fernery and tiny pond; small nursery. Due to the situation of the garden there may be some necessary restrictions to entry if busy. TEAS. *Adm £1.50 Chd free. Suns March 3 (1-5), May 19 (2-6), Oct 6 (1-5). Private visits by appt, please* Tel 01423 780291

Fernwood ✿✿ (Dick & Jean Feaster) Cropton. 4m NW of Pickering. From A170 turn at Wrelton signed Cropton. 1-acre garden created by the owners in the last 8yrs, containing herbaceous borders, a white garden, a scented garden, species and old roses, a wide variety of interesting plants, with a view of the N Yorkshire moors beyond. Morning coffee & TEAS. *Adm £1 Chd free. Sun July 7 (11-5)*

Fieldhead ✿✿ (Fiona Harrison & Chris Royffe) Boston Spa. Take A659 towards Boston Spa off A1 1m S of Wetherby. Chestnut Avenue on the R after ¾m. Please park on the main rd and walk up the avenue. A ⅓-acre garden recently created around an imposing Victorian house. Interestingly designed with a wide range of spaces, colours and textures; pools, terraces, a rose walk, shade and stone gardens. A large selection of plants; herbaceous, shrubs, ground cover and bamboos. Photographic exhibition showing development. Featured BBC 'Gardeners' World' 1995. Coffee/TEAS. *Adm £1.50 Chd free (Share to Northern Horticultural Society®). Suns May 19, June 16, 23 (11-5). Parties by appt please,* Tel 01937 843513

Gilling Castle ✿ (The Rt Revd the Abbot of Ampleforth) Gilling East, 18m N of York. Medium-sized terraced garden with steep steps overlooking golf course. Unsuitable for handicapped or elderly. *Adm £1 Chd free. For NGS July & Aug daily dawn to dusk. Large parties welcome, please* Tel 014393 206

¶Glebe House ✿ (Trisha & Graham Fairhurst) Park Lane, Thrybergh. Take A630 Rotherham to Doncaster. Turn R at Foster's petrol station and Garden Centre, ½m before church. Georgian stone house with small enclosed formal S-facing garden developed during last 5yrs, incorporating many new design features planted for summer colour and plant association. Herbaceous borders, lawn and interesting gravel garden with predominantly green planting scheme. TEA. *Adm £1 Chd free. Sun June 2 (1.30-5.30)*

Goddards ✿✿ (The National Trust Yorkshire Regional Office) 27 Tadcaster Rd, Dringhouses. 2m from York centre on A64, next to Swallow Chase Hotel. 1920s garden designed by George Dillistone, herbaceous borders, yew hedges, terraces with aromatic plants, rock gardens, pond. Partially suitable for wheelchairs. Guided tours, TEAS. *Adm £1.50 incl NT members. Sun June 23 (12-5). Large parties by appt May to Sept, please* Tel 01904 702021

The Green ✿✿ (Mr & Mrs Hugh Helm) Lund. 7m N of Beverley. Off B1248 Beverley Malton Rd. ¼-acre cottage garden; pool, rockery; climbing roses; shrubs; herbaceous plants, natural gravel garden. Established 11yrs in this delightful award winning "Britain in Bloom" village. Also open **5 Lockington Road.** *Adm £1 Chd free. Sun June 30 (2-5)*

Grimston Gardens ✿ The hamlet of Grimston is 1m S of Gilling East 7m S of Helmsley 17m N of York on B1363. Follow sign 1m S of Gilling East. TEA. *Adm £2 Chd free. Sun, Thurs July 7, 11 (1.30-5.30)*
    Bankside House (Clive & Jean Sheridan) ½-acre garden with sloping lawn, mature trees and shrubs with shaded walk, mixed herbaceous plants, semiformal beds, small Japanese area
    Grimston Manor Farm (Richard & Heather Kelsey) ½-acre garden with recent extension. The intricate design is profusely planted with a wide collection of herbaceous plants; trees and shrubs incorporating fine country views and old farm buildings

Harewood House ✿✿ (Harewood House Trust) Leeds. 9m N of Leeds on A61. Approx 80 acres of gardens within 1000 acres of Lancelot 'Capability' Brown landscaped parkland, formal terraces recently restored to original Sir Charles Barry design, 2m of box edging surrounding seasonal displays of Victorian bedding enhanced by Italianate fountains and statues, charming informal walks through woods around the lake to the cascade and rock garden with collections of hosta and rhododendrons. TEAS Cafeteria. *Adm £6 OAPs £5 Chd £4 gardens, grounds, house and bird garden incl. Adm £4 OAPs £3 Chd £2 gardens & grounds only. Daily March 16 to Oct 27 (10-7) (last adm 4.30pm). Weekends Nov to Dec. For NGS private groups by appt, please* Tel Trevor Nicholson 0113 288 6331

Harlsey Manor ✿✿ (Mr & Mrs Brian Holey) East Harlsey. Travelling N on the A19 drive past the Cleveland Tontine (A172 turn-off) and take next turn to the L marked East Harlsey. The driveway to Harlsey Manor is about ½m along this rd on the LH-side before the village. 6 acres of garden and woodland walks with wide variety of mature trees and shrubs. Long terrace with formal rose beds and views of Cleveland Hills; extensive replanting of rhododendrons and daffodils carried out in 1993. Herbaceous border replanted Autumn 1994. TEAS in aid of Guide Dogs for the Blind. *Adm £1.50 Chd free. Suns April 14 (1.30-5.30)*

¶Helmsley Gardens ✿ Teashops in Helmsley. *Adm £1 each gdn. Chd free. Sun June 9 (2-6)*
    Ryedale House (Dr & Mrs J A Storrow) 41 Bridge Street. On A170, 3rd house on R after bridge into Helmsley from Thirsk and York. ¼-acre walled garden; varieties of flowers, shrubs, trees, herbs. *Private visits welcome, please* Tel 01439 770231
    ¶Ryehill ✿✿ (Dr & Mrs C Briske) Follow yellow signs from bridge on A170. ¼-acre site interestingly divided into compartments. Intensely planted with many unusual varieties of flowering shrubs, roses, clematis and perennials. Baskets, containers, pond and well stocked conservatory

Hemble Hill Farm &❀ (Miss S K Edwards) Guisborough, on A171 between Nunthorpe and Guisborough opp the Cross Keys Inn. Dogs welcome, 7-acre garden facing the Cleveland Hills with formal and informal areas incl lake; young arboretum; heather, rhododendrons, large conservatory. TEAS. *Adm £1.25 Chd free. Sun May 12 (2-5.30). Private visits welcome June to Sept, please Tel 01287 632511*

High Farm ❀❀ (Mr & Mrs G R Cooper) Bilton. 5m E of Hull City Centre, take A165 Brid Rd, turn off at Ganstead Lane, onto B1238 to Bilton. Turn L opp Church. High Farm is at the bottom of Limetree Lane. Drive straight up the drive past the house, where parking is available in paddock. A mature garden of approx 1½ acres, harmoniously created and maintained by its present owners around a Georgian farmhouse. Many trees, shrubs, old species and climbing roses, herbaceous plants, as well as the thriving traditional kitchen garden. Flower arrangers will find much to interest them in the many unusual and rare plants to be found in the numerous beds and borders. TEAS. *Adm £1.50 Chd free. Suns May 26, June 30 (1-5)*

Hillbark ❀❀ (Malcom Simm & Tim Gittins) Bardsey. 4m SW of Wetherby, turn W off A58 into Church Lane. The garden is 150yds on L just before Church. Please use village hall car park (turn R opp Church into Woodacre Lane). A young 1-acre country garden. Past winner Sunday Express 'Large Garden of the Year'. Mixed planting with some English roses; paved and gravel terraces; descending to ponds and stream with ducks and marginal planting. TEAS. *Adm £1.50 Chd 50p (Share to Cookridge Hospital Cancer Research®). Suns May 19, June 23, Sept 8 (11-5). Private visits welcome by appt May to July, please Tel 01937 572065*

50 Hollins Lane ❀ (Mr & Mrs G Ellison) Hampsthwaite. 2m W of Harrogate, turn R off A59 Harrogate-Skipton rd. Small ¼-acre garden with limestone rockeries. Extensive varieties of alpines, dwarf plants, rhododendrons; azaleas and named hostas. Reconstructed for easier maintenance (no lawn), incorporating specimen shrubs, small trees, roses and fountain, surrounded by gravel. Plants sale in aid of Zimbabwe Lepers. *Adm £1.50 incl tea and biscuits. Private visits and parties May to Sept incl (max 30), please Tel 01423 770503*

Holly Cottage, Leas Gardens (Mr & Mrs John Dixon) Scholes. 8m S of Huddersfield on A616. Turn W at signpost to Scholes. ½-acre sloping garden of interest created from a field in 1988 with raised alpine bed and paved area with troughs; pond with small bog garden, rockery and herbaceous borders with good selection of plants. *Adm £1.50 Chd free. Private visits welcome Feb to end Oct, please Tel 01484 684083/662614*

¶**Holly Cottage, Wressle** &❀❀ (Maureen Read) 1m N of the A63 between Howden and Selby. From an overgrown field and orchard in 1986 to what is a seemingly long-established ¾-acre garden with pond, grass walks and woodland area. Mixed beds and borders feature many uncommon perennial plants suited to different aspects. TEAS. *Adm £1.50 Chd free. Sun June 30 (2-5)*

32 Hollybank Road ❀ (Mr & Mrs D Matthews) Holgate. A59 (Harrogate Rd) from York centre. Cross iron bridge, turn L after Kilima hotel (Hamilton Drive East). Fork slightly L (Hollybank Rd) after 400yds. Garden designer's small town garden planted for yr-round interest. Shrubs, small trees, climbers, clematis and container plants. Cobbled fountain, 4 separate patio areas, small pond. Finalist in Daily Mail National Gardens Competition. TEA. *Adm £1 Chd free. Sun June 30, Aug 18 (11-5). Private visits for parties of 6-10 by appt, please Tel 01904 627533*

Hovingham Hall &❀ (Sir Marcus & Lady Worsley) 8m W of Malton. House in Hovingham village, 20m N of York; on B1257 midway between Malton and Helmsley. Medium-sized garden; yew hedges, shrubs and herbaceous borders. C18 dovecote and riding school; cricket ground. Box Hedge Co performing Macbeth in Hop Garden at 7.30pm. Grounds open for picnics from 6pm. TEA in aid of Hovingham Church. *Adm £2 Chd free (Share to National Asthma Campaign®). Sun June 30 (2-6). Enquiries Tel 01653 628206*

Hunmanby Grange &❀❀ (Mr & Mrs T Mellor) Wold Newton. Hunmanby Grange is a farm 12½m SE of Scarborough, situated between Burton Fleming and Fordon. From Hunmanby take rd to Wold Newton 4m out of village turn R at Xrds towards Fordon garden 200yds on R. From A64 take B1039 towards Filey turn R before Flixton signed Fordon. In Fordon turn L at Xrds to Burton Fleming. Garden 1¼m on L. The garden has been created from exposed open fields over 12 yrs, on top of the Yorkshire Wolds near the coast, satisfying a plantswoman's and a young family's needs. Foliage colour, shape and texture have been most important in forming mixed borders, a gravel garden, a rose hedge, pond garden, orchard and laburnum tunnel. TEAS in aid of St Cuthbert's Church, Burton Fleming. *Adm £1 Chd free. Suns June 9, July 7 (11-5). Private visits welcome, Wed afternoons April to Sept please Tel 01723 891636*

Il Giardino &❀❀ (Peter & Marian Fowler) Bilton. 5m E of Hull City Centre. Take A165 Hull to Bridlington Rd. Turn off; take B1238 to Bilton Village. Turn L opp. St Peter's Church. "Il Giardino" is at bottom of Limetree Lane on L. No. 63. Once neglected garden approx ⅓ acre redesigned and revived over last 8yrs by present owners. Features incl mixed borders and island beds stocked with many old-fashioned pinks, erodiums, hardy geraniums and other unusual plants, shrubs and trees. Attractive beech hedge, small allotment, herb garden, orchard of old apple trees; pear; plum; cherries; medlar and filberts; entwined with many types of clematis. Cedarwood greenhouse with a collection of named pelargoniums; standard grapevine; potted citrus; fig tree and other less common plants. TEAS. *Adm £1 Chd free. Suns May 5, 26, June 30 (12-5)*

Inglemere Lodge ❀❀ (Mr & Mrs Peter Walker-Sharp) Ilkley. From Ilkley centre A65 towards Skipton, after ¾m opp post box turn L into Easby Dr. Owner built and maintained ⅙-acre garden surrounding L-shaped bungalow. Unusual layout on sloping site with small pond and large raised bed. Full of colour and interesting plants well displayed and labelled, many of which are for sale during the summer. TEAS in aid of British Red Cross. *Adm £1 Chd free. Sun June 16 (1.30-5). Private visits by appt, please Tel 01943 607333*

Kelberdale ✿❀ (Stan & Chris Abbott) Knaresborough. 1m from Knaresborough on B6164 Wetherby rd. House on L immed after new ring rd roundabout. Attractive owner-made and maintained, med-sized plantsman's garden with river views. Full of yr-round interest with large herbaceous border, conifer and colour beds. Alpines and pond. TEA. *Adm £1 Chd free (Share to St Michaels Hospice®). Suns June 23, 30 (10-6) Group visits welcome, please* Tel 01423 862140

54a Keldgate ❀✿ (Lenore & Peter Greensides) Beverley. Half-way between the double mini roundabout at SW entrance to Beverley on the B1230 and Beverley Minster. No private parking. ½-acre 'secret' garden within the charming town of Beverley. Largely created and solely maintained by the present owners over the last 17yrs. Clematis in variety, herbaceous plantings and shrubs, an inner garden of old roses, underplanted with peonies and geraniums; a recently redesigned kitchen garden, fruit trees and irises, spring bulbs in season. TEAS in aid of Shelter only on June 23. Plant stall on May 5. *Adm £1 Chd free. Suns May 5, June 23 (2-5). Group visits welcome, please* Tel 01482 866708

¶80 Lairgate ✿ (Mary & David Palliser) Beverley. In town centre on 1-way system. Enclosed ⅓-acre garden developed and maintained since 1986 by present owners, with many plants of interest to flower arrangers. Shrubs, climbers, old roses, bulbs, herbaceous and tender perennials, to provide yr-round and horticultural interest. *Adm £1 Acc chd free. Sun June 23 (2-5)*

Land Farm ✿❀ (J Williams Esq) Colden, nr Hebden Bridge. From Halifax at Hebden Bridge go through 2 sets traffic lights; take turning circle to Heptonstall. Follow signs to Colden. After 2¾m turn R at 'no thru' road, follow signs to garden. 4 acres incl alpine; herbaceous, heather, formal and newly developing woodland garden. Elevation 1000ft N facing. Has featured on 'Gardeners' World'. C17 house (not open). Art Gallery. *Adm £2 Chd free. May to end Aug; Open weekends and Bank Hols (10-5). By appt parties welcome evenings during week. Adm £3 incl refreshments, please* Tel 01422 842260

Langdale, Melsonby see County Durham

Lanhydrock Cottage ✿❀ (Mrs Jan Joyce) Skerne. 3m SE Driffield; follow signs to Skerne. Delightful small cottage garden of much interest and love, old-fashioned roses, herbs, fragrant perennials and wild flowers etc. Light refreshments. TEAS. *Adm £1 Chd free. Suns May 12, 26, June 9, 23 (11-4). Private visits welcome, please* Tel 01377 253727

30 Latchmere Rd ✿❀ (Mr & Mrs Joe Brown) Moor Grange, Leeds 16. A660 from City Centre to Lawnswood Ring Rd roundabout; turn sharp left on to ring rd A6120 for ⅓m to 3rd opening on left Fillingfir Drive; right to top of hill, turn right at top by pillar box, then left almost opposite into Latchmere Road, 3rd house on left. Bus stop at gate (Bus every 15 mins); 74 & 76 from City Centre; 54 from Briggate; 73 from Greenthorpe. Cars and coaches to park in Latchmere Drive please. A small garden full of interest; fern garden; herbaceous borders; alpine garden; glade; 2 pools; patio built of local York

stone; sink gardens; collection of 80 clematis. *Adm £1 Chd 50p (Share to GRBS®). Suns July 14, 21, 28, Aug 4 (2.30-5). Parties welcome, by written appt*

'Les Palmiers' 106 Vaughan Road ✿❀ (Richard Darlow & Christine Hopkins) Barnsley. 2m NW Barnsley Town centre. From M1 junction 37 take A628 towards Barnsley. After ½m turn L at major Xrds to hospital. Turn L at hospital Xrds into Gawber Rd, after ½m turn L into Vernon Way. Vaughan Rd is 1st cul-de-sac on R. Mediterranean garden to rear 60ft by 30ft. Planted entirely with 'warm climate' trees, shrubs, perennials, incl many tender subjects permanently planted eg palms, cordylines, yuccas, cacti and eucalyptus; spectacular flowering shrubs and exotic plants in pots. Mainly evergreen but most colourful April to Oct. Featured in BBC 2 Gardeners World, and many national magazine publications incl Journal of the European Palm Society and Practical Gardening Magazine. TEA. *Adm £1.50 OAP £1. Private visits welcome by appt only, weekends all yr, also evenings mid summer please* Tel 01226 291474. *Not suitable for young children due to many spiky plants!*

Ling Beeches ❀✿❀ (Mrs Arnold Rakusen) Ling Lane, Scarcroft 7m NE of Leeds. A58 mid-way between Leeds and Wetherby; at Scarcroft turn W into Ling Lane, signed to Wike on brow of hill; garden ⅓m on right. 2-acre woodland garden designed by owner emphasis on labour-saving planting; unusual trees and shrubs; ericaceous plants, some species roses, conifers, ferns, interesting climbers. Featured in The English Woman's Garden other publications and TV. TEA. *Adm £2. Sun April 28 (2-5); Private visits also welcome by appt, please* Tel 01132 892450

Littlethorpe Gardens ❀✿❀ nr Ripon. Littlethorpe lies 1½m SE of Ripon indicated by signpost close to Ripon Racecourse on the B6265 twixt Ripon and the A1. Teas at Littlethorpe Village Hall (nr Church). *Combined adm £2.50 Chd free. Sun June 9 (1.30-5.30)*
  Deanswood (Mrs J Barber) Garden of approx 1½ acres created during the last 10 years. Herbaceous borders; shrubs; special features streamside garden; 3 ponds with many unusual bog/marginal plants. Adjacent nursery also welcome. *Private visits also welcome, please* Tel 01765 603441
  Field Cottage (Mr & Mrs Richard Tite) A new 1-acre garden under development by owners. Informal herbaceous plantings, raised gravel and sleeper beds, bulbs and tender perennials. Small walled garden with terrace and an unusual range of plants in pots and containers
  Littlethorpe House (Mr & Mrs James Hare) 2 acres with many beautiful varieties of old-fashioned roses; extensive established mixed herbaceous and shrub borders

5 Lockington Road ❀ (Miss E Stephenson) Lund. Lund is off B1248 Beverley-Malton Rd. Small walled garden converted from old fold yard on edge of village with old-fashioned roses and cottage garden plants. "Charmingly English". Also open The Green. *Adm £1 Chd free. Sun June 30 (2-5). Private parties of 10 and over welcome, please* Tel 01377 217284

Low Askew ✉✿ (Mr & Mrs Martin Dawson-Brown) Cropton. 5m NW of Pickering between the villages of Cropton and Lastingham. Plantsman's garden full of interest incl scree, borders, roses & shrubs. Situated in beautiful countryside with stream and walk to River Seven. Troughs & pots are a speciality, filled with rare & species pelargoniums. Plant stalls by local nurserymen. Picnic area by river. Morning coffee, light lunches & TEAS in aid of NSPCC. *Adm £1.50 Chd free. Sun July 14 (11-5)*

Lullaby ✉✿ (Michael Whitton) Hull. From the A165 (Holderness Rd), travel along Saltshouse Rd towards Sutton Village. Turn R into Dunvegan Rd, R into Barra Close and R again, no 22 on L. Created by the owners from a building site, this compact 40' × 60' garden has developed into a peaceful retreat welcoming fox, squirrel, butterflies, frogs and a large variety of birds. A curving lawn leads the eye from a paved terrace, around herbaceous borders and an island bed and incl a pergola and a summerhouse. A small courtyard garden and a water feature. TEA. *Adm 85p Chd free. Suns June 30, July 14 (2-5). Private visits of minimum 10 people, please* **Tel 01482 783517**

Maspin House ♿✉✿ (Mr & Mrs H Ferguson) Hillam Common Lane. 4m E of A1 on A63 direction Selby. Turn R in Monk Fryston after Thrust Garage. L at T junction. Maspin House 1m on L. Ample off road parking. Garden of 1½ acres started in 1985 and still evolving. Owner made and maintained. Many unusual and beautiful plants giving good late colour. Lots of features made by handy husband incl paths, patios, ponds and waterfall, raised beds and separate gardens. TEAS in aid of Monk Fryston School. *Adm £1 Chd free. Sun Sept 15 (1.30-5.30). Private visits welcome, by appt please,* **Tel 01977 684922**

The Mews Cottage ✉✿ (Mrs Pat Clarke) 1 Brunswick Drive, Harrogate. W of town centre. From Cornwall Rd, N side of Valley Gardens, 1st R (Clarence Dr), 1st L (York Rd), first L (Brunswick Dr). A small garden on a sloping site of particular interest to hardy planters. Full of unusual and familiar plants but retaining a feeling of restfulness. A courtyard with trompe l'oeil and a gravelled area enclosed by trellising, provide sites for part of a large collection of clematis. TEAS. *Adm £1.50 Chd 50p. Private visits for groups, societies and parties welcome, please* **Tel 01423 566292**

Millgate House ✉✿ (Austin Lynch & Tim Culkin) Richmond Market Place. House is located at bottom of Market Place opp Barclays Bank. SE walled town garden overlooking the R Swale. Although small the garden is full of character, enchantingly secluded with plants and shrubs. Foliage plants incl ferns, hostas; old roses and interesting selection of clematis, small trees and shrubs. Featured in 'Homes & Gardens', 'Yorkshire Life', 'Daily Mail' and 'The Sunday Times'. Winner of 'Daily Mail'/RHS 1995 National Garden Competition. Full of ideas for small gardens. *Adm £1.50 Chd 50p. Sun July 7 (8am-8pm). Parties welcome, please* **Tel 01748 823571**

Nawton Tower ♿✉ (Mrs D Ward) Nawton, 5m NE of Helmsley. From A170, between Helmsley and Nawton village, at Beadlam turn N 2½m to Nawton Tower. Large garden; heathers, rhododendrons, azaleas, shrubs. Tea Helmsley and Kirbymoorside. *Adm £1.50 Chd 50p. Sat, Sun, Mon May 25, 26, 27 (2-6); private visits welcome, please* **Tel 01439 771218**

Ness Hall (Hugh Murray Wells Esq) Nunnington, 6m E of Helmsley, 22m N of York. From B1257 Helmsley-Malton rd turn L at Slingsby signed Kirbymoorside, 3m to Ness. Lge walled garden, mixed and herbaceous borders, emphasis on colour and design; orchard with shrubs and climbing roses. *Adm £1.50 Chd free (Share to Nunnington Church®). Weds June 26, July 3 (2-6)*

Netherwood House ♿✿ (Mr & Mrs Peter Marshall) 1m W of Ilkley on A65 towards Skipton; drive on L, car parking adjacent to house. Daffodils, spring flowering shrubs, duck pond; new rockery, bulb and stream plantings. Lovely views up Wharfedale. TEAS. *Adm £1.50 Chd free. Easter Sun April 7 (2-5.30)*

● **Newby Hall & Gardens** ♿✉✿ (R E J Compton Esq) Ripon. 40-acres extensive gardens laid out in 1920s; full of rare and beautiful plants. Winner of HHA/Christie's Garden of the Year Award 1987. Formal seasonal gardens, reputed longest double herbaceous borders to R. Ure and National Collection holder Genus Cornus. C19 statue walk; woodland discovery walk. Miniature railway and adventure gardens for children. Lunches & TEAS in licensed Garden Restaurant. The Newby shop and plant stall. *Adm House & garden £5.40 OAPs £4.50 Disabled/Chd £3.20, Garden only £3.80, OAPs £3.30, Disabled/Chd £2.50. April to Sept daily ex Mons (Open Bank Hols) (Gardens 11-5.30; House 12-5). Group bookings and further details from Administrator* **Tel 01423 322583**

Norton Conyers ♿✿ (Sir James & Lady Graham) Ripon. 4m NW of Ripon. Take Melmerby and Wath sign off A61 Ripon-Thirsk. Large C18 walled garden of interest to garden historians. Interesting borders and orangery; some hardy plants for sale. House which was visited by Charlotte Bronte, the original of 'Thornfield Hall' in 'Jane Eyre', also open. TEA. *Collecting box for NGS (£1 Chd free).* ▲*For NGS Sun June 23 (2-5)*

Nunburnholme Gardens ♿ A1079 Hull-York rd, turn to Nunburnholme in Hayton and follow signposts. *Combined adm £1.50 Chd free. Sun June 9 (1.30-5)*
   The Old Rectory ✉ (Mr & Mrs M Stringer) Owner maintained, large garden for chalk loving plants, with stream and herbaceous borders blending into surrounding countryside. Field parking. TEAS. *Private visits welcome May to Aug, please* **Tel 01759 302295**
   Wold View (Mrs Ann Westerdale) A wold village garden, unusual planting designed with surprises and variation. Ice cream

The Old Rectory, Mirfield ♿✉✿ (G Bottomley Esq) Exit 25 of M62; take A62 then A644 thru Mirfield Village; after approx ½m turn L up Blake Hall Drive, then 1st L, Rectory at top of hill. 1-acre garden surrounding Elizabethan Rectory. Mixed borders, Mulberry tree dating from C16; well, pergola and small ornamental pond. TEAS. *Adm £1 Chd free. Sun July 7 (2-5)*

Regular Openers. See end of county section.

Right An old apple tree in the garden of **North Court**, on the **Isle of Wight.** *Photograph by John Harrison.*

Below Water is a feature of many gardens, as at **Holly House** in **Lincolnshire**. *Photograph by Brian Chapple.*

Left "Head Over Heels" by Patrick Barker is one of the many contemporary sculptures in the garden of Lord and Lady Carrington at **The Manor House, Bledlow** in **Buckinghamshire**. *Photograph The National Gardens Scheme.*

Below **Sandringham, Norfolk** is graciously opened to the public by HM The Queen. *Photograph by Brian Chapple.*

Plant stalls are a great attraction at many gardens – this little girl is delighted with her purchase!
Photograph by Val Corbett.

Rich autumn colours enliven this flight of steps at **Plas Llidiardau, Dyfed** which is being developed by the owners from an existing Welsh country house garden. *Photograph by Jackie Newey.*

The Little Cottage, Hampshire, like many of the Scheme's gardens, welcomes private visits by appointment. Visitors are often shown round personally by the owners when they visit by appointment. *Photograph by Jackie Newey.*

This cottage garden, **The Graig, Gwent**, is wholly maintained by the 87 year-old owner, who this year will have been opening under the National Gardens Scheme for 22 years. *Photograph by Ron Evans.*

Right The Chairman of the National Gardens Scheme, Mrs Daphne Foulsham, presenting a trowel to the head gardener, Mr Neil Taylor at **Leckhampton Garden, Corpus Christi College, Cambridgeshire**, which has opened under the Scheme for 21 years. *Photograph The National Gardens Scheme.*

Below **The Old Rectory, Sudborough**. This Northamptonshire garden is an example of a classic English country garden and contains this decorative potager. *Photograph by Brian Chapple.*

Left Gardens even attract visitors in the rain! *Photograph by Val Corbett.*

Below **Parcevall Hall Gardens** in **Yorkshire** where conifers ensure this is a beautiful garden for all seasons. *Photograph by Brian Chapple.*

Old Sleningford ♿❀ (Mr & Mrs James Ramsden) 5m W of Ripon, off B6108. After North Stainley take 1st or 2nd L, follow sign to Mickley for 1m. An excellent example of an early C19 house and garden with original layout of interest to garden historians. Many acres with extensive lawns, interesting trees; woodland walk and Victorian fernery; exceptionally lovely lake and islands, streamside walk; watermill in the walled kitchen garden; long herbaceous border; yew and huge beech hedges. Flowers and grasses grown for drying. Several plant and other stalls. Home-made TEAS. *Adm £2 Chd 50p. (Share to N of England Christian Healing Trust®). Sat, Sun, Mon May 25, 26, 27 (1-5). Groups catered for, also private visits by appt, please* **Tel 01765 635229**

The Old Vicarage ✲❀ (Mr & Mrs R Marshall) Whixley, between York and Harrogate. ¾m from A59 3m E of A1. A delightful ¾-acre walled flower garden with mixed borders, unusual shrubs, climbers, roses, hardy and half-hardy perennials, bulbs. Paths and garden structures leading to new vistas using the gardens natural contours. Courtyard with small herb garden. TEAS. *Adm £1.50 Chd free. Mon, May 6, Sun June 16 (11-5)*

Otterington Hall ♿❀ (Sir Stephen & Lady Furness) Northallerton. 4m S of Northallerton. On A167 just N of S Otterington Village. 7 acres of garden and woodland walks, flowering shrubs, topiary, wonderful spring and kitchen garden, autumn colour. Designed for all seasons. Wheelchair users and families welcomed. TEAS. *Adm £2 Acc chd free. Sun March 31 (2-5). Private visits welcome by appt April to Oct, please* **Tel 01609 772061**

¶Oxenber House ❀ (Kath Robinson & Patrick Pickford) Austwick. 4m N of Settle A65. From village main st pass public house and school on L. Town Head Lane next L. ¾-acre planted for yr-round colour and interest. Gravel garden, scree, small pond and waterfall with alpines, ornamental grasses, foliage plants, ferns, spring bulbs, herbaceous and hardy perennials. Wild flower and vegetable area. Lovely views. TEA May 19. TEAS June 16 in aid of Action Research. *Adm £1 Chd 50p. Suns May 19, June 16 (11-5.30) Private visits welcome, please* **Tel 015242 51376**

Parcevall Hall Gardens ❀ (Walsingham College (Yorkshire Properties) Ltd) Skyreholme, 9m N of Skipton signs from B6160 Burnsall rd or off B6265 Grassington-Pateley Bridge rd. 20-acres in Wharfedale; shelter belts of mixed woodland, fine trees; terraces; fishponds; rock garden; tender shrubs inc desfontainea; crinodendron; camellia; bulbs; rhododendrons; orchard for picnics, old varieties of apples; autumn colour; birds in woodland; splendid views. TEAS. *Adm £2 Chd (5-12 yrs) 50p.* ▲*For NGS Suns April 21, June 16, July 14 (10-5)*

Park House ♿❀ (Mr & Mrs A T Preston) Moreby. 6m S of York. Between Naburn and Stillingfleet on B1222. Approx ½-acre, gardened since 1988, set within a 2-acre walled garden using some of the 16′ walls to display a wide variety of wall shrubs and climbers. Some herbaceous and mixed shrub borders. Large conservatory. TEAS. *Adm £1.20 Chd free. Sun June 23 (2-5.30)*

Parkview ♿✲❀ (Mr & Mrs Christopher Powell) 45 Church Street, South Cave. 12m W of Hull on A63 turn N to S Cave on A1034. In centre of village turn L by chemists, 250yds on L black gates under arch. ⅓-acre sheltered garden of perennial and shrub packed beds, pond and bog bed. New rose/honeysuckle pergola underplanted with 70+ varieties of hosta. Organic fruit and vegetable garden. TEAS. *Adm £1 Chd free if on lead (Share to Church Yard Fund©). Sun June 16 (2-5). Private visits welcome, please* **Tel 01430 423739**

Pennyholme (Mr C J Wills) Fadmoor, 5m NW of Kirbymoorside. From A170 between Kirbymoorside and Nawton, turn N, ½m before Fadmoor turn L, signed 'Sleightholmedale only' continue N up dale, across 3 cattlegrids, to garden. No Buses. Large, wild garden on edge of moor with rhododendrons, azaleas, primulas, shrubs. TEAS in aid of All Saints, Kirbymoorside. *Adm £1.50 Chd 50p (Share to St Aidan's, Gillamoor®). Sats, Suns June 1, 2, 8, 9 (11.30-5)*

¶Plants of Special Interest Nursery ♿❀ (Mr & Mrs Peter Dunstan) Braithwell. From M18 Junction 1 take A631. Turn L in Maltby to Braithwell. Nursery in centre of village. ¼-acre Mediterranean-style garden with patio and water feature adjacent to recently planted raised beds in small walled cottage garden. Nursery with excellent half-hardy and unusual plants incl zantedeschia Green Goddess. During August a colourful display of ornamental gourds, squashes and pumpkins growing behind the nursery. Menu featuring edible gourds in Tea-room. TEAS. *Adm £1 Chd 50p. Nursery open March to Dec Tues to Sats (9-5.30). Suns and Bank Hol Mons 10-5. For NGS Suns June 2, July 7, Sept 15 (10-5). Group bookings, please* **Tel 01709 812328**

55 Rawcliffe Drive ✲❀ (Mr & Mrs J Goodyer) Clifton. A19 from York centre, turn R at Clifton Green traffic lights (Water Lane). Rawcliffe Drive is 1st L after Clifton Hotel. A 30yd by 10yd suburban garden on 2 levels. Planted for yr-round interest with excellent use of foliage and colour. Many unusual shrubs, herbaceous plants and bulbs; around 90 clematis. *Adm £1.50 Chd free incl TEA. Suns June 9, July 21 (11-5). Also private visits welcome April to July, please* **Tel 01904 638489**

¶Rudston House ♿ (Mr & Mrs Simon Dawson) Rudston, nr Driffield. On B1253 5m W of Bridlington. S at Bosville Arms for approx 300yds. Birthplace of authoress Winifred Holtby. Victorian farmhouse (not open) and 2 acres of garden with fine old trees, lawns, paths with clipped box hedges, interesting potager with named vegetable varieties, roses, hosta bed and short woodland walk. Plenty of seats. TEA. *Adm £1.50 Chd free. Sun July 14 (11-5)*

St Nicholas ♿ (The Lady Serena James) 1m S of Richmond. On Brompton Catterick Bridge rd, ½ way down hill after leaving Maison Dieu. Bus: Darlington-Richmond; alight The Avenue, 500yds. Medium-large garden of horticultural interest; shrubs, topiary work. *Adm £1.50 Chd 50p. Sun April 28, (all day), also by appt parties only, please* **Tel 01748 2328**

Saltmarshe Hall ᏧᏫᏣ (Mr & Mrs Philip Bean) Howden. From Howden (M62, Jct 37) follow signs to Howden, Howdendyke and Saltmarshe. House in park W of Saltmarshe village. Large lawns, fine old trees, R Ouse and a regency house with courtyards provide a setting for shrubs, climbers, herbaceous plants and roses. Of special interest to plantsmen and garden designers are a pond garden, a walled garden and a large herbaceous border. Approx 10 acres. TEAS in aid of Laxton Church. *Adm £1.50 Acc chd free. Sun June 16 (2-5.30). Private visits welcome, please* Tel 01430 430199

Secret Garden, 10 Sherwood Grove ᏫᏣ (Mr & Mrs A C Downes) Acomb. From York on A59, turn L into Beckfield Lane at city boundary sign, before Western Ring Rd. Take 1st R, 2nd L. ¾-acre garden hidden behind suburban semi, developed and extended over 15 yrs. Features rockeries, pond, fruit cage but primarily extensive mixed plantings incl many unusual plants. 4 greenhouses with vines, cactus, succulent & tender plant collections. Small Nursery. TEA. *Adm £1 Chd free. Suns June 9, July 21 (10-5). Also private visits welcome, please* Tel 01904 796360

Sedbury Hall ᏧᏫ (Mr & Mrs W G Baker Baker) Richmond. A66 ½m W of Scotch Corner. Turn L immed after Sedbury Layby. Large established garden in approx 10 acres of grounds and parkland. Herbaceous border and roses leading to a secret garden. Wall shrubs and many varieties of climbing roses. Walled kitchen garden. Woodland walk with magnificent view over Dales. *Adm £2 Chd free. Sun July 14 (2.30-5.30)*

Shadwell Grange ᏧᏫᏣ (Mr & Mrs Peter Hartley) Shadwell Lane, Leeds 17. Turn L at traffic lights (signed Shadwell) ¼m from Moortown on A6120 (Leeds ring-rd) travelling E. A large 4-acre Victorian garden with established woodlands, rhododendrons, azaleas, mixed borders and new plantings. Water garden, orchard, wild garden and open views to the S. Parking in paddock. Plant stall, light refreshments in aid of British Red Cross. *Adm £1.50 Chd (over 5) 50p. Sun June 2 (11.30-4)*

Shandy Hall ᏫᏣ (The Laurence Sterne Trust) Coxwold, N of York. From A19. 7m from both Easingwold and Thirsk turn E signed Coxwold. C18 walled garden, unusual hardy perennials; old roses. 1-acre, with low-walled beds. 1-acre wild garden in Quarry adjoining garden. Home of C18 author, Laurence Sterne, who made the house famous. Craft shop in grounds. Unusual plants for sale. Wheelchairs with help. Teas in village, Coxwold (Schoolhouse Tea Room; home baking). *Adm £1.50 Chd 75p (Share to Laurence Sterne Trust®). House open Wed & Sun (2.30-4.30). Garden also open every afternoon except Sat (12-4.30) groups by appt on other days or evenings during the same period. For NGS Suns May 26, June 2, 30; Weds July 3, 10 (2-5)* Tel 01347 868465

Sinnington Gardens Ꮻ 4m W of Pickering on A170. A group of gardens which featured in Channel 4 series 'Nature Perfected', will be open in picturesque village. Tickets and parking on village green. TEAS. *Combined adm £2.50 Chd free. Sun June 16 (11-5)*

Sleightholme Dale Lodge Ꮳ (Mrs Gordon Foster; Dr & Mrs O James) Fadmoor, 3m N of Kirkbymoorside. 1m from Fadmoor. Hillside garden; walled rose garden; herbaceous borders. *Not* suitable for wheelchairs. No coaches. TEAS (Teas and plants not available June 1, 2). *Adm £1.50 Chd 50p. Sat, Sun, June 1, 2 (11.30-5) Sat, Sun July 13, 14 (2-6)*

Snilesworth ᏧᏣ (Viscount & Viscountess Ingleby) Halfway between Osmotherley and Hawnby. From Osmotherley bear L sign posted Snilesworth, continue for 4½m across the moor. 4½m from Hawnby on Osmotherley Rd. Turn R at top of hill. Garden created from moorland in 1957 by present owners father; rhododendrons and azaleas in a 30 acre woodland setting with magnificent views of the Hambleton and Cleveland hills; snowgums grown from seed flourish in a sheltered corner. TEAS. *Adm £1 Chd 20p (Share to Hawnby Church®). Sun June 9 (2-5)*

The Spaniels ᏧᏫᏣ (Janet & Dennis Tredgett) Hensall. 2m N of M62, 5m S of Selby. Turn E off A19 to Hensall. Field Lane is last turn on R in Hensall Village. A new ¾-acre garden planted over the past 2yrs on previous farmland. Long mixed borders in colour themes, incl young conifers, trees and shrubs, divided by curved lawns with island beds. Small wildlife pond. TEAS. *Adm £1 Chd 50p. Suns May 12, July 28 (12-5). Private visits welcome, please* Tel 01977 661858

Springfield House ᏧᏫᏣ (Mr & Mrs S B Milner) Tockwith. 5m E of Wetherby; 1m off B1224. Garden at west end of village. 1½ acres. Well established walled garden with herbaceous borders, water and rock gardens. Rose and conifer garden; shrub walk. Wide variety of plants. TEA. *Adm £1 Chd free. Sun June 16 (2-6)*

Stillingfleet Lodge ᏧᏫᏣ (Mr & Mrs J Cook) Stillingfleet 6m S of York, from A19 York-Selby take B1222 signed Sherburn in Elmet. ½-acre plantsman's garden subdivided into smaller gardens, each one based on a colour theme with emphasis on the use of foliage plants. Wild flower meadow and newly constructed pond, holders of National Collection of Pulmonaria. Adjacent nursery will be open. Homemade Teas in village hall in aid of local church. *Adm £1.50 Chd free. Suns May 19, June 30 (1.30-5.30)*

Stockeld Park ᏧᏫᏣ (Mr & Mrs P G F Grant) 2m NW of Wetherby. On A661 Wetherby-Harrogate Rd; from Wetherby after 2m entrance 2nd lodge on left. Bus: Wetherby-Harrogate, alight Stockeld lodge gates (¼m drive). 4-acres with lawns, grove and flowers, fine trees and roses. House built 1758 for Col Middleton by James Paine (listed Grade 1). C18 pigeon cote. Chapel 1890. *Open Thurs only April 4 to Oct 10 (2-5). For NGS Sun June 30. TEAS. Adm £2 Chd £1. House and Gardens £2.50, OAP's £1.50, Chd £1 (2-5)*

Stonegate Cottage ᏫᏣ (Mrs B Smith) Farnhill. 2m W Silsden. From Silsden or A629, follow directions to Farnhill. Stonegate Cottage is situated 100yds from Kildwick Hall towards Skipton. Cottage garden of approx 1 acre, on sloping site. Small pool and rockery. Unusual trees & shrubs. Wide variety of plants incl spring bulbs, herbaceous and roses. *Adm £1.50. Private visits by appt, please* Tel 01535 632388

Tan Cottage ✿ (Mr & Mrs D L Shaw) West Lane, Cononley. Take A629; turn off to Cononley 2¾m S of Skipton; top of village turn right onto Skipton rd. ¾-acre plantsman's garden adjoining C17 house (not open). Interesting plants, many old varieties; national collection of primroses. *Adm £1.50. Private visits by appt only, please* **Tel 01535 632030**

¶**Three Gables** (Jack Muirhead Esq) The Barrows, Markington, nr Harrogate. 1m from Wormald Green (A61 Harrogate-Ripon). ¾-acre garden set in woodland, approached over bridge of chinoiserie design crossing trout stream. On one side, herbaceous border with streamside plantings, the other a terrace garden with many container plants and pergola. Steep bank garden to rear. Some choice trees, shrubs; many unusual plants. Please park in lane. TEAS. *Adm £1.75 Chd 25p. Wed July 3, Sun Aug 18 (1.30- 6.30). Private visits by groups and societies welcome, following written application*

Victoria Cottage ✿ (John Bearder Esq) Beestonley Lane, Stainland. 6m SW of Halifax. Take the A629 (Huddersfield) from Halifax and fork R on the B6112 to Stainland. From Huddersfield take A640 Outlane, Sowood and Stainland. Turn at Black Horse Garage at top of Stainland Village, down Beestonley Lane. Victoria Cottage ¾m on R. ¾-acre plantsman garden, created by the owner from a NE sloping field since 1950. Daffodils; roses, flowering shrubs, some unusual for a hilly and wild part of the Pennines. Scenic setting. *Adm £1 Chd 30p. Suns April 14, May 12, June 2, 16; July 7 (10-5). Private visits welcome and parties by appt only, please* **Tel 01422 365215/374280**

Wass Gardens ✿❀ Nr Coxwold ¼m from Byland Abbey on Coxwold-Ampleforth rd. 6m SW of Helmsley turning from A170. 9m E of Thirsk; turn from A19 signed Coxwold. A variety of gardens in a picturesque hamlet set amid a broad cleft of deep wooded slopes. TEAS in aid of Wass Village Institute. *Adm £2 Chd free. Wed June 26 (12-5)*

8 Welton Old Road ❀ (Dr & Mrs O G Jones) Welton. In village of Welton 10m W of Hull off A63. Coming E turn L to village past church, turn R along Parliament St. and up hill. House 50yds on R opp Temple Close. From E take A63 and turn off at flyover to Brough; turn R for Welton and follow above instructions. Roadside parking in village. Informal 1-acre garden developed by owners over 30yrs. Imaginative planting with unusual shrubs, plants and less common trees; natural pond and lily pond. TEAS in aid of Leukaemia Research. *Adm £1 Chd free. Sun May 19 (2-5). Private visits welcome May to July* **Tel 01482 667488**

¶**26 West End** ✿ (Miss Jennifer Hall) Walkington. 2m from Beverley on the B1230, 100yds beyond Xrds in centre of village on the R. Interesting ½-acre cottage garden opening into an old wooded gravel pit still being developed by the owner single-handedly. Many rare plants collected over 15yrs. TEA. *Adm £1 Chd free. Sun July 7 (1.30-5)*

5 Wharfe Close ✿❀ (Mr & Mrs C V Lightman) Adel. Signposted off Leeds ring rd A6120 ¼m E of A660 Leeds-

Otley rd. Follow Long Causeway into Sir George Martin Drive. Wharfe Close adjacent to bus terminus. Please park on main rd. Medium-sized well stocked garden created from sloping site incorporating pools, rock gardens and mixed borders, small woodland walk filled with unusual plants grown on predominantly acid soil. TEAS. *Adm £1 Chd free. Sun July 14 (2-5) Private visits welcome June, July and August, please* **Tel 0113 261 1363**

The White Cottage ✿❀ (Mr & Mrs John Oldham) Halsham. 1m E of Halsham Arms on B1362, Concealed wooded entrance on R. Ample parking. The garden was created by its owners 25yrs ago. Delightful specialised and unusual planting in island beds. Natural pond and new water feature; vegetable and herb garden; architect designed sunken conservatory. Recently erected traditional pergola. Featured with Geoffrey Smith on BBC2 in 1992. Teas by Halsham Church. *Adm £1.50 Chd free (Share to Halsham Church Restoration Fund®). Suns May 19, July 14, Sept 15 (2-5). Private visits welcome by appt, please* **Tel 01964 612296**

The White House ✿❀ (Dr & Mrs A H Raper) Husthwaite. 3m N of Easingwold. Turn R off A19 signposted Husthwaite 1½m to centre of village opposite parish church. 1-acre garden created from scratch in 7 years now maturing and of particular interest to the plantswoman, containing herb garden, conservatory, gardens within the garden; herbaceous, particularly a hot summer border; shrubs; borders and many fascinating unusual plants. New landscaping and planting in the old orchard. Do visit throughout the day please to ease pressure. An opportunity to view this garden in a different season. Morning coffee and home-made food all day. Groups by prior arrangement. *Adm £1.50 Chd 25p (Share to Blenheim Project, Bradford®). Sun July 7 (11-5). Groups welcome by appt please,* **Tel 01347 868 688**

The Willows ✿❀ (Mr & Mrs Fleetwood) 172 Towngate, Clifton. From M62 exit 25, take A644 towards Brighouse. 1st R to Clifton. L at T junction; house approx 250 yds on L. ¾-acre owner created and maintained garden with oriental features, pools and waterfalls with herbaceous borders with many unusual plants of particular interest to flower arrangers and plantsmen. Containers and sink gardens. A wide variety of plantings in old orchard. TEAS. *Adm £1.50 Chd 50p. Sun June 16 (1-6). Groups welcome by appt, please* **Tel 01484 716513**

Wincroft ✿✿ (Mrs Mary Good) Swanland. From Humber Bridge N roundabout take A164 N to Beverley. After 1m turn L into Tranby Lane and proceed to 'Garden Open' signs on L. Park on roadside. Formal garden approx 1¼ acres laid out in and around attractive balustrading formerly at Swanland Manor. Long herbaceous border with good 'plant association' leads the eye towards views of the Humber estuary and beyond. Plants & TEAS in aid of Christ Church, Swanland, June 23 only. *Adm £1 Chd free. Suns June 23, July 14 (2-5)*

The National Gardens Scheme is a charity which traces its origins back to 1927. Since then it has raised a total of over £14 million for charitable purposes.

Windsong ❀ (Mr & Mrs Alan Gladwin) Osgodby. Take A63 2m N of Selby off A19, turn L into Sand Lane (signed Osgodby Village). A ½-acre garden created and maintained by the owners over the past 6 yrs. Many unusual features incl a moon gate; hardy plants and tender perennials packed into mixed borders. Ponds and stream-side plantings; orchard area. TEAS. *Adm £1 Chd free. Wed June 19, Sun June 23 (2-5). Private visits welcome by appt please* **Tel 01757 708802**

Windy Ridge ⚘❀ (Mr & Mrs J S Giles) Marsh Lane, Bolton Percy. 5m E of Tadcaster. Follw Bolton Percy signs off A64. 10m SW of York. Features a large collection of Barnhaven and Elizabethan primroses; Hose-in-Hose, Jack-in-the-Green, etc. Also wild and unusual hardy plants, grown in a natural cottage garden style sloping down to the Ings, greatly influenced by Margery Fish. Featured in channel 4 'Over the Garden Wall' 1994. Light lunches and teas available in village hall in aid of All Saints Church. *Combined adm with* **Betula and Bolton Percy Cemetery** *£2 Chd free. Suns April 14, June 30 (1-5)*

Woodcock ⚘❀ (Mr & Mrs David Price) ¾m E of Thirsk off A170 (Sutton Bank Rd). Turn R up bridle track. Proceed for 1m. 1½-acre garden laid out with some mature areas, always of interest. Plantings of shrubs, herbaceous, old- fashioned roses, spring bulbs, scree bed and developing camellia walk. Small woodland garden under construction. TEAS. *Adm £2 Chd free. Sun May 26 (2-5.30)*

Woodlands Cottage ❀ (Mr & Mrs Stark) Summerbridge. ½m W of Summerbridge on the B6165 (Ripley-Pateley Bridge). 1-acre country garden constructed and developed over the past 10yrs by the owners from a sloping site incorporating part of the existing woodland edge, field and natural stone outcrops with an attractive enclosed cottage style garden; herbaceous, formal herb garden, unusual hardy plants and separate vegetable area. Small nursery. TEAS in aid of Muscular Dystrophy Society. *Adm £1 Chd 50p. Suns May 19, Aug 11 (1.30-5). Private visits welcome by appt* **Tel 01423 780765**

Wytherstone House ⚘❀ (Maj N & Lady Clarissa Collin) Pockley, 3m NE of Helmsley from A170 signpost. Large garden, constantly being improved, consisting of shrubs (some choice and hard to find) shrub roses, perennials, terracotta pots, herb garden, mediterranean garden, beech hedges and magnificent views. The arboretum consisting of rare interesting trees has recently been landscaped with pond and small water garden. Suitable for wheelchairs if someone strong to push. TEAS in aid of Pockley Church and Village Hall. *Adm £2 Chd under 6 free. Over 6 50p. Specialist nursery open Easter to Oct Wed to Sun incl (10-5). Suns April 21, June 16 (1-5). Parties welcome, please* **Tel 01439 770012**

York Gate ⚘❀ (GRBS) Back Church Lane, Adel, Leeds 16. Behind Adel Church on Otley Rd out of Leeds (A660). Bus: WY 34 Leeds-Ilkley; alight Lawnswood Arms, ½m. A family garden created by father, son and mother. 1 acre of particular interest to the plantsman and containing pool, an arbour, miniature pinetum, dell with stream folly, nutwalk, peony bed, iris borders, fern border, herb garden, summerhouse, alley, white and silver garden, vegetable garden, pavement maze. Sybil's garden, all within 1-acre! NO COACHES. *Adm £2.50 Chd free (Share to GRBS®). Sat, Sun June 1, 2 (2-6)*

York House ⚘❀ (Mr & Mrs W H Pridmore) Claxton, 8m E of York, off A64. 1-acre plantsmans garden, created by owners since 1975; old roses, herbaceous, shrubs, fruit. *Adm £1 Chd free (Share to Northern Horticultural Society©). Only Sun May 19, plant stall. Private visits welcome, April to Sept please* **Tel 01904 468360**

NOTES

WALES
Clwyd

Hon County Organiser:
Denbighshire & Colwyn: Mrs Sebastian Rathbone, Bryn Celyn, Ruthin LL15 1TT Tel 01824 702077
Assistant Hon County Organiser: Miss Marion MacNicoll, Trosyffordd, Ystrad Rd, Denbigh LL16 4RL
Tel 01745 812247
Hon County Treasurer: Mr Alan Challoner, 13, The Village, Bodelwyddan LL18 5UR Tel 01745 583451
Hon County Organiser:
Flintshire and Wrexham: Mrs J R Forbes, Pen-y-Wern, Pontblyddyn, nr Mold CH7 4HN
Tel 01978-760531
Assistant Hon County Organiser: Mrs Gwen Manuel, Tir-y-Fron, Llangollen Rd, Ruabon, LL14 6RW
Tel 01978 821633
Hon County Treasurer: Mr Peter Manuel, Tir-y-Fron, Llangollen Rd, Ruabon, LL14 6RW
Tel 01978 821633

DATES OF OPENING

March 31 Sunday
Erddig Park, Wrexham
April 14 Sunday
Hawarden Castle, Hawarden
April 19 Friday
2 Woodside Cottages, Chirk
April 21 Sunday
Hartsheath, Pontblyddyn
April 24 Wednesday
Hartsheath, Pontblyddyn
April 28 Sunday
Hartsheath, Pontblyddyn
Welsh College of Horticulture,
Northop
May 8 Wednesday
2 Woodside Cottages, Chirk
May 11 Saturday
Dolhyfryd, Denbigh
Tir-y-Fron, Ruabon
May 12 Sunday
Dolhyfryd, Denbigh
Hawarden Castle, Hawarden
Tir-y-Fron, Ruabon
May 18 Saturday
Chirk Castle, nr Wrexham
May 19 Sunday
Three Chimneys, Rhostyllen
May 26 Sunday
Branas Lodge, Llandrillo ‡
Pen-y-Bryn, Llangollen
Rhagatt Hall, Carrog ‡
Tyn-y-Craig, Llandrillo ‡
2 Woodside Cottages, Chirk
June 2 Sunday
Berth and The Cottage, Llanbedr

June 5 Wednesday
Pen-y-Bryn, Llangollen
June 9 Sunday
33 Bryn Twr, Abergele
The Garden House, Erbistock
River House, Erbistock
June 12 Wednesday
2 Woodside Cottages, Chirk
June 16 Sunday
Castanwydden, Llandyrnog
June 23 Sunday
17 Broclywedog, Rhewl
The Garden House, Erbistock
Nantclwyd Hall, Ruthin
June 27 Thursday
17 Broclywedog, Rhewl
June 29 Saturday
Cerrigllwydion Hall, Llandyrnog
Dinbren Isaf, Llangollen
June 30 Sunday
Byrgoed, Llandderfel, nr Bala ‡
The Coach House, Llandyrnog
Dinbren Isaf, Llangollen
Dolwen, Cefn Coch
Fron Goch Farmhouse,
Llandrillo ‡
Gwaenynog, Denbigh ‡‡
Tal y Bryn Farm, Llanefydd ‡‡
Llangedwyn Hall,
Llangedwyn
Pen-y-Wern, Pontblyddyn
July 3 Wednesday
Byrgoed, Llandderfel, nr Bala
July 11 Thursday
Bryn Hafod, Treuddyn
July 13 Saturday
Tyddyn Uchaf, Carrog

July 14 Sunday
The Garden House, Erbistock
Llanasa Village Gardens
Tyddyn Uchaf, Carrog
July 18 Thursday
Bryn Hafod, Treuddyn
July 21 Sunday
Bodrhyddan, Rhuddlan
July 28 Sunday
The Garden House, Erbistock
September 1 Sunday
Eyarth House, nr Ruthin ‡
Plas Newydd, Llanfair DC ‡
September 15 Sunday
The Garden House, Erbistock
September 21 Saturday
Tyddyn Uchaf, Carrog
September 22 Sunday
Tyddyn Uchaf, Carrog
October 20 Sunday
Three Chimneys, Rhostyllen

By appointment only
For details see garden description

Alyn View, nr Mold
Argoed Cottage, nr Overton-on-Dee
Bryn Celyn, Llanbedr
Bryn Derwen, Mold
Cartref, Babell
Donadea Lodge, Babell
Merlyn, Moelfre, Abergele
Trem-Ar-For, Dyserth
Tyn Yr Odyn, Llannefydd

DESCRIPTIONS OF GARDENS

Alyn View, Rhydymwyn ✗ (Mr & Mrs Smith) nr Mold. Directions on appointment. A cottage garden of 1 acre. A shady private garden and a very sunny open garden. Both areas full of established trees, shrubs and herbaceous borders. *Adm £1 Chd 50p. Private visits welcome, please* **Tel 01352 741771**

Argoed Cottage ઇ✗ (Mr & Mrs C J Billington) Overton-on-Dee. App Overton-on-Dee from Wrexham on A528 cross over Overton Bridge and in about ¾m on brow of hill turn L into Argoed Lane. 1¾-acre garden. Interesting trees and shrubs. Herbaceous beds; roses and vegetable garden. *Adm £1 Chd free. Private visits by prior arrangement May to July. Please* **Tel 01978 710 707**

¶Berth & The Cottage ✗❀ (Mr & Mrs C Davey and Mrs F Davey) Llanbedr. From Ruthin take A494 towards Mold. After 1½m at the Griffin Inn turn L on to B5429. After 1m turn R at Xrds. Garden 1st L. 2½-acre garden; mixed borders, vegetable garden, cottage garden; water garden under construction. TEA. *Adm £1.50 Chd 25p. Sun June 2 (2-6)*

¶Bodrhyddan ✗❀ (The Lord & Lady Langford) Rhuddlan. From Rhuddlan take the A5151 to Dyserth. The garden is on the L. Parterre garden in the French style; formal garden, clipped yew hedges; water garden; woodland walk leading to St Mary's Well. TEAS. *Adm £1.50 Chd 50p (Share to St Kentigern's Hospice®). Sun July 21 (2-6)*

Branas Lodge ❀ (Mr & Mrs S C Lloyd) Llandrillo. [Grid Ref. SJ018378] 1m W of Llandrillo on B4401 Corwen to Bala rd take 2nd R by post box and cross R Dee. At T-junction turn L. Garden approx 150yds on R. Approx 2-acre hillside garden developed from scrub since 1975 with rhododendrons, azaleas and other shrubs. Waterfall approx 100' falling into garden. Views of Dee Valley and the Berwyns. TEAS at Tyn-y-Craig. *Adm £1.50 Chd 50p (Share to Llandrillo Parish Church®). Sun May 26 (2-5) Open with* **Tyn-y-Craig**

17 Broclywedog ✗❀ (Mel Royles) Rhewl, Ruthin. From Ruthin take A525 to Denbigh. Turn R in Rhewl onto Llandyrnog Rd. 2nd rd on R. A small attractive plantsmans garden packed with unusual varieties of geranium, erodium, sisyrinchium, alpine and others. TEA. *Adm £1 Chd 25p. Sun June 23, Thurs June 27 (2-6). Private visits welcome, please* **Tel 01824 702139**

Bryn Celyn ઇ✗ (Mr & Mrs S Rathbone) Llanbedr, Ruthin. [OS Ref SJ 133 603]. From Ruthin take A494 towards Mold. After 1½m at the Griffin Inn turn L onto B5429. 1¼m house and garden on R. 1-acre garden; mixed borders; walled garden; old-fashioned roses. TEAS. *Adm £1.50 Chd 50p. By appt only, please* **Tel 01824 702077**

Bryn Derwen ✗❀ (Roger & Janet Williams) Wrexham Road, Mold. ½m from Mold Cross on Mold-Wrexham rd B5444; opp Alun School and Sports Centre (large car park). ½-acre old walled garden with large sunken area. Plantsman's garden with wide variety of plants for sun and shade, giving interest from spring to autumn; allium, cistus, euphorbia, ferns, hostas, grasses, etc. Japanese garden. Featured on BBC Radio Wales Garddio and in The Good Garden Guide. *Adm £1 Chd 25p. Private visits welcome, please* **Tel 01352 756662**

Bryn Hafod ✗❀ (Rosemary & David Ffoulkes Jones) Treuddyn, Mold. Turn S off A5104 1m W of Treuddyn into Ffordd y Blaenau (signed). Follow lane for 1¼m. Country garden in elevated position of about 1 acre created from pasture 9yrs ago. A wide variety of plants in mixed borders and varied situations. TEAS in aid of Nightingale House Hospice, Wrexham. *Adm £1 Chd 50p. Thurs July 11, 18 (11-5)*

Bryn Meifod, see Gwynedd gardens

33 Bryn Twr ✗❀ (Mr & Mrs Colin Knowlson) Abergele. (To incl adjoining garden, **'Lynton'**) A55 W take slip rd to Abergele. Turn L at roundabout then over traffic lights; 1st L signed Llanfair T H. 3rd rd on L, no. 33 is on L. There are 2 connected gardens (Lynton) of approx ¾ acre in total, containing patio and pond areas; mixed herbaceous and shrub borders. TEAS. *Combined adm £2.50 OAPs £2 Chd free (Share to St Michaels, Abergele Scout Group©). Sun June 9 (2-6)*

Byrgoed ✗ (Alan & Joy Byrne) Llandderfel. 4½m NE Bala. Off B4401 Bala-Corwen rd. L into village 1st R over stream and up hill. Fork R at old chapel, Byrgoed is ⅝m on L [OS 125 990 372]. Densely stocked terraced cottage garden; thyme lawn, rockery, alpines, roses and fuschias. Yr-round interest. TEAS. *Adm £1 Chd 50p. Sun June 30, Wed July 3 (2-6)*

Cartref ✗ (Mrs D Jones) Caerwys Rd Babell, Holywell. Turn off A541 Mold to Denbigh rd at Afonwen signposted Babell. At T-junction turn R, Black Lion Inn turn L, 1st L 4th house. From Holywell old A55, turn L for Gorsedd then L again. L at Gorsedd Church for Babell, 2m down that rd turn R at Babell Chapel which is now Chapel House, 4th house. Very attractive well-stocked cottage garden; clematis, climbers, vegetables and roses. *Adm £1 Chd 25p (Share to Cancer Research®). Private visits welcome July only, please* **Tel 01352 720638**

Castanwydden ઇ❀ (A M Burrows Esq) Fforddlas, Llandyrnog. Take rd from Denbigh due E to Llandyrnog approx 4m. From Ruthin take B5429 due N to Llandyrnog. [OS ref 1264 (sheet 116)]. Approx 1-acre cottage garden with a considerable variety of plants and bulbs. Small nursery growing plants from the garden. TEAS. *Adm £1.50 Chd 25p. Sun June 16 (2-6) (Share to Llangynhafal Parish Church®). Private visits welcome, please* **Tel 01824 790404**

Cerrigllwydion Hall ✗❀ (Mr & Mrs D Howard) Llandyrnog. E of Denbigh. B5429 ½m from Llandyrnog village on Ruthin Road. Extensive grounds with mature trees; herbaceous borders; vegetables and greenhouses. TEAS. *Adm £1.50 Chd free (Share to Llanynys Church®). Sat June 29 (2-6)*

Chirk Castle ♿✂ (The National Trust) Chirk 7m SE of Llangollen. Off A5 in Chirk by War Memorial. 4½ acres trees and flowering shrubs, rhododendrons, azaleas, rockery, yew topiary. TEAS. *Adm to garden £2 OAPs/Chd £1. Sat May 18 (12-5)*

The Coach House ✂❀ (Mrs F A Bell) Llandyrnog. Take Mold rd out of Denbigh to village of Bodfari. Turn R to Llandyrnog on B5429. House approx 1m on L-hand side. Small cottage garden set in semi-walled garden. Created from rough farm land 8yrs ago. Some unusual and rare herbaceous plants and interesting features. TEAS. *Adm £1 Chd 50p. Sun June 30 (2-6)*

Dinbren Isaf ✂❀ (Mr & Mrs P Ault Walker) 1¾m N of Llangollen on rd to Worlds End and Minera. 1-acre garden. Wide variety of herbaceous plants and shrubs in alkaline soil at 850′ in woodland setting, as featured on S4C. TEAS. *Adm £1.50 Chd free (Share to Llantysilio Parish Church®). Sat, Sun June 29, 30 (2-6)*

Dolhyfryd ♿✂❀ (Capt & Mrs H M C Cunningham) The Lawnt, 1m from Denbigh on B5401 to Nantglyn. Several acres of park, woodland and shrub garden with river; magnificent native trees, many azaleas, rhododendrons, bulbs; walled kitchen garden; wild flower meadow. TEAS. *Adm £1.50 Chd 50p. Crocuses end of Feb and beginning of March. Sat, Sun May 11, 12 (2-6). Private visits welcome, please* **Tel 01745 814805**

Dolwen ✂❀ (Mrs F Denby) Cefn Coch Llanrhaedr-ym-Mochnant. From Oswestry take the B4580 going W to Llanrhaedr. Turn R in village and up narrow lane for 1m. Garden on R. 14m from Oswestry. 4 acres of hillside garden with pools, stream, small wood and many different types of plant and unusual annuals all backed by a stupendous mountain view. TEAS. *Adm £1 Chd free (Share to Oswestry Orthopaedic Hospital®). Every Fri and last Sun in month from May to Sept in aid of local charities. For NGS Sun June 30 (2-5). Private parties welcome, please* **Tel 01691 780 411**

Donadea Lodge ♿✂❀ (Mr & Mrs Patrick Beaumont) Babell. Turn off A541 Mold to Denbigh at Afonwen, signposted Babell; T-junction turn L. A55 Chester to St Asaph take B5122 to Caerwys, 3rd turn on L. Shady garden with unusual plants, shrubs; shrub and climbing roses; clematis; pink, yellow and white beds. Featured in Homes and Gardens 1994, and in The Good Gardens Guide 1996. *Private visits welcome from May 1 to 31, June 24 to Aug 11 please* **Tel 01352 720204**

Erddig Hall ♿✂❀ (The National Trust) 2m S of Wrexham. Signed from A483/A5125 Oswestry Road; also from A525 Whitchurch Road. Garden restored to its C18 formal design incl varieties of fruit known to have been grown there during that period and now incl the National Ivy Collection. TEAS. Tours of the garden by Head Gardener at 1pm, 2.30pm. *Adm £2 Chd £1. NT Shop & plant sales. For NGS Sun March 31 (12-4) Garden only*

Eyarth House ✂❀ (Mrs J T Fleming) 2m S of Ruthin off A525. Bus: Ruthin-Corwen, Ruthin-Wrexham. Large garden; rock garden; shrubs and ornamental trees. TEA. *Adm £1 Chd 50p (Share to St Mary's Church®). Sun Sept 1 (2.30-6) Private visits welcome, please* **Tel 01824 702745**

¶Fron Goch Farmhouse ✂❀ (Mrs S Stille) Llandrillo. Take B4401 off A5 W of Corwen. After 4m Fron Goch is on the R. Very pretty terraced garden in wonderful surroundings full of old-fashioned roses and unusual plants. TEAS. *Adm £1 Chd 25p. Sun June 30 (2-6)*

The Garden House ♿❀ (S Dyson-Wingett) Erbistock. 5m S of Wrexham on A528 Wrexham to Shrewsbury. Follow signs at Overton Bridge to Erbistock Church. Shrub and herbaceous plantings in monochromatic, analogous and complementary colour schemes. Rose pergolas and hydrangea avenue (over 200 species and cultivars). Victorian dovecote. Nursery plant centre. TEAS. *Adm £1 Chd free (Share to Frank Wingett Cancer Appeal©). Suns June 9, 23, July 14, 28, Sept 15 (2-6) Private visits welcome, please* **Tel 01978 780958**

Gwaenynog ♿✂❀ (Maj & Mrs Tom Smith & Mrs Frances Williams) Denbigh. 1m W of Denbigh on A543, Lodge on left. 2-acre garden incl the restored kitchen garden where Beatrix Potter wrote the Tale of the Flopsy Bunnies. Small exhibition of some of her work. C16 house visited by Samuel Johnson during his Tour of Wales. Coffee and biscuits 11-12.30pm. Refreshments available Broadleys Farm Restaurant. TEAS. *Adm £1.50 OAPs £1 Chd 25p (Share to St James's Church, Nantglyn®). Sun June 30 (11-6)*

Hartsheath ✂❀ (Dr M C Jones-Mortimer) Pontblyddyn. ½m S of intersection with A5104. Red brick lodge on E side of A541. Large woodland garden; many varieties of flowering cherries and crab apples. Tidy picnic lunchers welcomed. Lunch & Tea at Bridge Inn, Pontblyddyn. *Adm £1 Chd £1 (Share to Pontblyddyn Church®). Sun April 21 (12-5) Wed April 24 (2-5) Sun April 28 (12-5). Also private visits welcome weekdays Feb-May, Sept-Oct, please* **Tel 01352 770 204**

Hawarden Castle ♿✂ (Sir William & Lady Gladstone) On B5125 just E of Hawarden village. Large garden and picturesque ruined castle. *Adm £1.50 Chd/OAPs £1. Suns April 14, May 12 (2-6)*

Llanasa Village Gardens 3m SW of Prestatyn. Turn off A548 at Gwespyr or from A55 take A5151 turn off in Trelawnyd. TEAS. *Combined adm £3.50 Chd 50p. Sun July 14 (12-5)*

Golden Grove ✂ (Mr & Mrs Nigel Steele-Mortimer, & Mr & Mrs Mervyn Steele-Mortimer) A historic C17 manor house with Edwardian terraced garden. Yew topiary designed by Lady Aberconway. Part of C17 walled garden, orchard and water garden

Glanaber ♿✂❀ (Mrs J Spiller) 1-acre garden created from pastureland dominated by rare Maltese Oak; large duck pond, bridges, arches, footpaths create pleasant walks; spring bulbs; herbaceous and bedding plants. C18 house. Old tools, machinery display

¶Henblas ♿❀ (David & Bridget Lawton). C17 house in village. The garden and grounds are almost 1 acre with many mature trees, rhododendrons and clipped beech hedges. There is a small formal rose garden with pond, and the whole area is a sanctuary for many birds

¶**Henblas Lodge** ⚹ (Mr & Mrs J Williams) Medium-sized L-shaped cottage garden incorporating old with new to give yr-long colour

Tan y Fron ⚹ (Mr Meirion Ellis) Typical country cottage garden with outstanding splashes of brilliant colour and superb comprehensive vegetable garden

Cae Mawr ⚹⚹❀ (Mrs N A Leicester) New garden professionally landscaped, still under development; beautiful pond with carp. Future planning for small orchard and vegetable garden. Attractive shrubbery and flower beds. Large patio

Llangedwyn Hall ⚹⚹❀ (Mr & Mrs T M Bell) Llangedwyn; on the B4396 rd to Llanrhaedr about 5m W of the Llynclys Xrds. Approx 4 acres; formal terraced garden on 3 levels designed and laid out in late C17 and early C18. Sunken rose garden and small water garden. TEAS in aid of Llangedwyn Church. *Adm £1.50 OAP's & Chd 50p. Sun June 30 (2-6)*

Merlyn ⚹ (Drs J E & B E J Riding) Moelfre, Abergele. Leave A55 (Conwy or Chester direction) at Bodelwyddan Castle, proceed uphill by castle wall 1m to Xrds. 0.1m to T-junction. (white bungalow) R B5381 towards Betws yn Rhos for 2m, then fork L (signed Llanfair TH) after telephone box garden 0.4m on R. 2-acre garden developed from a field since 1987. Long mixed border; damp and gravel garden; many shrubs and old roses; rhododendrons and azaleas; spring garden. Views of sea. *Adm £1.50 Chd 50p. Private parties welcome Feb to Nov incl by prior arrangement, please Tel 01745 824435*

The Mount, Kinnerton, see Cheshire

¶**Nantclwyd Hall** ⚹ (Sir Phillip & Lady Isabella Naylor-Leyland) Ruthin. Take A494 from Ruthin to Corwen. The garden is 1½m from Pwllglas on L. Approx 3 acres of formal gardens and further grounds. Temples and follies by Sir Clough Williams-Ellis. TEA. *Adm £2 Chd 50p. Sun June 23 (2-6) Private visits welcome following written application*

¶**Pen-y-Bryn** ⚹⚹❀ (Mr & Mrs R B Attenburrow) Llangollen. Signs at t-lights on A5 in centre of Llangollen. Comfortable walking distance or field parking. 2-acre garden on wooded plateau overlooking town; panoramic views; on site of old hall with established trees, shrubs and rhododendrons, walled garden, water feature, extensive lawns and herbaceous borders. TEAS. *Adm £1.50 Chd free (Share to Friends of Llangollen International Musical Eisteddfod®). Sun May 26, Wed June 5 (2-6)*

Pen-y-Wern ⚹⚹❀ (Dr & Mrs Forbes) Pontblyddyn, 5m SE of Mold, 7m NW of Wrexham. On E side of A541, ½ way between Pontblyddyn and Caergwrle. 2½-acre terraced country-house garden incl interesting small gardens. Shrubs, conifers, grasses and herbaceous borders; rose garden spectacular in June/July. Magnificent copper beech with canopy circumference of 250ft and other splendid trees. TEAS. *Adm £1.50 Chd 50p (Share to Hope Parish Church®). Sun June 30 (2-6)*

Plas Newydd ⚹❀ (Mr & Mrs Geoffrey Jackson) Llanfair DC. Grid Ref [SJ 138 562] Take A525 from Ruthin for 1½m to Llanfair DC. Turn L at signpost to Graigfechan,

½m turn sharp L where rd bears R down lane, house and garden on L. 3½ acres of restored garden; shrubs, herbaceous, roses; walled garden and orchard. TEAS. *Adm £1 Chd 50p. Sun Sept 1 (2-6)*

Rhagatt Hall ⚹⚹❀ (Cdr & Mrs F J C Bradshaw) Carrog. 1m NE of Corwen. A5 from Llangollen, 3m short of Corwen, turn R (N) for Carrog at garage, cross R Dee and keep bearing L. 1st opening on R after Carrog and seeing river again. 5-acre garden with azaleas, rhododendrons, trees, rare magnolia, bluebell wood; extensive views. Georgian house. TEAS. *Adm £1 Chd 50p. Sun May 26 (2-6)*

River House ⚹⚹❀ (Mrs Gwydyr-Jones) Erbistock. 5m S of Wrexham. On A528 Wrexham-Shrewsbury rd, ¼m before Overton Bridge (opp turning A539 to Ruabon). Small garden with unusual shrubs and plants. *Adm £1 Chd free. Sun June 9 (2-6)*

¶**Tal y Bryn Farm** ⚹❀ (Mr & Mrs Gareth Roberts) Llanefydd. From Henllan take rd signed Llanefydd. After 2½m turn R signed Bont Newydd. Garden ½m on L. Newly designed working farmhouse garden planted to make best use of existing buildings and features framing wonderful views. TEA. *Adm £1 Chd 25p. Sun June 30 (2-6)*

Three Chimneys ⚹❀ (Mr & Mrs Hollington) 3m SW of Wrexham via Rhostyllen. From Wrexham A5152 fork R at Black Lion onto B5097. From Ruabon B5605 turn L onto B5426 signed Minera. Turn R ½m over bridge, L at Water Tower. Garden ¼m on L opp post box. Forester's garden of 1 acre; maples, conifers, cornus and sorbus species and varieties. Many small trees used in the manner of a herbaceous border. Very unusual and interesting. *Adm £1.50 Chd 25p. Suns May 19 (2-6) Oct 20 (1-5)*

Tir-y-Fron ⚹⚹❀ (Mr & Mrs P R Manuel) Llangollen Rd, Ruabon. 5m from Wrexham, take A539 from Ruabon By-Pass, signed Llangollen, turn R on brow of hill after 200yds. 1¾-acre garden with shrubs and herbaceous plants surrounded by mature trees with quarry. Offa's Dyke separates garden from drive. TEA May 11 TEAS May 12. (Share to Llangollen Canal Boat Trust©). *Adm £1.50 Chd free. Sat, Sun May 11, 12 (2-6)*

Trem-Ar-For ⚹ (Mr & Mrs L Whittaker) Dyserth. 125 Cwm Rd, Dyserth. From Dyserth to Rhuddlan rd A5151. Turn L at Xrds signed Cwm, fork L and at traffic de-restriction sign house on L. ¾-acre limestone terraced hillside garden with dramatic views towards Snowdon and Anglesey. A highly specialised garden with many rare and interesting plants with special emphasis on alpines, daphnes and specie paeonies. *Adm £1 Chd 50p (Share to North Wales Wildlife Trust©). Private visits welcome April to Sept, please Tel 01745 570349*

Tyddyn Uchaf ⚹❀ (Mandy & Nigel Dolby) Carrog. From Corwen take A5 to Llangollen. At Llidiart-y-Parc turn L to Carrog. R in middle of village. Garden 1½m on R or take A5104 from Wrexham, L at New Inn, house 2½m on L. Unusual, pretty, terraced cottage garden with rockeries, large pond; full of interesting plants. Small nursery. TEAS. *Adm £1 (Share to PTA Corrog School®). Sats, Suns, July 13, 14, Sept 21, 22 (11-5)*

Tyn-y-Craig ✍※ (Maj & Mrs Harry Robertson) Llandrillo. 1½m from Llandrillo towards Bala, L off the B4401 Corwen to Bala Rd. Developed over 25 yrs, a hillside garden approx 2 acres, incorporating 6 descending landscaped pools. Tea. *Adm £1.50 Chd 50p (Share to Christie Hospital NHS Trust©). Sun May 26 (2-5.30) Open with* **Branas Lodge**

Tyn yr Odyn ఉ※ (Mr & Mrs J S Buchanan) Llannefydd. 8m from Denbigh. B5382 signed Henllan and Llansannan. In Bryn Rhyd yr Arian, turn sharp R signed Llannefydd and Aled Plants. Garden ½m on L. Approx ⅔-acre cottage garden on the bank of R Aled, with stream, ponds and alpine garden; conifers, heathers, roses, shrubs, greenhouses and alpine house. Small nursery adjacent. *Adm £1 Chd 25p. Private visits welcome any day April to September, please* **Tel 01745 870394**

Welsh College of Horticulture ఉ※ Northop. Village of Northop is 3m from Mold and close to the A55 express-way. Mature gardens incorporating many national award winning features. Commercial sections. Garden Centre and retail sections where produce and garden sundries can be purchased. A Golf Course is being constructed for the teaching of Greenkeeping Skills. Car parking. TEA. *Adm £1 OAPs & Chd 50p families £3.50. Sun April 28 (10-4)*

2 Woodside Cottages ✍※ (Mrs J L Wilson) Halton. 7m N of Oswestry. Follow A5-A483. R off roundabout signed Halton. R at next roundabout ¼m under bridge and down hill. Garden on L. Alternatively N through Chirk (towards Llangollen) ¾m turn R (signed Black Park) ½m on R. A small but interesting cottage garden with a variety of different features incl alpine, heather, shrubbery, pond and bog areas. Over 100 hardy geraniums can be seen amongst the many unusual herbaceous plants and shrubs. TEAS. *Adm £1 Chd 50p. Fri April 19, Wed May 8, Sun May 26, Wed June 12 (2-5). Private visits welcome any time, please* **Tel 01691 777824**

Dyfed

Hon County Organisers:

North (Ceredigion District)   Mrs Stewart Neal, Llwyncelyn, Glandyfi, Machynlleth, Powys, SY20 8SS Tel 01654 781203

South (Carmarthen and Pembrokeshire)   Mrs Duncan Drew, Cwm-Pibau, New Moat, Clarbeston Road, Haverfordwest, Pembrokeshire SA63 4RE Tel 01437 532454

Dyfed North Treasurer   Mrs Peter Latham, Garreg, Glandyfi, Machynlleth, Powys SY20 8SS

DATES OF OPENING

April 20 Saturday
Colby Woodland Garden, Narberth
April 21 Sunday
Pant-yr-Holiad, Rhydlewis
May 5 Sunday
Post House, between
Whitland/St Clears
May 12 Sunday
Pant-yr-Holiad, Rhydlewis
May 19 Sunday
Llwyncelyn, Glandyfi
Mill House, Glandyfi
Picton Castle, The Rhos, nr
Haverfordwest
Post House, between
Whitland/St Clears
May 26 Sunday
Cae Hir, Cribyn
Ffynone, Boncath
Hean Castle, Saundersfoot
June 1 Saturday
Bryngoleu, Llannon
June 2 Sunday
Bryngoleu, Llannon

Crynfryn & Tynewydd Gardens,
midway, Aberaeron and
Tregaron
Pant-yr-Holiad, Rhydlewis
June 16 Sunday
Cae Hir, Cribyn
June 22 Saturday
Millinford, nr Haverfordwest
June 23 Sunday
Llanllyr, Talsarn
Millinford, nr Haverfordwest
June 30 Sunday
Living Garden, Bryn
Llygad yr Haul, Dryslwyn,
Carmarthen
Plas Llidiardau, Llanilar
July 6 Saturday
Dyffryn, Pennant, Llanon ‡
Felindre, Aberarth, Aberaeron ‡
Maesyrynn, Nantycaws,
Carmarthen
July 7 Sunday
Crynfryn & Tynewydd Gardens,
midway, Aberaeron and
Tregaron.
Maesyrynn, Nantycaws,
Carmarthen

July 14 Sunday
Cae Hir, Cribyn
July 28 Sunday
Picton Castle, The Rhos, nr
Haverfordwest
August 7 Wednesday
7 Maes yr Awel, Ponterwyd
August 11 Sunday
7 Maes yr Awel, Ponterwyd
August 25 Sunday
Llanerchaeron

Regular openings
For details see garden description

The Dingle, Crundale
Garreg, Glayndyfi
Hilton Court Nurseries, Roch
Picton Castle, The Rhos,
Haverfordwest
Saundersfoot Bay Leisure Park
Winllan, nr Lampeter
Ynyshir Hall, Eglwysfach,
Machynlleth

By appointment only
For telephone numbers and other
details see garden descriptions.
Private visits welcomed

Blaengwrfach Isaf, nr Llandyssul
Cwm-Pibau, New Moat,
    Haverfordwest

The Forge, Landshipping
Garreg, Glandyfi, Machynlleth
Old Cilgwyn Gardens, Newcastle
    Emlyn
Winllan, nr Lampeter

> **By Appointment Gardens.**
> These owners do not have a
> fixed opening day usually
> because they do not like crowds
> or have insufficient parking
> space. Owner will often give
> guided tour.

DESCRIPTIONS OF GARDENS

Blaengwrfach Isaf ⚘✿ (Mrs Gail M Farmer) Bancyffordd, 2m W of Llandysul. Leaving Llandysul on Cardigan rd, by Half Moon pub fork left; continue on this road;
approx 1½m, after village sign Bancyffordd farm track on
right. ¾-acre garden incorporating woodland, wild and
cottage garden aspects within a secluded and sheltered
area. Many specie and shrub roses; old-fashioned and
scented plants grown in variety of ways amongst unusual
trees planted for all-yr interest. Areas specially created
with bees, butterflies and birds in mind; new pathway
bordered by wild-flower meadow. Incl in 'English Private
Gardens'. *Adm £1 Chd free. Private visits welcome April,
May, June, Oct (10-4), please* **Tel 01559 362604**

Bryngoleu ♿✿ (Mr & Mrs Ivor Russell) Llannon. 13m
from Swansea, 7m from Llanelli. From junction 49 (Pont
Abraham) on M4 take A48(T) in the direction of Cross
Hands. Turn L after approx 3kms towards Village of Llwyn
Teg. At [map ref SN 56 E on OS 159.] ½-acre garden
with converted stable block, leading to extensive choice
of walks each about ½m long in mature and newly developing woodlands and alongside natural streams. 25
acres overall incl 2 lakes; fine views of the surrounding
countryside as shown on SC4 TV. Ample seating. TEA.
*Adm £1.50 Chd 50p. Sat, Sun June 1, 2 (2-6). Private par-
ties welcome, please* **Tel 01269 842343**

Cae Hir ⚘✿ (Mr Wil Akkermans) Cribyn. W on A482
from Lampeter. After 5m turn S on B4337. Cae Hir is 2m
on L. Beautiful and peaceful 6-acre garden on exposed W
facing slope. Entirely created and maintained by owner
from 4 overgrown fields of rough grazing. Started in
1985. Many unusual features found unexpectedly around
each corner incl red, yellow and blue sub-gardens, bonsai
'room', stonework, ponds, lovely views; new water and
bog garden and white garden. As featured on radio and
TV. TEA. *Adm £1.50 Chd 50p. Open daily except Mons
April to Oct (1-6). Also open Bank Hols.* ▲*For NGS Suns
May 26, June 16, July 14 (1-6)*

Colby Woodland Garden ✿ (The National Trust) ½m
inland from Amroth and 2m E of Saundersfoot. Signposted by Brown Tourist Signs on the coast rd and the
A477. 8-acre woodland garden in a secluded and tranquil
valley with a fine collection of rhododendrons and azaleas. Tea rooms and gallery. Walled garden open by kind
permission of Mr & Mrs A Scourfield Lewis. TEAS. *Adm
£2.60 Chd £1.30.* ▲*For NGS Sat April 20 (10-5). Large
parties by appt, please* **Tel 01834 811885**

¶**Crynfryn & Tynewydd Gardens** ⚘✿ TEAS. *Combined
adm £2 Chd free. Suns June 2, July 7 (10.30-6)*

¶**Crynfryn** (Mr & Mrs Tom Murton) Penuwch on
B4576 between Penuwch and Bwlchllan, 8m Aberaeron, 8m Tregaron. 1-acre woodland garden with
mature trees; pond; bog plants; meconopsis and
primulas; herbaceous borders and collection of old
shrub roses overlooking Cambrian Mts
¶**Tynewydd** (Mr & Mrs Robin Edwards) Bwlchllan.
½m S of Crynfryn. 2-acre garden; 2 large ponds; herbaceous planting; pergola; maturing trees and shrubs.
Extensive mountain views

Cwm Pibau ⚘ (Mrs Duncan Drew) New Moat. 10m NE
of Haverfordwest. 4-acre garden bordered by streams
and created since 1978; mainly young rare shrubs on a
hillside. *Adm £1 Chd free. Private visits welcome please*
Tel 01437 532 454

The Dingle ♿⚘✿ (Mrs A J Jones) Crundale. On approaching Haverfordwest from Carmarthen on A40, take
R turn at 1st roundabout signed Fishguard & Cardigan. At
next roundabout take R turn on to B4329. ½m on fork R
opp General Picton; then 1st right into Dingle Lane. 3-
acres plantsman's garden; rose garden; formal beds; scree;
herbaceous border; unusual shrubs; water garden; woodland
walk. Picturesque and secluded; free roaming peacocks.
Nursery adjoining. Tearoom. *Adm £1 Chd 50p (Share to
CRMF®). Weds to Suns March 13 to Oct 14 (10-6)*

¶**Dyffryn** ⚘✿ (Mr & Mrs O P J Richards) Pennant. SN
520, 637. From Aberarth, continue 100yds up hill, turn R,
B4577 to Pennant. Xrds at centre of village turn L. Follow
rd up hill past school. R fork, 250yds turn R. ⅔-acre partly woodland; many shrubs for flower arranging; small
ponds; small Japanese garden; open perennial border; interesting plants, local bird life. TEA *Combined adm with
Felindre. £2 or £1.50 each. Sat July 6 (11-5)*

¶**Felindre** ⚘✿ (Mr & Mrs Peter Davis) Felindre, Aberarth. 1m N of Aberaeron on A487. Turn L towards sea
after bridge. Roadside parking. 1-acre informal garden,
partly hillside with coastal trees and shrubs and unusual
herbaceous plants; pond pavement, kitchen garden;
pines, mulberry, salvias, geraniums and euphorbias. TEA
at Dyffryn. *Combined adm with* **Dyffryn** *£2 or £1.50 each.
Sat July 6 (11-5)*

Ffynone (Earl & Countess Lloyd George of Dwyfor) Boncath. From Newcastle Emlyn take A484 to Cenarth, turn L
on B4332, turn L again at Xrds just before Newchapel.
Large woodland garden in process of restoration. Lovely
views, fine specimen trees, rhododendrons, azaleas. Ask
for descriptive leaflet. House by John Nash (1793), not
shown. Later additions and garden terraces by F Inigo
Thomas c1904. TEA. *Adm £1 Chd free. Sun May 26 (2-6)*

The Forge ⅋ (I & S Mcleod-Baikie) Landshipping. Nearest town Narbeth. Landshipping well sign posted. Pass New Park with pillar box; 200yds further on, gate on R. Approx 9 acres recently planted woodland garden with many varieties of bulbs, trees and shrub roses. Small, pretty very charming. Featured in NGS video 2. *Private visits welcome mid-March to mid-April and also in June, please* Tel 01834 891279

Garreg ✄ (Lt Col & Mrs P A Latham) On A487 at Glandyfi. Between Aberystwyth (12m) and Machynlleth (5m). Old farm complex. 1st buildings on river side approaching from Machynlleth. Approx 1-acre garden; courtyard surrounding old Welsh farmhouse. *Adm £1.50 Chd free. Private visits welcome May 1 to Aug 31, please* Tel 01654 781251

Hean Castle ⅋✄❀ (Mr & Mrs T Lewis) Saundersfoot. 1m N of Saundersfoot. 1½m SE of Kilgetty. Take Amroth road from Saundersfoot or the Sardis road from Kilgetty. 2-acres; mixed borders with some unusual plants and shrubs; rose garden; walled garden and greenhouse; conifers; pot plants and troughs. Good view. TEAS. *Adm £1.50 Chd free. Sun May 26 (11-5). Also private visits welcome, please* Tel 01834 812222

Hilton Court Nurseries ⅋✄❀ (Mrs Cheryl Lynch) Roch. From Haverfordwest take the A487 to St Davids. 6m from Haverfordwest signs L to Hilton Court Nurseries. 4 acres of garden with superb setting overlooking ponds and woodlands. Spectacular lily ponds in July and August; wild flower walks; unusual trees and shrubs giving colour throughout the year. Nursery adjoining. TEAS. *Collecting box. Daily March to October 1 (9.30-5.30), October (10.30-4).* Tel 01437 710262

Living Garden ⅋✄❀ (Alan C Clarke Esq) 4a Brynmorlais Bryn, Llanelli; 2½m NE of town on B4297. Parking in layby on main rd please. Long, slim plantsman's garden subdivided for interest. Rare and attractive plants, containers, water features and pools. TEAS. *Adm £1 Chd 25p. Sun June 30 (2-5); also private visits welcome, please* Tel 01554 821274 *April to Sept*

Llanerchaeron ⅋✄❀ (The National Trust) Lampeter. 2m inland from Aberaeron, to the N of the A482 Lampeter to Aberaeron rd. Formerly the pleasure grounds and kitchen gardens to Llanerchaeron House, these 12-acre gardens are undergoing restoration by volunteers and others under the direction of The National Trust with very limited resources. The lake and surrounding woods and paths are yet to be restored. Visitors can see restoration at a very early stage. TEA. *Adm £2 Chd free. Sun Aug 25 (10-4)*

Llanllyr ⅋✄❀ (Mr & Mrs Robert Gee) Talsarn [SA48 8QB]. 6m NW of Lampeter on B4337 to Llanrhystud. Garden of about 4 acres, originally laid out in 1830s, renovated, replanted and extended since 1986. Mixed borders; lawns; bulbs; large fish pond with bog and water plants. Formal water garden. Shrub rose borders; foliage; species and old-fashioned plants. TEAS *Adm £1.50 Chd 50p. Sun June 23 (2-6). Private visits welcome April to Oct. Please write*

Llwyncelyn ✄❀ (Mr & Mrs Stewart Neal) and **The Mill House** (Prof & Mrs John Pollock) Glandyfi. On A487 from Aberystwyth (12m) Machynlleth (6m). Coming from Aberystwyth pass through Eglwysfach. Turn R just before Glandyfi sign. Part of old estate. 10-acre shrub and woodland garden with waterfalls and mill pond. More recent specialised plantings. TEAS. *Combined adm £2 Chd 50p Sun May 19 (2-6) Mill House also welcomes visitors by appt in May, Suns only. Collecting box.* Tel 01654 781342

¶**Llygad Yr Haul** ⅋✄❀ (Mrs Mari Harris) Dryslwyn, Carmarthen. 2m from the A40, 7m off the M4 at Cross Hands. Just under an acre, colourful flower garden incl herbs, mature trees and shrubs surrounding lawns. Overlooking the stunning Towy Valley. TEAS. *Adm £1 Chd under 12 free (Share to CRMF®). Sun June 30 (2-6)*

7 Maes yr Awel ✄❀ (Mrs Beryl Birch) Ponterwyd. From Aberystwyth take A44 towards Llangurig. At Ponterwyd Village, turn R on to A4120 Devil's Bridge rd, then turn 1st L almost immed. ½-acre hillside garden in mountainous surroundings; sheltered 'hidden' gardens, pools fountain, herbaceous plantings, flowering shrubs and specimen trees. Large conservatory for refreshments. TEA. *Adm £1 Acc chd free (Share to Haematology Fund, Bronglais Hospital©). Wed, Sun Aug 7, 11 (12-5)*

Maesyrynn ⅋❀ (Mr & Mrs Thomas) Nantycaws. From Carmarthen take A48 dual carriageway E towards Swansea. After approx 3m turn L for Nantycaws. From Swansea, sign reads Police HQ and Nantycaws. Drive 300yds BP garage on L. Turn R into lane opp; 2nd bungalow on L. Plantsman's cottage garden approx ½ acre. Mainly herbaceous beds and shrubs. Pond and water feature, pergolas and raised beds. Highly productive vegetable garden with greenhouses. Lovely views in rural setting. TEAS. *Adm £1 Chd free. Sat, Sun July 6, 7 (10-6). Parties welcome June to Sept, please* Tel 01267 234198

Millinford ⅋✄❀ (Drs B W & A D Barton) Millin, The Rhos, 3m E of Haverfordwest; on A40 to Carmarthen turn R signed The Rhos, take turn to Millin, R at Millin Chapel then immediate L over river bridge. 4 acres on bank of Millin Creek. Plantsman's garden, large collection of trees and shrubs with alpine area, herbaceous borders and small lake. TEAS. *Adm £1.50 Chd 50p (Share to NSPCC®). Sat, Sun June 22, 23 (11-6)*

Old Cilgwyn Gardens ⅋ (Mr & Mrs Fitzwilliams) Newcastle Emlyn. Situated 1m N of Newcastle Emlyn on the B4571, turn R into entrance. A mixed garden mainly woodland of 14 acres set in 900 acres of parkland, 53 acres of which are Sites of Special Scientific Interest; snowdrops, daffodils, bluebells, rhododendrons. For those prepared to walk, a large tulip tree and the site of the last duel fought in Wales can be seen in Cae Hislop field. *Adm £1.50. Private visits welcome all year, please* Tel 01239 710244

General Information. For general information on the use of this book see Page 15.

Pant-yr-Holiad ✿❀ (Mr & Mrs G H Taylor) Rhydlewis, 12m NW Llandysul. NE Cardigan. From coast rd take B4334 at Brynhoffnant S towards Rhydlewis; after 1m turn left; driveway 2nd L. 5-acres embracing walled garden housing tender plants, alpine beds, water features, rare trees and shrubs in woodland setting; extensive collection rhododendron species; fancy water-fowl. Collections of birch and unusual herbaceous plants. TEA. *Adm £1.50 Chd 50p (Share to Rhydlewis Village Hall®). Open Suns April 21, May 12, June 2 (2-5)*

¶**Picton Castle** ♿❀ (Picton Castle Trust) The Rhos. 3m E of Haverfordwest on A40 to Carmarthen, signposted off main rd. Mature 30-acre woodland garden with unique collection of rhododendrons and azaleas, many bred over 35yrs producing hybrids of great merit and beauty; rare and tender shrubs and trees like magnolia, myrtle, embothrium and eucryphia. Wild flowers abound. Walled garden with roses, fernery, herbaceous and climbing plants and large clearly labelled collection of herbs. Restaurant, 2 craft shops and garden nursery. *Adm £2 Chd £1, under 5 free. Open daily except Mons, April to Sept and Bank Hols. For NGS Suns May 19, July 28 (10.30-5).* **Tel 01437 751326**

Plas Llidiardau ♿✿❀ (L A Stalbow & G Taylor) Llanilar. 7m SE of Aberystwyth. Turn off A487 3m S of Aberystwyth onto A485 to Tregaron and Llanilar. From Llanilar take B4575 to Trawsgoed. Plas Llidiardau is ¾m on R. 7-acre old landscaped site redeveloped and planted since 1985. Wide selection of unusual plants and environments. Double herbaceous borders, formal pond, gravel garden, walled garden, organic raised beds, wooded areas, stream, wildlife pond. TEAS. *Adm £1.50 Chd 50p. Sun June 30 (1-6). Private visits welcome May to July, please* **Tel 01974 241434**

Post House ✿❀ (Mrs Jo Kenaghan) Cwmbach 6m N of St Clears. From Carmarthen W on A40. Take B4298 through Meidrim; leave by centre lane signed Llanboidy.

Turn right at Xrds signed Blaenwaun; right at Xrds to Cwmbach; garden bottom of hill. From Whitland E on A40, left at Ivydean nurseries, right at 3rd Xrds signed Cwmbach. 4-acre valley garden; rhododendrons, azaleas, camellias, unusual trees and shrubs underplanted with hardy orchids, anemones, trilliums, wild snowdrops, bluebells, etc. Large pool, bog garden. Old roses, herbaceous plants. Greenhouses and conservatory. Plants for sale. TEAS. *Adm £1.50 OAP's & Chd £1.* ▲*Suns May 5, 19 (2pm onwards). Private parties welcome, please* **Tel 01994 484213**

Saundersfoot Bay Leisure Park ♿❀ (Ian Shuttleworth Esq) Broadfield, Saundersfoot. On B4316, ¾m S from centre of Saundersfoot. Interesting layout of lawns, shrubs and herbaceous borders with many plants of botanical interest in 20-acre modern holiday leisure park. Large rock garden and water feature; laburnum walk; Japanese Garden. Holders of a National collection of Pontentilla fruticosa. Tea Saundersfoot. *Adm free. April 1 to Oct 28 daily (10-5)*

Winllan (Mr & Mrs Ian Callan) Talsarn. 8m NNW of Lampeter on B4342, Talsarn-Llangeitho rd. 6-acres wildlife garden with large pond, herb-rich meadow, small woodland and 600 yds of river bank walk. Over 200 species of wildflowers with attendant butterflies, dragonflies and birds. Limited suitability for wheelchairs. *Adm £1.50 Chd 50p (under 12 free). Open May & June daily (12-6). Also private visits welcome July & Aug, please* **Tel 01570-470612**

¶**Ynyshir Hall** (Mr & Mrs R J Reen) Machynlleth. Situated off main A487 in Eglwysfach Village, Ynyshir Hall has 14-acre landscaped gardens; mature ornamental trees. The mild climate allows many tender and unusual trees and shrubs; fine collection of rhododendrons and azaleas built up over many decades. TEAS *Adm £1.50. May 1 to 31 (9-5)*

The Glamorgans

Hon County Organiser:	Mrs Christopher Cory, Penllyn Castle, Cowbridge, South Glamorgan CF7 7RQ Tel 01446 772780
Assistant County Organiser:	Mrs L H W Williams, Llanvithyn House, Llancarfan, South Glamorgan Tel 01446 781232

DATES OF OPENING

April 14 Sunday
Trehedyn House,
Peterston-super-Ely
April 21 Sunday
Merthyr Mawr House, Bridgend
April 28 Sunday
Penllyn Castle, Cowbridge
May 12 Sunday
Coedarhydyglyn, Cardiff

9 Willowbrook Gardens, Mayals,
Swansea
May 18 Saturday
Cwmpennar Gardens, Mountain
Ash
May 19 Sunday
Cwmpennar Gardens, Mountain
Ash
May 26 Sunday
Springside, Pen-y-Turnpike, Dinas
Powys

June 2 Sunday
Marleigh Lodge, Old St Mellons
June 9 Sunday
Llanvithyn House, Llancarfan
June 16 Sunday
The Clock House, Llandaff
June 23 Sunday
Mwyndy House, nr Pontyclun
June 30 Sunday
11 Eastcliff, Southgate,
Swansea

July 7 Sunday
Fonmon Castle, nr Barry
Pontygwaith Farm,
Edwardsville

July 14 Sunday
Penylan Gardens

July 21 Sunday
29 Min-y-Coed, Radyr

July 28 Sunday
Gelly Farm, Cymmer

August 4 Sunday
29 Min-y-Coed, Radyr
Pontygwaith Farm, Edwardsville

By appointment only
For telephone numbers and other details see garden descriptions. Private visits welcomed

11 Arno Road, Little Coldbrook
10 Daniel Close, Sully
24 Elm Grove Place, Dinas Powis
Ffynnon Deilo, Pendoylan
Garth Madryn, Penderyn, Aberdare
19 Westfield Road, Glyncoch,
   Pontypridd

Regular Openers. Too many days to include in diary. Usually there is a wide range of plants giving year-round interest. See head of county section for the name and garden description for times etc.

1996 Special Events. For information on special National Gardens Scheme events in 1996 see Pages 18-19.

DESCRIPTIONS OF GARDENS

11 Arno Road ✗❀ (Mrs D Palmer) Little Coldbrook. From A4050 Cardiff to Barry, take roundabout marked Barry Docks and Sully. Then 2nd R into Coldbrook Rd, 2nd L into Langlands Rd, then 6th R into Norwood Cresc; 1st L into Arno Rd. 40ft × 30ft informal plantsman's garden with ponds, herbaceous plants, gravelled area planted with low growing plants. As featured on Radio Wales 'Gardening Matters' Aug '94. TEAS. *Adm £1. Private visits welcome weekends and Wednesdays May to Oct (2-5), please* **Tel 01446 743642**

The Clock House ☙✗❀ (Prof & Mrs Bryan Hibbard) Cathedral Close, Llandaff, 2m W of Cardiff. Follow signs to Cathedral via A4119. Bus: Cardiff alight Maltsters Arms. Small walled garden; fine old trees; wide variety of shrubs and plants; important collection of shrub, species and old roses. NT stall. TEA. *Adm £1.50 Acc chd free. Sun June 16 (2-6)*

Coedarhydyglyn ☙ (Executors of the late Sir Cennydd Traherne) 5m W of Cardiff. Natural terrain, pleasant situation; lawns, flowering shrubs, good collection of conifers; Japanese garden, fine trees. TEA. *Adm £1 Chd 20p (Share to Cardiff and District Samaritans®). Sun May 12 (2.30-6)*

Cwmpennar Gardens ✗❀ Mountain Ash 1m. From A4059 turn R 100yds past the traffic lights; follow sign to Cefnpennar, follow rd uphill through woods for ¾m, bear R sharply uphill before bus shelter, gardens 200yds. Car park 100yds past bus shelter. Mixture of formal and informal gardens with some natural woodland in all 3 of conservation interest. Variety of shrubs, rhododendrons and azaleas, rockeries, shrub roses; new plantings of shrubs and roses; water features. Rich in bird life, with nest boxes usually occupied. Gardens high on mountain side in secluded rural surroundings of coal mining valley. Gardens filmed for television. TEAS. Glamorgan Wildlife Trust Sales stall. *Combined adm £1 Chd 50p (Share to St Margarets Church Restoration Fund®). Sat, Sun May 18, 19 (2-6)*
> **The Cottage** (Judge & Mrs Hugh Jones)
> **Ivy Cottage** (Mr & Mrs D H Phillips)
> **Woodview** (Miss R & Miss A Bebb)

¶**10 Daniel Close** ✗❀ (Mrs Christine Richards) Sully. Via Penarth Sully Barry Rd. Sully Church in small layby on South Rd. Take Cog Rd, pass Sully Inn, 1st R into Bassett Rd, 1st R into Dispenser Rd. L into Daniel Close, bear R, house in L-hand corner. Small suburban garden mainly of summer interest; many unusual plants in containers; arbour with climbing plants, trees, shrubs, perennials. Pond for wild life. TEA. *Adm £1 Chd 25p. Private visits welcome July 1 to Aug 31 (2-6), please* **Tel 01222 531214**

11 Eastcliff ☙✗❀ (Mrs Gill James) Southgate. Take the Swansea to Gower road and travel 6m to Pennard. Go through the village of Southgate and take the 2nd exit off the roundabout. Garden 200yds on the L. Seaside garden approx ⅓ acre and developed in a series of island and bordered beds for spring and summer interest. A large number of white and silver plants. Unusual plants and shrubs. TEA. *Adm £1 Chd free. Sun June 30 (2-5). Also private visits welcome, please* **Tel 01792 233310**

24 Elm Grove Place ☙✗❀ (Mr & Mrs J Brockhurst) Dinas Powis. Elm Grove Place is a cul-de-sac 200yds E of Dinas Powis Railway Station on the Cardiff to Barry rd (A4055) under railway bridge, 4m from Cardiff, 3m from Barry. Plantsman's garden 60m × 30m, herbaceous, shrubs, greenhouse and several alpine and scree beds; patio area with some unusual container plants; pergola with clematis, wisteria and jasmine. TEA. *Adm £1 Chd free. Private visits welcome anytime between May 1 to Sept 1, please* **Tel 01222 513681**

Ffynnon Deilo (Mr & Mrs John Lloyd) Pendoylan Cowbridge 4½m. A48 Cardiff to Cowbridge. From Cardiff turn R at Sycamore Cross (½-way between St Nicholas and Bonvilston) to Peterston-Super-Ely; take 2nd L garden ¾m on R. Cottage garden with fish pond & Holy Well; interesting plants. Difficult for wheelchairs. TEA. *Adm £1.50 Chd free (£1 each for parties over 10). Private visits welcome April to Aug, please* **Tel 01446 760292**

¶**Fonmon Castle** ☙✗ (Sir Brooke Boothby) nr Barry. Take rd Cardiff-Llantwit Major, marked for Cardiff Airport. Take turning W of Penmark for Fonmon village, bear R round pond. Gate ¼m on. Medium-sized garden. Walled kitchen garden; flowering shrubs; good trees; fuchsias. Ancient castle (shown Tues & Weds April to Sept). TEAS. *Adm £1.50 Chd 50p. Sun July 7 (2-6)*

¶**Garth Madryn** ✿❀ (Mr & Mrs Christopher Williams) Penderyn, Aberdare. From Heads of the Valley Rd at Hirwaun follow signs to Brecon along Hirwaun by-pass. At Penderyn, pass Butchers Arms and turn L before Chapel and School. 3rd house on R in Church Rd. ½-acre mixed garden created since 1987 in the Brecon Beacons National Park. Collectors garden full of unusual plants featuring conifer beds, gravel garden, long herbaceous borders, island beds, formal and wildlife ponds. Huge collection of hardy geraniums and many polemoniums, rubus and aquilegias. Extensive area of unusual plants for sale especially hardy geraniums. *Adm £1 Chd free. Private visits welcome April to September weekdays and Sundays (10-6), please* **Tel 01685 811298**

Gelly Farm ✿❀ (Mrs A Appleton, Mrs L Howells, Mrs S Howells) Cymmer. 10m N E of Port Talbot, on A4107, ½m beyond Cymmer, towards Treorchy, turning off rd on R. 4 varied gardens grouped around the farmyard of a historically listed working hill farmstead on the slopes of a steep valley. Wildlife pond. Display of prize poultry, historical and other exhibitions. TEAS £1. *Adm £1.50 Chd free (Share to The Royal Agricultural Benevolent Institution®). Sun July 28 (2-6)*

Llanvithyn House ✿❀ (Mr & Mrs L H W Williams) Llancarfan 1.8m S of A48 at Bonvilston, sign for Llancarfan 100yds W of Bonvilston Garage, 1m N of Llancarfan. Medium-size garden on site of C6 monastery. C17 gatehouse. Lawns, interesting trees, shrubs, borders. TEAS if fine. *Adm £1.50 Chd 25p. Sun June 9 (2-6)*

¶**Marleigh Lodge** ❧✿❀ (Mr & Mrs J C Rees) Old St Mellons. A48 Cardiff-Newport. 5m from Cardiff turn L at White Hart Inn. Marleigh Lodge stands directly ahead between Began Rd and Druidstone Rd. 1½-acre family garden. Trees, rhododendrons, azaleas, camellias, flowering shrubs, water features. TEAS. *Adm £1.50 Chd 50p. Sun June 2 (2-6)*

Merthyr Mawr House ❧✿❀ (Mr & Mrs Murray McLaggan) Merthyr Mawr. 2m SW of Bridgend. Large garden with flowering borders, shrubs, scree garden; wood garden with chapel ruin C14 on site of Iron Age fort. TEA. *Adm £1.50 Chd £1 (Share to Merthyr Mawr Church Steeple Fund©). Sun April 21 (2-6)*

29 Min-y-Coed ✿❀ (Mr & Mrs J H Taylor) Radyr, 6m from Cardiff. On A4119 2m W of Llandaff turn R on B4262 towards Morganstown. From M4 junction 32 on A470 to Taffs Well turn L, then L to B4262 for Radyr. Hillside terraced informal garden with year round colour. TEAS. *Adm £1 Chd free. Suns July 21, Aug 4 (2-5.30)*

Mwyndy House ✿❀ (Mr & Mrs Dan Clayton Jones) Mwyndy. Exit 34 M4 for Llantrisant, A4119. Garden entrance on R, after 1st set of t-lights. Garden of approx 2 acres subdivided into 'rooms'. Walled garden and stream. Mature trees and shrubs with roses and water features. TEAS. *Adm £1.50 Chd 50p. Sun June 23 (2-6)*

Penllyn Castle ❧✿ (Mrs Christopher Cory) 3m NW of Cowbridge. From A48 turn N at Pentre Meyrick. Turn 1st R and at T-junction straight ahead through gate, leaving church on L. Large garden with fine views; old trees and

some new planting; spring shrubs (rhododendrons and magnolias) and bulbs. TEA. *Adm £1.50 Chd 50p. Sun April 28 (2-6)*

¶**Penylan Gardens** ✿❀ Penylan, Cardiff. N from city centre Ty Gwyn Rd links Penylan Hill (nr Roath Park) with Cyncoed Rd. Take Cardiff East (junction 29) off M4. Take Llanedeyrn interchange exit off Eastern Avenue. Take Cyncoed exit off small roundabout. *Combined adm £2 Chd £1. Sun July 14 (2-6)*

6 Alma Road (Mr Melvyn Rees) off Marlborough Road nr Albany Road. Take Llanedeyrn exit from A48. Redesigned S facing terraced house garden, with many species from southern and eastern hemispheres incl Dicksonia Antartica. Generally Japanese look, railway sleepers used as paving material with gravel infill. 30′ × 15′. TEA (Share to The Alzheimers Disease Soc®). *Private visits welcome, please* **Tel 01222 482200**

The George Thomas Centre for Hospice Care (The George Thomas Memorial Trust) City garden on 2 levels divided by a lovely wisteria. 1st level has an interesting herbaceous bed; 2nd level has a reclaimed bank and some good camellia shrubs; also well established pond. Much new planting. TEAS. *Private visits welcome, please* **Tel 01222 485345**

Pontygwaith Farm ❧❀ (Mr & Mrs R J G Pearce) Edwardsville. Take A4054 Old Cardiff to Merthyr Rd. Travel N for approx 3m through Quaker's Yard and Edwardsville. 1m out of Edwardsville turn sharp L by old bus shelter. Garden at bottom of hill. Medium-sized garden; surrounding C17. farmhouse adjacent to Trevithick's Tramway; situated in picturesque wooded valley; fish pond, lawns, perennial borders. TEAS. *Adm £1 Chd 50p. Suns July 7, Aug 4 (2-6). Private visits welcome, please* **Tel 01443 411137**

Springside ✿❀ (Prof & Mrs Michael Laurence) Dinas Powys. From Cardiff take B4055 to Penarth and Dinas Powys as far as the Leckwith (Cardiff Distributor Rd) roundabout. Then take B4267 to Llandough, up Leckwith Hill past Leckwith Village, take R-hand fork in rd into Pen-y-Turnpike as far as the 30mph sign. Turn R immed into Springside. Undulating 2-acre garden recently rescued after 30yrs of wilderness. Spacious, with views and newly planted trees: small ponds and old village water supply returned to nature, where children must be supervised; vegetable garden. Parking in the grounds only available in dry weather. TEA. *Adm £1.50 Chd 50p (Share to Dinas Powys Orchestra©). Sun May 26 (2-6)*

Trehedyn House ❧❀ (Mr & Mrs Desmond Williams) Peterston-Super-Ely. A 48 Cardiff to Cowbridge. Turn R at Sycamore Cross (½way between St Nicholas and Bonvilston). Take 2nd L. Garden ½m on L. Medium-sized garden. Interesting trees, shrubs, borders, bulbs and spring planting. TEAS. *Adm £1.50 Chd 50p. Sun April 14 (2-6)*

19 Westfield Road ✿❀ (Mr & Mrs Brian Dockerill) Glyn-coch Pontypridd. From Pontypridd travel 1.5m N along B4273. Take L turn by school. At top of hill follow rd to L. Take first R and R again into Westfield Rd. Enthusiasts collection of over 2,500 different varieties of plants, many unusual, grown in ½-acre garden designed as a series of interlinked enclosures each of different character. TEAS. *Adm £1 Chd 50p. Please* **Tel 01443 402999** *Prevented by limited parking from having specific open day, we welcome visitors by appt through the yr*

9 Willowbrook Gardens ✿ (Dr & Mrs Gallagher) May-als, 4m W of Swansea on A4067 (Mumbles) rd to Black-pill; take B4436 (Mayals) rd; 1st R leads to Westport Ave along W boundary of Clyne Park; 1st L into cul-de-sac. ½-acre informal garden designed to give natural effect with balance of form and colour between various areas linked by lawns; unusual trees suited to small suburban garden, esp conifers and maples; rock and water garden. TEAS. *Adm £1.50 Chd 30p. Sun May 12 (2-6) also private visits welcome, please* **Tel 01792 403268**

Gwent

Hon County Organiser: Mrs Glynne Clay, Lower House Farm, Nantyderry, Abergavenny NP7 9DP
Tel 01873 880257

Asst Hon County Organiser: Mrs R L Thompson, Llangwilym House, Llanfihangel Gobion, Abergavenny
Tel 01873 840269

DATES OF OPENING

April 7 Sunday
Llanover, nr Abergavenny
May 5 Sunday
Lower House Farm, Nantyderry
May 6 Monday
Lower House Farm, Nantyderry
May 12 Sunday
The Nurtons, Tintern
The Volland, Lower Machen
May 19 Sunday
Chwarelau Farm, Llanfapley,
nr Abergavenny
May 26 Sunday
Veddw House, The Veddw,
Devauden ‡
Wyndcliffe Court, St Arvans,
Chepstow ‡
May 27 Monday
Llan-y-Nant, Coed Morgan,
nr Abergavenny
June 2 Sunday
Bryngwyn Manor, Raglan ‡
The Graig, nr Raglan ‡
June 9 Sunday
Oakgrove, St Arvans, Chepstow ‡
Traligael, Whitebrook,
nr Monmouth ‡

June 16 Sunday
Penpergwm Lodge,
nr Abergavenny ‡
Trostrey Lodge, Bettws Newydd ‡
June 23 Sunday
Grace Dieu Court,
Dingestow
Wern Farm, Glascoed
June 29 Saturday
Castle House, Usk
June 30 Sunday
Court St Lawrence,
nr Usk ‡
Veddw House, The Veddw,
Devauden ‡
July 6 Saturday
Great Campston, Llangihangel
Crucorney
July 7 Sunday
Great Campston, Llanfihangel
Crucorney
Great Killough, nr Abergavenny
July 14 Sunday
Llanfair Court, nr Abergavenny ‡
Orchard House, Coed Morgan,
nr Abergavenny ‡
July 21 Sunday
Clytha Park, nr Abergavenny
Tredegar House & Park, Newport

July 28 Sunday
The Nurtons, Tintern ‡
Veddw House, The Veddw,
Devauden ‡
August 18 Sunday
Charters, Nantyderry
August 25 Sunday
Lower House Farm, Nantyderry
Veddw House, The Veddw,
Devauden
August 26 Monday
Lower House Farm, Nantyderry
September 1 Sunday
Castle House, Usk
September 8 Sunday
The Nurtons, Tintern
Tredegar House & Park, Newport

Regular openings
For details see garden description

Castle House, Usk
The Nurtons, Tintern
Penpergwm Lodge, nr Abergavenny
Tredegar House & Park, Newport
Veddw House, The Veddw, Devauden

DESCRIPTIONS OF GARDENS

Bryngwyn Manor ⌖✿❀ (Mr S Inglefield) 2m W of Raglan. Turn S off old A40 (Abergavenny-Raglan rd) at Croes Bychan (Raglan Garden Centre); house ¼m up lane. 3 acres; good trees, mixed borders, spring bulbs. TEAS. *Adm £1.50 Chd under 10 free. Sun June 2 (2-6)*

Castle House (Mr & Mrs J H L Humphreys) Usk; 200yds from Usk centre; turn up lane opp fire station. Medium-sized garden of orderly disorder with herb garden and ve-getables set around ruins of Usk Castle and medieval gatehouse which is open by appt. TEAS Sept 1 only. *Adm £2 Chd free. Sat June 29 as part of Usk Gardens Day (dona-tion to NGS) (10-6). For NGS Sun Sept 1 (2-6). Private visits also welcome, please* **Tel 01291 672563**

Charters &# (Mr & Mrs Peter Lang) Nantyderry, Abergavenny. From B4598 Usk to Abergavenny turn off at Chain Bridge, after 1m garden opp Foxhunter Inn. Approx 2½-acre garden. Mixed borders, shrubs and herbaceous. Kitchen garden, vegetables organically grown. Flowers for drying, dried arrangements and bunches for sale. TEAS. *Adm £1.50. Sun Aug 18 (2-6)*

Chwarelau Farm # (Mr & Mrs Maurice Trowbridge) On B4233 3½m E of Abergavenny. Medium-sized garden with magnificent views, approached down 200yd drive fringed by ornamental trees and shrubs. TEAS. *Adm £1 Chd 50p. Sun May 19 (2-6)*

Clytha Park & (Sir Richard Hanbury-Tenison) ½ way between Abergavenny and Raglan on old rd (not A40). 5 acres; C18 layout; trees, shrubs; lake. Teas in aid of CAFOD. *Adm £1.50 Chd 50p. Sun July 21 (2-6)*

Court St Lawrence &# (Mrs G D Inkin) Llangovan, 6m SW of Monmouth, 5m NE of Usk, between Pen-y-Clawdd and Llangovan. 5 acres of garden and woodland with trees, shrubs, lake, roses etc. TEAS, plants and produce stalls in aid of St David's Foundation, Newport. *Adm £1.50 Chd 50p. Sun June 30 (2-6)*

Grace Dieu Court &#& (Mr & Mrs David McIntyre) Dingestow. 1½m NW of Dingestow Village which is N of old Raglan-Monmouth rd (not dual carriageway). 3-acre open country garden in rolling countryside. Started from scratch in 1986. Mostly roses as shrubs, climbers and hedges; 2 lge ponds; herbaceous border, young specimen trees, shrubs and fine old oaks. TEAS. *Adm £1.50 Chd 50p. Sun June 23 (2-6)*

The Graig &# (Mrs Rainforth) Pen-y-Clawdd, SW of Monmouth. Turn S from Raglan-Monmouth rd (not motorway) at sign to Pen-y-Clawdd. Bus: Newport-Monmouth, alight Keen's shop, ½m. Mixed cottage garden with interesting shrubs and roses. TEAS. *Adm £1.50 Chd free. Sun June 2 (2-6). Private visits welcome, please Tel* **01600 740270**

Great Campston &# (Mr & Mrs A D Gill) 7m NE of Abergavenny; 2m towards Grosmont off A465 at Llanfihangel Crucorney. Drive on R just before brow of hill. Pretty 2-acre garden set in wonderful surroundings. Designed and planted from scratch by Mrs Gill, a garden designer; wide variety of interesting plants and trees enhanced by lovely stone walls, paving and summer house with fantastic views. The house stands 750ft above sea level on S facing hillside with spring fed stream feeding 2 ponds. TEAS. *Adm £2 Chd 50p (Share to 'Mind'®). Sat, Sun July 6, 7 (2-6). Private visits welcome, please Tel* **01873 890633**

The National Gardens Scheme is a charity which traces its origins back to 1927. Since then it has raised a total of over £14 million for charitable purposes.

1996 Special Events. For information on special National Gardens Scheme events in 1996 see Pages 18-19.

Great Killough &#& (Mr & Mrs John F Ingledew) Llantilio Crossenny, 6m E of Abergavenny. S of B4233. 3-acre garden created in the 1960s to complement mediaeval house. TEAS. *Adm £1.50 Chd free (Share to Barnardo's®). Sun July 7 (2-6)*

Llanfair Court & (Sir William Crawshay) 5m SE of Abergavenny. Route old A40 and B4598. Medium-sized garden, herbaceous border, flowering shrubs, roses, water garden; modern sculpture. TEAS. *Adm £1.50 Chd 50p. Sun July 14 (2-6)*

Llanover & (Robin Herbert, Esq) 4m S of Abergavenny. Bus: Abergavenny-Pontypool, alight drive gates. Large water garden; many rare plants, magnolias. TEAS. *Adm £1.50 Chd 50p. Sun April 7 (2-6)*

Llan-y-Nant &# (Mr & Mrs Charles Pitchford) Coed Morgan. 4m from Abergavenny, 5m from Raglan on old A40 (now B4598) Raglan to Abergavenny rd. Turn up lane opp 'Chart House' inn; pass Monmouthshire Hunt Kennels 500yds on R. 3 acres of garden and woodlands. Lawn, beds, shrubs, herbs, alpines and kitchen garden. Small lake with wild life. TEAS. *Adm £1.50 Chd 50p. Mon May 27 (2-6)*

Lower House Farm &# (Mr & Mrs Glynne Clay) Nantyderry, 7m SE of Abergavenny. From Usk-Abergavenny rd, B4598, turn off at Chain Bridge. Medium-sized garden designed for all-yr interest; mixed borders, fern island, bog garden, herb bed, paved area, unusual plants. Late flowering perennials. Featured in magazines, on T.V. and in NGS video 1. TEAS. *Adm £1.50 Chd 50p. Suns, Mons May 5, 6; Aug 25, 26 (2-6). Private visits also welcome, please Tel* **01873 880257**

The Nurtons & (Adrian & Elsa Wood) Tintern. On A466 opp Old Station, Tintern. 2-acre plantsman's garden; 2000 different species, cultivars for yr-round interest. Herbaceous borders, herb garden, rockery, shade beds, wildlife pond, mature trees. New areas being developed. 'Wye Valley Herbs' Nursery sells a range of unusual herbaceous plants incl full range of herbs. Teas nearby in Old Station at Tintern. Open daily (10.30-5) March to end Oct. (Share to Gwent Wildlife Trust®). *Adm £1.50 Chd free. For NGS Suns May 12, July 28, Sept 8 (10.30-5). Private visits also welcome, please Tel* **01291 689253**

Oakgrove &#& (Mr & Mrs C Hughes Davies) St Arvans. 1½m from Chepstow on A466 towards Monmouth, drive on L after racecourse. 2½ acres; fine beech trees, herbaceous borders, shrub roses; grey and silver border; recently established collection of fagus and nothofagus; wild garden. TEAS in aid of Friends of Royal Gwent Hospital. *Adm £1.50 Chd 50p. Sun June 9 (2-6)*

Orchard House &#& (Mr & Mrs B R Hood) Coed Morgan. 1½m N of old Raglan-Abergavenny rd. Approx 6m from Abergavenny. Turn opp King of Prussia or The Charthouse. A garden of approx 1½ acres with mixed borders of unusual herbaceous plants and shrubs, rosebeds and lawn. TEAS in aid of St David's Church. *Adm £1 Chd 30p. Sun July 14 (2-6). Private visits welcome April to Sept, please Tel* **01873 840289**

Penpergwm Lodge &✿ (Mr & Mrs Simon Boyle) 3m SE of Abergavenny. From Abergavenny take B 4598 towards Usk, after 2½m turn L opp King of Prussia Inn. Entrance 150yds on L. A 3-acre formal garden with mature trees, hedges & lawns; interesting potager, mixed unusual plants & vegetables; apple & pear pergola and S-facing terraces with sunloving plants. Nursery with rare plants, specialising in unusual hardy perennials. Home of Catriona Boyle's School of Gardening, now in its 10th yr. TEAS Sats only (and Sun June 16 in aid of St Cadoc's Church). *Adm £1.50 Chd free.*' *Thurs, Fris, Sats April 4 to Sept 30 (2-6). Sun June 16 (2-6). Private visits welcome, please* Tel 01873 840208

Traligael ✿ (Mr & Mrs E C Lysaght) 4m S of Monmouth via B4293 turn L for Whitebrook, or 3½m from A466 at Bigsweir Bridge past Whitebrook; garden alongside lane. 3-acre garden in woodland setting with water garden; rhododendrons and shrubs. *Adm £1.50 Chd free. Sun June 9 (2-6)*

Tredegar House & Park &✿✿ (Newport County Borough Council) 2m SW of Newport Town Centre. Signposted from A48 (Cardiff rd) and M4 junction 28. Series of walled formal gardens dating from the early C18 surrounding one of the most magnificent late C17 houses (also open). Orangery Garden recently restored to early C18 appearance with coloured mineral parterres, espaliered fruit trees, box hedging etc. Deep C19 herbaceous borders line the central cedar garden. On NGS days private gardens around **Home Farm Cottage** and **Curator's Cottage** are open, with orchard area and glasshouses. Restored Edwardian sunken garden also open. TEAS. *Adm £2 Chd 50p (Share to The Friends of Tredegar House and Park®). For NGS Suns July 21, Sept 8 (11-6). House, Gardens etc open Easter to end of Oct, for details, please* Tel 01633 815880

Trostrey Lodge ✿ (Mr & Mrs R Pemberton) Bettws Newydd. Half way between Raglan and Abergavenny on old road (not A40). Turning to Bettws Newydd opposite Clytha gates, 1m on R. Romantic, shaggy walled garden packed with interesting old-fashioned flowers, roses and herbs, small decorative orchard, all surrounded by fine landscape in one of the prettiest parts of Usk Valley. Ice creams. *Adm £1.50 Chd free. Sun June 16 (2-6)*

Veddw House ✿✿ (Mrs Anne Wareham & Mr Charles Hawes) The Veddw. Devauden is midway on B4293 Monmouth to Chepstow rd signposted from the green. 2½-acre garden still being developed with passionate enthusiasm. Emphasis on creating good garden pictures with colour harmonies. Formal vegetable garden with old roses and clematis; pool, conservatory; lovely views. Walk in 2-acre wood with interesting artifacts. *Adm £1.50 Chd 50p (Share to Heart Research Foundation for Wales®). Thurs May 30 to Aug 22, Mons May 27, Aug 26. For NGS Suns May 26, June 30, July 28, Aug 25 (2-6). Private visits welcome, please* Tel 01291 650836

¶**The Volland** &✿ (Mr & Mrs William Graham) Lower Machen. Between Newport and Caerphilly, 10mins from junction 28 (M4) W of Lower Machen Village, 1st R before county boundary. 1½-acres of interesting shrubs, trees and herbaceous plants; fern rockery under restoration. Natural garden - a continued fight against ground elder! TEAS. *Adm £1 Chd free. Sun May 12 (2-6)*

Wern Farm ✿✿ (Mr & Mrs W A Harris) Between Usk and Little Mill on A472. Turn at signpost for Glascoed village, 1m from main rd (Beaufort Inn or Monkswood Garage). 1½-acres pretty cottage garden; trees, shrubs, hardy perennials, alpines, rockery; herbs; veg garden. Demonstration of Bee-keeping and wool spinning. Small nursery with many rare and unusual plants for sale. TEAS. *Adm £1.50 Chd free. Sun June 23 (2-6)*

Wyndcliffe Court ✿ (HAP Clay Esq) St Arvans. 3m N of Chepstow, turn at Wyndcliffe signpost. Bus: Chepstow-Monmouth; alight St Arvans, Wyndcliffe stop, ¼m. Medium-sized garden; herbaceous borders; views, topiary, shrubs. Mentioned in The Historic Gardens of Wales. TEA. *Adm £1 chd free. Sun May 26 (2-6). Private visits welcome, please* Tel 0129162 2352

SYMBOLS USED IN THIS BOOK (See also Page 15)

‡   Following a garden name in the Dates of Opening list indicates that those gardens sharing the same symbol are nearby and open on the same day.

‡‡   Indicates a second series of nearby gardens open on the same day.

¶   Opening for the first time.

✿   Plants/produce for sale if available.

&   Gardens with at least the main features accessible by wheelchair.

✿   No dogs except guide dogs but otherwise dogs are usually admitted, provided they are kept on a lead. Dogs are not admitted to houses.

●   Gardens marked thus do not necessarily give all their takings to the National Gardens Scheme. Instead they give a guaranteed contribution.

▲   Where this sign appears alongside dates in the descriptive entry for a garden it denotes that this garden is also open regularly to the public on days other than those for the NGS.

Gwynedd

Hon County Organiser:
Anglesey, North Caernarfonshire,
North Merionethshire & Aberconwy

Mrs B S Osborne, Foxbrush, Port Dinorwic, Felinheli, Gwynedd LL56 4JZ
Tel 01248 670463

Hon County Organiser:
South Caernarfonshire &
South Merionethshire

Mrs W N Jones, Waen Fechan, Islaw'r Dref, Dolgellau LL40 1TS
Tel 01341 423479

DATES OF OPENING

March 17 Sunday
Bryniau, Boduan
April 7 Sunday
Bont Fechan Farm, Llanystumdwy
Bryniau, Boduan
Crug Farm, nr Caernarfon
April 14 Sunday
Foxbrush, Aber Pwll, Port
Dinorwic
April 21 Sunday
Penrhyn Castle,
nr Bangor
April 28 Sunday
Gilfach, Rowen, nr Conwy
May 5 Sunday
Bryniau, Boduan
May 12 Sunday
Bont Fechan Farm, Llanystumdwy
Foxbrush, Aber Pwll, Port
Dinorwic
May 18 Saturday
Farchynys Cottage, Bontddu
May 19 Sunday
Farchynys Cottage, Bontddu
Maenan Hall, Llanrwst
May 20 Monday
Farchynys Cottage, Bontddu
May 26 Sunday
Bryn Eisteddfod, Glan Conwy
Bryn Golygfa, Bontddu
Bryniau, Boduan
Crug Farm, nr Caernarfon

Glandderwen, Bontddu
Pen-y-Parc, Beaumaris
May 27 Monday
Bryn Golygfa, Bontddu
Crug Farm, nr Caernarfon
Glandderwen, Bontddu
June 16 Sunday
Bryniau, Boduan
Foxbrush, Aber Pwll, Port
Dinorwic
Henllys Lodge, Beaumaris
June 23 Sunday
Haulfryn, Llanberis
June 30 Sunday
Gilfach, Rowen, nr Conwy
Trysglwyn Fawr, Amlwch
July 6 Saturday
Bryn Castell, Llanddona, Anglesey
July 7 Sunday
Bont Fechan Farm,
Llanystumdwy
Bryniau, Boduan
Gwyndy Bach, Llandrygarn
July 14 Sunday
Crug Farm, nr Caernarfon
Henllys Lodge, Beaumaris
July 28 Sunday
Bryniau, Boduan
August 18 Sunday
Bont Fechan Farm,
Llanystumdwy
Gilfach, Rowen, nr Conwy
August 25 Sunday
Bryniau, Boduan

Crug Farm, nr Caernarfon
Maenan Hall, Llanrwst
September 15 Sunday
Bryniau, Boduan
October 6 Sunday
Bryniau, Boduan
October 27 Sunday
Bryniau, Boduan

Regular openings
For details see garden description

Bryn Meifod, Glan Conwy
Plas Muriau, Bettws-y-Coed
Plas Newydd, Anglesey
Plas Penhelig, Aberdyfi

By appointment only
*For telephone numbers and other
details see garden descriptions.
Private visits welcomed*

Brynmelyn, Ffestiniog
Bryn-y-Bont, Nantmor
Cefn Bere, Dolgellau
Hen Ysgoldy, Llanfrothen
Llys-y-gwynt, Llandegai
Pencarreg, Glyn Garth,
Menai Bridge

DESCRIPTIONS OF GARDENS

Bont Fechan Farm &⚶※ (Mr & Mrs J D Bean) Llanys-tumdwy. 2 m from Criccieth on the A497 to Pwllheli on the L-hand side of the main rd. Small garden with rock-ery, pond, herbaceous border, steps to river, large variety of plants. Nicely planted tubs. TEAS. *Adm 75p Chd 25p. Suns April 7, May 12, July 7, Aug 18 (11-5). Private visits welcome, please* Tel 01766 522604

Bryn Castell ※ (Lady Grace Gibson) Wern. 3m NW of Beaumaris. First L opp telephone box before entering vil-lage. 1m down single track rd towards Wern-y-Wylan. 2 acres semi-wild gardens surrounding remote farmhouse

with beautiful views. Pond and bog garden, wildflower lawns with bulbs and orchids; cottage garden with old roses and herbaceous plants; conservatory with vine. TEAS in aid of CRUSE Bereavement Care, Gwynedd Branch. *Adm £1 Chd free. Sat July 6 (11-5)*

Bryn Eisteddfod & (Dr Michael Senior) Glan Conwy. 3½m SE Llandudno 3m W Colwyn Bay; up the hill (Bryn-y-Maen direction) from Glan Conwy Corner where A470 joins A55. 8 acres of landscaped grounds incl mature shrubbery, arboretum, old walled 'Dutch' garden, large lawn with ha-ha. Extensive views over Conwy Valley, Snowdonia National Park, Conwy Castle, town and es-tuary. TEAS. *Adm £1 Chd 50p. Sun May 26 (2-5)*

Bryn Golygfa ❀ (Mrs K & Mr R Alexander) Dolgellau. 5m W of Dolgellau. Take A496 to Bontddu; garden is N 100yds past Bontddu Hall Hotel. Small garden on steep hillside; mixed planting incl rhododendrons and alpines. *Adm £1 Chd free. Sun, Mon May 26, 27 (11-6). Private visits welcome mid-May to mid-Aug, please* Tel 01341 430260

Bryn Meifod ❀❀ (Dr & Mrs K Lever) Graig Glan Conwy. Just off A470 1½m S of Glan Conwy. Follow signs for Aberconwy Nursery. ¾-acre garden developed over 25yrs but extensively replanted in the last 10yrs. Unusual trees and shrubs, scree and peat beds. Good autumn colours. Wide ranging collection of alpines especially autumn gentians. Extensive views towards Snowdonia and the Carneddau. *Collection Box. Open Wed, Thurs, Fris (2-5), May, June, Aug and Sept, please* Tel 01492 580875

Bryniau ❀ (P W Wright & J E Humphreys) Boduan. ½m down lane opp. St Buan's Church, Boduan, which is halfway between Nefyn and Pwllheli on the A497. New garden created since 1988 on almost pure sand. Over 80 types of trees; hundreds of shrubs, many unusual, showing that with a little effort, one can grow virtually anything anywhere. Plants & woodcraft for sale. TEAS. *Adm £1 Chd free. Suns March 17, April 7, May 5, 26, June 16, July 7, 28, Aug 25, Sept 15, Oct 6, 27 (11-6) and private visits welcome, please* Tel 01758 7213 38

Brynmelyn ❀ (Mr & Mrs A S Taylor) Cymerau Isaf. About 2m SW of Blaenau Ffestiniog, on A496 Maentwrog-Blaenau Ffestiniog Rd. Enter by lower gate in layby opp junction to Manod, by footpath sign. After 100yds leave car at garage and follow small footpath to R of garage, descending to stone bridge and Cymerau Falls. Continue over bridge and up hill, follow footpath L; garden about ¼m from garage. Upland garden surrounded by National Nature Reserve containing wide variety of plants providing interest throughout the season. *Adm £1 Chd 50p (Share to The National Osteoporosis Society®). Private visits welcome April 1 to Sept 15* Tel Ffestiniog 01766 762684. *Please telephone before 9.30 am or after dusk*

Bryn-y-Bont ❀ (Miss J Entwisle) Nantmor. 2½m S of Beddgelert, turn L over Aberglaslyn Bridge into A4085, 500yds turn L up hill, 2nd house on R. Small garden created since 1978 on S facing wooded hillside over looking Glaslyn Vale (As featured on Radio Wales 'Get Gardening' in 1990). *Adm £1 Chd free. Private visits welcome mid April to mid Sept (11-5pm). Private visits welcome, please* Tel 01766 890448

Cefn Bere ❀ (Mr & Mrs Maldwyn Thomas) Cae Deintur, Dolgellau. Turn L at top of main bridge on Bala-Barmouth Rd (not the by-pass); turn R within 20yds; 2nd R behind school and first L half way up short hill. Small garden; extensive collection of alpines, bulbs and rare plants. Tea Dolgellau. *Collecting box. Individuals and parties of up to 25 welcome, spring, summer and autumn months, please* Tel Dolgellau 01341 422768

Regular Openers. See end of county section.

Crug Farm ❀❀ (Mr & Mrs B Wynn-Jones) Griffiths Crossing. 2m NE of Caernarfon ¼m off main A487 Caernarfon to Bangor Road. Follow signs from roundabout to Bethel. Plantsman's garden; ideally situated; 2 to 3 acres grounds to old country house. Gardens filled with choice, unusual collections of climbers, and herbaceous plants; over 300 species of hardy geraniums. Featured in 'The Garden' and on BBC TV. Only partly suitable wheelchairs. TEAS in aid of local charities. *Collecting box for walled display garden open Thurs, Fri, Sat, Suns & Bank Hols Feb 26 to Sept 25 (10-6). See calendar for openings of private gardens. Adm £1 Chd free. Natural Rock garden only open Suns & Mons April 7, May 26, 27, Suns July 14, Aug 25 (10-6). Private parties welcome please,* Tel 01248 670232

Farchynys Cottage ❀❀ (Mrs G Townshend) Bontddu. On A496 Dolgellau-Barmouth rd; well signed W of Bontddu village. 4 acres; informal country garden on steep wooded hillside; unusual shrubs and trees; azaleas, over 75 species of rhododendron, giant liriodendron-tulipifera. Best mid-May, mid-June. TEA. *Adm £1 Chd free. Open May 1st to Sept 30, Tues, Wed, Thurs (11-5).* ▲*For NGS Sat, Sun, Mon May 18, 19, 20 (11-5).* Tel 01341 430245

Foxbrush ❀❀ (Mr & Mrs B S Osborne) Aber Pwll, Port Dinorwic, Felinheli. On Bangor to Caernarfon Road, entering village opp. layby with Felinheli sign post. Fascinating 3-acre country garden on site of old mill and created around winding river; rare and interesting plants; ponds and small wooded area. Extensive plant collections incl rhododendrons, ferns, primula, alpines, clematis and roses; 45ft long pergola; fan-shaped knot garden with traditional and unusual herbs; coaches welcome. A winner 1995 RHS/Today Gardening family of the year. TEA. *Adm £1 incl C16 cottage musuem Chd free. Suns April 14, May 12, June 16 (12-5). Also private visits and parties welcome, please* Tel 01248 670463

Gilfach ❀❀ (James & Isoline Greenhalgh) Rowen. At Xrds 100yds E of Rowen (4m S of Conwy) S towards Llanrwst, past Rowen School on L; turn up 2nd drive on L, signposted. 1-acre country garden on S-facing slope overlooking Conwy Valley; set in 35 acres farm and woodland; mature shrubs; herbaceous border; small pool. Partly suitable wheelchairs which are welcome. Magnificent views of River Conwy and mountains. TEAS. *Adm £1 Chd 10p. Suns April 28, June 30, Aug 18 (11-5)*

Glandderwen (A M Reynolds Esq) 5m W of Dolgellau. Take A496 to Bontddu. Garden is on S 100yds past Bontddu Hall Hotel. ½-acre on N bank of Mawddach Estuary facing Cader Idris; set amid large oaks; shrubs, trees; steep and rocky nature. *Adm £1 Chd free. Sun, Mon, May 26, 27 (11-6). Private visits welcome May 1 to Sept 30* Tel 01341 430229

Gwyndy Bach ❀❀❀ (Keith & Rosa Andrew) Llandrygarn. From Llangefni take the B5109 towards Bodedern, the cottage is exactly 5m out on the L. A ¾-acre artist's garden set amidst rugged Anglesey landscape. Romantically planted in intimate 'rooms' with interesting plants and shrubs, old roses and secluded lily pond. Studio attached. TEAS. *Adm £1 Chd free. Sun July 7 (11-5.30). Also private visits welcome, please* Tel 01407 720651

¶Haulfryn &⚘⚘ (Adrian & Diane Anthoine) Church Lane. 5 min walk from centre of Llanberis, up lane between garage and church. Garden approx 1 acre. Commenced 1987 from rough sheep pasture at foot of Snowdon. Numerous tree plantings, natural rock outcrop; variety of ericaceous shrubs, old roses and mixed herbaceous borders bounded by a natural mountain stream. Partly suitable wheelchairs. TEAS. *Adm £1 Chd free. Sun June 23 (11-5) Private visits welcome, please* **Tel 01286 870446**

Hen Ysgoldy ⚘ (Mr & Mrs Michael Jenkins) Llanfrothen. From Garreg via B4410, after ½m L; garden 200yds on R. Natural garden with streams and established trees, incl magnolias, eucalyptus and embothrium. Shrubs incl a variety of azaleas and rhododendrons, mixed borders planted for colour and interest most of the year round. *Collecting box. Private visits welcome April 1 to Aug 31* **Tel 01766 771231**

Henllys Lodge &⚘⚘ (Mr & Mrs K H Lane) Beaumaris. Past Beaumaris Castle, ½m turn L, 1st L again. Lodge at entrance to Henllys Hall Hotel drive. Approx 1-acre country garden, planted in traditional cottage style using perennials, shrubs, old roses and featuring extensive collection of hardy geraniums. Small woodland area. Stunning views across Menai Straits. TEAS. *Adm £1 Chd free. Suns June 16, July 14 (12-5.30). Private visits welcome, please* **Tel 01248 810106**

¶**Llys-y-Gwynt** &⚘ (Jennifer Rickards & John Evans) Llandegai. 3m S of Bangor and 300yds from Llandygai Roundabout. Just off B4409 which joins B4366 Pentir, Bethal, Caernarfon rd. 200yds from junction with A5 and 100yds from entrance to Esso Service Station and Travel Lodge. 2-acre rambling garden; well established trees and shrubs and magnificent views; pond, N-facing rockery; large Bronze Age burial cairn. Planting with emphasis on wind resistance, yr-round interest and encouraging wild life. *Adm £1 Chd free. Private visits welcome, please* **Tel 01248 353863**

Maenan Hall ⚘ (The Hon Christopher McLaren) Exactly 2m N of Llanrwst on E side of A470, ¼m S of Priory Hotel. Gardens created since 1956 by the late Christabel, Lady Aberconway and then present owner; 10 acres; lawns, shrub, rose and walled gardens; rhododendron dell; many species of beautiful and interesting plants, shrubs and trees set amongst mature oaks and other hardwoods; fine views of mountains across Conway valley. Home-made TEAS. *Adm £1.80 Chd 50p (Share to Margaret Mee Amazon Trust May 19; St David's Hospice Foundation Aug 25©). Suns May 19, Aug 25 (10-5) Last entry 4pm*

Pencarreg &⚘ (Miss G Jones) Glyn Garth. 1½m NE of A545 Menai Bridge towards Beaumaris, Glan Y Menai Drive is turning on R, Pencarreg is 100yds on R. Parking in lay-by on main rd, limited parking on courtyard for small cars & disabled. This beautiful garden, with a wealth of species planted for all-yr interest, has colour, achieved by the use of common & unusual shrubs. A small stream creates another delightful and sympathetically-exploited feature. The garden terminates at the cliff edge & this too has been skilfully planted. The views to the Menai Straits & the Carneddi Mountains in the distance make it obvious why this garden has been featured in 3 television programmes. *Collecting Box (Share to Snowdonia National Park Society©). Private visits welcome all year, please* **Tel 01248 713545**

Penrhyn Castle &⚘ (The National Trust) 3m E of Bangor on A5122. Buses from Llandudno, Caernarvon. Betwsy-Coed; alight: Grand Lodge Gate. Large gardens; fine trees, shrubs, wild garden, good views. Castle was rebuilt in 1830 for 1st Lord Penrhyn, incorporating part of C15 building on C8 site of home of Welsh Princes. Exhibition of National Trust Countryside; museum of locomotives and quarry rolling stock. NT Shop. TEAS and light lunches. Guide dogs admitted into Castle. *Adm £3 Chd £1.50. For NGS Sun April 21 (11-6). Last adm ½ hr prior to closing. Private visits welcome, please* **Tel 01248 353084**

Pen-y-Parc (Mrs E E Marsh) Beaumaris. A545 Menai Bridge-Beaumaris rd; after Anglesey Boatyard 1st left; after Golf Club 1st drive on left. NOT very easy for wheelchairs. 6 acres; beautiful grounds, magnificent views over Menai Strait; azaleas, rhododendrons and heathers; interesting terrain with rock outcrops used to advantage for recently planted conifer and rock gardens; small lake in natural setting; 2 further enclosed gardens. We would like to share the pleasure of this garden. TEA. *Adm £1 Chd 50p. Sun May 26 (11-5)*

Plas Muriau ⚘⚘ (Lorna & Tony Scharer) Betws-y-Coed. On A470 approx ¼m N of Waterloo Bridge, Betws-y-Coed; entrance by minor junction to Capel Garmon. A large garden dating from the 1870s recently restored. About 1 acre open to visitors. A structured garden within a woodland setting, with maginificent views. Unusual perennials and herbs, wild flowers, bulbs and roses. Many unusual plants for sale at adjacent nursery, Gwydir Plants. *Adm £1. Suns April to July (11-5) or by arrangement at nursery or by appt. Please,* **Tel 01690 710201**

Plas Newydd &⚘ (The Marquess of Anglesey; The National Trust) Isle of Anglesey. 1m SW of Llanfairpwll and A5, on A4080. Gardens with massed shrubs, fine trees, and lawns sloping down to Menai Strait. Magnificent views to Snowdonia. C18 house by James Wyatt contains Rex Whistler's largest wall painting; also Military Museum. TEAS and light lunches. *Adm house & garden £4 Chd £2, garden only £2, Chd £1, Family Adm £9.80. Every day except Sats March 29 to Sept 30. Fris and Suns only Oct 1 to 3 last entry 4.30pm. Garden open from (11-5)*

Plas Penhelig (Mr & Mrs A C Richardson) Aberdovey, between 2 railway bridges. Driveway to hotel by island and car park. 14 acres overlooking estuary, exceptional views. Particularly lovely in spring: bulbs, daffodils, rhododendrons, azaleas; rock and water gardens, mature tree heathers, magnolias, euphorbias; herbaceous borders, rose garden; wild and woodland flowers encouraged in large orchard; formal walled garden with herbaceous borders, large range of greenhouses, peaches, herbs. TEAS. *Adm £1.50 Chd 50p. Wed to Sun incl: April 1 to mid-Oct (2.30-5.30). Collecting box*

¶**Trysglwyn Fawr** & (Lord & Lady Stanley of Alderley) Rhosybol. Take the road S from Amlwch to Llanerchymedd. After 2m having passed the Parys Mountain mine shaft on your R, turn L, Trysglwyn Fawr is 1,000yds down that rd on your L. 1-acre garden overlooking farm land to fine view of Snowdonia. Mixed flower and shrub beds; vegetable garden, fruit garden and conservatory; farm walk showing amenity woodland and ponds. Planted during last 23yrs. TEA. *Adm £1 Chd free. Sun June 30 (2-6)*

Powys

Hon County Organisers:
(North – Montgomeryshire)   Captain R Watson, Westwinds, Kerry, Newtown, Powys Tel 01686 670605
(South – Brecknock & Radnor) Miss Shan Egerton, Pen-y-Maes, Hay on Wye, Hereford HR3 5PP
                              Tel 01497 820423

Assistant County Organiser:
S. Powys
Hon County Treasurer:
                              Lady Milford, Llanstephan House, Llanstephan, Brecon. Powys LD3 OYR
                              Tel 01982 560693

DATES OF OPENING

April 6 Saturday
Tan-y-Llyn Nurseries, Meifod
April 7 Sunday
Tan-y-Llyn Nurseries, Meifod
April 9 Tuesday
Diamond Cottage, Buttington
April 28 Sunday
Llanstephan House, Llyswen
May 4 Saturday
Glansevern Hall, Berriew,
   Welshpool
Tan-y-Llyn Nurseries, Meifod
May 5 Sunday
Tan-y-Llyn Nurseries, Meifod
May 7 Tuesday
Diamond Cottage, Buttington
May 11 Saturday
Cae Hywel,
   Llansantffraid-ym-Mechain
May 12 Sunday
Cae Hywel,
   Llansantffraid-ym-Mechain
Glanwye, Builth Wells
Trawscoed Hall, Welshpool
May 14 Tuesday
Diamond Cottage,
   Buttington
May 16 Thursday
The Bushes, Berriew
May 19 Sunday
Bronhyddon,
   Llansantffraid-ym-Mechain
Garth House, Llangammarch
   Wells
Gliffaes Country House Hotel,
   Crickhowell

May 21 Tuesday
Diamond Cottage, Buttington
May 23 Thursday
The Bushes, Berriew
May 27 Monday
Llysdinam, Newbridge-on-Wye
May 28 Tuesday
Diamond Cottage, Buttington ‡
Powis Castle Gardens,
   Welshpool ‡
May 30 Thursday
The Bushes, Berriew
June 1 Saturday
Glansevern Hall, Berriew,
   Welshpool
Tan-y-Llyn Nurseries, Meifod
June 2 Sunday
Bodynfoel Hall, Llanfechain
Gregynog, Tregynon
Tan-y-Llyn Nurseries, Meifod
June 4 Tuesday
Diamond Cottage, Buttington
June 6 Thursday
The Bushes, Berriew
June 9 Sunday
The Bushes, Berriew
June 11 Tuesday
Diamond Cottage, Buttington
June 13 Thursday
The Bushes, Berriew
June 16 Sunday
Pen-y-Maes, Hay-on-Wye
June 18 Tuesday
Diamond Cottage, Buttington
June 20 Thursday
The Bushes, Berriew
June 23 Sunday
Carrog, Llanfrynach ‡

Crossways, Newcastle on Clun
Manascin, Pencelli, Brecon ‡
Point Farm, Newtown
June 25 Tuesday
Diamond Cottage, Buttington
June 27 Thursday
The Bushes, Berriew
June 30 Sunday
Broadheath House, Presteigne ‡
Treberfydd, nr Bwlch
The Walled Garden, Knill, nr
   Presteigne ‡
July 2 Tuesday
Diamond Cottage, Buttington
July 4 Thursday
The Bushes, Berriew
July 6 Saturday
Glansevern Hall, Berriew,
   Welshpool
Tan-y-Llyn Nurseries, Meifod
Upper Dolley, Dolley Green,
   Presteigne
July 7 Sunday
Moor Park, nr Crickhowell
Tan-y-Llyn Nurseries, Meifod
Upper Dolley, Dolley Green,
   Presteigne
July 9 Tuesday
Diamond Cottage, Buttington
July 11 Thursday
The Bushes, Berriew
July 13 Saturday
Belan-yr-Argae, Welshpool
July 14 Sunday
Ashford House,
   Talybont on Usk
July 16 Tuesday
Diamond Cottage, Buttington

July 18 Thursday
The Bushes, Berriew
July 21 Sunday
Fraithwen, Tregynon, Newtown
July 23 Tuesday
Diamond Cottage, Buttington
July 25 Thursday
The Bushes, Berriew
July 28 Sunday
Treholford, Cathedine, Brecon
July 30 Tuesday
Diamond Cottage, Buttington
August 1 Thursday
The Bushes, Berriew
August 3 Saturday
Glansevern Hall, Berriew,
    Welshpool
Tan-y-Llyn Nurseries, Meifod
August 4 Sunday
Craig Llyn, Llanwrthwl
Lonicera, Talybont-on-Usk
Tan-y-Llyn Nurseries, Meifod
August 6 Tuesday
Diamond Cottage, Buttington
August 8 Thursday
The Bushes, Berriew

August 11 Sunday
Llysdinam, Newbridge-on-Wye
August 13 Tuesday
Diamond Cottage, Buttington
August 15 Thursday
The Bushes, Berriew
August 20 Tuesday
Diamond Cottage, Buttington
August 22 Thursday
The Bushes, Berriew
August 25 Sunday
Point Farm, Newtown
August 27 Tuesday
Diamond Cottage, Buttington
August 29 Thursday
The Bushes, Berriew
August 31 Saturday
Tan-y-Llyn Nurseries,
    Meifod
September 1 Sunday
The Bushes, Berriew
Tan-y-Llyn Nurseries, Meifod
September 5 Thursday
The Bushes, Berriew
September 12 Thursday
The Bushes, Berriew

October 5 Saturday
Tan-y-Llyn Nurseries, Meifod
October 6 Sunday
Gliffaes Country House Hotel,
    Crickhowell
Tan-y-Llyn Nurseries, Meifod

Regular openings
For details see garden description

Ashford House, Talybont
Glansevern Hall, Berriew
Mill Cottage, Abbeycwmhir

By appointment only
*For telephone numbers and other
details see garden descriptions.
Private visits welcomed*

Hill Crest, Brooks, Welshpool
Llangorse Gardens
Maenllwyd Isaf, Abermule
The Millers House, Welshpool

DESCRIPTIONS OF GARDENS

Ashford House ❀ (Mr & Mrs D A Anderson) Brecon. ¾m E of Talybont on Usk on B4558 signed from A40 through village. Walled garden of about 1 acre surrounded by woodland and wild garden approx 4 acres altogether. Mixed shrub and herbaceous borders; new small formal garden; meadow garden and pond; alpine house and beds; vegetables. The whole garden has gradually been restored and developed since 1979. Bring and buy plant stall. Suitable in parts for wheelchairs. TEAS. *Adm £1.50 Chd free (Share to Save the Children®). Open Tues April 2 to Oct 1 (2-6). For NGS Sun July 14 (2-6)*

¶**Belan-yr-Argae** (Ivy Pritchard Evans) Cefn-Coch. 14m SW of Welshpool via Llanfair Caereinion and Cefn Coch and 12m NW of Newtown via Tregynon and Adfa. Garden attached to an old-fashioned farm comprising formal and wild gardens with pools, unusual plants, shrubs and trees, all set in approx ½ acre. Yr-round interest. TEAS. *Adm £1.50 Chd free (Share to LUPUS®). Sat July 13 (2-5). Private visits welcome, please Tel 01938 810658*

Bodynfoel Hall &❀ (Maj & Mrs Bonnor-Maurice) Llanfechain, 10m N of Welshpool. Via A490 to Llanfyllin. Take B4393 to Llanfechain, follow signs. Approx 3½ acres; gardens and woodland; lakes; young and mature trees; shrub roses and heather bank. TEAS. *Adm £1 OAPs 50p Chd free. Sun June 2 (2-6) Tel 01691 648486*

¶**Broadheath House** &❀ (Mr & Mrs D MacDowell) 1m E of Presteigne on B4362. 2½-acre garden designed by Sir Clough William-Ellis. Sunken rose garden, ponds, enclosed yew garden, newly planted kitchen garden and orchard. Walk to Hindwell Brook. TEAS in loggia. *Combined adm with* **The Walled Garden** *£2.50 Chd free (Share to Council for the Preservation of Rural Wales®). Sun June 30 (2-5)*

Bronhyddon &❀ (Mr & Mrs R Jones-Perrott) Llansantffraid-ym-Mechain. 10m N Welshpool on A495 on E side in centre of village. Long drive; parking in fields below house. Wood having been almost clear felled now planted with choice young trees & shrubs on acid soil on S facing slope. Grass rides have been made and in spring is a mass of bluebells and foxgloves; a mature stand has anemones, snowdrops & primroses. Both areas lead out of small garden in front of house with elegant Regency verandahs & balconies. TEAS. *Adm £1 Chd free. Sun May 19 (2-6)*

The Bushes ❀❀ (Hywel & Eileen Williams) Pantyffridd Berriew. 8m Welshpool on B4390 midway Berriew and Manafon. Set in the picturesque Rhiew Valley, this pretty ⅔-acre garden surrounds the old stone cottage on a S-facing site. Designed into terraced colour co-ordinated 'rooms' and planted with interesting variety of perennials, shrub and climbers and use of groundcover plants; pools, cobbled and paved areas recently developed scented area. TEAS in aid of Cystic Fibrosis Trust on Suns. *Adm £1.50 Chd free. Suns June 9, Sept 1 (1-5). Every Thurs May 16 to Sept 12 incl (1-5). Private visits also welcome May 16 to Sept 12, please Tel 01686 650338*

Cae Hywel ❀ (Miss Judith M Jones) Llansantffraid-ym-Mechain, 10m N of Welshpool. On A495; on E (Oswestry) side of village. Car park in village. 1 acre; S facing slope on different levels; rock garden; herb garden; interesting shrubs, trees and plants. Partly suitable for wheelchairs. TEAS. *Adm £1 Chd free. Sat, Sun May 11, 12 (2-6)*

Carrog &❀ (Lt Col & Mrs R J M Sinnett) Llanfrynach. 3m SE of Brecon. LLanfrynach is signed from A40 flyover, just E of Brecon. The village is just off B4558. ⅔-acre of mixed borders of shrubs, herbaceous plants and roses. TEAS. *Adm £1 Chd free. Sun June 23 (2-6)*

Craig Llyn ❀ (Mrs M Munday) Llanwrthwl. 4m S of Rhayader towards Builth Wells on A470 signposted Llanwrthwl. By the church turn L signposted Hodrid. ¾m up that lane is Craig Llyn. Limited parking. 2-acre steep hillside garden overlooking R Wye and valley, planted with heathers, shrubs, rhododendrons, azaleas, sloping lawns, woodland and vegetable garden. Special features are natural stone paths (uneven) representing dry waterways in the Zen tradition. TEAS. *Adm £1.50 Chd free. Sun Aug 4 (11-5)*

¶**Crossways** ❀❀ (Mrs & Mr Smith) Newcastle on Clun, Shropshire. From Kerry take the B4368 signposted Clun. Travel past The Anchor for 1.5m then turn L at Xrds signposted Crossways, continue for 1m , cottage is at top of T-junction. Map ref. [205 859]. From Craven Arms take B4368 to Newcastle on Clun continue through village on B4368 for Newtown. 4m out of village turn R at Xrds signposted Crossways and continue. 1-acre cottage garden and nursery 1400ft on Shropshire/Welsh border. Extensively planted, and illustrates diversity of plants able to tolerate high altitude. Features incl ponds, wildlife and woodland area, herbaceous beds and borders, rock garden and vegetables. Wide range of plants grown incl hardy geraniums, foliage plants, plants to attract bees; many for sale in small nursery, open Suns April 1 to Oct 31. TEAS in aid of Shropshire and Mid-Wales Air Ambulance. *Adm £1. Sun June 23 (2-6). Private visits welcome, please* **Tel 01686 670890**

Diamond Cottage ❀❀ (Mr & Mrs D T Dorril) Buttington. From Welshpool on A458 3m turn R into Heldre Lane. From Shrewsbury, turn L past 'Little Chef' Trewern into Sale Lane. Then follow signs. 1.7-acre garden on steep N facing slope at 700ft. Unusual herbaceous plants and shrubs; wooded dingle with stream; vegetable garden, patio and pools. Extensive views to Berwyn Mountains. TEAS. *Adm £1.20 Chd free. Tues April 9, May 7, 14, 21, 28; June 4, 11,18, 25; July 2, 9, 16, 23, 30; Aug 6, 13, 20, 27 (2-6). Private visits welcome April to Sept, please* **Tel 01938 570570**

Fraithwen ❀❀ (Mr & Mrs David Thomas) Tregynon. 6m N of Newtown on B4389 midway between villages of Bettws Cedewain and Tregynon. 1-acre garden created in the last 10yrs; herbaceous borders, rockeries and ponds packed with interesting, unusual and rare plants and shrubs for colour throughout the year. Also on display antique horse-drawn machinery and implements. As featured in 'Womans Weekly'. Partially suitable for wheelchairs. TEAS. *Adm £1.50 Chd free (Share to Bettws Community Hall®). Sun July 21 (2-6). Private parties welcome, please* **Tel 01686 650307**

Garth House &❀ (Mr & Mrs F A Wilson) Garth on A483 6m W of Builth Wells. Drive gates in village of Garth by Garth Inn. Large wood with azaleas and rhododendrons; water and shrub garden; herbaceous garden; fine views. Historic connection with Charles Wesley & the Gwynne family. TEAS. *Adm £1.50 Chd free. Sun May 19 (2-6)*

Glansevern Hall Gardens &❀ (Mr & Mrs R N Thomas) Berriew. 4m SW of Powis Castle, Welshpool, on A483 at Berriew. 13-acre mature garden situated nr banks of R Severn. Centred on Glansevern Hall, a Greek Revival house of 1801. Noted for variety of unusual tree species; much new planting; lake with island; woodland walk; large rock garden and grotto. Walled rose garden; water features. Gift shop. TEAS. Free car/coach park. *Adm £2 Chd free. Fris, Sats, May to Sept. For NGS Sats May 4, June 1, July 6, Aug 3 (2-6)*

Glanwye &❀ (Mr & Mrs David Vaughan, G & H Kidston) 2m SE Builth Wells on A470. Large garden, rhododendrons, azaleas; herbaceous borders, extensive hedges, newly sown wild flower meadow; long woodland walk with bluebells and other woodland flowers. Good views of R Wye. Cream TEAS. *Adm £1.50 Chd free (Share to Llanddewi Cwm and Alltmawr Church®). Sun May 12 (2-5.30)*

Gliffaes Country House Hotel & (Mr & Mrs Brabner) 3m W of Crickhowell on A40. Large garden; spring bulbs; azaleas & rhododendrons, new ornamental pond; heathers; shrubs; ornamental trees; fine maples; autumn colour; fine position high above R. Usk. Cream Teas available at hotel. *April to Dec. For NGS Adm £1.50 Chd free (collecting box). Suns May 19, Oct 6 (2-5)*

Gregynog &❀❀ (University of Wales) Tregynon, 7m N of Newtown. A483 Welshpool to Newtown Rd, turn W at B4389 for Bettws Cedewain, 1m through village gates on left. Large garden; fine banks, rhododendrons and azaleas; dell with specimen shrubs; formal garden; colour-coded walks starting from car park. Descriptive leaflet available. Early C19 black and white house; site inhabited since C12. TEAS. *Adm £1 Chd 10p. Sun June 2 (2-6)*

Hill Crest ❀ (Mr J D & Mrs P Horton) Brooks. 9m W of Welshpool. Turn R to Berriew, then L by Lion Hotel, through village towards Bettws Cedewain. Turn R after 3m to Brooks then 1m up hill on L. 8m E from Newtown. Through Bettws Cedewain. Take Brooks Rd, after 3m turn L. House at top of hill on L. Approx 1 acre of mixed shrub borders, heathers, alpines and pool; hillside arboretum with rhododendron walk, pine, spruce conifers and deciduous wooded area planted with daffodils. *Adm £1 Chd 10p. Private visits welcome all year, please* **Tel 01686 640541**

Llangorse Gardens ❀ Llangorse is on B4560 4m off A40 at Bwlch, 6½m from Brecon and 4½m from Talgarth. Park in village
   The Neuadd (Mr & Mrs P Johnson) Informal garden of approx 1 acre with mixed borders of interesting trees, shrubs and herbaceous plants, emphasis on good foliage and unusual forms of cottage garden and native plants; small vegetable and fruit garden, meadow gardens and copse. Maintained by owners on organic lines to encourage wild life. *Private visits welcome, please* **Tel 01874 658 670**
   The Old Vicarage &❀ (Major & Mrs J B Anderson) Small family garden maintained by owners with interesting herbaceous and shrub borders; lawns, trees and vegetables. Plants usually for sale in aid of NGS. *Private visits welcome Spring to Oct, please* **Tel 01874 658639**

Llanstephan House &⚘❀ (Lord & Lady Milford) Llanstephan. Off small rd between Boughrood and Erwood Bridge on opp side of R Wye to A470 (Brecon-Builth Wells rd). Large garden with rhododendrons, azaleas, shrubs, old-fashioned roses, walled kitchen garden, woodland areas. Beautiful views of Wye Valley and Black Mountains. TEAS if fine. *Adm £1.50 Chd free. Sun April 28 (2-5)*

Llysdinam &⚘ (Lady Delia Venables-Llewelyn & Llysdinam Charitable Trust) Newbridge-on-Wye, SW of Llandrindod Wells. Turn W off A479 at Newbridge-on-Wye; right immed after crossing R Wye; entrance up hill. Large garden. Azaleas; rhododendrons, water garden and herbaceous borders; shrubs; woodland garden; kitchen garden; fine view of Wye Valley. TEAS. *Adm £1.50 Chd free (Share to NSPCC®). Mon May 27, Sun Aug 11 (2-6). Private parties welcome, please* **Tel 01597 860 200**

Lonicera &⚘❀ (Mr & Mrs G Davies) Talybont-on-Usk. ½m from turning off A40. 6m E of Brecon, signposted Talybont. Garden of varied interest incl several small feature gardens extending to approx ¼ acre; modern rose garden with dwarf conifers; herbaceous and woody perennials; colourful summer bedding displays; window boxes, hanging baskets and patio tubs forming extensive house frontage display; greenhouses. Teas in village. Plant stall. *Adm £1.50 Chd free (Share to Arthritis & Rheumatism Council®). Sun Aug 4 (2-6)*

Maenllwyd Isaf &⚘ (Mrs Denise Hatchard) Abermule, 5m NE of Newtown & 10m S of Welshpool. On B4368 Abermule to Craven Arms, 1½m from Abermule. 3 acres; unusual shrubs and plants; goldfish pool; 'wild' pool; R Mule. C16 listed house. *Adm £1 Chd free (Share to Winged Fellowship Trust®). Private visits welcome all year. Gardening clubs etc welcome, please* **Tel 01686 630204**

Manascin ❀ (Lady Watson) Pencelli. 3m SE of Brecon on B4558 pink house in Pencelli Village. Small garden, many features; small pond with water lilies and fountain; shrubs; roses, lilies and vegetable patch. TEAS at **Carrog**. *Adm £1 Chd free. Sun June 23 (2-6)*

Mill Cottage ⚘❀ (Mr & Mrs B D Parfitt) Abbeycwmhir. 8m N of Llandrindod Wells. Turning L off A483, 1m N of Crossgates Roundabout, then 3½m on L, signposted Abbeycwmhir. ⅓-acre garden of unusual and rare shrubs, small trees and climbers. Numerous ericaceae. Narrow paths and steps; limited parking. Many rare plants for sale. TEA. *Adm £1 Chd 50p. Sun to Sat incl, July 6 to 14, August 3 to 18 (mid-day to dusk)*

The Millers House & (Mr & Mrs Mark Kneale) Welshpool. About 1¼m NW of Welshpool on rd to Guilsfield A490; turn R into Windmill Lane; 4th cottage on L. 1½-acre country garden begun in 1988. Superb views. Mixed shrub and herbaceous borders, roses, climbers; pool. Ornamental and fruit trees incl a planting of 12 hardy eucalyptus. *Adm £1 Chd free. Private visits welcome, please* **Tel 01938 555432**

Moor Park & (Mr & the Hon Mrs L Price) Llanbedr. Turn off A40 at Fire Station in Crickhowell; continue 2m, signed Llanbedr. 5 acres; roses, borders, trees and walled kitchen garden. Lake, water garden under construction; woodland walk. TEAS. *Adm £1.50 Chd free. Sun July 7 (2-6)*

Pen-y-Maes &❀ (Miss S Egerton) 1m W of Hay on Wye on B4350 towards Brecon. Entrance on L. Small garden, mainly herbaceous. Walled kitchen garden with geometric box beds of vegetables and herbs. Old roses. Espaliered fruit trees. Featured in Gardens Illustrated Oct 1993. TEAS. *Adm £1.50 Chd free. Sun June 16 (2-5)*

Point Farm &⚘❀ (Mr & Mrs F Podmore) Bryn Lane, Newtown. From town centre head N across river to roundabout. Take R-hand rd off roundabout into Commercial St. L at fork into Llanfair Rd towards hospital. Bryn Lane is on L-hand side of the hospital. Point Farm is 1½m along Bryn Lane from the hospital, on R-hand side. The ½-acre garden is 750' above sea level with magnificent views of unspoilt countryside. Suitable herbaceous plants and shrubs have been planted to accommodate dry shade, sunny borders and boggy conditions. TEAS. *Adm £1 Acc chd free (Share to Diabetic Assoc.®). Suns June 23, Aug 25 (2-6). Private visits welcome, please* **Tel 01686 625709**

Powis Castle Gardens ⚘❀ (The National Trust) Welshpool. Turn off A483 ¾m out of Welshpool, up Red Lane for ¼m. Gardens laid out in 1720 with most famous hanging terraces in the world; enormous yew hedges; lead statuary, large wild garden. Part of garden suitable for wheelchairs, top terrace only. TEA. The date shown below is a *Special opening* for NGS; garden only. *Adm gardens only (Castle closed) £3.50 Chd £1.50 N.T. members also pay.* ▲*Tues May 28 (12-6)*

¶**Tan-y-Llyn** ⚘❀ (Callum Johnston & Brenda Moor) Meifod. From Oswestry on the A495 turn L in village, cross R Vyrnwy and climb hill for ½m bearing R at Y-junction. Map ref. [167125]. 3-acre sheltered garden and orchard in Montgomeryshire hills. Informally terraced, laid out to complement the proportions of existing hillside. Thorn grove, herb garden; extensive collection of container plants. Nursery specialising in alpines, herbaceous plants and herbs. TEAS. Events, demonstrations and exhibitions. *Adm £1 Chd free. Sats, Suns April 6, 7, May 4, 5, June 1, 2, July 6, 7, Aug 3, 4, Aug 31, Sept 1, Oct 5, 6 (2-6)*

Trawscoed Hall ⚘❀ (Mr & Mrs J T K Trevor) 3m N of Welshpool on Llanfyllin Road. Long drive through woodlands, lovely panoramic views from S facing sloping gardens with interesting plants. 2 acres. Magnificent wisteria covering front of fine Georgian house (not open) built 1777. Granary dating from 1772. Nature trails through prize-winning woodlands. TEAS in aid of Asthma Research. *Adm £1 Chd free. Sun May 12 (2-6)*

Treberfydd ⚘ (Lt Col & Mrs D Garnons Williams) Bwlch. 2¼m W of Bwlch. From A40 at Bwlch turning marked Llangorse then L for Pennorth. From Brecon, leave A40 at Llanhamlach. 2¼m to sign Llangasty Church but go over cattle grid to house. Large garden; lawns, roses, trees, rock garden. Plants for sale at commercial nursery. TEAS. *Adm £1.50 Chd free (Share to Llangasty Church®). Sun June 30 (2-6)*

Treholford (Mr & Mrs J A V Blackham) Cathedine. Turn off A40 between Crickhowell and Brecon at Bwlch for Llangorse. 2m on R. 5-acre garden overlooking Llangorse Lake; lawns with specimen trees, rock garden, pools and greenhouses incl a cacti house; walled kitchen garden with box hedges and rose arches. TEAS. *Adm £1.50 Chd free (Share to St Michael's Church, Cathedine®). Sun July 28 (2-6). Private visits welcome, please* **Tel 01874 730278**

Upper Dolley &✿ (Mrs B P Muggleton) Dolley Green. Take B4356 W out of Presteigne towards Whitton. At Dolley Green, 2m from Presteigne, turn L down 'No Through Road' by red brick church; Upper Dolley is 100yds on L. From Knighton take B4355 to turning for Whitton, B4357. Turn L at Whitton B4356 to brick church;

turn R. 2-acre country garden with open views of Lugg Valley; variety of borders with many shrub roses and large natural pond; C16 Grade 2 listed house (not open). Weather permitting. Cream TEAS and plants in aid of Bible Society. *Adm £1 Chd 50p. Sat, Sun July 6, 7 (2-6). Private visits welcome June, July, Aug, please* **Tel 01547 560273**

The Walled Garden & (Miss C M Mills) Knill, 3m from Kington and Presteigne. Off B4362 Walton-Presteigne rd to Knill village; right over cattle grid; keep right down drive. 3 acres; walled garden; stream; bog garden; primulas; shrub roses. Nr C13 Church in lovely valley. TEAS at **Broadheath House.** *Combined adm with Broadheath £2.50 Chd free. Sun June 30 (2-5). Private visits welcome any day (10-7), please* **Tel 01544 267411**

NOTES

The Counties of England and Wales

Note. The areas shown on this map are not necessarily precise geographic counties. Some are areas specific to the administration of the National Gardens Scheme

Index to Gardens

This index lists all gardens alphabetically and gives the counties in which they are to be found. Refer to the relevant county pages where the garden and its details will be found, again in alphabetical order. The following unorthodox county abbreviations are used: C & W—Cheshire and Wirral; L & R—Leicestershire and Rutland; G & A—Gwynedd and Anglesey. An * denotes a garden which will not be in its normal alphabetical order as it is a group garden and will be found under the Group Garden name but still within the county indicated.

F

G

M

N

Index to Advertisers

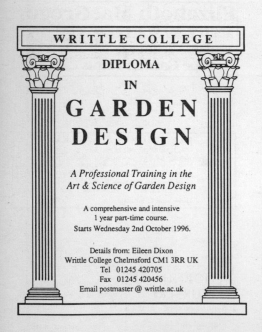

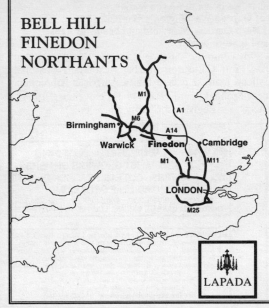

HATFIELD HOUSE

HATFIELD HERTFORDSHIRE AL9 5NQ
Tel No. (0707) 262823

Celebrated Jacobean Home (1611) of the Marquess of Salisbury

Close links with Elizabeth I including some possessions. Fine furniture, pictures, tapestries, armour. Adjacent to The Old Palace (1497) where Elizabeth I lived. Shops, Restaurant / Coffee Shop. Formal gardens originated by John Tradescant, gardener to Robert Cecil and King James I. Knot, scented and wilderness gardens, including rhododendrons, azaleas, old-fashioned roses, wild daffodils. Picnic area. Nature trails.

Adults £5.20   Children £3.30
(Special rates for parties of 20 or more, booked in advance.)

Open Daily, 25 March to 13 October 1996
(closed Good Friday and Mondays except Bank Holidays)

GARDENS: Daily 11-6
(except Good Friday)

HOUSE: Tues to Sat 12-4.00,
(Sundays 1.00-4.30; Bank Holidays 11-5)

FESTIVAL OF GARDENING
22–23 June 1996

Gardens and Farm

40 acres of Gardens and Woodland
Interesting variety of Unusual Plants
Organic Farm with Rare Breeds
Organic Kitchen Garden
Glasshouses, Walled Garden, Lakeside Walks
See main entry for visiting information

Farm Shop

All Produce Organically grown and reared
Fresh Vegetables and Fruit
Home made Jams and Chutneys
Fresh Dairy Produce
Farm Pork, Beef and Lamb.

Shop open Fridays 2pm – 5.30pm Saturdays 10am – 1pm

Waltham Place, White Waltham, Maidenhead, Berks.
Telephone 01628 825517.

TREHANE CAMELLIA CENTRE

At its best in March and April but worth a visit at any time. Camellias of all types and sizes including rarities and scented autumn flowering. Evergreen Azaleas, Magnolias, Pieris and Blueberries (P.Y.O. in August) Open Weekdays all year. Weekends also Spring and Summer.
Trehane Nursery Stapehill Road, Hampreston, Wimborne Dorset. BH21 7NE.   Tel: 01202 873490
(Next to Knoll Gardens)

THORNCROFT Clematis NURSERY

SPECIALIST CLEMATIS GROWER

Visit our large Clematis Display Garden where over 300 clematis can be seen in a natural setting.
The nursery has around 200 beautiful, and unusual, varieties available.
Open 1st March – 31st October   10.00am – 4.30pm
CLOSED WEDNESDAYS Winter times by appointment.
Please send 2 × 1st class stamps for catalogue.
Delivery can be arranged for our quality plants.
On B1135 exactly halfway between Wymondham & Dereham. The Lings, Reymerston, Norwich NR9 4QG.
Tel. 01953 850407.

RARE & UNUSUAL PLANT FAIRS '96

10–4
Adm £2.00

Over 30 specialist nurseries from across the country, offering an enormous range of hardy & tender perennials, cottage garden & foliage plants, herbs and wildflowers, shrubs & climbers, alpines & rock plants, new introductions, floral displays, expert advice, on-site catering, prestigious venues – AND LOTS MORE!

7th April   Fulbeck Hall, Fulbeck, Grantham, Lincs. The historic Georgian mansion & its superb Edwardian gardens, awash with the colour of spring bulbs, are also open to the public.

6th May   Barnsdale Lodge, Exton, Rutland Water, Leics. Set in the idyllic surroundings of Rutland.

12th May   Ryton Gardens, Ryton on Dunsmore, Coventry. The home of The Henry Doubleday Research Association, offering excellent facilities & attractions including an Organic Gardeners Question Time.

23rd June   Bressingham Plant Centre, Elton Hall, Elton, Peterborough. Set in the walled garden. Elegant & tranquil surroundings complimented by the local brass band.

7th Sept   Blooms of Bressingham, Diss, Norfolk. The home of the world famous horticulturists. Part of the Festival Weekend, including many attractions – display gardens, behind the scenes tours & numerous lectures.

Promoted by Primrose Fairs. Tel: – 01636 830756

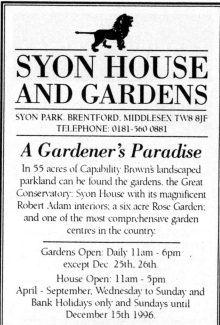

Great Comp Garden

This peaceful oasis in the heart of the Kent Countryside surrounds a fine early 17th Century Manor and is the delightful creation of Roderick Cameron and his late wife Joy.

The not so common combination of a well designed garden and a wealth of Trees, Shrubs and Perennials ensures a most satisfactory visit at any time of the year.

The new walled Italian Garden completed this year is only the latest of many additions and improvements in recent years. Amongst the fine collection of plants at Great Comp are over 50 magnolias in 30 varieties, 60 varieties of hardy Geranium, 100 different Conifers including a splendid 40 feet tall *Sequoia sempervirens* 'Cantab', and a breathtaking array of Rhododendrons and Azaleas.

Great Comp Music Festival, started by the Camerons in 1973 is unique in presenting six international chamber ensembles in the intimate setting of the old stable with only 80 seats.

As a special event for 1996 there will be a Garden Party on July 4th.

For further details of this and other events please send SAE to: The Curator, Great Comp Garden, Comp Lane, St Mary's Platt, Nr Borough Green, Kent TN15 8QS. FOR OPENING TIMES SEE LISTING.

376

378

BOTANICAL GARDENS

68 ACRES OF BEAUTIFUL GARDENS:

Vegetable and Fruit Trials
Flower Trials
Winter Garden, Foliage Garden,
Streamside, Roses, Bulbs, Alpines,
Rock Gardens
Wildflower Meadow
Woodland and Arboretum

Licensed Restaurant • Plant Centre
Gift Shop • Museum of Gardening
National Collections • Children's Play Area
Model Village

Harlow Carr Botanical Gardens
Crag Lane, Harrogate
Tel: 01423 565418

The Arley Garden Festival

Saturday 27th & Sunday 28th July 1996
10am - 5pm

AROUND THE SOUTH & WEST FRONTS OF
ARLEY HALL, CHESHIRE
(Near M6, Juncs. 19/20 & M56, Juncs. 9/10)

* Specialist nurseries selling lots of unusual plants.
* Floral displays.
* Garden Advice panel.
* 12 acres of award-winning gardens including the
  famous *Herbaceous Border* at its best.
* Hall beautifully decorated with flowers.

SPECIAL RATES FOR PRE-BOOKED PARTIES

*For more information contact Arley Estate Office, Nr
Northwich, Cheshire CW9 6NA   Tel: (01565) 777 353*

EXBURY GARDENS

*"The beauty and peace of the Gardens is so
wonderful. The colours, smells and texture of
the plants are exquisite.
Never have we seen such beauty in a garden.....
...it is a haven, away from this busy world."*

MR. & MRS B., WILTSHIRE.

THE WORLD-FAMOUS ROTHSCHILD GARDEN
ON THE EDGE OF THE NEW FOREST

SPRING & AUTUMN - 200 ACRES 🌿 SUMMER - 53 ACRES
LUNCHES & CREAM TEAS 🌿 PLANT CENTRE & GIFT SHOP
TELEPHONE: 01703 891203 OR 899422 (24 HOURS)

WHERE WONDERS NEVER CEASE

NEAR BEAULIEU, 20 MINUTES FROM M27 JUNCTION 2

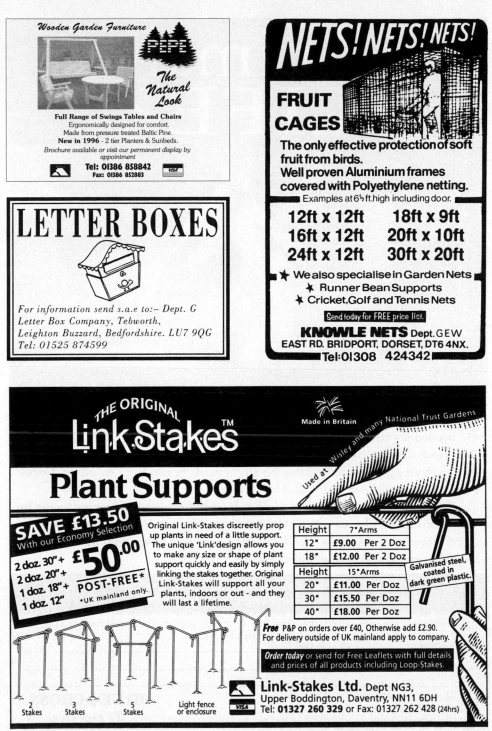

Animal LIFE?

Just two weeks old, thrown onto a building site and left to die.

This tiny bundle of fur came to Blue Cross so weak he could barely lift his head. He needed six stitches to his lower lip. We took him into our care and for the first time this kitten experienced human warmth. It took weeks of careful feeding with a dropper to build up his strength. *As he fought for his life he climbed so many mountains our staff called him Everest.*

To treat Everest's injuries and provide food and shelter for the nine weeks he was recovering with   us cost £298. Blue Cross relies entirely on your generosity to continue its life saving work. If 13 people give just £2 a month for a year, this would be enough to save another tiny life.

**If you want to help animals like Everest
please return the coupon below.**

Please send me more information about how I can help animals like Everest by becoming
a Blue Cross Friend.

Name (Mr/Mrs/Miss) _____

Address _____

_____ Postcode _____

Send to: Blue Cross, Freepost,
Room 562C, Shilton Road,
Burford, Oxon OX18 4BR   Reg Charity No. 224392

BLUE✚CROSS
We save lives

THE NATIONAL TRUST

Money raised by the National Gardens Scheme and donated to the Gardens Fund of the National Trust will once again help to conserve 20 of Britain's finest parks and gardens as well as train tomorrow's top gardeners. During 1996, you will see the National Gardens Scheme's donation working hard at:

CALKE ABBEY IN DERBYSHIRE, where the early 19th century Vinery will receive essential structural repairs.

DUDMASTON IN SHROPSHIRE, where the 1840s rockery will be restored.

PLAS NEWYDD IN GWYNEDD, where a vaulted cavern with tufa work and a pool will be created in the Italian Garden.

DINEFWR PARK IN DYFED, where the summerhouse will be repaired.

THE VYNE IN HAMPSHIRE, where the pleasure grounds will continue to be developed and replanted.

Ring 0181 315 1111 for a free National Trust Gardens Map Guide and be sure to visit us at the Chelsea and Hampton Court Flower Shows.

GARDENS

OF ENGLAND AND WALES
OPEN FOR CHARITY

1997 EDITION PUBLISHED FEB/MARCH

Price: £4.25 including UK postage. Airmail to Europe £5.25; Australia A$17.50; New Zealand NZ$21.50; USA US$18.00; Canada CDN$ 20.00

To The National Gardens Scheme, Hatchlands Park, East Clandon, Guildford, Surrey, GU4 7RT. Tel 01483 211535 (Fax 01483 211537)

Please send _____ copy/copies of *Gardens of England and Wales* for which I enclose PO/cheque for _____
Postal orders and cheques should be made payable to The National Gardens Scheme and crossed.
If sending money from abroad please use an international money order or sterling, dollar or euro cheques; other cheques are not acceptable. Add $1 to cheques for clearance.

_____

Name Mr/Mrs/Miss (Block letters)

_____

Address

_____

_____

The books will be posted on publication. If you wish to receive an acknowledgement of your order, please enclose an s.a.e.
Trade terms Supplies of this book on sale or return should be ordered direct from our trade distributors:
Seymour, 1270 London Road, Norbury, London, SW16 4DH (Tel 0181-679 1899)
The National Gardens Scheme is a registered charity, number 279284.

TO ADVERTISE IN

GARDENS OF ENGLAND AND WALES 1997

CONTACT:

AW PUBLISHING, PO BOX 38, ASHFORD, KENT TN25 6PR

TELEPHONE: 01303 813803 FAX: 01303 813737